PRECALCULUS

Second Edition

bju **press**®

Greenville, South Carolina

Note:
The fact that materials produced by other publishers may be referred to in this volume does not constitute an endorsement of the content or theological position of materials produced by such publishers. Any
references and ancillary materials are listed as an aid to the student or the teacher and in an attempt to
maintain the accepted academic standards of the publishing industry.

PRECALCULUS
Second Edition

Coordinating Writer
Mark Wetzel, MEd

Writers
Ben Adams, MEd
Gene Bucholtz, MEd
Jeffrey A. Jaeger, MEd
Timothy King
Tamera Knisely, MEd
Steve McKisic, MEd
Kathy Pilger, EdD
Sarah Ream, MPA

Academic Oversight
Jeff Heath

Editors
Heather Lonaberger, MA
Abigail Sivyer
Ron Tagliapietra, EdD

Biblical Worldview
Vern Poythress, PhD
Tyler Trometer, MDiv

Previous Edition Writers
Kathy Pilger, EdD
Ron Tagliapietra, EdD

Consultants
Steve McKisic, MEd
Kathy Pilger, EdD

Permissions
Sylvia Gass
Carrie Hanna
Ashleigh Schieber
Carrie Walker
Elizabeth Walker

Project Coordinator
Kyla J. Smith

Page Layout
Dzign Associates,
   Patricia Tirado

Designers and Illustrators
Chris Barnhart
Dzign Associates,
   Patricia Tirado
Drew Fields, MA
Josh Frederick
Emily Heinz
Pixel Mouse House,
   David Casas

Cover Designers
Chris Barnhart
Drew Fields, MA
Josh Frederick

Photograph credits appear on page 696.
Text acknowledgements appear on page 698.

All trademarks are the registered and unregistered marks of their respective owners.
BJU Press is in no way affiliated with these companies. No rights are granted by
BJU Press to use such marks, whether by implication, estoppel, or otherwise.

© 2020 BJU Press
Greenville, South Carolina 29609
First Edition © 2002, 2009 BJU Press

Printed in the United States of America
All rights reserved
ISBN 978-1-60682-934-9

15   14   13   12   11   10   9   8   7   6   5   4   3   2

Contents

Reaching the Pinnacle

In 1958 the first recorded ascent of the 3000 foot rock face of El Capitan in Yosemite National Park took the team of three climbers 47 days. The entire project took eighteen months as the climbers established multiple camps along the route—all connected by ropes. In 2017 Alex Honnold, using only a small bag of chalk strapped to his waist, climbed El Capitan free solo in under four hours.

Honnold did not accomplish this feat on a whim. He practiced climbing from a young age, noting that others had more natural ability, but he just kept on working. He trained hard (hanging by just his fingertips up to an hour every day), carefully plotted his route, and practiced particularly challenging parts of the climb by repeatedly rappelling down and climbing up.

In Precalculus you will hone and combine skills you have developed in algebra and geometry. For many of you, this course will be the final preparation you need before tackling a college-level calculus course. For others, it may be your final math class before you turn your focus to other areas. Either way, if you invest the necessary effort, you will expand both your skill in solving problems and your understanding of mathematics—its history, current use, and relevance from a biblical perspective. In the current Information Age with its data-driven algorithms, these skills are essential to understanding complex issues in health care, law enforcement, social media, space flight, and myriad other areas.

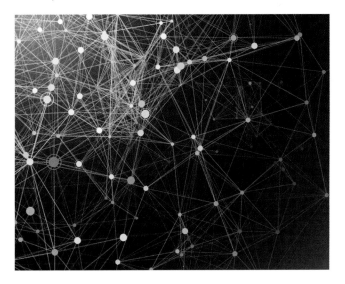

Over the next few pages you will be introduced to some of the special features contained in this book. The text integrates answers to critical questions regarding the genesis of mathematical ideas, modern applications of these ideas,

and the importance of these matters in today's world. Frequent technology instruction, tips, and step-by-step examples will assist you in your journey. In addition, margin notes in each section provide interesting bits of information that directly relate to the development or application of ideas in the accompanying text.

The Historical Connection, Data Analysis, and Biblical Perspective of Mathematics features found in each chapter provide context, application, and meaning to the mathematical ideas as they are introduced and will improve comprehension and retention. Woven together, these three features present a strong biblical worldview of mathematics. The Historical Connection features provide more than a timeline of events; they explore the factors leading to the development of particular mathematical ideas and the reasons why they were discovered at a particular time and place. The Data Analysis features offer an opportunity to work on real-world problems using the tools learned in that chapter. While the entire text is written from a biblical worldview that rejects the moral neutrality of mathematics, particular worldview topics are addressed in detail in the Biblical Perspective of Mathematics features.

We hope you are excited about this course! The material may be challenging, but the accomplishments are well worth the effort. Take advantage of the many features that are included in the text to help you along the way. Our goal is that you find this book useful, rigorous, and consistent with a biblical worldview.

Using This Book

Chapter Introduction
Preview the flow of lessons in the chapter and read a brief introduction to each of the three special features.

Biblical Perspective of Mathematics
Explore the philosophical basis of mathematics from a biblical worldview.

6 Vectors, Polar Graphs, and Complex Numbers

6.1 Vectors in the Plane
6.2 Dot Products
Biblical Perspective of Mathematics
6.3 Vectors in Space
6.4 Polar Coordinates
6.5 Graphs of Polar Equations
Historical Connection
6.6 Polar Forms of Complex Numbers
Data Analysis

 BIBLICAL PERSPECTIVE OF MATHEMATICS
Which types of reasoning are used to discover and verify mathematical truths?

 HISTORICAL CONNECTION
While vectors and polar coordinates are often presented before operations with complex numbers, the development of vectors lagged behind the development of complex numbers by about 200 years.

 DATA ANALYSIS
While some mathematicians studied operations thought to exist solely in the mind of man, these operations led to fractals, which are used to describe natural patterns occurring all around us and even inside of us.

Data Analysis
Discover how mathematical concepts are used in modern applications with engaging hands-on exercises.

Historical Connection
Consider why mathematical concepts were developed at a particular time and place.

VI

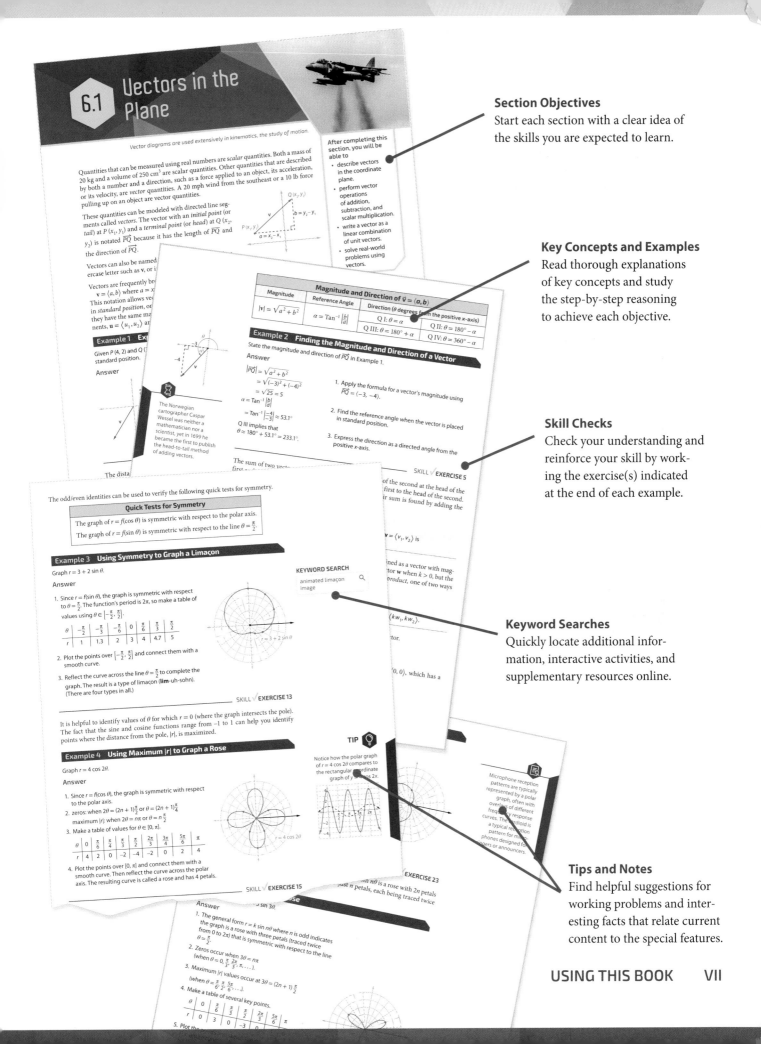

6.1 Vectors in the Plane

Vector diagrams are used extensively in kinematics, the study of motion.

Quantities that can be measured using real numbers are *scalar* quantities. Both a mass of 20 kg and a volume of 250 cm³ are scalar quantities. Other quantities that are described by both a number and a direction, such as a force applied to an object, its acceleration, or its velocity, are *vector* quantities. A 20 mph wind from the southeast or a 10 lb force pulling up on an object are vector quantities.

These quantities can be modeled with directed line segments called *vectors*. The vector with an *initial point* (or *tail*) at $P(x_1, y_1)$ and a *terminal point* (or *head*) at $Q(x_2, y_2)$ is notated $\overrightarrow{PQ}$ because it has the length of $\overrightarrow{PQ}$ and the direction of $\overrightarrow{PQ}$.

Vectors can also be named [...] ercase letter such as **v**, or [...]

Vectors are frequently br[...] $\mathbf{v} = \langle a, b \rangle$ where $a = $ [...] This notation allows vec[...] in *standard position*, or [...] they have the same ma[...] nents, $\mathbf{u} = \langle u_1, u_2 \rangle$ ar[...]

Example 1 Exp[...]

Given $P(4, 2)$ and $Q($ [...] standard position.

Answer

> The Norwegian cartographer Caspar Wessel was neither a mathematician nor a scientist, yet in 1699 he became the first to publish the head-to-tail method of adding vectors.

The dista[...]

After completing this section, you will be able to
- describe vectors in the coordinate plane.
- perform vector operations of addition, subtraction, and scalar multiplication.
- write a vector as a linear combination of unit vectors.
- solve real-world problems using vectors.

Magnitude and Direction of $\vec{v} = \langle a, b \rangle$		
Magnitude	Reference Angle	Direction (θ degrees from the positive x-axis)
$|v| = \sqrt{a^2 + b^2}$	$\alpha = \text{Tan}^{-1}\left|\frac{b}{a}\right|$	Q I: $\theta = \alpha$ Q II: $\theta = 180° - \alpha$ Q III: $\theta = 180° + \alpha$ Q IV: $\theta = 360° - \alpha$

Example 2 Finding the Magnitude and Direction of a Vector

State the magnitude and direction of $\overrightarrow{PQ}$ in Example 1.

Answer

$|\overrightarrow{PQ}| = \sqrt{a^2 + b^2}$
$= \sqrt{(-3)^2 + (-4)^2}$
$= \sqrt{25} = 5$

$\alpha = \text{Tan}^{-1}\left|\frac{b}{a}\right|$

$= \text{Tan}^{-1}\left|\frac{-4}{-3}\right| \approx 53.1°$

Q III implies that
$\theta \approx 180° + 53.1° = 233.1°$.

1. Apply the formula for a vector's magnitude using $\overrightarrow{PQ} = \langle -3, -4 \rangle$.

2. Find the reference angle when the vector is placed in standard position.

3. Express the direction as a directed angle from the positive x-axis.

SKILL ✓ EXERCISE 5

The sum of two vect[...]
first [...] of the second at the head of the [...] first to the head of the second. [...] sum is found by adding the [...]

$\mathbf{v} = \langle v_1, v_2 \rangle$ is

[...]ined as a vector with mag-[...]ector **w** when $k > 0$, but the [...]roduct, one of two ways

$\langle kw_1, kw_2 \rangle$.

KEYWORD SEARCH
animated limaçon image 🔍

The odd/even identities can be used to verify the following quick tests for symmetry.

Quick Tests for Symmetry
The graph of $r = f(\cos\theta)$ is symmetric with respect to the polar axis.
The graph of $r = f(\sin\theta)$ is symmetric with respect to the line $\theta = \frac{\pi}{2}$.

Example 3 Using Symmetry to Graph a Limaçon

Graph $r = 3 + 2\sin\theta$.

Answer

1. Since $r = f(\sin\theta)$, the graph is symmetric with respect to $\theta = \frac{\pi}{2}$. The function's period is 2π, so make a table of values using $\theta \in \left[-\frac{\pi}{2}, \frac{\pi}{2}\right]$.

θ	$-\frac{\pi}{2}$	$-\frac{\pi}{3}$	$-\frac{\pi}{6}$	0	$\frac{\pi}{6}$	$\frac{\pi}{3}$	$\frac{\pi}{2}$
r	1	1.3	2	3	4	4.7	5

2. Plot the points over $\left[-\frac{\pi}{2}, \frac{\pi}{2}\right]$ and connect them with a smooth curve.

3. Reflect the curve across the line $\theta = \frac{\pi}{2}$ to complete the graph. The result is a type of limaçon (**lim-uh-sohn**). (There are four types in all.)

$r = 3 + 2\sin\theta$

SKILL ✓ EXERCISE 13

It is helpful to identify values of θ for which $r = 0$ (where the graph intersects the pole). The fact that the sine and cosine functions range from -1 to 1 can help you identify points where the distance from the pole, $|r|$, is maximized.

Example 4 Using Maximum $|r|$ to Graph a Rose

Graph $r = 4\cos 2\theta$.

Answer

1. Since $r = f(\cos\theta)$, the graph is symmetric with respect to the polar axis.
2. zeros: when $2\theta = (2n + 1)\frac{\pi}{2}$ or $\theta = (2n + 1)\frac{\pi}{4}$ maximum $|r|$: when $2\theta = n\pi$ or $\theta = n\frac{\pi}{2}$
3. Make a table of values for $\theta \in [0, \pi)$.

θ	0	$\frac{\pi}{6}$	$\frac{\pi}{4}$	$\frac{\pi}{3}$	$\frac{\pi}{2}$	$\frac{2\pi}{3}$	$\frac{3\pi}{4}$	$\frac{5\pi}{6}$	π
r	4	2	0	-2	-4	-2	0	2	4

4. Plot the points over $[0, \pi)$ and connect them with a smooth curve. Then reflect the curve across the polar axis. The resulting curve is called a rose and has 4 petals.

$r = 4\cos 2\theta$

SKILL ✓ EXERCISE 15

Answer
[...] sin 3θ.

1. The general form $r = k\sin n\theta$ where n is odd indicates the graph is a rose with three petals (traced twice from 0 to 2π) that is symmetric with respect to the line $\theta = \frac{\pi}{2}$.
2. Zeros occur when $3\theta = n\pi$ (when $\theta = 0, \frac{\pi}{3}, \frac{2\pi}{3}, \pi, \ldots$).
3. Maximum $|r|$ values occur at $3\theta = (2n + 1)\frac{\pi}{2}$ (when $\theta = \frac{\pi}{6}, \frac{\pi}{2}, \frac{5\pi}{6}, \ldots$).
4. Make a table of several key points.

θ	0	$\frac{\pi}{6}$	$\frac{\pi}{3}$	$\frac{\pi}{2}$	$\frac{2\pi}{3}$	$\frac{5\pi}{6}$	π
r	0	3	0	-3	0		

5. Plot the[...]

[...] sin $n\theta$ is a rose with $2n$ petals [...]ust n petals, each being traced twice

[...] EXERCISE 23

TIP ⬡
Notice how the polar graph of $r = 4\cos 2\theta$ compares to the rectangular coordinate graph of $y = 4\cos 2x$.

Microphone reception patterns are typically represented by a polar graph, often with overlays of different frequency response curves. The cardioid is a typical reception pattern for micro-phones designed for singers or announcers.

Section Objectives
Start each section with a clear idea of the skills you are expected to learn.

Key Concepts and Examples
Read thorough explanations of key concepts and study the step-by-step reasoning to achieve each objective.

Skill Checks
Check your understanding and reinforce your skill by working the exercise(s) indicated at the end of each example.

Keyword Searches
Quickly locate additional information, interactive activities, and supplementary resources online.

Tips and Notes
Find helpful suggestions for working problems and interesting facts that relate current content to the special features.

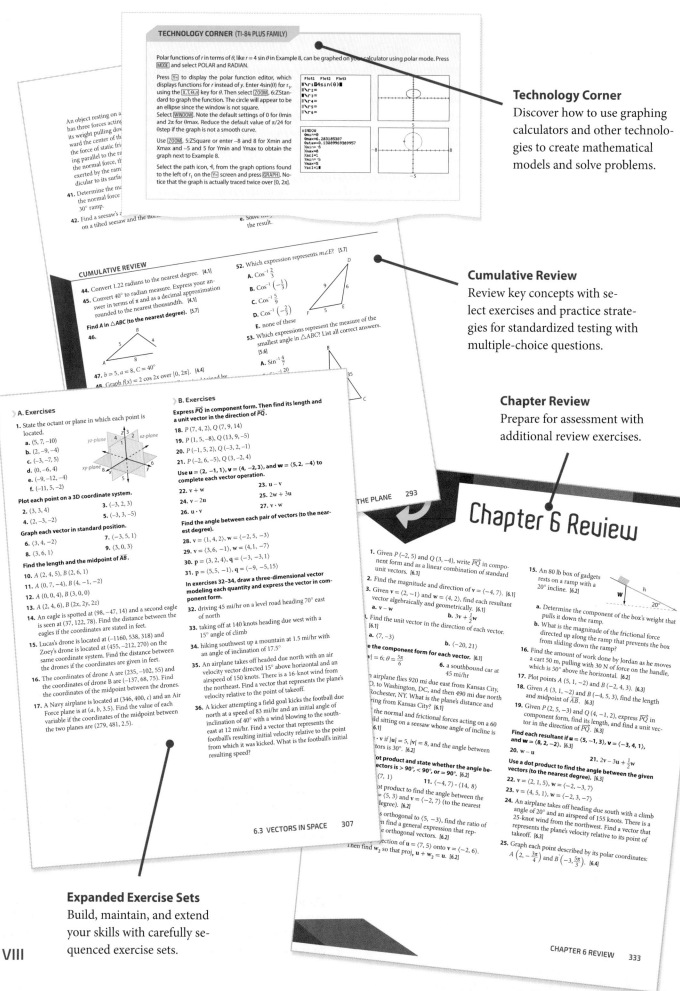

Technology Corner
Discover how to use graphing calculators and other technologies to create mathematical models and solve problems.

Cumulative Review
Review key concepts with select exercises and practice strategies for standardized testing with multiple-choice questions.

Chapter Review
Prepare for assessment with additional review exercises.

Expanded Exercise Sets
Build, maintain, and extend your skills with carefully sequenced exercise sets.

1 Analyzing Functions

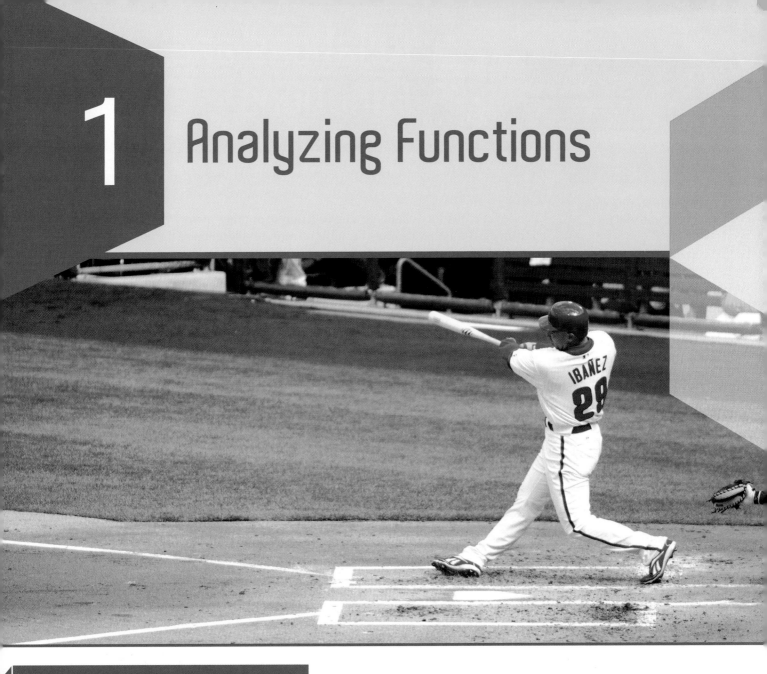

HISTORICAL CONNECTION

A culture's worldview affects how it explores and explains the physical world. Why was the concept of mathematical functions not developed until the seventeenth century?

BIBLICAL PERSPECTIVE OF MATHEMATICS

Is math a morally neutral discipline? After all, $2 + 2 = 4$ is true for all people, regardless of their religious beliefs. Should a Christian view mathematics as a human invention or a divine gift?

DATA ANALYSIS

Creating mathematical models of real-world data enables us to make informed predictions about future events. Can you develop a mathematical model that predicts whether a fly ball will clear the fence for a home run? How accurate is your model?

Relations and Functions

The speed of a tsunami is modeled with a mathematical function in exercise 35.

After completing this section, you will be able to

- use multiple representations of relations.
- identify relations that are functions.
- use interval notation.

While René Descartes (1596–1650) developed the idea of graphing relations, he likely studied the writings of Nicole Oresme, a fourteenth-century scholastic who plotted the results of heat transfer experiments using horizontal and vertical axes.

The idea of a quantity changing as a function of another quantity is a relatively recent mathematical concept. Its roots lie in the scientific exploration of the physical world that flourished under a Christian worldview in the seventeenth century. The study of relations and functions led to the development of calculus and is the basis of most of modern mathematics. The pairing of numbers in a relation or function is frequently represented by a set of ordered pairs.

> **DEFINITION**
>
> A **relation** is any set of ordered pairs.

The set $A = \{(4, -2), (1, -1), (0, 0), (1, 1), (4, 2)\}$ is a relation since it is a set of ordered pairs. A relation can also be represented by a table, a mapping diagram, or a graph.

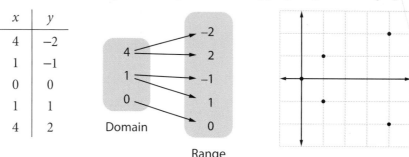

x	y
4	−2
1	−1
0	0
1	1
4	2

The mapping diagram for relation A illustrates its *domain*, the set of first elements $D = \{4, 1, 0\}$, and its *range*, the set of second elements $R = \{-2, -1, 0, 1, 2\}$. In mathematics, we are typically concerned with relations in which each first coordinate is associated with exactly one second coordinate.

> **DEFINITION**
>
> A **function** is a relation in which every first coordinate has one and only one second coordinate associated with it.

Relation A is not a function because the element 4 in the domain is associated with both −2 and 2 in the range. Relation $B = \{(-2, -3), (0, 1), (1, 3)\}$ is a function because each first coordinate is associated with exactly one second coordinate.

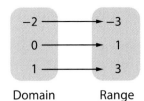

Domain   Range

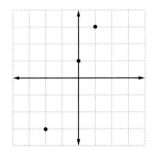

The *Vertical Line Test* can be used to determine whether a graphed relation is a function.

VERTICAL LINE TEST

If two or more points of a graphed relation lie on the same vertical line, the relation is not a function.

Example 1 Using the Vertical Line Test

Determine whether each relation is a function.

a.

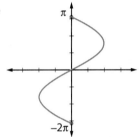

b.

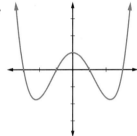

Answer

a. No; a vertical line can intersect the graph at more than one point.

b. Yes; no vertical line intersects the graph at more than one point.

_____ SKILL ✓ **EXERCISE 5**

The relationship between the first coordinate (the *abscissa*) and the second coordinate (the *ordinate*) in a relation is usually described by an equation. For example, $y = 2x + 1$ describes the relationship between the ordered pairs in relation B. Functions are named with lowercase letters (particularly f and g) and their equations are frequently written in *function notation*, where y is replaced by $f(x)$, read "f of x": $f(x) = 2x + 1$.

A function can be defined by its function rule and a statement of its domain:
$$g(x) = x^2 - 1; D = \{x \mid -2 < x < 2\}.$$

You can determine as many of the function's ordered pairs as needed by choosing a value for x from the domain and using the function rule to calculate the corresponding y-value. Because the value of y depends on the value chosen for x, y is called the *dependent variable* and x is called the *independent variable*. Plotting several ordered pairs of a function and recognizing a pattern often allows us to sketch the function's graph.

Example 2 Graphing a Function

Graph $g(x) = x^2 - 1$; $D = \{x \mid -2 \leq x \leq 2\}$.

Answer

$g(-2) = (-2)^2 - 1 = 3$
$g(-1) = (-1)^2 - 1 = 0$
$g(0) = (0)^2 - 1 = -1$
$g(1) = (1)^2 - 1 = 0$
$g(2) = (2)^2 - 1 = 3$

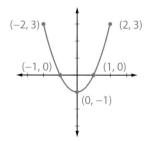

1. Evaluate the function at several points.

2. Plot the ordered pairs.

3. Since the domain contains all real numbers from −2 to 2, connect the points with a smooth curve.

SKILL ✔ **EXERCISE 19**

TIP

The context determines whether the notation represents an ordered pair or an interval.

The range of $g(x)$ in Example 2 can be described with an inequality: $\{y \mid -1 \leq y \leq 3\}$. A shorter *interval notation* can also be used. *Closed* intervals include both endpoints and are indicated by brackets: $[-1, 3]$. *Open* intervals, such as $0 < x < 5$, exclude both endpoints and are indicated with parentheses: $(0, 5)$. Intervals may also be *half-open* (or *half-closed*). The symbols used in interval notation are frequently used instead of open circles and solid points when the interval is graphed on a number line. Unbounded intervals extend infinitely and are indicated using ∞ for positive infinity or $-\infty$ for negative infinity.

Bounded Intervals			Unbounded Intervals		
Graph	Inequality	Interval	Graph	Inequality	Interval
$\overset{[\quad\quad]}{a \quad\quad b}$	$a \leq x \leq b$	$[a, b]$	$\overset{[\quad\quad\quad}{a}$	$x \geq a$	$[a, \infty)$
$\overset{(\quad\quad)}{a \quad\quad b}$	$a < x < b$	(a, b)	$\overset{(\quad\quad\quad}{a}$	$x > a$	(a, ∞)
$\overset{[\quad\quad)}{a \quad\quad b}$	$a \leq x < b$	$[a, b)$	$\overset{\quad\quad)}{b}$	$x < b$	$(-\infty, b)$
$\overset{(\quad\quad]}{a \quad\quad b}$	$a < x \leq b$	$(a, b]$	$\overset{\quad\quad]}{b}$	$x \leq b$	$(-\infty, b]$

Example 3 Representing Intervals

Write each inequality in interval notation, then graph the interval on a number line.

a. $-1 < x \leq 3$ **b.** $x \geq 2$

Answer

a. $(-1, 3]$ **b.** $[2, \infty)$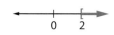

SKILL ✔ **EXERCISE 11**

When the domain of a function is not stated, its domain is assumed to be the real numbers except those values that would cause the dependent variable to be undefined. Determining the range of a function algebraically is more difficult. It can be helpful to examine the function's graph.

Example 4   Finding the Domain and Range

State the domain and range of each function.

a. $g(x) = \sqrt{2x - 3}$

b. $f(x) = \dfrac{1}{x + 2}$

Answer

a. $g(x) = \sqrt{2x - 3}$

$2x - 3 \geq 0$

$x \geq \dfrac{3}{2}$

$\therefore D = [1.5, \infty)$

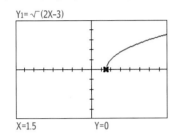

Y₁= √(2X-3)

X=1.5   Y=0

$\therefore R = [0, \infty)$

1. The radicand of an even root must be greater than or equal to 0.

2. Solve.

3. Write the domain in interval notation.

4. Use technology to graph $g(x)$ and confirm the domain.

5. Use the graph to determine that there are no points with negative y-values and that the y-values increase without bound.

The willingness of Western civilizations to accept the idea of infinity and explore its implications was based on their general acceptance of a biblical worldview, which includes an infinite God.

b. $f(x) = \dfrac{1}{x + 2}$

$x + 2 \neq 0$

$x \neq -2$

$\therefore D = \{x \mid x \neq -2\}$ or

$D = (-\infty, -2) \cup (-2, \infty)$

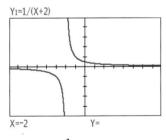

Y₁=1/(X+2)

X=-2   Y=

$0 = \dfrac{1}{x + 2}$

$0(x + 2) = 1$

$0 = 1$

$\therefore R = \{x \mid x \neq 0\}$ or

$R = (-\infty, 0) \cup (0, \infty)$

1. Since division by 0 is undefined, the denominator cannot be equal to 0.

2. Solve.

3. Write the domain in set-builder notation or in interval notation.

4. Use technology to graph $g(x)$ and confirm that y is undefined when $x = -2$.

5. It appears that the y-values of the function extend forever in each direction but may not include 0. This can be checked algebraically.

   a. Set the function value, $f(x)$ or y, equal to 0.

   b. Multiply both sides by $x + 2$ and simplify.

   c. Since $0 \neq 1$, $f(x) \neq 0$.

—————————— SKILL ✓ **EXERCISE 29**

Your graphing calculator can be used to display several representations of a function. Be sure that the calculator is in function mode by selecting FUNCTION on the [MODE] menu. Then press [Y=] to enter the function editor and enter the function rule $f(x) = \frac{1}{x+2}$ as Y1.

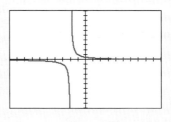

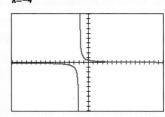

Use the [TABLE] command ([2nd], [GRAPH]) to view the ordered pairs for the defined function. The [TBLSET] command ([2nd], [WINDOW]) displays the TABLE SETUP menu. TblStart and ∆Tbl define the initial value and the increment for the independent variable. Setting Indpnt to Ask enables you to search for individual x-values in the table.

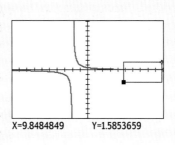

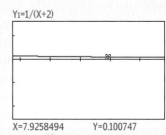

Use the [GRAPH] command to display a graph of the function. The [ZOOM] command can be used to adjust the portion of the graph that is viewed. Selecting ZStandard from the [ZOOM] menu causes the function to be graphed in a window with $-10 \leq x \leq 10$ and $-10 \leq y \leq 10$. Use ZSquare to produce a graph where the scales of the axes are the same.

Selecting ZBox from the [ZOOM] menu allows you to zoom in and further examine a rectangular region that is defined using the cursor keys and [ENTER] to position the opposite vertices. The [TRACE] command allows you to see the function's coordinates as you move across the graph or enter a particular value for x.

The [WINDOW] menu allows you to enter an exact minimum, maximum, and scale for each axis. With experience, you will be able to quickly determine the best window to display the graph's key characteristics.

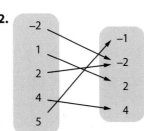

X=9.8484849   Y=1.5853659

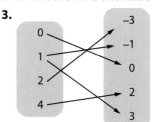

Y1=1/(X+2)

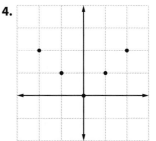

X=7.9258494   Y=0.100747

❯ A. Exercises

Graph each relation and state its domain and range using set-builder notation.

1. {(1, 2), (3, 4), (6, 2), (4, −1)}

2.

Write each relation as a set of ordered pairs and determine whether it is a function.

3.

4.

Determine whether each relation is a function.

5.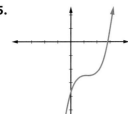

6.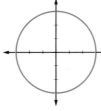

7.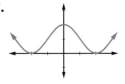

8.

Write each inequality in interval notation, then graph the interval on a number line.

9. $x < 12$

10. $x \geq -7$

11. $-4 < x \leq 10$

12. $x < 5$ or $x > 18$

State the domain and range of each function, using interval notation where possible. Remember that an open circle implies an excluded endpoint in the graph.

13.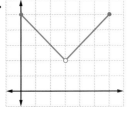

14.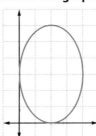

15.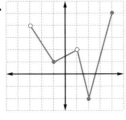

16.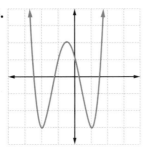

17.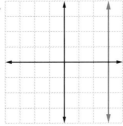

18.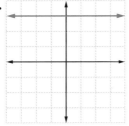

❯ B. Exercises

Represent each function as a set of ordered pairs, a mapping diagram, and a graph.

19. $f(x) = 2x - 5$ where $D = \{x \mid x = -1, 1, 4\}$

20. $g(x) = 2x^2 - 3$ where $D = \{-2, -1, 0, 1, 2\}$

21. $h(x) = -x + 4$ where $D = \{-2, -1, 0, 3\}$

22. $l(x) = x^3 - 2x^2 - 4$ where $D = \{-1, 0, 1, 2, 3\}$

23. Give an example of a relation consisting of 4 ordered pairs.

24. Give an example of a function consisting of 4 ordered pairs.

25. Give an example of a relation that is not a function.

Use technology to graph each function. Then state the domain and range of each function, using interval notation where possible.

26. $f(x) = 3x - 4$

27. $g(x) = -3$

28. $h(x) = \sqrt{x + 4}$

29. $f(x) = \dfrac{3}{x - 1}$

Determine whether each relation is a function.

30. $y = x$

31. $x = \dfrac{1}{y^2}$

32. a relation where the input value x is the day of the month and the output value y is the dollar amount for individual debit transactions for a hardware store

33. a pairing of a golf hole number and the score recorded by a golfer during a round

34. Jenni started a home business making backpacks and spent $300 to purchase enough supplies to make 15 backpacks. Her profit can be modeled by $f(n) = 50n - 300$ where n represents the number of bags sold.

   a. How much is she charging for each bag?

   b. How much did she spend on supplies for each bag?

   c. How many bags must she sell to break even?

   d. State the function's domain and range.

35. The speed at which a tsunami moves across the ocean can be calculated using the formula $s = \sqrt{9.8d}$ where s is the speed in meters per second and d is the ocean's depth in meters.

   a. Describe the domain and range using interval notation.

   b. Find the speed of a tsunami in kilometers per hour at an ocean depth of 3600 m.

> **C. Exercises**

36. If $g(x) = \frac{x}{2} + 1$, find the following.

   a. $g\left(\frac{1}{4}\right)$ **b.** $g(-b)$

   c. $g(4x)$ **d.** $g(6x - 6)$

37. Find $\dfrac{f(x + h) - f(x)}{h}$ for each function.

   a. $f(x) = x - 2$ **b.** $f(x) = x^2 + 2x - 4$

38. Explain: Is Stacy correct in claiming that the domain of $f(x) = \dfrac{1}{\sqrt{3x - 5}}$ is $\left[\frac{5}{3}, \infty\right)$? Explain why or why not.

39. Analyze: State the domain of $f(x) = \dfrac{1}{2x + 11}$ and $g(x) = \sqrt{6 - x}$ in both set-builder notation and interval notation. Describe which notation you prefer for each function and explain why.

40. Discuss: Describe a case in which interval notation would not be appropriate for stating a domain or range.

CUMULATIVE REVIEW

List any of the following subsets of the real numbers to which each number belongs: $\mathbb{Z}, \mathbb{N}, \mathbb{W}, \mathbb{Q}, \mathbb{Q}', \mathbb{R}$.
[Appendix 1]

41. $1.191191119\ldots$ **42.** π

Choose which of the following subsets is the most specific subset of the real numbers to which each number belongs: $\mathbb{Z}, \mathbb{N}, \mathbb{W}, \mathbb{Q}, \mathbb{Q}', \mathbb{R}$. [Appendix 1]

43. -8 **44.** 0 **45.** $\sqrt{6}$ **46.** $\frac{2}{9}$

Use the Venn diagram to complete exercises 47–50.
[Appendix 1]

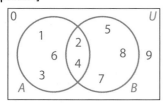

47. Which set represents the universal set?

   A. $\{0, 9\}$ **D.** $\{x \mid x \leq 9, x \in \mathbb{Z}\}$

   B. $\{x \mid 0 \leq x \leq 9\}$ **E.** none of these

   C. $\{x \mid x \leq 9, x \in \mathbb{W}\}$

48. Find $(A \cap B)'$.

   A. U **D.** $\{1, 3, 5, 6, 7, 8\}$

   B. $\{0, 9\}$ **E.** $\{0, 1, 3, 5, 6, 7, 8, 9\}$

   C. $\{2, 4\}$

49. Which of the following statements is true?

   I. $A \subset U$ **II.** $U \in \mathbb{W}$ **III.** $7 \in A'$

   A. I only   **D.** I and III only

   B. II only   **E.** II and III only

   C. I and II only

50. Which of the following statements is true?

   I. $A \cup B = U$ **II.** $A \cup B \subset U$ **III.** $A' \subset U$

   A. I only   **D.** I and III only

   B. II only   **E.** II and III only

   C. III only

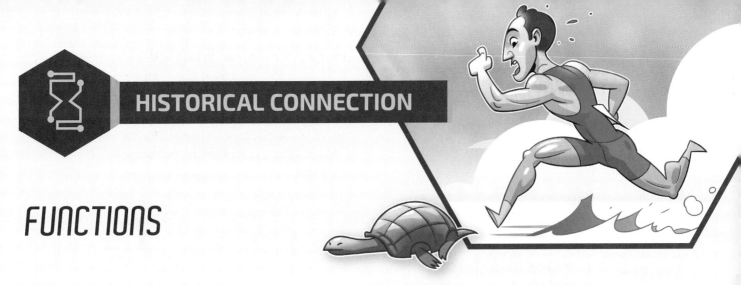

FUNCTIONS

Imagine an Olympic sprinter who cannot catch up to a tortoise! Such a paradox was proposed by Zeno, a Greek philosopher of the fifth century BC. Zeno proposed that the tortoise be given a head start, however small. In the time it would take the sprinter to reach the tortoise's position, the tortoise would have moved ahead to a new position. If time is composed of an infinite number of instants, this process would continue and the sprinter would continue to get closer but would never catch the tortoise.

Zeno was attempting to show that a belief in infinity leads to absurdity. His famous paradoxes were written in support of Parmenides's view that reality consists of "the one" as opposed to "the many," a perspective that rejected the ideas of infinity and motion. Ancient Greek philosophers deified man's reasoning ability and rejected anything they could not fully understand since it would transcend their god. To Parmenides, any motion was simply an illusion. However, a

biblical worldview accepts the idea that God is three persons in one (triune) and recognizes that His creation exhibits characteristics of both "the one" and "the many."

The ancient Greeks demonstrated magnificent reasoning in their development of geometry, but because of their worldview, they did not develop the idea of a function. Their geometry was static, exploring unchanging shapes. If motion was considered at all, it was circular motion that had a beginning and an end, never linear motion that was infinite. Since functions were developed primarily through the study of motion, this necessary prerequisite of calculus awaited a worldview that was not afraid of infinity.

A biblical worldview recognizes an infinite Creator, a finite creation, and a triune God. The Western world's acceptance of these ideas explains, at least in part, the development of the idea of a function in the Middle Ages, when according to math historian Howard Eves, "the meditations of scholastic philosophers led to subtle theorizing on motion, infinity, and the continuum, all of which are fundamental concepts in modern mathematics . . . [and] may, to some extent, account for the remarkable transformation from ancient to modern mathematical thinking."

Nicole Oresme, a fourteenth-century French scholastic, studied motion and heat transfer by plotting functions on a rectangular coordinate system centuries before Descartes. Scholastics like Oresme were the academics of the Middle Ages. They generally held a biblical worldview and expected natural processes to be orderly and to follow observable laws laid down by a sovereign Creator.

COMPREHENSION CHECK

1. Name the Greek philosopher whose paradoxes questioned the idea of infinity.

2. Describe in your own words the paradox of the sprinter and the tortoise. Why would this paradox be viewed as an argument against the idea of infinity?

3. In what century did Oresme plot functions?

4. What was the predominant worldview of Western cultures during the Middle Ages?

5. Why were scholastics more willing than Greek philosophers to explore changing natural processes involving concepts of motion and infinity?

The vertical velocity of an object in free fall is modeled by a linear equation in Example 7.

After completing this section, you will be able to

- graph linear equations.
- find intercepts.
- write an equation for a line.
- apply the distance and midpoint formulas.

The graph of a linear function, such as $f(x) = \frac{1}{2}x + 3$, can be constructed by plotting several ordered pairs from the function, noticing that the points lie on a line, and then drawing the line through the points to illustrate all the ordered pairs that define the function.

$$f(-4) = \tfrac{1}{2}(-4) + 3 = 1$$

$$f(-2) = \tfrac{1}{2}(-2) + 3 = 2$$

$$f(2) = \tfrac{1}{2}(2) + 3 = 4$$

$$f(4) = \tfrac{1}{2}(4) + 3 = 5$$

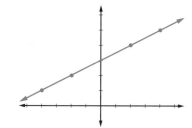

Since any real number could have been chosen for x, the domain of $f(x)$ is the real numbers. The range of the function is also the real numbers since the line continues infinitely.

Remembering key characteristics of linear functions will help you quickly graph and describe these functions. Recall that the slope of a line describes its incline or steepness.

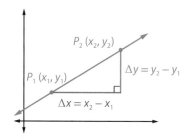

DEFINITION

The **slope** of a line, m, is the ratio of its *rise* (vertical change) to the corresponding *run* (horizontal change).

$$m = \frac{rise}{run} = \frac{\Delta y}{\Delta x} = \frac{y_2 - y_1}{x_2 - x_1}$$

When Nicole Oresme plotted data from heat transfer experiments in the Middle Ages, he recognized that a constant slope indicated uniform variance in the tested material.

Example 1 Finding the Slope of a Line

Find the slope of the line passing through $(-2, 2)$ and $(4, 5)$.

Answer

$$m = \frac{y_2 - y_1}{x_2 - x_1} = \frac{5 - 2}{4 - (-2)} = \frac{3}{6} = \frac{1}{2}$$

1. Substitute and simplify.

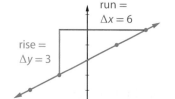

2. Confirm graphically.

$$m = \frac{rise}{run} = \frac{\Delta y}{\Delta x} = \frac{3}{6} = \frac{1}{2}$$

SKILL ✓ **EXERCISE 3**

Notice that the line in Example 1 is the linear function $f(x) = \frac{1}{2}x + 3$ where the coefficient of x is the line's slope, $\frac{1}{2}$, and the constant, 3, is the *y*-value of its *y*-intercept, the point where the line intersects the *y*-axis. The function notation for a linear function with slope m and *y*-intercept $(0, b)$ is called the *slope-intercept form* of a line.

$f(x) = mx + b$ or $y = mx + b$

Example 2 Graphing a Linear Function

Graph $f(x) = -3x + 2$. Then state its domain and range.

Answer

$m = -3$ and $b = 2$

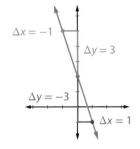

$D = \mathbb{R}; R = \mathbb{R}$

1. Compare $y = -3x + 2$ to $y = mx + b$.

2. Plot the *y*-intercept $(0, b) = (0, 2)$.

3. Use the *y*-intercept and $m = \dfrac{\Delta y}{\Delta x} = \dfrac{-3}{1} = \dfrac{3}{-1}$ to graph at least one more point, $(1, -1)$ or $(-1, 5)$, and draw the line through these points.

4. The graph shows that all real numbers are included in both the domain and range.

In *Discourse on the Method of Rightly Conducting the Reason, and Seeking Truth in the Sciences*, the French philosopher and mathematician René Descartes proposed that mathematical truths are established by human reasoning.

_____ SKILL ✔ **EXERCISE 7**

Every line in a plane, including vertical lines, can be written in *general linear form*: $Ax + By = C$ where A is not negative and the coefficients A and B and the constant C are expressed as integers if possible.

A line's *x*-intercept, the point at which the line crosses the *x*-axis, can be determined by letting $y = 0$ and solving for x.

$$Ax + B(0) = C$$

$$x = \frac{C}{A}$$

$\therefore$ the *x*-intercept is $\left(\dfrac{C}{A}, 0\right)$.

The slope and *y*-intercept of a line in general form can be determined by converting the equation to slope-intercept form.

$$Ax + By = C$$

$$By = -Ax + C$$

$$y = -\frac{A}{B}x + \frac{C}{B}$$

$\therefore$ the *y*-intercept is $\left(0, \dfrac{C}{B}\right)$ and the slope $m = -\dfrac{A}{B}$.

Note that the *y*-intercept could also be found by letting $x = 0$ and solving for y.

Example 3 Using the General Linear Form

Find the intercepts and slope of $2x - 3y = 9$. Then graph the equation.

Answer

x-intercept: $\left(\frac{9}{2}, 0\right) = (4.5, 0)$ 1. Use $\left(\frac{C}{A}, 0\right)$ to find the x-intercept.

y-intercept: $\left(0, \frac{9}{-3}\right) = (0, -3)$ 2. Use $\left(0, \frac{C}{B}\right)$ to find the y-intercept.

$m = -\frac{2}{(-3)} = \frac{2}{3}$ 3. Use $m = -\frac{A}{B}$ to find the slope.

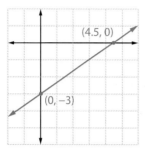

4. Plot the intercepts and graph the line. Start at the y-intercept and use $m = \frac{2}{3}$ to confirm that the point 2 units up and 3 units to the right, $(3, -1)$, is also on the line.

SKILL ✓ **EXERCISE 29**

The *point-slope form* of a line through a particular point (x_1, y_1) with slope m can be derived by letting (x, y) represent any other point on the line and applying the slope formula.

$$m = \frac{y - y_1}{x - x_1}; \therefore y - y_1 = m(x - x_1)$$

Example 4 Finding the Equation of a Line

Write the slope-intercept form equation of the line passing through $(1, 6)$ and $(3, -1)$.

Answer

$m = \frac{-1 - 6}{3 - 1} = -\frac{7}{2}$ 1. Find the slope.

$y - y_1 = m(x - x_1)$ 2. Apply the point-slope form.

$y - 6 = -\frac{7}{2}(x - 1)$

$y - 6 = -\frac{7}{2}x + \frac{7}{2}$

$y = -\frac{7}{2}x + \frac{19}{2}$

SKILL ✓ **EXERCISE 19**

Many real-world functions can be modeled using linear equations. Even the rate of change for a non-linear function at a specific point is calculated using the slope of the tangent to the curve at that point.

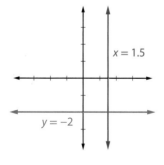

Since every point of the graph of $y = -2$ has a y-coordinate of -2, the graph is a horizontal line with a slope of $m = \frac{0}{run} = 0$. Similar linear functions of the form $f(x) = 0x + k$ or $y = k$ are called *constant functions* and their graphs are horizontal lines with a y-intercept of $(0, k)$.

Likewise, every point of the graph of $x = 1.5$ has an x-coordinate of 1.5, so the graph is a vertical line with a slope of $m = \frac{rise}{0}$, which is undefined. Similar equations of the form $x = k$ are vertical lines with an x-intercept of $(k, 0)$. These equations do not represent functions and cannot be written in function notation or in slope-intercept form.

In previous classes you have seen the relationship between the slopes of parallel and perpendicular lines.

1. Two non-vertical lines are parallel if and only if they have equal slopes: $m_1 = m_2$.

2. Two non-vertical lines are perpendicular if and only if the product of their slopes is -1: $m_1 \cdot m_2 = -1$. This implies the slopes are negative reciprocals of each other: $m_1 = -\dfrac{1}{m_2}$.

TIP 💡

Do not confuse the zero slope of horizontal lines with the undefined slope of vertical lines.

Example 5 Finding Equations of Parallel and Perpendicular Lines

Write the equation of each line in slope-intercept form.

a. the line parallel to $2x + 3y = 6$ and through $(-2, -1)$

b. the line perpendicular to $y = \frac{3}{4}x - 5$ and through $(3, -2)$

Answer

a. $m_G = -\dfrac{A}{B} = -\dfrac{2}{3}$ 1. Find the slope of the given line.

    $m_\parallel = m_G = -\dfrac{2}{3}$ 2. Parallel lines have the same slope.

    $y - (-1) = -\dfrac{2}{3}[x - (-2)]$ 3. Substitute the slope and the known coordinates into $y - y_1 = m(x - x_1)$ and convert to slope-intercept form.

        $y + 1 = -\dfrac{2}{3}x - \dfrac{4}{3}$

             $y = -\dfrac{2}{3}x - \dfrac{7}{3}$

b. $m_\perp = -\dfrac{1}{m_G} = -\dfrac{1}{\left(\frac{3}{4}\right)} = -\dfrac{4}{3}$ 1. Find the negative reciprocal of the slope of the given line.

    $-2 = -\dfrac{4}{3}(3) + b$ 2. Find the y-intercept by substituting the slope and the known coordinates into $y = mx + b$ and solving for b.

    $-2 = -4 + b$

      $2 = b$

    $y = -\dfrac{4}{3}x + 2$ 3. Use the slope and y-intercept to write the equation.

SKILL ✔ **EXERCISES 21, 23**

Review the following formulas for the distance between two points and the midpoint of a segment in the coordinate plane. The distance formula is derived using the Pythagorean Theorem and the midpoint's coordinates are averages of the endpoints' coordinates.

Distance Formula	Midpoint Formula
The distance, d, between $P_1(x_1, y_1)$ and $P_2(x_2, y_2)$ is $d = \sqrt{(x_2 - x_1)^2 + (y_2 - y_1)^2}.$	The midpoint of the segment connecting $P_1(x_1, y_1)$ and $P_2(x_2, y_2)$ is $M\left(\dfrac{x_1 + x_2}{2}, \dfrac{y_1 + y_2}{2}\right).$

Example 6 Applying the Distance and Midpoint Formulas

Find the length and midpoint of $\overline{AB}$ with A $(-3, 7)$ and B $(2, -4)$.

Answer

$$AB = \sqrt{(2 - (-3))^2 + (-4 - 7)^2} = \sqrt{5^2 + (-11)^2} = \sqrt{146}$$

$$M\left(\frac{-3 + 2}{2}, \frac{7 + (-4)}{2}\right) = \left(-\frac{1}{2}, \frac{3}{2}\right)$$

SKILL ✓ EXERCISE 23

The vertical velocity of a projectile (with negligible air resistance) can be modeled with the following linear function of the time it has been in the air: $v(t) = -gt + v_0$. Vertical velocities and the initial vertical velocity, v_0, are positive when the projectile is traveling up from the earth and negative when the projectile is traveling down toward the earth. The magnitude of g, the *acceleration due to gravity*, is about 32 ft/sec^2 or 9.8 m/sec^2.

Example 7 Modeling Vertical Velocity

Use the linear function to model the vertical velocity of a firework shot upward with an initial vertical velocity of 144 ft/sec and determine how long it takes the firework to reach its highest point.

Answer

$v(t) = -32t + 144$ 1. Substitute $g = 32$ ft/sec^2 and $v_0 = 144$ ft/sec into $v(t) = -gt + v_0$.

$0 = -32t + 144$ 2. At its peak, the firework has a vertical velocity of 0.

$32t = 144$ 3. Solve for t.

$t = 4.5$ sec

SKILL ✓ EXERCISE 33

Review the following summary of equations before completing the exercises.

Forms of Linear Equations		Slope Formulas	
$Ax + By = C$	general linear	$m = \dfrac{y_2 - y_1}{x_2 - x_1}$	definition
$y - y_1 = m(x - x_1)$	point-slope	$m_2 = m_1$	parallel lines
$y = mx + b$	slope-intercept	$m_2 = -\dfrac{1}{m_1}$	perpendicular lines

A. Exercises

1. The graph of a function in the form $f(x) = ax + b$ ($a, b \in \mathbb{R}$) is always a _____.

2. State the domain and range of any non-constant linear function.

State the slope of each line.

3.
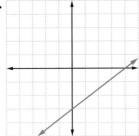

4.
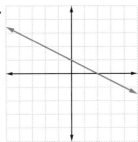

Graph each linear equation using its slope and y-intercept.

5. $y = 3x - 1$

6. $y = -\frac{3}{2}x + 2$

7. $y = -2x + \frac{3}{2}$

8. $x - 4y = 12$

Graph each linear equation using its x- and y-intercepts.

9. $5x + 2y = 10$

10. $6x + 3y = 9$

11. $3x - 4y = 6$

12. $4x - 3y = -4$

State the x-intercept, y-intercept, and slope of each line.

13. $x + 2y = 2$

14. $5x + 2y = 8$

15. $2x + 3 = -7$

16. $3y - 4 = 11$

17. $y = -\frac{2}{3}x + 1$

18. $y = \frac{2}{5}x - \frac{1}{3}$

B. Exercises

Write the slope-intercept form equation of each described line.

19. passing through $(3, 4)$ and $(-9, -4)$

20. passing through $(-5, 2)$ and $(6, -9)$

21. passing through $(2, -3)$ and parallel to $y = \frac{4}{3}x - 1$

22. passing through $(-10, 2)$ and parallel to $3x - y = 12$

23. passing through $(0, 5)$ and perpendicular to the line containing $(9, 3)$ and $(-7, -4)$

24. passing through $(6, -2)$ and perpendicular to $x + 2y = 7$

Find the distance between each pair of points. Then find the midpoint of the connecting segment.

25. $(5, 6)$ and $(-4, -6)$

26. $(5, 8)$ and $(2, 10)$

27. $(-11, 3)$ and $(2, 19)$

28. $(-3, 7)$ and $(2, -4)$

29. Find the length of a radius of the circle that is centered at $(2, -3)$ and contains the point $(-10, 2)$.

30. Find the length of a diameter of the circle that is centered at $(-3, 1)$ and contains the point $(4, -6)$.

31. Find the center and length of a radius of the circle whose diameter has endpoints $(-3, 2)$ and $(1, 5)$.

32. Find the center and length of a radius of the circle whose diameter has endpoints $(1, 4)$ and $(6, -1)$.

In exercises 33–34 model the vertical velocity of a projectile using the linear function $v(t) = -gt + v_0$ where g, the magnitude of the acceleration due to gravity, is 32 ft/sec^2 and v_0 is the initial vertical velocity.

33. Determine the velocity at which a watermelon strikes the ground if it takes 2.5 sec to fall when John drops it from a cliff. Why is the final velocity negative?

34. John launches a watermelon from a cliff with an initial vertical velocity of 44 ft/sec.

   a. How long will it take the watermelon to reach its highest point?

   b. If the time it takes to fall from its highest point back to the height of the cliff is the same as the time it took to reach its highest point, at what velocity does the watermelon pass the cliff on its way down to the ground?

   c. Determine the final vertical velocity if it takes the watermelon 4.2 sec from its initial launch to strike the ground.

35. The cost of a ride-sharing service is a function of the distance traveled and the type of car. Write a linear function modeling the cost and find the cost for a 5 mi ride.

   a. ShareCarX has a $2.00 base fare with a $3.00/mi charge.

   b. ShareCarXL has a $3.00 base fare with a $3.25/mi charge.

   c. ShareCarSelect has a $5.00 base fare with a charge of $3.50/mi.

   d. ShareCarPremium has an $8.00 base fare with a $4.00/mi.

36. **Write:** State the equation of a line that is not a function and describe this type of line.

37. **Write:** State the equation of a line whose range is not the set of real numbers and describe this type of line.

38. **Explain:** Why is a linear function in the form $y = k$ called a *constant function*?

Applying the distance formula to the definition of a circle and squaring both sides produces the following equation for a circle centered at (h, k) with radius r: $(x - h)^2 + (y - k)^2 = r^2$.

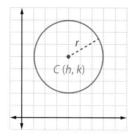

39. Write an equation for each circle.

 a. a circle centered at the origin with a radius of 7

 b. a circle centered at $(1, -4)$ with a radius of 2

40. Graph each circle.

 a. $x^2 + y^2 = 16$ **b.** $(x + 2)^2 + (y - 1)^2 = 9$

❯ C. Exercises

Graph each system of equations. Then describe how the change in the function rule from $f(x)$ to $g(x)$ and $h(x)$ affects the slope and y-intercept of the graph of $f(x)$.

41. $f(x) = x$
 $g(x) = x + 2$
 $h(x) = x - 3$

42. $f(x) = x + 5$
 $g(x) = 2x + 5$
 $h(x) = -2x + 5$

43. Write the slope-intercept form equation of the perpendicular bisector of a segment with endpoints $(2, 9)$ and $(-10, -7)$.

44. Find two pairs of points in the form of $(3x, -4)$ and $(8, x)$ where the distance between the points is 20 units.

Use the figure for exercises 45–46.

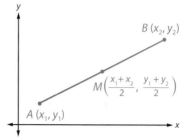

45. Prove the distance formula.

46. Verify the midpoint formula by showing that $AM = MB = \frac{1}{2}AB$.

CUMULATIVE REVIEW

Simplify each exponential expression. [Appendix 4]

47. 8^0 **48.** 8^{-2} **49.** $8^{\frac{1}{3}}$

50. Write $32^{\frac{2}{3}}$ as a simplified radical. [Appendix 4]

51. Which type of line is not a function? [1.1]

52. Simplify i^{15}. [Appendix 5]

53. Simplify $\sqrt[3]{4320}$. [Appendix 4]

 A. $12\sqrt{30}$ **C.** $2\sqrt[3]{90}$ **E.** none of these
 B. $12\sqrt{5}$ **D.** $6\sqrt[3]{20}$

54. What is the area of the shaded part of the square? [Geometry]

 A. $12\pi \, u^2$
 B. $(9\pi + 27) \, u^2$
 C. $(36 - 9\pi) \, u^2$
 D. $(36 - 6\pi) \, u^2$
 E. none of these

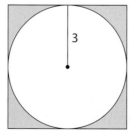

Write and solve an equation or inequality to complete the following exercises. [Appendix 2]

55. What is the product of two consecutive odd numbers whose sum is 48?

 A. 551   **C.** 567   **E.** none of
 B. 572   **D.** 575   these

56. What is the largest of three consecutive even numbers whose sum is -144?

 A. -46 **C.** -50 **E.** none of
 B. -42 **D.** -47 these

The Gift of Mathematics

The miracle of appropriateness of the language of mathematics for the formulation of the laws of physics is a wonderful gift which we neither understand nor deserve.

—*Eugene Wigner (recipient of the 1963 Nobel Prize in Physics)*

Many modern secular mathematicians maintain that mathematics is simply a creation of human minds. But God created the world (Gen. 1:1) with a system of orderly, transcendent principles that govern creation. Through the centuries, human minds have developed the symbols and terms of mathematics as they quantitatively described the created world. God is the origin of the underlying principles that provide the foundation and consistency for their work.

The practical arithmetic operations of addition and multiplication work the same from culture to culture, even though the abstract notation used may vary. The same is true for the independent discoveries of calculus by Newton in England using "fluxions" and by Leibniz in Europe using "differentials," terms referring to the same calculus concept. Important formulas such as $F = ma$ and $E = mc^2$ are man's descriptions of universal laws put in place by God. Eugene Wigner could not understand how the human-created language of mathematics could be so successful in modeling our physical universe. His reference to the appropriateness of mathematics as a "wonderful gift" points to the underlying connections established by God.

The mathematics created by human minds owes its origin to God, who created man in His image (Gen. 1:27) as a thinking, reasoning being. It is God who makes it possible for sinful humans to develop logical mathematical systems. Famous Protestant theologian John Calvin concluded, ". . . since it is manifest that men whom the Scriptures term carnal, are so acute and clear-sighted in the investigation of inferior things, their example should teach us how many gifts the Lord has left in possession of human nature . . . . But if the Lord has been pleased to assist us by the work and ministry of the ungodly in physics, dialectics, mathematics, and other similar sciences, let us avail ourselves of it, lest, by neglecting the gifts of God spontaneously offered to us, we be justly punished for our sloth." Calvin understood that human mathematical and scientific abilities are inherent gifts from our Creator.

Many prominent men have recognized that their important discoveries are not their exclusive creations. Heinrich Hertz, the German physicist who first proved the existence of Maxwell's electromagnetic waves, stated that "one cannot escape the feeling that these mathematical formulas have an independent existence and an intelligence of their own, that they are wiser than we are, wiser even than their discoverers, that we get more out of them than was originally put into them." James Nickel, a prominent Christian mathematician, contrasted man's knowledge with God's, stating that "man's mathematical knowledge will never exhaust the infinite panorama of God's knowledge (I Sam. 2:3; Ps. 147:5). At best, man is gifted with an infinitesimal subset of God's exhaustive wisdom and knowledge (Ps. 104:24)."

❯ Exercises

1. What is the original source of mathematical laws and truth?

2. Describe the view of the origin of mathematics held by many modern secular mathematicians.

3. What two terms did Newton and Leibniz use to describe the same calculus concept?

4. How did Eugene Wigner describe "the miracle of the appropriateness of the language of mathematics" in developing the laws of physics?

5. Why did John Calvin say that even the ungodly can make great discoveries in mathematics and the sciences?

6. **Discuss:** Why do mathematical systems designed by man owe their origin to God?

7. **Discuss:** Explain the statement "Mathematics is a gift from God."

8. **Discuss:** Should man's role in the development of mathematics be described as creating, discovering, or both? Explain why.

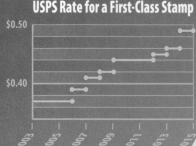

1.3 Piecewise Functions and Continuity

After completing this section, you will be able to

- define and graph the basic absolute value and greatest integer functions.
- graph and analyze piecewise functions.
- use limits to identify points of discontinuity.

Many graphs cannot be defined by a single rule.

A *piecewise function* is defined by two or more function rules for various intervals of its domain. The correct rule is selected based on the value of x. The *absolute value function* is likely the first piecewise function you have encountered.

$$f(x) = |x| = \begin{cases} x \text{ if } x \geq 0 \\ -x \text{ if } x < 0 \end{cases}$$

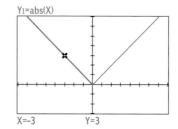

Y₁=abs(X)

X=-3   Y=3

If $x \geq 0$, then $|x|$ is x. If $x < 0$ (a negative number), then $|x|$ is the opposite of x (a positive number). This implies that an absolute value is always nonnegative.

The graph of the absolute value function consists of two linear pieces: $y = -x$ when $x < 0$ and $y = x$ when $x \geq 0$. Notice that the domain is all real numbers and the range is the nonnegative real numbers.

Example 1   Evaluating an Absolute Value Function

Find $g(x) = |2x - 3|$ with $D = \{-4, -2, 0, 1, 2, 4\}$.

Answer

$g(-4) = |2(-4) - 3| = |-11| = 11$
$g(-2) = |2(-2) - 3| = |-7| = 7$
$g(0) = |2(0) - 3| = |-3| = 3$
$g(1) = |2(1) - 3| = |-1| = 1$
$g(2) = |2(2) - 3| = |1| = 1$
$g(4) = |2(4) - 3| = |5| = 5$

1. Evaluate the function at each member of the domain.

$g = \{(-4, 11), (-2, 7), (0, 3), (1, 1), (2, 1), (4, 5)\}$

2. List the set of ordered pairs.

In Excel spreadsheets the greatest integer function, INT, is a special case of a FLOOR function, while rounding up to the next integer is an example of a CEILING function.

SKILL ✓ EXERCISE 1

The graph of the *greatest integer function* consists of an infinite number of pieces. Each range value is the greatest integer less than or equal to the given domain value. The function is represented using square brackets: $f(x) = [x]$. Its domain is the set of real numbers, but its range consists of the set of integers. The rule for the greatest integer function can be written as a piecewise function.

$$f(x) = [x] = \begin{cases} \vdots \\ -2 \text{ if } -2 \leq x < -1 \\ -1 \text{ if } -1 \leq x < 0 \\ 0 \text{ if } 0 \leq x < 1 \\ 1 \text{ if } 1 \leq x < 2 \\ \vdots \end{cases}$$

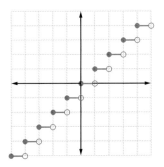

Since the *y*-value of each piece is constant, each of the infinitely many pieces is a portion of a horizontal line. Notice how the open circles and solid dots are used to indicate whether the endpoint of each portion is included or excluded in the graph.

Example 2 Evaluating the Greatest Integer Function

Find $f(x) = [x]$ where $D = \left\{ -5, -\frac{3}{2}, -\frac{3}{4}, 0, \frac{1}{4}, \frac{5}{2} \right\}$.

Answer

$f(-5) = [-5] = -5$ 1. The greatest integer less than or equal to −5 is −5.

$f\left(-\frac{3}{2}\right) = \left[-\frac{3}{2}\right] = -2$ 2. The greatest integer less than or equal to −1.5 is −2.

$f\left(-\frac{3}{4}\right) = \left[-\frac{3}{4}\right] = -1$ 3. The greatest integer less than or equal to −0.75 is −1.

$f(0) = [0] = 0$ 4. The greatest integer less than or equal to 0 is 0.

$f\left(\frac{1}{4}\right) = \left[\frac{1}{4}\right] = 0$ 5. The greatest integer less than or equal to 0.25 is 0.

$f\left(\frac{5}{2}\right) = \left[\frac{5}{2}\right] = 2$ 6. The greatest integer less than or equal to 2.5 is 2.

$f = \left\{ (-5, -5), \left(-\frac{3}{2}, -2\right), \left(-\frac{3}{4}, -1\right), (0, 0), \left(\frac{1}{4}, 0\right), \left(\frac{5}{2}, 2\right) \right\}$

SKILL ✓ **EXERCISE 3**

The definition of a mathematical function has broadened considerably since the development of calculus in the eighteenth century. While the term initially referred only to continuous functions, these are a small subset of the vast number of relations that are considered to be functions today.

A function that has no gaps, jumps, or holes is a *continuous function*. You can graph a continuous function without lifting your pencil from the paper. The absolute value function is continuous, while the greatest integer function is discontinuous because of the jumps between pieces. Many piecewise functions are discontinuous.

Example 3   Graphing Piecewise Functions

Graph $f(x) = \begin{cases} x^2 & \text{if } x \leq -1 \\ |x| & \text{if } -1 < x \leq 2 \\ -x+5 & \text{if } x > 2 \end{cases}$.

Then list the function's domain and range and state whether the function appears to be continuous.

KEYWORD SEARCH

piecewise grapher $\mathcal{Q}$

Answer

x	x^2	x	$|x|$	x	$-x+5$
-2	4	-1	1	2	3
-1	1	0	0	5	0
		2	2		

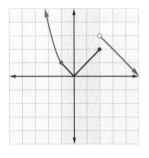

$D = \mathbb{R}; R = \mathbb{R}$
The function appears to be discontinuous when $x = 2$.

Check

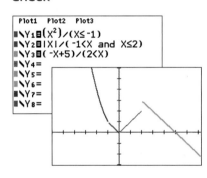

Plot1 Plot2 Plot3
■\Y₁🔲(X²)/(X≤-1)
■\Y₂🔲|X|/(-1<X and X≤2)
■\Y₃🔲(-X+5)/(2<X)
■\Y₄=
■\Y₅=
■\Y₆=
■\Y₇=
■\Y₈=

X	Y₁	Y₂	Y₃
-1.005	1.01	ERROR	ERROR
-1.004	1.008	ERROR	ERROR
-1.003	1.006	ERROR	ERROR
-1.002	1.004	ERROR	ERROR
-1.001	1.002	ERROR	ERROR
-1	1	ERROR	ERROR
-0.999	ERROR	0.999	ERROR
-0.998	ERROR	0.998	ERROR
-0.997	ERROR	0.997	ERROR
-0.996	ERROR	0.996	ERROR
-0.995	ERROR	0.995	ERROR

X=-1

X	Y₁	Y₂	Y₃
1.995	ERROR	1.995	ERROR
1.996	ERROR	1.996	ERROR
1.997	ERROR	1.997	ERROR
1.998	ERROR	1.998	ERROR
1.999	ERROR	1.999	ERROR
2	ERROR	2	ERROR
2.001	ERROR	ERROR	2.999
2.002	ERROR	ERROR	2.998
2.003	ERROR	ERROR	2.997
2.004	ERROR	ERROR	2.996
2.005	ERROR	ERROR	2.995

X=2

TIP

Use TEST ([2nd], [MATH]) to enter inequalities or logical operators. To [TRACE] along the graph of a piecewise function, use ▲ or ▼ to select the desired function rule.

1. Divide the coordinate plane into the domain's three subsets: $x \leq -1, -1 < x \leq 2$, and $x > 2$.

2. Assign each function to its domain and evaluate it at selected values within the domain or at an excluded endpoint.

3. Graph each piece of the function.

4. Verify whether the endpoint of each piece is open or closed.

5. The function is defined for all real numbers. The graph implies that the function ranges from $-\infty$ to ∞.

6. To graph each piece of the function with a graphing calculator, divide its function rule by the inequality representing its domain as shown. The expressions in the denominator evaluate to 1 when the inequality is true and to 0 when the inequality is false.

7. While the graphed function may appear to have breaks at -1, examining the first table of values shows that the pieces would "connect" at $(-1, 1)$.

8. Examining the second table around $x = 2$ shows that the function's value jumps from 2 to almost 3.

SKILL ✓ EXERCISE 11

If a function $f(x)$ is continuous at $x = a$, then the value of the function must approach $y = f(a)$ from both the left and the right. The number that a function approaches, even if that number is never reached, is called a *limit*.

DEFINITIONS

The **left-hand limit** of $f(x)$ as x approaches a, denoted $\lim\limits_{x \to a^-} f(x)$, is the number to which $f(x)$ gets closer and closer as x gets closer to a from the left.

The **right-hand limit** of $f(x)$ as x approaches a, denoted $\lim\limits_{x \to a^+} f(x)$, is the number to which $f(x)$ gets closer and closer as x gets closer to a from the right.

Left- and right-hand limits are often referred to as *one-sided limits*.

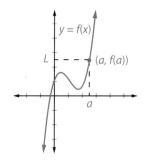

In Example 3, the left-hand limit is $\lim\limits_{x \to 2^-} f(x) = 2$ since $f(x) = |x|$ gets closer and closer to 2 as x approaches 2 from the left. The right-hand limit is $\lim\limits_{x \to 2^+} f(x) = 3$ since $f(x) = -x + 5$ gets closer and closer to 3 as x approaches 2 from the right.

DEFINITION

The **limit** of $f(x)$ as x approaches a, denoted $\lim\limits_{x \to a} f(x)$, is L if and only if
$$\lim\limits_{x \to a^-} f(x) = \lim\limits_{x \to a^+} f(x) = L.$$

TIP

This "two-sided" limit of the piecewise function in Example 3 at $x = -1$ exists and $\lim\limits_{x \to -1} f(x) = 1$ since $\lim\limits_{x \to -1^-} f(x) = \lim\limits_{x \to -1^+} f(x) = 1$. Because $\lim\limits_{x \to -1} f(x) = f(-1)$, the function is continuous at $x = -1$.

An infinite discontinuity indicates the presence of a vertical asymptote. A point discontinuity is also called a removable discontinuity.

Notice that $\lim\limits_{x \to 2} f(x)$ does not exist since $\lim\limits_{x \to 2^-} f(x) = 2$ and $\lim\limits_{x \to 2^+} f(x) = 3$. This difference between left- and right-hand limits indicates a jump in the value of the function.

The following table illustrates different possible types of discontinuity at $x = 2$.

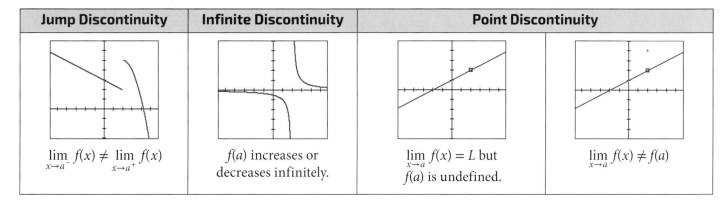

Jump Discontinuity	Infinite Discontinuity	Point Discontinuity	
$\lim\limits_{x \to a^-} f(x) \neq \lim\limits_{x \to a^+} f(x)$	$f(a)$ increases or decreases infinitely.	$\lim\limits_{x \to a} f(x) = L$ but $f(a)$ is undefined.	$\lim\limits_{x \to a} f(x) \neq f(a)$

DEFINITION

A function is **continuous** at $x = a$ if $f(a)$ and $\lim\limits_{x \to a} f(x)$ exist and $\lim\limits_{x \to a} f(x) = f(a)$.
A function is *continuous on an interval* (a, b) if and only if it is continuous at every point in (a, b).

Example 4 Identifying Discontinuities

Determine if $f(x) = \dfrac{x-2}{x^2-2x}$ is continuous at each value. If it is discontinuous, identify the type of discontinuity.

a. $x = -2$ **b.** $x = 0$ **c.** $x = 2$

Answer

a. At $x = -2$, $f(-2) = \dfrac{-4}{8} = -\dfrac{1}{2}$.

	$x \to -2^-$ →				← $x \to -2^+$		
x	−2.1	−2.01	−2.001	−2	−1.999	−1.99	−1.9
$f(x)$	−0.4762	−0.4975	−0.4998	−0.5	−0.5003	−0.5025	−0.5263

$f(x)$ → −0.5 ← $f(x)$

$\lim\limits_{x \to -2} f(x) = -0.5$ since $\lim\limits_{x \to -2^-} f(x) = -0.5$ and $\lim\limits_{x \to -2^+} f(x) = -0.5$.

The function is continuous at $x = -2$ since $\lim\limits_{x \to -2} f(x) = f(-2)$.

b. At $x = 0$, $f(0) = \dfrac{-2}{0}$, which is undefined.

	$x \to 0^-$ →				← $x \to 0^+$		
x	−0.1	−0.01	−0.001	0	0.001	0.01	0.1
$f(x)$	−10	−100	−1000		1000	100	10

$f(x)$ → −∞ ∞ ← $f(x)$

$\lim\limits_{x \to 0} f(x)$ does not exist since $\lim\limits_{x \to 0^-} f(x) = -\infty$ and $\lim\limits_{x \to 0^+} f(x) = \infty$.

The function has an infinite discontinuity at $x = 0$.

c. At $x = 2$, $f(2) = \dfrac{0}{0}$, which is undefined.

	$x \to 2^-$ →				← $x \to 2^+$		
x	1.9	1.99	1.999	2	2.001	2.01	2.1
$f(x)$	0.5263	0.5025	0.5003		0.4998	0.4975	0.4762

$f(x)$ → 0.5 ← $f(x)$

$\lim\limits_{x \to 2} f(x) = 0.5$ since $\lim\limits_{x \to 2^-} f(x) = 0.5$ and $\lim\limits_{x \to 2^+} f(x) = 0.5$.

The function has a point discontinuity at $x = 2$.

Check

Graphing the function clearly illustrates the infinite discontinuity at $x = 0$. Use the trace function or view a table of values to confirm the point discontinuity at $x = 2$.

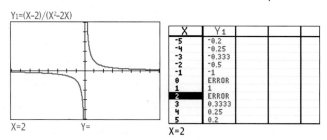

The intervals of continuity for the function in Example 4 are $(-\infty, 0)$, $(0, 2)$, and $(2, \infty)$.

SKILL ✓ **EXERCISE 36**

A. Exercises

Find the set of ordered pairs for each function rule when $D = \{-4, -\frac{1}{2}, 0, \frac{3}{4}, 2\}$.

1. $g(x) = |4x|$

2. $f(x) = |x - 4|$

3. $h(x) = [x]$

4. $g(x) = [3x + 1]$

5. $h(x) = \begin{cases} -6x & \text{if } x < 0 \\ x + 2 & \text{if } x \geq 0 \end{cases}$

6. $f(x) = \begin{cases} 2x + 5 & \text{if } x < -1 \\ x & \text{if } -1 \leq x \leq 1 \\ x - 1 & \text{if } x > 1 \end{cases}$

Graph each function. Then state its domain, range, and whether it is continuous or discontinuous.

7. $f(x) = |x|$

8. $h(x) = |x - 6|$

9. $f(x) = |x + 3| + 1$

10. $p(x) = \begin{cases} 0 & \text{if } x = 3 \\ 5 & \text{if } x \neq 3 \end{cases}$

11. $g(x) = \begin{cases} -x & \text{if } x < 1 \\ 2x - 3 & \text{if } x \geq 1 \end{cases}$

12. $f(x) = \begin{cases} x + 3 & \text{if } x < -2 \\ 3^x & \text{if } x > -1 \end{cases}$

Classify each function as continuous or discontinuous. Further classify any discontinuities as jump, infinite, or point.

13.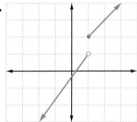

14.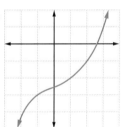

15.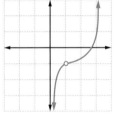

16.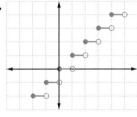

17.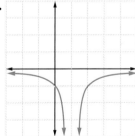

18.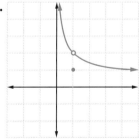

19. Which is a continuous function?
   A. the number of people attending church as a function of the week of the year
   B. the area of a triangle as a function of its height
   C. the cost of gasoline as a function of time

20. Which is a discontinuous function?
   A. the cost of filling your tank with gasoline as a function of the number of gallons
   B. the distance traveled as a function of time
   C. the number of minutes charged to your cell phone account as a function of the length of the call

B. Exercises

Graph each function. Then state its domain, range, and whether it is continuous or discontinuous.

21. $g(x) = [x]$

22. $y = [x - 4]$

23. $y = \begin{cases} x & \text{if } x < 1 \\ 2x - 4 & \text{if } 1 \leq x \leq 4 \\ \frac{1}{3}x & \text{if } x > 4 \end{cases}$

24. $f(x) = \begin{cases} x^2 & \text{if } -2 < x < 2 \\ 4 & \text{otherwise} \end{cases}$

Use the graph of $f(x)$ to complete exercises 25–33.

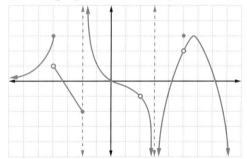

Find the one-sided limits.

25. $\lim\limits_{x \to -4^-} f(x)$ and $\lim\limits_{x \to -4^+} f(x)$

26. $\lim\limits_{x \to -2^-} f(x)$ and $\lim\limits_{x \to -2^+} f(x)$

27. $\lim\limits_{x \to 2^-} f(x)$ and $\lim\limits_{x \to 2^+} f(x)$

28. $\lim\limits_{x \to 5^-} f(x)$ and $\lim\limits_{x \to 5^+} f(x)$

Use the graph of $f(x)$ above to find each limit. Justify your answer using the definition of a limit.

29. $\lim\limits_{x \to 2} f(x)$

30. $\lim\limits_{x \to 3} f(x)$

31. $\lim\limits_{x \to -2} f(x)$

32. List the values for which a limit of $f(x)$ does not exist.

33. Name the value of x for which the limit of $f(x)$ is not equal to the defined value of the function.

State whether each function is continuous or discontinuous at $x = -2$ and classify any discontinuities as jump, infinite, or point. Justify your answer using the definition of continuity.

34. $f(x) = \dfrac{x}{x+1}$

35. $g(x) = \dfrac{x}{x^2 - 4}$

36. $h(x) = \dfrac{x^2 + 6x + 8}{x^2 - 2x - 8}$

37. $r(x) = \dfrac{4x}{x^2 + 4}$

38. $t(x) = [x]$

❯ C. Exercises

39. Classify each type of function as *always*, *sometimes*, or *never* continuous.

   a. linear   **b.** greatest integer   **c.** piecewise

40. Determine whether $f(x) = \sqrt{x+1}$ is continuous in each case.

   a. at $x = -2$

   b. over its domain

   c. over the real numbers

41. Graph $y \geq |x - 3|$.

42. Refer to the graph of $f(x)$ in exercises 25–33.

   a. Find $\lim\limits_{x \to -\infty} f(x)$.

   b. What characteristic of the graph is indicated by this limit?

CUMULATIVE REVIEW

43. Given $g(x) = -3x^3$, find $g(2)$, $g(-1)$, $g(0)$, and $g(5)$. [1.1]

44. Given $f(x) = 3x^{-1}$, find $f(2)$, $f(-1)$, $f(0)$, and $f(5)$. [1.1]

45. Solve $\dfrac{x}{8} = \dfrac{21}{28}$. [Appendix 2]

46. State the slope of the line $y = -2$. [1.2]

Write a function rule describing the line through each pair of points. [1.2]

47. $(1, 3)$ and $(-2, -6)$

48. $(0, 5)$ and $(3, 8)$

49. Producing a Wi-Fi device costs $12 per device plus a one-time setup expense of $3200. How many Wi-Fi devices must a company sell at $20 each to make a profit? [1.2]

   A. > 160   **C.** > 200   **E.** > 400

   B. < 200   **D.** > 300

50. If $M(-1, 2)$ is the midpoint of $\overline{CD}$ with D at $(5, 1)$, what are the coordinates of C? [1.2]

   A. $(-7, 3)$ **C.** $(-7, 1)$ **E.** none of these

   B. $(4, 1)$ **D.** $(4, 3)$

Write and solve an equation or inequality to complete the following exercises. [Appendix 2]

51. Find a number such that two-thirds of the sum of the number and 9 is twice the number.

   A. $\dfrac{9}{4}$ **C.** $\dfrac{9}{2}$ **E.** none of these

   B. $\dfrac{27}{4}$ **D.** $\dfrac{27}{2}$

52. Which interval describes the set of real numbers such that the sum of 3 times a number and 5 is no more than -16?

   A. $\left(-\infty, -\dfrac{11}{3}\right)$ **D.** $(-\infty, -7]$

   B. $\left(-\infty, -\dfrac{11}{3}\right]$ **E.** none of these

   C. $(-\infty, -7)$

The electrostatic force between two charged objects varies inversely with the square of the distance between them.

Power functions include several basic functions that serve as building blocks for other functions.

DEFINITION

A **power function** is a function in the form $f(x) = kx^n$ where k and the power n are non-zero constants.

Functions such as $y = -3x^2$, $y = 2x^{\frac{1}{3}}$, and $y = \dfrac{1}{5x^4}$ are power functions, but $y = 2^x$ and $y = 6$ are not. While the exponent n can be any rational or irrational value, we will limit our discussion in this section to power functions with integral exponents. The simplest power function, $y = kx$, is a linear function through the origin with a slope of k. Examine the basic quadratic and cubic functions $y = kx^2$ and $y = kx^3$ where $k = 1$.

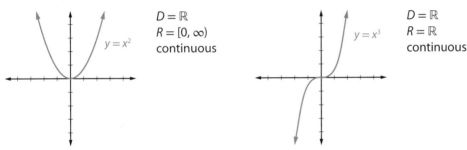

$D = \mathbb{R}$
$R = [0, \infty)$
continuous

$y = x^2$

$D = \mathbb{R}$
$R = \mathbb{R}$
continuous

$y = x^3$

After completing this section, you will be able to

- describe power functions.
- describe end behaviors.
- describe intervals in which a function is increasing, decreasing, or constant.
- classify functions as even, odd, or neither.
- use power functions to model variations.

The *end behavior* of a function can be described as limits of the values of $f(x)$ as x increases or decreases without bound. Notice how end behaviors of the quadratic and cubic functions are expressed using the notation of limits.

Examining End Behavior			
$f(x) = x^2$		$f(x) = x^3$	
Left-End	Right-End	Left-End	Right-End
$\lim\limits_{x \to -\infty} x^2 = \infty$	$\lim\limits_{x \to \infty} x^2 = \infty$	$\lim\limits_{x \to -\infty} x^3 = -\infty$	$\lim\limits_{x \to \infty} x^3 = \infty$

Examining the graph of a function will help you find intervals where the function is *increasing*, *decreasing*, or *constant* as you move from left to right. Notice that $f(x) = x^2$ decreases over $(-\infty, 0]$ and increases over $[0, \infty)$, and that $f(x) = x^3$ increases over its entire domain.

DEFINITIONS

Given a function $f(x)$ and an interval I in which $x_2 > x_1$ for all x_1 and $x_2 \in I$,

the function is **increasing** over I if $f(x_2) > f(x_1)$,

the function is **decreasing** over I if $f(x_2) < f(x_1)$, and

the function is **constant** over I if $f(x_2) = f(x_1)$.

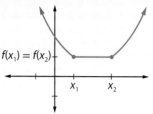

Many power functions can be classified as either even or odd.

DEFINITIONS

A function is **even** when $f(-x) = f(x)$ for all $x \in D$.
A function is **odd** when $f(-x) = -f(x)$ for all $x \in D$.

A function in which $f(-x) \neq f(x)$ and $f(-x) \neq -f(x)$ is neither even nor odd. The basic quadratic function $f(x) = x^2$ is an even function since $f(-x) = (-x)^2 = x^2 = f(x)$. Notice that its graph exhibits line symmetry with respect to the y-axis, a characteristic of any even function. The basic cubic function $f(x) = x^3$ is an odd function since $f(-x) = (-x)^3 = -x^3 = -f(x)$. Notice that its graph exhibits point symmetry with respect to the origin, a characteristic of any odd function. In exercises 40–41 you will show that all power functions of even degree are even functions and that all power functions of odd degree are odd functions.

Example 1 Describing Power Functions with Positive Exponents

Graph each function. Then describe its domain; range; end behavior; intervals of continuity; intervals for which the function is increasing, decreasing, or constant; whether the function is even, odd, or neither; and any symmetry.

a. $f(x) = \frac{1}{4}x^5$

b. $g(x) = -2x^4$

Answer

a.

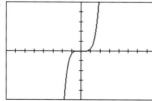

$D = \mathbb{R}; R = \mathbb{R}$
$\lim\limits_{x \to -\infty} \frac{1}{4}x^5 = -\infty, \lim\limits_{x \to \infty} \frac{1}{4}x^5 = \infty$
The function is continuous and increases over its entire domain.
The function is odd and exhibits point symmetry with respect to the origin.

b.

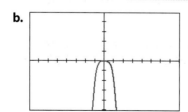

$D = \mathbb{R}; R = (-\infty, 0]$
$\lim\limits_{x \to -\infty} -2x^4 = -\infty, \lim\limits_{x \to \infty} -2x^4 = -\infty$
The function is continuous over its domain.
It increases over $(-\infty, 0]$ and decreases over $[0, \infty)$.
The function is even and exhibits line symmetry with respect to the y-axis.

SKILL ✔ EXERCISE 19

The graph of a power function $y = kx^2$ with $k < 0$ is a reflection across the x-axis of the graph of the corresponding power function with $k > 0$. For example, $f(x) = 2x^4$ approaches ∞ as x approaches both $-\infty$ and ∞, but $f(x) = -2x^4$ approaches $-\infty$ as x approaches both $-\infty$ and ∞.

While the graphs of power functions with positive exponents are continuous functions, the graphs of power functions with negative exponents contain a discontinuity. Notice that the graph of $f(x) = x^{-1} = \frac{1}{x}$ has an infinite discontinuity at $x = 0$, where the function is undefined. The end behaviors of power functions with negative exponents also differ from those of power functions with positive exponents.

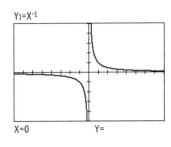

$f(x) = x^{-1}$	
Left-End	**Right-End**
$\lim\limits_{x \to -\infty} x^{-1} = 0$	$\lim\limits_{x \to \infty} x^{-1} = 0$

Example 2 Describing Power Functions with Negative Exponents

Graph each function. Then describe the domain; range; end behavior; intervals of continuity; intervals for which the function is increasing, decreasing, or constant; whether the function is even, odd, or neither; and any symmetry.

a. $f(x) = 3x^{-2}$

b. $g(x) = -\frac{1}{4}x^{-3}$

Answer

a.

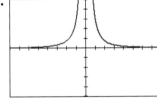

$D = \{x \mid x \neq 0\}$; $R = \{y \mid y > 0\}$

$\lim\limits_{x \to -\infty} 3x^{-2} = 0$, $\lim\limits_{x \to \infty} 3x^{-2} = 0$

The function has an infinite discontinuity at $x = 0$.

It increases over $(-\infty, 0)$ and decreases over $(0, \infty)$. The function is even and exhibits line symmetry with respect to the y-axis.

b.

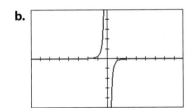

$D = \{x \mid x \neq 0\}$; $R = \{y \mid y \neq 0\}$

$\lim\limits_{x \to -\infty} -\frac{1}{4}x^{-3} = 0$, $\lim\limits_{x \to \infty} -\frac{1}{4}x^{-3} = 0$

The function has an infinite discontinuity at $x = 0$.

It increases over $(-\infty, 0)$ and over $(0, \infty)$. The function is odd and exhibits point symmetry with respect to the origin.

SKILL ✓ **EXERCISE 21**

You have studied direct and inverse variations in previous courses. Any variation of two variables can be viewed as a power function of the form $y = kx^n$ where k, the *constant of variation* (or *constant of proportion*), is positive.

If y varies *directly* with (or is *directly proportional* to) x, then $y = kx$. The fact that the circumference of a circle varies directly with the length of its radius is described by the function $c = 2\pi r$ where the constant of variation is 2π.

Example 3   Modeling a Direct Variation

When an object is traveling at a constant speed, the distance traveled varies directly with the elapsed time. If it took 2 hr to travel 50 mi, find the distance traveled in 7 hr.

Answer

$d = kt$ 1. Distance varies directly with time.

$k = \dfrac{d}{t} = \dfrac{50 \text{ mi}}{2 \text{ hr}} = 25 \text{ mi/hr}$ 2. Solve for the constant of variation, k.

$d = \left(25 \dfrac{\text{mi}}{\text{hr}}\right)t$ 3. Use the variation from step 1 to write a function modeling the variation.

$\quad = \left(25 \dfrac{\text{mi}}{\text{hr}}\right)(7 \text{ hr}) = 175 \text{ mi}$ 4. Evaluate the function for $t = 7$ hr.

SKILL ✔ **EXERCISE 27**

A variable may also vary directly with a power of another variable. For example, the fact that the area of a circle varies directly with the square of its radius can be modeled with the function $A = \pi r^2$, where the constant of variation is π.

Example 4   Modeling a Direct Variation with a Power of a Variable

The volume of a sphere is directly proportional to the cube of its radius. If a sphere with a radius of 6 cm has a volume of 288π cm^3, find the volume of a sphere with a radius of 12 cm.

Answer

$V = kr^3$ 1. The volume of a sphere varies directly with the cube of its radius.

$k = \dfrac{V}{r^3} = \dfrac{288\pi \text{ cm}^3}{(6 \text{ cm})^3} = \dfrac{4}{3}\pi$ 2. Solve for k.

$V = \dfrac{4}{3}\pi r^3$ 3. Write a function modeling the variation.

$\quad = \dfrac{4}{3}\pi(12 \text{ cm})^3 = 2304\pi \text{ cm}^3$ 4. Evaluate the function when $r = 12$ cm.

SKILL ✔ **EXERCISE 29**

In a direct variation the exponent in the power function is positive, but in an inverse variation, the exponent of the power function is negative. If y *varies inversely* with (or is *inversely proportional* to) x, then $y = kx^{-1}$ or $y = \dfrac{k}{x}$. The fact that the gravitational force between two objects varies inversely with the square of the distance between their centers can be modeled by the equation $F = kd^{-2}$ or $F = \dfrac{k}{d^2}$. Rearranging this equation shows that the product of inversely proportional quantities remains constant: $Fd^2 = k$.

Example 5   Modeling an Inverse Variation

The illumination, I, of an object is inversely proportional to the square of its distance, d, from the light source. What is the illumination of an object 6 m from a lamp if the illumination 2 m from the lamp is 150 lumen/m^2?

Answer

$I = kd^{-2} = \dfrac{k}{d^2}$

1. Illumination varies inversely with the square of the distance from the light source.

$k = Id^2 = \left(150\,\dfrac{\text{lumen}}{\text{m}^2}\right)(2\text{ m})^2$

$\quad = 600\text{ lumen}$

2. Solve for k.

$I = \dfrac{600\text{ lumen}}{d^2}$

3. Write a function modeling the variation.

$I = \dfrac{600\text{ lumen}}{(6\text{ m})^2} \approx 16.7\text{ lumen/m}^2$

4. Evaluate the function when $d = 6$ m.

——————————————————————— SKILL ✔ EXERCISE 31

Notice that tripling the distance caused the illumination to be one-ninth of the original illumination.

❯ A. Exercises

1. State the power and constant of variation for each power function.

   a. $f(x) = -\dfrac{1}{4}x^3$ **b.** $g(x) = -\dfrac{2}{3x^7}$

   c. $P = \dfrac{22.4}{V}$ **d.** $A = \dfrac{\sqrt{3}}{4}x^2$

2. Explain why each function is not a power function.

   a. $y = 10$ **b.** $h(x) = 5^x$

Sketch a graph of each function. Then use limit notation to state its end behavior.

3. $f(x) = \dfrac{1}{4}x^3$ 4. $f(x) = -x^4$

5. $g(x) = 2x^{-5}$

Sketch a graph of each function. Then describe intervals for which the function is increasing, decreasing, or constant.

6. $f(x) = 2x^2$ 7. $f(x) = -3x^{-5}$

8. $g(x) = -\dfrac{x^3}{2}$

Sketch a graph of each function. Then state whether the function is even, odd, or neither and describe any symmetry.

9. $g(x) = 2x^3$ 10. $f(x) = x^{-2}$

11. $f(x) = 4x^{-3}$

Write a power function modeling each variation.

12. q varies directly with r; $q = 3$ when $r = 12$

13. m varies directly with the cube of n; $m = 96$ when $n = 2$

14. r varies inversely with p; $r = 15$ when $p = 3$

15. d varies inversely with the square of a; $d = 8$ when $a = \dfrac{1}{2}$

❯ B. Exercises

Use technology to graph each function. Then describe the domain; range; end behavior; intervals of continuity; intervals for which the function is increasing, decreasing, or constant; whether the function is even, odd, or neither; and any symmetry.

16. $f(x) = \dfrac{1}{2}x^{-1}$ 17. $f(x) = -\dfrac{1}{8}x^2$

18. $f(x) = -4x^{-2}$ 19. $f(x) = -0.25x^3$

20. $f(x) = \dfrac{1}{4}x^4$ 21. $f(x) = 3x^{-3}$

Match the values given for $f(x) = kx^n$ to each described graph.

A. $k > 0$, n is even   **C.** $k < 0$, n is even
B. $k > 0$, n is odd   **D.** $k < 0$, n is odd

22. symmetric with respect to the origin and $\displaystyle\lim_{x \to -\infty} f(x) = \infty$

23. symmetric with respect to the y-axis and $\displaystyle\lim_{x \to \infty} f(x) = -\infty$

24. symmetric with respect to the y-axis and $\displaystyle\lim_{x \to \infty} f(x) = \infty$

25. symmetric with respect to the origin and $\displaystyle\lim_{x \to -\infty} f(x) = -\infty$

Use a power function to model each variation.

26. Ohm's law states that current in an electric circuit with a given resistance varies directly with the voltage. If the current is 3 amps at 10 volts, what is the voltage if the current is 5 amps?

27. Hooke's law states that the distance a spring stretches is directly proportional to the force applied to the spring. Find the distance a spring stretches under 42 lb of force if a force of 12 lb stretches the spring 1.4 in.

28. If the number of days it takes to complete a project is inversely proportional to the number of workers hired for the project, and if it takes 54 days for 4 workers to complete the project, how many days are needed to complete a project with 18 workers?

29. If the stopping distance of a motor vehicle is directly proportional to the square of the vehicle's speed, and if it takes 96 ft for a vehicle to stop when traveling 40 mi/hr, find the stopping distance for the vehicle when traveling 60 mi/hr.

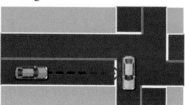

30. If the distance a stone falls varies directly with the square of the time it has been falling, and if a stone falls 4 ft in the first 0.5 sec, how far does the stone fall in 3 sec?

31. The electrostatic force between two charged particles is inversely proportional to the square of the distance between them. If the force between two particles 0.02 m apart is 8×10^{-20} N, find the force when the particles are 0.08 m apart.

32. Bill's grade point average (GPA) varies inversely with the time he spends playing video games. Bill has a GPA of 2.8 when playing video games for 18 hr/week. How many hours should Bill limit his video game playing to if he wants to achieve a 3.5 GPA?

33. The strength of a magnetic field is inversely proportional to the cube of the distance from the magnet. By what factor does the strength of the field increase when the distance to the magnet is halved?

34. The relative illumination of a photograph's subject is inversely proportional to the square of its distance from the light source. If the subject's relative illumination at 1 m is 100%, what is its relative illumination at 2 m? 5 m? 10 m?

35. Graph the following power functions in the same window: $y = x$; $y = x^3$; $y = x^5$; $y = x^7$.
    a. State the domain; range; end behavior; intervals of continuity; intervals for which the function is increasing, decreasing, or constant; and the symmetry for any odd power function with $k = 1$.
    b. What points are included in all the graphs?
    c. Describe how the graph changes as the exponent increases.

36. Graph the following power functions in the same window: $y = x^2$; $y = x^4$; $y = x^6$; $y = x^8$.
    a. State the domain; range; end behavior; intervals of continuity; intervals for which the function is increasing, decreasing, or constant; and the symmetry for any even power function for which $k = 1$.
    b. What points are included in all the graphs?
    c. Describe how the graph changes as the exponent increases.

37. In what ways would the description of each function differ from the description of the even power functions in exercise 36a?
    a. $y = x^0$ b. $y = kx^0$

❯ C. Exercises

38. State whether each function is a power function. If not, give the reason. Then state whether the function is even, odd, or neither.

    a. $f(x) = 5\sqrt[3]{x}$ **b.** $f(x) = 2x^0$

    c. $f(t) = 5^x$ **d.** $f(x) = x^{\sqrt{3}}$

39. Use the graph of each function to state whether the function is even, odd, or neither. Then verify your answer algebraically.

    a. $y = 6x$ **b.** $y = 3x + 5$

    c. $y = x^4 - 3x^2 + 5$ **d.** $y = x^3 - 4x$

    e. $y = x^2 - 5x - 2$

40. Prove: Show that power functions in which the exponent is even are even functions.

41. Prove: Show that power functions in which the exponent is odd are odd functions.

42. Prove: Prove that if functions f and g are increasing functions, then $f + g$ is also an increasing function.

43. Kepler's third law of planetary motion states that the square of a planet's orbital period is directly proportional to the cube of the planet's average distance from the sun.

    a. Using T for the planet's orbital period and R for its average distance from the sun, express the relation as a variation.

    b. If Earth has an orbital period of 365.2 days and an average distance of 93 million miles from the sun, find k for our sun's solar system.

    c. Use the data about Earth's orbit to estimate Neptune's orbital period (in Earth years) if Neptune's average distance from the sun is 2.8 billion miles.

CUMULATIVE REVIEW

Write each quadratic expression as a binomial squared. [Algebra]

44. $x^2 - 8x + 16$ **45.** $9x^2 + 12x + 4$

46. Simplify $(x - 1)^2 - 3(x - 1) + 5$. [Algebra]

47. Write the linear function rule for
$f = \{(x, y) \mid (-4, -7), (-1, -1), (3, 7)\}$. [1.2]

48. Graph $g(x) = \begin{cases} -2x & \text{if } x < 0 \\ x - 2 & \text{if } x \geq 0 \end{cases}$. [1.3]

49. Find each limit of $g(x)$ from exercise 48. [1.3]

    a. $\lim\limits_{x \to 0^+}$ **b.** $\lim\limits_{x \to 0^-}$ **c.** $\lim\limits_{x \to 0}$

50. Describe the continuity of $g(x)$ from exercise 48 at $x = 0$. [1.3]

    A. continuous   **D.** point discontinuity

    B. infinite discontinuity   **E.** none of these

    C. jump discontinuity

51. Which point is on the line passing through $(4, 7)$ with a slope of $-\frac{5}{2}$? [1.2]

    A. $(2, 2)$ **D.** $(-1, 5)$

    B. $(2, 12)$ **E.** none of these

    C. $(6, 12)$

Write and solve an equation or inequality to complete the following exercises. [Appendix 2]

52. Which interval describes the numbers such that the difference of 5 and twice the number is at least 37?

    A. $(-\infty, 16)$ **D.** $(-\infty, -16]$

    B. $[-16, \infty)$ **E.** none of these

    C. $(16, \infty)$

53. A commercial flight allows 5 hr for the plane to travel 2380 nautical miles while cruising at an average air speed of 500 knots. What is the average headwind speed that is expected during the flight?

    A. 120 knots   **D.** 220 knots

    B. 34 knots   **E.** none of these

    C. 24 knots

1.5 Transformations of Functions

The arches of the Sydney Harbour Bridge can be modeled by transformations of the basic quadratic function.

A *family of functions* is a group of functions whose graphs share similar characteristics. The basic function with the simplest graph within the family is called the *parent function*. This section explores several ways that the graph of a parent function can be transformed to acquire the graph of a related function.

A *translation* of the parent function occurs when the graph is shifted horizontally or vertically.

Imagine texting without abbreviations or acronyms! The study of mathematics would be especially difficult without generalized algebraic notation. Much of this notation was not developed until the writings of François Viète were published in the sixteenth century.

Vertical Translation	Horizontal Translation
$g(x) = f(x) + k$	$g(x) = f(x - h)$
(graph: $g(x) = \lvert x \rvert + 2$, $f(x) = \lvert x \rvert$, $g(x) = \lvert x \rvert - 3$)	*(graph: $g(x) = (x + 3)^3$, $f(x) = x^3$, $g(x) = (x - 2)^3$)*
k units up if $k > 0$ k units down if $k < 0$	h units right if $h > 0$ h units left if $h < 0$

If $g(x) = f(x - h) + k$ (with h and $k \neq 0$), then $f(x)$ has been translated both horizontally and vertically.

Example 1   Translating a Parent Function

Graph $g(x) = (x + 1)^2 - 2$, then state the function's domain and range.

Answer

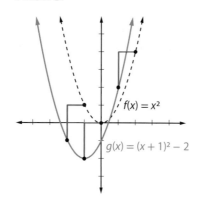

1. Sketch a graph of the parent function $f(x) = x^2$.

2. Since $g(x) = f(x - (-1))^2 + (-2)$ with $h = -1$ and $k = -2$, slide the graph of the parent function 1 unit left and 2 units down.

3. $D = \mathbb{R}; R = \{y \mid y \geq -2\}$

SKILL ✔ EXERCISE 11

A *reflection* across a coordinate axis produces a mirror image. Notice that a "vertical" reflection occurs when the "output" of the function is negated and a "horizontal" reflection occurs when the "input" of the function is negated.

Reflection in the *x*-axis	Reflection in the *y*-axis
$g(x) = -f(x)$	$g(x) = f(-x)$

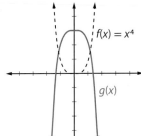

Example 2   Reflecting and Translating Parent Functions

Describe the transformation of the graph of $f(x)$ that results in the graph of $g(x)$. Then write an equation for $g(x)$.

a.

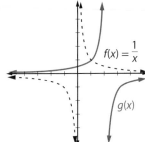

b.

Answer

a. The graph of $g(x)$ is a reflection of $f(x) = x^4$ in the *x*-axis followed by a translation 3 units up.

$\therefore g(x) = -x^4 + 3$.

b. The graph of $g(x)$ is a translation of $f(x) = \frac{1}{x}$ two units to the right followed by a reflection in the *x*-axis.

$\therefore g(x) = -\frac{1}{x-2}$.

SKILL ✓ **EXERCISE 13**

Translations and reflections are called *rigid transformations* since they maintain the shape of the graph, changing only the graph's position in the plane. The graph of a function can also be stretched or shrunk vertically or horizontally. These *nonrigid transformations* distort the shape of the graph.

Vertical Stretch or Shrink	Horizontal Stretch or Shrink
$g(x) = af(x)$	$g(x) = f(bx)$
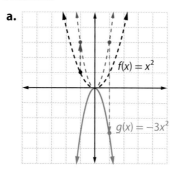	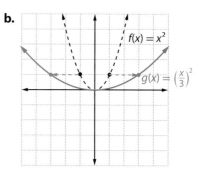
stretch by a factor of a if $|a| > 1$ or shrink by a factor of a if $0 < |a| < 1$	shrink by a factor of $\frac{1}{|b|}$ if $|b| > 1$ or stretch by a factor of $\frac{1}{|b|}$ if $0 < |b| < 1$

TIP

To stretch a function vertically by a factor of 3, triple the y-coordinate (output) of each ordered pair. To stretch a function horizontally by a factor of 3, triple the x-value (input) of each ordered pair.

The horizontal shrink of $h(x) = \sqrt{2x}$ could also be viewed as a vertical stretch when the function is written as $g(x) = 1.414\sqrt{x}$. Similarly, the horizontal stretch of $h(x) = \sqrt{0.5x}$ can be viewed as a vertical shrink when the function is written as $g(x) = 0.707\sqrt{x}$.

Example 3 Stretching and Shrinking Parent Functions

Sketch the graph of the parent function $f(x) = x^2$ and use it to graph each function.

a. $g(x) = -3x^2$

b. $h(x) = \left(\frac{x}{3}\right)^2$

Answer

a.

The graph of $f(x)$ is stretched vertically by a factor of 3 and then reflected in the x-axis.

b.

The graph of $f(x)$ is stretched horizontally by a factor of
$$\frac{1}{b} = \frac{1}{\left(\frac{1}{3}\right)} = 3.$$

SKILL ✓ **EXERCISE 15**

What happens when several transformations are combined? Consider the following illustrations of transformations of $f(x) = x^2$. The vertical transformations in $g(x)$ are the result of operations on the output of the parent function $f(x) = x^2$ and the horizontal transformations in $h(x)$ are the result of operations on the input of $f(x) = x^2$.

$$g(x) = -2x^2 + 3$$

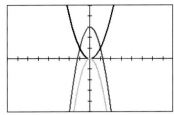

$$h(x) = (-2x + 3)^2$$

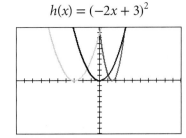

1. a reflection in the x-axis and a vertical stretch by a factor of 2

2. then a slide up 3 units

1. a slide left 3 units

2. then a reflection in the y-axis and a horizontal shrink by a factor of $\frac{1}{2}$

The vertical transformations related to the output of the parent function follow the order of operations. You may have noticed that the horizontal shift and shrink seem to be opposites of the vertical shift and stretch. These horizontal transformations are related to the input of the parent function (within the parentheses). They are performed in an order that is opposite of the order of operations. While horizontal and vertical transformations do not affect each another, horizontal transformations are typically completed first.

Example 4   Combining Transformations

Use transformations of a basic parent function to sketch the graph of $g(x) = \frac{1}{3}(2 - x)^3 - 4$.

Answer

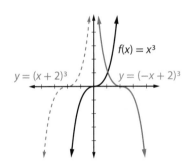

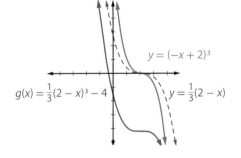

1. Sketch a graph of the parent function $f(x) = x^3$.

2. Complete the horizontal transformations implied by operations on the input of the parent function: $(2 - x)$ or $(-x + 2)$.

   a. a shift 2 units left

   b. then a reflection in the y-axis

3. Complete the vertical transformations implied by operations on the output of the parent function: $\frac{1}{3}f(x) - 4$.

   a. a vertical shrink by a factor of 3

   b. then a shift 4 units down

_____ SKILL ✓ **EXERCISE 21**

Describing the graph of a function as a transformation of a known parent function can help you write a function rule for the graph.

KEYWORD SEARCH

parent function chart 🔍

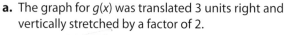

Example 5 Writing Function Rules

Describe each graph as a transformation of $f(x) = x^2$.
Then write its function rule.

Answer

Knowing the general shape of parent functions helps to determine the equation that best models collected data.

a. The graph for $g(x)$ was translated 3 units right and vertically stretched by a factor of 2.

$$\therefore g(x) = 2(x - 3)^2$$

b. The graph for $h(x)$ was reflected in the x-axis and vertically shrunk by a factor of $\frac{1}{2}$ before being translated 1 unit down.

$$\therefore h(x) = -\frac{1}{2}x^2 - 1$$

SKILL ✓ **EXERCISE 25**

❯ A. Exercises

Describe the graph of $g(x)$ as a transformation of $f(x) = x^2$. Confirm your answer by graphing $f(x)$ and $g(x)$ in the same window.

1. $g(x) = x^2 - 3$

2. $g(x) = (x + 2)^2$

3. $g(x) = -\frac{1}{4}x^2$

4. $g(x) = \left(\frac{x}{3}\right)^2$

5. Match each function to the described transformation of $f(x)$.

   a. $f(x) + c$ **I.** reflection in the x-axis

   b. $f(x + c)$ **II.** reflection in the y-axis

   c. $-f(x)$ **III.** vertical translation

   d. $f(-x)$ **IV.** horizontal translation

6. Match each function to the described transformation of $g(x)$.

   a. $g(cx); |c| > 1$ **I.** vertical stretch

   b. $g(cx); 0 < |c| < 1$ **II.** vertical shrink

   c. $cg(x); 0 < |c| < 1$ **III.** horizontal stretch

   d. $cg(x); |c| > 1$ **IV.** horizontal shrink

Describe the graph of each function as a transformation of $f(x) = x^3$. Confirm your answer by graphing $f(x)$ and $g(x)$ in the same window.

7. $g(x) = \left(\frac{x}{2}\right)^3 - 5$

8. $g(x) = (x - 1)^3 + 2$

9. $g(x) = 2x^3 - 3$

10. $g(x) = -\frac{3}{4}(x + 4)^3$

Draw a graph of the parent function $f(x)$. Then graph $g(x)$ and $h(x)$ as transformations of $f(x)$ on the same coordinate plane.

11. $f(x) = |x|; g(x) = |x + 3|; h(x) = |x| - 2$

12. $f(x) = x^2; g(x) = x^2 - 3; h(x) = (x - 3)^2$

13. $f(x) = x^2; g(x) = -x^2 + 2; h(x) = (-x + 2)^2$

14. $f(x) = x^3; g(x) = \frac{x^3}{4}; h(x) = \left(\frac{x}{4}\right)^3$

15. $f(x) = x^4; g(x) = -2x^4; h(x) = (-2x)^4$

16. $f(x) = x; g(x) = \frac{2}{3}x - 1; h(x) = -\frac{2}{3}x + 1$

❯ B. Exercises

Graph each function as a transformation of a parent function. Then state the function's domain and range.

17. $g(x) = -2[x]$

18. $h(x) = \left[-\frac{x}{2}\right]$

19. $m(x) = \frac{1}{x + 2} - 1$

20. $n(x) = \frac{2}{(x - 3)^2}$

21. $p(x) = -2(x - 3)^2 + 4$

22. $q(x) = \frac{1}{2}|x + 1| - 3$

Write a function rule for each illustrated transformation of $f(x) = \sqrt{x}$.

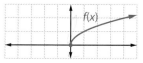

23.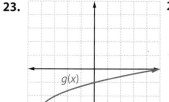

24.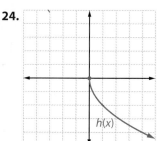

25.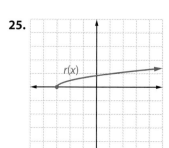

26.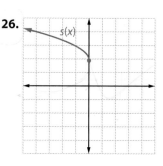

Write a function rule for g(x), the described transformation of f(x). Then confirm your answer by graphing f(x) and g(x) in the same window.

27. $f(x) = |x|$ translated 2 units left and 3 units down

28. $f(x) = |x|$ vertically stretched by a factor of 4 and reflected in the x-axis

29. $f(x) = x^2$ translated 5 units right and vertically shrunk by a factor of $\frac{1}{3}$

30. $f(x) = x^3$ vertically shrunk by a factor of $\frac{1}{2}$ and then translated 5 units up

31. $f(x) = x^4$ reflected in the x-axis and then translated 3 units up

32. $f(x) = x^2$ reflected in the x-axis and stretched vertically by a factor of 2, then translated 3 units left and 1 unit up

Describe how the graph of f(x) is transformed into the graph of g(x). You may want to graph each function to verify your answer.

33. $f(x) = |x + 2|^2 - 1$ and $g(x) = |x - 5|^2 + 3$

34. $f(x) = (x + 3)^2$ and $g(x) = -(x - 4)^2$

> **C. Exercises**

35. Write a function rule for each described transformation of $f(x) = x^2$. Then confirm each answer by using technology to graph the new function in the same window with $f(x)$.

   a. $g(x)$: reflected in the x-axis and then translated 2 units up

   b. $h(x)$: translated 2 units up and then reflected in the x-axis

36. **Analyze:** Describe the graph of $y = mx + b$ as a transformation of the parent function $y = x$.

37. **Prove:** Show algebraically that the result of reflecting $f(x) = (x - 2)^2 + 1$ in both the x- and y-axes is $h(x) = -(x + 2)^2 - 1$.

38. Suppose a parabolic arch is used to form a building that is 25 ft tall and 30 ft wide at ground level.

   a. Write the equation for the transformation of $f(x) = x^2$ that has been translated 15 units right, reflected across the x-axis, and then translated 25 units up.

   b. Graph your function and explain why it is not a good model for the building's arch.

   c. Adjust the coefficient of the squared term to vertically stretch or shrink the function until it passes through the origin and (30, 0).

39. Use technology to graph $f(x) = (x - 2)^2 - 3$ and each composition of the absolute value function and $f(x)$ in the same window. Then match the composed function to the described transformation of $f(x)$.

   a. $|f(x)|$ **b.** $f(|x|)$

   I. Any portion of $f(x)$ below the x-axis is reflected in the x-axis.

   II. Any portion of $f(x)$ to the left of the y-axis is reflected in the y-axis.

   III. The portion of $f(x)$ below the x-axis is replaced by a reflection in the x-axis of the portion of $f(x)$ that is above the x-axis.

   IV. The portion of $f(x)$ to the left of the y-axis is replaced by a reflection in the y-axis of the portion of $f(x)$ that is to the right of the y-axis.

40. Match each function to its graph given the graph of $f(x)$.

I.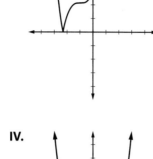

II.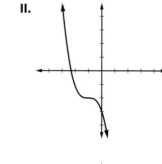

III.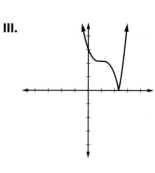

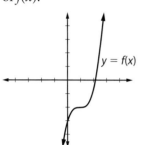

$y = f(x)$

IV.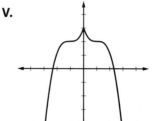

V.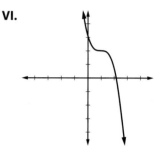

VI.

a. $g(x) = -f(x)$
b. $g(x) = f(-x)$
c. $g(x) = |f(x)|$
d. $g(x) = f(|x|)$
e. $g(x) = |f(-x)|$
f. $g(x) = -f(|x|)$

CUMULATIVE REVIEW

Solve by factoring. [Algebra]

41. $x^2 + 10x - 24 = 0$

42. $6y^2 - 40y - 64 = 0$

Solve by taking roots. [Algebra]

43. $2a^2 - 64 = 0$

44. $3(x + 5)^2 = 48$

Solve by completing the square. [Algebra]

45. $x^2 - 4x = 45$

46. $y^2 + 6y = -1$

47. Express x in terms of y if $5y = 4x - 16$. [Appendix 4]

   A. $x = \frac{5}{4}y + 16$ **D.** $x = \frac{4}{5}y - 4$

   B. $x = \frac{5}{4}y + 4$ **E.** $x = \frac{4}{5}y + 16$

   C. $x = \frac{4}{5}y + 4$

48. The graph of $3x - 4y = 12$ lies in which quadrants of the coordinate plane? [1.2]

   A. I, II, and III   **D.** II and IV only

   B. I, III, and IV   **E.** I and III only

   C. II, III, and IV

49. Which equation represents a line parallel to $\overleftrightarrow{AB}$ with $A(-1, 4)$ and $B(3, 12)$? [1.2]

   A. $y = -2x + 2$ **D.** $y = -\frac{1}{2}x + 6$

   B. $y = 2x - 4$ **E.** $y = \frac{1}{2}x + 3$

   C. $y = 2x + 6$

50. Which graph represents an odd function? [1.4]

  A. 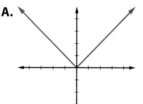   **C.**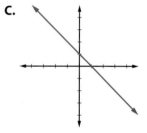

  B. 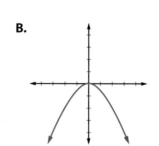   **D.**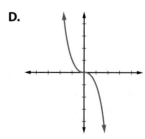

  E. none of these

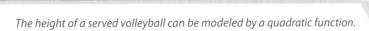

1.6 Quadratic Functions

The height of a served volleyball can be modeled by a quadratic function.

The graph of the basic quadratic function $f(x) = x^2$ was examined in Section 1.4. Horizontal and vertical shifts, reflections, stretches, and shrinks of this parent function produce a family of *quadratic functions* whose graphs are called *parabolas*.

The *axis of symmetry* divides a parabola into mirror-image halves and intersects the parabola at its *vertex*, which is either a minimum or maximum point. The axis of symmetry for the parent function $f(x) = x^2$ is the line $x = 0$ (the y-axis) and its vertex is the origin, which is a minimum point.

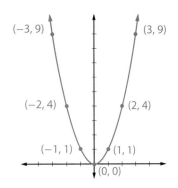

After completing this section, you will be able to

- graph quadratic functions.
- identify the vertex and classify it as a maximum or minimum.
- find the zeros of a quadratic function.

Example 1 Transforming the Parent Quadratic Function

Transform the graph of $f(x) = x^2$ to obtain the graph of $g(x) = -2(x - 3)^2 + 4$. Then identify the new parabola's domain, range, axis of symmetry, vertex, and whether the vertex is a maximum or minimum point.

Answer

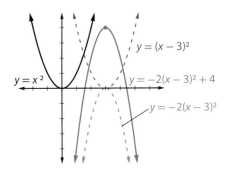

1. Transform the graph.
   a. Shift the graph 3 units right.
   b. Then reflect it in the x-axis and stretch it vertically by 2.
   c. Finally, translate it 4 units up.

2. Describe the graph.
   a. $D = \mathbb{R}$; $R = (-\infty, 4]$
   b. The axis of symmetry is $x = 3$.
   c. The vertex $(3, 4)$ is a maximum point.

SKILL ✓ **EXERCISE 7**

When supply and demand graphs are linear, the total revenue can be modeled by a quadratic function. The parabola's vertex indicates the number of units that provides the greatest revenue.

When written in *vertex form*, $f(x) = a(x - h)^2 + k$, a parabola's axis of symmetry $x = h$ and vertex (h, k) are easily identified. If $a > 0$ the parabola opens upward and the vertex is a minimum point. If $a < 0$ the parabola opens downward and the vertex is a maximum point.

Quadratic functions are also frequently expressed in *standard form* as a sum of a quadratic term, a linear term, and a constant.

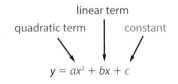

linear term
quadratic term | constant

$$y = ax^2 + bx + c$$

DEFINITION

A **quadratic function** is a function that can be written in the form $f(x) = ax^2 + bx + c$ where a, b, and $c \in \mathbb{R}$ and $a \neq 0$.

Converting a standard form quadratic function to its vertex form will help when analyzing and graphing the function. This conversion usually involves a process called *completing the square*. Recall that completing the square of a binomial in the form $x^2 + dx$ is done by adding $\left(\frac{1}{2}d\right)^2$.

KEYWORD SEARCH

interactive completing 🔍
square proof

Example 2 Graphing a Quadratic Function in Standard Form

Graph $f(x) = 3x^2 + 12x + 8$. Then identify the domain, range, axis of symmetry, vertex, and whether the vertex is a maximum or minimum point.

Answer

$f(x) = 3x^2 + 12x + 8$

1. Convert to vertex form by completing the square.

$f(x) = 3(x^2 + 4x + \underline{\hspace{1cm}}) + 8$

   a. Factor the leading coefficient out of the quadratic and linear terms, leaving an expression in the form of $x^2 + dx$.

$f(x) = 3(x^2 + 4x + 4) + 8 - 12$

   b. Add $\left(\frac{1}{2}d\right)^2 = \left(\frac{4}{2}\right)^2 = 4$ within the parentheses. Since any amount added within the parentheses is multiplied by the leading coefficient, compensate by subtracting $3(4) = 12$.

$f(x) = 3(x + 2)^2 - 4$

   c. Rewrite the expression within the parentheses as a binomial squared and simplify the remaining terms.

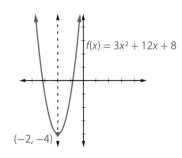

2. Use the function's vertex form, $f(x) = 3(x - (-2))^2 + (-4)$, to analyze the function and graph the parabola.

   a. Since $a = 3$, the parabola opens upward and is obtained by stretching $y = x^2$ vertically by a factor of 3.

   b. The axis of symmetry is $x = -2$ and the vertex $(-2, -4)$ is a minimum point.

   c. $D = \mathbb{R}$; $R = [-4, \infty)$

SKILL ✔ **EXERCISE 23**

By completing the square for $f(x) = ax^2 + bx + c$, we can develop formulas for h and k.

$f(x) = a\left(x^2 + \frac{b}{a}x\right) + c$

1. Factor the leading coefficient from the quadratic and linear terms.

$= a\left(x^2 + \frac{b}{a}x + \frac{b^2}{4a^2}\right) + c - \frac{b^2}{4a}$

2. Complete the square by adding $\left(\frac{1}{2} \cdot \frac{b}{a}\right)^2 = \frac{b^2}{4a^2}$ within the parentheses. Since $a\left(\frac{b^2}{4a^2}\right) = \frac{b^2}{4a}$ is added to the function, subtract $\frac{b^2}{4a}$ from the constant term.

$= a\left(x + \frac{b}{2a}\right)^2 + \left(c - \frac{b^2}{4a}\right)$

3. Factor the trinomial.

$h = -\frac{b}{2a}$ and $k = c - \frac{b^2}{4a}$

4. Comparing the resulting function to $f(x) = a(x - h)^2 + k$ provides general expressions for h and k.

The formula for h is easy to remember and use, but it is often easier to find the value of k by evaluating $f(h)$.

Another key characteristic describing a parabola is the location of the x- and y-intercepts. The y-intercept of any function has an x-coordinate of 0, and its y-coordinate is found by evaluating $f(0)$. Therefore the y-intercept of $f(x) = ax^2 + bx + c$ is $(0, c)$. Since the x-intercepts of a graph have a y-coordinate of 0, the x-intercepts can be found by letting $f(x) = 0$ and solving the resulting equation.

▌DEFINITION

A **zero** (or **root**) of a function is any value of x for which $f(x) = 0$.

Quadratic functions can have real or imaginary zeros. The real zeros of a function are the x-coordinates of the parabola's x-intercepts. When the function has only one zero, the x-intercept is the parabola's vertex. The graph of a function with imaginary zeros does not intersect the x-axis.

Some quadratic equations can be solved by factoring and applying the Zero Product Property.

▌ZERO PRODUCT PROPERTY

A product of real numbers is 0 if and only if one or more of its factors is 0. Symbolically, $pq = 0$ iff $p = 0$ or $q = 0$.

Example 3   Finding Zeros by Factoring

Find the y-intercept and the zeros of $y = -x^2 + 6x$. Then graph the function.

Answer

y-intercept: $(0, 0)$

$-x^2 + 6x = 0$

$-x(x - 6) = 0$

$-x = 0$ or $x - 6 = 0$

$x = 0; x = 6$

The zeros are 0 and 6.

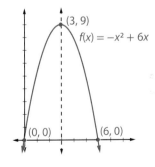

1. The y-intercept of $f(x) = ax^2 + bx + c$ is $(0, c)$.
2. Set the function equal to 0.
   a. Factor.
   b. Apply the Zero Product Property.
   c. Solve.
3. The roots of $f(x) = 0$ are the zeros of the function.
4. Use the standard form $y = ax^2 + bx + c$ to analyze the function and graph the parabola.
   a. Since $a = -1$, the graph of $y = x^2$ is reflected in the x-axis and opens downward.
   b. The axis of symmetry is $x = h = -\dfrac{b}{2a} = -\dfrac{6}{2(-1)} = 3$.
   c. The vertex (h, k) lies on the axis of symmetry. $k = f(h) = f(3) = -(3)^2 + 6(3) = 9; V(3, 9)$
   d. The x-intercepts are $(0, 0)$ and $(6, 0)$.

SKILL ✓ **EXERCISE 9**

You can also use the quadratic formula (derived in exercise 39) to find the zeros of a quadratic function.

If $ax^2 + bx + c = 0$ and $a \neq 0$, then $x = \dfrac{-b \pm \sqrt{b^2 - 4ac}}{2a}$.

Notice that any real zeros are equidistant from the axis of symmetry, $x = -\dfrac{b}{2a}$.

Example 4 Finding Zeros Using the Quadratic Formula

Find the y-intercept and zeros of $f(x) = \frac{1}{2}x^2 + 2x + 3$. Then graph the function.

Answer

y-intercept: $(0, 3)$

$\frac{1}{2}x^2 + 2x + 3 = 0$

$x = \dfrac{-b \pm \sqrt{b^2 - 4ac}}{2a}$

$= \dfrac{-(2) \pm \sqrt{(2)^2 - 4\left(\frac{1}{2}\right)(3)}}{2\left(\frac{1}{2}\right)}$

$= -2 \pm \sqrt{-2}$

$= -2 \pm \sqrt{2}\,i$

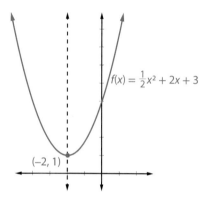

$f(x) = \frac{1}{2}x^2 + 2x + 3$

$(-2, 1)$

1. The y-intercept of $f(x) = ax^2 + bx + c$ is $(0, c)$.

2. Set $f(x) = 0$.

  a. Solve the equation using the quadratic formula since $f(x)$ does not factor easily.

  b. Express the imaginary number $\sqrt{-2}$ as $\sqrt{2}\,i$ and state the zeros in the standard form for a complex number, $a + bi$.

3. Use the standard form $y = ax^2 + bx + c$ to analyze the function and graph the parabola.

  a. Since $a = \frac{1}{2}$, the graph of $y = x^2$ shrinks vertically by $\frac{1}{2}$ and opens upward.

  b. The axis of symmetry is $x = h = -\dfrac{b}{2a} = -\dfrac{(2)}{2\left(\frac{1}{2}\right)} = -2.$

  c. The vertex (h, k) lies on the axis of symmetry. $k = f(h) = f(-2) = \frac{1}{2}(-2)^2 + 2(-2) + 3 = 1$ $V(-2, 1)$

  d. The imaginary zeros confirm that the parabola does not cross the x-axis.

—————— SKILL ✓ **EXERCISE 13**

If the vertex and one other point on the parabola are known, the vertex form can be used to derive the quadratic function.

Example 5 Writing a Quadratic Function Rule

Write the standard form of a parabola passing through $(2, 7)$ with a vertex at $(-4, 1)$.

Answer

$y = a(x - h)^2 + k$

$7 = a(2 - (-4))^2 + 1$

$7 = a(2 + 4)^2 + 1$

$6 = 36a$

$a = \frac{1}{6}$

$f(x) = \frac{1}{6}(x + 4)^2 + 1$

$= \frac{1}{6}(x^2 + 8x + 16) + 1$

$f(x) = \frac{1}{6}x^2 + \frac{4}{3}x + \frac{11}{3}$

1. Substitute the coordinates of the vertex (h, k) and any other point on the parabola (x, y) into the vertex form.

2. Solve to find a.

3. Write the equation of the parabola in vertex form.

4. Expand and simplify to write the function in standard form.

CONTINUED ➡

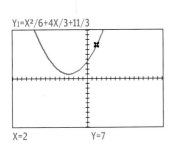

$Y_1 = X^2/6 + 4X/3 + 11/3$

X=2   Y=7

5. Graph the function to confirm that it passes through (2, 7) and has a vertex at (−4, 1).

_____ SKILL ✓ **EXERCISE 31**

In Section 1.2 the vertical velocity of a projectile was modeled by the linear function $v(t) = -gt + v_0$. The *height of a projectile* can be modeled by the quadratic function $h(t) = -\frac{1}{2}gt^2 + v_0 t + h_0$ where g, the acceleration due to gravity, is approximately 32 ft/sec² or 9.8 m/sec², v_0 is the initial vertical velocity, and h_0 is the initial height.

Example 6   Modeling the Height of a Projectile

A ball is thrown upward from a height that is 10 m above the ocean with an initial vertical velocity of 25 m/sec. Find the time it takes for the ball to hit the ocean and the maximum height of the ball (above the ocean).

Answer

$v_0 = 25$ m/sec; $h_0 = 10$ m, $g = 9.8$ m/sec²

$h(t) = -\frac{1}{2}(9.8)t^2 + 25t + 10$

$\quad = -4.9t^2 + 25t + 10$

$-4.9t^2 + 25t + 10 = 0$

$t = \dfrac{-(25) \pm \sqrt{(25)^2 - 4(-4.9)(10)}}{2(-4.9)}$

$\quad \approx -0.373 \text{ or } 5.475$

It takes the ball about 5.5 sec to hit the ocean.

$t = -\dfrac{25}{2(-4.9)} \approx 2.55$ sec

$h(2.55) = -4.9(2.55)^2 + 25(2.55) + 10$

$\quad \approx 41.9$ m

1. Use $h(t) = -\frac{1}{2}gt^2 + v_0 t + h_0$ to model the height of the ball.

2. To determine when the ball's height is 0 m, apply the quadratic formula.

3. The maximum height lies on the axis of symmetry: $t = -\dfrac{b}{2a}$.

4. Evaluate the function at the time the ball is at its maximum height.

5. Graph the function and use the Max and Zero functions to confirm your results.

TIP

The function can be quickly and accurately evaluated by entering it as Y1 and then entering Y1(Ans) after calculating $t \approx 2.55$.

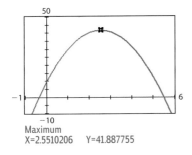

Maximum
X=2.5510206   Y=41.887755

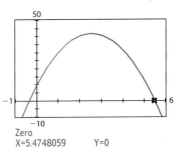

Zero
X=5.4748059   Y=0

_____ SKILL ✓ **EXERCISE 33**

A. Exercises

State the vertex of each parabola, whether it has a maximum or minimum point, and its axis of symmetry.

1. $f(x) = 3x^2$

2. $f(x) = -2x^2 - 10$

3. $f(x) = -(x - 5)^2 + 7$

4. $f(x) = (x + 2)^2 + \frac{7}{3}$

Graph each parabola as a transformation of the parent function $f(x) = x^2$.

5. $y = -\frac{1}{3}x^2$

6. $y = x^2 - 3$

7. $y = 2(x + 3)^2 + 1$

8. $y = -\left(x - \frac{1}{2}\right)^2 + 4$

Find the zeros of each quadratic function by factoring.

9. $y = 2x^2 + 9x - 56$

10. $y = -x^2 + x + 20$

Find the zeros of each quadratic function using the quadratic formula.

11. $y = x^2 + 5x - 2$

12. $y = x^2 - 4x + 5$

13. $f(x) = -2x^2 + 2x - 5$

14. $g(x) = 3x^2 + 4x - 5$

Find the y-intercept and zeros of each quadratic function.

15. $f(x) = x^2 - 10x + 24$

16. $f(x) = -2x^2 + x + 3$

17. $f(x) = 2(x + 2)^2 - 8$

18. $f(x) = -\frac{1}{4}(x - 2)^2 + 4$

B. Exercises

Write each quadratic function in vertex form and then graph the function.

19. $f(x) = x^2 - 2x$

20. $g(x) = x^2 + 8x + 17$

21. $h(x) = x^2 + 5x + \frac{9}{4}$

22. $f(x) = -x^2 - 4x - 7$

23. $g(x) = 4x^2 + 8x - 1$

24. $h(x) = -2x^2 + 12x - 16$

Identify the vertex of each parabola and state whether it is a maximum or minimum point. Then state the y-intercept and any x-intercepts.

25. $g(x) = x^2 + 4x$

26. $f(x) = -x^2 + 10x - 28$

27. $g(x) = x^2 - 2x + \frac{1}{2}$

28. $h(x) = 2x^2 - 10x + 8$

29. Determine if each statement relating to the characteristics of $f(x) = ax^2 + bx + c$, with $a \neq 0$, is *always*, *sometimes*, or *never* true.

    a. The domain is the real numbers.

    b. The range is the real numbers.

    c. The function is continuous.

30. Describe the end behavior of $f(x) = ax^2 + bx + c$ in each case.

    a. if $a > 0$

    b. if $a < 0$

31. Write the standard form of a parabola that passes through $(8, 3)$ and has a vertex at $(2, -1)$.

32. Write the standard form of a parabola that passes through $(1, -13)$ and has a vertex at $(-2, 5)$.

33. Use the function for the height of a projectile, $h(t) = -\frac{1}{2}gt^2 + v_0t + h_0$, to model the height of a watermelon thrown from a height of 384 ft with an initial vertical velocity of 32 ft/sec.

    a. Write the quadratic function modeling the height of the watermelon during its flight.

    b. How long does it take for the watermelon to reach its maximum height?

    c. What is the maximum height of the watermelon?

    d. How long does it take to hit the ground below?

34. A company analyst studying the cost of producing an item uses $C(x) = 0.03x^2 - 7.8x + 15,000$ to model the cost as a function of x, the number of items produced each week. Use the model to determine how many items should be produced each week to minimize the cost and to estimate the cost of producing those items.

35. A major retailer sells 10,050 high-end TVs a month at $950 each. Research indicates that for every $20 drop in price, 300 more units would be sold each month.

    a. If x represents the number of $20 price drops and the monthly revenue is the product of the price $(950 - 20x)$ and the number of units sold $(10,050 + 300x)$, write the standard form of the function modeling the monthly revenue.

    b. Determine the number of price drops that will generate the most revenue and state the related selling price for the televisions.

    c. What is the expected monthly revenue at the optimal price point?

36. A farmer plans the timing of his wheat harvest to maximize his income. He estimates his current yield at 45,000 bushels priced at $4/bu. For every week he waits, his harvest is predicted to increase by 2000 bushels, but the price will drop $0.15/bu.

    a. If x represents the number of weeks the farmer waits to harvest and the income is the product of price and number of bushels harvested, write the standard form of the function modeling the income.

    b. Determine the number of weeks to wait before harvest that generates the most income; then estimate the number of bushels that will be harvested at that time.

    c. What is the expected income after waiting the optimal number of weeks?

C. Exercises

37. Use the function for the height of a projectile, $h(t) = -\frac{1}{2}gt^2 + v_0t + h_0$, to model the height of a volleyball served from a height of 2 m with an initial vertical velocity of 4 m/sec.

   a. Write the quadratic function modeling the height of the volleyball during its flight.

   b. Determine the maximum height of the ball and how long it takes to reach that height.

   c. How long does it take the volleyball to hit the floor?

   d. If the ball's horizontal velocity during its flight is 15 m/sec, does the ball clear the 2.24 m tall net located 9 m from the serve? If so, does the ball land within the out-of-bounds line 18 m from where it was served? Explain your reasoning.

38. Convert $y = ax^2 + bx + c$ to vertex form. Then state the coordinates of the vertex and the axis of symmetry.

39. Derive the quadratic formula by completing the square to solve the standard form of a quadratic equation, $ax^2 + bx + c = 0$.

Complete the square to identify the vertex of each parabola and state whether it is a maximum or minimum point. Then state the y-intercept and any x-intercepts.

40. $f(x) = \frac{1}{2}x^2 - 12x + 15$ **41.** $f(x) = -\frac{3}{2}x^2 + 12x - 18$

CUMULATIVE REVIEW

Express the domain of each function using interval notation. [1.1]

42. $f(x) = \sqrt{4 - x^2}$ **43.** $g(x) = \frac{3}{2x - 1}$

44. Find the equation of the line through $(2, 3)$ and perpendicular to $x = 2$. [1.2]

Write a function rule for each variation. [1.4]

45. The value of y varies directly with the cube of x, and $y = 128$ when $x = 4$.

46. The value of y varies inversely with x, and $y = 20$ when $x = 4$.

47. If the annual interest earned varies directly with the amount invested and $1500 invested earns $108 annually, how much must be invested in order to earn $180? [1.4]

48. Simplify i^{54}. [Appendix 5]

   A. 1   **C.** $-i$ **E.** none of these

   B. -1 **D.** i

49. Which function passes through $(0, a)$ and $(a, 0)$? [1.2]

   A. $y = ax$ **C.** $y = -x + a$ **E.** none of these

   B. $y = x - a$ **D.** $y = x + a$

50. If $g(x)$ is a translation of $f(x) = x^2$, which equation represents $g(x)$? [1.5]

   A. $g(x) = (x - 2)^2 - 3$

   B. $g(x) = (x - 3)^2 - 2$

   C. $g(x) = (x + 2)^2 - 3$

   D. $g(x) = (x - 2)^2 + 3$

   E. $g(x) = (x + 2)^2 + 3$

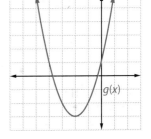

51. Which function represents $f(x) = (x + 4)^2 - 9$ after it has been shifted 3 units left and 5 units down? [1.5]

   A. $g(x) = (x + 7)^2 - 14$ **D.** $g(x) = (x + 9)^2 - 12$

   B. $g(x) = (x + 1)^2 - 14$ **E.** none of these

   C. $g(x) = (x - 1)^2 - 12$

Consumer costs can often be represented with a composition of functions.

After completing this section, you will be able to

- perform function operations including composition.
- determine the domain for combinations of functions.
- decompose a composite function.
- model and solve real-world problems using combinations and compositions of functions.

Many functions are algebraic combinations of simpler functions. The four basic operations of addition, subtraction, multiplication, and division can be performed on functions as well as real numbers.

Function Operations	
addition	$(f + g)(x) = f(x) + g(x)$
subtraction	$(f - g)(x) = f(x) - g(x)$
multiplication	$(fg)(x) = f(x) \cdot g(x)$
division	$\dfrac{f}{g}(x) = \dfrac{f(x)}{g(x)}$, where $g(x) \neq 0$

The domain of the resulting function is the intersection of the domains of the two functions, except where the domain is further limited by the fact that division by 0 is undefined.

Example 1   Arithmetic Operations with Functions

If $f(x) = x^2 - 4$ and $g(x) = x + 2$, write a function rule representing the result of each function operation and state the resulting function's domain.

a. $(f + g)(x)$ **b.** $(f - g)(x)$ **c.** $(fg)(x)$ **d.** $\dfrac{f}{g}(x)$

Answer

a. $(f + g)(x) = f(x) + g(x)$
$$= (x^2 - 4) + (x + 2)$$
$$= x^2 + x - 2$$
$$D_f = \mathbb{R}; D_g = \mathbb{R}; \therefore D_{f+g} = \mathbb{R}$$

b. $(f - g)(x) = f(x) - g(x)$
$$= (x^2 - 4) - (x + 2)$$
$$= x^2 - x - 6$$
$$D_f = \mathbb{R}; D_g = \mathbb{R}; \therefore D_{f-g} = \mathbb{R}$$

c. $(fg)(x) = f(x) \cdot g(x)$
$$= (x^2 - 4)(x + 2)$$
$$= x^3 + 2x^2 - 4x - 8$$
$$D_f = \mathbb{R}; D_g = \mathbb{R}; \therefore D_{fg} = \mathbb{R}$$

d. $\dfrac{f}{g}(x) = \dfrac{f(x)}{g(x)}$
$$= \dfrac{x^2 - 4}{x + 2}, \text{ where } x \neq -2$$
$$= \dfrac{(x - 2)(x + 2)}{x + 2}$$
$$= x - 2, x \neq -2$$
$$D_f = \mathbb{R}; D_g = \mathbb{R}; \therefore D_{f/g} = \{x \mid x \neq -2\}$$

SKILL ✔ **EXERCISES 3, 7**

The value for $(f + g)(-1)$ in Example 1 is $f(-1) + g(-1) = -3 + 1 = -2$. Alternately, the resulting function rule can be used: $(f + g)(-1) = (-1)^2 + (-1) - 2 = -2$.

Another function operation involves substituting an algebraic expression into a function.

Example 2 Substituting Expressions

If $f(x) = 5x - 7$ and $g(x) = x^2 + 3x - 2$, evaluate each function.

a. $f(a + b)$ **b.** $f(x^2 - 9)$ **c.** $g(4a)$ **d.** $g(3x + 1)$

Answer

a. $f(a + b) = 5(a + b) - 7$
$$= 5a + 5b - 7$$

b. $f(x^2 - 9) = 5(x^2 - 9) - 7$
$$= 5x^2 - 45 - 7$$
$$= 5x^2 - 52$$

c. $g(4a) = (4a)^2 + 3(4a) - 2$
$$= 16a^2 + 12a - 2$$

d. $g(3x + 1) = (3x + 1)^2 + 3(3x + 1) - 2$
$$= (9x^2 + 6x + 1) + (9x + 3) - 2$$
$$= 9x^2 + 15x + 2$$

SKILL ✓ **EXERCISE 11**

This fifth function operation is *composition*. To compose two functions, the function rule for the second function is substituted into the first function. The range (output) of the second function becomes the domain (input) of the first function.

▌DEFINITION

The **composition** of two functions f and g, denoted $f \circ g$, is defined as $(f \circ g)(x) = f(g(x))$, read "f of g of x."

Example 3 Composing Functions

If $f(x) = x^2 - 9$ and $g(x) = x + 3$, write a function rule representing each composition.

a. $(f \circ g)(x)$ **b.** $(g \circ f)(x)$

Answer

a. $(f \circ g)(x) = f(g(x))$
$$= (x + 3)^2 - 9$$
$$= x^2 + 6x + 9 - 9$$
$$= x^2 + 6x$$

1. Apply the definition of composition.
2. Substitute $g(x) = x + 3$ for x in $f(x)$.
3. Simplify.

b. $(g \circ f)(x) = g(f(x))$
$$= (x^2 - 9) + 3$$
$$= x^2 - 6$$

1. Apply the definition of composition.
2. Substitute $f(x) = x^2 - 9$ for x in $g(x)$.
3. Simplify.

SKILL ✓ **EXERCISE 17**

TIP

Note that the composition of functions is not commutative.

The value for the composition $(f \circ g)(2)$ in Example 3 is $f(g(2))$, where $g(2) = 5$ and $f(5) = 16$. Alternately, the resulting function rule can be used: $(f \circ g)(2) = (2)^2 + 6(2) = 16$.

The domain of $(f \circ g)(x)$ is not the intersection of the domains of $f(x)$ and $g(x)$. Instead, it is the domain of g, the inner function, less any values that are undefined in the rule for $f(g(x))$, the composite function.

Example 4 Composing Functions with Restricted Domains

If $f(x) = x^2$ and $g(x) = \sqrt{4-x}$, write a function rule for each composition and state its domain.

a. $(f \circ g)(x)$ **b.** $(g \circ f)(x)$

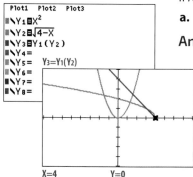

Answer

a. $(f \circ g)(x) = f(g(x))$

$\qquad = (\sqrt{4-x})^2$

$\qquad = |4-x|$

$D_{f(g(x))} = (-\infty, 4]$

$(f \circ g)(x) = 4-x,$
$D = (-\infty, 4]$

1. Apply the definition of composition.
2. Substitute $g(x) = \sqrt{4-x}$ for x in $f(x)$.
3. Simplify.
4. $D_g = (-\infty, 4]$. The composition $f(g(x))$ does not imply additional restrictions.
5. The rule can be simplified if the domain is stated.
6. The function rule and domain can be verified with your graphing calculator.

b. $(g \circ f)(x) = g(f(x))$

$\qquad = \sqrt{4-x^2}$

$4 - x^2 \geq 0$

$x^2 \leq 4$

$\sqrt{x^2} \leq \sqrt{4}$

$|x| \leq 2$

$D_{g/f(x)} = [-2, 2]$

1. Apply the definition of composition.
2. Substitute $f(x) = x^2$ for x in $g(x)$.
3. $D_f = \mathbb{R}$ but $g(f(x))$ implies that $4 - x^2 \geq 0$.

4. The function rule and domain can be verified with your graphing calculator.

_____ SKILL ✓ EXERCISE 21

Just as it can be beneficial to see a function as the result of arithmetic operations on simpler functions, it can be helpful to view a more complicated function as a composition of simpler functions. To *decompose* $h(x)$, find simpler inner and outer functions $g(x)$ and $f(x)$ such that $h(x) = f(g(x))$. For instance, one way to decompose $h(x) = (2x-1)^2$ is with $g(x) = 2x - 1$ and $f(x) = x^2$.

Example 5 Decomposing a Function

Find $f(x)$ and $g(x)$ such that $h(x) = (f \circ g)(x)$.

a. $h(x) = \sqrt{x^5 - 3}$ **b.** $h(x) = 2x^2 - 12x + 5$

Answer

a. If $g(x) = x^5 - 3$,
then $f(x) = \sqrt{x}$, and
$f(g(x)) = \sqrt{x^5 - 3}$.

or

If $g(x) = x^5$,
then $f(x) = \sqrt{x-3}$, and
$f(g(x)) = \sqrt{x^5 - 3}$.

More than one decomposition may be possible.

b. $h(x) = 2x^2 - 12x + 5$

$\qquad = 2(x + 6x + \underline{\quad}) + 5$

$\qquad = 2(x + 6x + 3^2) + 5 - 2(9)$

$\qquad = 2(x+3)^2 - 13$

If $g(x) = x + 3$,
then $f(x) = 2x^2 - 13$.

or

If $g(x) = (x+3)^2$,
then $f(x) = 2x - 13$.

1. Complete the square to isolate the variable.

2. More than one decomposition may be possible.

_____ SKILL ✓ EXERCISES 27, 29

Example 6 Applying a Composite Function

A spherical water balloon is filled at a faucet whose flow rate is 45 cm^3/sec. Use the formula for the volume of a sphere, $V = \frac{4}{3}\pi r^3$, to write a rule for the diameter of the balloon as a function of time. Then use the function to determine the diameter of a balloon after being filled for 10 sec and the time required to fill a balloon to a width of 12 cm.

The French mathematician Joseph Fourier, when considering the work of Archimedes, Galileo, and Newton, concluded that "they have taught us that the most diverse phenomena are subject to a small number of fundamental laws which are reproduced in all the acts of nature."

Answer

$V = \frac{4}{3}\pi r^3$

$\frac{3}{4\pi}V = r^3$

$r = \sqrt[3]{\dfrac{3V}{4\pi}}$

1. Solve the volume formula for the radius, r.

Since $d = 2r$,

$d(V) = 2\sqrt[3]{\dfrac{3V}{4\pi}}$.

2. Write a function rule for diameter in terms of volume.

$V(t) = 45t$

3. Write a function rule for volume in terms of time.

$d(V(t)) = 2\sqrt[3]{\dfrac{3(45t)}{4\pi}}$

$d(V(t)) = 6\sqrt[3]{\dfrac{5t}{4\pi}}$

4. Find $(d \circ V)(t)$ to express diameter in terms of time.

$d(V(10)) = 6\sqrt[3]{\dfrac{5(10)}{4\pi}}$

5. Evaluate the composite function when $t = 10$.

$= 6\sqrt[3]{\dfrac{25}{2\pi}} \approx 9.5$ cm

$12 = 6\sqrt[3]{\dfrac{5t}{4\pi}}$

$2^3 = \dfrac{5t}{4\pi}$

$t = \dfrac{32\pi}{5} \approx 20.1$ sec

6. Substitute a diameter of 12 cm into the composite function and solve for t.

SKILL ✓ **EXERCISE 33**

⟫ A. Exercises

Write the function rule for $(f + g)(x)$, $(g − f)(x)$, and $(fg)(x)$ and state each domain.

1. $f(x) = -2x + 7$
$g(x) = x - 9$

2. $f(x) = -2x + 7$
$g(x) = 5x^2$

3. $f(x) = 5x^2$
$g(x) = \frac{1}{x}$

4. $f(x) = \sqrt{x}$
$g(x) = (x - 4)^2$

Write the function rule for $\frac{f}{g}(x)$ and $\frac{g}{f}(x)$ and state each domain.

5. $f(x) = x - 2$
$g(x) = x$

6. $f(x) = x + 7$
$g(x) = 2x - 3$

7. $f(x) = x^2 - 4$
$g(x) = \frac{2}{x}$

8. $f(x) = x^2 - 9$
$g(x) = \sqrt{x - 2}$

Evaluate each expression when $f(x) = -2x + 7$, $g(x) = 5x^2$, and $h(x) = x - 9$.

9. $f(x^2)$

10. $h(x - 4)$

11. $g(3a + b)$

12. $f(x^2 + 4)$

13. $f(a^2 + 4a - 9)$

14. $g(2a)$

Use the graphs of $f(x) = x^2 + 2x + 1$ and $g(x) = x - 2$ for exercises 15–16.

a. Sketch the graph of each function by adding or multiplying the y-coordinates of $f(x)$ and $g(x)$.

b. State the function rule for the resulting function.

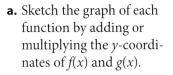

c. Confirm your answer by comparing your sketch to a graph of the function rule on your calculator.

15. $(f + g)(x)$

16. $(fg)(x)$

Write the function rule for $(f \circ g)(x)$ and $(g \circ f)(x)$. Then find $(f \circ g)(3)$ and $(g \circ f)(3)$.

17. $f(x) = x - 7$
$g(x) = x^2 + 8$

18. $f(x) = 5x - 4$
$g(x) = x^2 + 8$

19. Write: In exercises 17–18, which property is shown not to apply in compositions? Explain your reasoning.

20. The Smith family's average power bill is modeled by $p(d) = 5.3d + 8.5$ and their average water bill is modeled by $w(d) = 0.4d + 14$ where d is the number of days in the billing cycle.

   a. Find $(p + w)(d)$ and $(p - w)(d)$.

   b. Find $(p + w)(31)$ and $(p - w)(29)$ and explain what each value represents.

B. Exercises

Write the function rule for $(f \circ g)(x)$ and $(g \circ f)(x)$ and state each domain.

21. $f(x) = x^2 - 4x - 24$
   $g(x) = x + 7$

22. $f(x) = \frac{9}{x}$
   $g(x) = x - 7$

23. $f(x) = \sqrt{x - 5}$
   $g(x) = x^2 - 4$

24. $f(x) = \sqrt{7 - x}$
   $g(x) = x^2 - 3$

25. $f(x) = x^2 - 10$
   $g(x) = \frac{1}{x - 2}$

26. $f(x) = \sqrt{x - 2}$
   $g(x) = \frac{1}{x}$

Find $f(x)$ and $g(x)$ such that $h(x) = (f \circ g)(x)$.

27. $h(x) = \sqrt{x^2 - 3}$

28. $h(x) = \dfrac{1}{\sqrt{x - 4}}$

29. $h(x) = x^2 + 4x - 3$

30. $h(x) = 3x^2 - 36x + 100$

31. There are 1000 m in 1 km and 100 cm in 1 m.

   a. Write a function rule $m(x)$ to change kilometers to meters and a function rule $c(x)$ to convert meters to centimeters.

   b. Find the composition of the function rules that converts kilometers directly to centimeters.

   c. Use the composite function to find the number of centimeters in 5 km.

32. A cylindrical dunk tank with a diameter of 5 ft is being filled at 3 ft³/min.

   a. Write a function, $V(t)$, for the volume of water after t minutes.

   b. Use $V = \pi r^2 H$ to write a function, $H(V)$, for the water's height in terms of its volume.

   c. Find a composite function for the water's height in terms of the time the tank is being filled.

   d. Use the composite function to determine the depth of the water in the tank after being filled for 20 min.

   e. How long will it take for the tank to be filled to a depth of 5.5 ft?

33. A programmer animating travel through a tunnel increases the radius of a circle from an initial length of 3 mm at a rate of 2 mm/sec.

   a. Write function $A(r)$ describing the area of the circle in terms of its radius, and a second function $r(t)$ describing the radius in terms of the time.

   b. Find $A \circ r$. What does this composition represent?

   c. How long will it take for the area of the circle to be 169π mm²?

34. A store offers an employee discount of 25% as well as a coupon for $10 off any purchase over $10.

   a. Write function $e(x)$ that calculates the price with the employee discount, and function $c(x)$ that calculates the price of any purchase over $10 with the coupon.

   b. If the coupon is applied before the employee discount, find the composite function that calculates the final price and state its domain. Then use the function to calculate the final price of a $60 sweater.

   c. If the employee discount is applied before the coupon, find the composite function that calculates the final price and state its domain. Then use the function to calculate the final price of a $60 sweater.

   d. If line a represents the regular price, state the type of discount represented by each of the other lines.

C. Exercises

35. Given $f(x) = x^2 + 5x - 6$ and $g(x) = x - 1$, find $\dfrac{f}{g}(x)$ and state its domain and range. Then graph the function and describe its end behavior and any discontinuities.

Determine whether each statement is *always, sometimes,* or *never* true. Explain your reasoning.

36. The domain of $(f + g)(x)$ is the union of the domains of $f(x)$ and $g(x)$.

37. The domain of $(fg)(x)$ is the intersection of the domains of $f(x)$ and $g(x)$.

38. The domain of $\frac{f}{g}(x)$ is the domain of $f(x)$.

39. The domain of $(f \circ g)(x)$ is the domain of $g(x)$.

Use $f(x) = 2x + 3$, $g(x) = \frac{1}{x}$, and $h(x) = \sqrt{x}$ to state the function rule and domain for each composition.

40. Examine $(f \circ g \circ h)(x)$ by finding the following.
    a. $(f \circ (g \circ h))(x)$ **b.** $((f \circ g) \circ h)(x)$

41. Examine $(g \circ h \circ f)(x)$ by finding the following.
    a. $(g \circ (h \circ f))(x)$ **b.** $((g \circ h) \circ f)(x)$

42. Write: Which property of composition is illustrated in exercises 40–41? Explain your reasoning.

CUMULATIVE REVIEW

Solve each equation for the indicated variable.
[Algebra]

43. $p = 2l + 2w$ for l **44.** $b = \frac{a - c}{a + c}$ for a

45. $x = y^2 - z$ for y

46. Find the slope of a line that is perpendicular to $3x + 5y = 6$. [1.2]

47. Write a function rule for the line through $(2, 5)$ that is parallel to $f(x) = -3x + 7$. [1.2]

48. Graph $f(x) = \begin{cases} -1 \text{ if } x < -1 \\ x + 2 \text{ if } -1 \le x \le 1 \\ -\frac{1}{2}x + 2 \text{ if } x > 1 \end{cases}$. [1.3]

49. Describe the continuity of $y = \frac{x + 2}{x^2 - x - 6}$ at $x = 3$.
[1.3]

    A. continuous   **D.** point discontinuity
    B. infinite discontinuity   **E.** none of these
    C. jump discontinuity

50. The US Postal Service increased the per-ounce rate of a standard-sized domestic letter 17 times in the twentieth century. What type of continuity would be present in a line graph of twentieth-century postal rates? [1.3]

    A. continuous   **D.** point discontinuity
    B. infinite discontinuity   **E.** none of these
    C. jump discontinuity

51. Which could be the graph of $f(x) = -x^2 - 4x - 2$? [1.6]

    A. 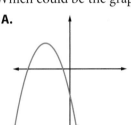   **C.**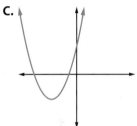

    B. 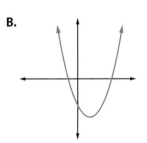   **D.**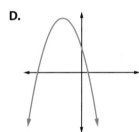

    E. none of these

52. Describe the solution(s) of $f(x) = 0$. [1.6]
    A. 2 positive
    B. 2 negative
    C. 1 negative
    D. 1 positive
    E. 1 negative and 1 positive

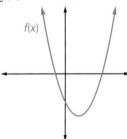

1.8 Parametric Equations and Inverses

Projectile motion is often modeled by parametric equations.

After completing this section, you will be able to

- define relations and functions parametrically.
- find a rule for the inverse of a function.
- graph the inverse of a function.
- determine whether the inverse of a graphed function is a function.
- determine whether two functions are inverses.

The correlation between two variables may be caused by their relationship to a third variable. For example, a convenience store may see that ice-cream sales are directly proportional to sales of sunscreen, but this correlation is probably caused by their common relationship to daily high temperatures. In these cases it may be desirable to define each coordinate of the relation's ordered pairs with a pair of *parametric equations*, both in terms of the third variable, called a *parameter*.

Example 1 Graphing a Relation Represented by Parametric Equations

Given the relation P defined by $x = t^2 - 3$ and $y = t + 1$ with $-3 \le t \le 3$;

a. find the ordered pairs for the relation when $t = -3, -2, -1, 0, 1, 2, 3$;

b. plot the points and draw the graph of the relation; and

c. state whether the relation is a function.

Answer

a.

t	−3	−2	−1	0	1	2	3
x	6	1	−2	−3	−2	1	6
y	−2	−1	0	1	2	3	4

Evaluate x and y for each value of t.

b.

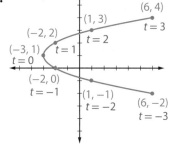

Plot the resulting points and connect them with a smooth curve.

c. The relation is not a function.

The graph fails the Vertical Line Test.

SKILL ✔ **EXERCISE 3**

The process of expressing y in terms of x when given a set of parametric equations is called *eliminating the parameter*. Solve for t in the equation for x and substitute the solution into the equation for y. This process is illustrated using $x = t^2 - 3$ and $y = t + 1$ from Example 1.

$$x = t^2 - 3 \qquad\qquad y = t + 1$$
$$t^2 = x + 3 \qquad\qquad y = \pm\sqrt{x + 3} + 1$$
$$t = \pm\sqrt{x + 3}$$

The path of a ball thrown from a height of 6 ft at an approximate angle of 37° above the horizontal with a speed of 80 ft/sec can be modeled by $y = -\frac{1}{256}x^2 + \frac{3}{4}x + 6$. A limitation of this representation is that it does not indicate the time when the object is at a particular point on its parabolic path.

When the horizontal displacement x and vertical displacement (or height) y are modeled as functions of time t, the parametric equations allow the x- and y-coordinates to be determined at any time during the projectile's flight.

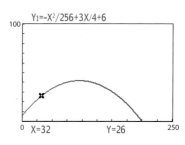

Example 2 Modeling a Projectile's Path with Parametric Equations

Use your calculator and the parametric equations below to graph the trajectory of a ball thrown with an initial speed of 80 ft/sec at an approximate angle of 37° above horizontal. Then eliminate the parameter to show that the parametric equations are equivalent to the original functional representation above.

$x = 64t$ and $y = -16t^2 + 48t + 6$

Answer

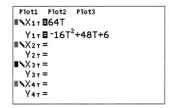

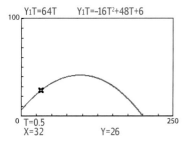

$x = 64t; t = \dfrac{x}{64}$

$y = -16\left(\dfrac{x}{64}\right)^2 + 48\left(\dfrac{x}{64}\right) + 6$

$ = -\dfrac{1}{256}x^2 + \dfrac{3}{4}x + 6$

1. Change your calculator's mode from function to parametric, and enter the equations for x and y as separate functions in the [Y=] screen. (Use the [X,T,Θ,n] key to enter the parameter t.)

2. [GRAPH] the function and resize the [WINDOW] to show the ball's trajectory.

   a. Set Tmin = 0 and Tmax = 5 to ensure that sufficient points are plotted. Use Tstep = 0.05 to adjust the incrementation of T values.

   b. The [TRACE] function can be used to display the coordinates at a given time t.

   c. The [CALC] functions zero, min, max, and intersect are not available in parametric mode.

3. Solve $x = 64t$ for t, and substitute the resulting expression for t into the equation for y.

SKILL ✓ **EXERCISE 37**

The impact that modeling dynamic versus static processes had on the development of calculus is seen in Isaac Newton's use of the term *fluxion* (Latin for "flow"). He thought of curves as being formed by a point as it moved along a path.

When a relation is expressed parametrically, it is easy to find parametric equations for its *inverse*.

▌DEFINITION

If a relation S contains the ordered pair (a, b), its **inverse relation** S^{-1} contains the ordered pair (b, a).

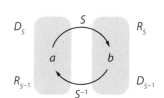

The range of the relation is the domain of its inverse, and the domain of the relation is the range of its inverse. The inverse of the relation in Example 1 can be found by interchanging the equations for the first and second coordinates.

$$P: x = t^2 - 3 \text{ and } y = t + 1 \text{ with } -3 \leq t \leq 3$$

$$P^{-1}: x = t + 1 \text{ and } y = t^2 - 3 \text{ with } -3 \leq t \leq 3$$

When the relation is expressed as a single equation in terms of x and y, the inverse can be found by interchanging the variables and solving for y.

TIP

Use ZOOM, 5:ZSquare when graphing inverses so the scales of the axes are identical and reflections are not distorted.

$$P: y = \pm\sqrt{x + 3} + 1$$
$$P^{-1}: x = \pm\sqrt{y + 3} + 1$$
$$x - 1 = \pm\sqrt{y + 3}$$
$$(x - 1)^2 = y + 3$$
$$y = (x - 1)^2 - 3$$

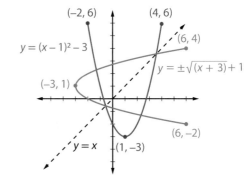

Notice that the graphs of P and P^{-1} are reflections of each other in the line $y = x$, and that the inverse is a function since it passes the Vertical Line Test. The fact that the inverse passes the Vertical Line Test can be predicted by a Horizontal Line Test of the original relation.

HORIZONTAL LINE TEST

If a horizontal line can be drawn through more than one point of a relation's graph, the relation's inverse is not a function.

Every relation has an inverse, which may or may not be a function. The Horizontal Line Test confirms that the inverse of the relation in Example 1 is a function. Likewise, every function has an inverse, which may or may not be a function. Notice how the Horizontal Line Test indicates that the inverse of the function in Example 2 is not a function.

Example 3   Finding the Inverse

Find the inverse of $f(x) = \frac{1}{3}x + 1$. Then graph $f(x)$ and its inverse and determine whether the inverse is a function.

Answer

$$y = \frac{1}{3}x + 1$$
$$x = \frac{1}{3}y + 1$$

1. Express the function in terms of x and y and interchange the independent and dependent variables.

$$x - 1 = \frac{1}{3}y$$
$$y = 3x - 3$$

2. Solve for y.

CONTINUED ➡

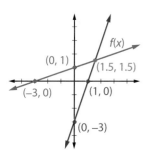

The inverse $y = 3x - 3$ is a function.

3. Graph the function $y = \frac{1}{3}x + 1$ and its inverse $y = 3x - 3$, noting that they are reflections of each other in the line $y = x$.
   Note that the y-intercept becomes the x-intercept and the x-intercept becomes the y-intercept.

4. The graph of the original function passes the Horizontal Line Test.

SKILL ✓ EXERCISES 9, 15

Restrictions on the domain of a function can cause difficulty when finding the inverse.

Example 4   Finding the Inverse with a Restricted Domain

Find an equation for the inverse of $y = \sqrt{x + 2}$. Then determine whether the inverse is a function, state the inverse's domain and range, and sketch its graph.

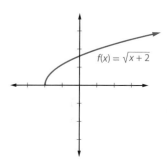

Answer

$x = \sqrt{y + 2}$
$x^2 = y + 2$
$y = x^2 - 2$
The inverse is a function.

$D_{inv} = [0, \infty)$; $R_{inv} = [-2, \infty)$

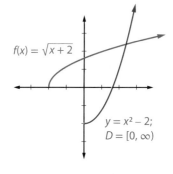

1. Switch the variables and solve for y.

2. The graph of the original function passes the Horizontal Line Test.

3. Switch the original function's domain, $D_f = [-2, \infty)$, and range, $R_f = [0, \infty)$, to obtain the domain and range of the inverse function.

4. Graph the inverse.
   Notice that without its restricted domain, $y = x^2 - 2$ is not the inverse of the original function (a reflection across $y = x$).

SKILL ✓ EXERCISE 33

The inverse of $f(x) = \sqrt{x + 2}$ in Example 4 is a function since each member of its domain is paired with exactly one element of its range. When the inverse of a function f is also a function, the inverse is notated as f^{-1} and read "f inverse": $f^{-1}(x) = x^2 - 2$, $D = [0, \infty)$. Functions that pass the Horizontal Line Test are further classified as *one-to-one functions* since each member of the range is paired with exactly one member of the domain.

TIP

The notation $f^{-1}(x)$ does not indicate the reciprocal of the function, which must be indicated as $\frac{1}{f(x)}$.

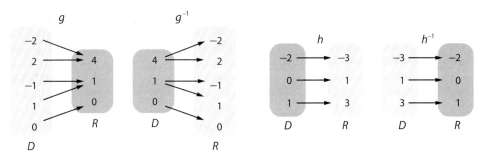

Notice that function g is not one-to-one. Since the domain of its inverse has a value that is paired with two range values, its inverse is not a function. Since h is a one-to-one function, $h(1) = 3$ and $h^{-1}(3) = 1$. Therefore, $(h^{-1} \circ h)(1) = 1$ and $(h \circ h^{-1})(3) = 3$. In fact, $(h^{-1} \circ h)(x) = x$ and $(h \circ h^{-1})(x) = x$ for all x in their domains. When composed, a function and its inverse function "reverse" each other.

▌DEFINITION

The functions $f(x)$ and $g(x)$ are **inverse functions** if $(f \circ g)(x) = (g \circ f)(x) = x$ for all x in their domains.

Example 5   Verifying Inverse Functions

Show that $f(x) = \frac{1}{3}x + 1$ and $g(x) = 3x - 3$ are inverse functions.

Answer

$(f \circ g)(x) = f(g(x))$

$\qquad = \frac{1}{3}(3x - 3) + 1$

$\qquad = x - 1 + 1$

$\qquad = x$

1. Find $(f \circ g)(x)$ by substituting $g(x)$ into $f(x)$.

$(g \circ f)(x) = g(f(x))$

$\qquad = 3\left(\frac{1}{3}x + 1\right) - 3$

$\qquad = x + 3 - 3$

$\qquad = x$

2. Find $(g \circ f)(x)$ by substituting $f(x)$ into $g(x)$.

$f(x)$ and $g(x)$ are inverse functions.

3. $(f \circ g)(x) = (g \circ f)(x) = x$

SKILL ✔ **EXERCISE 21**

> **A. Exercises**

Find the ordered pair defined by the parametric equations.

1. $x = -2t - 3$ and $y = 3t - 4$, $t = 3$

2. $x = t + 3$ and $y = t^2 - 5$, $t = -4$

Graph the relation represented by each pair of parametric equations and state whether each relation is a function.

3. $x = t + 3$ and $y = 2t + 1$, $-2 \le t \le 2$

4. $x = t + 1$ and $y = t^2 - 1$, $-2 \le t \le 2$

5. $x = t^2 + 3$ and $y = t + 3$, $-2 \le t \le 2$

6. $x = t^3$ and $y = 2t - 1$, $-2 \le t \le 2$

State whether each relation is a function. Then determine whether the inverse is a function, and if not, explain why.

7. $P = \{(4, 7), (2, -3), (5, 7), (1, 8)\}$

8. $Q = \{(-1, 7), (-6, 2), (3, 4)\}$

9.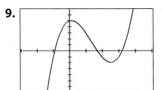

10.

Use technology to graph each function and then use the Horizontal Line Test to determine if the inverse is a function.

11. $f(x) = |x|$

12. $y = 3x^5 - 4x$

13. $y = x^3$

14. $y = \sqrt{25 - x^2}$

Find the inverse of each function.

15. $f(x) = -4x + 6$

16. $g(x) = \frac{x}{2} + 3$

17. $h(x) = x^3 + 3$

18. $f(x) = \frac{x+1}{2x}$

19. The function $f(x) = 0.2642x$ converts a number of liters, x, to an equivalent number of gallons.

   a. Find $f^{-1}(x)$, which converts a number of gallons to an equivalent number of liters.

   b. Express a volume of 4.5 gal in liters.

20. The function $f(x) = \frac{9}{5}x + 32$ converts a temperature in degrees Celsius, x, to degrees Fahrenheit.

   a. Find $f^{-1}(x)$, which converts a temperature in degrees Fahrenheit to degrees Celsius.

   b. Express a temperature of 98.6°F in degrees Celsius.

> **B. Exercises**

Confirm that $f(x)$ and $g(x)$ are inverse functions by showing that $(f \circ g)(x) = x = (g \circ f)(x)$.

21. $f(x) = 3x + 9$

   $g(x) = \frac{x-9}{3}$

22. $f(x) = \frac{x^5 - 1}{2}$

   $g(x) = \sqrt[5]{2x + 1}$

23. $f(x) = \frac{x-1}{x+7}$

   $g(x) = \frac{-7x - 1}{x - 1}$

Find $(f \circ g)(x)$ and $(g \circ f)(x)$ and state whether $f(x)$ and $g(x)$ are inverse functions.

24. $f(x) = x + 6$

   $g(x) = x - 6$

25. $f(x) = 2x + 1$

   $g(x) = \frac{x}{2} - 1$

26. $f(x) = \frac{x}{x+1}$

   $g(x) = \frac{x}{1-x}$

Sketch the graph of the inverse of each function.

27.

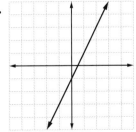

28.

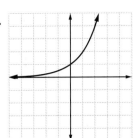

29.

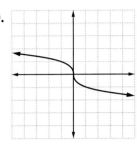

Find $f^{-1}(x)$ for each function. Confirm your results by using technology to graph the function and its inverse.

30. $f(x) = 2x - 3$

31. $f(x) = 3x^5 - 4$

32. $f(x) = \frac{1}{x+2}$

Find the inverse of each function and specify any restricted domains. Confirm your results by using technology to graph the function and its inverse.

33. $h(x) = \sqrt{x - 2}$

34. $g(x) = \frac{3}{\sqrt{x-4}}$

35. $f(x) = \frac{3}{2\sqrt{x+1}}$

36. $h(x) = \sqrt{\frac{3(x+4)}{2}}$

37. The horizontal distance traveled and height of the served volleyball described in Section 1.6 exercise 37 can be modeled (in meters) by the following parametric equations where the service line acts as the origin.

$$x = 15t$$
$$y = -4.9t^2 + 4t + 2$$

   a. Use technology to graph the parametric function. Then determine the ordered pair describing the position of the volleyball at each quarter-second until the ball hits the floor.

   b. Eliminate the parameter to find a function, $f(x)$, for the ball's height in terms of the horizontal distance traveled. Use technology to graph the function and use the ordered pairs from part a to confirm your answer.

   c. Find the maximum height of the serve and the horizontal distance it traveled to that point.

   d. How far from the service line does the ball land?

38. The men's PE instructor wants to write a linear formula to grade the results of the 12-minute run. A 1.75 mi run would earn a 95% (1.75, 95) and a 1 mi run would earn a 65% (1, 65).

   a. Find the linear function $f(x)$ that assigns a percentage grade for various recorded distances.

   b. Find $f^{-1}(x)$ and describe what its independent and dependent variables represent.

   c. Find the percentage grade for a student who runs 1.125 mi.

   d. Find the distance needed to earn an 85%.

C. Exercises

39. Write: Find expressions for the slope of a linear function given in standard form, $ax + by = c$, and the slope of its inverse. Describe the relationship between the slopes.

State whether each statement is *always*, *sometimes*, or *never* true. Explain your reasoning.

40. The inverse of a linear function is also a function.

41. The inverse of an odd function is an even function.

42. The inverse of an increasing function is an increasing function.

43. Explain: Why is the inverse of $g(x)$ not a function? State a least restrictive domain of $g(x)$ for which the inverse is a function.

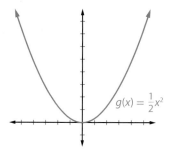

$g(x) = \frac{1}{2}x^2$

44. Find the inverse of $f(x) = \begin{cases} \dfrac{x - 14}{4} & \text{if } x \leq 2 \\ \dfrac{9}{1 - 2x} & \text{if } x > 2 \end{cases}$.

Confirm your result by using technology to graph the function and its inverse.

CUMULATIVE REVIEW

Graph each function. [1.3–1.4]

45. $f(x) = 3[x]$

46. $g(x) = \left[\frac{1}{2}x\right]$

47. Determine whether $f(x) = \begin{cases} |x| & \text{if } x \leq 2 \\ x^2 & \text{if } x > 2 \end{cases}$ is continuous or discontinuous. Explain your reasoning. [1.3]

Classify each function as even, odd, or neither. [1.4]

48. $f(x) = 3x^2$

49. $f(x) = 2x^5$

50. $f(x) = x^2 + 2$

51. Which equation describes $g(x)$, a transformation of $f(x)$? [1.5]

A. $g(x) = 3f(x - 4) + 2$
B. $g(x) = -3f(x - 4) + 2$
C. $g(x) = -3f(x + 4) - 2$
D. $g(x) = 3f(x + 4) + 2$
E. $g(x) = -3f(x + 4) + 2$

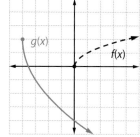

52. What is the sum of the roots of the equation $4x^2 - 12x - 25 = 3x^2 - 20$? [1.6]

A. 12   **C.** −18   **E.** −15
B. −12   **D.** 18

53. Find $f(g(x))$ if $f(x) = 3x - 2$ and $g(x) = x^2 + 1$. [1.7]
A. $f(g(x)) = 9x^2 + 5$
B. $f(g(x)) = 3x^2 + 1$
C. $f(g(x)) = 9x^2 - 6x + 5$
D. $f(g(x)) = 3x^3 - 2x^2 + 3x - 2$
E. none of these

54. If $f(x) = 3x - 2$ and $g(x) = x^2 + 1$, what is the domain of $\frac{f}{g}(x)$? [1.7]
A. $\{x \mid x \neq -1\}$
B. $\left\{x \mid x > \frac{2}{3}\right\}$
C. $\left\{x \mid x \neq \frac{2}{3}\right\}$
D. $\{x \mid x > -1\}$
E. $\mathbb{R}$

The American alligator can grow up to a foot a year in the wild and up to three feet a year on an alligator farm. A biologist studying alligator growth patterns recorded the lengths and weights of fourteen alligators.

Data containing two related variables, such as length and weight, is called *bivariate* data. A *scatterplot* of the ordered pairs can be drawn to illustrate the relationship between the two variables. A *trend line* can be drawn to model the relationship between the data and make predictions related to other values of either variable. This trend line should minimize the distances from the data points. While trend lines drawn by visual inspection can provide imprecise estimates, a variety of technologies can be used to draw a scatterplot and complete a *linear regression* using a statistical algorithm to find the *line of best fit.*

Length (in.)	Weight (lb)
58	28
63	33
86	90
69	36
147	640
78	57
114	197
128	366
85	84
88	70
72	61
74	54
90	106
94	130

After completing this section, you will be able to

- find linear and quadratic models for data.
- evaluate how well a function models data.
- use a model to make predictions.

Joseph Fourier, in the preliminary discourse to his 1822 *The Analytical Theory of Heat*, wrote that "profound study of nature is the most fertile source of mathematical discoveries."

Graphing Calculator	Spreadsheet	Internet
See the Technology Corner in Section 6.6 of BJU Press's ALGEBRA 1, 3rd ed., or use the Internet keyword search *TI-84 regression.*	See the Technology Corner in Section 2.4 of BJU Press's ALGEBRA 2, 3rd ed., or use the Internet keyword search *spreadsheet trend line.*	Use the Internet keyword search *best fit line applet* or *regression app.*

Example 1 Finding the Line of Best Fit

Use technology to create a scatterplot and determine the equation of the line of best fit for the data collected by the biologist. Then use the equation to predict the following.

a. the weight of a 100 in. long alligator

b. the weight of a 3 ft long alligator

c. the length of an alligator that weighs 100 lb

Answer

Let x = length (in inches) and $y = f(x)$ = weight (in pounds).

1. Weight is more likely to be a function of length.

CONTINUED ➡

$$f(x) \approx 6.252x - 417.000$$

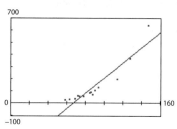

2. Input the data into a graphing calculator, spreadsheet, or Internet applet and complete the linear regression to determine the equation of the line of best fit.

3. Graph the function on the scatterplot.

a. $f(100) \approx 6.252(100) - 417.00 = 208.2$ lb

b. $f(36) \approx 6.252(36) - 417.00 = -191.9$ lb

4. Find $f(100)$.

5. Find $f(36)$, using 3 ft = 36 in.

c. $f(x) \approx 6.252x - 417.00 = 100$
$$x \approx \frac{517.00}{6.252} \approx 82.7 \text{ in.}$$

6. Set $f(x) = 100$ and solve for x.

SKILL ✔ **EXERCISE 9**

Attempts to model natural phenomena drove mathematical innovation in Europe. Surprisingly, problems in diverse areas (hydrodynamics, heat transfer, electricity, magnetism, optics, etc.) were found to have similar mathematical solutions. The wave equation, developed during the mid-1700s, led to John Maxwell's discovery of radio waves a century later.

In this model, the prediction within the range of data points (*interpolation*) is fairly reasonable while the prediction outside the range of data points (*extrapolation*) is not reasonable. In general, interpolation tends to produce better estimates than extrapolation.

The *linear correlation* of the data describes how closely the data points are clustered along the trend line. The *correlation coefficient*, r, where $-1 \leq r \leq 1$, numerically describes the degree to which the two variables are related. A positive correlation indicates that the two quantities increase or decrease together. A negative value of r represents an inverse correlation, where one variable increases as the other decreases.

The closer $|r|$ is to 1, the stronger the correlation is between the variables. If $r = 1$ or -1, all the data points will be on a line with a positive or negative slope, respectively. If r is near 0, the points appear to be randomly scattered. The correlation is usually considered to be strong when $|r| > 0.8$ and weak when $|r| < 0.5$, but these guidelines vary with the context of the data.

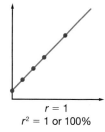
$r = 1$
$r^2 = 1$ or 100%

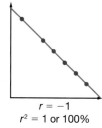
$r = -1$
$r^2 = 1$ or 100%

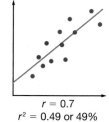
$r = 0.7$
$r^2 = 0.49$ or 49%

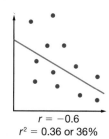
$r = -0.6$
$r^2 = 0.36$ or 36%

Many statistical applications also state the value of r^2, the *coefficient of determination*. If r is -0.8, then r^2 is 0.64. This indicates that 64% of the variation in the dependent variable can be explained by variation in the independent variable.

Outliers are points that do not seem to fit the trend of the scatterplot. These points typically represent extreme variations or unusual circumstances and are often ignored when mathematical models are constructed. We should ask if the last one or two data points in Example 1 are outliers or if a different function would serve as a better model for the data.

The *residuals*, the differences between the actual y-value of each data point and its value predicted by the modeling function, also indicate how well the model fits the data. If there is a pattern within the residuals, continue to search for a better model.

Example 2　Evaluating a Linear Model

Evaluate the linear model of the line of best fit for the alligator data.

a. State and interpret the values of the coefficient of determination and the linear correlation coefficient.

b. Plot the residuals and interpret the graph.

Answer

a. $r^2 \approx 0.866$
86.6% of the variation in weight is explained by variation in length.
$r \approx 0.931$
There is a strong positive correlation between length and weight.

Use technology to display the correlation coefficient, r, or the coefficient of determination, r^2, or both. You may have to calculate r from r^2, using the slope of the line to determine whether r is positive or negative.

b.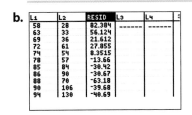

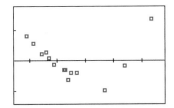

The curved pattern of the residuals suggests that a quadratic function might be a better model.

1. To view the residuals calculated by your graphing calculator while completing the regression, display the list editor ([STAT], [1]), use ▶ and ▲ to select L3, and select [INS] to place an empty column in the list editor. Then select [LIST] ([2nd], [STAT]), choose RESID from the list name menu, and press [ENTER] to name the list and display the residual for each data point.
2. Use [STAT PLOT] to turn off Plot1 and turn on Plot2, using L_1 for the Xlist and defining the Ylist by selecting LIST and choosing RESID from the NAMES submenu. Press [Y=], [◀], [ENTER] to turn off the graph of Y1, and then select ZoomStat ([ZOOM], [9]) to display a graph of the residuals.

TIP

When using other technologies, you may have to calculate the list of residuals before creating a similar scatterplot.

SKILL ✔ **EXERCISE 21**

The process of completing a *quadratic regression* with technology is similar to the process used to complete a linear regression. The coefficient of determination, r^2, is calculated, but a correlation coefficient, r, is not since this measure applies only to linear models.

Example 3　Creating and Evaluating a Quadratic Model

Complete a quadratic regression to find a quadratic function that models the alligator data. Then examine and interpret the coefficient of determination and a plot of the residuals.

Answer

$f(x) \approx 0.088x^2 - 11.656x + 425.841$

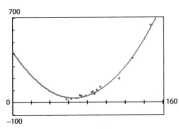

1. Complete a quadratic regression and plot the parabola on the data's scatterplot.

CONTINUED ➡

$r^2 \approx 0.987$
With this model, 98.7% of the variation in weight is explained by variation in length.

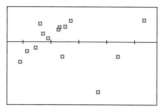

A random distribution suggests that a quadratic function might be the best model.

2. Use technology to display the coefficient of determination, r^2.

3. Use Plot2 to display a scatterplot of the updated residuals.

SKILL ✓ **EXERCISE 22**

While r^2 values and plots of residuals are indicators of the value of a model, the usefulness of the model still needs to be examined. Our quadratic model appears to be a good fit within the data set and may continue to work for longer alligators. However, the fact that the parabola's minimum value occurs when $x \approx 66$ in. makes it clear that it is not a good model for alligators much shorter than this. In later chapters, we will study other functions that may provide an even better model for this type of data.

Raw data is frequently transformed when creating a model. Years are frequently expressed as the number of years after a convenient reference point, and large numbers can be expressed in thousands, millions, or billions.

Example 4 Transforming Data

Find a function modeling the population of New York City during the nineteenth century. Then use the model to predict its population in 1900.

New York City					
Year	Population	Year	Population	Year	Population
1800	60,515	1840	312,710	1880	1,206,299
1810	96,373	1850	515,547	1890	1,515,301
1820	123,706	1860	813,669		
1830	202,589	1870	942,292		

TIP

Using the exact regression equation eliminates rounding errors, which can be significant when the x-values are relatively large.

Answer

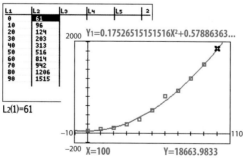

$f(x) \approx 0.175x^2 + 0.579x + 53.445$

The model predicts a population of approximately 1,864,000 in 1900.

1. Let x be the number of years since 1800 and let y be the population (in thousands).

2. The scatterplot suggests a quadratic model, and an r^2 value of 0.99 implies that the resulting quadratic regression produces a good fit for the data.

3. Use TRACE on Y1 and enter 100 to find the approximate population in 1900.

SKILL ✓ **EXERCISES 26–29**

We must be careful not to assume that a high coefficient of determination implies a cause-and-effect relationship between the independent variable and the dependent variable. The cause-and-effect relationship may be reversed, both variables might be related to a third variable or a combination of other variables, or the relationship may be coincidental.

❯ A. Exercises

Match each scatterplot to the best description of its linear correlation.

A. strong positive   C. weak positive
B. strong negative   D. weak negative

1.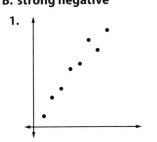

2.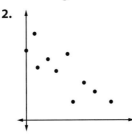

3.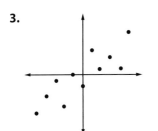

4.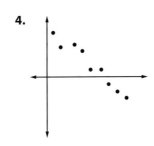

Refer to the data set for exercises 5–8.

x	0	2	4	6	8	10	12	14
y	21	17	14	11	7	2	1	−3

5. Is the function increasing, decreasing, or both? What does this imply about the linear correlation?

6. Use technology to create a scatterplot and determine the linear function that best models the data. Round coefficients to the nearest thousandth.

7. State the coefficient of determination. What does this value indicate?

8. Use your model to predict the value of *y* (to the nearest tenth) when *x* is 20. Is this an example of interpolation or extrapolation?

Refer to the data set for exercises 9–12.

x	−5	−3	−1	1	3	5
y	−6	−3	0	2	5	11

9. Use technology to create a scatterplot and determine the linear function that best models the data. Round coefficients to the nearest thousandth.

10. State the coefficient of determination. What does this value indicate?

11. How does the regression equation algebraically confirm the type of linear correlation?

12. Use your model to predict the value of *y* (to the nearest tenth) when *x* is 4. Is this an example of interpolation or extrapolation?

Refer to the data set for exercises 13–16.

x	2	5	7	10	13	15	18	20
y	2	8	16	20	23	21	13	3

13. Is the function increasing, decreasing, or both? What does this imply about the linear correlation?

14. Use technology to create a scatterplot and determine the quadratic function that best models the data. Round coefficients to the nearest thousandth.

15. State the coefficient of determination. What does this value indicate?

16. Use your model to predict the value of *y* (to the nearest tenth) when *x* = 13; then find the difference between the actual and predicted values. What is this difference called?

B. Exercises

Use technology to create a scatterplot of each set of data. Then determine the linear or quadratic function that best models the data. Round coefficients to the nearest thousandth.

17.

x	y
−2	−10.7
−1	−8.0
0	−5.2
2	0.9
4	7.1
7	15.9

18.

x	y
−3	5.0
−1	3.7
0	2.0
2	2.3
3	1.0
5	0.0

19.

x	y
−2	11.1
−1	4.9
0	1.0
2	−0.9
5	11.0
6	18.7

20.

x	y
−3	6.8
−2	−0.8
−1	−3.6
0	−4.0
1	−4.4
2	−7.2

For exercises 21–25, use technology to create a scatterplot of gasoline prices. Let x represent the number of years since 1940 and let y represent the price per gallon (in cents).

Average US Gas Prices	
Year	$/gal
1940	0.18
1950	0.27
1960	0.31
1970	0.36
1980	1.19
1990	1.15
2000	1.51
2010	2.79

21. Find the best linear function modeling the data; then find the corresponding coefficient of determination and create a graph of the residuals. Do the residuals appear to form a pattern?

22. Find the best quadratic function modeling the data; then find the corresponding coefficient of determination and create a graph of the residuals. Do the residuals appear to form a pattern?

23. Using the better model from exercises 21 and 22, estimate the average price of gasoline for each year.
   a. 1995   **b.** 2015   **c.** this year

24. The actual average price for gasoline was $1.15/gal in 1995 and $2.45/gal in 2015. Was the interpolation or extrapolation more accurate in exercise 23? Is this unusual?

25. Discuss: State several reasons why gas price predictions may not be accurate. Then state why mathematical models are valuable even if their predictions are not as accurate as we would like.

Communications networks use various *topologies*, or configurations of connectivity. A full mesh topology increases network reliability by connecting every *node* (device such as computer or printer) to every other node so that communications can be redirected when a connection fails. The number of connections often makes such configurations expensive.

Nodes	Connections
2	
3	
4	
5	
6	15

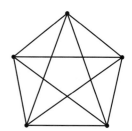

26. Complete the table by listing the number of connections in full-mesh networks with each number of nodes.

27. Create a scatterplot of the data and complete linear and quadratic regressions to find best-fit linear and quadratic models for the data. State each function and corresponding r^2 value.

28. Analyze: What does the coefficient of determination for the quadratic model indicate?

29. Determine the number of connections needed for a full-mesh network of 100 nodes.

Dallas, Texas, had the ninth largest population in a 2015 survey of US cities. Use technology to create a scatterplot of the following population data. Let *x* represent the number of years since 1900 and let *y* represent the population (in thousands).

Dallas, Texas			
Year	Population	Year	Population
1920	158,976	1970	844,401
1930	260,475	1980	904,075
1940	294,734	1990	1,006,877
1950	434,462	2000	1,188,580
1960	679,684		

30. In which decade did Dallas experience its greatest population increase?

31. Find the best linear function modeling the data and the corresponding coefficient of determination. Then create a graph of the residuals. Do they appear to form a pattern?

32. Use the linear model found in exercise 31 to estimate the population of Dallas for each year.
    a. 2010   **b.** 1900   **c.** 1860

33. **Analyze:** Compare the predicted populations in exercise 32 to the actual populations in the table below and the actual 2010 population of 1,197,816. Does the linear model appear to be a good fit for the data? Explain your reasoning.

Use technology to create a scatterplot of a second set of population data for Dallas. Let *x* represent the number of years since 1900 and let *y* represent the population (in thousands).

Dallas, Texas			
Year	Population	Year	Population
1860	678	1940	294,734
1880	10,358	1960	679,684
1900	42,639	1980	904,075
1920	158,976	2000	1,188,580

34. Find the best quadratic function modeling the data and the corresponding coefficient of determination. Then create a graph of the residuals. Do they appear to form a pattern?

35. Use the quadratic model found in exercise 34 to estimate the population of Dallas for each year.
    a. 2010   **b.** 1990   **c.** 1930

36. **Analyze:** Calculate the percent error of each predicted population from exercise 35 using the table for exercises 30–33 and the actual 2010 population of 1,197,816. Which values were more accurate: the interpolated values or the extrapolated values? Is this unusual?

⟩ C. Exercises

Use the life expectancy data to create scatterplots for both males and females. Let *x* represent the number of decades since 1900.

US Life Expectancy		
Year Born	Males	Females
1930	58.1	61.6
1940	60.8	65.2
1950	65.6	71.1
1960	66.6	73.1
1970	67.1	74.7
1980	70.0	77.4
1990	71.8	78.8
2000	74.3	79.7

37. Referring to the numeric data in the table, in which decade did life expectancy increase the most for males? for females?

38. Complete linear regressions to determine the best linear functions modeling the male and the female life expectancies and state the coefficient of determination for each model.

39. **Analyze:** What does comparing the slopes of the lines allow us to conclude about the life expectancy of the genders?

40. Use the linear models found in exercise 38 to estimate the US life expectancies for both males and females born in each year.
    a. 1985   **b.** 2010

41. Complete quadratic regressions to determine the best quadratic function modeling the male and the female life expectancies and state the coefficient of determination for each model.

42. Determine the vertex for each regression equation and interpret its significance.

43. Many factors affect life expectancy. The psalmist considers life expectancy in Psalm 90:10–12.

  a. How do the models from exercises 38 and 40 compare with these estimates made thousands of years ago?

  b. According to this passage and Ephesians 5:16, what is the purpose of recognizing our life expectancy?

CUMULATIVE REVIEW

Graph each function and then list its domain and range. Use limit notation to describe its end behavior. [1.3–1.6]

44. $y = [x] + 6$

45. $y = -2x^2$

46. $y = 2(x + 3)^3 + 1$

47. $y = 2x^{-2}$

Write a function rule for $g(x)$, the described transformation of $f(x)$. [1.5]

48. $f(x) = x^2$ translated 2 units right and reflected in the x-axis

49. $f(x) = x^3$ stretched vertically by a factor of 2 and then translated 3 units down and 1 unit left

50. What is the maximum value of $f(x) = -3(x + 4)^2 - 2$? [1.6]

  A. -4 **C.** -2 **E.** 4

  B. -3 **D.** 2

51. If $f(x)$ and the $g(x)$ are inverse functions, what is $g(f(5))$? [1.7]

  A. 5 **C.** $\frac{1}{5}$ **E.** 25

  B. -5 **D.** $-\frac{1}{5}$

52. Which function has an inverse function? [1.8]

  A. $f(x) = 3x^2$ **D.** $h(x) = 2x - 4$

  B. $g(x) = |x - 2|$ **E.** all of these

  C. $r(x) = 3x^4$

53. If the equations $x = 2t + 1$ and $y = t - 7$ represent a parametric function, what is the x-intercept? [1.8]

  A. $(7, 0)$ **C.** $(15, 0)$ **E.** $\left(-\frac{1}{2}, 7\right)$

  B. $(0, 7)$ **D.** $\left(0, -\frac{15}{2}\right)$

DATA ANALYSIS

Home Run

Horizontal Distance (ft)	Height (ft)
0.0	3.4
50.3	28.7
100.6	52.1
149.6	72.8
198.7	85.6
250.2	86.2
300.5	72.4

Mathematical models are powerful tools for making predictions and informing decisions. They can be used to estimate unknown values within a data set (interpolation) and to predict values beyond a data set (extrapolation). However, you need to be aware of the limitations of mathematical models so that the resulting estimates are properly interpreted and applied.

Aristotle's assertion that all motion on earth is linear, circular, or a combination of the two was believed and taught for about 2000 years. Galileo studied Aristotle's laws of motion but later showed that projectile motion can be modeled by a parabolic path. You will investigate both linear and parabolic models of the flight of a batted ball, predict whether the ball clears the outfield wall for a home run, and evaluate the usefulness of your model.

1. Use technology to complete a scatterplot and linear regression of the data. Record the equation of the line of best fit, the correlation coefficient, and the coefficient of determination.

   a. Describe the linear correlation of the data.

   b. Interpret the coefficient of determination for the linear model.

   c. Explain why the line of best fit would not be a good model for the ball's flight.

2. Use technology to graph the residuals. What characteristic of this graph indicates that you should attempt to find a different model?

3. Complete a quadratic regression of the data. Record the resulting quadratic function and its coefficient of determination and graph your quadratic model on the scatterplot.

   a. Interpret the coefficient of determination for the quadratic model.

   b. Does the quadratic model appear to be a good model for the data?

4. Use the quadratic model to make predictions.

   a. Predict the maximum height of the ball.

   b. Predict whether the batter hit a home run if the ball is headed to the 10 ft tall left-center field wall (381 ft from home plate). Justify your prediction.

   c. Predict how far from home plate the ball will land (assuming level ground and no obstructions).

5. Evaluate your predictions.

   a. How can you know that the model's prediction for the maximum height is not exact? Determine the smallest possible error in the model's prediction of the maximum height.

   b. The batted ball was actually a home run landing 397 ft from home plate. Determine the amount of error in the model's prediction.

   c. When evaluating a model, consider factors that are not included by the model. What is likely the most significant factor excluded by the quadratic model?

While our quadratic model is not perfect, quadratic equations are frequently used to model the trajectory of a projectile. There are many other factors that can be included to make the model more accurate. Video game developers utilize mathematical models like these to simulate the path of projectiles. While some games strive to be as realistic as possible, others play with physics by intentionally altering the gravitational force or eliminating air resistance or friction.

6. What factors affect the accuracy of the mathematical model of the baseball's trajectory?

7. What could help provide a more accurate mathematical model?

8. Why is mathematical modeling an important tool even if some predictions are not perfectly accurate?

9. How do the strengths and weaknesses of mathematical models relate to the roles of God and humans in the development of mathematics?

Chapter 1 Review

State the domain and range, using interval notation when possible. Determine whether the relation is a function. [1.1]

1.

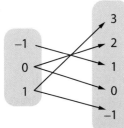

2. {(1, 3), (4, 6), (−3, −1), (0, 3)}

3. $y = \dfrac{1}{x + 5}$

4. $y^2 = x − 3$

5. Represent $f(x) = |x − 2|$ where $D = \{−4, −2, 0, 2, 4\}$ as a set of ordered pairs, with a mapping diagram, and with its graph. [1.1]

State the x-intercept, y-intercept, and slope of each line. Then graph the function. [1.2]

6. $y = −\dfrac{3}{5}x + 6$

7. $2x − 3y = 12$

8. Given $A\,(9, −5)$ and $B\,(−5, −3)$, find AB and the midpoint of $\overline{AB}$. [1.2]

9. Write the slope-intercept form equation of the line passing through $(−3, 7)$ and $(6, 1)$. [1.2]

10. Write the general form equation of the line passing through the point $(−4, −5)$ and perpendicular to $x − 2y = 6$. [1.2]

Graph each function and state its domain and range. Then identify the function as continuous or discontinuous. [1.3, 1.5]

11. $f(x) = |x − 1|$

12. $g(x) = [x] + 2$

13. $h(x) = \begin{cases} −1 & \text{if } x < 0 \\ x^2 & \text{if } 0 \le x \le 2 \\ −x + 6 & \text{if } x > 2 \end{cases}$

14. Find each limit of the function in exercise 13. Justify your answer. [1.3]

    a. $\lim\limits_{x \to 0} h(x)$

    b. $\lim\limits_{x \to 2} h(x)$

15. Classify each discontinuity below as jump, infinite, or point. [1.3]

  a.

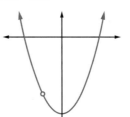

  b.

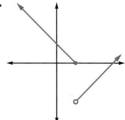

  c.

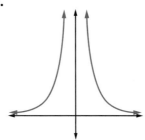

Use technology to graph each function. Then describe its domain; range; end behavior; intervals of continuity; intervals for which the function is increasing, decreasing, or constant; whether the function is even, odd, or neither; and any symmetry. [1.4]

16. $y = −2x^4$

17. $y = \dfrac{x^3}{2}$

18. $y = −3x^{−2}$

Use a power function to model each variation in exercises 19–21. [1.4]

19. If Jennie pays $15 dollars for supplies to clean 3 homes and the cost varies directly with the number of homes, what is the cost for the supplies needed to clean 10 homes?

20. The number of days needed to complete a project is inversely proportional to the number of workers on the project. Determine the number of days needed to complete a project with 2 workers if it takes 3 days for 7 workers to complete the project.

21. The volume of a hemisphere is directly proportional to the cube of its radius. Determine the volume of a hemisphere with a radius of 14 ft if a hemisphere with a 2 ft radius has a volume of $\dfrac{16\pi}{3}$ ft^3.

22. Write a function rule for $g(x)$, the described transformation of $f(x)$. Confirm your answer by graphing $f(x)$ and $g(x)$ in the same window. [1.5]

  a. $f(x) = |x|$ translated 4 units right and 2 units up

  b. $f(x) = x^3$ vertically stretched by a factor of 2 and then translated 1 unit down

  c. $f(x) = x^2$ reflected across the x-axis, vertically shrunk by a factor of $\frac{1}{3}$, and then translated 5 units up

Graph each function as a transformation of a parent function. Then state the function's domain and range. [1.5–1.6]

23. $g(x) = -2|x - 3| + 1$

24. $g(x) = \left(\frac{x}{2}\right)^3 - 2$

25. $g(x) = 2[x]$

26. $f(x) = -2(x - 1)^2 + 3$

27. $h(x) = \frac{1}{2}(x + 2)^2$

28. $g(x) = 3x^2 - 18x + 25$

Identify the vertex of each parabola and state whether it is a maximum or minimum point. Then state the y-intercept and any zeros. [1.6]

29. $f(x) = -(x - 1)^2 + 4$

30. $f(x) = 2x^2 + 5x - 12$

Use $f(x) = x^2 - 4x + 4$ and $g(x) = x - 2$ to write function rules for each function operation in exercises 31–33. [1.7]

31. Find $(f + g)(x)$, $(g - f)(x)$, and $(fg)(x)$.

32. Find $(f \circ g)(x)$ and $(g \circ f)(x)$.

33. Find $\frac{f}{g}(x)$, graph the function, state its domain and range, and describe any discontinuities.

34. If $f(x) = \sqrt{x - 3}$ and $g(x) = x^2 - 1$, find $(f \circ g)(x)$ and $(g \circ f)(x)$ and state the domain of each. [1.7]

35. Find $f(x)$ and $g(x)$ such that $h(x) = (f \circ g)(x) = -2x^2 + 12x - 13$. [1.7]

Use composition to determine whether $f(x)$ and $g(x)$ are inverse functions. [1.8]

36. $f(x) = \frac{x}{3} - 2$
    $g(x) = 3x + 2$

37. $f(x) = \frac{x^5 + 1}{4}$
    $g(x) = \sqrt[5]{4x - 1}$

Find the inverse of each function. Confirm your results by using technology to graph the function and its inverse in the same square window. [1.8]

38. $f(x) = \frac{x - 3}{4}$

39. $f(x) = \frac{1}{x - 3}$

40. Use technology to graph $y = -x^4 + 5x^2 + x + 1$. Determine whether the inverse is a function and justify your answer. [1.8]

41. A relation is defined by the parametric equations $x = t + 4$ and $y = t^2 - 1$ with $-3 \leq t \leq 3$. [1.8]

  a. Draw a graph of the relation.

  b. Eliminate the parameter to express y in terms of x.

42. The horizontal distance traveled and height of a punted football are modeled (in feet) by the following parametric equations. [1.8]
$$x = 45t$$
$$y = -16t^2 + 60t + 3$$

  a. Use technology to graph the parametric functions and determine the ordered pair describing the position of the football at each second before it hits the ground.

  b. Eliminate the parameter to find a function expressing the football's height in terms of the horizontal distance traveled. Use technology to graph the function and use the ordered pairs from part a to confirm your answer.

  c. Find the maximum height of the football.

  d. Find the horizontal distance the football travels before hitting the ground (in yards).

43. A swimming pool with a diameter of 20 ft and a depth of 4 ft is being filled by a garden hose at 4 ft³/min. [1.7]

  a. Write a function $V(t)$ for the volume of water in the pool after t minutes.

  b. Use $V = \pi r^2 H$ to write a function $H(V)$ that expresses the water's height in terms of its volume.

  c. Compose the functions to find a function that expresses the water's height in terms of the time.

  d. Find the height of the water after 3 hr.

  e. How long will it take for the pool to be filled to a depth of 4 ft?

44. A quarterback throws a pass from a height of 6 ft at the 20 yd line. The pass is caught at the same height at the 50 yd line after the football reached a maximum height of 15 ft. Write a quadratic function modeling the path of the ball, using the team's goal line as the origin. [1.6]

45. The height of a projectile can be modeled by the quadratic function $h(t) = -\frac{1}{2}gt^2 + v_0 t + h_0$ where g, the acceleration due to gravity, is approximately 32 ft/sec². A firework is launched with an initial vertical velocity of 270 ft/sec from a barge at a point 15 ft above the river. Ignoring the effect of air resistance, predict the maximum height the firework reaches (above the river) and the time it takes to reach that height. [1.6]

Use technology to create a scatterplot of median new home prices in the US. Let *x* represent the number of years since 1970, and let *y* represent the price in thousands of dollars. [1.9]

Median New Home Prices in the US	
Year	Price
1970	$23,400
1975	$39,300
1980	$64,600
1985	$84,300
1990	$122,900
1995	$133,900
2000	$169,000

46. Find the best linear function modeling the data and the corresponding coefficient of determination.

47. Create a graph of the residuals. Do the residuals appear to form a pattern?

48. Find the best quadratic function modeling the data and the corresponding coefficient of determination.

49. Use the linear model to estimate the median price of a new home in 1983.

50. Use both the linear model and the quadratic model to estimate the median price of a new home in 2010. Then determine the difference between each estimate and the actual 2010 median price of $221,300.

2 Radical, Polynomial, and Rational Functions

HISTORICAL CONNECTION

During the Middle Ages, interest in using algebraic techniques to solve problems in science, commerce, and finance flourished. Gutenberg's printing press (ca. 1440) led to the proliferation of mathematical texts. This encouraged the adoption and standardization of symbolic notation, a key development in the study of functions.

BIBLICAL PERSPECTIVE OF MATHEMATICS

Do mathematical laws evidence the divine nature of God? Are attributes of God found in simple arithmetical truths?

DATA ANALYSIS

Mathematicians analyze the key characteristics of functions that model raw data, enabling informed predictions and decisions to be made. You will learn how to find zeros, asymptotes, point discontinuities, end behavior, and relative minimum and maximum points of several types of nonlinear functions.

An athlete's hang time is a function of the height of the jump.

After completing this section, you will be able to

- graph a radical function and describe its key characteristics.
- relate radical functions and their inverse power functions.
- solve radical equations.

Power functions with integral exponents were examined in Section 1.4. Recall that the radical expression $\sqrt[r]{x}$ can also be written as a power with a rational exponent, $x^{\frac{1}{r}}$. Therefore, a function of the form $f(x) = k\sqrt[r]{x}$ is a power function with a fractional exponent.

> **DEFINITION**
>
> A **radical function** contains a radical expression with the independent variable in the radicand.

One of the simplest radical functions is the square root function, $f(x) = \sqrt{x}$ or $f(x) = x^{\frac{1}{2}}$. The domain is restricted to $[0, \infty)$ since negative values for x result in imaginary values for y. The range is also $[0, \infty)$ since the notation indicates the principal (or positive) square root. The function is continuous and increasing over its domain.

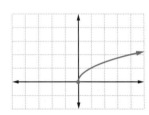

Fractional exponents were first used by Nicole Oresme in the fourteenth century. He expressed $2^{\frac{1}{2}}$ as $\frac{1}{2}2^p$ and $4^{\frac{3}{2}}$ as $\left|1\,p\,\frac{1}{2}\right|4$.

Example 1 Analyzing Radical Functions

Use technology to graph each radical function. State its domain and range and then determine the intervals in which the function is increasing or decreasing. Then state whether the function is continuous or discontinuous and whether it is odd, even, or neither.

a. $g(x) = \sqrt[3]{x}$ **b.** $h(x) = \sqrt[4]{x}$

Answer

a.

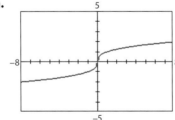

$D = \mathbb{R}; R = \mathbb{R}$
increasing: $\mathbb{R}$
continuous; odd

b.

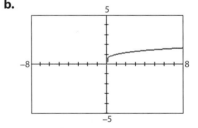

$D = [0, \infty); R = [0, \infty)$
increasing: $[0, \infty)$
continuous; neither

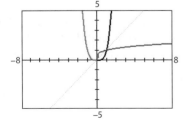

_____ SKILL ✔ **EXERCISE 3**

The graph of $g(x) = \sqrt[3]{x} = x^{\frac{1}{3}}$ in Example *1a* suggests that $g(x)$ is the inverse function of $f(x) = x^3$. This can be verified by showing that $f(g(x)) = \left(x^{\frac{1}{3}}\right)^3 = x$ and $g(f(x)) = (x^3)^{\frac{1}{3}} = x$.

Since $f(x) = x^4$ is an even function and does not pass the Horizontal Line Test, its inverse is not a function unless the function's domain is restricted. When the domain of $f(x) = x^4$ is restricted to $D_f = [0, \infty)$, its inverse function is $h(x) = \sqrt[4]{x} = x^{\frac{1}{4}}$.

Notice the first-quadrant shapes of the illustrated parent power functions of the form $f(x) = x^n$. The functions all contain the point $(1, 1)$. When $n > 0$, $\lim\limits_{x \to 0^+} x^n = 0$ and $\lim\limits_{x \to \infty} x^n = \infty$; but when $n < 0$, $\lim\limits_{x \to 0^+} x^n = \infty$ and $\lim\limits_{x \to \infty} x^n = 0$. When n is a rational exponent, such as $x^{\frac{p}{r}}$ where $\frac{p}{r}$ is simplified, $f(x) = \sqrt[r]{x^p}$. The radical function $f(x) = x^{\frac{p}{r}}$ is restricted to $D = [0, \infty)$ when r is even. The shape of the remaining portion of each graph will be explored in exercise 9.

Many radical functions can be graphed by transforming a parent function of the form $f(x) = \sqrt[r]{x^p}$.

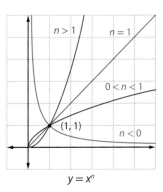

$y = x^n$

Example 2   Graphing the Transformation of a Radical Function

Use transformations of a parent radical function to graph $g(x) = 4 - \sqrt{x + 3}$. Then state its domain and range.

Answer

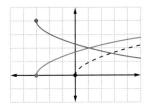

1. Rewrite the function $g(x) = -\sqrt{x + 3} + 4$.
2. Sketch a graph of the parent function $f(x) = \sqrt{x}$.
3. Translate the graph 3 units left.
4. Reflect the graph in the x-axis and translate the graph 4 units up.

$x + 3 \geq 0; x \geq -3;$
$D = [-3, \infty); R = (-\infty, 4]$

5. The radicand of an even root cannot be negative.

_____ SKILL ✔ **EXERCISE 19**

Note also that the inverse of $f(x) = x^{\frac{p}{r}}$ is $g(x) = x^{\frac{r}{p}}$ with any necessary restrictions on the domains.

Example 3   Finding and Graphing the Inverse of a Radical Function

Find the inverse function of $f(x) = -\sqrt{x - 1}$. Then graph $f(x)$ and $f^{-1}(x)$.

Answer

$y = -\sqrt{x - 1}$
$D = [1, \infty); R = (-\infty, 0]$

1. State the function's domain and range.

$x = -\sqrt{y - 1}$
$x^2 = \left(-\sqrt{y - 1}\right)^2$
$x^2 = y - 1$
$y = x^2 + 1$

2. Find the inverse by switching the variables and solving for y. Recall that squaring both sides eliminates the radical.

$f^{-1}(x) = x^2 + 1; D = (-\infty, 0]$

3. Use the range of $f(x)$ to restrict the domain of the parabola, $y = x^2 + 1$, so that the function is the inverse.

CONTINUED ➡

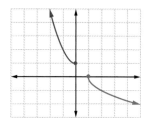

4. Graph $f(x)$ and $f^{-1}(x)$.

A *radical equation* contains a radical expression with a variable in the radicand. To solve a radical equation, isolate the radical expression and raise both sides to the appropriate power. You must check each solution of the resulting equation, since *extraneous roots* can appear when you raise both sides to a power.

Example 4   Solving a Radical Equation

Solve $\sqrt{x+5} + 1 = x$.

Answer

$\sqrt{x+5} = x - 1$

1. Subtract 1 from each side to isolate the radical.

$x + 5 = x^2 - 2x + 1$

2. Square both sides.

$0 = x^2 - 3x - 4$

3. Solve for x.

$0 = (x-4)(x+1)$

$x = 4$ or $x = -1$

$\sqrt{(4)+5} + 1 \ ? \ (4) \qquad \sqrt{(-1)+5} + 1 \ ? \ (-1)$

4. Substitute into the original equation to check for extraneous roots.

$3 + 1 = 4 \qquad\qquad 2 + 1 \ne -1$

solution: $x = 4$

5. Exclude -1 since it is extraneous.

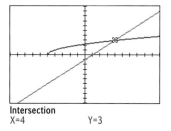

Intersection
X=4   Y=3

The solutions from Example 4 can also be checked by graphing the left side of the equation as Y_1 and the right side as Y_2. The x-coordinate of any intersection is a solution to the equation (use 5:intersect from the [CALC] menu). If the graphs do not intersect, there are no real solutions.

If an equation has several radicals containing the variable, isolate one of them, raise both sides to the appropriate power, isolate a remaining radical, and repeat the process. The solutions can be checked graphically.

Example 5 Solving Equations with Multiple Radicals

Solve $\sqrt{x^2 + 5x + 3} - \sqrt{x^2 + 3x} = 1$.

Answer

$\sqrt{x^2 + 5x + 3} = \sqrt{x^2 + 3x} + 1$ 1. Isolate one of the radicals.

$x^2 + 5x + 3 = x^2 + 3x + 2\sqrt{x^2 + 3x} + 1$ 2. Square both sides.

$2x + 2 = 2\sqrt{x^2 + 3x}$ 3. Simplify and isolate the remaining radical.

$x + 1 = \sqrt{x^2 + 3x}$

$x^2 + 2x + 1 = x^2 + 3x$ 4. Square both sides again.

$1 = x$ 5. Solve for x.

$\sqrt{(1)^2 + 5(1) + 3} - \sqrt{(1)^2 + 3(1)}\ ?\ 1$ 6. Check the solution.

$\qquad\qquad\qquad\qquad 3 - 2 = 1$

SKILL ✓ **EXERCISE 29**

Equations of the form $x^{\frac{p}{r}} = k$ are also radical equations and can be solved by raising each side to the power of $\frac{r}{p}$. Notice that $\left(x^{\frac{p}{r}}\right)^{\frac{r}{p}} = \sqrt[p]{\left(x^{\frac{p}{r}}\right)^r} = \sqrt[p]{x^p}$. Therefore when p is even, $\left(x^{\frac{p}{r}}\right)^{\frac{r}{p}} = \sqrt[p]{x^p} = |x| = \pm x$, and when p is odd, $\left(x^{\frac{p}{r}}\right)^{\frac{r}{p}} = \sqrt[p]{x^p} = x$.

Example 6 Solving Radical Equations by Raising Powers

Solve $x^{\frac{2}{3}} - 1 = 15$.

Answer

$x^{\frac{2}{3}} = 16$ 1. Isolate the variable.

$\left(x^{\frac{2}{3}}\right)^{\frac{3}{2}} = 16^{\frac{3}{2}}$ 2. Raise both sides to the power of $\frac{3}{2}$.

$|x| = \left(4^2\right)^{\frac{3}{2}} = 4^3$ 3. Solve the resulting equation.

$x = \pm 64$

$(64)^{\frac{2}{3}} - 1\ ?\ 15$ $(-64)^{\frac{2}{3}} - 1\ ?\ 15$ 4. Check.

$\quad 4^2 - 1\ ?\ 15$ $(-4)^2 - 1\ ?\ 15$

$\quad 16 - 1 = 15$ $16 - 1 = 15$

SKILL ✓ **EXERCISE 33**

A. Exercises

Use technology to graph each radical function. State its domain, range, and the intervals for which the function is increasing or decreasing. State whether the function is continuous or discontinuous and whether it is odd, even, or neither.

1. $f(x) = \sqrt[5]{x}$
2. $f(x) = \sqrt[6]{x}$
3. $f(x) = x^{\frac{5}{2}}$
4. $f(x) = x^{\frac{3}{7}}$
5. $g(x) = \sqrt{4 - x}$
6. $g(x) = \sqrt[4]{2x + 4}$
7. $h(x) = \sqrt[3]{x - 5}$
8. $h(x) = \sqrt[5]{11 - 2x}$

9. **Explore:** Use technology to graph several power functions to illustrate each case of $f(x) = x^n$ or $f(x) = x^{\frac{p}{r}}$ where $\frac{p}{r}$ is simplified. Then state whether each type of function is even, odd, or neither.

   a. $f(x) = x^n$, $n \in$ even $\mathbb{Z}$
   b. $f(x) = x^n$, $n \in$ odd $\mathbb{Z}$
   c. $f(x) = x^n$, $n \in \mathbb{Q}'$
   d. $f(x) = x^{\frac{p}{r}}$, $r \in$ even $\mathbb{Z}$
   e. $f(x) = x^{\frac{p}{r}}$, $r \in$ odd $\mathbb{Z}$, $p \in$ even $\mathbb{Z}$
   f. $f(x) = x^{\frac{p}{r}}$, $r \in$ odd $\mathbb{Z}$, $p \in$ odd $\mathbb{Z}$

State a rule for g(x), the inverse of f(x), and use technology to graph both f(x) and g(x). State the restricted domain for either f(x) or g(x) that is required for f(x) and g(x) to be inverses of each other.

10. $f(x) = x^3$
11. $f(x) = x^{\frac{3}{4}}$
12. $f(x) = \sqrt{x^3}$
13. $f(x) = \sqrt[3]{x^5}$

Solve. Be sure to check for extraneous solutions.

14. $\sqrt{3x + 4} = 5$
15. $\sqrt[3]{x} + 6 = 2$
16. $\sqrt{x + 4} = x - 2$
17. $2x = 3 + \sqrt{7x - 3}$
18. $\sqrt[3]{n^2 + 2} + 1 = 4$

B. Exercises

Use transformations of a parent radical function to graph each function. Then state its domain and range.

19. $g(x) = \sqrt[3]{x} + 2$
20. $h(x) = -\sqrt{x - 2}$
21. $m(x) = 2\sqrt{x + 3}$
22. $n(x) = 3 + \sqrt[3]{x + 1}$
23. $r(x) = \sqrt{2 - x}$
24. $t(x) = 3 - 2\sqrt[3]{x}$

Find the inverse of each function, then graph f(x) and $f^{-1}(x)$.

25. $f(x) = \sqrt{x - 1}$
26. $f(x) = \sqrt{x} + 2$
27. $f(x) = \sqrt[3]{x - 2}$
28. $f(x) = 2 - \sqrt{x}$

Solve.

29. $\sqrt{x} + \sqrt{x + 5} = 5$
30. $\sqrt{n + 6} - \sqrt{n} = \sqrt{2}$
31. $\sqrt{4x + 5} + 2\sqrt{x - 3} = 17$
32. $\sqrt{r^2 + 3r + 3} + \sqrt{r^2 + r - 1} = 2$

Solve by raising powers.

33. $x^{\frac{2}{3}} + 6 = 10$
34. $x^{\frac{3}{4}} + 1 = 9$
35. $\sqrt{x^3} + 10 = 74$
36. $100 - \sqrt[3]{x^4} = 19$

37. Solve $d = 2\sqrt{\dfrac{V}{h\pi}}$ for V and use the resulting equation to find the volume of a 5 ft tall cylinder with a diameter of 20 ft.

38. Solve $r = \sqrt[3]{\dfrac{3V}{4\pi}}$ for V and use the resulting equation to find the volume of a soccerball whose diameter is 22 cm.

39. The equation $I = \sqrt{\dfrac{P}{R}}$ expresses electrical current I (in amps) as a function of power P (in watts) and resistance R (in ohms). Solve the equation for R and use the result to find the resistance of a motor drawing 10 amps of current and using 1100 watts of power.

40. Kadour Ziani, a professional basketball dunker, set a world record with a 5 ft vertical leap. His hang time, the total time he was airborne, can be modeled by $t = \dfrac{\sqrt{h}}{2}$ where t is in seconds and h is in feet.

   a. What is the hang time for a vertical leap of 2 ft?
   b. What was the hang time for Ziani's world record jump?
   c. Find the vertical leap of an athlete with a hang time of 1 sec.
   d. Approximate the height of a punted football with a 4.40 sec hang time.

C. Exercises

Solve.

41. $\sqrt[3]{7x + 1} = x + 1$
42. $\sqrt{n} + \sqrt{n - 3} = \dfrac{3}{\sqrt{n - 3}}$

State a rule for the inverse of f(x) and graph both f(x) and its inverse. If the inverse is not a function, restrict the domain of f(x) so that its inverse is a function $f^{-1}(x)$ and state the rule for $f^{-1}(x)$.

43. $f(x) = x^2 - 4$
44. $f(x) = x^2 + 2x + 1$

45. Multiply $(-5a^3 + 7b)(-5a^3 - 7b)$.   [Algebra]

Factor. [Algebra]

46. $8x^2 + 20x - 28$

47. $x^3 - 7x^2 - 4x + 28$

48. Draw a mapping diagram of $R = \{(0, -3), (2, 2),$ $\left(-\frac{1}{2}, -3\right), (1, 5)\}$ and state whether the relation is a function or not.   [1.1]

49. A city's population is found to vary inversely with the square root of its unemployment rate. If the population is 137,800 with 5% unemployment, predict the population if unemployment rises to 6%.   [1.4]

50. Write the equation of the transformation of $f(x) = x^2$ that has been translated 5 units left, stretched vertically by a factor of 3, and translated 1 unit up.   [1.5]

51. Which of the following relations represents a function?   [1.1]

A. $x = 2$

B. $x = \dfrac{1}{y^2}$

C. $x = y$

D. $\{(-1, 0), (2, 0.5),$ $(1, -3), (-1, 1)\}$

E. none of these

52. Which function results when $f(x) = \sqrt{x}$ is reflected across the x-axis and translated 6 units up?   [1.5]

A. $g(x) = \sqrt{-x} + 6$

B. $g(x) = -\sqrt{x} + 6$

C. $g(x) = -\sqrt{x} - 6$

D. $g(x) = \sqrt{x} - 6$

E. none of these

53. Write the standard form of a parabola that passes through $(2, 4)$ and has a vertex at $(1, 1)$.   [1.6]

A. $f(x) = 3x^2 - 2x + 1$

B. $f(x) = 3x^2 - 6x + 3$

C. $f(x) = 3x^2 + 6x + 4$

D. $f(x) = 3x^2 - 6x + 4$

E. none of these

54. Which of the following statements is true when $f(x) = x^2 - 3$ and $g(x) = \sqrt{x + 3}$?   [1.7]

A. The domain of $f(g(x))$ is $(0, \infty)$.

B. $f(g(x)) = x$ for all real numbers

C. $g(f(x)) = |x|$

D. $f(g(x)) = g(f(x))$

E. none of these

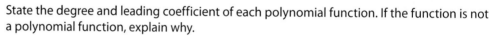

Video game sales can be modeled with a polynomial function.

After completing this section, you will be able to

- graph and describe the key characteristics of a polynomial function.
- find zeros of a polynomial function by factoring.
- apply the Intermediate Value Theorem.

Power functions of the form $f(x) = kx^n$ where n is a natural number and constant functions of the form $f(x) = c$ where c is a real number are called *monomial functions*. You learned how to graph transformations of parent power functions of the form $g(x) = a(x - h)^3 + k$ in Section 1.5. Constant functions such as $f(x) = c$, linear functions such as $f(x) = mx + b$, and quadratic functions such as $f(x) = ax^2 + bx + c$ were also studied in Chapter 1. All of these are examples of a larger class of functions called *polynomial functions*.

▌DEFINITION

A **polynomial function** of degree n is a function that can be written in the form $p(x) = a_n x^n + a_{n-1} x^{n-1} + a_{n-2} x^{n-2} + \cdots + a_1 x + a_0$ where n is a whole number, $a_n, a_{n-1}, \ldots, a_0 \in \mathbb{R}$, and the *leading coefficient* $a_n \neq 0$. When its terms are written in order of descending degree, a polynomial function is said to be in *standard form*.

Quadratic functions have a degree of 2, linear functions have a degree of 1, and constant functions have a degree of 0 since $a_0 x^0 = a_0(1) = a_0$. The zero function has no degree since $f(x) = 0 = 0x^n$ and a specific power of x cannot be determined.

Example 1   Identifying Polynomial Functions

State the degree and leading coefficient of each polynomial function. If the function is not a polynomial function, explain why.

a. $f(x) = 2x^3 - 24x^2 + 96x - 127$

b. $g(x) = 3x^{-1} + x - 5$

c. $h(x) = \sqrt{2}x - x^4$

d. $j(x) = \sqrt{x^2 + 4}$

Answer

a. degree: 3; leading coefficient: 2

b. $g(x)$ is not a polynomial function since the exponent of the first term is not a whole number.

c. $h(x) = -x^4 + \sqrt{2}x$; degree: 4; leading coefficient: -1

d. $j(x)$ cannot be written as a polynomial. $\left(\sqrt{x^2 + 4} \neq x + 2\right)$

SKILL ✔ **EXERCISE 1**

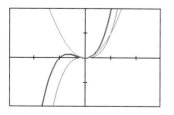

◉ TIP

Polynomial functions of degrees 3, 4, and 5 are called cubic, quartic, and quintic functions, respectively.

Polynomial functions can be viewed as the sum or difference of one or more monomial functions. The graph of $f(x) = x^3 + x^2$ illustrates that it is not a simple transformation of either $y = x^3$ or $y = x^2$. Like monomial functions, polynomial functions are defined and continuous over the real numbers. Unlike the absolute value function, the graph of a polynomial function is smooth, with no sharp corners.

Another key characteristic of polynomial functions is illustrated by the graph of $f(x) = x^3 + x^2$. The function's end behavior can be predicted using the end behavior of the leading term.

LEADING TERM TEST

The end behavior of a polynomial function
$$p(x) = a_n x^n + a_{n-1} x^{n-1} + a_{n-2} x^{n-2} + \cdots + a_1 x + a_0$$
is determined by its degree, n, and its leading coefficient, a_n.

n is odd and $a_n > 0$.	n is odd and $a_n < 0$.
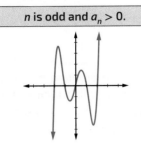	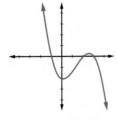
$\lim\limits_{x \to -\infty} p(x) = -\infty;\ \lim\limits_{x \to \infty} p(x) = \infty$	$\lim\limits_{x \to -\infty} p(x) = \infty;\ \lim\limits_{x \to \infty} p(x) = -\infty$
n is even and $a_n > 0$.	n is even and $a_n < 0$.
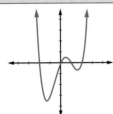	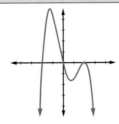
$\lim\limits_{x \to -\infty} p(x) = \infty;\ \lim\limits_{x \to \infty} p(x) = \infty$	$\lim\limits_{x \to -\infty} p(x) = -\infty;\ \lim\limits_{x \to \infty} p(x) = -\infty$

Example 2   Applying the Leading Term Test

Describe the end behavior of each polynomial function.

a. $f(x) = -2x^3 + 5x$

b. $g(x) = -3x^2 + x^4 - 2$

Answer

a. Since $n = 3$ is odd and $a_n = -2 < 0$,
$$\lim_{x \to -\infty} f(x) = \infty \text{ and } \lim_{x \to \infty} f(x) = -\infty.$$

b. Writing the function in standard form, $g(x) = x^4 - 3x^2 - 2$, makes it easy to see that $n = 4$ is even and $a_n = 1 > 0$.
$$\lim_{x \to -\infty} g(x) = \infty \text{ and } \lim_{x \to \infty} g(x) = \infty$$

Check

The graphs of the functions confirm the predicted end behavior.

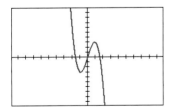

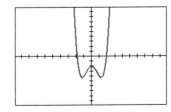

SKILL ✓ **EXERCISE 7**

In addition to modeling data sets, quartic equations are used by robotic milling machines where the intersection of a line and a torus must be computed.

The zeros and number of turning points are key characteristics of the graph of a polynomial. If $(c, 0)$ is an x-intercept of the function's graph, the following statements are also true:

$x = c$ is a solution to the equation $p(x) = 0$,
$(x - c)$ is a factor of the polynomial $p(x)$,
and c is a zero of $p(x)$.

Note that the cubic function $f(x)$ in Example 2 has three zeros and two turning points, called *relative extrema* (one *relative minimum* and one *relative maximum*). The quartic function $g(x)$ in Example 2 has two zeros and three relative extrema (two relative minimums and one relative maximum). It would have four zeros if it were translated up 3 units.

ZEROS AND RELATIVE EXTREMA OF POLYNOMIAL FUNCTIONS

A polynomial function with degree n has at most n real zeros and $n - 1$ relative extrema.

Are there formulas, like the quadratic formula, that can be used to find the zeros of polynomial functions with higher degree? Formulas for cubic and quartic functions were found by the Italian mathematicians Niccolò Tartaglia and Lodovico Ferrari and published in 1545 by Gerolamo Cardano. Unfortunately both equations are too complicated to be of practical use. In the early 1800s the Norwegian genius Niels Abel proved that a formula for finding the zeros of quintic equations does not exist.

The zeros of many polynomial functions can be found by factoring the polynomial and applying the Zero Product Property.

KEYWORD SEARCH

Niels Abel

Example 3   Finding Zeros by Factoring

State the maximum number of real zeros and relative extrema for $p(x) = -2x^3 + 4x^2$. Then find the real zeros.

Answer

A cubic function has at most 3 real zeros and 2 relative extrema.

$-2x^3 + 4x^2 = 0$

$-2x^2(x - 2) = 0$

$-2x^2 = 0$ or $x - 2 = 0$

$x = 0$ $x = 2$

Check

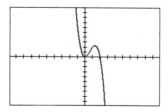

1. A polynomial function with degree n has at most n real zeros and $n - 1$ relative extrema.

2. Set $p(x) = 0$.

3. Factor.

4. Apply the Zero Product Property.

5. Solve the resulting equations.

6. Graphing the function confirms the zeros.

SKILL ✓ **EXERCISE 19**

If the completely factored form of $p(x)$ contains a repeated factor $(x - c)^m$, c is a repeated zero with a *multiplicity* of m. When m is odd, the graph crosses the x-axis at $(c, 0)$, but when m is even, the graph touches the x-axis at $(c, 0)$ without crossing the axis. The graph of $p(x) = (x - 2)^3(x + 1)^2$ has a repeated zero of 2 with a multiplicity of 3 and a repeated zero of -1 with a multiplicity of 2.

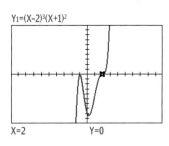

Example 4 Using Technology to Find Zeros and Relative Extrema

Use technology to find the real zeros and relative extrema for $p(x) = x^4 - 7x^2 + 6$.

Answer

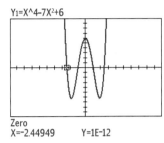

Zero
X=-2.44949   Y=1E-12

zeros at $x \approx \pm 2.45$ and $x = \pm 1$

rel. max.: $(0, 6)$
rel. min.: $\approx (-1.87, -6.25)$
           $\approx (1.87, -6.25)$

1. Graph the function in a window that illustrates the function's x-intercepts and relative extrema.

2. Select the zero function from the [CALC] menu. Then respond to the prompts to enter a search interval and an estimated zero. Repeat the process to find all the zeros.

3. Select the maximum or minimum function from the [CALC] menu and enter a search interval and an estimate for the x-values of the local extrema.

Check

$(x^2)^2 - 7(x^2) + 6 = 0$
$(x^2 - 6)(x^2 - 1) = 0$
$x^2 - 6 = 0$ or $x^2 - 1 = 0$
$x^2 = 6$ $x^2 = 1$
$x = \pm\sqrt{6} \approx \pm 2.45$ $x = \pm 1$

4. Factoring and applying the Zero Product Property produces exact values for the zeros and verifies the approximations found using technology.

—————————————— SKILL ✓ EXERCISE 25

Polynomials that can be written as $au^2 + bu + c$, such as $p(x)$ in Example 4 where $u = x^2$, are said to be in quadratic form.

Since a polynomial function is continuous, the only place the value of the function can change signs from positive to negative or from negative to positive is at a zero of the function.

Placing the distinct real zeros on the x-axis divides the function's domain into *test intervals* in which the function is always positive or always negative. You can sketch the basic shape of a polynomial function by determining its end behavior, finding the real zeros and their multiplicity, and plotting a few additional points.

Example 5   Sketching the Graph of a Polynomial Function

Sketch the graph of $p(x) = -2x^4 - x^3 + 6x^2$.

Answer

Since n is even and $a_n < 1$,
$\lim\limits_{x \to -\infty} p(x) = -\infty$ and
$\lim\limits_{x \to \infty} p(x) = -\infty$.

$-x^2(2x^2 + x - 6) = 0$

$-x^2(2x - 3)(x + 2) = 0$

$x = 0, \frac{3}{2}, -2$

x	-1	1
y	5	3

1. Use the Leading Term Test to determine the function's end behavior.

2. Find and plot the zeros. End behaviors indicate that that the function is negative over $(-\infty, -2)$ and $\left(\frac{3}{2}, \infty\right)$.

3. The multiplicity of roots implies that the function is positive over $(-2, 0)$ and $\left(0, \frac{3}{2}\right)$.

   Plot at least one point between each zero and sketch the graph.

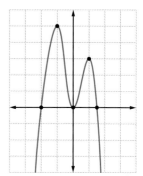

SKILL ✓ **EXERCISE 29**

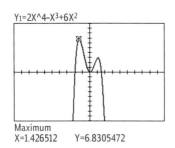

Y₁=2X^4-X³+6X²

Maximum
X=1.426512   Y=6.8305472

The even multiplicity of the repeated root 0 implies that $(0, 0)$ is a relative minimum of the function. We cannot assume the additional points $(-1, 5)$ and $(1, 3)$ are relative maximums, but the function must contain these points. Technology can be used to obtain a more accurate graph and to find the relative maximums of approximately $(-1.43, 6.83)$ and $(1.05, 3.03)$. Calculus provides a direct method of locating local extrema.

We have seen that a sign change in the value of the function indicates the presence of a zero. This statement is a specific application of the more general Intermediate Value Theorem.

▌ INTERMEDIATE VALUE THEOREM

If a function is continuous over $[a, b]$ and there exists a value n that is between $f(a)$ and $f(b)$, then c exists in $[a, b]$ such that $f(c) = n$.

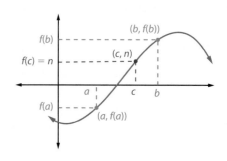

This theorem guarantees that the function includes every value between $f(a)$ and $f(b)$ in the interval $[a, b]$. When either $f(a)$ or $f(b)$ is negative and the other is positive, applying this theorem with $n = 0$ guarantees the presence of c such that $f(c) = 0$, a real root.

Example 6 Applying the Intermediate Value Theorem

Use the Intermediate Value Theorem to determine which consecutive integers the real zeros of $p(x) = 3x^3 - 2x^2 - 6x + 4$ occur between.

Answer

x	−2	−1	0	1	2
$p(x)$	−16	5	4	−1	8

Real zeros occur between
a. −2 and −1,
b. 0 and 1, and
c. 1 and 2.

There are no other zeros.

1. Evaluate the polynomial at several points.

2. Apply the Intermediate Value Theorem where
   a. $p(-2)$ is negative and $p(-1)$ is positive,
   b. $p(0)$ is positive and $p(1)$ is negative, and
   c. $p(1)$ is negative and $p(2)$ is positive.

3. We have located 3 zeros, the maximum number for a cubic polynomial function.

Simon Stevin, a Dutch scientist born in 1548, was the first proponent of a decimal system. He developed a decimal expansion algorithm to find the roots of any polynomial. This same algorithm (in binary form) was used by Augustin-Louis Cauchy in his proof of the Intermediate Value Theorem.

_____ SKILL ✓ **EXERCISES 15, 33**

Note that the lack of a sign change between two values does not guarantee the absence of real zeros. The function could cross the x-axis twice within the defined interval.

❯ A. Exercises

1. State the degree and leading coefficient of each polynomial function. If the function is not a polynomial function, explain why.
   a. $f(x) = 7x^5 + 3x^3 - 4x$
   b. $f(x) = 2x^{-1} + 1$
   c. $f(x) = 2x - 6x^4$
   d. $f(x) = 28$

State whether the degree, n, of the graphed polynomial is odd or even and whether its lead coefficient, a_n, is positive or negative.

2.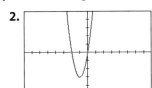
3.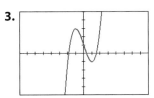
4.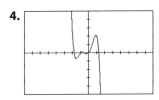
5.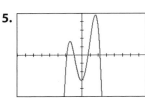

Use the Leading Term Test to describe each function's end behavior.

6. $p(x) = -x^2 + 3x + 1$
7. $p(x) = -2x^5 - 3x$
8. $p(x) = x^3 - x^2 + 4x + 2$
9. $p(x) = 3x^4 + 6x^2 - 4$

Find the zeros for each polynomial function, including the multiplicity of any repeated zeros.

10. $p(x) = (x^2 - 16)(x^2 - 4)$
11. $p(x) = (x - 6)^4$
12. $p(x) = x^2$
13. $p(x) = (x - 4)^2(x + 1)^3$

Use the Intermediate Value Theorem to show that there is a zero within the given interval.

14. $p(x) = -x^4 + 5x^2 + x - 2; [-1, 0]$
15. $p(x) = x^5 + 3x^4 - x^3 + x^2 - 7; [1, 2]$

❯ B. Exercises

State the maximum number of real zeros and relative extrema for each function. Then find the real zeros.

16. $p(x) = x^2 - 11x + 28$
17. $p(x) = 4x^2 - 8x + 4$
18. $p(x) = 3x^4 - 12x^2$
19. $p(x) = 16x^3 + 8x^2 + x$
20. $p(x) = 2x^2 + x - 6$
21. $p(x) = x^5 - 2x^3 + x$
22. $p(x) = 3x^4 - 10x^2 + 8$
23. $p(x) = 4x^5 - 13x^3 + 9x$

Use technology to graph each function in a window that shows all the zeros and relative extrema. Then state each zero and any relative extrema (to the nearest hundredth).

24. $p(x) = -x^3 - x^2 + 6x$
25. $p(x) = 2x^3 - 7x^2 - 17x + 10$
26. $p(x) = -x^4 + 2x^3 + 5x^2 - x + 3$
27. $p(x) = 8x^4 - 16x^3 - 2x^2 + 14x + 5$

Identify the function's zeros, y-intercepts, and end behavior. Then sketch its graph.

28. $p(x) = x^4 - 4x^2$

29. $p(x) = 2x^3 - x^2 - 6x$

30. $p(x) = \frac{1}{2}x^3 - 2x$

31. $p(x) = x^4 - 6x^2 + 8$

Use the Intermediate Value Theorem to determine which consecutive integers the real zeros occur between.

32. $p(x) = x^3 + 5x^2 - 1$

33. $p(x) = -x^3 + 4x^2 - 2x - 2$

34. Sales in the video game market from August 2015 through January 2016 can be modeled by $p(x) = -37.5x^4 + 452x^3 - 1846x^2 + 3150x - 1447$ where x is the month, beginning with August, and y is the sales in millions of dollars.

   a. According to the model, which month had the highest sales?

   b. What was the dollar amount for these sales?

35. A box without a lid is formed by cutting squares of length x in. from each corner of an 18 in. by 20 in. sheet of cardboard.

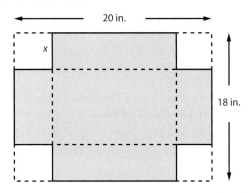

   a. Find the polynomial function that models the volume of the box and graph the function.

   b. Considering the context, state a reasonable domain for the function. Explain your reasoning.

   c. Find the maximum volume for the box and the corresponding dimensions (to the nearest tenth of an inch).

36. Explore: Graph each function using technology and examine its symmetry to classify it as even, odd, or neither.

   a. $p(x) = 3x^4 - 4x^2 - 5$

   b. $p(x) = 3x^5 - 4x^3 - 5x$

   c. $p(x) = 3x^4 - 4x - 5$

37. Explore: Examine $p(-x)$ for each function to classify the function as even, odd, or neither.

   a. $p(x) = 3x^5 - 4x^2 - 5$

   b. $p(x) = 3x^6 - 4x^4 - 5x^2$

   c. $p(x) = 3x^7 - 4x^5 - 5x^3$

38. Analyze: Use the results of exercises 36–37 to make a conjecture describing the terms in each type of polynomial function.

   a. an even polynomial function

   b. an odd polynomial function

❯ C. Exercises

39. Determine the zeros of the binomial function $p(x) = x^n - x^{n-1}$. Then state the multiplicity of each zero.

40. Explore: Consider $p(x) = x^3 + 4x^2 - 5x + 1$.

   a. Evaluate $p(0)$ and $p(1)$. Does the Intermediate Value Theorem predict a zero within $[0, 1]$?

   b. Use technology to graph the function and find any zeros within $[0, 1]$.

   c. Do the results of steps a and b demonstrate an inconsistency in the Intermediate Value Theorem? Explain why or why not.

41. Explain: Is it possible for a quartic function to have just two relative extrema? Explain your answer.

42. A method for finding the tangent to a curve at a point is learned in calculus. Consider $p(x) = -x^3 + 2x^2 + x - 3$ and the line $f(x) = -3x + 5$.

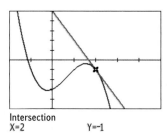

Intersection
X=2   Y=-1

   a. Algebraically verify that $(2, -1)$ is a solution to both equations.

   b. Algebraically find a second point of intersection of $f(x)$ and $p(x)$.

   c. Use technology to verify the second point of intersection.

   d. Use the two points of intersection to verify the slope of the secant line that represents the curve's average rate of change between the two points.

Multiply. [Algebra]

43. $(x - 3)(x^2 + 3x + 9)$ **44.** $(x^2 - 9)(x^2 - 3x + 9)$

Factor. [Algebra]

45. $2x^2 + 9x - 18$ **46.** $x^3 + 3x^2 - 9x - 27$

Divide. [Algebra]

47. $(x^3 + 9x^2 + 29x + 66) \div (x + 6)$

48. $(-x^3 - 3x + 18) \div (x - 3)$

49. If $f(x) = \dfrac{5}{x - 4}$, find $\lim\limits_{x \to 4^-} f(x)$ and $\lim\limits_{x \to 4^+} f(x)$. [1.3]

   A. ∞, ∞ **D.** $-\infty, -\infty$

   B. $\infty, -\infty$ **E.** undefined

   C. $-\infty, \infty$

50. Which of the following functions is *not* a power function? [1.4]

   A. $y = \sqrt{x}$ **D.** $y = 5^x$

   B. $y = -\dfrac{3}{5x^4}$ **E.** $y = -6x^{-3}$

   C. $y = x$

51. Given $h(x) = \dfrac{1}{\sqrt{x^2 - 4}}$, find $f(x)$ and $g(x)$ such that $h(x) = (f \circ g)(x)$. [1.7]

   A. $f(x) = \dfrac{1}{\sqrt{x - 4}}$; $g(x) = x^2$

   B. $f(x) = \dfrac{1}{\sqrt{x}}$; $g(x) = x^2 - 4$

   C. $f(x) = \dfrac{1}{x}$; $g(x) = \sqrt{x^2 - 4}$

   D. all of these

   E. none of these

52. Which equation represents the inverse of $f(x) = \sqrt[5]{x^2}$ where $x \geq 0$? [2.1]

   A. $y = \dfrac{5}{2}\sqrt{x}$

   B. $y = \sqrt{x^{\frac{2}{5}}}$

   C. $y = x^{\frac{2}{5}}$

   D. $y = x^{-\frac{2}{5}}$

   E. $y = x^{\frac{5}{2}}$

TECHNOLOGY CORNER (TI-84 PLUS FAMILY)

Your graphing calculator may have several limitations when graphing functions. Graphing $f(x) = \dfrac{x^4 - 2x^3 - x^2 + 2x}{2x^2 + 2x - 4} = \dfrac{x(x - 1)(x + 1)(x - 2)}{2(x - 1)(x + 2)}$ in the standard window is not sufficient to illustrate the entire graph. Increasing the range of the window to [–10, 30] reveals the true shape of the graph.

When graphing rational functions containing discontinuities, the calculator will not draw vertical asymptotes. In Connected mode, some calculators may connect plotted points on either side of a vertical asymptote in an attempt to produce a smooth curve. For example, notice the nearly vertical line drawn near $x = -2$. This line is often misinterpreted as an asymptote.

The point discontinuity at $x = 1$ may not be accurately represented in the graph. Examining the table of functional values, an ERROR occurs at each attempted division by 0 and indicates either a vertical asymptote (at $x = -2$) or a point discontinuity (at $x = 1$). The exact number of zeros may be difficult to determine from a graph unless you zoom in. The magnified view helps define the search interval when using the zero function found on the CALC menu. The table also confirms zeros at $x = -1$, 0, and 2.

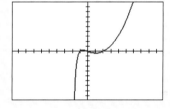

TI-83 Plus

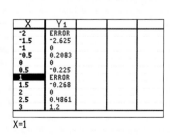

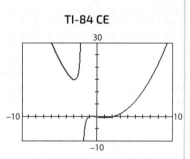

TI-84 CE

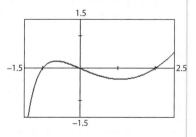

2.3 The Remainder and Factor Theorems

Cubic polynomials are frequently used to model a volume as in exercise 34.

After completing this section, you will be able to

- divide polynomials using long division and synthetic division.
- evaluate polynomial functions using the Remainder Theorem.
- determine the linear factors of a polynomial using the Factor Theorem.
- write a polynomial function with given zeros.

The factoring of a polynomial of higher degree often involves dividing the polynomial by another polynomial. The long-division algorithm can be used when the dividend has a degree higher than that of the divisor.

Example 1 Long Division of Polynomials

Divide $p(x) = 2x^3 + 7x^2 - 15$ by $d(x) = 3 + 2x$ and state whether $d(x)$ is a factor of $p(x)$.

Answer

$$
\begin{array}{r}
x^2 + 2x - 3 \quad \text{R.} -6 \\
2x + 3 \overline{)\; 2x^3 + 7x^2 + 0x - 15} \\
-(2x^3 + 3x^2) \\
\hline
4x^2 + 0x \\
-(4x^2 + 6x) \\
\hline
-6x - 15 \\
-(-6x - 9) \\
\hline
-6
\end{array}
$$

$d(x)$ is not a factor of $p(x)$.

1. Express the dividend $p(x)$ and divisor in standard form and insert a place-holding term of $0x$ in $p(x)$.

2. Use the steps of the long-division algorithm to divide, multiply, and subtract until the remaining expression has a lower degree than the divisor.

3. The division produces a remainder, so the divisor is not a factor of the dividend.

SKILL ✔ **EXERCISE 1**

The result of the division in Example 1 can be expressed as

$$(2x^3 + 7x^2 - 15) \div (2x + 3) = x^2 + 2x - 3 - \frac{6}{2x + 3} \text{ or}$$

$$\frac{p(x)}{d(x)} = q(x) + \frac{r(x)}{d(x)} \text{ where } q(x) = x^2 + 2x - 3 \text{ and } r(x) = -6.$$

The fact that $p(x) = d(x)\left[q(x) + \frac{r(x)}{d(x)}\right] = d(x) \cdot q(x) + r(x)$ can be used to check the division.

$$(2x + 3)(x^2 + 2x - 3) - 6 = 2x^3 + 7x^2 - 15$$

Synthetic division, a shortened version of the long-division algorithm, can be used when dividing a polynomial by a linear polynomial of the form $x - c$. You will understand the shortcut better if you compare the colored coefficients in each shortened version of the following long division. Notice that c, the zero of $x - c$, is used in the shortened versions instead of $-c$.

In 1804 Paolo Ruffini's new synthetic division won him the gold medal in an Italian Scientific Society contest to present the best method of finding roots of equations. Ruffini was also a philosopher and medical doctor, publishing articles on the immortality of the soul and contagious typhoid.

| Long Division | Elimination of Variables | Synthetic Division |

Long Division

$$\begin{array}{r} 3x^2 - 2x - 4 \quad \text{R. } 6 \\ x - 2 \overline{)\ 3x^3 - 8x^2 + 0x + 14} \\ \underline{-(3x^3 - 6x^2)} \\ -2x^2 + 0x \\ \underline{-(-2x^2 + 4x)} \\ -4x + 14 \\ \underline{-(-4x + 8)} \\ 6 \end{array}$$

Elimination of Variables

$$\begin{array}{r} 3 - 2 - 4 \ \text{R. } 6 \\ -2\overline{)\ 3 - 8 + 0 + 14} \\ \underline{-(3 - 6)} \\ -2 + 0 \\ \underline{-(-2 + 4)} \\ -4 + 14 \\ \underline{-(-4 + 8)} \\ 6 \end{array}$$

Synthetic Division

$$\begin{array}{r} 2\ \big|\ \ \ 3 \ -8 \ \ \ 0 \ \ 14 \\ \ \ \ \ \ \ \ \ \ 6 \ -4 \ -8 \\ \hline \ \ \ \ 3 \ -2 \ -4 \ \ \ 6 \end{array}$$

Collapse the algorithm vertically and indicate the subtractions as additions of the opposite.

When dividing a polynomial by a divisor of the form $x - c$, the degree of the quotient is one less than the degree of the dividend and any remainder is a real number. Reinsert the powers of x to state the result of the division:

$$(3x^3 - 8x^2 + 14) \div (x - 2) = 3x^2 - 2x - 4 + \frac{6}{x - 2}.$$

Example 2 Synthetic Division of Polynomials

Use synthetic division to divide $p(x) = 2x^5 - 3x^3 + 7x^2 + 3x + 18$ by $d(x) = x + 2$. Then state whether $x + 2$ is a factor of $p(x)$.

Answer

$$\begin{array}{r} -2\ \big|\ \ \ 2 \ \ \ 0 \ -3 \ \ \ 7 \ \ \ 3 \ \ 18 \\ \downarrow \\ \hline \ \ \ \ 2 \end{array}$$

1. List the coefficients of the dividend in descending degree, inserting 0 for the missing quartic term. Place -2 from the *divisor*, $x - (-2)$, to the left and bring down the leading coefficient.

$$\begin{array}{r} -2\ \big|\ \ \ 2 \ \ \ 0 \ -3 \ \ \ 7 \ \ \ 3 \ \ 18 \\ \ \ \ \ \ \ -4 \\ \hline \ \ \ \ 2 \ -4 \end{array}$$

2. Multiply -2 by 2 and place the product, -4, under the second coefficient, 0. Then add the coefficient and the product: $0 + (-4) = -4$.

$$\begin{array}{r} -2\ \big|\ \ \ 2 \ \ \ 0 \ -3 \ \ \ 7 \ \ \ 3 \ \ 18 \\ \ \ \ \ \ \ -4 \ \ \ 8 \ -10 \ \ \ 6 \ -18 \\ \hline \ \ \ \ 2 \ -4 \ \ \ 5 \ -3 \ \ \ 9 \ \ \ 0 \end{array}$$

3. Repeat this process of multiplying by -2 and adding until you reach the remainder, which in this case is 0.

$\dfrac{p(x)}{d(x)} = q(x) = 2x^4 - 4x^3 + 5x^2 - 3x + 9$

$x + 2$ is a factor of $p(x)$.

4. The last line provides the coefficients of the quotient polynomial in descending degree and shows that there is no remainder.

SKILL ✓ **EXERCISE 7**

The division of $p(x)$ by $(ax + b)$ can be done synthetically if both the dividend and the divisor are divided by the constant a to obtain an equivalent division with a divisor of the form $x - \frac{b}{a}$.

Englishman William George Horner independently developed the same synthetic division process as Ruffini. Some evidence suggests that Chinese mathematicians used the same algorithm half a century earlier. What does this independent development suggest about mathematics?

Example 3   Factoring with Synthetic Division

Use synthetic division to divide $p(x) = 2x^3 - 3x^2 - 4x + 6$ by $d(x) = 2x - 3$. Then state whether $2x - 3$ is a factor of $p(x)$.

Answer

$$\frac{(2x^3 - 3x^2 - 4x + 6) \div 2}{(2x - 3) \div 2} = \frac{x^3 - \frac{3}{2}x^2 - 2x + 3}{x - \frac{3}{2}}$$

$$\begin{array}{c|cccc} \frac{3}{2} & 1 & -\frac{3}{2} & -2 & 3 \\ & & \frac{3}{2} & 0 & -3 \\ \hline & 1 & 0 & -2 & 0 \end{array}$$

$$\frac{p(x)}{d(x)} = q(x) = x^2 - 2$$

$2x - 3$ is a factor of $p(x)$.

1. Divide both $p(x)$ and $d(x)$ by 2 to derive an equivalent division with a divisor of the form $x - \frac{b}{a}$.

2. Complete the equivalent division by $x - \frac{3}{2}$.

3. The last line provides the coefficients of the quotient polynomial in descending degree and shows that there is no remainder.

SKILL ✓ **EXERCISES 9, 23**

When the remainder is 0, the quotient $q(x)$ is called the *depressed polynomial* and is also a factor of $p(x)$ since $p(x) = d(x) \cdot q(x)$.

Given the polynomial function $p(x) = 3x^3 - 6x^2 + 2x - 4$, compare the value of $p(3)$ and the remainder of $p(x) \div (x - 3)$.

$$p(3) = 3(3)^3 - 6(3)^2 + 2(3) - 4$$
$$= 81 - 54 + 6 - 4$$
$$= 29$$

and   using synthetic division:

$$\begin{array}{c|cccc} 3 & 3 & -6 & 2 & -4 \\ & & 9 & 9 & 33 \\ \hline & 3 & 3 & 11 & 29 \end{array}$$

$$3x^2 + 3x + 11 \quad \text{R. } 29$$

The fact that $p(3)$ equals the remainder when $p(x)$ is divided by $x - 3$ is guaranteed by the Remainder Theorem.

▶ REMAINDER THEOREM

If a polynomial $P(x)$ is divided by a binomial $x - c$, the remainder $R = P(c)$.

Proof:

Given $p(x) = d(x) \cdot q(x) + r(x)$ where $d(x) = x - c$, $r(x)$ must be a constant, R, with a degree of 0, since $r(x)$ has a degree less than the divisor $x - c$, which has a degree of 1.
$\therefore p(x) = (x - c) \cdot q(x) + R$.
Substituting c for x:
$\quad p(c) = (c - c) \cdot q(c) + R,$
$\quad p(c) = 0 \cdot q(c) + R$, and
$\quad p(c) = R$.

Synthetic division and the Remainder Theorem provide alternate methods of evaluating a polynomial and finding a remainder.

Example 4   Finding a Remainder with the Remainder Theorem

Use the Remainder Theorem to find the remainder when $p(x) = x^4 - 6x^3 - x^2 + 2x + 7$ is divided by $x - 1$.

Answer

$$R = p(1) = 1 - 6 - 1 + 2 + 7 \qquad \text{Find } R \text{ by evaluating } p(1).$$
$$= 3$$

SKILL ✓ **EXERCISE 13**

A compressed form of synthetic division omits the intermediate step of recording each product before the product is added mentally, leaving just the coefficients of $q(x)$ and the remainder. This can be especially helpful when using synthetic division to evaluate several values of a function, a process sometimes called *synthetic substitution*.

Example 5   Synthetic Substitution

Given $p(x) = x^3 + 5x^2 - 4$, apply the Remainder Theorem to evaluate $p(-4)$, $p(-3)$, $p(-2)$, and $p(-1)$.

Answer

c	1	5	0	−4	
−4	1	1	−4	12	$p(-4) = 12$
−3	1	2	−6	14	$p(-3) = 14$
−2	1	3	−6	8	$p(-2) = 8$
−1	1	4	−4	0	$p(-1) = 0$

Use compressed synthetic division to find $p(c) = R$ when $p(x)$ is divided by $(x - c)$.

SKILL ✓ **EXERCISE 15**

The Remainder Theorem and synthetic substitution can be used to find zeros of a function. The Factor Theorem formally states the relationship between the zeros of a polynomial function and its factors. Recall that the proof of a biconditional $p \leftrightarrow q$ requires the proof of both conditionals, $p \rightarrow q$ and $q \rightarrow p$.

▌ FACTOR THEOREM

$p(c) = 0$ if and only if $(x - c)$ is a factor of $p(x)$.

Proof:

Using the Remainder Theorem, if $p(c) = 0$,
then $p(x) \div (x - c) = q(x) + 0$ and $(x - c)$ divides $p(x)$ exactly.
Therefore, $p(x) = (x - c) \cdot q(x)$ and $(x - c)$ is a factor of $p(x)$.

Conversely, if $(x - c)$ is a factor of $p(x)$,
then $p(x) = (x - c) \cdot q(x) + 0$ and
the Remainder Theorem guarantees that $p(c) = 0$ if $R = 0$.

Using synthetic division, the Remainder Theorem, and the Factor Theorem together allows you to check whether $(x - c)$ is a factor of a polynomial function and provides the coefficients of the depressed polynomial when it is a factor.

Example 6 Factoring Polynomials

If 2 is a zero of $p(x) = x^3 + 6x^2 - x - 30$, factor $p(x)$ completely and list all of its zeros.

Answer

$$
\begin{array}{r}
\ 1 \quad 6 \ -1 \ -30 \\
\hline
2\,|\ \ 1 \quad 8 \quad 15 \quad 0
\end{array}
$$

$\therefore p(x) = (x - 2)(x^2 + 8x + 15)$

$\quad\quad = (x - 2)(x + 3)(x + 5)$

$(x - 2)(x + 3)(x + 5) = 0$
$x = 2, -3, -5$

1. Since 2 is a zero, $x - 2$ is a factor. Use compressed synthetic division to find the depressed polynomial.

2. Continue to factor the polynomial.

3. Apply the Zero Product Property and list all the zeros.

————— SKILL ✓ EXERCISE 25

The Factor Theorem enables you to construct polynomials with known zeros. While there are many polynomials that could have the given roots, we will find a polynomial with the least possible degree. While the leading coefficient of a polynomial is often 1 (a *monic polynomial*), we usually find a polynomial in which all the coefficients are integers.

Example 7 Writing a Polynomial Function with Given Zeros

Write a polynomial function of least degree with integral coefficients that has zeros of $-1, \frac{5}{4}$, and 3 (with a multiplicity of 2).

Answer

$p_1(x) = (x + 1)\left(x - \frac{5}{4}\right)(x - 3)^2$

1. Use the Factor Theorem to list all the factors of a least degree polynomial with the stated roots. The multiplicity of a zero is assumed to be 1 unless otherwise stated.

$p_2(x) = (x + 1)(4x - 5)(x - 3)^2$

2. Multiplying the second factor by 4 produces another polynomial (without fractions) with the same zeros.

$\quad = (4x^2 - x - 5)(x^2 - 6x + 9)$

$\quad = 4x^4 - 25x^3 + 37x^2 + 21x - 45$

3. Multiply the factors, writing the polynomial in standard form.

————— SKILL ✓ EXERCISE 31

❯ A. Exercises

Use long division to find each quotient.

1. $(2x^2 + 5x + 1) \div (x + 4)$

2. $(3x^3 + 8x^2 - 15x + 4) \div (3x - 1)$

3. $(8x^3 - 1331) \div (2x - 11)$

4. $(x^4 - 3x^3 + 9x^2 - 12x + 17) \div (x^2 + 4)$

Use synthetic division to find each quotient.

5. $(x^4 - 7x^3 + 10x^2 + 9x - 4) \div (x - 4)$

6. $(x^4 - 5x^2 - 17x + 15) \div (x - 3)$

7. $(3x^2 - x^5 + 4x - x^3) \div (x + 1)$

8. $(4x^2 - 6x^4) \div (x + 2)$

9. $(6x^3 - 13x^2 + 9x - 2) \div (2x - 1)$

10. $(3x^3 - 7x^2 - 9x - 2) \div (3x + 2)$

Use the Remainder Theorem to find the remainder when $p(x)$ is divided by each binomial.

11. $p(x) = x^4 - 8x^2 + 16$

   a. $x - 1$

   b. $x + 2$

   c. $x - 2$

12. $p(x) = x^3 - 8$

   a. $x - 1$

   b. $x + 2$

   c. $x - 2$

13. $p(x) = x^3 - 4x^2 - 20x - 7$
   a. $x + 1$
   b. $x - 7$
   c. $x - 1$

14. $p(x) = x^5 - 1$
   a. $x + 1$
   b. $x + 2$
   c. $x - 1$

Use synthetic substitution to evaluate $p(1)$, $p(2)$, and $p(-1)$ for each function.

15. $p(x) = 3x^2 + x - 2$

16. $p(x) = x^4 + 2x^3 - 7x^2 - 8x + 12$

17. $p(x) = -2 + 7x - 3x^2$

18. $p(x) = x^3 + 3x^2 - x - 3$

❭ B. Exercises

19. Which of the following must be true if $x - 4$ is a factor of $p(x)$? List all correct answers.
   A. $x + 4$ is a factor of $p(x)$.   **D.** $p(4) = 0$
   B. 4 is a zero of $p(x)$.   **E.** $p(-4) = 0$
   C. -4 is a zero of $p(x)$.

20. Explain: A classmate claims that $p(x) = x^3 + 3x^2 - x - 3$ has a factor of $x - 3$. Is this correct? Use the Remainder Theorem to explain why or why not.

21. Consider $(x^3 + 64) \div (x + 4)$.
   a. Use synthetic division to find the quotient.
   b. Write the factorization of $x^3 + 64$.

22. Use each of the following to show that $x - 1$ is a factor of $p(x) = x^5 - 1$.
   a. synthetic division
   b. the Remainder Theorem

Completely factor each polynomial using the given information. Then list all the real zeros of the function.

23. $p(x) = x^3 - 3x^2 - 6x + 8$ if $p(1) = 0$

24. $p(x) = 2x^3 + 7x^2 + 2x - 3$ if $x + 3$ is a factor

25. $p(x) = 2x^4 - 5x^3 + x^2 + 5x - 3$ if 1 is a zero (multiplicity 2)

26. $p(x) = x^4 + 4x^3 - 13x^2 - 40x + 48$ if $x - 1$ and $x + 4$ are factors

27. $p(x) = 27x^3 - 343$; $p\left(\frac{7}{3}\right) = 0$

Write a standard form polynomial function with integral coefficients having the following zeros.

28. 1 and 4

29. 2 (multiplicity 3)

30. $\frac{1}{6}$ and $\frac{5}{7}$

31. $\frac{1}{2}$ (multiplicity 2) and 5

32. 3, -2 (multiplicity 2), $\frac{2}{3}$

33. ± 1, $\pm \frac{1}{3}$

34. Joe wants to enlarge his raised garden box, which is 2 ft wide by 5 ft long and 1 ft high. He plans to increase the length and width by three times the amount that he increases the height.
   a. Write a polynomial function, $V(x)$, for the volume of the enlarged box in terms of its increase in height.
   b. Use the function to find the volume (in ft^3) if the enlarged box is 27 in. tall.
   c. What is the length and width of the new box?

35. The Table lists the median values of homes in Massachusetts.

Year	x	Median Value ($\$/ft^2$)
1996	0	101
1999	3	122
2002	6	181
2005	9	322
2008	12	268
2011	15	204
2014	18	271

   a. Letting x represent the number of years since 1996, complete a regression to find a quartic model for the data.
   b. Use the model to approximate the cost in 2000 and in 2007.
   c. Use the model to approximate the year that housing prices began to decrease and the year they began to increase again.

❭ C. Exercises

Find k so that $d(x)$ is a factor of $p(x)$.

36. $p(x) = 2x^2 + 9x + k$; $d(x) = x + 5$

37. $p(x) = x^4 - x^3 - kx^2 + 11x + 6$; $d(x) = (x + 3)$

38. Find k if $g(x) = x^2 + 6x - 1$ and $h(x) = kx^3 - x^2 - 2x - 1$ have the same remainder when divided by $x - 2$.

39. Find the values of j and k if the function $p(x) = -2x^2 - jx + k$ has a remainder of 7 when divided by $x + 1$ and a remainder of 5 when divided by $x + 2$.

40. Prove: Show that $x - 1$ is always a factor of $x^n - 1$.

41. Simplify $(3x^5 - 2x^4 + x - 4) - (4x^4 - x^3 + x - 7)$.
[Algebra]

42. Simplify $\sqrt{-104}$. [Appendix 5]

Solve. [1.6]

43. $x^2 + 2x + 5 = -3x^2 + 2x - 4$ [1.6]

44. $x^3 + 729 = 0$ [1.6]

45. Graph the compound inequality $x \geq \frac{1}{4}$ or $x < -2$ on a number line and express it using interval notation. [1.1]

46. If $f(x) = 5x^2 + 34x - 7$ and $g(x) = x + 7$, find $\frac{f}{g}(x)$. [1.7]

47. Simplify $\dfrac{5x^3 + 3x + 5x^2y + 3y}{x^4 - y^4}$. [Algebra]

 A. $\dfrac{5x^2 + 3}{\left(x^2 + y^2\right)(x - y)}$

 D. $\dfrac{5x^2 + 3}{\left(x^2 - y^2\right)(x - y)}$

 B. $\dfrac{5x^2 + 3}{\left(x^2 + y^2\right)(x + y)}$

 E. none of these

 C. $\dfrac{5x^2 + 3y}{\left(x^2 + y^2\right)(x + y)}$

48. Which equation represents the line $y = \frac{2}{3}x - \frac{5}{6}$? [1.2]

 A. $4x - 5y = 6$

 D. $4x - 6y = 5$

 B. $4x + 6y = 5$

 E. none of these

 C. $4x + 6y = -5$

49. What is the result when $f(x) = 2x^2$ is translated 2 units right and 3 units down? [1.5]

 A. $g(x) = 2x^2 + 8x + 5$

 D. $g(x) = 2x^2 + 8x - 3$

 B. $g(x) = 2x^2 - 2x - 3$

 E. none of these

 C. $g(x) = 2x^2 - 8x + 5$

50. Find the zeros of $f(x) = 4x^2 + 3x + 10$. [1.6]

 A. $x = \dfrac{-3 \pm i\sqrt{151}}{8}$

 D. $x = -2, \dfrac{5}{4}$

 B. $x = \dfrac{-3 \pm \sqrt{151}}{8}$

 E. none of these

 C. $x = \dfrac{-3 \pm 13i}{8}$

SYMBOLS

Can you calculate the zenzizenzizenzic of 2?

Modern mathematicians express this intimidating notation as the much more manageable 2^8. The introduction and acceptance of symbols such as 2^8 in mathematical publications was driven by the study of algebra and enabled by the invention of movable-type printing.

The first published use (in English) of the now familiar addition and subtraction signs occurred in *The Whetstone of Wit*, an algebra text published by Robert Recorde in 1557. Recorde also introduced the sign for equality in this text, commenting that nothing could be more equal than two parallel lines.

The full title of Recorde's book is *The whetstone of wit, which is the second part of Arithmetic: containing the extraction of roots: The Cossic practice, with the rule of Equation: and the works of Surd Numbers*.

The archaic German word for the unknown value in an equation is *coss*. So prolific were German mathematical authors in the sixteenth century that for a while *coss* was used instead of

algebra throughout Europe when referring to the mathematics of unknown quantities.

The first German algebra text, commonly known as *The Coss*, was published in 1525. In 1553 Michael Stifel published a new edition with extensive notes. Stifel was an Augustinian monk who, partly because of his distaste for the sale of indulgences, became a follower of Martin Luther. Nearly 200 years later, Leonhard Euler would be taught mathematics by his father from Stifel's edition.

The Coss was written by Christoff Rudolff and contained the first use of the modern radical symbol to indicate roots. The vinculum (horizontal bar) was added by René Descartes in his 1637 volume on geometry. Indices to indicate other roots besides the square root were not adopted until the end of the century.

Nicole Oresme introduced the idea of a mathematical function in the fourteenth century, but it would be another 200 years before the scientific explorations of Galileo and Kepler led to the fuller development of the power of functions in modeling natural phenomena. In the interim, Gutenberg published the first Bible printed on a movable-type press, Columbus discovered the New World, Magellan circumnavigated the globe, and Martin Luther nailed his Ninety-Five Theses to the church door in Wittenberg.

As the concept of a function developed and symbols became more standardized and useful, mathematicians began to study functions as abstract ideas in their own right, even when they saw no practical application. This development of "pure mathematics" led some mathematicians to conclude that all math is created by man.

COMPREHENSION CHECK

1. When did the first use of addition, subtraction, and equality signs occur in print in English?

2. Why would a sixteenth-century algebra book be called *The Coss*?

3. What famous eighteenth-century mathematician learned mathematics from *The Coss*?

4. What key invention of the fifteenth century helped standardize mathematical notation?

5. Why did the use and development of functions flourish during a time of scientific exploration?

6. State a factor contributing to the belief by some that mathematics is solely a human creation.

2.4 Zeros of Polynomial Functions

Germany honored Carl Gauss, "the Prince of Mathematics," on the 10 deutsche mark note in 1991.

After completing this section, you will be able to

- identify the possible rational zeros of a polynomial.
- apply Descartes's Rule of Signs and the Upper and Lower Bound Tests.
- find complex zeros of a polynomial function.
- find a polynomial function of least degree for a given set of zeros.

Christianity is built on fundamental doctrines, such as the infallibility of God's Word, the deity of Christ, Christ's resurrection, and salvation through Christ alone. These fundamentals are foundational to other truths. Similarly, there are several fundamental theorems in mathematics that form the foundation for other theorems. These include the Fundamental Theorem of Algebra, first proved by Carl Friedrich Gauss.

FUNDAMENTAL THEOREM OF ALGEBRA

Every polynomial function of degree greater than 0 has at least one complex zero.

The complex root(s) may be real or imaginary. This theorem is used to prove a second theorem describing the factorization of polynomial functions and leads to a corollary describing the exact number of zeros.

COMPLETE LINEAR FACTORIZATION THEOREM

Every polynomial function of positive degree n can be factored into n *linear factors* so that $p(x) = a(x - z_1)(x - z_2) \ldots (x - z_n)$ where $z_1, z_2, \ldots, z_n$ are the complex zeros of $p(x)$.

Proof:

The Fundamental Theorem of Algebra guarantees that $p(x)$ has at least one complex zero, z_1.

Thus $p(z_1) = 0$, and by the Factor Theorem $p(x) = (x - z_1)[q_1(x)]$, where $q_1(x)$ is a depressed polynomial.

The Fundamental Theorem also guarantees that $q_1(x)$ has a complex zero; let it be z_2. Therefore, $p(x) = (x - z_1)(x - z_2)[q_2(x)]$.
Repeating this process decreases the degree of $q(x)$ by 1 until $q(x)$ is of degree 0 (a constant) and $p(x) = a(x - z_1)(x - z_2) \ldots (x - z_n)$.

COROLLARY OF THE FUNDAMENTAL THEOREM OF ALGEBRA

A polynomial function of positive degree n has exactly n zeros, which may be repeated. Therefore, there are at most n roots to the equation $p(x) = 0$.

These *existence theorems* guarantee that the zeros and factors exist, but do not explain how to find them. The rest of this section discusses several ways to find the zeros of certain polynomial functions, whether they are rational, irrational, or imaginary.

The linear function $f(x) = 3x - 5$ has one zero: $x = \frac{5}{3}$. Factoring the cubic $g(x) = x^3 - 4x = x(x^2 - 4)$ allows you to quickly find its three zeros: 0, ±2. Factoring the quadratic $h(x) = 2x^2 - x - 6 = (x - 2)(2x + 3)$ produces its two rational zeros: 2 and $-\frac{3}{2}$. Notice that the numerators of these zeros, 2 and –3, are factors of the polynomial's constant, –6, and that their denominators, 1 and 2, are factors of the leading coefficient, 2. This observation leads to the following theorem.

RATIONAL ZERO THEOREM

If $p(x) = a_n x^n + a_{n-1} x^{n-1} + \cdots + a_2 x^2 + a_1 x + a_0$ with integral coefficients and $\frac{c}{d}$ is a reduced rational zero of $p(x)$, then c is a factor of a_0 and d is a factor of a_n.

Example 1   Using the Rational Zero Theorem

Find the zeros of $p(x) = 6x^3 + 7x^2 - 1$.

Answer

factors of -1: ± 1

factors of 6: $\pm 1, \pm 2, \pm 3, \pm 6$

possible zeros: $\frac{c}{d} = \pm 1, \pm \frac{1}{2}, \pm \frac{1}{3}, \pm \frac{1}{6}$

$p(1) = 6 + 7 - 1 = 12$
$p(-1) = -6 + 7 - 1 = 0$

$$
\begin{array}{r|rrrr}
-1 & 6 & 7 & 0 & -1 \\
   &   & -6 & -1 & 1 \\
\hline
   & 6 & 1 & -1 & 0
\end{array}
$$

$p(x) = (x + 1)(6x^2 + x - 1)$

$(x + 1)(3x - 1)(2x + 1) = 0$

$\therefore x = -1, \frac{1}{3}, -\frac{1}{2}$

1. Make a list of possible rational zeros by listing possible factors of the constant term and the leading coefficient.

2. The Remainder Theorem can be used to quickly check some of the simpler possible zeros.

3. Use synthetic division to divide $p(x)$ by $(x + 1)$ and find the coefficients of the depressed polynomial.

4. Set $p(x) = 0$ and factor the depressed polynomial.

5. Solve for the zeros using the Zero Product Property.

SKILL ✓ **EXERCISE 5**

Example 2   Solving a Polynomial Equation

Solve $x^4 + 9x^3 + 15x^2 + 9x = -14$.

Answer

$x^4 + 9x^3 + 15x^2 + 9x + 14 = 0$

factors of 14: $\pm 1, \pm 2, \pm 7, \pm 14$

factors of 1: ± 1

possible zeros: $\frac{c}{d} = \pm 1, \pm 2, \pm 7, \pm 14$

Test only $-1, -2, -7$, and -14.

$$
\begin{array}{r|rrrrr}
   & 1 & 9 & 15 & 9 & 14 \\
-1 & 1 & 8 & 7 & 2 & 12 \\
-2 & 1 & 7 & 1 & 7 & 0
\end{array}
$$

$(x + 2)(x^3 + 7x^2 + x + 7) = 0$

$(x + 2)[x^2(x + 7) + (x + 7)] = 0$

$(x + 2)(x + 7)(x^2 + 1) = 0$

$\therefore x = -2, -7$, and $\pm i$

1. Set the equation equal to 0.

2. Make a list of possible rational zeros by listing possible factors of the constant term and the leading coefficient.

3. Note that all the coefficients are positive and no positive number will make $p(x) = 0$.

4. Use compressed synthetic division to test these possible roots.

   Since -2 is a zero, $(x + 2)$ is a factor of $p(x)$.

5. Factor $p(x)$ completely into linear factors. You can factor the cubic by grouping or by further synthetic division, trying only the possible negative roots of the depressed polynomial, -1 and -7.

6. Solve using the Zero Product Property.

SKILL ✓ **EXERCISE 19**

While the Rational Zero Theorem requires integral coefficients, Example 3 illustrates how it can be used when the polynomial's coefficients are rational.

Example 3 Using the Rational Zero Theorem with Rational Coefficients

Find the zeros of $p(x) = x^3 - \frac{13}{12}x^2 + \frac{3}{8}x - \frac{1}{24}$.

Answer

$24p(x) = 24x^3 - 26x^2 + 9x - 1$

1. Multiply by the least common denominator to obtain integral coefficients.

factors of -1: ± 1

factors of 24: $\pm 1, \pm 2, \pm 3, \pm 4, \pm 6, \pm 8, \pm 12, \pm 24$

possible zeros: $\pm 1, \pm \frac{1}{2}, \pm \frac{1}{3}, \pm \frac{1}{4}, \pm \frac{1}{6}, \pm \frac{1}{8}, \pm \frac{1}{12}, \pm \frac{1}{24}$

2. Make a list of the possible rational zeros for $24p(x)$.

$$
\begin{array}{r|rrrr}
 & 24 & -26 & 9 & -1 \\
\frac{1}{2} & & & & \\
\hline
 & 24 & -14 & 2 & 0 \\
\end{array}
$$

3. Compressed synthetic division reveals that $\left(x - \frac{1}{2}\right)$ is a factor of $24p(x)$ and provides the coefficients of the depressed polynomial.

$24p(x) = \left(x - \frac{1}{2}\right)(24x^2 - 14x + 2)$

4. Factor $24p(x)$.

$24p(x) = 2\left(x - \frac{1}{2}\right)(12x^2 - 7x + 1)$

   a. Factor 2 out of the depressed polynomial.

$24p(x) = 2\left(x - \frac{1}{2}\right)(3x - 1)(4x - 1)$

   b. Factor the remaining quadratic.

$p(x) = \frac{1}{12}\left(x - \frac{1}{2}\right)(3x - 1)(4x - 1)$

5. Divide both sides by 24 to solve for $p(x)$.

The zeros of $p(x)$ are $x = \frac{1}{2}, \frac{1}{3},$ and $\frac{1}{4}$.

6. Apply the Zero Product Property.

SKILL ✓ EXERCISE 25

When all possible roots suggested by the Rational Zero Theorem fail, you know that the zeros are irrational or imaginary. For example, it can be shown (either by synthetic division or substitution) that ± 1 and ± 3 are not zeros of $p(x) = x^2 + 3x - 3$. Fortunately, the quadratic formula can be used to find the function's two irrational roots: $\frac{-3 \pm \sqrt{21}}{2}$.

The following theorems can help limit your search for real zeros of a polynomial function whether they are rational or irrational.

Descartes's Rule of Signs was contained in the geometry appendix of his famous *Discourse*, published in 1637.

▌ DESCARTES'S RULE OF SIGNS

If $p(x) = a_n x^n + a_{n-1} x^{n-1} + \cdots + a_2 x^2 + a_1 x + a_0$ with real coefficients, then

- the number of positive real zeros of $p(x)$ is the number of variations in the sign of $p(x)$ or less than that number by an even number and
- the number of negative real zeros of $p(x)$ is the number of variations in the sign of $p(-x)$ or less than that number by an even number.

This rule allows you to describe the possible number of positive and negative zeros.

Example 4   Applying Descartes's Rule of Signs

Describe the possible number of positive and negative zeros of
$p(x) = 3x^4 - 5x^3 + 4x^2 - 10x - 4$.

Answer

$p(x)$ has 3 or 1 positive zero.

1. There are 3 sign changes in the coefficients of $p(x)$.
$$p(x) = 3x^4 - 5x^3 + 4x^2 - 10x - 4$$
$$\quad\quad\quad 1 \quad 2 \quad 3$$

$p(x)$ has 1 negative zero.

2. The coefficients of $p(-x)$ have only 1 sign change.
$$p(-x) = 3x^4 + 5x^3 + 4x^2 + 10x - 4$$
$$\quad\quad\quad\quad\quad\quad 1$$

SKILL ✓ **EXERCISE 9a**

The Upper and Lower Bound Tests can establish an interval containing all of a function's real zeros.

▌UPPER AND LOWER BOUND TESTS

If $p(x)$ is a polynomial function of degree $n \geq 1$ with a positive leading coefficient and $p(x)$ is divided by $x - c$ using synthetic division,

(1) $c \geq 0$ is an **upper bound** of the zeros if every coefficient of the depressed polynomial is nonnegative and

(2) $c \leq 0$ is a **lower bound** of the zeros if the coefficients of the depressed polynomial and its remainder are alternately nonnegative and nonpositive.

The Upper and Lower Bound Tests can ensure that a graphing window illustrates all the real zeros of a function.

If the leading coefficient of $p(x)$ is negative, simply find the zeros for $-p(x)$, which are also the zeros of $p(x)$ since $p(x)$ and $-p(x)$ are reflections of each other in the x-axis.

Example 5   Applying the Upper and Lower Bound Tests

Show that any real zeros of $p(x) = 3x^4 - 5x^3 + 4x^2 - 10x - 4$ lie within the interval $[-1, 2]$.

Answer

$$\begin{array}{c|ccccc} & 3 & -5 & 4 & -10 & -4 \\ 2 & & & & & \\ \hline & 3 & 1 & 6 & 2 & 0 \end{array}$$

1. Since all the coefficients of the depressed polynomial when $p(x) \div (x - 2)$ are nonnegative, 2 is an upper bound of the zeros for $p(x)$.

$$\begin{array}{c|ccccc} & 3 & -5 & 4 & -10 & -4 \\ -1 & & & & & \\ \hline & 3 & -8 & 12 & -22 & 18 \end{array}$$

2. Since the coefficients of the depressed polynomial when $p(x) \div [x - (-1)]$ are alternately nonnegative and nonpositive, −1 is a lower bound of the zeros for $p(x)$.

SKILL ✓ **EXERCISE 9b**

The synthetic division testing the upper bound of 2 in Example 5 reveals that 2 is also a zero and that $p(x)$ can be factored into

$$p(x) = (x - 2)(3x^3 + x^2 + 6x + 2).$$

The graph of $p(x)$ suggests that $-\frac{1}{3}$ is a zero and can be used to factor the depressed polynomial.

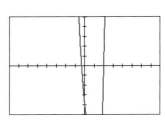

$$\begin{array}{c|cccc} & 3 & 1 & 6 & 2 \\ -\frac{1}{3} & & & & \\ \hline & 3 & 0 & 6 & 0 \end{array}$$

$$p(x) = (x - 2)\left(x + \frac{1}{3}\right)(3x^2 + 6)$$

$$p(x) = 3(x - 2)\left(x + \frac{1}{3}\right)(x^2 + 2)$$

The remaining two zeros, $x = \pm\sqrt{2}i$, are complex numbers, which are neither positive nor negative.

The following theorems describe the occurrence of irrational and complex roots for polynomials with appropriate coefficients.

▌ CONJUGATE ROOT THEOREMS

1. If $p(x)$ is a polynomial with rational coefficients and $a + c\sqrt{b}$ is a zero of $p(x)$, then its conjugate, $a - c\sqrt{b}$, is also a zero of $p(x)$.

2. If $p(x)$ is a polynomial with real coefficients and $a + bi$ is a zero of $p(x)$, then its conjugate, $a - bi$, is also a zero of $p(x)$.

Example 6   Applying a Conjugate Root Theorem

List all the zeros of $p(x) = x^4 + 2x^3 - x^2 + 2x - 2$ if $-i$ is a zero.

Answer

Note that i is also a zero of $p(x)$.

1. Apply the second Conjugate Root Theorem since all coefficients are real.

$(x - i)$ and $(x + i)$ are linear factors of $p(x)$.

2. Apply the Factor Theorem using the zeros $\pm i$.

$p(x) = (x + i)(x - i) \cdot q(x)$
$p(x) = (x^2 + 1) \cdot q(x)$

3. Express $p(x)$ as the product of known factors and an unknown quotient polynomial, $q(x)$.

$$
\begin{array}{r}
x^2 + 2x - 2 \\
x^2 + 1 \overline{)\, x^4 + 2x^3 - x^2 + 2x - 2} \\
-(x^4 \quad\quad + x^2) \\
\hline
2x^3 - 2x^2 + 2x \\
-(2x^3 \quad\quad + 2x) \\
\hline
-2x^2 \quad -2 \\
-(-2x^2 \quad -2) \\
\hline
0
\end{array}
$$

4. Divide to find the factor $q(x)$. Synthetic division cannot be used since the divisor has a degree of 2.

$q(x) = x^2 + 2x - 2$

$x = \dfrac{-2 \pm \sqrt{2^2 - 4(1)(-2)}}{2(1)}$

$= -1 \pm \sqrt{3} \approx -2.73, 0.73$

$\therefore p(x) = 0$ when $x = \pm i, -1 \pm \sqrt{3}$

5. Since $q(x)$ cannot be factored with integral coefficients, use the quadratic formula to find its irrational zeros.

SKILL ✓ EXERCISE 17

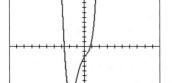

Note that Descartes's Rule of Signs predicts that the function in Example 6 has either 3 or 1 positive real root and 1 negative real root, and that the Upper and Lower Bound Tests can confirm that there are no real zeros outside the interval $[-3, 1]$.

Bound Tests		1	2	−1	2	−2	
Upper	1	1	3	2	4	2	(all positive coefficients)
Lower	−3	1	−1	2	−4	10	(alternating nonnegative and nonpositive coefficients)

The graph of the function confirms the two irrational zeros. The Complete Linear Factorization Theorem guarantees that the four zeros can be used to write the complete linear factorization of the polynomial.

$$p(x) = (x - i)[x - (-i)][x - (-1 + \sqrt{3})][x - (-1 - \sqrt{3})]$$

If the zeros occur in conjugate pairs, those factors are frequently combined and written as an *irreducible quadratic factor*.

$$p(x) = (x^2 + 1)(x^2 + 2x - 2)$$

The Conjugate Root Theorems and the Factor Theorem enable you to construct a polynomial of least degree with integral coefficients from the known zeros.

Example 7 Writing a Polynomial Function with Given Zeros

Write a standard form polynomial function of least degree with integral coefficients that has zeros of 0 (multiplicity 3), $\frac{2}{3}$, $1 + \sqrt{2}$, and $3 - 2i$.

Answer

$(x - 0)^3 = x^3$

1. The multiplicity of 3 implies that the factor $(x - 0)$ appears 3 times.

$3\left(x - \frac{2}{3}\right) = 3x - 2$

2. Multiply the factor from the zero of $\frac{2}{3}$ by a constant to eliminate fractions.

$[x - (1 + \sqrt{2})][x - (1 - \sqrt{2})]$
$= [(x - 1) - \sqrt{2}][(x - 1) + \sqrt{2}]$
$= [(x - 1)^2 - 2] = x^2 - 2x - 1$

3. A zero of $1 + \sqrt{2}$ implies that its conjugate $1 - \sqrt{2}$ is also a zero. Note how the Associative Property is used to multiply the related factors using the difference of squares pattern.

$[x - (3 - 2i)][x - (3 + 2i)]$
$= [(x - 3) + 2i][(x - 3) - 2i]$
$= (x - 3)^2 - 4i^2 = x^2 - 6x + 13$

4. The complex zero $3 - 2i$ implies that its conjugate $3 + 2i$ is also a zero. The Associative Property is used to multiply the related factors using the difference of squares pattern.

$p(x) = x^3(3x - 2)(x^2 - 2x - 1)(x^2 - 6x + 13)$
$\quad = (3x^4 - 2x^3)(x^4 - 8x^3 + 24x^2 - 20x - 13)$
$\quad = 3x^8 - 26x^7 + 88x^6 - 108x^5 + x^4 + 26x^3$

5. Multiply the factors to find a least degree polynomial with integral coefficients.

SKILL ✓ EXERCISE 31

A. Exercises

List all the possible rational zeros for each polynomial function.

1. $p(x) = 2x^3 + 3x^2 - x + 2$
2. $p(x) = 6x^3 + 5x^2 - 12x + 4$

Find all the zeros for each polynomial function. Indicate any multiplicities greater than 1.

3. $p(x) = (x^2 - 4)(x^2 - 16)$
4. $p(x) = x^3 - 2x^2 - 5x + 6$
5. $p(x) = x^3 - 13x - 12$
6. $p(x) = x^3 - 6x^2 + 12x - 8$

7. $p(x) = x^4 - 10x^3 + 33x^2 - 40x + 16$
8. $p(x) = x^4 - 9x^2 + 4x + 12$

Given the polynomial function $p(x)$,
a. **use Descartes's Rule of Signs to describe the possible number of positive and negative zeros and**
b. **use Upper and Lower Bound Tests to show that any real zeros lie within the given interval.**

9. $p(x) = x^4 - 4x^3 + 4x^2 - 4x + 3$, $[0, 4]$
10. $p(x) = x^4 + x^3 - x^2 + x - 2$, $[-3, 2]$

Write a polynomial function of least degree with integral coefficients that has the given zeros.

11. $x = 3, \pm\sqrt{2}$
12. $x = 1, \pm 4i$

B. Exercises

Use the given zero to find the remaining zeros for each polynomial function.

13. $p(x) = 2x^3 - 12x^2 - 6x + 36;\ x = \sqrt{3}$

14. $p(x) = x^3 + 3x^2 + x + 3;\ x = i$

15. $p(x) = x^4 + x^3 + 4x^2 + 4x;\ x = 2i$

16. $p(x) = x^3 - 9x^2 + 22x - 10;\ x = 2 - \sqrt{2}$

17. $p(x) = x^3 + x^2 + 3x - 5;\ x = -1 - 2i$

Solve.

18. $x^3 - x^2 + 3x - 3 = 0$

19. $x^4 - 3x^3 - 4x^2 + 12x = 0$

20. $x^3 - x^2 = x$

21. $x^3 + \frac{7}{2}x^2 = 14x - 6$

Find all the zeros of each polynomial function.

22. $p(x) = x^3 - x^2 - 8x + 12$

23. $p(x) = x^3 + 3x^2 - x + 45$

24. $p(x) = 5x^4 - 16x^3 + 18x^2 - 48x + 9$

25. $p(x) = x^4 - \frac{11}{4}x^3 + \frac{9}{4}x^2 - \frac{1}{4}x - \frac{1}{4}$

26. $p(x) = x^3 - \frac{17}{30}x^2 - \frac{1}{10}x + \frac{1}{15}$

27. $p(x) = x^4 + \frac{11}{6}x^3 + \frac{1}{4}x^2 - \frac{11}{24}x - \frac{1}{8}$

28. $p(x) = x^4 - \frac{11}{4}x^3 + \frac{1}{2}x^2 + \frac{29}{16}x + \frac{3}{8}$

Write a standard form polynomial function of least degree with integral coefficients that has the given zeros.

29. $x = 2,\ 1 \pm \sqrt{3}$

30. $x = -2,\ 3 \pm 2i$

31. $x = -\frac{3}{4},\ 4 - 3i$

32. $x = -\frac{1}{2},\ \frac{2}{3},\ 2 + i$

33. $x = -2$ (multiplicity 2), $1 + \sqrt{5},\ 2 - 3i$

Use technology to find a zero. Then use synthetic division to factor the polynomial.

34. $p(x) = 21x^3 + 29x^2 - 24x + 4$

35. $p(x) = 5x^3 + 2x^2 - 10x - 4$

Use the Upper and Lower Bound Tests to determine if the window illustrates all the real zeros of each function. If not, state and verify another integral interval that contains all the real zeros of the function.

36. $p(x) = x^5 - 6x^4 - 10x^3 + 5x^2 + 8x + 1$

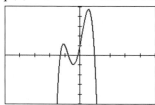

37. $p(x) = x^4 + x^3 - x^2 + x - 2$

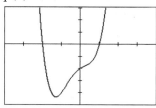

38. $p(x) = x^3 + 8x^2 - 6x - 3$

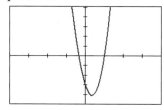

39. $p(x) = -x^4 - 4x^3 + 13x^2 + 4x - 12$

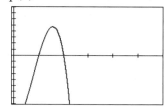

40. Explain: If a fifth-degree polynomial function with rational coefficients has zeros at $x = \pm1$ and $x = \sqrt{3}$, what is the maximum multiplicity for each given zero? Explain your reasoning.

C. Exercises

41. Discover: Consider a polynomial function whose only zeros are $x = \sqrt{3}$ and $x = -2$.

    a. Find a quadratic function with these zeros.

    b. Show that $x = -\sqrt{3}$ is not a zero of the function found in step *a*.

    c. Explain why your findings are not a contradiction of the first Conjugate Root Theorem.

42. Discover: Consider a polynomial function whose only zeros are $x = -2i$ and $x = 1$.

    a. Find a quadratic function with these zeros.

    b. Show that $x = 2i$ is not a zero of the function found in step *a*.

    c. Explain why your findings are not a contradiction of the second Conjugate Root Theorem.

43. Generalize: Find the general form of a quadratic function having the given zero.

    a. $a + bi$ **b.** $a - c\sqrt{b}$

44. Use technology to graph $p(x) = x^3 + 2x^2 - 5x - 6$.

    a. State the function's zeros.

    b. Does the greatest positive zero pass the Upper Bound Test? Does the least negative zero pass the Lower Bound Test?

    c. Some might think that the results of part *b* show that one of the tests is invalid. Explain why this is not true.

CUMULATIVE REVIEW

45. Given A $(-2, 5)$ and B $(4, -1)$, find AB and the midpoint of $\overline{AB}$. **[1.2]**

46. Classify $f(x) = \dfrac{2}{x^2}$ as a continuous or discontinuous function. Further classify any discontinuities as jump, infinite, or point. **[1.3]**

47. Describe how the graph of $f(x) = \dfrac{1}{x^2}$ is transformed to get the graph of $g(x) = \dfrac{1}{x^2 - 4} + 3$. **[1.5]**

48. Write the function rule for $\dfrac{g}{f}(x)$ if $f(x) = x + 1$ and $g(x) = 7x^2 + 15x + 8$. **[1.7]**

Use $p(x) = 2x^4 - 3x^3 + x^2 - 73x + 5$ for exercises 49–50.

49. Use the Leading Term Test to describe the function's end behavior. **[2.2]**

50. Use the Remainder Theorem to find the remainder when $p(x)$ is divided by $x - 4$. **[2.3]**

51. Factor the polynomial $f(x) = x^3 - 27$. **[Algebra]**

    A. $(x + 3)(x^2 - 3x + 9)$ **D.** $(x - 3)(x^2 + 3x - 9)$

    B. $(x - 3)(x^2 - 3x + 9)$ **E.** none of these

    C. $(x + 3)(x^2 + 3x + 9)$

52. State the domain of $f(x) = \sqrt{x - 5}$. **[1.1]**

    A. $(-5, \infty)$ **D.** $(0, \infty)$

    B. $[5, \infty)$ **E.** $[0, \infty)$

    C. $(-\infty, \infty)$

53. Describe the continuity of $g(x) = \dfrac{x^2 - 9}{x + 3}$ at $x = -3$. **[1.3]**

    A. continuous   **D.** point discontinuity

    B. jump discontinuity   **E.** none of these

    C. infinite discontinuity

54. Find the zeros of $f(x) = -3x^2 - x + 4$. **[1.6]**

    A. $x = -\dfrac{3}{4}, 4$ **D.** $x = -\dfrac{3}{4}, 1$

    B. $x = -\dfrac{4}{3}, 1$ **E.** none of these

    C. $x = \dfrac{4}{3}, 1$

Math's Divine Nature

2 + 2 = 4 is true at all times and at all places. We have classic terms to describe this situation: the truth is omnipresent (present at all places) and eternal (there at all times) . . . . The attributes of omnipresence and eternity are only the beginning. On close examination, other divine attributes seem to belong to arithmetical truths.

—Vern S. Poythress (American theologian, mathematician, and author)

Mathematics can be defined as the science of number, quantity, and space. The inadequacy of the human intellect to fully understand these concepts should be immediately obvious as we contemplate the infinite set of natural numbers, the infinite quantity of real numbers between 0 and 1, or the infinite space suggested by our universe. Our mathematics contains transcendent truth originating with our infinite God, who has been gracious in making mathematical knowledge accessible to mankind. We should not be surprised that our mathematics reflects several characteristics of God.

Vern S. Poythress characterizes mathematical truth as both omnipresent and eternal. In *Redeeming Mathematics*, he explains that mathematical facts have other divine attributes because they come from God. For example, the fact $2 + 2 = 4$ does not change with the passage of time; it is immutable. Furthermore, "two apples and two apples always make four apples. No event escapes the 'hold' or dominion of arithmetical laws. The power of these laws is absolute, in fact, infinite. In classical language, the law is omnipotent ('all powerful')."

The divine nature of mathematical truth is clarified by a comparison to God's Word. Poythress explains: "The Bible indicates that God rules the world through his speech. He speaks, and it is done [Ps. 33:6] . . . . We may then conclude that the same principle applies in particular to numerical truths about the world. God governs *everything*, including numerical truth. His word specifies what is true. The apples in a group of four apples are created things. What God says about them is divine."

With that in mind we can say that "$2 + 2 = 4$ is both transcendent and immanent. It transcends the creatures of the world by exercising power over them, conforming them to its dictates. It is immanent in that it touches and

holds in its dominion even the smallest bits of this world. $2 + 2 = 4$ transcends the galactic clusters and is immanently present in the behavior of the electrons surrounding a beryllium nucleus. Transcendence and immanence are characteristics of God."

A Christian view of mathematics realizes that our transcendent God controls all things, including mathematics, and that He has authority over all mathematical truth. Because God created finite man in His image, "as human beings we are capable of thinking God's thoughts after him. In particular, we can know that $2 + 2 = 4$, a truth that is in God's mind before it is in ours." Our immanent God gives this mathematical truth to us; it is observed in our created universe and comprehended in our finite minds.

The mathematics crafted and applied by mankind is derived from God's perfect body of mathematical truth. Our understanding of God's truths has grown over time. For example, the mathematical notation developed by past civilizations may be ineffective. Performing multiplication and division is certainly more difficult with Roman numerals than it is with decimal numbers. Each construction of a superior notation or an illuminating concept is a blessing from God.

While human knowledge increases as we interact with God's revelation in His creation, our understanding of His knowledge is still limited. Our work in mathematics provides undeniable evidence of these limitations. We often make logical or computational errors as we create proofs or apply theory. The work of a professional mathematician is thoroughly examined for errors by peers before it is accepted by the mathematics community. Mathematical modeling uses data from the past to make predictions about future events, sometimes with unreliable results. Inferential statistics presents conclusions with margins of error. These limitations contrast with the omniscient character of God. God does not operate in a world of uncertainty; His sovereignty is complete and unfailing.

Despite the limitations of our understanding, humanly crafted mathematics can express transcendent truths that originate with God. When our mathematics agrees with and expresses transcendent truth, it reflects God's own faithfulness. $2 + 2 = 4$ is certainly and always true. God's knowledge of $2 + 2 = 4$ exceeds ours, but God has allowed us to know this truth, reflecting His mind and the certainty of who He is.

⟩ Exercises

1. What example does Poythress use to illustrate the immanence of mathematics in the "the smallest bits of the world"?

2. Which prominent past civilization utilized an inferior number system?

3. Describe two types of errors made in geometric proofs and algebraic solutions.

4. Why is the work of a professional mathematician reviewed by peers before gaining acceptance in the mathematics community?

5. Which mathematical discipline describes conclusions in terms of a margin of error?

6. When is humanly crafted mathematics true?

7. Which divine characteristic provides the sense of certainty for mathematical truths like $2 + 2 = 4$?

8. Match each divine characteristic of mathematical truth to its description.

   a. all powerful
   b. present at all places
   c. existing forever
   d. not subject to the limitations of the universe
   e. involved in the universe
   f. unchanging over time

   I. eternal
   II. immanent
   III. immutable
   IV. omnipotent
   V. omnipresent
   VI. transcendent

9. **Discuss:** Contrast human mathematics with God's transcendent mathematical truths.

A photographer changes the distance between the camera's lens and the image sensor to bring the image into focus.

TIP

Each continuous portion of these graphs is called a *branch*. The graph of $f(x) = \frac{1}{x}$ is a *hyperbola*.

In the seventeenth century Evangelista Torricelli showed that the solid created by rotating the graph of the rational function $f(x) = \frac{1}{x}$ where $x \geq 1$ about the x-axis has a finite volume but an infinite surface area. Such mysteries emphasize our limited understanding of creation (Job 38–41) and should inspire awe and worship of the Creator.

In mathematics, the word *rational* conveys the idea of a ratio. Just as the rational numbers, $\mathbb{Q} = \{\frac{a}{b} \mid a, b \in \mathbb{Z}, b \neq 0\}$, are ratios of integers, rational functions are ratios of polynomials.

DEFINITION

A **rational function** is a function that can be expressed as $f(x) = \frac{a(x)}{b(x)}$ where $a(x)$ and $b(x)$ are polynomials and $b(x) \neq 0$.

The domain of any rational function excludes the zeros of $b(x)$. Examining the end behaviors and the value of the function near the excluded values provides a general idea of the shape of the function's graph. Reciprocal power functions such as $f(x) = \frac{1}{x}$ and $g(x) = \frac{1}{x^2}$ are some of the simplest rational functions. Notice that the graphs of these functions approach specific x- and y- values called *asymptotes*.

$$f(x) = \frac{1}{x} \qquad\qquad\qquad g(x) = \frac{1}{x^2}$$

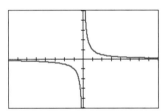 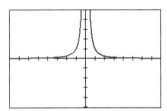

$D = \{x \mid x \neq 0\}; R = \{y \mid y \neq 0\}$
end behavior:
$$\lim_{x \to -\infty} f(x) = 0; \lim_{x \to \infty} f(x) = 0$$
one-sided limits for $x = 0$:
$$\lim_{x \to 0^-} f(x) = -\infty; \lim_{x \to 0^+} f(x) = \infty$$

$D = \{x \mid x \neq 0\}; R = \{y \mid y > 0\}$
end behavior:
$$\lim_{x \to -\infty} g(x) = 0; \lim_{x \to \infty} g(x) = 0$$
one-sided limits for $x = 0$:
$$\lim_{x \to 0^-} g(x) = \infty; \lim_{x \to 0^+} g(x) = \infty$$

VERTICAL AND HORIZONTAL ASYMPTOTES

The line $x = c$ is a **vertical asymptote** if $\lim_{x \to c^-} f(x) = \pm\infty$ or $\lim_{x \to c^+} f(x) = \pm\infty$.

The line $y = c$ is a **horizontal asymptote** if $\lim_{x \to -\infty} f(x) = c$ or $\lim_{x \to \infty} f(x) = c$.

A function of the form $f(x) = \frac{a}{(x - h)^n} + k$ where $n \in \mathbb{N}$ is a rational function that can be graphed as a transformation of a power function with a negative exponent.

Example 1   Graphing a Transformed Reciprocal Power Function

Identify the asymptotes of $g(x) = \dfrac{2}{(x-1)^2} + 3$. Then graph the function.

Answer

$g(x) = 2\left(\dfrac{1}{(x-1)^2}\right) + 3$

$\quad = 2f(x-1) + 3$

1. Express $g(x)$ as a transformation of $f(x) = \dfrac{1}{x^2}$. Note that

   $g(x)$ is $f(x)$ translated 1 unit right, stretched vertically by a factor of 2, and then translated 3 units up.

vertical asymptote: $x = 1$
horizontal asymptote: $y = 3$

2. Use the translations to identify the vertical asymptote and horizontal asymptote. $D_g = \{x \mid x \neq 1\}$ confirms the vertical asymptote.

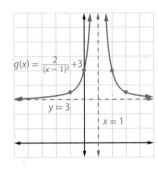

3. The graph of $f(x)$ has been stretched vertically from its horizontal asymptote by a factor of 2. Evaluating several points ensures an accurate graph.

Check

4. Confirm your results by examining the end behavior, $\lim\limits_{x \to -\infty} g(x) = 3$ and $\lim\limits_{x \to \infty} g(x) = 3$, and the one-sided limits at the domain's excluded value, $\lim\limits_{x \to 1^-} g(x) = \infty$ and $\lim\limits_{x \to 1^+} g(x) = \infty$.

SKILL ✔ **EXERCISE 5**

Rational functions that are not transformations of basic power functions can be graphed by identifying vertical asymptotes and point discontinuities, describing the end behavior, and identifying several strategic points before sketching the graph. Analyzing the discontinuities of a rational function $f(x) = \dfrac{a(x)}{b(x)}$ caused by the zeros of $b(x)$ is essential to understanding the shape of the graph.

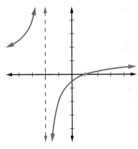

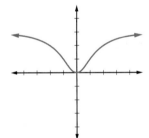

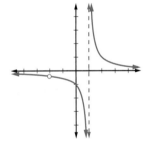

$$f(x) = \frac{x-1}{x+2} \qquad\qquad g(x) = \frac{3x^2}{x^2+2} \qquad\qquad h(x) = \frac{x+2}{x^2+x-2}$$

The function $f(x) = \dfrac{x-1}{x+2}$, which could be rewritten as a transformed reciprocal function $f(x) = \dfrac{-3}{x+2} + 1$, has an infinite discontinuity at its vertical asymptote, $x = -2$. Since the denominator in $g(x) = \dfrac{3x^2}{x^2+2}$ has no real zeros, it is a continuous function.

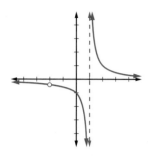

The numerator and denominator of $h(x) = \dfrac{x+2}{x^2+x-2}$ contain a common factor; therefore the function can be rewritten as a *reduced rational function* with a stated restriction on the domain:

$$h(x) = \dfrac{x+2}{(x+2)(x-1)} = \dfrac{1}{x-1}, \ x \neq -2.$$

This equivalent form of $h(x)$ indicates that the graph is a translated hyperbola that is undefined when $x = -2$. Therefore, the zeros of the denominator in $h(x) = \dfrac{x+2}{(x+2)(x-1)}$ indicate different types of discontinuity. The function has an infinite discontinuity at its vertical asymptote, $x = 1$, and a point discontinuity, or *hole*, at $x = -2$.

Discontinuities of $f(x) = \dfrac{a(x)}{b(x)}$	
vertical asymptote	at any zero of $b(x)$ without a matching zero in $a(x)$
point discontinuity	where zeros of $b(x)$ have matching zeros in $a(x)$

Example 2   Finding Vertical Asymptotes and Point Discontinuities

Identify the discontinuities in the graph of $f(x) = \dfrac{(x+3)(x-2)}{(x+3)(x-2)(x-2)}$.

Answer

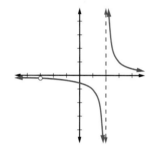

$f(x) = \dfrac{(x+3)(x-2)}{(x+3)(x-2)(x-2)} = \dfrac{1}{x-2}, \ x \neq -3$

$b(x)$: $x = -3, 2$ (multiplicity 2)
$a(x)$: $x = -3, 2$

1. Identify the zeros of $b(x)$ and $a(x)$.

point discontinuity at $x = -3$
vertical asymptote: $x = 2$

2. The zero of -3 in $b(x)$ is matched by a zero of $a(x)$, but one of the repeated zeros of 2 in $b(x)$ has no match in $a(x)$.

SKILL ✓ **EXERCISE 9**

The end behavior of a rational function can be described by a horizontal, slant, or non-linear asymptote, depending on the degrees of $a(x)$ and $b(x)$. In *proper rational functions*, such as $f(x)$ in the following table, the numerator's degree is less than the denominator's degree. In *improper rational functions*, such as $g(x)$, $h(x)$, and $j(x)$ in the following table, the numerator's degree is the same as or greater than the denominator's degree.

End Behavior of $f(x) = \dfrac{a(x)}{b(x)} = \dfrac{a_n x^n + a_{n-1}x^{n-1} + \cdots + a_1 x + a_0}{b_m x^m + b_{m-1}x^{m-1} + \cdots + b_1 x + b_0}$			
Comparison of the Degrees of $a(x)$ and $b(x)$			
$n < m$	$n = m$	$n = m + 1$	$n > m + 1$
horizontal asymptote		slant asymptote	nonlinear asymptote
$y = 0$	$y = \dfrac{a_n}{b_m}$	$y = q(x)$ where $\dfrac{a(x)}{b(x)} = q(x) + r(x)$	
$f(x) = \dfrac{x}{x^2 - 4}$	$g(x) = \dfrac{8x^2}{4x^2 - 9}$	$h(x) = \dfrac{x^2}{x + 1}$	$j(x) = \dfrac{x^3 - x^2 - x - 1}{x - 1}$

While a function's graph may cross a non-vertical asymptote (such as the graph of $f(x)$ above), these asymptotes indicate the function's end behavior. The horizontal asymptote of a proper rational function is the x-axis, $y = 0$. Improper rational functions having a numerator and denominator with the same degree have a horizontal asymptote $y = k$, where k is the ratio of the leading coefficients.

When the degree of the numerator is greater than the degree of the denominator, the asymptote is the quotient polynomial from the stated division (without any remainder). Completing the division in $h(x) = \dfrac{x^2}{x + 1}$ shows that $h(x) = x - 1 + \dfrac{1}{x + 1}$. Since the value of the fractional term gets closer to 0 as $x \to \pm\infty$, the function approaches the linear slant asymptote, $q(x) = x - 1$. Completing the division in $j(x)$ shows that $j(x) = x^2 - 1 - \dfrac{2}{x - 1}$ and reveals that the function approaches the parabola $y = x^2 - 1$ asymptotically.

The sketch of the graph of a rational function should indicate any asymptotes or point discontinuities and the x- and y-intercepts. The x-intercepts can be found by examining the zeros of the numerator, $a(x)$, and the y-intercept can be found by evaluating $f(0)$ when it exists.

After being taught from *The Coss*, Leonhard Euler wrote a complete algebra text intended for self-study in 1765. Since Euler had gone blind by this time, he dictated the book to a young man he had hired as a servant.

Example 3   Graphing a Proper Rational Function ($n < m$)

Graph $f(x) = \dfrac{x - 2}{x^2 - 5x + 6}$.

Answer

$f(x) = \dfrac{x - 2}{(x - 2)(x - 3)} = \dfrac{1}{x - 3}, x \neq 2$

vertical asymptote: $x = 3$
point discontinuity at $x = 2$

horizontal asymptote: $y = 0$

1. Find the excluded values of the domain and identify the location of any vertical asymptotes or point discontinuities.

2. Identify the horizontal asymptote of a proper rational function ($n < m$).

CONTINUED ➡

y-intercept: $f(0) = \dfrac{1}{(0)-3} = -\dfrac{1}{3}$;

$\therefore \left(0, -\dfrac{1}{3}\right)$

x-intercept: $a(x) = 1 \neq 0; \therefore$ none

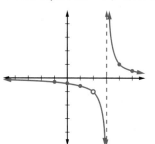

3. Identify any x- or y-intercepts.

4. Plot at least one point in each interval defined by the vertical asymptote. Using the reduced function allows you to find the exact location of the point discontinuity.

x	-1	1	2	4	5
$y = \dfrac{1}{x-3}$	$-\dfrac{1}{4}$	$-\dfrac{1}{2}$	-1	1	$\dfrac{1}{2}$

Note that $\lim\limits_{x \to 3^-} f(x) = -\infty$, $\lim\limits_{x \to 3^+} f(x) = \infty$, and the absence of any x-intercepts indicates that neither branch crosses the x-axis.

_____ SKILL ✔ **EXERCISE 29**

Example 4   Graphing an Improper Rational Function ($n = m$)

Graph $g(x) = \dfrac{1 - 4x^2}{x^2}$.

Answer

$g(x) = \dfrac{-4x^2 + 1}{x^2}$

vertical asymptote: $x = 0$

horizontal asymptote: $y = -4$

y-intercept: $g(0) = \dfrac{-4(0) + 1}{(0)^2}$; undefined.

$\therefore$ none

x-intercept: $a(x) = (1 + 2x)(1 - 2x) = 0$;

$\therefore \left(\pm\dfrac{1}{2}, 0\right)$

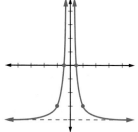

1. The zero of $b(x)$ is not a zero of $a(x)$, indicating a vertical asymptote.

2. When $n = m$, there is a horizontal asymptote at $y = \dfrac{a_n}{b_m}$.

3. Identify any x- or y-intercepts.

4. Plot at least one point in each interval defined by the vertical asymptote.

x	-1	1
y	-3	-3

Note that $\lim\limits_{x \to 0^-} g(x) = \infty$ and $\lim\limits_{x \to 0^+} g(x) = \infty$ and the x-intercepts indicate that each branch crosses the x-axis just once. Since $g(x)$ is an even function, its graph is symmetric with respect to the y-axis.

_____ SKILL ✔ **EXERCISE 33**

💡 **TIP**

Dividing to express $g(x) = \dfrac{1}{x^2} - 4$ illustrates that $g(x)$ is $f(x) = \dfrac{1}{x^2}$ translated down 4 units.

Example 5 Graphing an Improper Rational Function ($n = m + 1$)

Graph $h(x) = \dfrac{x^3}{1 - x^2}$.

Answer

$b(x) = 1 - x^2 = 0; x = \pm 1$
vertical asymptote: $x = \pm 1$

$$-x^2 + 0x + 1 \overline{\smash{)}\,x^3 + 0x^2 + 0x + 0} \quad \begin{array}{r} -x \quad\quad R.\ x \end{array}$$
$$\underline{-(x^3 + 0x^2 - \quad x)}$$
$$x + 0$$

$h(x) = -x + \dfrac{x}{1 - x^2}$

oblique asymptote: $y = -x$

y-intercept: $h(0) = \dfrac{(0)}{1 - (0)^2} = 0; \therefore (0, 0)$

x-intercept: $a(x) = x^3 = 0; \therefore (0, 0)$

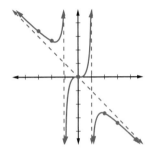

1. The zeros of $b(x)$ are not zeros of $a(x)$, indicating vertical asymptotes.

2. When $n > m$, complete the stated division to find $q(x)$, the equation of the oblique asymptote. Notice that as $x \to \pm\infty$, $\dfrac{x}{1 - x^2} \to 0$ since x^2 increases much faster than x. Therefore $h(x) \to -x$ as $x \to \pm\infty$.

3. Identify the x- and y-intercepts. Note that the origin is the only x-intercept and its multiplicity of 3 indicates that the graph crosses the axis at this point.

4. Plot at least one point in each interval defined by the asymptotes.

x	-3	-2	2	3
y	$\dfrac{27}{8}$	$\dfrac{8}{3}$	$-\dfrac{8}{3}$	$-\dfrac{27}{8}$

Note that $\lim\limits_{x \to 1^-} h(x) = \infty$ and $\lim\limits_{x \to 1^+} h(x) = -\infty$.

Since $h(-x) = \dfrac{(-x)^3}{1 - (-x)^2} = \dfrac{-x^3}{1 - x^2} = -h(x)$, it is an odd function whose graph is symmetric with respect to the origin.

SKILL ✔ **EXERCISE 35**

> **A. Exercises**

Identify any asymptotes and state each function's domain and range.

1. $f(x) = -\dfrac{1}{x^2}$ **2.** $f(x) = \dfrac{1}{x^3}$

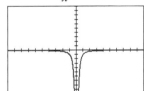   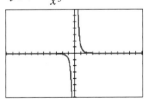

Identify the asymptotes and graph each function as a transformation of a reciprocal power function.

3. $g(x) = \dfrac{1}{(x + 1)^2} - 2$ **4.** $g(x) = -\dfrac{1}{x^3} + 1$

5. $g(x) = \dfrac{2}{(x - 3)^3}$ **6.** $g(x) = -\dfrac{1}{(x + 2)^2} - 1$

Identify any vertical asymptotes or point discontinuities of each function.

7. $f(x) = \dfrac{x - 2}{x^2 - 4}$

8. $f(x) = \dfrac{(x + 1)(x - 5)}{(x + 1)(x^2 - 10x + 25)}$

9. $f(x) = \dfrac{(x + 2)(x - 4)}{(x + 2)(x^2 - 16)}$

10. $f(x) = \dfrac{(x - 1)(x + 3)}{(x^2 - 9)(x + 3)}$

Match each description of a rational function $f(x) = \dfrac{a(x)}{b(x)}$ to the characteristic exhibited by its graph.
A. a zero at $x = k$
B. vertical asymptote at $x = k$
C. point discontinuity at $x = k$

11. A factor of $(x - k)$ in $b(x)$ is not matched in $a(x)$.

12. The factor of $(x - k)$ in $a(x)$ is not in $b(x)$.

13. All factors of $(x - k)$ are matched in $a(x)$ and $b(x)$.

Match each description of a rational function

$$f(x) = \frac{a_n x^n + a_{n-1} x^{n-1} + \cdots + a_1 x + a_0}{b_m x^m + b_{m-1} x^{m-1} + \cdots + b_1 x + b_0}$$ **to the character-istic exhibited by its graph.**

14. $n < m$

15. $n = m$

16. $n = m + 1$

17. $n > m + 1$

A. horizontal asymptote at $y = \dfrac{a_n}{b_m}$

B. horizontal asymptote at $y = 0$

C. nonlinear asymptote

D. slant asymptote

❯ B. Exercises

Classify each rational function as proper or improper. Then identify all asymptotes and any point discontinuities.

18. $f(x) = \dfrac{x}{x^2 - 9}$

19. $f(x) = \dfrac{x + 4}{x^2 - 16}$

20. $g(x) = \dfrac{x^2 + 4x + 3}{x^2 + 3x}$

21. $g(x) = \dfrac{6x^2 - 5}{3x^2 - 12}$

22. $h(x) = \dfrac{x^2}{x - 2}$

23. $h(x) = \dfrac{x^3}{x^2 - 1}$

24. $f(x) = \dfrac{x^3}{x + 2}$

25. $f(x) = \dfrac{x^3 + x^2 - 2x}{x - 2}$

Identify any asymptotes, point discontinuities, and intercepts for each function. Then use these characteristics to sketch its graph.

26. $f(x) = \dfrac{x + 1}{x^2 - 1}$

27. $f(x) = \dfrac{x + 2}{x - 1}$

28. $f(x) = \dfrac{3 - x}{x - 1}$

29. $f(x) = \dfrac{1}{x^2 - 4x}$

30. $f(x) = \dfrac{x + 1}{x^2 - 4}$

31. $h(x) = \dfrac{x^2 - 1}{x^3}$

32. $f(x) = \dfrac{3x^2}{x^2 + 2x}$

33. $f(x) = \dfrac{9 - x^2}{x^2 - 3x}$

34. $f(x) = \dfrac{x^2 + 2}{2 - 2x}$

35. $f(x) = \dfrac{x^3 - x^2 - 2x}{x^2 - 3x + 2}$

36. $f(x) = \dfrac{x^4 + x^2 - 2}{2x^3 + 4x^2 + 4x + 2}$

37. $f(x) = \dfrac{x^4 - 3x^2 - 4}{x^3 - 8}$

38. How does the graph of $f(x) = \dfrac{(x - 3)(x + 1)}{x + 1}$ compare to the graph of $g(x) = x - 3$?

39. Algebraically determine if the graph of each function is linear or parabolic. Explain your reasoning.

a. $f(x) = \dfrac{2x^2 + x - 15}{x + 3}$

b. $f(x) = \dfrac{2x^3 - x^2 - x}{2x + 1}$

40. Write a rational function with the given characteristics.

a. a horizontal asymptote at $y = 2$, a vertical asymptote at $x = -5$, and a point discontinuity at $x = 3$

b. a nonlinear asymptote, a vertical asymptote at $x = 1$, and a point discontinuity at $x = -2$

41. Model: The function $f(x) = \dfrac{5x}{x - 5}$ models the distance from a particular camera lens to the focused image in terms of the distance x (in centimeters) from the lens to the photographed object.

a. Use technology to graph the function. Then state a reasonable domain for the function.

b. State the equation of any asymptotes and explain their significance.

c. How far from the lens is the focused image when the photographed object is 2 m in front of the lens?

42. Model: Complete the following steps to derive and apply a function modeling the percent concentration of the resulting solution when x ml of pure acid is added to 150 ml of a 20% acid solution.

a. Write expressions for the amount of acid and the total volume of the final solution.

b. Write a function for the percent concentration of the solution. State a reasonable domain for the function.

c. Use technology to graph the function. Then state the equation of any asymptotes and explain their significance.

d. How many milliliters of pure acid must be added to reach a final concentration of 50%?

❯ C. Exercises

Identify any asymptotes, point discontinuities, and intercepts for each function. Then use these characteristics to sketch its graph.

43. $f(x) = \dfrac{x^3 - x^2 + x}{1 - x}$

44. $f(x) = \dfrac{2x^4 - x^3 - x^2}{2x^2 - 3x + 1}$

45. Explain: Why can every polynomial function also be classified as a rational function?

46. Reduce the rational function $f(x) = \dfrac{x^{n+2} + 2x^{n+1} + 4x^n}{x^{n+2} - 8x^{n-1}}$. Then state all asymptotes, point discontinuities, and intercepts of the function.

Add or subtract. [Algebra]

47. $\dfrac{a+3}{a^2-1} + \dfrac{2a}{a+1}$

48. $\dfrac{x+3}{x^2+3x-10} - \dfrac{5x}{x^2-4}$

Solve. [1.6]

49. $x^2 - 10x + 9 = -x^2 - 5x + 6$

50. $5x^2 + x - 3 = 0$

Let $f(x) = 3x^5 - 23x^4 + 61x^3 - 61x^2 + 8x + 12$. [2.4]

51. List all possible integral zeros.

52. Factor $f(x)$.

53. If $f(x) = -x^3 + 7$, what is $f(-3)$? [1.1]

   A. −2   **D.** 20

   B. 16   **E.** 34

   C. −20

54. Which of the following functions is both odd and continuous? [1.4]

   A. $y = 3x^2$ **D.** $y = 5$

   B. $y = \dfrac{6}{x^{-3}}$ **E.** none of these

   C. $y = \frac{2}{7}(x-3)^{-5}$

55. Which function has an inverse function? [1.8]

   A. $f(x) = 4|x|$ **D.** $y = \sqrt{16 - x^2}$

   B. $y = 6x^5 - 4x$ **E.** none of these

   C. $y = x^3$

56. Use technology to find the linear or quadratic function that best models the data. Round coefficients to the nearest thousandth. [1.9]

   A. $y = -0.010x + 3.904$

   B. $y = -0.092x^2 + 0.909x + 5.970$

   C. $y = -0.092x + 3.904$

   D. $y = 0.036x^2 + 0.410x + 3.904$

   E. none of these

x	y
−5	−1
−2	3
0	7
5	9
8	7
12	2
15	0

2.6 Solving Rational Equations

After completing this section, you will be able to

- solve a rational equation, identifying any extraneous solutions.
- use rational functions to model and solve real-life problems.

Rational equations such as $P(s) = \dfrac{1}{ms + b}$ are used to express the dynamics of an adaptive cruise control (ACC) system.

A *rational equation* contains at least one ratio of polynomials, $\dfrac{a(x)}{b(x)}$, where $b(x) \neq 0$. When solving a rational equation, multiplying both sides of the equation by the least common multiple of the denominators of the rational expressions (the LCD) eliminates the fractions. When an equation is multiplied by an expression containing variables, there is a possibility that you will introduce some answers that are not solutions of the rational equation. You *must* check for extraneous solutions resulting from such a multiplication.

Example 1   Solving a Rational Equation

Solve $\dfrac{3n}{n-5} = \dfrac{3n+1}{n-4}$.

Answer

$$(n-5)(n-4)\left[\frac{3n}{n-5} = \frac{3n+1}{n-4}\right]$$ 1. Multiply both sides by the LCD, $(n-5)(n-4)$.

$$3n(n-4) = (n-5)(3n+1)$$

$$3n^2 - 12n = 3n^2 - 14n - 5$$ 2. Simplify and solve.

$$2n = -5$$

$$n = -\frac{5}{2}$$

Check

$$\frac{3\left(-\frac{5}{2}\right)}{-\frac{5}{2}-5} = \frac{3\left(-\frac{5}{2}\right)+1}{-\frac{5}{2}-4}$$ 3. Substitute the answer into the original equation.

$$\frac{-\frac{15}{2}}{-\frac{15}{2}} = \frac{-\frac{13}{2}}{-\frac{13}{2}}$$

$$1 = 1$$

SKILL ✓ **EXERCISE 1**

A proportion, such as the equation in Example 1, is a special type of rational equation. In this case, setting the product of the extremes equal to the product of the means (cross-multiplying) quickly produces the same result as multiplying both sides by the least common denominator (LCD).

If $\dfrac{18}{x+3} = \dfrac{12}{x}$, then $18x = 12(x+3)$.

Example 2 illustrates another way of checking for extraneous roots. Any result that is an excluded value of a rational expression in the original equation is an extraneous solution and must be omitted.

Example 2   Using Domains to Identify Extraneous Solutions

Solve $\dfrac{x+2}{x-4} - \dfrac{30}{x^2 - 3x - 4} - \dfrac{4}{x+1} = 0$.

Answer

$\dfrac{x+2}{x-4} - \dfrac{30}{(x-4)(x+1)} - \dfrac{4}{x+1} = 0$

1. Factor the denominators to identify the LCD, $(x-4)(x+1)$.

$(x-4)(x+1)\left[\dfrac{x+2}{x-4} - \dfrac{30}{(x-4)(x+1)} - \dfrac{4}{x+1} = 0\right]$

$(x+1)(x+2) - 30 - 4(x-4) = 0$

2. Multiply both sides by the LCD to eliminate the rational expressions.

$(x^2 + 3x + 2) - 30 - 4x + 16 = 0$

$x^2 - x - 12 = 0$

$(x+3)(x-4) = 0$

$x = -3, 4$

3. Simplify the resulting equation and solve.

Check

$\dfrac{-3+2}{-3-4} - \dfrac{30}{(-3)^2 - 3(-3) - 4} - \dfrac{4}{-3+1} = 0$

$\dfrac{1}{7} - \dfrac{15}{7} + 2 = 0$

4. Since −3 is in the domain of each expression, it is not an extraneous solution.

If $x = 4$, two of the original expressions are undefined, so this solution is extraneous.

5. The extraneous solution is introduced in step 2, where both sides are multiplied by 0 when $x = 4$.

The only solution is $x = -3$.

_____ SKILL ✓ EXERCISE 17

Any rational equation can be expressed in the form $\dfrac{c(x)}{d(x)} = 0$. The solutions are then the zeros of $f(x) = \dfrac{c(x)}{d(x)}$. Adding the rational expressions in Example 2,

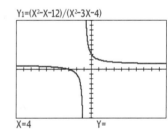

$\dfrac{(x+2)(x+1)}{(x-4)(x+1)} - \dfrac{30}{(x-4)(x+1)} - \dfrac{4(x-4)}{(x+1)(x-4)} = 0$

$\dfrac{(x^2+3x+2) - 30 - 4x + 16}{(x-4)(x+1)} = 0$

$\dfrac{x^2 - x - 12}{x^2 - 3x - 4} = 0.$

The graph of $f(x) = \dfrac{x^2 - x - 12}{x^2 - 3x - 4} = \dfrac{(x-4)(x+3)}{(x-4)(x+1)}$ indicates a zero at $x = -3$ and contains a point discontinuity at $x = 4$.

Example 3   Applying a Rational Equation

Find every number whose opposite is equal to the reciprocal of the sum of the number and 3.

Answer

$-x = \dfrac{1}{x+3}$

1. Let x represent the number and translate the statement into an equation.

$(x+3)\left[-x = \dfrac{1}{x+3}\right]$

$-x^2 - 3x = 1$

2. Multiply both sides by the LCD to clear the fraction.

$0 = x^2 + 3x + 1$

$x = \dfrac{-(3) \pm \sqrt{(3)^2 - 4(1)(1)}}{2(1)}$

3. Solve the resulting quadratic equation.

$= \dfrac{-3 \pm \sqrt{5}}{2} \approx -2.62, -0.38$

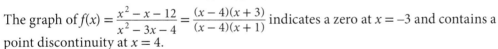

Check

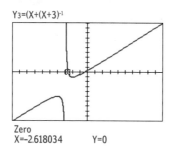

Y3=(X+(X+3)⁻¹

Zero
X=-2.618034   Y=0

4. The zeros of $f(x) = x + \dfrac{1}{x+3}$ confirm that these solutions are not excluded values for the rational expression.

SKILL ✓ **EXERCISE 23**

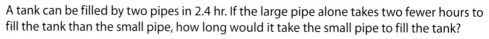

Rational equations are often used to solve problems involving the rate at which work is accomplished. If a job can be completed in 8 hr, the rate is $\dfrac{1 \text{ job}}{8 \text{ hr}} = \dfrac{1}{8}$ of the job per hour. The rate of working together is assumed to be the sum of the individual rates.

Example 4   Solving a Rate-of-Work Problem

A tank can be filled by two pipes in 2.4 hr. If the large pipe alone takes two fewer hours to fill the tank than the small pipe, how long would it take the small pipe to fill the tank?

Answer

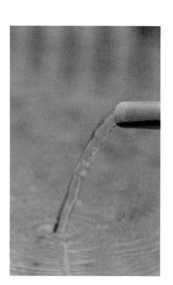

$$rate_{large} + rate_{small} = rate_{together}$$

$$\frac{1}{t-2} + \frac{1}{t} = \frac{1}{2.4}$$

$$2.4t(t-2)\left[\frac{1}{t-2} + \frac{1}{t} = \frac{1}{2.4}\right]$$

$$2.4t + 2.4(t-2) = t(t-2)$$

$$4.8t - 4.8 = t^2 - 2t$$

$$0 = t^2 - 6.8t + 4.8$$

$$t = \frac{-(-6.8) \pm \sqrt{(-6.8)^2 - 4(1)(4.8)}}{2(1)}$$

$$= 6, 0.8$$

The small pipe will fill the tank in 6 hr.

Check

$$\frac{1}{4} + \frac{1}{6} = \frac{3}{12} + \frac{2}{12} = \frac{5}{12} = \frac{10}{24} = \frac{1}{2.4}$$

1. Letting t represent the time it takes the small pipe to fill the tank, write an equation relating the rates of work.

2. Multiply both sides by the LCD.

3. Solve the resulting quadratic equation and interpret the answer.

4. A time of 0.8 hr for the small pipe would cause the time for the large pipe to be negative.

5. Substitute into the original equation.

SKILL ✓ **EXERCISE 27**

Some distance problems are solved by using $r = \dfrac{d}{t}$ or $t = \dfrac{d}{r}$ and then writing and solving a rational equation relating the rates or times of each part of a trip.

Example 5 Solving a Distance Problem

Due to construction, Sarah averages only 25 mi/hr during the first fourth of her drive from Tryon to Anderson. What average speed does she maintain for the rest of the trip if she averages 40 mi/hr over the entire trip?

Answer

Let d = the entire distance driven and r = Sarah's average speed for the rest of the trip.

1. Assign variables to represent the unknowns.

	Rate	Time	Distance
First Part	25	$\dfrac{\frac{1}{4}d}{25} = \dfrac{d}{4(25)}$	$\frac{1}{4}d$
Last Part	r	$\dfrac{\frac{3}{4}d}{r} = \dfrac{3d}{4r}$	$\frac{3}{4}d$
Total Trip	40	$\dfrac{d}{40}$	d

2. Using a table to organize the information, write simplified expressions for each time using $t = \dfrac{d}{r}$.

$$\frac{d}{100} + \frac{3d}{4r} = \frac{d}{40}$$

$$\frac{1}{100} + \frac{3}{4r} = \frac{1}{40}$$

$$400r\left[\frac{1}{100} + \frac{3}{4r} = \frac{1}{40}\right]$$

$$4r + 300 = 10r$$

$$300 = 6r$$

$$r = 50 \text{ mi/hr}$$

3. Write and solve an equation relating the times for the trip.

   a. Divide each term by d. Note that we do not need to know the total distance.

   b. Multiply both sides by a common denominator to clear the fractions.

   c. Solve the resulting equation.

Check

$$\frac{d}{\frac{d}{4(25)} + \frac{3d}{4(50)}} \cdot \frac{200}{200} = \frac{200d}{2d + 3d} = \frac{200d}{5d} = 40 \text{ mi/hr}$$

4. The average speed = $\dfrac{\text{total distance}}{\text{total time}}$.

SKILL ✔ **EXERCISE 31**

The universal consistency of arithmetical truths allows for diverse applications. From creating safer automobiles with adaptive cruise control to modeling motion, this consistency is an indicator of the "goodness" of mathematics.

❯ A. Exercises

Solve.

1. $\dfrac{x}{x-2} = \dfrac{x-4}{x-5}$

2. $\dfrac{3}{x} + \dfrac{x}{10} = \dfrac{11}{2x}$

3. $\dfrac{1}{x-8} = \dfrac{2x}{x^2-64}$

4. $x - \dfrac{10}{x} = -3$

5. $\dfrac{2x^2 + x + 2}{x^2 - 2x + 1} = 2$

6. $\dfrac{3}{4n^2 - 7n - 2} + \dfrac{2}{2-n} = \dfrac{4}{28n+7}$

7. $\dfrac{2}{r^2 + 3r - 4} = \dfrac{2}{3r+12} - \dfrac{r}{r-1}$

8. $\dfrac{6}{x-1} = \dfrac{x}{x+2} - \dfrac{18}{x^2+x-2}$

9. $\dfrac{11 - n^2}{3n^2 - 5n + 2} = \dfrac{2n+3}{3n-2} - \dfrac{n-3}{n-1}$

10. $\dfrac{1}{t^3 + t^2 - 25t - 25} + \dfrac{2}{t^2 - 25} = \dfrac{3}{t^2 + 6t + 5}$

Use technology to graph each rational equation and identify the real roots of the function. Round answers to the nearest thousandth.

11. $\dfrac{8x^2 + 2x - 5}{3x + 4} = 0$

12. $\dfrac{-2x}{x+4} = \dfrac{5.5x - 7}{x+5}$

B. Exercises

Solve.

13. $\dfrac{x+4}{x^2-1} = \dfrac{3x}{x+1}$

14. $x - \dfrac{1}{x} = -2$

15. $\dfrac{x}{x-3} - \dfrac{4}{x+5} = \dfrac{11}{x^2+2x-15}$

16. $\dfrac{y+2}{y} - \dfrac{y+1}{y-1} = 4$

17. $\dfrac{r}{r-5} = \dfrac{7r}{r^2-3r-10} - \dfrac{3}{r+2}$

18. $\dfrac{2}{x+3} + \dfrac{6}{x^2+3x} = \dfrac{2-x}{x}$

19. $\dfrac{x^2+3x-60}{2x^2+9x+4} = \dfrac{8x}{2x+1} - \dfrac{2x}{x+4}$

20. $\dfrac{3}{b} + \dfrac{5}{b-1} - \dfrac{6}{b-2} = \dfrac{-5}{b^2-3b+2}$

21. Explain what each type of solution of $f(x) = 0$ implies about the graph of $f(x)$.

   a. real solutions

   b. extraneous solutions

   c. imaginary solutions only

22. One number is three times another number. Find the two numbers if the sum of their reciprocals is $\frac{1}{6}$.

23. What number must be added to both the numerator and the denominator of $\frac{2}{17}$ to produce a fraction equivalent to $\frac{2}{5}$?

24. Find all numbers whose difference is 4 and the sum of whose reciprocals is $\frac{2}{3}$.

25. A number is 4 more than twice another number. Find all such numbers if the sum of their reciprocals is $\frac{1}{3}$.

26. Josiah and his younger brother Lucas volunteered to paint a community center. They did the job in 8 hr. Josiah could do the job alone in 12 hr. How long would it have taken Lucas to do the job alone?

27. Karleigh can detail a car in half the time that it would take her trainee, Mallory. Working together they can do the job in 40 min. How long would it take Mallory to do the job alone?

28. A swimming pool that usually takes 4 hr to fill took 6 hr to fill because a small drain was left open. How long would it take the drain to empty a full pool?

29. It took 18 hr to fill a tank when the drain was accidentally left open. Determine how long it normally takes to fill and to empty the tank if it normally takes 3 hr longer to empty the tank than it takes to fill it.

30. An avid cyclist sets out to break his personal record by averaging 20 mi/hr on a ride but realizes that he has averaged only 18 mi/hr at the halfway point. What will his average speed need to be for the second half of the ride if he is to meet his goal?

31. Two planes that fly at 600 mi/hr in still air leave the Kansas City airport in opposite directions. If the plane flying with the wind flies 990 mi in 20 min less time than the plane flying into the wind, find the wind speed.

32. Determine the average speed of a boat in still water if it makes a 280 mi trip downriver but takes an extra 8 hr to return upriver against a 2 mi/hr current.

33. **Analyze:** Explain the advantage of multiplying both sides of the equation in exercise 13 by the LCD instead of using cross multiplication to solve the proportion.

C. Exercises

34. If a flask in a medical lab contains a mixture of 5 cm³ of medicine and 11 cm³ of water, how much medicine must be added for the mixture to be $\frac{2}{3}$ medicine?

35. A circuit contains three parallel resistors of 10 ohms, 40 ohms, and 60 ohms. The total resistance for n parallel resistors is $\dfrac{1}{R_T} = \dfrac{1}{R_1} + \dfrac{1}{R_2} + \dfrac{1}{R_3} + \cdots + \dfrac{1}{R_n}$.

   a. Calculate the total resistance of the parallel resistors in the circuit.

   b. If a total resistance of 15 ohms is desired, what size resistor should replace the 10 ohm resistor?

36. Write a rational function $p(w)$ for the perimeter of a 100 ft^2 rectangle in terms of its width. Then use technology to graph the function and determine the minimum perimeter for such a rectangle.

37. Write a rational function $p(w)$ representing the perimeter of a 37 ft^2 rectangle in terms of its width.

   a. Find the exact dimensions of such a rectangle whose perimeter is 44 ft.

   b. Verify that the area of the rectangle is 37 ft^2.

38. A cyclist desiring to average 20 mi/hr during a training ride wants a function that expresses the required average speed during the second half of a ride based on the average speed to the halfway point.

   a. Write a function for the second half's average speed (r_2) in terms of the first half's average speed (r_1).

   b. Use technology to graph the function and to find the second half's averages for first-half averages of 15 mi/hr, 13 mi/hr, and 10mi/hr.

   c. State a reasonable domain for the function. Explain your reasoning

   d. State the equation and explain the meaning of any asymptotes.

CUMULATIVE REVIEW

State whether the value of $p(x) = (x + 1)^4(x - 2)^5$ changes its sign at the given zero. [2.2]

39. $x = -1$ **40.** $x = 2$

Use limit notation to describe each function's end behavior. [2.2, 2.5]

41. $f(x) = -3x^3 + 2x - 1$ **42.** $f(x) = \dfrac{2}{(x - 3)^5}$

Add or subtract. [Algebra]

43. $\dfrac{1}{x^2 - 9} + \dfrac{x - 3}{x^2 - 6x + 9}$ **44.** $\dfrac{x}{x^2 + 5x + 6} - \dfrac{6}{x^2 + x - 2}$

45. Find the slope-intercept form of the line passing through (1, 2) and perpendicular to $x + y = 3$. [1.2]

   A. $y = x - 1$ **D.** $y = x + 1$

   B. $y = -x - 1$ **E.** none of these

   C. $y = -x + 1$

46. Find a function rule for the relation containing $\{(-1, -1), (0, 0), (1, 1), (2, 8), (3, 27)\}$. [1.3]

   A. $f(x) = x$ **D.** $f(x) = [x]$

   B. $f(x) = -x^2$ **E.** none of these

   C. $f(x) = x^3$

47. Which is the inverse of $f(x) = \dfrac{1}{x + 5}$? [1.8]

   A. $f^{-1}(x) = x - 5$ **D.** $f^{-1}(x) = \dfrac{1 - 5x}{x}$

   B. $f^{-1}(x) = \dfrac{1}{x - 5}$ **E.** none of these

   C. $f^{-1}(x) = \dfrac{1}{5x}$

48. Which of the following statements about modeling with functions is true? [1.9]

   A. If $|r| > 0.5$, there is a strong linear correlation.

   B. The correlation coefficient is represented by r^2.

   C. The value of r^2 indicates the percentage of the variation in the independent variable that is explained by variation in the dependent variable.

   D. Outliers are points that do not seem to fit the trend of the scatterplot.

   E. all of these

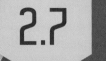

2.7 Nonlinear Inequalities

A polynomial inequality can be solved to find an acceptable range of values for the height of an origami box.

After completing this section, you will be able to

- solve polynomial inequalities.
- solve rational inequalities.

A *polynomial inequality* can be written in the form $p(x) > 0$, $p(x) \geq 0$, $p(x) < 0$, $p(x) \leq 0$, or $p(x) \neq 0$ where $p(x)$ is a polynomial function.

Since a polynomial function is continuous, a change in the sign of the function's value can only occur at a zero. Expressing the inequality as a polynomial on one side with 0 on the other allows us to use the zeros to define intervals for which the function takes on exclusively positive or exclusively negative values. A *sign chart* showing the sign values of the function over each interval can be used to state solutions to the following inequalities.

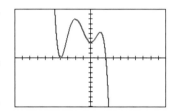

$p(x) > 0$ over $(-\infty, -4) \cup (-4, 2)$ $p(x) \geq 0$ over $(-\infty, 2]$
$p(x) < 0$ over $(2, \infty)$ $p(x) \leq 0$ over $[2, \infty)$

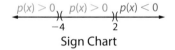

Sign Chart

By examining the sign of each factor for a single x-value in each interval, you can quickly determine the sign of the function's values over that entire interval.

Example 1 Solving a Polynomial Inequality

Solve $x^2 > x + 2$.

Answer

$x^2 - x - 2 > 0$

1. Express as an equivalent inequality in the form $p(x) > 0$.

$(x + 1)(x - 2) = 0$
The zeros are at $x = -1, 2$.

2. Solve $p(x) = 0$ to find the zeros of the function.

$$\underset{(-)(-)}{\overset{p(x) > 0}{\xleftarrow{\hspace{1cm}}}} \underset{-1}{)(} \underset{(+)(-)}{\overset{p(x) < 0}{\hspace{1cm}}} \underset{2}{)(} \underset{(+)(+)}{\overset{p(x) > 0}{\xrightarrow{\hspace{1cm}}}}$$

3. Make a sign chart by examining the signs of the factors within each interval.

   a. When $x = -3$, $(x + 1)$ and $(x - 2)$ are negative, $\therefore p(x)$ is positive over $(-\infty, -1)$.

   b. When $x = 0$, $(x + 1)$ is positive and $(x - 2)$ is negative, $\therefore p(x)$ is negative over $(-1, 2)$.

   c. When $x = 3$, both $(x + 1)$ and $(x - 2)$ are positive, $\therefore p(x)$ is positive over $(2, \infty)$.

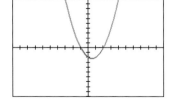

$x \in (-\infty, -1) \cup (2, \infty)$

4. State the solution to $x^2 > x + 2$.

Check

5. Note how the graph of $p(x) = x^2 - x - 2$ confirms this result.

SKILL ✓ EXERCISE 5

Recall that the graph of a polynomial function crosses the x-axis at zeros with odd multiplicity but touches the x-axis without crossing it at zeros with even multiplicity. There are no x-intercepts or sign changes associated with complex zeros. Combining these facts with the function's end behavior provides a second method of predicting the sign of the function's values over each interval.

Example 2 Solving a Polynomial Inequality

Solve $(2 - x)(x^2 + 1)(x + 4)^2 \leq 0$.

Answer

$x = 2, -4$ (multiplicity 2)
$x^2 + 1$ has only complex zeros.

1. Find the zeros, noting the multiplicity of any repeated zeros.

$\lim\limits_{x \to -\infty} p(x) = \infty$; $\lim\limits_{x \to \infty} p(x) = -\infty$

2. Note the end behavior of a fifth-degree polynomial with a negative leading coefficient.

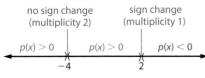

3. Make a sign chart using the end behavior and the sign changes indicated by the multiplicity of each real zero.

$x \in \{-4\} \cup [2, \infty)$

4. State the solution to the inequality.

Check

$$\underset{(+)(+)(+)-4 \quad (+)(+)(+) \quad 2 \quad (-)(+)(+)}{\overset{p(x) > 0 \qquad p(x) > 0 \qquad p(x) < 0}{\xleftrightarrow{\hspace{4cm}}}}$$

5. Evaluating when each factor is positive produces the same sign chart for $p(x)$.
   $(2 - x)$ is positive when $x < 2$.
   $(x^2 + 1)$ is always positive.
   $(x + 4)^2$ is never negative.

—————————————————————————— SKILL ✔ **EXERCISE 7**

The solution for a polynomial inequality where $p(x)$ has no real zeros is either the set of all real numbers or the empty set, $\varnothing$.

Example 3 Solving a Polynomial Inequality with No Real Zeros

Solve $4x^4 + 9 \leq -37x^2$.

Answer

$4x^4 + 37x^2 + 9 \leq 0$
$(4x^2 + 1)(x^2 + 9) = 0$
$x = \pm\dfrac{i}{2}, \pm 3i$

1. Find the zeros of the equivalent inequality in the form $p(x) \leq 0$.

$\lim\limits_{x \to \pm\infty} p(x) = \infty$

2. Note the end behavior of a fourth-degree polynomial with a positive leading coefficient.

∴ There are no solutions.

3. The end behavior and the fact that there are no real zeros implies that $p(x) > 0$ for all x.

Check

$4x^2 + 1 > 0$; $x^2 + 9 > 0$;   4. Examining each factor confirms that $p(x) > 0$ for all x.
always   always

—————————————————————————— SKILL ✔ **EXERCISE 29**

When solving a *rational inequality* (an inequality containing rational expressions), write the inequality with a single rational function on one side and 0 on the other. Since the value of a rational function can change its sign at either a zero or at a discontinuity, the zeros of both the numerator and the denominator are included in the sign chart.

Example 4 Solving a Rational Inequality

Solve $\dfrac{x}{x+3} \le -2$.

Answer

$$\frac{x}{x+3} + 2 \le 0$$
1. Express the inequality with 0 on one side.

$$\frac{x}{x+3} + 2\left(\frac{x+3}{x+3}\right) \le 0$$
2. Combine the terms to express the nonzero side as a single rational function, $f(x) = \dfrac{a(x)}{b(x)}$.

$$\frac{3x+6}{x+3} \le 0$$

zeros of $a(x)$: -2, a zero of $f(x)$
zeros of $b(x)$: -3, a discontinuity

3. Find the zeros of the numerator and the denominator.

4. Make a sign chart by examining values within each interval.

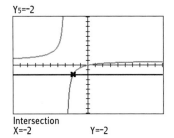

    a. When $x = -4$, both $(3x + 6)$ and $(x + 3)$ are negative.

    b. When $x = -2.5$, $(3x + 6)$ is negative and $(x + 3)$ is positive.

    c. When $x = 0$, both $(3x + 6)$ and $(x + 3)$ are positive.

$x \in (-3, -2]$
5. State the solution to $\dfrac{x}{x+3} \le -2$.

Check

6. Note how the graphs of $Y_1 = \dfrac{x}{x+3}$ and $Y_2 = -2$ confirm the result.

Y5=-2

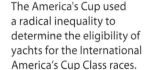

Intersection
X=-2   Y=-2

SKILL ✓ **EXERCISE 21**

Graphical solutions are used in many real-life applications of polynomial and rational inequalities.

Example 5 Applying a Rational Inequality

The Cantin Corporation is designing a 500 cm³ soup can. Find the range of possible radii lengths (to the nearest hundredth of a centimeter) for the can if its surface area cannot exceed 380 cm².

Answer

$$V = \pi r^2 H$$

$$H = \frac{V}{\pi r^2} = \frac{500}{\pi r^2}$$

$$SA = 2\pi r^2 + 2\pi r H$$
$$= 2\pi r^2 + 2\pi r\left(\frac{500}{\pi r^2}\right)$$
$$= 2\pi r^2 + \frac{1000}{r}$$

1. Letting r represent the radius of the can, find an expression for the height and surface area of the can in terms of the radius.

The America's Cup used a radical inequality to determine the eligibility of yachts for the International America's Cup Class races.

$$2\pi r^2 + \frac{1000}{r} \le 380$$

$$2\pi r^2 - 380 + \frac{1000}{r} \le 0$$

$$\frac{2\pi r^3 - 380r + 1000}{r} \le 0$$

2. Write a rational inequality modeling the restriction on the can's surface area and combine the terms on the left side.

CONTINUED ➡

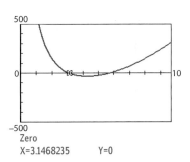

Zero
X=3.1468235   Y=0

$r \in [3.15 \text{ cm}, 5.71 \text{ cm}]$

3. Solve graphically using the zero option from the [CALC] menu.

SKILL ✓ EXERCISE 33

A. Exercises

Find the zeros for each polynomial function and then use a sign chart to determine intervals where the function's values are (a) positive and (b) negative.

1. $p(x) = (x + 4)(x - 3)$

2. $p(x) = (x + 2)(x - 1)(x - 3)$

3. $p(x) = (x + 3)^3(x - 1)^2$

4. $p(x) = (2x - 3)(x^2 + 1)(x - 3)$

Solve each polynomial inequality by factoring and using a sign chart.

5. $2x^2 - 11x - 6 \geq 0$

6. $x^3 - 2x^2 - x + 2 \leq 0$

7. $x^3 - 3x^2 + 4 < 0$

8. $x^4 + 4x^2 + 3 < 0$

Find the zeros and points of discontinuity for each rational function. Then use a sign chart to determine the intervals where the function's values are (a) positive and (b) negative.

9. $f(x) = \dfrac{x}{x - 2}$

10. $f(x) = \dfrac{x - 2}{x^2 - 1}$

11. $f(x) = \dfrac{x + 1}{5x^2 + x - 4}$

12. $f(x) = \dfrac{x + 5}{x - 1} - 2$

13. Which statements are true of sign charts?

   A. Unique linear factors change signs only once.

   B. The sign of the function must change at a point of discontinuity.

   C. Odd multiplicity of a linear factor implies a sign change.

14. At which value(s) is $f(x) = \dfrac{x + 1}{x^2 - 1}$ discontinuous?

   A. $x = 1$ **C.** $x = \pm 1$

   B. $x = -1$ **D.** none of these

B. Exercises

Solve each inequality using a sign chart.

15. $\dfrac{x - 3}{2x^2 - 3x - 9} \leq 0$

16. $\dfrac{x - 2}{x^2 - 9} > 0$

17. $\dfrac{x^2 + 5x - 14}{2x^2 - 5x + 2} \geq 0$

18. $\dfrac{x^2 + 2x - 15}{x^2 + 7x + 10} < 0$

19. $\dfrac{2x + 11}{x^2 + 3} \geq 1$

20. $\dfrac{x^2 - 10}{2x - 5} \geq 3$

21. $\dfrac{(2x + 1)(x + 2)}{(x + 5)(x - 1)} \geq 2$

22. $\dfrac{2x^2 - x - 27}{x^2 - x - 12} \leq 1$

23. $x^3 + 2x^2 > 8x$

24. $x^3 - 3x^2 + 3x - 1 < 0$

25. $2x^3 + 6 \leq 3x^2 + 11x$

26. $x^4 + 20 \leq 2x^3 + 15x^2 + 4x$

27. $x^4 + 2x^3 - 11x^2 - 12x + 36 \geq 0$

28. $2x^4 + 2x^3 + 4x \geq x^6 + 2x^5 + x^2 + 4$

29. $x^5 + x^3 - 4x < 4x^4 - 10x^2 + 8$

30. A church grounds crew is designing a playground whose area must be no more than 4000 ft². Find the largest possible dimensions (to the nearest foot) if its length is to be 10 ft longer than its width.

31. The Cantin Corporation is redesigning its large fruit cans to hold 3.6 L (3600 cm³). Find the range of possible radii lengths (to the nearest hundredth of a centimeter) for the can if its surface area cannot exceed 1325 cm².

32. The cost per square foot for a three-bedroom home in Denver, Colorado, between 2006 and 2016 can be modeled by the polynomial function
$f(x) = -0.0058x^4 + 0.58x^3 - 12.26x^2 + 92x - 41$
where x represents the number of years since 2000. Use technology to determine when the cost per square foot was less than \$185.

33. An origami gift box can be made by folding an 8" × 11" piece of cardstock. Find the range of possible heights for the box if its volume needs to be at least 55 in.^{3}

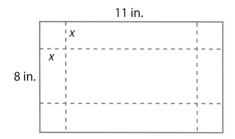

11 in.

8 in.

x

x

> **C. Exercises**

Solve each inequality using a sign chart.

34. $\dfrac{x+3}{2x+5} \geq \dfrac{x+2}{x-3}$

35. $\dfrac{x^2-49}{x^2-x-42} \leq \dfrac{6-x}{x^2+6x}$

Sign charts can be adapted for other types of inequalities. Use a modified sign chart to solve each inequality.

36. $\dfrac{x}{\sqrt{x+3}} \geq 0$

37. $\dfrac{2-x}{\sqrt{x-5}} < 0$

38. $\dfrac{x}{|x+3|} < 0$

39. $\dfrac{\sqrt{5-2x}}{|x-1|} > 0$

40. The formula $\dfrac{L+1.25\sqrt{S}-9.8\sqrt[3]{DSP}}{0.686} \leq 24.00$ m was used to determine the eligibility of a yacht for the International America's Cup Class races. In the formula, L is the rated length in meters, S is the rated sail area in square meters, and DSP is the volume of water displaced in cubic meters. Determine the minimum displacement for a yacht that is 25 m long with a rated sail area of 325 m^2.

41. An Internet company is planning a new cloud storage facility of at least 12 acres on their 800-acre campus. The engineers recommend that the structure have a length 150 ft longer than twice its width. Use the fact that 1 acre = 43,560 ft^2 to write a polynomial inequality modeling the area of the planned facility in square feet. Use technology to find the smallest dimensions for the storage facility (to the nearest foot).

42. Adam has decided that his rectangular cornfield will have a length twice as long as its width, with an option to add 50 yd to the length in later years. He eventually wants to plant 25 acres of corn. Write an inequality that would represent the total area of the enlarged field. Use technology to find the smallest dimensions that would meet the requirements. (1 acre = 4840 yd^2)

43. Graph the function $f(x) = \begin{cases} 2x^2 - 4x \text{ if } x \le 2 \\ 2 \text{ if } x > 2 \end{cases}$. Then state its domain, range, and whether it is continuous or discontinuous. **[1.3]**

44. Write $f(x) = -3x^2 + 12x - 9$ in vertex form and graph the function. **[1.6]**

45. Write the function rule and domain for $\frac{f}{g}(x)$ if $f(x) = x^3 + 3x^2 + 2x + 6$ and $g(x) = x^2 + 2$. **[1.7]**

46. Classify each statement as *always*, *sometimes*, or *never* true. **[1.8]**

  a. A relation has an inverse.

  b. A relation has an inverse that is a function.

  c. A function has an inverse.

  d. A function has an inverse function.

  e. A one-to-one function has an inverse function.

47. Complete a linear regression to find a model for the data. **[1.9]**

x	y
−3	−1
0	2
4	4
6	7
8	10
9	14

48. Use limits to describe the end behavior of $f(x) = -x^6 + 7x - 1$. **[2.2]**

49. Charles's law states that the volume of gas is directly proportional to the temperature of the gas (in Kelvin). A helium-filled balloon has a volume of 2.86 L at 293 K. At what temperature (to the nearest degree) will its volume be 2.72 L? **[1.4]**

  A. 292 K   **D.** 279 K

  B. 287 K   **E.** none of these

  C. 268 K

50. Which equation describes $g(x)$ as a transformation of $f(x)$? **[1.5]**

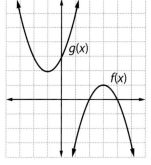

  A. $g(x) = f(x - 4) + 1$

  B. $g(x) = -f(x + 4) + 1$

  C. $g(x) = f(x + 4) + 3$

  D. $g(x) = -f(x + 4) + 3$

  E. none of these

51. Find $h(x) = (fg)(x)$ if $f(x) = \sqrt{x}$ and $g(x) = \sqrt{x^3 + 2x^2 + x}$. **[1.7]**

  A. $h(x) = x\sqrt{x^2 + 2x + 1}; D = \mathbb{R}$

  B. $h(x) = x\sqrt{x(x + 1)}; D = [0, \infty)$

  C. $h(x) = x(x + 1); D = [0, \infty)$

  D. $h(x) = x^2(x + 1); D = \mathbb{R}$

  E. none of these

52. Solve $\sqrt{x + 9} = x - 3$. **[2.1]**

  A. no solution   **D.** $x = 0, 7$

  B. $x = 0$ **E.** none of these

  C. $x = 7$

Year	Median Home Price ($1000s)	Year	Median Home Price ($1000s)
2000	149.8	2009	309.5
2001	157.4	2010	240.2
2002	176.7	2011	203.3
2003	205.5	2012	195.4
2004	243.4	2013	222.1
2005	310.2	2014	266.6
2006	392.1	2015	304.2
2007	445.1	2016	337.4
2008	425.6		

The Housing Market

To buy or not to buy? The prospect of purchasing your own home can be exciting, but it can also involve some risk. The housing market was booming during the years leading up to 2008. Then suddenly the market crashed, putting millions of individuals and businesses in financial jeopardy.

Some attribute the 2008 housing market crash to greed. As housing values increased in the early 2000s, lenders made riskier loans, some home buyers overextended their means, and speculators purchased homes hoping to make quick profits.

This feature examines several mathematical models of three-bedroom home prices in Miami, Florida, during the years before and after the market crash of 2008. Mathematical models of the housing market can provide insight into what will likely become your most significant financial investment.

1. Use technology to complete a scatterplot where x represents the number of years since 2000.

2. Although the plot clearly is not linear, a linear trend line indicates the general trend of prices over time.

   a. Find the linear function that best models the data.

   b. What does the slope of the trend line indicate?

3. Complete the following steps to find a better model for the pricing data.

   a. Would a quadratic, cubic, or quartic polynomial appear to be the best model for the graphed data?

   b. Complete a regression and state the polynomial function that best models the data.

   c. Recall that an outlier is an extreme or unusual value. The classification of a data point as an

outlier is often subjective and must be evaluated in context. Examining the scatterplot and the graph of the polynomial model, list several years that could be considered outliers.

As data analysis tools, mathematical models are used for much more than determining unknown data and making estimates and predictions. Models can help us evaluate when, how, and why certain events happened. Combined with wisdom and discernment, especially from God's Word, models can provide insights on the past and prepare us for the future.

4. Describe the end behavior of the polynomial model. What does its end behavior tell us about the reliability of the model outside the known data set?

5. Note the sharp increase before the relative maximum and the sharp decrease before the relative minimum. What events are indicated by this portion of the model? How might this have affected homeowners who had made recent home purchases?

6. Describe the characteristics of a model that would be realistic and useful for estimating home values outside the known data set.

7. What conclusions can be drawn about investing in the housing market by looking at the linear model? the polynomial model?

8. From your analysis of the polynomial model, when is the best time to buy a home? What other factors would a buyer need to consider?

9. Buying a home can be a good investment, but caution is important. Explain how Proverbs 22:3, 7 should influence your perspective when purchasing a home.

Chapter 2 Review

1. Which of the following are true for $f(x) = \sqrt[r]{x}$? [2.1]
   A. The domain of $f(x)$ is $[0, \infty)$ when r is even.
   B. The function $f(x)$ is an even function when r is even.
   C. The domain of $f(x)$ is $(-\infty, \infty)$ when r is odd.
   D. The function $f(x)$ is odd when r is odd.

Use technology to graph each function. State its domain, range, and the intervals for which the function is increasing or decreasing. State whether the function is continuous or discontinuous and whether it is odd, even, or neither. [2.1]

2. $g(x) = \sqrt[4]{x - 3} - 1$
3. $h(x) = x^{\frac{2}{3}} + 2$
4. Graph $g(x) = \sqrt[3]{x + 3} - 2$ as a transformation of a parent radical function. Then state its domain and range. [2.1]
5. Find the inverse of $f(x) = \sqrt{x} - 1$. Then graph $f(x)$ and $f^{-1}(x)$. [2.1]

Solve. [2.1]

6. $\sqrt{x + 4} + 1 = \sqrt{2x + 1}$
7. $\sqrt[3]{x^2} + 15 = 24$
8. Solve $m^2 = \sqrt[3]{\dfrac{rp}{g^2}}$ for p. [2.1]

Use the Leading Term Test to describe each function's end behavior. [2.2]

9. $p(x) = -x^3 + 2x^2 - x - 7$
10. $p(x) = x^6 - x^3 - 4$
11. Use technology to graph $p(x) = x^4 - x^3 - 3x^2$ and find the relative extrema. [2.2]

Factor to find all the real zeros of each polynomial function. Indicate any multiplicities greater than 1. [2.2]

12. $p(x) = 4x^2 + 12x + 9$
13. $p(x) = x^4 - 5x^2 - 24$

Identify each function's zeros, y-intercepts, and end behavior. Then sketch its graph. [2.2]

14. $p(x) = 2x^4 - x^3 - 6x^2$
15. $p(x) = -x^4 + 5x^2 - 4$
16. Use long division to find $(3x^2 + 7x - 5) \div (x + 3)$. [2.2]

Use synthetic division to find each quotient. [2.3]

17. $(2x^3 - x^2 - 5x - 1) \div (x - 2)$
18. $(2x^3 - 9x^2 + x + 12) \div (2x - 3)$
19. Use the Remainder Theorem to find the remainder when $p(x) = x^4 - 3x^3 + x^2 - 3x$ is divided by each binomial. [2.3]
    a. $x - 2$
    b. $x - 3$
    c. $x + 1$

Completely factor each polynomial function using the given information. [2.3]

20. $p(x) = 2x^4 - x^3 - 33x^2 - 56x - 20$ if -2 is a zero (multiplicity 2)
21. $p(x) = 27x^3 - 54x^2 + 36x - 8$ if $p\left(\frac{2}{3}\right) = 0$

Write a polynomial function of least degree with integral coefficients that has the given zeros. [2.3]

22. -2 (multiplicity 4) [2.3]
23. $\frac{1}{2}, -\frac{3}{4}$ [2.3]
24. Analyze $p(x) = 2x^3 - x^2 - 6x + 5$. [2.4]
    a. List all possible rational zeros.
    b. Use Descartes's Rule of Signs to describe the possible number of positive and negative real roots.
    c. Do the Upper and Lower Bound Tests show that all the real zeros are within $[-2, 2]$? If not, state and verify another integral interval that contains all the real zeros of the function.

Find all the zeros of each polynomial function. [2.4]

25. $p(x) = x^3 - 2x^2 - 5x + 6$
26. $p(x) = 2x^4 - 9x^3 + 17x^2 - 19x - 15$

Write a polynomial function of least degree with integral coefficients that has the given zeros. [2.4]

27. $2 + \sqrt{3}, -5$
28. $1, 3 + 4i$

Identify each function's zeros, y-intercepts, and end behavior. Then sketch its graph. [2.4]

29. $p(x) = x^3 - 2x^2 - 5x + 6$
30. $p(x) = -4x^3 + 4x^2 + 5x - 3$

Describe the rational function

$$f(x) = \frac{a(x)}{b(x)} = \frac{a_n x^n + a_{n-1} x^{n-1} + \cdots + a_1 x + a_0}{b_m x^m + b_{m-1} x^{m-1} + \cdots + b_1 x + b_0}$$

if its graph has the stated characteristic. [2.5]

31. a horizontal asymptote at $y = \dfrac{a_n}{b_m}$

   A. $n < m$ **C.** $n = m + 1$

   B. $n = m$ **D.** $n > m + 1$

32. a point discontinuity at $x = k$

   A. A factor of $(x - k)$ in $b(x)$ is not matched in $a(x)$.

   B. The factor of $(x - k)$ in $a(x)$ is not in $b(x)$.

   C. All factors of $(x - k)$ are matched in $a(x)$ and $b(x)$.

Identify the asymptotes and graph each function as a transformation of a reciprocal power function. [2.5]

33. $g(x) = 1 - \dfrac{1}{x^3}$ **34.** $g(x) = \dfrac{2}{(x-3)^2} - 4$

Classify each rational function as proper or improper. Then identify all asymptotes and any point discontinuities. [2.5]

35. $f(x) = \dfrac{x + 6}{x^2 - 36}$ **36.** $f(x) = \dfrac{x^4 + x^3}{x^2 - 4x - 5}$

Identify any asymptotes, point discontinuities, and intercepts for each function. Then use these characteristics to sketch its graph. [2.5]

37. $f(x) = \dfrac{x - 2}{x^2 - 4}$ **38.** $f(x) = \dfrac{x^2}{2x^2 - 2x}$

39. $f(x) = \dfrac{x^3 - x}{x^2 + 2x + 1}$

Solve. [2.6]

40. $\dfrac{x + 1}{x - 5} = \dfrac{x}{x + 3}$

41. $\dfrac{4}{n^2 - n - 6} + \dfrac{3}{n^2 - 2n - 3} = \dfrac{8}{n^2 + 3n + 2}$

42. $\dfrac{4}{2r^2 + r - 1} = \dfrac{1}{2r - 2} - \dfrac{r}{r^2 - 1}$

43. Find two numbers whose sum is 18 and the sum of whose reciprocals is $\frac{1}{4}$.

44. Olivia can process 300 applications twice as fast as Ava can. If they work together, they can finish the job in 8 hr. How much time would it take each of them to do the job alone?

45. A small outlet can drain a water tank in 8 hr. If a large outlet is also opened, the tank can be drained in 3 hr. How long would it take to drain the tank with just the large outlet?

46. A boat that travels 15 mi/hr in still water takes 40% more time to make a trip upriver than it takes to make the trip back downriver. Determine the average speed of the river's current.

47. Jen ran the first third of her race at 7 mi/hr (a pace of 8:34 min/mi). If her goal is to average 8 mi/hr for the race (a pace of 7:30 min/mi), at what speed should she run the rest of the course? What is the equivalent pace (in min/mi)?

Use a sign chart to determine the intervals where the function's values are (a) positive and (b) negative. [2.7]

48. $p(x) = (3x + 4)(x^2 + 2)(x - 5)$

49. $f(x) = \dfrac{(x + 3)}{(x - 1)(2x + 1)}$

Solve each polynomial inequality by factoring and then using a sign chart. [2.7]

50. $2x^3 + x^2 - 6x < 0$

51. $2x^4 + 68x \le 3x^3 + 24x^2 + 48$

52. $\dfrac{x^2 + x - 6}{x^2 - 9x + 14} \ge 0$

53. $\dfrac{x^2 + 16}{3x + 4} \le 2$

54. A large family-size box for Alge-Crunch cereal is being designed. The 12.5 oz box is 10" × 8" × 2" and the company wants to increase the dimensions as illustrated. Find the range of possible values of x if the volume of the new box is to be no more than 425 in.³ [2.7]

3 Exponential and Logarithmic Functions

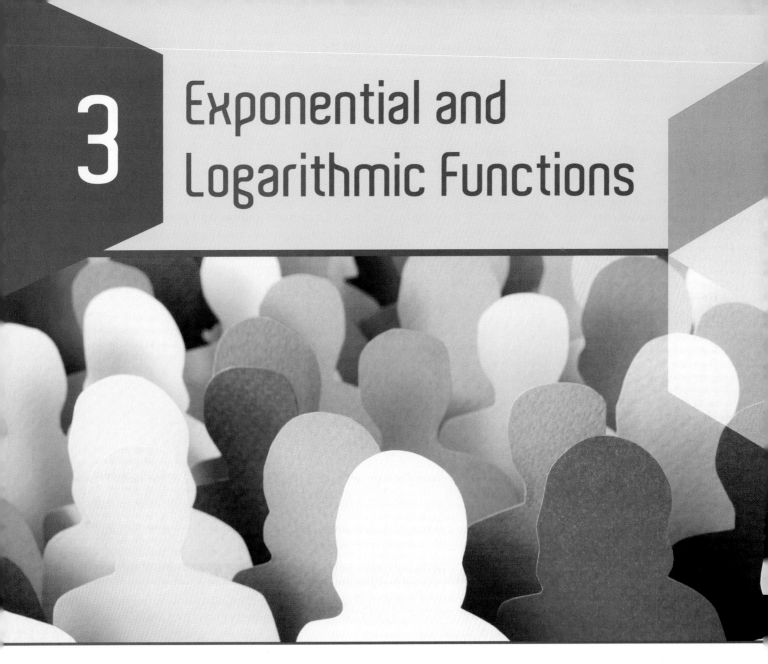

HISTORICAL CONNECTION

In 1919 the mathematical historian Florian Cajori stated that "the miraculous powers of modern calculation are due to three inventions: the Arabic Notation, Decimal Fractions, and Logarithms."

BIBLICAL PERSPECTIVE OF MATHEMATICS

John Napier, who developed logarithms, is a prime example of a man who recognized that his gifts were from God and used them in a conscious effort to serve others, thus bringing glory to God.

DATA ANALYSIS

While populations of living organisms may initially experience exponential growth, limited resources within their environments tend to restrict their growth. Is it reasonable to apply logistic functions and their carrying capacities to human populations?

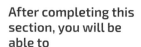

3.1 Exponential Functions

The resurgent population of bald eagles can be modeled using an exponential function.

After completing this section, you will be able to

- identify exponential functions.
- graph exponential functions.
- model and solve real-world problems involving exponential growth and decay.

In Chapters 1–2 we studied polynomial, rational, radical, and power functions with rational exponents. These *algebraic functions* involve only the algebraic operations of addition, subtraction, multiplication, division, and raising a variable to a rational power. In Chapters 3–5 we will study exponential, logarithmic, and trigonometric functions. These functions are called *transcendental functions* because they go beyond, or transcend, the basic algebraic operations.

While exponential functions may appear to be similar to power functions, they are distinguished by the location of the variable. In a power function the variable is in the base and the exponent is a constant. In an *exponential function* the base is a constant and the variable is in the exponent.

$f(x) = x^4$ is a power function with a degree of 4, and
$g(x) = 4^x$ is an exponential function with a base of 4.

> **DEFINITION**
>
> A function of the form $f(x) = ab^x$ where $a \neq 0$, $b > 0$, and $b \neq 1$ is an **exponential function** with base b.

The coefficient $a = 0$ is excluded since $f(x) = 0 \cdot b^x = 0$ is the zero function. The base $b = 1$ is excluded since $f(x) = a \cdot 1^x = a$ is a constant function.

Example 1 Graphing an Exponential Function

Graph each exponential function. Then state each function's domain and range, any asymptotes and intercepts, its end behavior, and the intervals in which the function is increasing or decreasing.

a. $f(x) = 2^x$　　　　　**b.** $g(x) = \left(\frac{1}{2}\right)^x$

Answer

1. Make a table of ordered pairs for each function.

x	$f(x)$	$g(x)$
-3	$\frac{1}{8}$	8
-2	$\frac{1}{4}$	4
-1	$\frac{1}{2}$	2
0	1	1
1	2	$\frac{1}{2}$
2	4	$\frac{1}{4}$
3	8	$\frac{1}{8}$

2. Plot the ordered pairs and draw the graphs.

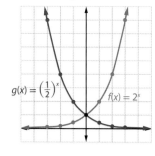

3. Analyze each function.

$f(x) = 2^x$	$g(x) = \left(\frac{1}{2}\right)^x$
$D = \mathbb{R}$; $R = (0, \infty)$	$D = \mathbb{R}$; $R = (0, \infty)$
y-intercept: $(0, 1)$	y-intercept: $(0, 1)$
asymptote: $y = 0$	asymptote: $y = 0$
$\lim\limits_{x \to -\infty} g(x) = 0$	$\lim\limits_{x \to -\infty} g(x) = \infty$
$\lim\limits_{x \to \infty} g(x) = \infty$	$\lim\limits_{x \to \infty} g(x) = 0$
increasing $(-\infty, \infty)$	decreasing $(-\infty, \infty)$

SKILL ✓ EXERCISE 7

The arithmetic operations of exponentiation and finding roots allow us to evaluate exponential functions, such as $f(x) = 2^x$, for rational values of x. For example, $f(3) = 2^3 = 8$ and $f(1.5) = 2^{\frac{3}{2}} = \sqrt{8} \approx 2.83$.

The fact that exponential functions are defined and continuous over the real numbers enables us to extend our evaluations to irrational values of x, such as $f(\pi) = 2^\pi$, using successively closer rational approximations of x.

x	3	3.1	3.14	3.141	3.1415	3.14159
$f(x)$	8	≈ 8.5742	≈ 8.8152	≈ 8.8214	≈ 8.8244	≈ 8.8250

You can see that $f(\pi) = 2^\pi \approx 8.825$.

Example 1 illustrates several general characteristics of exponential functions of the form $y = b^x$. Since $b^0 = 1$, the y-intercept of the graph is $(0, 1)$. There is no x-intercept since there is a horizontal asymptote at $y = 0$. If $b > 1$, the function is increasing and can model *exponential growth* with a *growth factor* of b. If $0 < b < 1$, the function is decreasing and can model *exponential decay* with a *decay factor* of b.

The fact that $g(x) = \left(\frac{1}{2}\right)^x$ is a reflection of $f(x) = 2^x$ in the y-axis can be verified algebraically by rearranging $g(x) = (2^{-1})^x = 2^{(-1)x} = 2^{-x}$. Exponential functions of the form $g(x) = ab^x$ are vertical stretches or compressions of the parent function $f(x) = b^x$ and have a y-intercept of $(0, a)$. Horizontal and vertical transformations are easily identified in functions of the form $g(x) = ab^{x-h} + k$.

Example 2 Transforming a Parent Exponential Function

Describe each transformation of $f(x) = 3^x$. Then sketch $g(x)$.

a. $g(x) = -2 \cdot 3^x$

b. $g(x) = 3^{x-2}$

c. $g(x) = 3^x - 2$

d. $g(x) = 3^{-x}$

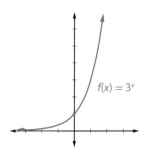

Answer

a. Reflect $f(x)$ in the x-axis and stretch it vertically by a factor of 2.

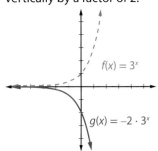

b. Translate $f(x)$ right 2 units.

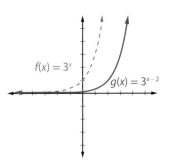

c. Translate $f(x)$ down 2 units.

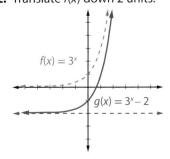

d. Reflect $f(x)$ in the y-axis.

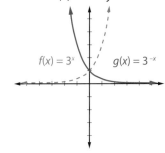

SKILL ✓ **EXERCISE 11**

Approximating e	
x	$\left(1+\frac{1}{x}\right)^x$
1	2
10	2.59374
100	2.70481
1000	2.71692
10,000	2.71814
$e \approx 2.71828$	

Many real-life instances of continuous exponential growth can be modeled using the irrational number e as the base. The *natural base* is defined as $e = \lim\limits_{x \to \infty} \left(1 + \frac{1}{x}\right)^x$ and $e \approx 2.71828$. The function $f(x) = e^x$ is called the *natural exponential function* and has several properties that simplify calculations done in calculus.

Example 3 Transforming the Natural Exponential Function

Describe each transformation of $f(x) = e^x$.
Then sketch the transformed function.

a. $g(x) = \frac{1}{4}e^x$

b. $h(x) = e^{-x} + 2$

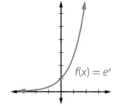

Answer

a. Shrink $f(x)$ vertically by a factor of $\frac{1}{4}$.

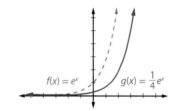

b. Reflect $f(x)$ in the y-axis and translate the result up 2 units.

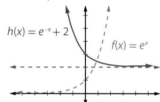

SKILL ✓ EXERCISE 17

Compound interest is modeled by an exponential function. While simple interest is paid only on the original investment, interest is frequently reinvested, or compounded, at the end of a given period so that in subsequent periods it earns interest along with the original investment.

Examine the account balance after t years when a principal P is invested at an annual interest rate r (frequently called the *annual percentage rate*, or APR) and is compounded annually.

Year	Balance
0	$A_0 = P$
1	$A_1 = P + rP = P(1 + r)$
2	$A_2 = A_1(1 + r) = P(1 + r)(1 + r) = P(1 + r)^2$
3	$A_3 = A_2(1 + r) = P(1 + r)^2(1 + r) = P(1 + r)^3$
$\vdots$	$\vdots$
t	$A_t = A_{t-1}(1 + r) = P(1 + r)^{t-1}(1 + r) = P(1 + r)^t$

The symbol e owes its acceptance primarily to Leonhard Euler. His first use of e occurred in a paper that he wrote at the age of twenty exploring the mathematics of cannon fire.

If the interest is compounded n times a year (quarterly, monthly, or daily),
the rate for each compounding period is $\frac{r}{n}$,
the number of compounding periods is nt, and
the function rule for the account balance after t years is $A(t) = P\left(1 + \frac{r}{n}\right)^{nt}$.

A formula for continuously compounded interest can be derived by letting $\frac{n}{r} = x$ and letting the number of compoundings per year approach infinity.

$$A(t) = P\left(1 + \frac{r}{n}\right)^{nt} \qquad\qquad \text{Note that } n = xr \text{ and that } \frac{r}{n} = \frac{1}{x}.$$
$$= P\left(1 + \left(\frac{1}{x}\right)\right)^{(xr)t} \qquad \text{Substitute.}$$
$$= P\left(\left(1 + \frac{1}{x}\right)^{x}\right)^{rt} \qquad \text{Power Property of Exponents}$$
$$= Pe^{rt} \qquad\qquad\qquad \text{definition of the natural base, } e$$

Compound Interest Formulas	
compounded n times annually: $A(t) = P\left(1 + \frac{r}{n}\right)^{nt}$	compounded continuously: $A(t) = Pe^{rt}$

Example 4 Compounding Interest

If $30,000 is invested at 6% APR, calculate the account balance after 15 yr with each compounding.

a. annually   b. quarterly   c. monthly

d. daily   e. continuously

Answer

using $A(t) = P\left(1 + \frac{r}{n}\right)^{nt}$:

a. $n = 1; A(15) = \$30{,}000\left(1 + \frac{0.06}{1}\right)^{1(15)} \approx \$71{,}896.75$

b. $n = 4; A(15) = \$30{,}000\left(1 + \frac{0.06}{4}\right)^{4(15)} \approx \$73{,}296.59$

c. $n = 12; A(15) = \$30{,}000\left(1 + \frac{0.06}{12}\right)^{12(15)} \approx \$73{,}622.81$

d. $n = 365; A(15) = \$30{,}000\left(1 + \frac{0.06}{365}\right)^{365(15)} \approx \$73{,}782.64$

e. using $A(t) = Pe^{rt}$: $A(15) = \$30{,}000e^{0.06(15)} \approx \$73{,}788.09$

SKILL ✔ EXERCISE 27

Some of the oldest cuneiform tablets contain problems related to the computation of interest. It is likely that the exploration of increasing compounding periods led to the first contemplation of e.

Populations and other quantities frequently experience exponential growth or decay, which can both be modeled as compounding annually or continuously where r is the *growth rate*.

Exponential Growth ($r > 0$) and Decay ($r < 0$) Formulas	
compounded annually: $P(t) = P_0(1 + r)^t$	compounded continuously: $P(t) = P_0 e^{rt}$

TIP

Since $f(x) = ab^x$ or $P(t) = P_0(1 + r)t,$ $P_0 = a$ and $1 + r = b.$

Example 5 Modeling Population Growth

In 1963 the US Fish and Wildlife Service counted 487 pairs of nesting bald eagles in the 48 contiguous United States. After being placed on the US endangered species list in 1967, their number increased to 3035 nesting pairs in 1990. Assuming exponential growth, find the average annual percent increase in nesting pairs from 1963 to 1990. Then use an exponential growth model to predict the number of nesting pairs in 2006.

Answer

$$P(t) = P_0(1 + r)^t$$
$$3035 = 487(1 + r)^{27}$$
$$\frac{3035}{487} = (1 + r)^{27}$$
$$\sqrt[27]{\frac{3035}{487}} = 1 + r$$
$$r = \sqrt[27]{\frac{3035}{487}} - 1$$
$$\approx 0.0701$$
or 7.01% annually

1. Let $t = 0$ in 1963 so that $t = 27$ in 1990, $P_0 = 487$, and $P(27) = 3035$.

2. Solve for r.

$$P(t) = P_0(1 + r)^t$$
$$P(43) \approx 487(1 + 0.0701\ldots)^{43}$$
$$\approx 8975 \text{ nesting pairs}$$

3. Substitute $t = 43$ and the unrounded annual rate of increase into the exponential growth function and evaluate. Using the rounded rate of increase produces a slightly different estimate.

SKILL ✔ **EXERCISE 31**

The speed at which a radioactive element decays is described by its *half-life*, H, the time it takes for half the radioactive isotope to decay into a stable isotope of another element. The number of half-lives in a given time period t is found using $\frac{t}{H}$, and the amount of the radioactive element remaining is modeled by the following exponential decay equation:

$$P(t) = P_0\left(1 - \frac{1}{2}\right)^{\frac{t}{H}} = P_0\left(\frac{1}{2}\right)^{\frac{t}{H}}.$$

The mathematical model makes several assumptions, including a constant rate of decay.

Example 6 Modeling Radioactive Decay

The half-life of carbon-14 (C-14) is estimated to be 5730 yr. Organic remains near Ale's Stones in Sweden have been used to date the monument near AD 600. Suppose a sample of the remains contains 68 mg of C-14.

a. Estimate the original amount of C-14 in the sample 1400 yr ago.

b. Predict the amount of C-14 remaining in the sample 50 yr from now.

These 59 large boulders, weighing up to 4000 lb each, form the oval outline of a ship that is 220 ft long.

TIP

Part *b* could also be solved by evaluating $P(50)$, using 68 mg as the initial amount of C-14.
$$P(50) = 68\left(\frac{1}{2}\right)^{\frac{50}{5730}}$$
$$\approx 67.6 \text{ mg}$$

Answer

a. $P(t) = P_0\left(\frac{1}{2}\right)^{\frac{t}{H}}$

$$68 = P_0\left(\frac{1}{2}\right)^{\frac{1400}{5730}}$$

$$P_0 = \frac{68}{\left(\frac{1}{2}\right)^{\frac{1400}{5730}}} \approx 80.5 \text{ mg}$$

Substitute the current amount, the number of elapsed years, and the isotope's half-life into the function modeling radioactive decay; then solve for P_0.

b. $P(1450) \approx 80.5\left(\frac{1}{2}\right)^{\frac{1450}{5730}}$

$$\approx 67.6 \text{ mg}$$

Evaluate $P(1450)$ using P_0 from part *a*.

SKILL ✔ **EXERCISE 33**

A. Exercises

1. Classify each function as a power function or an exponential function.
   - a. $f(x) = 7^x$
   - b. $g(x) = x^7$
   - c. $h(x) = \left(\frac{2}{3}\right)^x$
   - d. $j(x) = x^e$

2. Classify each function as modeling exponential growth or decay.
   - a. $f(x) = 2.4^x$
   - b. $k(x) = 35\left(\frac{1}{2}\right)^x$
   - c. $p(x) = 3 \cdot 5^{-x}$
   - d. $g(x) = 500(1.25)^x$

3. Evaluate.
   - a. $f(-1)$ when $f(x) = 3^x$
   - b. $p(3)$ when $p(x) = 4\left(\frac{1}{2}\right)^x$
   - c. $q(-2)$ when $q(x) = \left(\frac{3}{5}\right)^x$

4. Use a calculator to evaluate, rounding your answer to the nearest ten thousandth.
   - a. $g(0.001)$ when $g(x) = 4^x$
   - b. $h(\sqrt{3})$ when $h(x) = 2\left(\frac{1}{3}\right)^x$
   - c. $j(-e)$ when $j(x) = \left(\frac{5}{2}\right)^x$

Graph the following exponential functions by finding several ordered pairs. State each function's domain and range, then classify the function as exponential growth or decay.

5. $y = 3^x$
6. $y = \left(\frac{1}{3}\right)^x$
7. $y = 4^{-x}$
8. $g(x) = 2 \cdot 2^x$

Describe each transformation of $f(x) = 3^x$ and then graph $f(x)$ and $g(x)$.

9. $g(x) = 3^{x+3} - 2$
10. $g(x) = 2 \cdot 3^{x-4}$

Describe each transformation of $f(x) = 2^x$ and then graph $f(x)$ and $g(x)$.

11. $g(x) = -2^x + 3$
12. $g(x) = -\frac{1}{4} \cdot 2^{x-1}$

Write a function rule for $g(x)$, the described transformation of $f(x) = 3^x$. Then confirm your answer by graphing $f(x)$ and $g(x)$ in the same window.

13. $f(x)$ reflected in the y-axis and then translated 2 units up

14. $f(x)$ reflected in the x-axis, stretched vertically by a factor of 4, and translated 5 units to the left

Use technology to graph each function and then state its domain, range, intercepts, asymptotes, and end behavior.

15. $f(x) = 1.23^x$
16. $f(x) = -2\pi^{x-4} + 1$

B. Exercises

Describe each transformation of $f(x) = e^x$. Then sketch the graph and state the translated function's domain and range, any asymptotes and intercepts, and the function's end behavior.

17. $g(x) = e^{x-3} + 4$
18. $g(x) = -\frac{1}{3}e^{x+2}$
19. $g(x) = e^{4-x}$
20. $g(x) = 2e^{-x} + 1$

Describe the transformation of $f(x) = 2^x$ and then graph $f(x)$ and $g(x)$.

21. $g(x) = 3 \cdot 2^{x-3} + 1$
22. $g(x) = \frac{1}{3} \cdot 2^{-x} - 1$

23. Use technology to graph $f(x) = 2^x$, $g(x) = 3^x$, $h(x) = 5^x$, and $j(x) = 10^x$ in the same window. Describe the rate of growth in $f(x) = b^x$ in the first quadrant as b gets larger.

24. State the domain, range, and intercepts of the exponential function $f(x) = ab^x$.

25. Describe the end behavior of $f(x) = ab^x + k$.
   - a. when $a > 0$ and $b > 1$
   - b. when $a > 0$ and $0 < b < 1$

26. State whether each function represents exponential growth, exponential decay, or neither.
   - a. $y = ab^x$, where $a > 0$ and $b > 1$
   - b. $y = ab^x$, where $a > 0$ and $0 < b < 1$
   - c. $y = ab^{-x}$, where $a > 0$ and $b > 1$
   - d. $y = ab^x$, where $a > 0$ and $b < 0$
   - e. $y = ab^x$, where $a > 0$ and $b = 1$

Determine the account balance of each investment when compounded (a) annually, (b) quarterly, (c) monthly, (d) daily, and (e) continuously.

27. $10,000 at 1.25% annual interest for 5 yr

28. $4000 deposited at 6% annual interest in 2000 and withdrawn on the same date in 2042

29. From which bank will you earn more money in 8 yr if Bank A compounds monthly and Bank B compounds semiannually? Explain your reasoning.
   - a. if both banks offer the same interest rate
   - b. if Bank A offers 4% and Bank B offers 5%

30. In 2015 the average student loan debt was $30,000. How much will a student with this debt compounded daily at 6.3% APR owe if payment is deferred for 5 yr? for 10 yr?

31. In 1979 the Steller sea lion was placed on the endangered species list with an estimated population of 18,313 sea lions. It was removed from the list after the population increased to an estimated 70,174 in 2010. Determine the population's average annual rate of increase from 1979 to 2010. Then use an exponential growth model to predict the population in 2017.

32. A radiation source with an activity of 1 becquerel (Bq) transforms one nucleus per second. Scientists estimate that 800 terabecquerels (TBq) of cesium-137 (Cs-137) reached California in 2016 as a result of the 2011 Fukushima nuclear disaster. The half-life of Cs-137 is approximately 30 yr. Find the radiation emission of this amount of Cs-137 after 50 yr and after 150 yr.

33. The antibiotic ciprofloxacin has a half-life of 4 hr. If a patient is administered a dose of 750 mg at 10:30 AM, estimate the amount present in the patient's body at 1:45 PM.

34. If a culture of 250 initial bacteria doubles every 20 min, write a function modeling its growth. Then use the model to estimate the number of bacteria in the culture after each amount of time.

    a. 1 hr   **b.** 3 hr   **c.** 9 hr

Interest rates with different compounding periods can be compared using the *annual percentage yield* (APY). The APY is the equivalent annual rate for an investment at a given annual percentage rate (APR) compounded n times after 1 yr.

$$P(1 + APY) = P\left(1 + \frac{APR}{n}\right)^n$$

35. Solve the equation above to derive a formula for the APY. Explain why the APY does not depend on the amount invested.

36. Find the APY and account balance of a $3600 investment compounded daily at 6% APR after 5 yr.

37. Bobby is considering investing $50,000 in either a certificate of deposit at 2% APR compounded daily or a money market account with 2.25% APR compounded quarterly. Find the APY of both accounts and determine the difference between the investments after 10 yr.

C. Exercises

Use the properties of exponents to write each function in the form $y = a \cdot b^x$. Then state which functions are equivalent.

38. $f(x) = 4 \cdot 2^{2x}$, $g(x) = 2^{4x+2}$, and $h(x) = 4^{2x+1}$

39. $f(x) = \frac{1}{27} \cdot 3^{2x}$, $g(x) = \left(\frac{1}{9}\right)^{2x}$, and $h(x) = 3^{2x-3}$

40. Use technology to solve each inequality.

    a. $2^x < 3^x$ **b.** $2^x > 3^x$

41. Use technology to solve each inequality.

    a. $\left(\frac{1}{2}\right)^x < \left(\frac{1}{5}\right)^x$ **b.** $\left(\frac{1}{2}\right)^x > \left(\frac{1}{5}\right)^x$

42. Gail purchased a used car in 2012 for $12,500. After 5 yr Gail used an appraisal website to determine that the value of her car was $4555. Determine the car's annual rate of depreciation and estimate the car's value in 2020.

43. Ron is comparing two 3-yr-old used cars. Determine the depreciation rate for each car and each car's value 3 yr from now.

Car	Original Price	Price After 3 Yr
A	$19,190	$9970
B	$17,400	$8816

44. A metal bar at 875°C is placed in 20°C water to cool. Its temperature can be modeled using Newton's law of cooling: $T(t) = T_S + (T_0 - T_S)e^{-kt}$ where T_0 is the object's initial temperature, T_S is the surrounding medium's temperature (assumed to be constant), k is the cooling constant, and t is the time.

    a. State the equation modeling the object's temperature if the cooling constant $k = 0.1$ sec^{-1}.

    b. What is the temperature of the bar after 45 sec?

    c. Find the initial temperature of a second bar placed in the water if its temperature after 1 min is 22.3°C.

    d. State one factor that may cause this model to be inaccurate.

45. Write the equation of a line passing through $(-3, 1)$ and parallel to $5x - 8y = 10$. [1.2]

46. State another classification for any power function with degree 1. [1.4]

47. When is a quadratic function also a power function? [1.4]

Evaluate each function. [2.1]

48. $f(x) = x^{\frac{2}{3}}$ when $x = -27$

49. $g(x) = \sqrt[3]{x}$ when $x = \dfrac{8}{343}$

50. $h(x) = x^{\frac{4}{5}}$ when $x = 32$

51. Which of the following is equivalent to $\dfrac{5x\sqrt{54y}}{3\sqrt{6x^2}}$?
  [Algebra]

  A. $15\sqrt{y}$ **D.** $5y$

  B. $5\sqrt{y}$ **E.** none of these

  C. $\dfrac{5\sqrt{y}}{3}$

52. Which of the following functions is odd and increasing over the real numbers? [2.1]

  A. $f(x) = 3x^2$ **D.** $h(x) = x^{\frac{2}{3}}$

  B. $g(x) = -2x^5$ **E.** none of these

  C. $j(x) = \sqrt[3]{x}$

53. Which describes the end behavior of $f(x) = -4x^5 + 3x$? [2.2]

  A. $\lim\limits_{x \to \pm\infty} f(x) = -\infty$

  B. $\lim\limits_{x \to \pm\infty} f(x) = \infty$

  C. $\lim\limits_{x \to -\infty} f(x) = \infty,\ \lim\limits_{x \to \infty} f(x) = -\infty$

  D. $\lim\limits_{x \to -\infty} f(x) = -\infty,\ \lim\limits_{x \to \infty} f(x) = \infty$

  E. none of these

54. Which of the following is not a factor of $f(x) = x^3 - 3x^2 - 10x + 24$? [2.3]

  A. $x + 1$ **D.** $x + 3$

  B. $x - 2$ **E.** none of these

  C. $x - 4$

The magnitude of an earthquake is measured by the logarithmic Richter scale.

After completing this section, you will be able to

- convert between exponential and logarithmic forms of an equation.
- evaluate common and natural logarithms.
- graph logarithmic functions.
- model and solve real-world problems using logarithmic functions.

the exponent

$$y = \log_b x \text{ iff } b^y = x$$

the base   the number

Consider the graph of the exponential function $y = 2^x$. Since its graph passes the horizontal line test, the function is one-to-one and its inverse is also a function. Recall that the graph of a function's inverse is the reflection of the function across the line $y = x$, and that the function rule for the inverse is found by interchanging x and y and solving for y. Doing this with an exponential function, such as $f(x) = 2^x$, presents a challenge. How do you solve $x = 2^y$ for y? Logarithmic functions provide the means for solving such an equation.

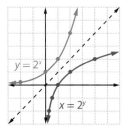

DEFINITION

A **logarithmic function** with base b is the inverse of an exponential function of the form $y = b^x$ where x and b are positive numbers and $b \neq 1$: $y = \log_b x$ if and only if $b^y = x$.

The notation $y = \log_b x$ is read "y equals the logarithm of x with base b." The base b logarithm of a number is the exponent when the number is expressed as a power of b. The logarithmic function $f(x) = \log_2 x$ is the inverse of the exponential function $f(x) = 2^x$.

Example 1   Evaluating Logarithms

Evaluate each logarithm.

a. $\log_2 64$ **b.** $\log_4 \frac{1}{16}$ **c.** $\log_5 \sqrt[3]{5}$ **d.** $\log_3 1$

Answer

Set each expression equal to y, convert it to exponential form, and then solve.

a. $\log_2 64 = y$
$2^y = 64$
$2^y = 2^6$
$y = 6$
$\therefore \log_2 64 = 6$

b. $\log_4 \frac{1}{16} = y$
$4^y = \frac{1}{16}$
$4^y = 4^{-2}$
$y = -2$
$\therefore \log_4 \frac{1}{16} = -2$

c. $\log_5 \sqrt[3]{5} = y$
$5^y = 5^{\frac{1}{3}}$
$y = \frac{1}{3}$
$\therefore \log_5 \sqrt[3]{5} = \frac{1}{3}$

d. $\log_3 1 = y$
$3^y = 1$
$3^y = 3^0$
$y = 0$
$\therefore \log_3 1 = 0$

SKILL ✔ EXERCISES 5, 9

The following properties of logarithms can be demonstrated by converting from logarithmic to exponential form, or from exponential form to logarithmic form.

Basic Properties of Logarithms

If x and b are positive numbers and $b \neq 1$,

1. $\log_b 1 = 0$ since $b^0 = 1$;
2. $\log_b b = 1$ since $b^1 = b$;
3. $\log_b b^x = x$ since $b^x = b^x$; and
4. $b^{\log_b y} = y$ since $\log_b y = \log_b y$.

The last two properties follow directly from the fact that logarithms and exponents with the same base are inverse functions of each other. These properties allow the evaluation of certain logarithmic and exponential expressions.

Example 2   Applying Properties of Logarithms

Evaluate each expression.

a. $\log_2 1$ **b.** $\log_7 7$ **c.** $\log_2 64$ **d.** $6^{\log_6 3.5}$

Answer

a. $\log_2 1 = 0$ **b.** $\log_7 7 = 1$ **c.** $\log_2 2^6 = 6$ **d.** $6^{\log_6 3.5} = 3.5$
     since $2^0 = 1$ since $7^1 = 7$

SKILL ✓ **EXERCISES 11, 13**

While the base of a logarithmic function can be any positive number except 1, base 10 is commonly used. The base 10 logarithmic function is called the *common logarithmic function* and is usually written without the base. Therefore, $y = \log x$ and $y = 10^x$ are inverse functions. The basic properties of logarithms apply to common logs.

1. $\log 1 = 0$ 2. $\log 10 = 1$ 3. $\log 10^x = x$ 4. $10^{\log y} = y$

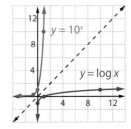

Common logs of powers of ten can be evaluated using these properties. The $\boxed{\text{LOG}}$ key on your calculator is used to find decimal approximations of other common logs.

Example 3   Common Logarithms

Evaluate each expression.

a. $\log 1000$ **b.** $\log 0.01$ **c.** $\log 4.39$

d. $\log \frac{1}{4}$ **e.** $10^{\log 63}$ **f.** $\log (-3)$

Answer

a. $\log 10^3 = 3$

b. $\log 10^{-2} = -2$

c. using your calculator: $\log 4.39 \approx 0.6425$

d. using your calculator: $\log \frac{1}{4} \approx -0.6021$

e. using inverse functions: $10^{\log 63} = 63$

f. Not a real number. Logarithmic functions have $D = (0, \infty)$.

Common logarithms are sometimes called Briggsian logarithms after Henry Briggs, the Oxford mathematician who published the first table of common logs in 1619.

KEYWORD SEARCH

common log table 🔍

SKILL ✓ **EXERCISES 19, 21**

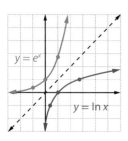

The inverse of $y = e^x$ is the *natural logarithmic function*, $y = \log_e x$ or $y = \ln x$, both of which are read "y is the natural log of x." The basic properties of logarithms apply to natural logs.

1. $\ln 1 = 0$ 2. $\ln e = 1$ 3. $\ln e^x = x$ 4. $e^{\ln y} = y$

The $\boxed{\text{LN}}$ key of your calculator is used to find decimal approximations of natural logs.

Example 4   Natural Logarithms

Evaluate each expression.

a. $\ln e^2$ **b.** $\ln e^{-1}$ **c.** $\ln 4.39$

d. $\ln \frac{1}{4}$ **e.** $e^{\ln 3}$ **f.** $\ln 0$

KEYWORD SEARCH

natural log table   🔍

Answer

a. $\ln e^2 = 2$

d. using a calculator:

     $\ln \frac{1}{4} \approx -1.3863$

b. $\ln e^{-1} = -1$

e. using inverse functions:

     $e^{\ln 3} = 3$

c. using a calculator:

     $\ln 4.39 \approx 1.479$

f. Not a real number. Logarithmic functions have $D = (0, \infty)$.

SKILL ✔ **EXERCISES 23, 25**

The fact that $y = b^x$ and $y = \log_b x$ are inverse functions can help when graphing basic logarithmic functions.

Example 5   Graphing a Logarithmic Function

Graph $f(x) = \log_3 x$.

Answer

Joost Bürgi, a Swiss clock maker, published a book of logarithms similar to John Napier's in 1620. The fact that Bürgi discovered the logarithmic calculation process independently points to a divine origin of mathematical truths.

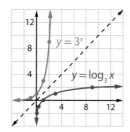

a. Make a table of values for the inverse function $g(x) = 3^x$, plot the points, and connect them with a smooth curve to graph the exponential function.

x	–2	–1	0	1	2
$g(x) = 3^x$	$\frac{1}{9}$	$\frac{1}{3}$	1	3	9

b. Since $f(x)$ is the inverse of $g(x)$, plot the ordered pairs $(g(x), x)$ and connect them with a smooth curve to graph the logarithmic function $f(x) = \log_3 x$.

c. Notice that the graphs are reflections of each other in the line $y = x$.

SKILL ✔ **EXERCISE 27**

$y = b^x$	$y = \log_b x$
$D = \mathbb{R}$; $R = (0, \infty)$	$D = (0, \infty)$; $R = \mathbb{R}$
HA: $y = 0$	VA: $x = 0$
no x-intercept; y-intercept: $(0, 1)$	no y-intercept; x-intercept: $(1, 0)$
contains $(1, b)$ and $\left(-1, \frac{1}{b}\right)$	contains $(b, 1)$ and $\left(\frac{1}{b}, -1\right)$

The graphs of other basic logarithmic functions with $b > 1$ have similar characteristics, while logarithmic functions with $0 < b < 1$ are rare. The graphs of logarithmic functions of the form $g(x) = a \log_b (x - h) + k$ can be drawn as transformations of the parent function $f(x) = \log_b x$.

Example 6 Graphing Transformed Logarithmic Functions

Describe the transformation of $f(x) = \log_3 x$ that produces each function. Then sketch both the parent function and the transformed function on the same coordinate plane.

a. $g(x) = \log_3 (x + 2)$ **b.** $h(x) = \log_3 x + 2$ **c.** $j(x) = -2 \log_3 x$

Answer

a. $f(x)$ translated 2 units left   **b.** $f(x)$ translated 2 units up   **c.** $f(x)$ reflected in the x-axis and stretched vertically by a factor of 2

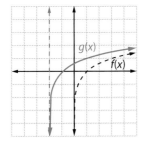 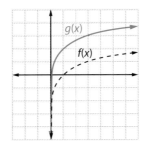 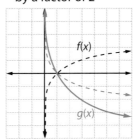

SKILL ✓ **EXERCISE 31**

It can be difficult to measure quantities that vary by extremely large amounts, such as the intensity of sound, the amplitude of seismic waves, or the concentration of ions in acids and bases. Logarithmic measures such as decibels, the Richter scale, pH, or pOH are used to describe the vast differences between measured quantities in terms of powers of ten or some other base.

Example 7 Applying a Logarithmic Measure

The Richter magnitude scale uses a logarithmic function, $R = \log \frac{A}{A_0}$, to compare the amplitude of an earthquake, A, to a small reference amplitude, A_0.

a. What does an earthquake measure on the Richter scale if its amplitude is 10,000 times the small reference amplitude?

b. By what factor was A_0 magnified in the 1964 Alaskan earthquake, which measured 9.2 on the Richter scale?

Answer

a. $R = \log \dfrac{(10{,}000\, A_0)}{A_0}$ 1. Find R when $A = 10{,}000 A_0$.

$\quad = \log 10{,}000 = \log 10^4 = 4.0$

---

b. $R = \log \dfrac{A}{A_0} = 9.2$ 1. Substitute for R.

$\quad \dfrac{A}{A_0} = 10^{9.2}$ 2. Convert to exponential form.

$\quad A = 10^{9.2} A_0$ 3. Solve for A in terms of A_0.

The earthquake's amplitude was $10^{9.2}$ (about 1.6 billion) times the reference amplitude.

SKILL ✓ **EXERCISE 39**

A. Exercises

1. Convert to logarithmic form.

   a. $5^3 = 125$ **b.** $8^2 = 64$

   c. $2^{-4} = \frac{1}{16}$ **d.** $\left(\frac{1}{3}\right)^2 = \frac{1}{9}$

2. Convert to exponential form.

   a. $\log_2 8 = 3$ **b.** $\log_5 25 = 2$

   c. $\log_{12} 144 = 2$ **d.** $\log_{\frac{1}{4}} \frac{1}{16} = 2$

3. Convert to exponential form.

   a. $\log 1 = 0$ **b.** $\log 1000 = 3$

   c. $\log 7 \approx 0.8451$ **d.** $\log 0.01 = -2$

4. Convert to exponential form.

   a. $\ln 1 = 0$ **b.** $\ln 5 \approx 1.6094$

   c. $\ln e = 1$ **d.** $\ln \frac{1}{e} = -1$

Evaluate each logarithm.

5. $\log_2 256$ **6.** $\log_4 64$

7. $\log_2 \frac{1}{8}$ **8.** $\log_6 \frac{1}{1296}$

9. $\log_7 \sqrt{7}$ **10.** $\log_2 \sqrt[3]{4}$

Use the properties of logarithms to evaluate each expression.

11. $\log_4 4$ **12.** $\log_5 1$

13. $2^{\log_2 \frac{1}{4}}$ **14.** $5^{\log_5 2}$

15. $10^{\log 0.001}$ **16.** $e^{\ln 1}$

Evaluate each common log. Round to the nearest ten thousandth if necessary.

17. $\log 10$ **18.** $\log 100,000$

19. $\log 0.0001$ **20.** $\log 25$

21. $\log e$

Evaluate each natural log. Round to the nearest ten thousandth if necessary.

22. $\ln 1$ **23.** $\ln \frac{1}{e^7}$

24. $\ln \sqrt[5]{e^2}$ **25.** $\ln 100$

26. $\ln \frac{2}{3}$

B. Exercises

Graph each logarithmic function. Then state its domain and range.

27. $y = \log_4 x$ **28.** $y = \log_5 x$

29. $y = \log_8 x$

30. Analyze: Compare the graphs of $y = \log_2 x$, $y = \ln x$, $y = \log x$, and your graphs from exercises 21–23. Describe the rate of growth of $f(x) = \log_b x$ beyond its x-intercept as the value of b increases.

Describe each transformation of $f(x) = \log_2 x$. Then use a graph of $f(x)$ to sketch the graph of $g(x)$.

31. $g(x) = \log_2 x - 3$ **32.** $g(x) = \log_2 (x + 2) + 4$

33. $g(x) = -\frac{1}{2} \log_2 x$

Write a function rule for $g(x)$, the described transformation of $f(x)$. Then confirm your answer by graphing $f(x)$ and $g(x)$ in the same window.

34. $f(x) = \log x$ translated 2 units left and 3 units down

35. $f(x) = \ln x$ translated 5 units left and then reflected in the y-axis

36. $f(x) = \log x$ reflected in the x-axis and translated 2 units up

37. Explain: Why is 0 not in the domain of $f(x) = \log x$?

38. Specify the intervals of x for which $f(x) = \ln x$ is (a) positive, (b) negative, (c) zero, and (d) undefined. Are these intervals the same for $f(x) = \log x$?

39. Example 7 illustrates how the Richter scale is used to compare earthquakes. Earthquakes with a magnitude less than 3.0 are often not felt, while the most severe earthquakes may measure 7.0 or higher.

Use $R = \log \frac{A}{A_0}$ to find the magnitude of the 2017 earthquake near Brenas, Puerto Rico, if its amplitude was 1200 times as great as A_0.

40. Model: Prolonged exposure to sounds greater than 85 decibels (dB) is known to contribute to noise-induced hearing loss. The loudness of a sound (in decibels) is calculated using $L = 10 \log \frac{I}{I_0}$, where I is the sound's intensity (in watts per square meter) and I_0 is the intensity of sound at the threshold of hearing.

  a. Find the missing measures to the nearest decibel.

Sound Source	Intensity (W/m²)	Loudness (dB)
threshold of hearing	10^{-12}	0
normal conversation	10^{-7}	
vacuum cleaner	10^{-4}	
symphonic orchestra	10^{-2}	
car horn	10^{0}	

  b. Prolonged exposure to which of the listed sound sources can contribute to hearing loss?

41. Students at Smithville High School took their statistics exam on January 5. Researchers found that when students took an equivalent exam t months later without studying, the average score could be modeled by the function $f(t) = 78 - 17 \log (t + 1)$ where $0 \leq t \leq 12$. Use the model to estimate the following average scores.

   a. the score on the original exam

   b. the score after 2 months

   c. the score after 6 months

❯ C. Exercises

Describe $g(x)$ as a transformation of $f(x)$, then use the graph of $f(x)$ to sketch the graph of $g(x)$. State the transformed function's domain and range, any asymptotes and intercepts, and the end behavior.

42. $f(x) = \log_2 x$ and   **43.** $f(x) = \log x$ and
    $g(x) = -\frac{1}{2} \log_2 (x + 4)$ $g(x) = \log (4 - x)$

44. $f(x) = \ln x$ and
    $g(x) = 2 \ln (-x)$

45. Explain: Determine whether the following statements are true or false. Justify your answers algebraically.

   a. $e^{\log 10^e} = e^e$ **b.** $\log_2 \frac{1}{2\sqrt[3]{2}} = \frac{4}{3}$

   c. $\log \frac{1}{\sqrt{0.00001}} = \frac{5}{2}$

46. Compare: Describe the relationship between the graphs of each pair of functions. Verify your answer algebraically.

   a. $f(x) = \log_2 x$ and $g(x) = \log_{\frac{1}{2}} x$

   b. $g(x) = \log_{\frac{1}{2}} x$ and $h(x) = -\log_2 x$

47. The number of months M required to repay a loan balance B at an annual percentage rate r with monthly payments of P is modeled by the equation

$$M = -\frac{\log \left(1 - \frac{rB}{12P}\right)}{\log \left(1 + \frac{r}{12}\right)}.$$ Determine the number of months required to repay a \$20,000 car loan at 6% APR for each payment amount.

P	M
\$300	
\$350	
\$400	
\$450	
\$500	

48. The number of years T that it takes to double an investment at a given annual percentage yield is given by the formula $T = \frac{\ln 2}{\ln (1 + APY)}$. How many years will it take Cathy to double \$100,000 invested in a certificate of deposit with each annual percentage yield?

   a. 5% APY   **b.** 3% APY

   c. 1.5% APY

CUMULATIVE REVIEW

Simplify each expression. [Algebra]

49. $3^x \cdot 81^2$ **50.** $2^x \cdot 16^{x+1}$ **51.** $\frac{128^{x+2}}{4}$

Solve. [2.1]

52. $\sqrt{2x + 5} = \sqrt{3}$ **53.** $\sqrt[4]{\frac{x}{2}} - 5 = -2$

54. $\sqrt{3x + 4} = x$

55. Which of the following is true if $(x + 2)$ is a factor of $p(x)$? [2.3]

   A. $x - 2$ is a factor of $p(x)$.   **D.** $p(-2) = 0$

   B. 2 is a zero of $p(x)$.   **E.** none of these

   C. The degree of $p(x)$ is at least 2.

56. Describe the possible number of positive and negative zeros of $p(x) = 2x^4 + 5x^3 - 2x^2 + x - 8$. [2.4]

   A. 1 positive zero; 1 or 3 negative zeros

   B. 1 or 3 positive zeros; 1 negative zero

   C. 0, 2, or 4 positive zeros; 0 negative zeros

   D. 3 positive zeros; 1 or 3 negative zeros

   E. none of these

57. Which of the following functions represents exponential growth? [3.1]

   A. $f(x) = 3 \cdot \left(\frac{1}{5}\right)^x$ **D.** $j(x) = 3 \cdot 5^{-x}$

   B. $g(x) = 3 \cdot (-5)^x$ **E.** none of these

   C. $h(x) = 3 \cdot 5^x$

58. If \$20,000 is invested at 3% APR, which of the following represents the account balance after 10 yr compounding monthly? [3.1]

   A. \$26,878.33   **D.** \$26,997.18

   B. \$26,970.46   **E.** none of these

   C. \$26,987.07

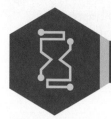

NAPIER'S ARTIFICIAL NUMBERS

Imagine an invention that would allow you to work twice as fast as you do now. That would mean two-and-a-half day school weeks, a two-year college degree, and twenty-hour work weeks!

The logarithms proposed by John Napier seemed almost this revolutionary to the mathematicians and astronomers who lauded their introduction. Johannes Kepler, who discovered laws describing the elliptical orbits of planets, even dedicated one of his published works to Napier in praise of his logarithms. Such enthusiasm is understandable, considering the tedious and error-prone nature of multiplying, dividing, and extracting roots of very large numbers by hand.

Napier did not "stumble upon" his discovery, but rather set out purposefully to ease the burden of calculating products, quotients, powers, and roots of large numbers. While developing his ideas and tables over the course of twenty years, Napier initially called his logarithms "artificial numbers" but coined the term *logarithms* from the Greek words *logos* (ratio) and *arithmos* (number) before publishing his results in 1614.

Rather than thinking in terms of the inverses of exponential functions, Napier developed logarithms by noting the

relationship between arithmetic and geometric sequences. In fact, the historian Florian Cajori says, "It is one of the greatest curiosities of the history of science that Napier constructed logarithms before exponents were used."

Before Napier invented his logarithms, the method of prosthaphaeresis was used to convert multiplication to addition by means of a trigonometric equation. The Danish astronomer Tycho Brahe and his assistant Paul Wittich simplified calculations with the formula $2 \sin A \sin B = \cos (A - B) - \cos (A + B)$.

While history remembers Napier for his logarithms, his first book, published in 1593, was a commentary titled *A Plaine Discovery of the whole Revelation of Saint John*. He believed this was his most important work and the one for which he would be remembered. Using mathematics and reasoning, he constructed a chronology of the events in Revelation and predicted that the Second Coming of Christ and the destruction of the world would occur in 1688. Napier dedicated his book to the Scottish ruler King James VI (who would later commission the King James Version of the Bible), but the dedication was dropped after the king ignored Napier's encouragement to purge the court of ungodly influences.

The English mathematician Henry Briggs was so fascinated by Napier's logarithms that he made a difficult four-day journey to meet with him personally in 1615. Briggs and Napier eventually agreed that the most useful logarithmic system would be based on the powers of ten, where log 10 = 1 and log 1 = 0. Due to Napier's failing health, the completion of the resulting logarithmic tables was left to Briggs, who published them in 1617. These tables endured as the primary means of calculation for more than three and a half centuries until they and calculating devices that used them (such as slide rules) were replaced by computers and handheld calculators.

You guys sure are eccentric!

COMPREHENSION CHECK

1. Name the two men most responsible for developing logarithms.

2. What is prosthaphaeresis?

3. What was the subject of Napier's first published book?

4. Why were logarithms so readily accepted and frequently utilized for hundreds of years?

5. **Discuss:** Referencing Matthew 24:36, evaluate Napier's attempt to decode a mathematical system in Revelation to predict the date of Christ's return. Did he approach his study of Revelation appropriately? Why or why not?

Properties of Logarithms

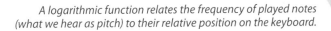

A logarithmic function relates the frequency of played notes (what we hear as pitch) to their relative position on the keyboard.

The properties of logarithms have historically been used to simplify complicated products, quotients, powers, and roots. While calculators now assist us with these tasks, these properties still have other practical applications. Because logarithms are the exponents when numbers are expressed as a power of the given base, their properties follow directly from the properties of exponents.

Property	of Logarithms*	of Exponents
Equality	$\log_b m = \log_b n$ iff $m = n$	$b^m = b^n$ iff $m = n$
Product	$\log_b mn = \log_b m + \log_b n$	$b^m \cdot b^n = b^{m+n}$
Quotient	$\log_b \frac{m}{n} = \log_b m - \log_b n$	$\frac{b^m}{b^n} = b^{m-n}$
Power	$\log_b m^p = p \log_b m$	$(b^m)^p = b^{mp}$

*where $m > 0$ and $n > 0$

The Product Property of Logarithms is derived from the Product Property of Exponents.

Let $\log_b m = x$ and $\log_b n = y$.

$\quad b^x = m$ and $b^y = n$ Convert to exponential form.
$\quad mn = b^x \cdot b^y$ Substitute.
$\quad mn = b^{x+y}$ Product Property of Exponents
$\log_b mn = x + y$ Convert to logarithmic form.
$\log_b mn = \log_b m + \log_b n$ Substitute.

These properties can be used to expand logarithmic expressions, converting multiplication and division into addition and subtraction and converting the evaluation of powers and roots into multiplication and division.

Example 1 Expanding a Logarithmic Expression

Expand each logarithmic expression.

a. $\log \dfrac{a^2 b}{c^4}$ **b.** $\ln \dfrac{\sqrt[3]{2c - 1}}{b^2}$

Answer

a. $\log \dfrac{a^2 b}{c^4} = \log a^2 b - \log c^4$ 1. Quotient Property

$\qquad\qquad\ = \log a^2 + \log b - \log c^4$ 2. Product Property

$\qquad\qquad\ = 2 \log a + \log b - 4 \log c$ 3. Power Property

---

b. $\ln \dfrac{\sqrt[3]{2c - 1}}{b^2} = \ln (2c - 1)^{\frac{1}{3}} - \ln b^2$ 1. Quotient Property

$\qquad\qquad\qquad = \frac{1}{3} \ln (2c - 1) - 2 \ln b$ 2. Product Property; Note that $\ln (2c - 1)$ cannot be further expanded.

SKILL ✓ EXERCISE 5

After completing this section, you will be able to

- evaluate, expand, and condense logarithmic expressions.
- use the change of base formula.
- model and solve real-world problems using logarithmic functions.

Before devising his logarithms, John Napier designed a system of rods imprinted with numbers that could be arranged in sequence to aid in multiplication. These popular seventeenth-century computing devices were called "Napier's Bones" because of their appearance.

KEYWORD SEARCH

Napier's Bones   🔍

An expression involving logarithms may need to be expressed as a single logarithm.

Example 2   Condensing a Logarithmic Expression

Write each expression as a single logarithm.

a. $3 \log ab - \frac{1}{2} \log c$ **b.** $\ln (b + 1) + 5 \ln b$

Answer

a. $3 \log ab - \frac{1}{2} \log c$

$= \log (ab)^3 - \log c^{\frac{1}{2}}$ 1. Power Property

$= \log \frac{(ab)^3}{\sqrt{c}}$ or $\log \frac{a^3 b^3}{\sqrt{c}}$ 2. Quotient Property

b. $\ln (b + 1) + 5 \ln b$

$= \ln (b + 1) + \ln b^5$ 1. Power Property

$= \ln b^5(b + 1)$ or $\ln (b^6 + b^5)$ 2. Product Property

SKILL ✓ **EXERCISE 9**

These properties allow logarithms to be expressed in terms of other logarithms. This skill is critical when solving logarithmic equations.

Example 3   Applying Properties of Logarithms

Using $\log_7 2 \approx 0.3562$ and $\log_7 3 \approx 0.5646$, find a decimal approximation of each logarithm.

a. $\log_7 12$ **b.** $\log_7 \frac{49 \sqrt{3}}{2}$

Answer

a. $\log_7 12 = \log_7 (2^2 \cdot 3)$
$= \log_7 2^2 + \log_7 3$
$= 2 \log_7 2 + \log_7 3$
$\approx 2(0.3652) + 0.5646$
$= 1.2950$

b. $\log_7 \frac{49 \sqrt{3}}{2} = \log_7 7^2 + \log_7 3^{\frac{1}{2}} - \log_7 2$
$= 2 \log_7 7 + \frac{1}{2} \log_7 3 - \log_7 2$
$\approx 2(1) + \frac{1}{2}(0.5646) - (0.3562)$
$= 1.9261$

SKILL ✓ **EXERCISE 23**

Working with logarithms with bases other then 10 or e can be difficult since most calculators have only [LOG] and [LN] keys. Converting $\log_3 8 = y$ to exponential form and rewriting it in terms of common logs enables us to find a decimal approximation of the logarithm.

Let $\log_3 8 = y$.

$3^y = 8$ Convert to exponential form.
$\log 3^y = \log 8$ Equality Property of Logarithms
$y \log 3 = \log 8$ Power Property of Logarithms
$y = \dfrac{\log 8}{\log 3}$ Multiplication Property of Equality
≈ 1.8928 Evaluate using technology.

Generalizing this process produces a formula that converts a logarithmic expression into one with a more convenient base.

CHANGE OF BASE FORMULA

For positive a, b, and x with $a \neq 1$ and $b \neq 1$, $\log_b x = \dfrac{\log_a x}{\log_a b}$.

Logs of other bases are usually converted to common or natural logs.

$$\log_b x = \frac{\log x}{\log b} \quad \text{or} \quad \log_b x = \frac{\ln x}{\ln b}$$

Example 4 Applying the Change of Base Formula

Find $\log_2 5.89$.

a. using common logs

b. using natural logs

Answer

a. $\log_2 5.89 = \dfrac{\log 5.89}{\log 2}$

≈ 2.5583

b. $\log_2 5.89 = \dfrac{\ln 5.89}{\ln 2}$

≈ 2.5583

Check

Use technology to verify that $2^{2.5583} \approx 5.89$.

SKILL ✓ **EXERCISE 15**

The change of base formula can be used to show that the graph of any logarithmic function $g(x) = \log_b x$ is a vertical stretch or shrink of $f(x) = \ln x$ by a factor of $\dfrac{1}{\ln b}$.

$$g(x) = \log_b x = \frac{\ln x}{\ln b} = \left(\frac{1}{\ln b} \right) \ln x$$

Example 5 Graphing Base b Logarithmic Functions

Describe how the graph of $f(x) = \ln x$ is transformed to obtain the graph of each function.

a. $g(x) = \log_7 x$

b. $h(x) = \log_{\frac{1}{7}} x$

Answer

a. Using the change of base formula, $g(x) = \log_7 x = \dfrac{1}{\ln 7} \ln x$.

Therefore, $g(x)$ is a vertical shrink of $f(x)$ by a factor of $\dfrac{1}{\ln 7} \approx 0.5$.

b. $h(x) = \log_{\frac{1}{7}} x$

$= \dfrac{\ln x}{\ln \frac{1}{7}} = \dfrac{1}{\ln 7^{-1}} \ln x$ change of base formula

$= \dfrac{1}{-\ln 7} \ln x$ Power Property of Logarithms

Therefore, $h(x)$ is a vertical shrink of $f(x)$ by a factor of $\dfrac{1}{\ln 7} \approx 0.5$ that is reflected in the x-axis.

Check

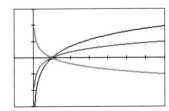

Use technology to graph and compare the functions.

$Y_1 = \ln(X)$

$Y_2 = \ln(X)/\ln(7)$

$Y_3 = \ln(X)/\ln(1/7)$

SKILL ✓ **EXERCISE 33**

Note that $\log_{\frac{1}{7}} x = -\log_7 x$ since $Y_3 = \log_{\frac{1}{7}} x$ is a reflection of $Y_2 = \log_7 x$ across the x-axis. The properties of logarithms and the change of base formula can be used to show that when $b > 1$ (and therefore $0 < \frac{1}{b} < 1$), $\log_{\frac{1}{b}} x = -\log_b x$.

Understanding the properties of logs and the change of base formula enables mathematicians to easily work with mathematical models of natural phenomena.

J. S. Bach promoted the tuning of musical instruments so that the ratios of the frequencies of any two adjacent notes are constant. This method, known as *equal* or *even temperament*, causes the frequencies to follow a logarithmic spiral.

Example 6 Modeling Frequencies of the Piano

The frequency of a note played by a key on the piano is related to the key's position on the keyboard. The number of notes, n, that one key is above another is modeled by the function $n = 12 \log_2 \left(\frac{f_2}{f_1} \right)$ where f_2 is the higher frequency and f_1 is the lower frequency.

a. The note C_5 is one octave higher than middle C and has twice its frequency. How many notes above middle C is C_5?

b. If middle C has a frequency of 261.63 Hertz (Hz), how many notes above middle C is A_4, which has a frequency of 440 Hz?

Answer

a. $n = 12 \log_2 \left(\frac{2f_1}{f_1} \right) = 12 \log_2 2$ 1. Substitute $2f_1$ for f_2.

$= 12(1) = 12$ notes   2. Apply the fact that $\log_n n = 1$.

b. $n = 12 \log_2 \left(\frac{440}{261.63} \right)$ 1. Substitute the frequencies into the function rule.

$= \frac{12}{\ln 2} \ln \left(\frac{440}{261.63} \right) = 9$ notes   2. Evaluate by applying the change of base formula.

SKILL ✓ **EXERCISE 37**

▶ A. Exercises

Expand each logarithmic expression. Assume all variables are positive values.

1. $\log xy^3$ **2.** $\ln ab^2 c$ **3.** $\ln 7x^4$

4. $\log \frac{3}{x^2}$ **5.** $\ln \frac{a^4}{b^2}$ **6.** $\log \frac{x^a y^b}{z}$

7. $\log \frac{\sqrt[5]{x^3}}{y}$ **8.** $\log \sqrt[3]{a^2 b^5}$

Write each expression as a single logarithm.

9. $\log x + 2 \log y$

10. $4 \log x + 2 \log 5$

11. $3 \ln y - 2 \ln 3$

12. $2 \ln x + 3 \ln 2 - \ln y$

13. $\frac{1}{3}(2 \log x + \log 1000)$

14. $\frac{1}{5}(\log x + 3 \log y) - 2 \log 10$

Use common logs to evaluate each logarithm. Round answers to the nearest ten thousandth.

15. $\log_2 50$ **16.** $\log_5 175$ **17.** $\log_8 95.7$

Use natural logs to evaluate each logarithm. Round answers to the nearest ten thousandth.

18. $\log_2 50$ **19.** $\log_4 212$ **20.** $\log_7 34.75$

▶ B. Exercises

Use $\log_7 2 \approx 0.3562$, $\log_7 3 \approx 0.5646$, and $\log_7 5 \approx 0.8271$ to find a decimal approximation of each logarithm.

21. $\log_7 \frac{1}{2}$ **22.** $\log_7 100$

23. $\log_7 4900$ **24.** $\log_7 \frac{5\sqrt{6}}{7}$

Expand each logarithmic expression. Assume all variables are positive values.

25. $\log 100 \sqrt[3]{x^2}$ **26.** $\log_3 \sqrt{27xy^2}$

27. $\log_7 \frac{49 \sqrt{y}}{x}$ **28.** $\log_2 \frac{\sqrt{2x}}{16y}$

Write each expression as a single logarithm.

29. $x \log 3 - 2 \log y + \frac{1}{3} \log z$

30. $x \ln 3 + y \ln 2 - z \ln 3$

31. $\ln 2x + 3 \ln 4x^2 - \ln 8x^4$

32. $3 \log \frac{3}{2} + 2 \log 6x - 2 \log 3$

Describe the graph of $g(x)$ as a transformation of $f(x) = \ln x$.

33. $g(x) = \log_{20} x$

34. $g(x) = \log_{\frac{1}{3}} x$

35. Rewrite the Richter scale formula, $R = \log \frac{A}{A_0}$, in terms of natural logs.

36. The loudness of sound is measured in decibels using the equation $L = 10 \log \frac{I}{I_0}$ where I is the intensity of the sound and I_0 is the intensity of sound at the threshold of hearing, 10^{-12} W/m^2. Write the expanded form of the equation. Then use the equation to find the loudness of a mosquito's buzz, which has an intensity of 10^{-8} W/m^2.

37. A composer must understand which combinations of frequencies create a desired sound.

Use $n = 12 \log_2 \left(\frac{f_2}{f_1} \right)$ (introduced in Example 6) to answer the following questions.

a. A clarinet is playing the F$\sharp$ below middle C at a frequency of 370 Hz while a flute is playing a note at a frequency of 1976 Hz. How many notes above the clarinet's note is the flute's note?

b. A bassoon is playing a G$_2$ with a frequency of 98 Hz. What is the frequency of a clarinet playing two octaves (24 notes) above the bassoon?

Use the following table to answer questions 38–39.

Substance	pH	pOH
vinegar	2.2	11.8
tomato	4.5	9.5
milk	6.6	7.4
distilled water	7.0	7.0
baking soda	8.3	5.7
ammonia	11.0	3.0
lye	13.0	1.0

38. The acidity of a solution is measured on the pH scale by pH $= -\log [H_3O^+]$ where $[H_3O^+]$ represents the concentration of hydronium ions (in moles/L).

a. Which substance listed in the table has $[H_3O^+] = 6.3 \times 10^{-12}$ moles/L?

b. What is the concentration of hydronium ions in distilled water?

c. What is the concentration of hydronium ions in vinegar? Is this more or less than the concentration of H_3O^+ in distilled water?

d. Approximately how many times greater is $[H_3O^+]$ in baking soda than in lye?

39. The pOH scale quantifies the basicity of a solution using pOH $= -\log [OH^-]$ where $[OH^-]$ represents the concentration of hydroxide ions (in moles/L). The sum of a solution's pH and pOH is 14.

a. What is the concentration of hydroxide ions in distilled water?

b. What is the concentration of hydroxide ions in vinegar? Is this more or less than $[OH^-]$ in distilled water?

c. Given that the pH of an unknown substance is 3.7, find $[OH^-]$.

d. Derive an equation relating $[H_3O^+]$ and $[OH^-]$.

40. Prove each property of logarithmic functions.

a. $\log_b \frac{1}{x} = -\log_b x$ **b.** $\log_{\frac{1}{b}} x = -\log_b x$

C. Exercises

41. Prove the Quotient Property of Logarithms: $\log_b \frac{m}{n} = \log_b m - \log_b n$.

42. Prove the Power Property of Logarithms: $\log_b m^p = p \log_b m$.

43. Prove the change of base formula: $\log_b x = \frac{\log_a x}{\log_a b}$.

44. Explain: Use technology to graph $f(x) = \log (x - 2) - \log x$ and $g(x) = \log \left(\frac{x-2}{x} \right)$. Why are the functions not equivalent?

Determine whether $f(x)$ and $g(x)$ are inverses of each other. [1.8]

45. $f(x) = 2x - 6$
  $g(x) = \frac{x}{2} + 3$

46. $f(x) = \frac{7}{x+2}$
  $g(x) = \frac{x+2}{7}$

47. List the possible rational zeros for the function $f(x) = x^3 + 2x^2 - 5x - 6$ and then factor $f(x)$. [2.4]

48. Identify the asymptotes of $g(x) = -\dfrac{1}{(x+1)^2} + 3$. Then graph the function as a transformation of a reciprocal power function. [2.5]

49. Solve $\dfrac{5}{3x^2 + 16x - 12} + \dfrac{3x-2}{x+6} = \dfrac{x}{3x-2}$. [2.6]

50. What is best description of the linear correlation of the following graph? [1.9]

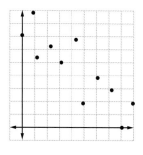

  A. strong positive
  B. strong negative
  C. weak positive
  D. weak negative
  E. none of these

51. What are points that do not seem to fit the trend of a scatterplot of the data called? [1.9]

  A. correlators
  B. outliers
  C. residuals
  D. regressions
  E. determinates

52. Which of the following cannot be true in the exponential function $f(x) = ab^x$? [3.1]

  A. $a < 0$
  B. $0 < a < 1$
  C. $b < 0$
  D. $0 < b < 1$
  E. all of these

53. Between what two integers does $\log_2 3$ lie? [3.2]

  A. 0, 1
  B. 3, 4
  C. 2, 3
  D. 1, 2
  E. none of these

54. A biology class took an exam on June 1. When students took an equivalent exam without preparation in the subsequent months, their average score could be modeled by the function $f(t) = 74 - 16 \log (t + 1)$ where $0 \le t \le 12$. Use the model to estimate the average score 6 months after the original exam. [3.2]

  A. 61%
  B. 60%
  C. 45%
  D. 42%
  E. none of these

Exponential and Logarithmic Equations

Newton's law of cooling can be used to determine how long ice cream should be out of a commercial freezer before it is served.

In an *exponential equation*, such as $e^x = 9$, the variable occurs in an exponent. In a *logarithmic equation*, such as $\log x = -2$, the variable occurs in the argument (input) of a logarithmic expression. Many simple exponential and logarithmic equations can be solved by simply converting to the alternative form.

If $\log x = -2$ then $x = 10^{-2} = 0.01$, and if $e^x = 9$ then $x = \ln 9 \approx 2.1972$.

A variety of strategies are used when solving more complicated exponential equations. When both sides of the equation can be expressed as powers of the same base, apply the *Equality Property of Exponents* ($b^x = b^y$ if and only if $x = y$) and solve the resulting equation.

After completing this section, you will be able to

- solve exponential and logarithmic equations.
- model and solve real-world problems using exponential and logarithmic equations.

Example 1 Solving by Using Like Bases

Solve $27^x = \left(\frac{1}{9}\right)^{x+5}$.

Answer

$(3^3)^x = (3^{-2})^{x+5}$ 1. Express each base as a power of 3.

$3^{3x} = 3^{(-2x-10)}$ 2. Power Property of Exponents

$3x = -2x - 10$ 3. Equality Property of Exponents

$5x = -10$ 4. Solve for x.

$x = -2$

SKILL ✓ **EXERCISE 3**

When the two sides of an exponential equation cannot be expressed using the same base, solve by finding a logarithm of each side. This is an application of the *Equality Property of Logarithms*:

$\log_b x = \log_b y$ if and only if $x = y$. Use the base of the exponential expression when it has a base of 10 or e.

Example 2 Solving by Finding Logarithms

Solve each exponential equation.

a. $10^{x+1} = 4$ **b.** $e^{-5x} = 17$

Answer

a. $\log 10^{x+1} = \log 4$ **b.** $\ln e^{-5x} = \ln 17$ 1. Take the common or natural log of both sides of the equation.

$x + 1 = \log 4$ $-5x = \ln 17$ 2. Simplify using the inverse property of logarithms.

$x = -1 + \log 4$ $x = -\frac{1}{5}\ln 17$ 3. Solve for x.

≈ -0.3979 ≈ -0.5666 4. Use a calculator to find a decimal approximation.

SKILL ✓ **EXERCISE 5**

This process can also be viewed as converting to logarithmic form and then solving for x.

$$10^{x+1} = 4 \qquad\qquad e^{-5x} = 17$$

$$x + 1 = \log 4 \qquad -5x = \ln 17 \qquad \text{Write the equation in logarithmic form.}$$

$$x = -1 + \log 4 \qquad x = -\tfrac{1}{5}\ln 17 \qquad \text{Solve for } x.$$

When the exponential equation has a base other than 10 or e, the strategy of finding either the natural or common log of each side will produce the same result.

Example 3 Solving by Finding Logarithms

Solve each exponential equation.

a. $5^x = 7$ $\qquad\qquad$ **b.** $3^{2x-1} = 5^x$

Answer

a. $\log 5^x = \log 7$ $\qquad$ **b.** $\qquad \ln 3^{2x-1} = \ln 5^x$ $\qquad$ 1. Take the logarithm of both sides.

$\quad x \log 5 = \log 7$ $\qquad\qquad (2x - 1)\ln 3 = x \ln 5$ $\qquad$ 2. Power Property of Logarithms

$\qquad x = \dfrac{\log 7}{\log 5}$ $\qquad\qquad\quad 2x \ln 3 - \ln 3 = x \ln 5$ $\qquad$ 3. Solve for x.

$\qquad\qquad\qquad\qquad\qquad 2x \ln 3 - x \ln 5 = \ln 3$

$\qquad\qquad\qquad\qquad\qquad x(2 \ln 3 - \ln 5) = \ln 3$

$\qquad\qquad\qquad\qquad\qquad\qquad x = \dfrac{\ln 3}{\ln 9 - \ln 5}$ $\qquad$ (The power property can be used to express 2 ln 3 as ln 9.)

$\qquad\qquad x \approx 1.209$ $\qquad\qquad\qquad\qquad x \approx 1.869$ $\qquad$ 4. Use a calculator to find a decimal approximation.

SKILL ✔ **EXERCISE 7**

In Example 3a you could convert directly to logarithmic form, obtaining $x = \log_5 7$. While this is an equivalent solution, you would need to use the change of base formula to express $\log_5 7 = \dfrac{\log 7}{\log 5}$ or $\dfrac{\ln 7}{\ln 5}$ before using a calculator to evaluate the expression.

Exponential equations in quadratic form can be solved by factoring or using the quadratic formula.

Example 4 Solving by Factoring

Solve $e^{2x} - 4e^x - 5 = 0$.

Answer

$(e^x)^2 - 4(e^x) - 5 = 0$ $\qquad$ 1. Write the equation in the quadratic form.

$(e^x - 5)(e^x + 1) = 0$ $\qquad$ 2. Factor.

$e^x - 5 = 0 \;\;\text{or}\;\; e^x + 1 = 0$ $\qquad$ 3. Zero Product Property

$\qquad e^x = 5 \qquad\qquad e^x = -1$ $\qquad$ 4. Solve the resulting exponential equations.

$\qquad x = \ln 5 \qquad\quad x = \ln(-1)$

$\qquad x \approx 1.6094$ $\qquad\qquad\qquad\qquad$ 5. The natural log of a negative number is not real.

Check

6. Finding the zeros of $Y_1 = e^{2x} - 4e^x - 5$ confirms that $x = \ln 5$ is the only solution.

SKILL ✔ **EXERCISE 27**

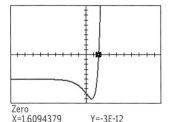

Zero
X=1.6094379 $\qquad$ Y=-3E-12

There are several strategies used to solve more complicated logarithmic equations. When both sides of the equation can be expressed using a logarithmic expression, apply the Equality Property of Logarithms and solve the resulting equation.

Example 5 Solving with the Equality Property of Logarithm

Solve $2 \ln x = \ln 9$.

Answer

$\ln x^2 = \ln 9$	1. Power Property of Logarithms
$x^2 = 9$	2. Equality Property of Logarithms
$x = \pm 3$	3. Take the square root of each side.
The solution is $x = 3$.	4. Since the domain of $\ln x$ is $(0, \infty)$, -3 is an extraneous solution.

SKILL ✓ **EXERCISE 15**

Other logarithmic equations can be solved by converting to exponential form after writing the equation as a single logarithmic expression isolated on one side of the equation.

A Sumerian tablet in the Louvre asks how long it will take to double an investment at 20% interest. Interestingly, the normal interest rate for silver was around 20% while the rate for grain was typically 33%.

Example 6 Solving by Converting to Exponential Form

Solve $\log_5 x = 1 - \log_5 (2x - 3)$.

Answer

$\log_5 x + \log_5 (2x - 3) = 1$	1. Isolate the logarithmic functions on one side.
$\log_5 x(2x - 3) = 1$	2. Write that side as a single logarithmic expression using the Product Property of Logarithms.
$x(2x - 3) = 5^1$	3. Convert to exponential form.
$2x^2 - 3x = 5$	
$2x^2 - 3x - 5 = 0$	4. Solve for x.
$(2x - 5)(x + 1) = 0$	
$x = \frac{5}{2} \text{ or } x = -1$	
The solution is $x = \frac{5}{2}$.	5. Since -1 is not in the domain of either original logarithmic expression, it is extraneous.

Check

6. Confirm by finding the intersections of
$$Y1 = \frac{\log x}{\log 5} \text{ and } Y2 = 1 - \frac{\log (2x - 3)}{\log 5}.$$

SKILL ✓ **EXERCISE 37**

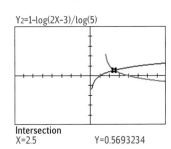

The ability to solve exponential and logarithmic equations enables the solving of many real-life problems.

Example 7   Doubling an Investment

While the charging of interest on loans to a fellow Israelite in need is forbidden (Deut. 15:1–7, 23:19), the parable of the talents teaches that investing what has been entrusted to us is expected if we are to be faithful servants (Matt. 25:14–30).

How long does it take for $4000 invested at 6% annual interest to grow to $8000 if interest is compounded monthly?

Answer

$$A(t) = P\left(1 + \frac{r}{n}\right)^{nt}$$

$$8000 = 4000\left(1 + \frac{0.06}{12}\right)^{12t}$$

$$2 = 1.005^{12t}$$

$$\log 2 = \log 1.005^{12t}$$

$$\log 2 = 12t \log 1.005$$

$$t = \frac{\log 2}{12 \log 1.005} \approx 11.6 \text{ years}$$

1. Substitute the given information into the compound interest formula.
2. Simplify the exponential equation.
3. Take the common log of both sides.
4. Solve for t.

Check

10,000   Y1=4000(1.005)^((12X))

0
   Intersection
   X=11.58131   Y=8000
15

5. Confirm by finding the intersection of $Y_1 = 4000(1.005)^{12t}$ and $Y_2 = 8000$.

SKILL ✔ **EXERCISE 41**

▷ A. Exercises

Solve each exponential equation. Round answers to the nearest thousandth if necessary.

1. $2^x = 64$
2. $3^x = \frac{1}{243}$
3. $27^{x-3} = 9^{x-1}$
4. $10^x = 77$
5. $e^{x+1} = 10$
6. $4e^x = 20$
7. $6^x = 12$
8. $5^x = \frac{1}{12}$
9. $3^{5x} = 2$
10. $5^{x+2} = 15$

Solve each logarithmic equation.

11. $\log_3 (4x - 7) = 2$
12. $\log_3 (x + 1) = 2$
13. $\log_{27} x = \frac{1}{3}$
14. $\ln (2x + 1) = \ln (4x - 5)$
15. $2 \log_3 x = \log_3 8$
16. $\frac{1}{2} \log_3 x = 2$

17. The formula for the Richter magnitude scale, $R = \log \frac{A}{A_0}$, compares an earthquake's amplitude A to a small reference amplitude, A_0. If the April 2017 earthquake in Atacama, Chile, had a magnitude of 6.2, approximately how many times larger than A_0 was its amplitude?

18. The loudness of a sound is measured in decibels using the equation $L = 10 \log \frac{I}{I_0}$, where I is the intensity of the sound and I_0 is the intensity of sound at the threshold of hearing, 10^{-12} W/m². If a phone app warns users when the volume of the device is at or above 64 dB, find the lowest sound intensity that triggers the warning.

▷ B. Exercises

Find all real solutions for x. Round answers to the nearest thousandth if necessary.

19. $\left(\frac{2}{3}\right)^x = \frac{81}{16}$
20. $\left(\frac{1}{625}\right)^{2x-10} = 25^{10x}$
21. $4^{1-x} = 5^x$
22. $3^{x+1} = 17^{2x}$
23. $e^x = 10^{x+1}$
24. $e^{2x-1} = 10^x$
25. $12^{x-4} = 3^{x-2}$
26. $3^{-x-1} = 6^{-x+2}$
27. $e^{2x} - 27e^x + 72 = 0$
28. $e^{2x} + 5e^x = 6$
29. $e^{2x} + 11e^x = -24$
30. $3e^{4x} - 11e^{2x} + 8 = 0$

Find all real solutions for x.

31. $\frac{1}{4} \log_4 x^2 = \log_4 8$
32. $\log_2 3x = \log_2 (x + 4) - \log_2 3$
33. $\log_3 x = 2 \log_3 5 + \log_3 16$
34. $\ln x + \ln(x - 3) = \ln 54$
35. $\log_2 8^x = -3$
36. $\log_{16} x^2 = -\frac{1}{2}$
37. $\log_2 (x - 2) = 3 - \log_2 x$
38. $\log_3 \frac{1}{4} - \log_3 \frac{3}{4} = x$

39. Explore: Complete the following to explore the properties of equality for powers and exponents.

   a. If $x^2 = 3^2$, is $x = 3$ the only solution? Explain why.

   b. If $x^3 = 3^3$, is $x = 3$ the only solution? Explain why.

   c. Compare the graphs of $f(x) = x^2$ and $g(x) = x^3$. Which properties of the graphs explain the difference between the answers in part a and part b?

   d. According to the Equality Property for Exponents, if $b^x = b^n$, then $x = n$. What characteristic of the graph of $h(x) = b^x$ supports this conclusion?

40. Contrast: Solve the following equations. Then explain the general process used to solve each equation.

   a. $\log_5 x = 7$ **b.** $\log_7 5 = x$ **c.** $\log_x 5 = 7$

41. Model: In a Sierpinski fractal, the number of black triangles T surrounding the central white triangle is modeled by the equation $T = 3^n$ where n is number of iterations. How many iterations are needed to produce 1,594,323 black triangles?

Iterations

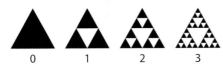

0   1   2   3

42. How many years will it take for a $60,000 investment with 3% APR compounded monthly to match an $80,000 investment with 2% APR compounded quarterly? Verify your answer graphically.

❯ C. Exercises

Find all real solutions for x.

43. $\ln(2x + 5) + \ln(3x + 1) = \ln 8$

44. $\log_2 \sqrt{\dfrac{3x + 4}{x}} = 0$

45. $\log_4 x^8 = \dfrac{4}{3} \log_4 64$

46. $x^{\log_3 5} = 125$

47. An object's temperature may be modeled using Newton's law of cooling (and heating): $T(t) = T_S + (T_0 - T_S)e^{-kt}$ where T_0 is the object's initial temperature, T_S is the surrounding medium's temperature (assumed to be constant), k is the heating constant, and t is the time. A tub of ice cream stored in a freezer at –20°C is placed in a room at 25°C.

   a. Find k if the temperature of the ice cream increased to –15°C after 5 min.

   b. Write a function modeling the temperature of the ice cream after t min in the room.

   c. Estimate the temperature of the ice cream after 20 min in the room.

48. The periodic payment P for a car loan of B dollars can be calculated using the equation $P = \dfrac{iB}{1 - (1 + i)^{-n}}$ where i is the periodic interest rate and n is the number of payments. Use the formula and an APR of 3% to complete the following.

   a. Find the monthly payment on a 3 yr loan of $12,500.

   b. Solve the equation for B. Then use the result to find the maximum 3 yr loan with a monthly payment of $300.

   c. Solve the equation for n. Then determine the number of monthly $300 payments needed to repay a $9000 car loan.

Solve. [2.6]

49. $\dfrac{x+1}{x-1} = \dfrac{6x+1}{x^2-1}$

50. $\dfrac{4}{x-6} + \dfrac{8x}{x+3} = \dfrac{3}{x^2-3x-18}$

Describe each transformation of $f(x) = \log_5 x$. Then use a graph of $f(x)$ to sketch the graph of $g(x)$. [3.2]

51. $g(x) = \log_5 x + 3$

52. $g(x) = \log_5 (x-4) + 2$

Expand each logarithmic expression. Assume all variables are positive values. [3.3]

53. $\log 10\sqrt[3]{x^2 y}$

54. $\log_5 \dfrac{25\sqrt{x}}{yz}$

55. Identify any asymptotes of $f(x) = \dfrac{x^3 - x^2 - 2x}{x^2 - 3x + 2}$. [2.5]

    A. HA: $y = 1$; VA: $x = 2$ and $x = 1$

    B. VA: $x = 1$; SA: $y = x + 2$

    C. VA: $x = 2$ and $x = 1$; SA: $y = x + 2$

    D. VA: $x = 2$ and $x = 1$; SA: $y = x + 2$

    E. HA: $y = 1$; VA: $x = 2$ and $x = 1$; SA: $y = x$

56. Find the solution of $\dfrac{x^2 - 2x - 15}{2x^2 + 9x + 9} \geq 0$. [2.7]

    A. $(-\infty, -3) \cup \left(-3, -\dfrac{3}{2}\right) \cup [5, \infty)$

    B. $\left(-3, -\dfrac{3}{2}\right)$

    C. $(-\infty, -3) \cup (-\dfrac{3}{2}, 5]$

    D. $\left(-\infty, -\dfrac{3}{2}\right) \cup [5, \infty)$

    E. $(-\infty, -3) \cup \left(-\dfrac{3}{2}, 5\right)$

57. Find the account balance in 12 yr if $4500 is invested at 6.5% compounded semiannually. [3.1]

    A. $4801.37   **C.** $9695.58   **E.** $9816.63

    B. $9580.93   **D.** $9795.98

58. Which describes $f(x) = \log_5 x$ translated 2 units left, reflected across the x-axis, and then translated 4 units up? [3.2]

    A. $g(x) = 2 \log_5 x + 2 + 4$

    B. $g(x) = \log_5 (-x + 2) + 4$

    C. $g(x) = -\log_5 (x - 2) + 4$

    D. $g(x) = -\log_5 (x + 2) + 4$

    E. $g(x) = -\log_5 (x - 4) + 2$

Glorifying God with Math

The work of the sixteenth, seventeenth, and even some eighteenth-century mathematicians was a religious quest. . . . The search for the mathematical laws of nature was an act of devotion. It was the study of the ways and nature of God which would reveal the glory and grandeur of his handiwork. . . . Man could not hope to perceive the divine plan as clearly as God himself understood it, but man could with humility and modesty seek to at least approach the mind of God. . . . Each discovery of a law of nature was hailed as evidence testifying more to God's brilliance than to the ingenuity of the investigator.

—*Morris Kline (American mathematics historian and philosopher)*

The German mathematician and astronomer Johannes Kepler (1571–1630) stated that astronomers "ought to keep in their minds not the glory of their own intellect, but the glory of God above everything else." Everything in a Christian's life should bring glory to God (1 Cor. 10:31). Morris Kline observed that mathematicians before the nineteenth century had, if not a strictly biblical worldview, at least a religious worldview. Their goal was to glorify God as they worked. Colossians 1:18 provides additional focus for Christians, stating that our Lord Jesus Christ should have the preeminence in all things. But how can we glorify God with mathematics?

Acknowledging God as the origin of mathematical truth allows us to praise Him as the reason for the divine characteristics apparent in the subject. Christian mathematician Larry Zimmerman observed that the knowledge of mathematics "unveils not only vistas of beauty and power unsuspected before but also an order, symmetry and infinitude which stuns and awes the beholder." As we study mathematics and marvel at its beauty and order, we should praise God, the giver of that beauty and order. Everything we do should be done in thanksgiving to God (Col. 3:17). We can glorify God by recognizing the power of algebra, the symmetry of geometry, and the infinitude of calculus as reflections of our Creator.

We can also glorify God with mathematics by using it to fulfill the Creation Mandate (Gen. 1:26–28, Ps. 8). Gottfried Leibniz, one of the founders of calculus, stated that "the principal goal of the whole of mankind must be the knowledge and development of the wonders of God, and that this is the reason that God gave him the empire of the globe." The knowledge, skills, and principles used in proper stewardship of the earth and its resources are due in large part to mathematics. American educator H. F. Fehr asserted that "mathematics serves as a handmaiden for the explanation of the quantitative situations in other subjects, such as economics, physics, navigation, finance, biology and even the arts." Our mathematical knowledge has enabled advances in science, medicine, and technology, resulting in opportunities to better manage our God-given domain.

Many careers depend on mathematical proficiencies acquired through diligent study of mathematics. Galileo declared, "I do not feel obliged to believe that the same God who has endowed us with senses, reason, and intellect has intended us to forgo their use and by some other means to give us knowledge which we can attain by them." Your senses, reason, and intellect come from God. You should use them for His glory.

Exercises

1. According to Morris Kline, in which centuries did mathematicians view their work as a religious quest?

2. What is the primary purpose of math for a Christian?

3. What did Kepler admonish scientists and mathematicians not to glory in?

4. According to Leibniz, why did God give people dominion over the earth?

5. Which mathematician believed that God would not use other means to reveal to us those things that we could determine using the intellect that He gave us?

6. Cite two Scripture passages that state that everything we do should glorify God.

7. Cite two Scripture passages describing the mandate that people are to exercise dominion over the earth.

8. According to Colossians 1:18, who specifically should have the preeminence in all that we do?

9. According to Zimmerman, what five characteristics of mathematics should stun and awe the beholder?

10. **Discuss:** Describe several specific ways that God can be glorified through mathematics.

3.5 Exponential, Logistic, and Logarithmic Models

Exponential, logistic, and logarithmic models help further our understanding of population growth.

After completing this section, you will be able to

- use exponential, logistic, and logarithmic functions to model data and solve problems.
- use transformations to linearize data.

Compare the growth of $f(x) = \frac{1}{2}x + 1$ and $g(x) = 2\left(\frac{3}{2}\right)^x$.

x	-2	-1	0	1	2
$f(x)$	0	$\frac{1}{2}$	1	$\frac{3}{2}$	2

$+\frac{1}{2}$ $+\frac{1}{2}$ $+\frac{1}{2}$ $+\frac{1}{2}$

x	-2	-1	0	1	2
$g(x)$	$\frac{8}{9}$	$\frac{4}{3}$	2	3	$\frac{9}{2}$

$\times\frac{3}{2}$ $\times\frac{3}{2}$ $\times\frac{3}{2}$ $\times\frac{3}{2}$

The linear function $f(x)$ grows by the consistent amount of $\frac{1}{2}$, but the exponential function grows by the consistent factor of $\frac{3}{2}$, or 1.5, which can also be expressed as a growth rate of 50%. If a population is experiencing exponential growth or decay, a function modeling its growth can be determined given two data points.

Example 1 Modeling Exponential Growth

The Denver metro area grew from 2.4 million residents in 2000 to 2.8 million in 2010.

a. Determine the average annual percent increase between 2000 and 2010 and write an exponential function modeling the population.

b. Use your exponential model to estimate the population in 2015.

c. Use your exponential model to predict the year in which the population will reach 4 million.

Answer

a. $P(t) = ab^t$ where $a = 2.4$

        1. Let $P(t)$ represent the population t years after 2000 so that $P(0) = ab^0 = 2.4$.

$2.8 = 2.4b^{10}$

$b^{10} = \frac{2.8}{2.4}$

        2. Use $P(10) = 2.8$ to find b, the growth factor.

$b = \sqrt[10]{\frac{2.8}{2.4}} \approx 1.0155$

$r = b - 1 \approx 0.0155$ or 1.55%

        3. Use $b = 1 + r$ to find r, the growth rate.

$P(t) \approx 2.4(1.0155)^t$

        4. State the exponential model.

b. $P(15) \approx 2.4(1.0155)^{15}$

       ≈ 3.0 million people

Evaluate $P(15)$.

c.

$4 \approx 2.4(1.0155)^t$

$\frac{4}{2.4} \approx 1.0155^t$

$\ln\frac{4}{2.4} \approx \ln 1.0155^t$

$\ln 4 - \ln 2.4 \approx t \ln 1.0155$

$t \approx \frac{\ln 4 - \ln 2.4}{\ln 1.0155} \approx 33$

Substitute 4 into $P(t) \approx 2.4(1.0155)^t$ and solve for t.

The model predicts that the population of the Denver metro area will reach 4 million in 2033.

SKILL ✓ EXERCISE 17

When there are multiple data points from a population experiencing exponential growth or decay, an exponential regression can be performed using technology to determine a function modeling the population over time.

Example 2   Using an Exponential Regression

Find a function $P(t)$ modeling the population of the Denver metro area t years after 1900 by completing an exponential regression for the data in the table. Then use the model to estimate the population in 2015 and the year in which the population will reach 4 million.

Year	Population (millions)	Year	Population (millions)
1910	0.28	1970	1.24
1920	0.33	1980	1.62
1930	0.39	1990	1.85
1940	0.45	2000	2.40
1950	0.62	2010	2.78
1960	0.93		

Answer

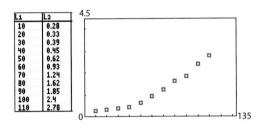

1. Enter the data, using L_1 = years since 1900 and L_2 = the population. The scatterplot indicates that an exponential model may be a good fit.

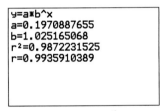

$P(t) \approx 0.1971(1.0252)^t$

2. Complete an exponential regression (STAT, [CALC], 0:ExpReg) with Diagnostics On and store the regression equation as Y_1.

   The high coefficient of determination implies that the exponential model is a good fit.

   Note the average annual growth rate:
   $b - 1 \approx 1.025 - 1 = 0.025$ or 2.52%.

$$P(115) \approx 0.1971(1.0252)^{115}$$
$$\approx 3.44 \text{ million people}$$

3. Evaluate $Y_1(115)$ to estimate the 2015 population.

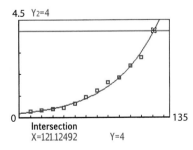

4. To solve $4 \approx 0.1971(1.0252)^t$ graphically, find the intersection of the exponential regression equation (stored as Y_1) and $Y_2 = 4$. Then interpret its x-value of ≈ 121.1.

The model predicts that the population will reach 4 million in 2021.

TIP

The most recent regression equation can be entered in the Y= equation editor using VARS, 5:Statistics, EQ, and selecting 1:RegEQ. Other related constants, including a, b, r^2, and r, can be entered in other contexts using this menu.

SKILL ✓ EXERCISES 19–21

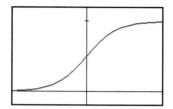

Exponential growth requires a consistent rate of growth. It is difficult for a population to sustain unrestricted exponential growth as supporting resources are stressed. In reality, its growth eventually slows and the graph levels out, approaching a maximum sustainable population. A *logistic function* provides a good model for the restricted growth of a population.

DEFINITION

A **logistic growth function** can be written in the form $f(x) = \dfrac{c}{1 + ae^{-bx}}$ where a, b, and c are positive constants.

Notice that the function has two horizontal asymptotes: $y = 0$ describes the left end behavior; the right end behavior is described by $y = c$, the limit of growth when the *carrying capacity* of the supporting environment is reached.

Example 3   Using a Logistic Regression

Using the data from Example 2, find a logistic function modeling the restricted population growth of the Denver metro area t years after 1900. Then use the model to estimate the population in 2015 and the year in which the population will reach 4 million.

Answer

While carrying capacity can be determined experimentally for bacteria or animal populations, no consensus exists on how to determine the carrying capacity for a human population, primarily because people can exercise stewardship over their environment.

```
            Logistic
y=c/(1+ae^(-bx))
a=34.63850517
b=0.0333429525
c=5.264911957
```

$$P(t) \approx \dfrac{5.2649}{1 + 34.6385\,e^{-0.0333t}}$$

$Y_3(115) \approx 3.01$ million people

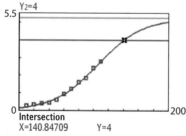

Intersection
X=140.84709   Y=4

1. Complete a logistic regression of the data ([STAT], [CALC], B:Logistic) and store the regression equation as Y_3.

   There is no coefficient of determination associated with a logistic regression.

   Note that the model estimates the limit of growth for the Denver metro area population to be about 5.26 million.

2. Evaluate $Y_3(115)$ to estimate the 2015 population.

3. Find the intersection of the logistic regression equation (stored as Y_3) and $Y_2 = 4$. Then interpret the x-value of ≈ 140.85.

The model predicts that the population will reach 4 million in 2040.

SKILL ✔ **EXERCISE 23**

Notice we have developed three different models to make predictions regarding the Denver metro area population. The actual 2015 population of about 2.8 million may indicate that the logistic function is the best model to predict when the population would reach 4 million.

Logarithmic functions are used to model rapid initial growth followed by slower growth over time. Measures of productivity, language or skill acquisition, and weight loss frequently exhibit logarithmic growth.

Example 4   Using a Logarithmic Regression

Mark has instituted a 13-week eating and exercise plan in order to improve his overall fitness. Use the data to create a function $W(t)$ modeling his overall weight loss. Then use the model to predict how many additional weeks are required to reach his goal of losing 10 lb.

Answer

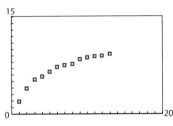

1. Complete a scatterplot of the data. The shape indicates that a logarithmic model may be a good fit.

$W(t) \approx 1.9398 + 2.8725 \ln t$

2. Complete a logarithmic regression of the data ([STAT], CALC, 9:LnReg) and store the regression equation as Y_1.

   Note the high coefficient of determination.

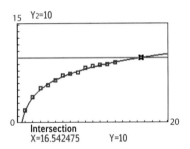

3. Find the intersection of the logarithmic regression equation (stored as Y_1) and $Y_2 = 10$ and interpret the x-value.

Week	Cumulative Weight Loss (lb)
1	1.9
2	3.9
3	5.3
4	5.8
5	6.5
6	7.2
7	7.5
8	7.7
9	8.4
10	8.7
11	8.9
12	9.0
13	9.2

The model predicts that a weight loss of 10 lb will be achieved around week 16.5, so another 3.5 weeks is needed for Mark to reach his goal.

_____ SKILL ✔ **EXERCISE 25**

The preceding example illustrates how the natural tendency to assume linear growth when the growth is actually logarithmic can lead to frustration as weight loss slows over time.

A visual inspection of a scatterplot may not be sufficient to determine whether the data is best modeled by a power function, an exponential function, or a logarithmic function. In this case, exploring transformed data sets using $X = \ln x$, $Y = \ln y$, or both and determining whether they are linear can help establish the appropriate model for the original data.

Linearization of a Nonlinear Data Set		
Original Data Model		Linear Transformed Data
power function	$y = ax^b$	$(X, Y) = (\ln x, \ln y)$
exponential function	$y = ab^x$	$(X, Y) = (x, \ln y)$
logarithmic function	$y = a + b \ln x$	$(X, Y) = (\ln x, y)$

TIP

See the Technology Corner at the end of this lesson for detailed instructions on entering L_3 and L_4 and completing the scatterplots.

A scatterplot of the following data indicates the data may best be modeled by a power function (with $b > 1$) or an exponential function.

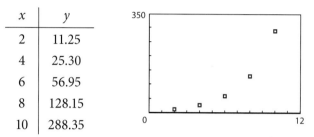

x	y
2	11.25
4	25.30
6	56.95
8	128.15
10	288.35

Use technology to create the transformed data sets $X = \ln x = L_3$ and $Y = \ln y = L_4$. The non-linear scatterplot of $(X, Y) = (\ln x, \ln y)$ indicates that a power function may not be the best model. The linear scatterplot of $(X, Y) = (x, \ln y)$ indicates that an exponential model will be a good fit for the original data.

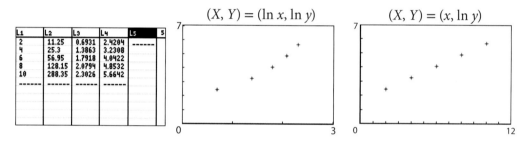

Completing a linear regression using L_1 and L_4 for (X, Y) produces the modeling function $Y \approx 0.4055X + 1.6091$. Substituting into this equation using $X = x$ and $Y = \ln y$ allows us to derive an equation modeling the original data.

$\quad Y \approx 0.4055X + 1.6091$

$\ \ln y \approx 0.4055x + 1.6091$ — Substitute.

$\qquad y \approx e^{(0.4055x + 1.6091)}$ — Convert to exponential form.

$\qquad y \approx (e^{0.4055})^x e^{1.6091}$ — Apply properties of exponents to obtain the form $y = ab^x$.

$\quad y \approx (1.5)^x(4.9983)$ — Simplify.

or $y \approx 5(1.5)^x$

You may have wondered why correlation coefficients, which apply only to linear regressions, are listed with the results of power, exponential, and logarithmic regressions. This is because technology uses the process of linearizing the data in order to complete these other regressions.

Example 5   Modeling Orbits

Use the data to determine the relationship between a planet's orbital period (the time it takes to orbit the sun) and its average orbital radius (its distance from the sun).

	Orbital Period (days)	Mean Radius (10^6 km)
Mercury	88.0	57.9
Venus	224.7	108.2
Earth	365.2	149.6
Mars	687.0	227.9
Jupiter	4331	778.6
Saturn	10,747	1433.5

Answer

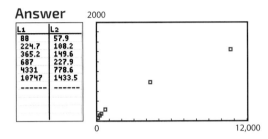

1. A visual inspection of a scatterplot of the data indicates that either a power function ($b < 1$) or a logarithmic function may be the best model for the relationship between the variables.

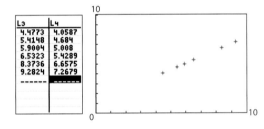

2. A scatterplot of $(X, Y) = (\ln x, \ln y)$ illustrates the linear relationship of the transformed data and indicates that a power function will be a good model for the original data.

$Y \approx 0.6677X + 1.0686$

3. Find the linear regression equation for the transformed data.

$\ln y \approx 0.6677 \ln x + 1.0686$

4. Use $X = \ln x$ and $Y = \ln y$ to substitute into the linear equation.

$y \approx e^{0.6677 \ln x + 1.0686}$
$y \approx (e^{\ln x})^{0.6677} e^{1.0686}$
$y \approx x^{0.6677} e^{1.0686}$
$y \approx 2.9113 \, x^{0.6677}$
or $y \approx 2.9113 x^{\frac{2}{3}}$

5. Convert to exponential form and simplify to derive a power function modeling the original data.

SKILL ✓ **EXERCISES 29–31**

Cubing both sides of our result produces the equation $y^3 \approx 24.6752x^2$ where x represents the orbital period and y represents the average radius. This is a mathematical expression of Kepler's third law of planetary motion, which states that the square of the orbital period of a planet is directly proportional to the cube of the orbit's average radius.

TECHNOLOGY CORNER (TI-84 PLUS FAMILY)

When transforming the data on page 160, lists L_3 and L_4 can be quickly generated by selecting the column header, pressing [CLEAR], and then entering $\ln(L_1)$ and $\ln(L_2)$, respectively.

To graph the transformed data $(X, Y) = (\ln x, \ln y)$, be sure all stat plots are turned off except Plot 2. Enter L_3 for the Xlist and L_4 for the Ylist, using [2nd], [3] and [2nd], [4]. Then use [ZOOM], 9:ZoomStat to display the graph. The test for a power function does not appear to be linear.

To graph the transformed data $(X, Y) = (x, \ln y)$, return to Plot 2 and change the Xlist to L_1. Use 9:ZoomStat to display the new scatterplot. The test for an exponential model appears to be linear. Use L_1 and L_4 when completing the linear regression of the transformed data.

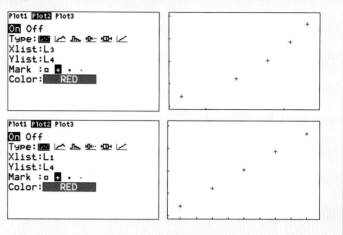

> ## A. Exercises

1. Identify the model that best fits each type of growth.

    I. exponential   **III.** logarithmic

    II. linear   **IV.** logistic

    a. Values regularly change by the same amount.

    b. Values regularly change by the same factor.

    c. Growth eventually slows and the graph approaches a maximum value.

    d. There is rapid initial growth with slower growth over time.

Classify each function.
A. exponential growth
B. exponential decay
C. logarithmic growth
D. logistic growth

2. $y = \dfrac{c}{1 + ae^{-bx}}$

3. $y = a + b \ln x$

4. $y = ab^x$ with $0 < b < 1$

5. $y = ab^x$ with $b > 1$

6.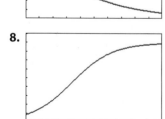

7.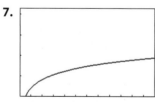

8.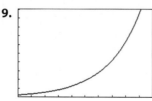

9.

Make a scatterplot of each data set. Then complete a regression to find an exponential function that models the data, rounding each constant to the nearest ten thousandth. Finally, use the model to estimate $f(14)$.

10.

x	y
1	9
2	14
3	20
4	30
5	45
6	68

11.

x	y
0	76.8
2	49.4
4	31.6
6	20.1
8	12.9
10	8.3

Make a scatterplot of each data set. Then complete a regression to find a logistic function that models the data, rounding each constant to the nearest ten thousandth. Finally, use the model to estimate $f(14)$.

12.

x	y
1	2.9
3	6.4
5	11.6
7	16.0
9	18.9
11	20.1

13.

x	y
0	2.3
2	4.7
4	8.7
6	14.4
8	20.1
10	24.6
12	27.2

Make a scatterplot of each data set. Then complete a regression to find a logarithmic function that models the data, rounding each constant to the nearest ten thousandth. Finally, use the model to estimate f(19).

14.

x	y
1	8
2	15
3	19
4	22
5	24
6	26

15.

x	y
1	2.0
3	10.7
5	14.9
7	17.5
9	19.7
11	21.0

16. Match each type of growth to the best modeling function.

   I. exponential   **II.** logistic   **III.** logarithmic

   a. rapid initial growth that slows over time

   b. slow initial growth that increases over time

   c. slow initial growth that increases before the growth slows as it approaches a limit

> **B. Exercises**

17. In 2000, New York City had a population of 8,008,278, making it the first US city to exceed 8 million people. The city's population in 2010 was 8,175,133.

   a. Using t to represent the number of years since 2000, find the city's average annual rate of growth from 2000 to 2010 and write an exponential function modeling the population.

   b. Use your exponential model to estimate the city's population in 2017 (to the nearest hundred thousand).

   c. Use your exponential model to predict the year in which the city's population will reach 8.5 million.

18. Chicago, Illinois, experienced its first ever population drop when its population declined from 3,620,962 in 1950 to 3,550,404 in 1960.

   a. Using t to represent the number of years since 1950, find the population's average annual rate of decline from 1950 to 1960 and write an exponential function modeling the population.

   b. Use your exponential model to estimate the city's population (to the nearest thousand) in 1955.

   c. If the decline in population continued at the same average annual rate, in which year would the population have fallen to 3.2 million?

The table lists typical atmospheric pressures at various altitudes.

Altitude (1000 ft)	Atmospheric Pressure (psi)
0	14.70
5	12.23
10	10.11
15	8.30
20	6.76
25	5.46
30	4.37

19. Use technology to create a scatterplot and complete an exponential regression to find a function that models atmospheric pressure in terms of thousands of feet in altitude.

20. Use the function to estimate the atmospheric pressure at 36,000 ft, the altitude of a cruising airliner.

21. Estimate the altitude (to the nearest hundred feet) with an atmospheric pressure of 3 psi.

In 1782 when the United States adopted it as the national bird, the American bald eagle population consisted of an estimated 100,000 nesting pairs. By 1963, the bald eagle was placed on the endangered species list with an estimated 487 nesting pairs. Letting x represent the number of years since 1900, create a scatterplot of the data.

Year	Nesting Pairs
1963	487
1974	791
1981	1188
1984	1757
1990	3035
1996	5094
2000	6471

22. Complete a regression to find an exponential function that models the data. Then use the model to predict (to the nearest hundred) the number of nesting pairs in 2006 and 2010.

23. Complete a regression to find a logistic function that models the data. Then use the model to predict (to the nearest hundred) the number of nesting pairs in 2006 and 2010.

24. Which model produces lower estimates? Explain why.

The table lists the frequencies for several keys on the piano.

Note	Frequency (Hz)	Key Number
A_0	27.5000	1
$A\sharp/Bb_0$	29.1352	2
C_1	32.7032	4
E_1	41.2034	8
F_1	43.6536	9
G_1	48.9994	11
A_1	55.0000	13

25. Use technology to create a scatterplot and complete a regression to find a logarithmic function that models each note's key number on the piano in terms of its frequency.

26. Use the function to find the key on the piano with a frequency of 3951.07 Hz.

27. Find the frequency for piano key number 68.

28. Concrete gets stronger as it cures over time. The table lists the maximum compressive pressures (in megapascals, MPa) that columns of fabric-formed concrete were able to withstand while curing. Create a scatterplot and complete a regression to find a logarithmic function that models the data. Then use the model to estimate the maximum pressure the columns can withstand 2.5 weeks after being formed.

Curing Time (weeks)	Max. Pressure (MPa)
1	22
2	27
3	31
4	34
5	36
6	38
7	39
8	40

Create a scatterplot of the data for exercises 29–31.

x	y
1	26
2	33
3	44
4	57
5	74
6	96
7	126
8	163

29. Which two types of modeling functions does the scatterplot suggest?

30. Use technology to create linearization data and scatterplots to test which type of function provides the best model. Use your results to complete a linear regression and state the linear function modeling the transformed data. Round constants to the nearest ten thousandth.

31. Substitute for X and Y in the linear model of the transformed data and derive a function modeling the original data.

Create a scatterplot of the data for exercises 32–34.

x	y
1	1
2	3.7
3	5.4
4	6.5
5	7.4
6	8.2
7	8.8
8	9.3

32. Which two types of modeling functions does the scatterplot suggest?

33. Use technology to create linearization data and scatterplots to test which type of function provides the best model. Use your results to complete a linear regression and state the linear function modeling the transformed data. Round constants to the nearest ten thousandth.

34. Substitute for X and Y in the linear model of the transformed data and derive a function modeling the original data.

35. **Explain:** Why are logistic functions typically used to model population growth instead of exponential functions?

36. **Analyze:** Identify the carrying capacity of the logistic function $f(x) = \dfrac{5}{1 + 3e^{-2x}}$.

37. **Research:** List several primary factors that affect an environment's carrying capacity for a population.

> ## C. Exercises

38. Derive a formula for average annual rate of growth from an initial amount P_i to a final amount P_f in n years.

39. **Explain:** What is the result of completing a logarithmic regression on the following data? Which value causes this result? Explain why.

x	15	7	3	1	0
y	6	5	4	3	2

Create a scatterplot of the data for exercises 40–44.

40. Which two possible types of modeling functions does the scatterplot suggest?

41. Use technology to create linearization data and scatterplots to test which type of function provides the best model. Use your results to complete a linear regression and state the linear function modeling the transformed data and the coefficient of determination. Round constants to the nearest ten thousandth.

x	y
2	0.3010
3	0.4771
4	0.6021
5	0.6990
6	0.7782
7	0.8451
8	0.9031
9	0.9542
10	1.0000

42. Substitute for X and Y in the linear model of the transformed data and derive a function modeling the original data.

43. Use the modeling function to evaluate $f(100)$, $f(1000)$, and $f(10,000)$.

44. Use the change of base formula to express $f(x) = \log x$ in terms of natural logs. What does your solution reveal about the data set in the table?

CUMULATIVE REVIEW

Identify all asymptotes and point discontinuities in each function. [2.5]

45. $f(x) = \dfrac{5-x}{x^2 - 25}$

46. $f(x) = \dfrac{x^2 - x - 6}{x^3 + x^2 - x - 1}$

Solve each inequality by factoring and using a sign chart. [2.7]

47. $2x^2 + 3x - 20 \leq 0$

48. $x^3 - 3x^2 + 2x - 6 > 0$

49. Determine the account balance of a $12,000 investment compounded quarterly at 1.5% interest for 10 yr. [3.1]

50. Write a function rule for $g(x)$, the described transformation of $f(x) = 5^x$, if $f(x)$ is translated 2 units left, reflected in the y-axis, stretched vertically by a factor of 3, and translated 1 unit down. [3.1]

51. Which of the following are not inverse functions? [1.8, 3.2]

A. $y = 2x$ and $y = \frac{1}{2}x$

B. $y = x^2$ and $y = \sqrt{x}$

C. $y = x^3$ and $y = \sqrt[3]{x}$

D. $y = 3^x$ and $y = \log_3 x$

E. These are all inverse functions.

52. Which expression is equivalent to $3 \ln x + 2 \ln 3 - 4 \ln y$? [3.3]

A. $\ln \dfrac{x^3 + 9}{y^4}$

B. $\ln \dfrac{6x^3}{y^4}$

C. $\ln \dfrac{9x^3}{y^4}$

D. $\ln 9x^3 y^4$

E. none of these

53. Solve $\left(\dfrac{1}{3}\right)^{x-2} = 81$. [3.4]

A. $x = -2$

B. $x = 2$

C. $x = 6$

D. $x = 4$

E. none of these

54. Solve $\log_3 (x + 1) + \log_3 (x + 3) = 1$. [3.4]

A. $x = 4$

B. $x = -4$

C. $x = 0, -4$

D. $x = 0$

E. none of these

DATA ANALYSIS

Year	Population (billions)
1927	2
1960	3
1974	4
1987	5
1999	6
2011	7

A World Population Crisis?

How long can the earth sustain its current population growth? Will we run out of space for people to live? Will we experience widespread food and water shortages? Many people are looking for answers to these questions. We can use mathematical analysis of world population data to see patterns in population growth and to predict future populations. At the same time, God's Word provides insight into how we should respond to these concerns.

1. Use technology to complete a scatterplot of the world population data where x represents the number of years since 1900. Which type of function(s) might be used to model world population?

2. Complete a linear regression and state the resulting linear function and its coefficient of determination. Round constants to the nearest ten thousandth.

3. Apply the linear model.
   a. What is the average annual population increase (in millions) during this time?
   b. Estimate the world's population in 2030.
   c. Predict the year in which the world's population will reach 9 billion.

4. Analyze the linear model.
   a. Does the coefficient of determination indicate a strong correlation?
   b. Use technology to plot the residuals. What conclusion can be drawn from this graph?

5. Using technology, create linearization data and scatterplots to test whether a power, exponential, or logarithmic function provides the best model. Which model is suggested by these graphs? Use your results to complete a linear regression and state the linear function modeling the transformed data. Round constants to the nearest ten thousandth.

6. Substitute for X and Y in the linear model of the transformed data and derive a function modeling the original data.

7. Complete a regression for the original data to find the equation for the best-fit model and state its coefficient of determination. Compare this function to the one derived in exercise 6.

8. Apply the nonlinear model.
   a. What is the average annual population growth rate during this time?
   b. Estimate the world's population in 2030.
   c. Predict the year in which the world's population will reach 9 billion.

9. Analyze the nonlinear model.
   a. Does the coefficient of determination indicate a stronger correlation?
   b. Use technology to plot the residuals. What conclusion can be drawn from this graph?
   c. The US Census Bureau estimates that the world population will reach 8 billion in 2024 and 9 billion in 2042. Do they expect the population to grow at about the same rate, at a significantly faster rate, or at a significantly slower rate than your exponential model predicts?

10. State reasons for and against the use of a logistic function to model the world population.

11. List several factors that might restrict human population growth.

12. Since bacteria, plants, and animals have very little control over their environment, they cannot voluntarily affect the carrying capacity for their populations. How does the fact that we are created in God's image allow us to affect the carrying capacity of human populations? State several examples.

13. How can population growth models help us fulfill our biblical responsibilities?

While data can help us make informed decisions, our worldview influences our response to world population growth. Responses shaped by biblical and secular worldviews, such as making clean water more available, can be similar. However, there are times when these worldviews generate very different responses.

14. List several unethical practices that have affected human population growth.

15. What are some ways in which a biblical worldview will affect our response to a growing world population?

16. Consider this quote from former president George H. W. Bush: "Every human being represents hands to work, and not just another mouth to feed." How should we relate the biblical commands to exercise dominion and fill the earth (Gen. 1:28) to concerns about the world's population growth?

Chapter 3 Review

1. Classify each function as a power function, an exponential function, or neither. **[3.1]**

   a. $f(x) = 4^x$ **b.** $h(x) = \left(\frac{1}{6}\right)^x$ **c.** $q(x) = \frac{1}{2}x^3$

Graph each exponential function by finding several ordered pairs. State the function's domain and range, then classify it as exponential growth or decay. [3.1]

2. $g(x) = 3 \cdot 2^x$ 3. $y = \left(\frac{1}{4}\right)^x$

4. Describe how the graph of $f(x) = 2^x$ is transformed to obtain the graph of $g(x) = 2^{x-3} + 1$. Use the graph of $f(x)$ to sketch the graph of $g(x)$ and then state the domain and range of $g(x)$. **[3.1]**

5. Describe how the graph of $f(x) = 2^x$ is transformed to obtain the graph of $g(x) = -4 \cdot 2^{x-3} + 1$. Use the graph of $f(x)$ to sketch the graph of $g(x)$ and then state the domain, range, intercepts, asymptotes, and end behavior of $g(x)$. **[3.1]**

Write a function rule for $g(x)$, the described transformation of $f(x)$. Then confirm your answer by graphing $f(x)$ and $g(x)$ in the same window. [3.1]

6. $f(x) = 5^x$ is translated 4 units to the left and 1 unit up.

7. $f(x) = e^x$ is reflected in the x-axis, vertically stretched by a factor of 3, then translated 2 units to the right and 1 unit down.

8. Determine the account balance of an investment of $25,000 at 1.5% APR after 10 yr when compounded (a) annually, (b) monthly, and (c) continuously.

9. In 1989 the population of the Florida panther was estimated to be 46, and the species was placed on the endangered list. By 2017 the panther's population had increased to approximately 100. Determine the population's average annual rate of increase during this time. Then use an exponential growth model to predict the population in 2025. **[3.1]**

10. A sample is determined to contain 27 g of barium-139, an isotope with a half-life of 83 min. How much barium-139 remains 2.5 hr later? **[3.1]**

11. Convert to logarithmic form. **[3.2]**

   a. $7^2 = 49$ **b.** $4^3 = 64$

   c. $6^{-2} = \frac{1}{36}$ **d.** $\left(\frac{1}{5}\right)^3 = \frac{1}{125}$

12. Convert to exponential form. **[3.2]**

   a. $\log_4 16 = 2$ **b.** $\log_{\frac{1}{3}} \frac{1}{27} = 3$

   c. $\log 0.00001 = -5$ **d.** $\ln \frac{1}{e^2} = -2$

Evaluate each expression. Round answers to the nearest ten thousandth if necessary. [3.2]

13. $\log_3 81$ 14. $\ln \sqrt{e}$

15. $e^{\ln 5}$ 16. $\log 50$

17. Graph $f(x) = \log_6 x$. Then state its domain and range. **[3.2]**

18. Describe $g(x) = \log_2 (x + 3)$ as a transformation of $f(x) = \log_2 x$, then graph both functions. **[3.2]**

19. Describe $g(x) = -2 \log_3 x + 2$ as a transformation of $f(x) = \log_3 x$, then use a graph of $f(x)$ to sketch the graph of $g(x)$. State the transformed function's domain and range, any asymptotes and intercepts, and the end behavior. **[3.2]**

20. Use the investment doubling formula, $T = \dfrac{\ln 2}{\ln (1 + APY)}$, to determine how many years, T, it will take Robert to double his $10,000 investment in a certificate of deposit (CD) with an APY of 2.5%. **[3.2]**

Expand each logarithmic expression. Assume all variables are positive values. [3.3]

21. $\log x^2 y$ 22. $\log \frac{x^3}{15}$

23. $\ln \sqrt[3]{\dfrac{a^2}{b^4}}$

Write each expression as a single logarithm. [3.3]

24. $\log x + 2 \log 3$

25. $\frac{1}{2}(4 \log x + \log y) - 3 \log z$

26. $2 \ln 5x + \ln 10y - \ln 5$

27. Use $\log_7 2 \approx 0.3562$ and $\log_7 3 \approx 0.5646$ to find a decimal approximation of each logarithm. [3.3]

   a. $\log_7 24$ **b.** $\log_7 14\sqrt{2}$

28. Use common logs to evaluate each logarithm. [3.3]

   a. $\log_2 40$ **b.** $\log_6 108$

29. Use natural logs to evaluate each logarithm. [3.3]

   a. $\log_4 24$ **b.** $\log_3 21$

30. Describe the graph of $g(x)$ as a transformation of $f(x) = \ln x$. [3.3]

   a. $g(x) = \log_5 x$ **b.** $g(x) = \log_{\frac{1}{2}} x$

Solve each exponential equation. [3.4]

31. $5^x = \dfrac{1}{625}$ **32.** $8^x = \left(\dfrac{1}{32}\right)^{-3x+12}$

Solve each logarithmic equation. [3.4]

33. $\log_2 (3x + 11) = 5$ **34.** $\ln (x - 5) = \ln x - \ln 6$

Find all real solutions for x. Round answers to the nearest thousandth. [3.4]

35. $5^{x+3} = e^{4x}$

36. $e^{2x} + 2e^x - 48 = 0$

37. $\log_5 2 - \log_5 \frac{2}{5} = 12x$

38. $\ln x + \ln (x + 5) = \ln 14$

39. A customer was served a cup of 186°F coffee in a café whose temperature was 71°F. The coffee cooled to 171°F in 3 min. Its temperature can be modeled using Newton's law of cooling: $T(t) = T_S + (T_0 - T_S)e^{-kt}$, where T_0 is the object's initial temperature, T_S is the surrounding medium's temperature, k is the cooling constant, and t is the time. [3.4]

   a. Find the value of k and state the function modeling the coffee's temperature.

   b. Estimate the temperature of the coffee 10 min after being served.

40. The periodic payment P for a home mortgage of B dollars can be calculated using the equation $P = \dfrac{iB}{1 - (1 + i)^{-n}}$ where i is the periodic interest rate and n is the number of payments. [3.4]

   a. Calculate the monthly payment for a 30 yr mortgage of $300,000 with a 4.2% APR.

   b. Solve the equation for n and determine the number of payments required to pay off the loan with monthly payments of $1700.

41. The population around Austin, Texas, grew from 465,622 people in 1990 to 656,562 people in 2000. Determine the average annual rate of growth during this time and use it to write an exponential function modeling the population. [3.5]

   a. Use the exponential function to estimate the population (to the nearest thousand) in 2015.

   b. Use the exponential function to predict the year in which the population will reach 1.25 million.

Use the population data for Austin, Texas, (rounded to the nearest thousand) to complete exercises 42–43. [3.5]

Year	Population	Year	Population
1920	35,000	1970	254,000
1930	53,000	1980	346,000
1940	88,000	1990	466,000
1950	132,000	2000	657,000
1960	187,000	2010	790,000

42. Letting t represent the number of years since 1900, complete a regression to find an exponential function $P(t)$ that models the population of Austin, Texas (in thousands).

   a. Use your model to estimate the 2015 population (to the nearest thousand).

   b. Use your model to estimate the year in which the population will reach 1.25 million.

43. Letting t represent the number of years since 1900, complete a regression to find a logistic function $P(t)$ that models the population of Austin, Texas (in thousands).

   a. State the carrying capacity predicted by your model (to the nearest thousand).

   b. Use your model to graphically estimate the 2015 population (to the nearest thousand).

   c. Use your model to graphically estimate the year in which the population will reach 1.25 million.

44. Create a scatterplot and complete a regression to find a logarithmic function that models the data. Then estimate $f(12)$. [3.5]

x	y
1	5.00
2	13.30
3	18.18
4	21.64
5	24.31
6	26.50

45. Identify the type of function associated with each linearized data transformation. [3.5]

   a. $(X, Y) = (\ln x, y)$

   b. $(X, Y) = (\ln x, \ln y)$

   c. $(X, Y) = (x, \ln y)$

Use the following data to complete exercises 46–47.
[3.5]

x	y
1	0.12
2	2.00
3	10.13
4	32.00
5	78.12
6	163.00

46. Use technology to create a scatterplot for the data. Then create linearization data and scatterplots to test whether a power, exponential, or logarithmic function provides the best model. Which model is suggested by your graphs?

47. Complete a regression for the linear transformed data set and state the linear function modeling the transformed data. (Round constants to 4 decimal places.) Then substitute into the linear equation and derive a function modeling the original data.

4 Trigonometric Functions

 HISTORICAL CONNECTION

Trigonometry, born out of an effort to understand movement in the "celestial sphere," initially had as much to do with circles and spheres as it did with triangles.

 BIBLICAL PERSPECTIVE OF MATHEMATICS

The development of abstract mathematics has allowed us to explore the vastness of God's creation. Stanley L. Jaki notes in *The Relevance of Physics* that "the science of trigonometry was in a sense a precursor of the telescope. It brought faraway objects within the compass of measurement and first made it possible for man to penetrate in a quantitative manner the far reaches of space."

 DATA ANALYSIS

Regularly recurring (cyclic) patterns are found in abundance in natural and manmade systems. Since trigonometric functions are cyclical, they are used to model many practical applications, including the occurrence of sunspots.

This statue on Nepean Point in Ottawa depicts the French explorer Samuel de Champlain holding an astrolabe, which would have helped him navigate by using the sun's angle of elevation above the horizon.

After completing this section, you will be able to

- draw an angle in standard position.
- convert between degrees, minutes, and seconds; decimal degrees; and radian measures of angles.
- identify coterminal angles.
- calculate arc length and sector area using angle measure and radius length.
- calculate angular and linear speeds.

The term *trigonometry* is derived from Greek words meaning "triangle measure." Ancient civilizations used the relationships between the sides and angles of right triangles in surveying, navigation, engineering, and astronomy. Trigonometry was then expanded to explain circular and harmonic phenomena, including orbits, vibrating strings, pendulums, and electrical current.

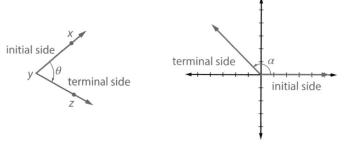

In geometry, an angle is often defined as the union of two rays with a common endpoint, or *vertex*. An angle can also be viewed as the sweep of a ray moving from an initial position to a final position, similar to the sweep of a clock's hand in a given period of time. An angle is in *standard position* when it is placed on the coordinate plane with its vertex at the origin and the initial position of the ray aligned with the positive x-axis. The final position of the sweeping ray is the *terminal side* of the angle.

An angle is often named by its vertex, such as $\angle Y$. When more than one angle has its vertex at Y, three letters are used to avoid confusion, as in $\angle XYZ$. In this text, $m\angle Y$ is frequently notated simply as Y. Lowercase Greek letters such as α (alpha), β (beta), or θ (theta) are also used to name an angle or indicate its measure.

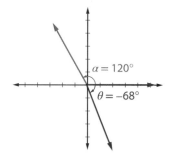

When an angle is viewed as a rotation, its measure includes both the direction and amount of rotation. In mathematics, a counterclockwise rotation is described as a *positive angle* and a clockwise rotation is described as a *negative angle*. The amount of rotation can be measured in *degrees*, where $1°$ represents $\frac{1}{360}$ of a circle. In the illustration, $\alpha = 120°$ and $\theta = -68°$. Degrees can be further divided using decimal degrees (DD) or degrees, minutes, and seconds (DMS), in which a *minute* ($1'$) is $\frac{1}{60}$ of a degree and a *second* ($1''$) is $\frac{1}{60}$ of a minute (or $\frac{1}{3600}$ of a degree). In navigation, angles representing bearings are measured from due north where clockwise rotations are positive.

Example 1 Describing a Navigational Bearing

Represent a ship's bearing, given in DMS form as 127°30′9″, as a standard position angle in DD form.

The DMS divisions of a circle are rooted in the Babylonian sexagesimal (base 60) number system and the ease of dividing a circle's circumference into equal arcs with 6 equilateral triangles. The fact that a year is approximately 360 days may also have been an influencing factor.

Answer

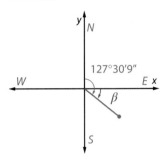

1. Sketch the ship's bearing.

$$127° + 30′\left(\frac{1°}{60′}\right) + 9″\left(\frac{1°}{3600″}\right)$$
$$\approx 127° + 0.5° + 0.0025°$$
$$\approx 127.5025°$$

2. Convert DMS form to DD form.

$$127.5025° - 90° = 37.5025°$$
$$\beta = -37.5025°$$

3. Express the terminal ray as a negative rotation from the positive *x*-axis.

Check

$$0.5025°\left(\frac{60′}{1°}\right) = 30.15′$$

4. Convert the decimal portion of the degrees to minutes.

$$30′ + 0.15′\left(\frac{60″}{1′}\right) = 30′\,9″$$

5. Convert the decimal portion of the minutes to seconds.

SKILL ✓ **EXERCISE 9**

While degrees work well for navigation and construction, many applications involving trigonometric functions require the domain to be real numbers. Using *radian measure* allows both the domain and the range to be expressed with real numbers having similar units.

> ▌**DEFINITIONS**
>
> The **radian measure** of an angle θ is the ratio of its intercepted arc's length s to the circle's radius r: $\theta = \frac{s}{r}$. A central angle that intercepts an arc whose length is the same as the circle's radius has a measure of 1 **radian**.

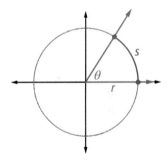

Note that a radian measure is a real number with no units since it is a ratio of two lengths. The relationship between radian and degree measures can be derived by considering the arc length of one complete rotation of 360°: $s = 2\pi r$, the circumference of a circle.

$$\theta = \frac{s}{r} = \frac{2\pi r}{r} = 2\pi \text{ radians} = 360°$$
$$\pi \text{ radians} = 180°$$

This relationship produces two unit multipliers that can be used to convert between radians and degrees.

$$\frac{\pi \text{ radians}}{180°} = 1 \text{ and } \frac{180°}{\pi \text{ radians}} = 1$$

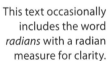
TIP

This text occasionally includes the word *radians* with a radian measure for clarity.

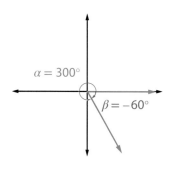

Example 2 Converting between Degree and Radian Measures

Convert each degree measure to radians and each radian measure to degrees.

a. 90° **b.** −225° **c.** $\frac{2\pi}{3}$ **d.** 6

Answer

a. $90°\left(\frac{\pi \text{ radians}}{180°}\right) = \frac{\pi}{2} \approx 1.57$ **b.** $-225°\left(\frac{\pi \text{ radians}}{180°}\right) = -\frac{5\pi}{4} \approx -3.93$

c. $\frac{2\pi}{3}\left(\frac{180°}{\pi \text{ radians}}\right) = 120°$ **d.** $6\left(\frac{180°}{\pi \text{ radians}}\right) = \frac{1080}{\pi} \approx 343.8°$

SKILL ✔ **EXERCISE 11**

The terminal side of an *acute* angle (radian measure $0 < \theta < \frac{\pi}{2}$) lies in Quadrant I, and the terminal side of an *obtuse* angle ($\frac{\pi}{2} < \theta < \pi$) lies in Quadrant II. The terminal side of a *quadrantal angle* ($\theta = n\frac{\pi}{2}, n \in \mathbb{Z}$) lies on one of the axes.

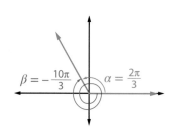

Two angles in standard position with the same terminal ray are called *coterminal angles*. Since the dynamic view of angles allows a ray to sweep in either direction or to sweep through one or more complete circles before taking its terminal position, any angle has an infinite number of coterminal angles. Coterminal angles can be found by adding or subtracting multiples of 360° or 2π radians. For example, a 300° angle is coterminal with angles of −60°, 660°, and −420°.

Example 3 Finding Coterminal Angles

Write an expression for all angles coterminal with $\theta = -\frac{4\pi}{3}$.
Then specify one positive and one negative coterminal angle.

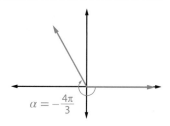

Answer

$-\frac{4\pi}{3} + n2\pi, n \in \mathbb{N}$ 1. Coterminal angles can be found by adding and subtracting multiples of 2π.

$\alpha = -\frac{4\pi}{3} + (1)2\pi = \frac{2\pi}{3}$ 2. Let $n = 1$ and add 2π to find a positive coterminal angle.

$\beta = -\frac{4\pi}{3} - (1)2\pi = -\frac{10\pi}{3}$ 3. Let $n = -1$ and subtract 2π to find a negative coterminal angle.

SKILL ✔ **EXERCISE 21**

Solving the definition of radian measure, $\theta = \frac{s}{r}$, for r leads directly to a formula for *arc length*.

▌ARC LENGTH FORMULA

A central angle of radian measure θ in a circle with radius length r intercepts an arc with length $s = r\theta$.

Note that when $r = 1$, the arc length is equal to the radian measure of the central angle. When the central angle is given in degrees, convert to radian measure before applying the arc length formula.

Example 4 Finding Arc Length

A nautical mile has historically been defined as 1 minute of latitude at the earth's equator. Determine the relationship between a (statute) mile and a nautical mile (nm), given that the earth's average radius at the equator is 3959 mi.

Answer

$\theta = \frac{1°}{60}\left(\frac{\pi \text{ radians}}{180°}\right) = \frac{\pi}{10{,}800}$

1. Convert 1 minute to radian measure.

$s = r\theta = (3959 \text{ mi})\left(\frac{\pi}{10{,}800}\right)$
$\approx 1.15 \text{ mi}$

2. Apply the arc length formula.

$\therefore 1 \text{ nm} \approx 1.15 \text{ mi}$

SKILL ✓ **EXERCISE 37**

The study of *uniform circular motion* analyzes the linear and angular speeds of an object moving in a circular path at a constant speed. The *angular speed*, usually denoted with the lowercase Greek letter omega (ω), is the ratio of the angle of rotation (in radians) per unit of time: $\omega = \frac{\theta}{t}$. Angular speed stated in terms of revolutions can be converted to radians using the unit multiplier $\frac{2\pi \text{ radians}}{1 \text{ revolution}}$. The *linear speed* is the ratio of arc length, or distance traveled, per unit of time: $v = \frac{s}{t}$. Since $s = r\theta$, $v = \frac{r\theta}{t} = r\left(\frac{\theta}{t}\right) = r\omega$.

> ▎**UNIFORM CIRCULAR MOTION FORMULAS**
>
> If θ is the radian measure of the angle of rotation,
> then the angular speed is $\omega = \frac{\theta}{t}$ and the linear speed is $v = \frac{s}{t} = r\omega$.

Example 5 Analyzing Uniform Circular Motion

Karyn is playing an LP vinyl record at $33\frac{1}{3}$ rpm (revolutions per minute) on her vintage record player. Determine the angular speed of the record (in radians per second). Then find the linear speed (in inches per second) of a point at the edge of the record (6 in. from the center) and the linear speed of a point at the edge of its label (2 in. from the center).

Answer

$\omega = \frac{100 \text{ revolutions}}{3 \text{ min}}\left(\frac{2\pi \text{ radians}}{1 \text{ revolution}}\right)\left(\frac{1 \text{ min}}{60 \text{ sec}}\right)$
$= \frac{10\pi \text{ radians}}{9 \text{ sec}} \approx 3.49 \text{ radians/sec}$

1. Convert the angular speed from revolutions per minute to radians per second.

$v_6 = r\omega = (6 \text{ in.})\left(\frac{10\pi}{9 \text{ sec}}\right)$
$= \frac{20\pi \text{ in.}}{3 \text{ sec}} \approx 20.94 \text{ in./sec}$

$v_2 = (2 \text{ in.})\left(\frac{10\pi}{9 \text{ sec}}\right) = \frac{20\pi \text{ in.}}{9 \text{ sec}} \approx 6.98 \text{ in./sec}$

2. Substitute into $v = r\omega$ to find each linear speed.
Since the radian measure is a ratio of two lengths, it is a real number and the label is not needed.

SKILL ✓ **EXERCISE 33**

Radian measure provides a convenient formula for the area of a *sector* of a circle, the region bounded by two radii and the intercepted arc. Recall from GEOMETRY that the ratio of the area of a sector and the circle's area is equal to ratio of the central angle and a complete rotation: $\frac{A_{sector}}{\pi r^2} = \frac{\theta}{2\pi}$. Solving for the area of the sector, $A_{sector} = \left(\frac{\theta}{2\pi}\right)\pi r^2 = \frac{1}{2}r^2\theta$.

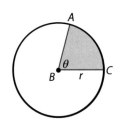

Example 6   Finding the Area of a Sector

If the shaded sector has an area of 24π m^2 and $BA = 12$ m, find the radian measure and the degree measure of $\angle ABC$.

Answer

$A_{sector} = \frac{1}{2}r^2\theta$

$\theta = \frac{2A_{sector}}{r^2}$

$\theta = \frac{2(24\pi \text{ m}^2)}{(12 \text{ m})^2} = \frac{48\pi \text{ m}^2}{144 \text{ m}^2} = \frac{\pi}{3}$

$\frac{\pi}{3}$ radians $\left(\frac{180°}{\pi \text{ radians}}\right) = 60°$

1. Solve the formula for the area of a sector for θ, the radian measure of the angle.

2. Substitute and simplify to express θ in radians.

3. Convert radians to degrees.

SKILL ✓ **EXERCISE 31**

A. Exercises

1. Sketch a standard position angle with each degree measure.

   a. 45°   **b.** −30°

   c. −225°   **d.** 500°

2. Sketch a standard position angle with each radian measure.

   a. $\frac{5\pi}{4}$ **b.** $-\pi$

   c. $\frac{-4\pi}{3}$ **d.** $\frac{15\pi}{4}$

Convert to degrees, minutes, and seconds (DMS).

3. −2.87°   **4.** 110.51°   **5.** 48.362°

Convert to decimal degrees (DD).

6. −58°54′   **7.** 98°45′43.2″   **8.** 135°35′38.4″

Convert each degree measure to radian measure. Express the answer in terms of π and as a decimal approximation rounded to the nearest hundredth.

9. 35°   **10.** −40°

11. 1080°   **12.** 154.5°

Convert each radian measure to degrees. Round answers to the nearest tenth of a degree if necessary.

13. $\frac{\pi}{5}$ **14.** $-\frac{7\pi}{2}$

15. $\frac{\pi}{12}$ **16.** 5

17. Identify the missing degree or radian measure of the standard position angle whose terminal side passes through each point (A–K).

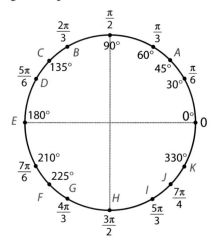

B. Exercises

18. How many degrees (to the nearest tenth) are in one radian? How many radians (to the nearest ten thousandth) are in one degree?

For each angle, write an expression for all coterminal angles. Then state one positive and one negative coterminal angle.

19. $\alpha = 148°$ **20.** $\alpha = -200°$

21. $\alpha = \frac{\pi}{4}$ **22.** $-\frac{5\pi}{3}$

23. Which of the following angles are coterminal to $\alpha = \frac{\pi}{5}$? Select all that apply.

   A. $\frac{4\pi}{5}$ **B.** $\frac{11\pi}{5}$ **C.** 756°   **D.** −324°

Find the missing arc length, radius measure, or angle measure (in radians).

	Arc (s)	Radius (r)	Angle (θ)
24.		8	$\frac{\pi}{4}$
25.	6π	4	
26.	$\frac{\pi}{2}$		$\frac{\pi}{6}$
27.	3π	6	

28. An air traffic controller notes that an airplane flying from Kansas City to Los Angeles at a bearing of 259°38′6″ will be landing shortly. Represent the plane's bearing as a standard position angle in decimal degrees (DD).

29. If the pendulum of a grandfather clock is 94 cm long, how far does the end of the pendulum travel as it swings through an angle of 6°? If the pendulum is lengthened by 2 cm to prevent the clock from running too fast, how much farther does the end swing through its 6° arc? Round answers to the nearest hundredth of a centimeter.

30. If a sprinkler rotates 60° and the nozzle streams water 5 ft away, find the area watered (to the nearest tenth of a square foot).

31. A 24 in. diameter prize wheel is divided into 16 equal sectors. Find the arc length and the area of one sector. Round answers to the nearest tenth.

32. A compact circular saw operates at a maximum speed of 3500 rpm and has a blade with a diameter of 4.5 in. Find the angular speed of the blade (in radians per second) and the linear speed (in inches per second) for a tip of the sawblade. Round answers to the nearest tenth.

33. A floor buffer with a 20 in. radius operates at 1500 rpm. Find the angular speed of the buffer (in radians per second) and the difference of the linear speeds (in miles per hour) for a point on the outer edge of the buffer pad and a point on the edge of the 3 in. diameter hole in the center of the pad. Round answers to the nearest tenth.

34. Show algebraically that every angle coterminal with 2π is an even multiple of π.

35. Show algebraically that every angle coterminal with π is an odd multiple of π.

36. Write an equation expressing the difference of any two coterminal angles α and θ.

C. Exercises

37. Minneapolis, Minnesota, is located at 44°59′ N and Springfield, Missouri, is located at 37°13′ N on the same longitudinal line. Estimate the distance between the cities (to the nearest mile), using 3959 mi as the radius of the earth.

38. Samuel is making a 3D pie chart with a 3 ft diameter for a presentation and plans to cover each slice with fabric. If the pie chart is 6 in. thick, how much fabric (to the nearest tenth of a square foot) will be used to cover the top and the sides of the slice that represents 40% of the spending?

39. An amusement park is planning the *Centrihuge*, a new ride that presses passengers against the wall of a circular cylinder as it spins at 24 rpm.
    a. Determine the angular speed of the ride (in radians per second).
    b. Find the linear speed (in miles per hour) of a person on the wall for rides with diameters of 45 ft and 48 ft.

40. A 1300 ft long center-pivot irrigation system with 10 equally spaced trusses takes 72 hr for each rotation over a circular field.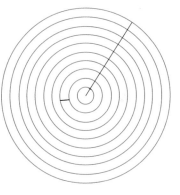
    a. Find the distance that the third irrigation truss from the center travels in 9 hr.
    b. How many acres are irrigated between the third and outermost trusses in 9 hr? (1 acre = 43,560 ft²)
    c. Find the angular speed (in radians per hour) of the irrigation system.
    d. Find the linear speed (in feet per hour) of the first truss and the ninth truss.

41. A freestyle bike competitor pedals at his maximum speed of 24 mi/hr as he approaches a ramp on an obstacle course. If the diameters of his rear wheel, wheel sprocket, and pedal sprocket are 20 in., 3 in., and 6 in., respectively, find the angular speed (in radians per second) of each component. *Hint*: Every point along the chain moves at the same linear speed.

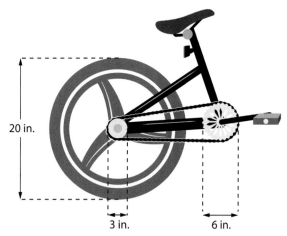

20 in.

3 in.   6 in.

42. Use the table listing the maximum speed for each gear of a racecar with 25.8 in. diameter tires to find the maximum angular speed of its tires in each gear (in radians per second and revolutions per second).

Gear	1st	2nd	3rd	4th	5th
Max Speed (mi/hr)	60	92	124	158	202

a. 1st   **b.** 5th

CUMULATIVE REVIEW

State the domain of each function. [2.1]

43. $f(x) = \sqrt{x + 7}$

44. $f(x) = \sqrt{x - 12}$

List all the possible rational zeros for each polynomial function. [2.4]

45. $p(x) = x^4 + 16$

46. $p(x) = 4x^3 - 5x^2 - 7x + 2$

47. A fishpond has an expected annual growth rate of 8%. Write an exponential function that models the fish population, given a current population of 2000 fish. [3.1]

48. Solve $3^{x-7} = 26.2$. [3.4]

49. Solve for x. [Algebra]

A. $2\sqrt{13}$ **D.** $4\sqrt{13}$
B. $2\sqrt{17}$ **E.** none of these
C. $4\sqrt{17}$

x

9

17

50. Which of the following is true if $x + 3$ is a factor of $p(x)$? [2.3]

A. $x - 3$ is a factor of $p(x)$.
B. -3 is a zero of $p(x)$.
C. 3 is a zero of $p(x)$.
D. $p(3) = 0$
E. none of these

51. Determine the account balance of a $25,000 investment compounded quarterly at 3.75% interest for 15 yr. [3.1]

A. $43,761.55   **D.** $43,875.10
B. $43,648.43   **E.** none of these
C. $43,837.90

52. Use the properties of logarithms to evaluate $3^{\log_3 \frac{1}{9}}$. [3.2]

A. 3   **D.** $\frac{1}{3}$
B. $\frac{1}{9}$ **E.** none of these
C. 9

Right Triangle Trigonometry

The change in altitude when climbing from Lake Phelps to the peak of the Grand Teton can be estimated using trigonometry.

We will initially limit our study of *trigonometric functions* (frequently abbreviated as *trig functions*) to the acute angles found in right triangles. The hypotenuse of the illustrated right triangle is the side opposite right $\angle C$. The angles are commonly designated by uppercase letters such as A and B, or by Greek letters such as α and β. Lowercase letters a, b, and c represent the lengths of sides opposite the corresponding vertices A, B, and C. Recall that the lengths of the three sides in the illustrated right triangle are related by the Pythagorean Theorem: $a^2 + b^2 = c^2$.

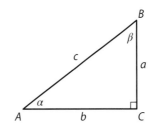

After completing this section, you will be able to

- evaluate the six trigonometric ratios of an acute angle.
- solve right triangles.
- solve real-world problems involving angles of elevation and depression.

The trigonometric functions describe the six possible ratios of side lengths in terms of their relationship to an acute angle of a right triangle.

Basic Trigonometric Functions	Reciprocal Trigonometric Functions
sine of $\angle A = \sin A = \dfrac{\text{leg opposite } \angle A}{\text{hypotenuse}}$ $= \dfrac{opp.}{hyp.} = \dfrac{a}{c}$	**cosecant** of $\angle A = \csc A = \dfrac{1}{\sin A}$ $= \dfrac{hyp.}{opp.} = \dfrac{c}{a}$
cosine of $\angle A = \cos A = \dfrac{\text{leg adjacent } \angle A}{\text{hypotenuse}}$ $= \dfrac{adj.}{hyp.} = \dfrac{b}{c}$	**secant** of $\angle A = \sec A = \dfrac{1}{\cos A}$ $= \dfrac{hyp.}{adj.} = \dfrac{c}{b}$
tangent of $\angle A = \tan A = \dfrac{\text{leg opposite } \angle A}{\text{leg adjacent } \angle A}$ $= \dfrac{opp.}{adj.} = \dfrac{a}{b}$	**cotangent** of $\angle A = \cot A = \dfrac{1}{\tan A}$ $= \dfrac{adj.}{opp.} = \dfrac{b}{a}$

The tangent and cotangent functions can be expressed as quotients of the sine and cosine functions.

$$\tan A = \frac{\sin A}{\cos A} \text{ since } \frac{\sin A}{\cos A} = \frac{\frac{a}{c}}{\frac{b}{c}} = \frac{a}{b} = \tan A, \text{ and}$$

$$\cot A = \frac{\cos A}{\sin A} \text{ since } \frac{\cos A}{\sin A} = \frac{\frac{b}{c}}{\frac{a}{c}} = \frac{b}{a} = \cot A.$$

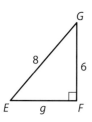

Example 1 Evaluating Trigonometric Functions

Evaluate the six trigonometric functions for $\angle G$.

Answer

$g^2 + 6^2 = 8^2$

$\qquad g = \sqrt{8^2 - 6^2} = \sqrt{28} = 2\sqrt{7}$

1. Use the Pythagorean Theorem to find g.

$\sin G = \dfrac{opp.}{hyp.} = \dfrac{2\sqrt{7}}{8}$ $\qquad \csc G = \dfrac{1}{\sin G} = \dfrac{1}{\frac{\sqrt{7}}{4}} = \dfrac{4}{\sqrt{7}}$

2. Use the definitions to find the six trigonometric ratios.

$\qquad = \dfrac{\sqrt{7}}{4} \approx 0.6614$ $\qquad\qquad = \dfrac{4\sqrt{7}}{7} \approx 1.5119$

$\cos G = \dfrac{adj.}{hyp.} = \dfrac{6}{8}$ $\qquad \sec G = \dfrac{1}{\cos G} = \dfrac{1}{\frac{3}{4}}$

$\qquad = \dfrac{3}{4} = 0.75$ $\qquad\qquad = \dfrac{4}{3} \approx 1.3333$

$\tan G = \dfrac{opp.}{adj.} = \dfrac{2\sqrt{7}}{6}$ $\qquad \cot G = \dfrac{1}{\tan G} = \dfrac{1}{\frac{\sqrt{7}}{3}} = \dfrac{3}{\sqrt{7}}$

$\qquad = \dfrac{\sqrt{7}}{3} \approx 0.8819$ $\qquad\qquad = \dfrac{3\sqrt{7}}{7} \approx 1.1339$

SKILL ✓ **EXERCISE 3**

The Angle-Angle Similarity Postulate guarantees that any two right triangles are similar if they have a corresponding pair of congruent acute angles. Since ratios of corresponding sides of similar figures are equal, these trigonometric ratios of a given angle are the same for similar right triangles of any size.

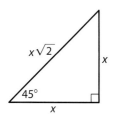

Recall that the leg:leg:hypotenuse ratio in an isosceles right triangle is $1:1:\sqrt{2}$ and that the short leg:long leg:hypotenuse ratio in a 30-60-90 triangle is $1:\sqrt{3}:2$. These ratios allow you to state exact trigonometric ratios for 45°, 30°, and 60° angles without the use of a calculator.

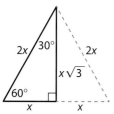

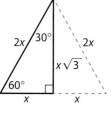

$m\angle A$	$\sin A$	$\cos A$	$\tan A$	$\csc A$	$\sec A$	$\cot A$
30° or $\frac{\pi}{6}$	$\frac{1}{2}$	$\frac{\sqrt{3}}{2}$	$\frac{\sqrt{3}}{3}$	2	$\frac{2\sqrt{3}}{3}$	$\sqrt{3}$
45° or $\frac{\pi}{4}$	$\frac{\sqrt{2}}{2}$	$\frac{\sqrt{2}}{2}$	1	$\sqrt{2}$	$\sqrt{2}$	1
60° or $\frac{\pi}{3}$	$\frac{\sqrt{3}}{2}$	$\frac{1}{2}$	$\sqrt{3}$	$\frac{2\sqrt{3}}{3}$	2	$\frac{\sqrt{3}}{3}$

A ca. 1700 BC clay tablet known as Plimpton 322 shows that ancient Babylonians were aware of the relationship expressed by the Pythagorean Theorem and that they could derive many Pythagorean triples, including 4601, 4800, and 6649, well over 1000 yr before the Pythagoreans (ca. 500 BC).

Notice that $\sin 60° = \cos 30° = \dfrac{\sqrt{3}}{2}$; $\tan 60° = \cot 30° = \sqrt{3}$, and that $\sec 60° = \csc 30° = 2$. In fact, the trigonometric function of any acute angle is equal to the *cofunction* of its complement. This generalized statement will be proved in later sections using the definitions of sine, tangent, secant, and their respective cofunctions cosine, cotangent, and cosecant.

If one trigonometric ratio of an acute angle is known, the other five trigonometric ratios of that angle can be found.

Example 2   Using One Ratio to Find the Other Trig Ratios

Given acute θ where $\sin \theta = 0.8$, find the other five trigonometric ratios for θ.

Answer

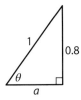

$$a^2 + 0.8^2 = 1^2$$
$$a = \sqrt{1^2 - 0.8^2}$$
$$= \sqrt{0.36} = 0.6$$

$$\cos \theta = \frac{0.6}{1} = 0.6$$

$$\tan \theta = \frac{0.8}{0.6} = \frac{4}{3} \approx 1.3333$$

$$\csc \theta = \frac{1}{\sin \theta} = \frac{1}{0.8} = 1.25$$

$$\sec \theta = \frac{1}{\cos \theta} = \frac{1}{0.6} \approx 1.6667$$

$$\cot \theta = \frac{1}{\tan \theta} = \frac{1}{\frac{4}{3}} = \frac{3}{4} = 0.75$$

1. Sketch a right triangle with θ such that $\sin \theta = \frac{opp.}{hyp.} = \frac{0.8}{1}$.

2. Use the Pythagorean Theorem to find the length of the adjacent leg.

3. Apply the definitions to find the values of the other two basic trigonometric functions.

4. Find the values of the reciprocal trigonometric functions.

— SKILL ✓ **EXERCISE 15**

It is important to know whether your calculator is set to radian or degree mode when evaluating trigonometric functions. Most calculators require cotangents, secants, and cosecants to be evaluated using their reciprocal functions.

Example 3   Using a Calculator to Evaluate Trig Functions

Evaluate $\cos 37°$, $\tan 61°40'$, and $\sin \frac{\pi}{6}$ with the calculator in degree mode. Then evaluate $\tan \frac{\pi}{4}$, $\csc 30°15'$, and $\sec \frac{\pi}{6}$ with the calculator in radian mode.

Answer

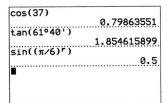

1. Press [MODE] and check that Degree is selected. Then select [QUIT] ([2nd], [MODE]).

2. Enter [COS], [3], [7], [)] to find $\cos 37°$.

3. Evaluate $\tan 61°40'$, using the [ANGLE] menu ([2nd], [APPS]) to enter the function in DMS.

4. Use the Angle menu to identify $(\pi/6)$ as a radian measure.

5. Press [MODE], highlight Radian, and press [ENTER], to set the calculator to Radian mode.

6. Enter [TAN], [2nd], [^], [÷], [4], [)] to evaluate $\tan \frac{\pi}{4}$.

7. Express $30°15'$ in decimal degrees. Use the Angle menu to indicate degree measure when evaluating
$$\csc 30.25° = \frac{1}{\sin 30.25°}$$ in radian mode.

8. Evaluate $\sec \frac{\pi}{6}$ using the reciprocal key, [x⁻¹], to represent the function as the reciprocal of $\cos \frac{\pi}{6}$.

— SKILL ✓ **EXERCISE 7**

TIP

Be careful not to use one of the inverse functions ($\sin^{-1}$, $\cos^{-1}$, or $\tan^{-1}$) when attempting to evaluate reciprocal functions.

When the lengths of two sides in a right triangle are known, the measures of the acute angles can be determined. *Inverse trigonometric functions* are defined by reversing the functional relationship between angle measure and the ratio of the sides in a right triangle.

Inverse Trigonometric Functions (of acute $\angle A$ with measure α)			
	Inverse Sine	**Inverse Cosine**	**Inverse Tangent**
Definition	If $\sin \alpha = x$, then $\sin^{-1} x = \alpha$.	If $\cos \alpha = x$, then $\cos^{-1} x = \alpha$.	If $\tan \alpha = x$, then $\tan^{-1} x = \alpha$.
Example	If $\sin \frac{\pi}{6} = \frac{1}{2}$, then $\sin^{-1} \frac{1}{2} = \frac{\pi}{6}$.	If $\cos \frac{\pi}{6} = \frac{\sqrt{3}}{2}$, then $\cos^{-1} \frac{\sqrt{3}}{2} = \frac{\pi}{6}$.	If $\tan \frac{\pi}{6} = \frac{\sqrt{3}}{3}$, then $\tan^{-1} \frac{\sqrt{3}}{3} = \frac{\pi}{6}$.

Inverse trigonometric functions are frequently used when *solving a triangle* (finding any unknown angle measures or side lengths). A right triangle can be solved if one side length and either of the acute angles or a second side length is known.

Example 4 Solving a Right Triangle

Solve $\triangle ABC$, stating angle measures to the nearest tenth of a degree.

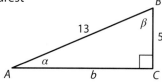

Answer

$$5^2 + b^2 = 13^2$$
$$b = \sqrt{13^2 - 5^2} = \sqrt{144} = 12$$

1. Use the Pythagorean Theorem to find b.

$$\sin \alpha = \frac{5}{13}$$

$$\sin^{-1} \frac{5}{13} = \alpha \approx 22.6°$$

2. Use the inverse sine function to find α. (Be sure the calculator is in degree mode.)

$$\cos \beta = \frac{5}{13}$$

$$\cos^{-1} \frac{5}{13} = \beta \approx 67.4°$$

3. Use the inverse cosine function to find β.

Check

$$22.6° + 67.4° = 90°$$

The acute angles of a right triangle are complementary.

SKILL ✓ **EXERCISE 27**

Many practical problems can be solved by finding the measure of an angle or a side in a right triangle modeling the scenario.

The first recorded estimate of the relative distances of the moon and sun from the earth was made by Aristarchus (ca. 300 BC) using the right triangle formed by the sun, the earth, and a half-moon.

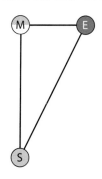

Example 5   Applying Right Triangle Trigonometry

A ship is spotted at a bearing of 90° from a lighthouse and at a bearing of 137°20′ from a Coast Guard station that is 10 km due north of the lighthouse. Determine the distance to the ship from the lighthouse and from the Coast Guard station.

Answer

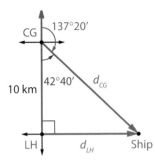

1. Sketch a right triangle modeling the scenario.

$$180° - 137°20′ = 42°40′$$

2. Find the measure of an acute angle in the triangle.

$$\tan 42°40′ = \frac{d_{LH}}{10}$$
$$10 \tan 42°40′ = d_{LH}$$
$$d_{LH} \approx 9.2 \text{ km}$$

3. Use the tangent ratio to find the length of the leg opposite the given angle when you know the length of the adjacent leg.

$$10^2 + 9.2^2 = d_{CG}^2$$
$$d_{CG} = \sqrt{184.95} \approx 13.6 \text{ km}$$

4. Use the Pythagorean Theorem to solve for the distance between the ship and the Coast Guard station.

SKILL ✓ **EXERCISE 33**

Solving practical problems often requires the use of angles of elevation and depression. The *angle of elevation* is the angle formed by a horizontal line and the line of sight as the observer looks at an object above the horizontal. The *angle of depression* is the angle formed by a horizontal line and the line of sight as the observer looks at an object below the horizontal.

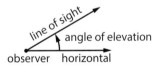
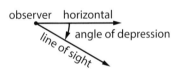

Example 6   Using Overlapping Right Triangles

Tyler views the peak of Grand Teton from Phelps Lake at an 11° angle of elevation. After kayaking 1.5 mi toward Grand Teton, the angle of elevation is 14°. Calculate the peak's height above the lake (to the nearest foot).

Answer

1. Sketch a diagram of the scenario.

$$\tan 11° = \frac{h}{x + 1.5}$$
$$h = (x + 1.5) \tan 11°$$
$$h = x \tan 11° + 1.5 \tan 11°$$
$$x = \frac{h - 1.5 \tan 11°}{\tan 11°}$$

$$\tan 14° = \frac{h}{x}$$
$$x = \frac{h}{\tan 14°}$$

2. Use the overlapping right triangles to write equations relating each angle of elevation to the peak's height and solve each equation for x.

CONTINUED ➡

$$\frac{h - 1.5\tan 11°}{\tan 11°} = \frac{h}{\tan 14°}$$

$$\tan 14°(h - 1.5\tan 11°) = h\tan 11°$$

$$h\tan 14° - 1.5\tan 11°(\tan 14°) = h\tan 11°$$

$$h(\tan 14° - \tan 11°) = 1.5\tan 11°(\tan 14°)$$

$$h = \frac{1.5\tan 11°(\tan 14°)}{\tan 14° - \tan 11°} \approx 1.323\text{ mi}$$

$$1.323\text{ mi}\left(\frac{5280\text{ ft}}{1\text{ mi}}\right) \approx 6986\text{ ft}$$

3. Solve the system of equations using substitution.

4. Convert miles to the nearest foot.

_____ SKILL ✔ **EXERCISE 41**

❯ A. Exercises

Find the six trigonometric ratios in exact fractional form for the given acute angles in each triangle.

1. ∠A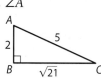

2. ∠N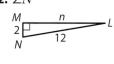

3. ∠Q

Use the triangles from exercises 1–3 to find the six trigonometric ratios for each angle in decimal form. Round answers to the nearest ten thousandth when necessary.

4. ∠C   **5.** ∠L   **6.** ∠P

7. Use a calculator in degree mode to evaluate the following trigonometric ratios (to the nearest ten thousandth).

  a. $\cos 26°20'$ **b.** $\tan 17°$ **c.** $\sin \frac{2\pi}{5}$

8. Use a calculator in radian mode to evaluate the following trigonometric ratios (to the nearest ten thousandth).

  a. $\csc \frac{\pi}{15}$ **b.** $\sec 1.15$ **c.** $\cot 86°50'$

Find each indicated length (to the nearest tenth).

9. 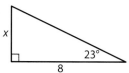   **10.**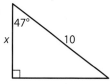

Find the measure of ∠A (to the nearest degree).

11. 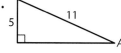   **12.**

Solve. Round answers to the nearest tenth.

13. The bottom of a rectangular pool rises at a constant 8° grade from 12 ft at the deep end to 3 ft at the shallow end. How long is the pool?

14. A wire supporting a 150 ft radio antenna stretches from the top of the antenna to the ground 32 ft away from the base of the antenna. Find the angle formed by the wire and the ground.

❯ B. Exercises

Find the remaining trigonometric ratios for each acute angle θ in a right triangle.

15. $\cos \theta = \frac{7}{25}$ **16.** $\tan \theta = \frac{8}{15}$ **17.** $\sec \theta = \frac{13}{12}$

18. $\cot \theta = \frac{4}{9}$ **19.** $\sin \theta = 0.5$ **20.** $\sec \theta = 1.25$

Find the six trigonometric ratios for each angle. Use exact values when possible.

21. $\frac{\pi}{3}$ **22.** 30°   **23.** 42°   **24.** $\frac{\pi}{4}$

Solve right △ABC. State side lengths to the nearest hundredth and angle measures to the nearest tenth of a degree.

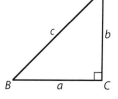

25. $a = 5, c = 9$

26. $\angle A = 49°, a = 6$

27. $\angle B = 12.7°, a = 20$

28. $c = 14, b = 8$

29. $\angle A = 64.2°, c = 16$

30. Use △ABC to prove each statement.

  a. $\sin A = \cos B$

  b. $\sin^2 A + \cos^2 A = 1$
  (Note that $\sin^2 \alpha$ is a simplified notation for $(\sin \alpha)^2$.)

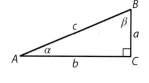

31. Explain: Why are the trigonometric ratios the same for all 30-60-90 triangles?

Solve. Round answers to the nearest tenth unless specified otherwise.

32. Safety guidelines recommend that the angle formed by an extension ladder and level ground not exceed 76°. How high against the side of a building can a 20 ft long ladder be safely placed? How far from the building should the ladder be placed to reach this height?

33. A plane leaves airport A traveling at 210 mi/hr. After 1.5 hr, the plane is due east of airport B. If airport A is 230.4 mi due south of airport B, what was the bearing of the plane as it took off from airport A?

34. A ship's captain sights an anchored ship at a bearing of 128°. After the ship travels south for 63 nautical miles, the anchored ship is due east of the moving ship. How far apart are the two ships at the second sighting?

35. A pilot flying at 3000 ft approaches a runway with an angle of depression of 16° to the start of the runway and 9°20′ to the end of the runway. Find the length of the runway (to the nearest foot).

36. A missile travels at a speed of 900 ft/sec at a constant angle of elevation of 73°. After 5 sec what is its altitude (to the nearest foot)?

37. The angle of depression from the top of a 75 ft lighthouse to a ship at sea is 0°40′. How far is the ship from the lighthouse?

› C. Exercises

Solve for *x*, *y*, and *z* (to the nearest tenth).

38.

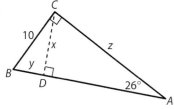

39.

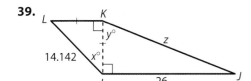

40. Samantha is checking the height of a tethered blimp. She measures a 30° angle of elevation, then walks 60 ft toward the blimp and measures a 35° angle of elevation. If her line of sight is 5 ft above the ground, estimate the height of the blimp.

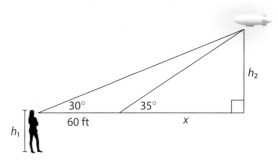

41. When a hot-air balloon is directly over the highway, the pilot measures a 4° angle of depression to the base of the town's tallest building. Estimate the height of the balloon (to the nearest foot) if the angle of depression is 5° after flying 1 mi toward the building without changing altitude.

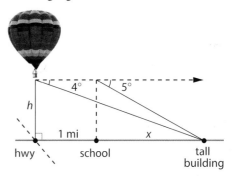

42. From your location on a ferry, the angle of elevation to the top of the Statue of Liberty's torch is 7°, and the angle of elevation to the base of her feet is 3.5°. Determine the height of the statue (*y*) and your ferry's distance from the monument if the height of the entire monument is 305.5 ft. Round answers to the nearest foot.

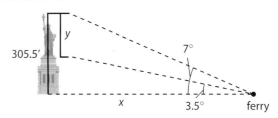

43. A plane 6 nm from the Lexington airport approaches the airport from a bearing of 295° at an altitude of 2000 ft. A second plane 5 nm from the airport approaches at an altitude of 1500 ft from a bearing of 25°. (1 nm ≈ 6076 ft)

   a. Find the horizontal distance between the planes (to the nearest tenth of a nautical mile).

   b. Find the angle of descent (depression) for each plane (to the nearest tenth of a degree).

44. A compass points toward the magnetic north pole instead of true north, the direction of the geographic North Pole. At Trent's location, true north is 8° east of magnetic north. He follows a compass bearing of 327° for 2 mi to avoid a lake, but his final destination is a point 5 mi true north of his starting point. After the detour, what compass bearing should he follow to reach his final destination? How far will he have traveled?

CUMULATIVE REVIEW

Algebraically find the *y*-intercept, the domain, and any vertical asymptotes for each function. Then use technology to verify your answers. [2.5]

45. $f(x) = \dfrac{6}{x+2}$

46. $f(x) = \dfrac{x+3}{x^2-4}$

Use the properties of logarithms to find the value of *x*. [3.4]

47. $\log_2 (x^2 + 3x + 4) = 1$

48. $\log (x^2 - 144) = 1 + \log (x + 12)$

Convert each degree measure to radian measure. Express the answer in terms of π and then as a decimal approximation rounded to the nearest hundredth. [4.1]

49. 36°

50. −148°

51. Solve $\sqrt{x} - \sqrt{2x-2} + 4 = 5$. [2.1]

   A. $x = 1$ **D.** $x = 9$

   B. $x = 1, 9$ **E.** none of these

   C. $x = -1, -9$

52. Solve $e^{6x} = 36$. [3.4]

   A. $\ln 2$ **D.** $\frac{1}{2} \ln 3$

   B. $\frac{1}{2} \ln 6$ **E.** none of these

   C. $\frac{1}{3} \ln 6$

53. Solve $3e^{2x+1} - 6 = 0$. [3.4]

   A. $\ln 2 - \frac{1}{2}$ **D.** $\ln 2$

   B. $\frac{1}{2}(\ln 2 - 2)$ **E.** none of these

   C. $-\ln 2 + 1$

54. Which of the following angles is not coterminal with $\frac{5\pi}{4}$? [4.1]

   A. $\frac{13\pi}{4}$ **D.** $-\frac{11\pi}{4}$

   B. $-\frac{3\pi}{4}$ **E.** $\frac{21\pi}{4}$

   C. $\frac{9\pi}{4}$

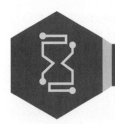
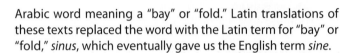

TRIGONOMETRY

If you have ever camped far from the city and artificial lights, you have likely experienced the awe of a brilliant night sky (Ps. 19:1). When you consider that ancient civilizations regularly enjoyed such views, it is no wonder that they realized the constellations maintained their relative positions as they moved across the sky. This consistency proved useful in navigation and developing calendars. However, a few of the heavenly lights were different—they moved among the fixed stars, and even seemed to move backwards at times! The Babylonians (like the Greeks, Arabs, and Europeans after them) assumed that the earth was stationary at the center of the universe and that the stars were on a sphere (or spheres) that revolved around the earth. Attempting to explain the retrograde motion of the planets occupied astronomers for millennia. Trigonometry developed as an aid in their study of celestial motion and the mapping of the night sky.

In his second-century treatise *Almagest*, Ptolemy references the oldest known Greek trigonometric table, produced by the astronomer Hipparchus ca. 140 BC. Ptolemy's description of the table's construction includes a theorem that now bears his name: "In an inscribed quadrilateral, the sum of the products of the opposite sides is equal to the product of the diagonals." When using Ptolemy's table, it was often necessary to find half the chord of twice the angle. For convenience, Hindu astronomers added a half-chord column to their trigonometric tables. The Sanskrit word for *half* was mistranslated into an

Arabic word meaning a "bay" or "fold." Latin translations of these texts replaced the word with the Latin term for "bay" or "fold," *sinus*, which eventually gave us the English term *sine*.

Ptolemy also authored works on astrology, optics, and geography. Maps in his text *Geography* included latitude and longitude and influenced cartography for over a thousand years. Ptolemy's maps were based on an 18,000 mi estimate of the earth's circumference attributed to the Stoic philosopher Posidonius, instead of Eratosthenes's more accurate calculation of roughly 25,000 mi. Since the maps used by Christopher Columbus in the fifteenth century were still based on Ptolemy's projections, they greatly underestimated the distance to India. Many sources suggest that Columbus may not have attempted his epic journey if the maps had been more accurate.

Trigonometry began with the astronomy of the Babylonians and Greeks, was further developed by Hindus and Arabs, and eventually came to Europe in Latin translations of the ancient texts. In the fifteenth century Johann Müller summarized this heritage in his five-volume work *On Triangles of Every Kind*. This text was studied by Nicolaus Copernicus, who developed a heliocentric model of the universe. Copernicus placed the sun at the center of the universe but preserved much of Ptolemy's model, which explained retrograde motion using circular orbits and epicycles (small circles traversed by a planet as it makes its larger orbit around the sun). Nevertheless, Copernicus's model could not completely solve the mystery of retrograde motion. The accurate plotting of planetary positions provided by trigonometry and the development of logarithms as an aid in calculations eventually enabled Johannes Kepler to discover the key to planetary motion—elliptical orbits.

COMPREHENSION CHECK

1. Why was trigonometry developed?

2. Who published the oldest known Greek trigonometric table?

3. State Ptolemy's Theorem.

4. What English word for a common trigonometric function has its origin in the Hindu word for "half"?

5. Explain how Ptolemy's *Geography* may have influenced Columbus's discovery of America.

6. **Discuss:** Explain the role of trigonometry in the development of the current model of the solar system.

4.3 Extending Trigonometric Functions

The change in height of this Foucault pendulum in Paris is modeled by $\Delta h = L(1 - \cos \theta)$.

After completing this section, you will be able to

- evaluate trig functions using coordinates of a point on its terminal side, its reference angle, or the unit circle.
- use the unit circle to explain symmetry (odd and even) and the periodic nature of trig functions.

In this section we will expand the definitions of trigonometric functions beyond angles found in right triangles to angles of any measure. We will then use radian measure to extend the domain of trigonometric functions to real numbers.

The trigonometric functions can be defined for any angle drawn in standard position using a point $P(x, y)$ on its terminal side.

DEFINITIONS

Given point $P(x, y)$ on the terminal side of angle θ in standard position and $r = \sqrt{x^2 + y^2}$, the six trigonometric ratios are defined as follows.

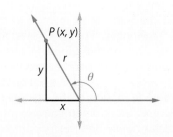

$$\sin \theta = \frac{y}{r} \qquad \cos \theta = \frac{x}{r} \qquad \tan \theta = \frac{y}{x}$$

$$\csc \theta = \frac{r}{y} \qquad \sec \theta = \frac{r}{x} \qquad \cot \theta = \frac{x}{y}$$

Example 1 Evaluating Trig Functions Using a Point on the Terminal Side

State the six trigonometric functions of an angle θ in standard position if its terminal side passes through (–6, –8).

Answer

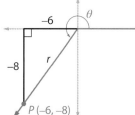

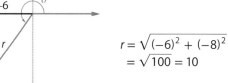

1. Sketch the angle in standard position.

$$r = \sqrt{(-6)^2 + (-8)^2}$$
$$= \sqrt{100} = 10$$

2. Determine r, the distance from the origin to P.

$$\sin \theta = \frac{y}{r} = \frac{-8}{10} = -\frac{4}{5} \qquad \csc \theta = \frac{r}{y} = \frac{10}{-8} = -\frac{5}{4}$$

$$\cos \theta = \frac{x}{r} = \frac{-6}{10} = -\frac{3}{5} \qquad \sec \theta = \frac{r}{x} = \frac{10}{-6} = -\frac{5}{3}$$

$$\tan \theta = \frac{y}{x} = \frac{-8}{-6} = \frac{4}{3} \qquad \cot \theta = \frac{x}{y} = \frac{-6}{-8} = \frac{3}{4}$$

3. Apply the expanded definitions of the trigonometric functions.

SKILL ✓ EXERCISE 3

The German clergyman Bartholomaeus Pitiscus was the first to use the word *trigonometry* in the title of a book. His *Trigonometriae sive de dimensione triangulorum libri quinque* (Trigonometry, the properties of triangles in five books) was published in Frankfurt in 1595.

The terminal side of a *quadrantal angle* lies on one of the coordinate axes. The expanded definitions allow us to quickly evaluate the trigonometric functions of these angles whose measures are multiples of $\frac{\pi}{2}$ or 90°.

Example 2   Evaluating Trig Functions for a Quadrantal Angle

Evaluate the six trigonometric functions for an angle measuring $\frac{3\pi}{2}$.

Answer

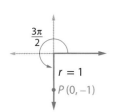

$P = (0, -1)$

$r = 1$

1. Sketch the angle and choose a convenient point on the terminal ray.
2. The point P is 1 unit from the origin.

$\sin\theta = \frac{y}{r} = \frac{-1}{1} = -1$ $\csc\theta = \frac{r}{y} = \frac{1}{-1} = -1$

$\cos\theta = \frac{x}{r} = \frac{0}{1} = 0$ $\sec\theta = \frac{r}{x} = \frac{1}{0}$; undefined

$\tan\theta = \frac{y}{x} = \frac{-1}{0}$; undefined $\cot\theta = \frac{x}{y} = \frac{0}{-1} = 0$

3. Apply the definitions. Note that the secant and tangent functions are not defined for $\frac{3\pi}{2}$.

SKILL ✓ **EXERCISE 5**

Any nonquadrantal angle θ has an associated *reference angle* α, the acute angle formed by the terminal side and the *x*-axis when θ is in standard position. The triangle formed by a perpendicular drawn to the *x*-axis from $P(x, y)$ on the terminal side of a nonquadrantal angle forms a *reference triangle*.

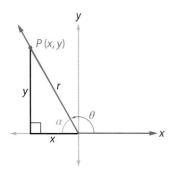

$\theta = 120°$; $\alpha = 60°$

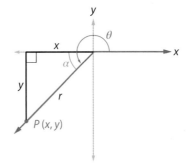

$\theta = 225°$; $\alpha = 45°$

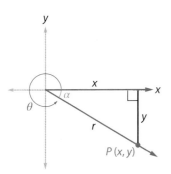

$\theta = 330°$; $\alpha = 30°$

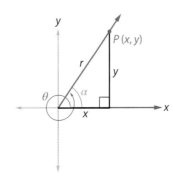

$\theta = 420°$; $\alpha = 60°$

The quadrant sign chart on the left:

Q II: (−, +)
$\sin\theta = \frac{+}{r} = +$
$\cos\theta = \frac{-}{r} = -$
$\tan\theta = \frac{+}{-} = -$

Q I: (+, +)
$\sin\theta = \frac{+}{r} = +$
$\cos\theta = \frac{+}{r} = +$
$\tan\theta = \frac{+}{+} = +$

Q III: (−, −)
$\sin\theta = \frac{-}{r} = -$
$\cos\theta = \frac{-}{r} = -$
$\tan\theta = \frac{-}{-} = +$

Q IV: (+, −)
$\sin\theta = \frac{-}{r} = -$
$\cos\theta = \frac{+}{r} = +$
$\tan\theta = \frac{-}{+} = -$

Because r is always positive, the sign of a trigonometric function is determined by the signs of x and y in the quadrant containing the terminal side. Reference angles and the ratios of side lengths in a 30-60-90 or 45-45-90 triangle allow us to quickly evaluate the exact values of trigonometric functions for angles whose measures are multiples of 30° or 45° $\left(\frac{\pi}{6} \text{ or } \frac{\pi}{4}\right)$.

Example 3   Using Reference Angles to Evaluate Trig Functions

State the exact values of the three basic trigonometric functions for each angle.

a. −240°

b. $\frac{7\pi}{4}$

Answer

a.

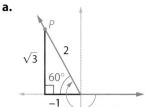

b.

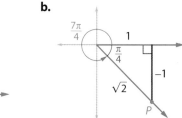

1. Sketch each angle, its reference angle, and an associated reference triangle.

$\sin(-240°) = \frac{\sqrt{3}}{2}$

$\cos(-240°) = \frac{-1}{2} = -\frac{1}{2}$

$\tan(-240°) = \frac{\sqrt{3}}{-1} = -\sqrt{3}$

$\sin\frac{7\pi}{4} = \frac{-1}{\sqrt{2}} = -\frac{\sqrt{2}}{2}$

$\cos\frac{7\pi}{4} = \frac{1}{\sqrt{2}} = \frac{\sqrt{2}}{2}$

$\tan\frac{7\pi}{4} = \frac{-1}{1} = -1$

2. Apply the expanded definitions:
$\sin\theta = \frac{y}{r}$, $\cos\theta = \frac{x}{r}$, and $\tan\theta = \frac{y}{x}$.

SKILL ✔ EXERCISE 11

Your calculator will give decimal approximations for trigonometric functions of other nonacute angles.

Example 4   Using a Calculator to Evaluate Trig Functions

Use your calculator (in radian mode) to evaluate each function.

a. cos 337°

b. $\sin\left(-\frac{4\pi}{5}\right)$

c. cot 2

Answer

```
cos(337°)
                0.9205048535
sin(-4π/5)
                -0.5877852523
tan(2)⁻¹
                -0.4576575544
1/tan(2)
                -0.4576575544
```

Be sure your calculator is in Radian mode.

a. Enter cos(337°), using the [ANGLE] menu to insert the degree symbol.

b. Enter sin(−4π/5).

c. Find cot 2 by entering tan(2)[x⁻¹], or 1/tan(2).

Check

Use the quadrant of the terminal side to verify that the sign of each value is correct.

a. 270° < 337° < 360°; The cosine is positive in Q IV.

b. $-\pi < -\frac{4\pi}{5} < -\frac{\pi}{2}$; The sine is negative in Q III.

c. $\frac{\pi}{2} < 2 < \pi$ (or 1.57 < 2 < 3.14); The cotangent is negative in Q II.

SKILL ✔ EXERCISE 15

If the value of one of the trigonometric functions of an angle and the quadrant of the terminal side is known, you can use the reference triangle to determine the values of the other trigonometric functions of the angle.

Example 5   Finding Other Trigonometric Ratios

If $\cos \theta = -\frac{2}{3}$ and $\sin \theta > 0$, find $\tan \theta$ and $\csc \theta$.

Answer

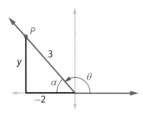

1. Sketch θ and the reference triangle in Q II since it is the only quadrant where $\cos \theta < 0$ and $\sin \theta > 0$.

$$2^2 + y^2 = 3^2$$
$$y = \pm\sqrt{9 - 4} = \sqrt{5}$$

2. Use $\cos \theta = \frac{x}{r}$ and the Pythagorean Theorem to find y, which is positive in Q II.

$$\tan \theta = \frac{y}{x} = \frac{\sqrt{5}}{-2} = -\frac{\sqrt{5}}{2} \qquad \csc \theta = \frac{r}{y} = \frac{3}{\sqrt{5}} = \frac{3\sqrt{5}}{5}$$

3. Use x, y, and r to find the other trigonometric ratios.

SKILL ✓ **EXERCISE 17**

While we have extended the definitions of trigonometric functions to angles of any measure, calculus and many applications require that the trigonometric functions use domains containing real numbers instead of angle measures. This is accomplished using the *unit circle*.

▌DEFINITION

The **unit circle** is the circle centered at the origin and having a radius of 1 unit. Its equation is $x^2 + y^2 = 1$.

Placing a vertical real number line so that its origin is at $A\,(1, 0)$ and wrapping it around the unit circle allows a real number t to be mapped to a point $P\,(x, y)$ on the unit circle where t = the length of $\overarc{AP}$. Point P defines the standard position angle θ with radian measure of $\theta = \frac{s}{r} = \frac{t}{1} = t$. This allows the independent variable of a trigonometric function to be viewed as either an angle measure of θ radians or a real number t.

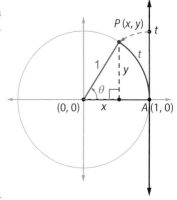

▌DEFINITIONS

If t is a real number on the number line wrapped around the unit circle so that t = the length of $\overarc{AP}$, the trigonometric functions of t are defined in terms of $P\,(x, y)$ as follows.

$$\sin t = y \qquad\qquad \cos t = x \qquad\qquad \tan t = \frac{y}{x}, x \neq 0$$

$$\csc t = \frac{1}{y}, y \neq 0 \qquad \sec t = \frac{1}{x}, x \neq 0 \qquad \cot t = \frac{x}{y}, y \neq 0$$

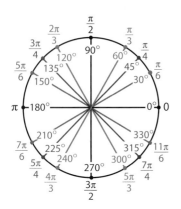

Since a unit circle is used in these definitions, these trigonometric functions are also called *circular functions*.

Notice that $P(x, y)$ has coordinates $(\cos t, \sin t)$. The following reference triangles and quadrantal angles can be used to quickly identify these coordinates on the unit circle and the exact values of each trigonometric function for the illustrated angle measures and arc lengths.

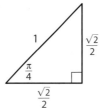 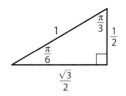

Example 6   Using the Unit Circle to Evaluate Trig Functions

Use the unit circle to state the exact value of each expression.

a. $\cos \dfrac{2\pi}{3}$ **b.** $\csc 225°$ **c.** $\tan \pi$

Answer

TIP

The following patterns can be used to remember the values of sine and cosine functions for special values.

θ	$\cos\theta$	$\sin\theta$
0	$\dfrac{\sqrt{4}}{2}$	$\dfrac{\sqrt{0}}{2}$
$\dfrac{\pi}{6}$	$\dfrac{\sqrt{3}}{2}$	$\dfrac{\sqrt{1}}{2}$
$\dfrac{\pi}{4}$	$\dfrac{\sqrt{2}}{2}$	$\dfrac{\sqrt{2}}{2}$
$\dfrac{\pi}{3}$	$\dfrac{\sqrt{1}}{2}$	$\dfrac{\sqrt{3}}{2}$
$\dfrac{\pi}{2}$	$\dfrac{\sqrt{0}}{2}$	$\dfrac{\sqrt{4}}{2}$

a.

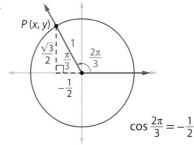

$$\cos \frac{2\pi}{3} = -\frac{1}{2}$$

1. Sketch the angle and the related reference triangle within the unit circle.
2. Identify $P(x, y) = \left(-\dfrac{1}{2}, \dfrac{\sqrt{3}}{2}\right)$.
3. Since $P(x, y) = (\cos t, \sin t)$, $\cos\theta = x$.

b.

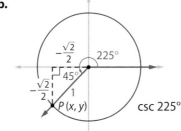

$$\csc 225° = \frac{1}{-\dfrac{\sqrt{2}}{2}}$$
$$= -\sqrt{2}$$

1. Sketch the angle and the related reference triangle within the unit circle.
2. Identify $P(x, y) = \left(-\dfrac{\sqrt{2}}{2}, -\dfrac{\sqrt{2}}{2}\right)$.
3. Use $P(x, y) = (\cos t, \sin t)$ and $\csc t = \dfrac{1}{\sin t} = \dfrac{1}{y}$.

c.

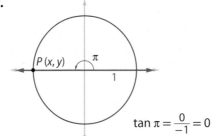

$$\tan \pi = \frac{0}{-1} = 0$$

1. Sketch the quadrantal angle within the unit circle.
2. Identify $P(x, y) = (-1, 0)$.
3. Use $P(x, y) = (\cos t, \sin t)$ and $\tan t = \dfrac{\sin t}{\cos t} = \dfrac{y}{x}$.

SKILL ✔ **EXERCISE 23**

Viewing $f(t) = \cos t$ and $g(t) = \sin t$ as the x- and y-coordinates of the endpoint of an arc on the unit circle helps to explain several characteristics of trigonometric functions. Both functions have a domain of the real numbers and a range of $[-1, 1]$. The domains and ranges of other trigonometric functions will be investigated in future sections.

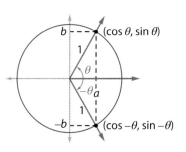

The figure illustrates that $\cos(-\theta) = \cos\theta$ and $\sin(-\theta) = -\sin\theta$. Therefore, cosine is an even function and sine is an odd function. It can be shown that secant is an even function and that tangent, cotangent, and cosecant are odd functions by expressing these functions in terms of sine and cosine or in terms of x, y, and r.

The definitions related to the unit circle make it clear that evaluating the same trigonometric function for coterminal angles will produce the same result. If $n \in \mathbb{Z}$, $\sin(\theta + n2\pi) = \sin\theta$ and $\cos(\theta + n2\pi) = \cos\theta$. A function is *periodic* if, for some given constant c, $f(x + c) = f(x)$ for all x. The smallest such positive value of c is called the *period* of the function. All six trigonometric functions are periodic, with sine, cosine, secant, and cosecant having periods of 2π. In Section 4.5 you will learn why the period of the tangent and cotangent functions are both π.

Example 7 Using the Period of a Trig Function

Find the exact value of $\sin\left(-\frac{29\pi}{3}\right)$.

Answer

$\sin\left(-\frac{29\pi}{3}\right) = -\sin\frac{29\pi}{3}$

1. Apply the fact that sine is an odd function.

$= -\sin\left(\frac{5}{3}\pi + \frac{24}{3}\pi\right)$

$= -\sin\left(\frac{5}{3}\pi + (4)2\pi\right)$

$= -\sin\frac{5\pi}{3}$

2. Use the fact that sine has a period of 2π to rewrite the expression in terms of a coterminal angle within $[0, 2\pi)$.

$-\sin\frac{29\pi}{3} = -\sin\frac{5\pi}{3} = -\left(-\frac{\sqrt{3}}{2}\right) = \frac{\sqrt{3}}{2}$

3. Evaluate $\sin\frac{5\pi}{3} = -\frac{\sqrt{3}}{2}$ using a Q IV reference angle of $\frac{\pi}{3}$.

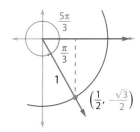

SKILL ✓ **EXERCISE 29**

God's creation has many periodic phenomena that can be modeled with trigonometric functions. He promised in Genesis 8:22 that the yearly cycle of the seasons and the daily cycle of sunlight and darkness would continue throughout the earth's existence. Other cycles in nature include lunar phases, tides, sunspots, comets, prevailing winds, and animal migrations.

Seventeenth-century scientists used pendulums and spring bobs (springs with weights attached) to measure time since these devices, like the sun and the moon, have cyclical properties. Hooke's law, which describes the linear relationship between the force applied to a spring and the spring's displacement, is the basis for the balance wheel found in wristwatches.

A. Exercises

Evaluate the six trigonometric functions for an angle in standard position whose terminal ray passes through each point.

1. $(1, 4)$ **2.** $(-6, -1)$

3. $(-3, 2)$ **4.** $(8, -7)$

Evaluate the six trigonometric functions for each quadrantal angle.

5. $\theta = \frac{\pi}{2}$ **6.** $\theta = 180°$

Sketch each angle θ and a reference triangle. Then state the measure of the reference angle α.

7. $\theta = 160°$ **8.** $\theta = -120°$

9. $\theta = -\frac{11\pi}{6}$ **10.** $\theta = 2$

Use reference angles to find the exact value of each expression.

11. $\cos 150°$ **12.** $\sin (-135°)$

13. $\tan (-60°)$ **14.** $\csc 315°$

15. Use a calculator in radian mode to evaluate each expression (to four decimal places).

     a. $\sin (-100°)$ **b.** $\sec 2.75$ **c.** $\cot \frac{3\pi}{8}$

16. Use a calculator in degree mode to evaluate each expression (to four decimal places).

     a. $\tan (-50°)$ **b.** $\cot 117°$ **c.** $\sin \frac{9\pi}{5}$

B. Exercises

17. If $\cos \theta = -\frac{20}{29}$ and $\tan \theta < 0$, find $\sin \theta$ and $\cot \theta$.

18. If $\sin \theta = -\frac{8}{17}$ and $\cos \theta > 0$, find $\tan \theta$ and $\sec \theta$.

19. If $\sec \theta = \frac{7}{3}$ and $\sin \theta < 0$, find $\sin \theta$, $\cos \theta$, and $\tan \theta$.

20. If $\cot \theta = \frac{12}{13}$ and $\sin \theta > 0$, find $\sin \theta$, $\cos \theta$, and $\tan \theta$.

Use the unit circle to find the exact value of each expression.

21. $\sin 120°$ **22.** $\cos 270°$

23. $\tan \frac{5\pi}{6}$ **24.** $\cot (-\pi)$

25. $\sec 210°$ **26.** $\cot \frac{5\pi}{3}$

27. $\csc \frac{5\pi}{4}$

Evaluate each expression.

28. $\sin \frac{16\pi}{3}$ **29.** $\tan \frac{17\pi}{2}$

30. $\cos (-3\pi)$ **31.** $\sin \left(-\frac{11\pi}{2}\right)$

32. Sketch each angle θ in standard position and label its reference angle α. Then express α in terms of θ.

     a. $0 < \theta < \frac{\pi}{2}$ **b.** $\frac{\pi}{2} < \theta < \pi$

     c. $\pi < \theta < \frac{3\pi}{2}$ **d.** $\frac{3\pi}{2} < \theta < 2\pi$

33. Find $\sin (-\theta)$ if $\sin \theta = \frac{7}{8}$.

34. Find $\cos (-\theta)$ if $\cos \theta = \frac{5}{13}$.

An object hanging from a spring is pulled down k inches below its equilibrium position and released. Its height (relative to its equilibrium position) t seconds after its release is modeled by $f(t) = -a \cos \frac{2\pi}{p}t$ where p is the time it takes to return to the released position.

35. Find and interpret the height of the object at each time if $a = 3$ and $p = 0.5$.

     a. 0.125 sec   **b.** 0.25 sec

     c. 0.6 sec   **d.** 2.0 sec

36. Use $t = 0$ to explain why $g(t) = -k \sin \frac{2\pi}{c}t$ does not correctly model the object's height.

37. Make a copy of the unit circle illustrating the degree and radian measures of all angles $\theta \in [0, 2\pi)$ whose measures are multiples of $\frac{\pi}{6}$ or $\frac{\pi}{4}$. Then label each endpoint of the related arc lengths with the ordered triplet $(\cos \theta, \sin \theta, \tan \theta)$.

C. Exercises

For a pendulum with length L swinging through relatively small angles of θ, the formula relating the change in height Δh and the angle θ it makes with its stationary position is $\Delta h = L(1 - \cos \theta)$.

38. Foucault's pendulum suspended from the dome of the Pantheon in Paris was 67 m long.

     a. Find Δh when $\theta = 19°$.

     b. Find θ when $\Delta h = 2$ m.

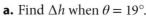
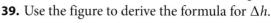

39. Use the figure to derive the formula for Δh.

40. Using the fact that cosine is an even function and sine is an odd function, algebraically prove each statement.

     a. Tangent is an odd function.

     b. Secant is an even function.

41. Use the drawing and unit circle definitions to prove each relationship.

a. $\cos(\pi - \theta) = -\cos\theta$

b. $\sin(\pi - \theta) = \sin\theta$

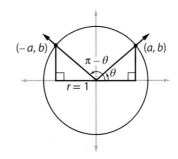

CUMULATIVE REVIEW

Describe the graph of $g(x)$ as a transformation of $f(x) = x^2$. [1.5]

42. $g(x) = (x - 8)^2$

43. $g(x) = -4x^2$

44. Write a function rule for $g(x)$, a reflection of $f(x) = x^3$ in the x-axis that has been translated 7 units left and 9 units up. [1.5]

45. Determine the type of discontinuity for each function at $x = 3$. [1.3, 2.5]

  I. jump   **II.** infinite   **III.** point

  a. $f(x) = \dfrac{x + 3}{x^2 - 6x + 9}$

  b. $g(x) = \dfrac{x - 3}{x^2 - x - 6}$

  c. $h(x) = [3x]$

Determine whether each function is even, odd, or neither. [2.2]

46. $p(x) = 8x^6 + 2x^3 - 5$

47. $p(x) = 7x^8 - 6x^2$

48. Find the radian measure for $42°$. [4.1]

  A. $\dfrac{7\pi}{6}$

  B. $\dfrac{7\pi}{30}$

  C. $\dfrac{5\pi}{6}$

  D. $\dfrac{17\pi}{30}$

  E. none of these

49. The radii of the two similar shaded sectors have a ratio of $4 : 3$. If the larger sector has an area of $10\ \text{cm}^2$, find the arc length defined by the smaller sector. [4.1]

  A. 15 cm

  B. 7.5 cm

  C. 3.75 cm

  D. 2.5 cm

  E. none of these

50. If $\csc\theta = \dfrac{17}{15}$, find $\sec\theta$. [4.2]

  A. $\dfrac{17}{8}$

  B. $\dfrac{8}{17}$

  C. $\dfrac{16}{17}$

  D. $\dfrac{15}{17}$

  E. none of these

51. Find m if a line perpendicular to $y = mx + b$ has a slope of $-\sec\theta$. [4.2]

  A. $\csc\theta$

  B. $-\cos\theta$

  C. $-\sin\theta$

  D. $\cos\theta$

  E. none of these

Drawing graphs of the parent trigonometric functions and the unit circle can help you understand how the shapes of the graphs are generated. Press MODE and select RADIAN, PAR, and SIMUL to graph parametric equations simultaneously.

Press Y= and enter $X_{1T} = \cos T$ and $Y_{1T} = \sin T$ for the unit circle. Enter $X_{2T} = T$ and $Y_{2T} = \sin T$ for the sine function. Cursor to the left of each set of parametric equations and select the path icon ⤵. Then press WINDOW and enter the following window values before graphing the functions.

$Tmin = 0$, $Tmax = 2\pi$, $Tstep = \pi/36$
$Xmin = -\pi/2$, $Xmax = 5\pi/2$, $Xscl = \pi/4$
$Ymin = -2.9$, $Ymax = 2.9$, $Yscl = 1$

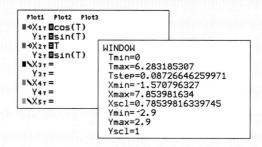

Notice how the value of the sine function is the height of the point moving along the unit circle.

1. Draw the graphs of the other trigonometric functions by entering each function in Y_{2T}.

2. Explore the graph of the inverse of $y = \sin x$ by entering $X_{2T} = T$ and $Y_{2T} = \sin T$ and switching these expressions in X_{1T} and Y_{1T}. Adjust the window as needed. Can you change the domain of the trigonometric function using Tmin and Tmax so that the inverse is also a function?

3. Explore the graphs of the inverse of $y = \cos x$ and the inverse of $y = \tan x$.

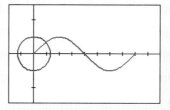

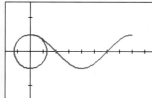

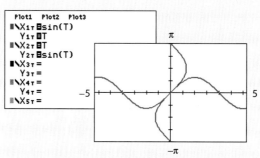

4.4 Sinusoidal Functions

A bore tide (a large wave or series of waves coming in with the tide) can be modeled by a sinusoidal function of time.

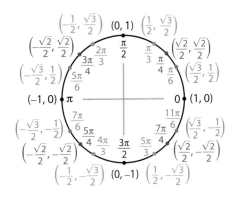

Just as we used the unit circle to extend the definitions of the trigonometric functions to real numbers, it can be used to draw graphs of the basic sine and cosine functions. Recall from Section 4.3 that wrapping a real number around the unit circle allows the value of sine to be viewed as the y-coordinate (the height) of the endpoint of an arc on the unit circle. Similarly, the cosine value may be viewed as the x-coordinate (the directed horizontal distance) of the endpoint. In Section 4.3 we saw that the period (the length of one complete cycle of values) of both functions is 2π.

After completing this section, you will be able to

- analyze and graph sinusoidal functions.
- write function rules for sinusoidal functions.
- model real-world data and solve problems using sinusoidal functions.

Plotting the coordinates from the 16 special values on the unit circle illustrates the pattern of values during the first period of each function. This cycle of values can be repeated to extend the graphs. The Technology Corner at the end of the previous section shows how to produce parametric representations of these functions.

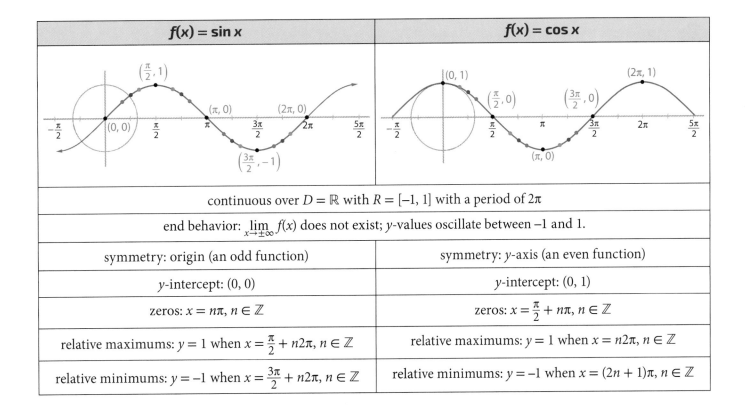

$f(x) = \sin x$	$f(x) = \cos x$

continuous over $D = \mathbb{R}$ with $R = [-1, 1]$ with a period of 2π

end behavior: $\lim\limits_{x \to \pm\infty} f(x)$ does not exist; y-values oscillate between -1 and 1.

$f(x) = \sin x$	$f(x) = \cos x$
symmetry: origin (an odd function)	symmetry: y-axis (an even function)
y-intercept: $(0, 0)$	y-intercept: $(0, 1)$
zeros: $x = n\pi, n \in \mathbb{Z}$	zeros: $x = \dfrac{\pi}{2} + n\pi, n \in \mathbb{Z}$
relative maximums: $y = 1$ when $x = \dfrac{\pi}{2} + n2\pi, n \in \mathbb{Z}$	relative maximums: $y = 1$ when $x = n2\pi, n \in \mathbb{Z}$
relative minimums: $y = -1$ when $x = \dfrac{3\pi}{2} + n2\pi, n \in \mathbb{Z}$	relative minimums: $y = -1$ when $x = (2n + 1)\pi, n \in \mathbb{Z}$

Notice that the graph of the cosine function can be obtained by shifting the graph of the sine function $\frac{\pi}{2}$ units to the left. Any function that is a transformation of a sine function is called a *sinusoid*. A *sinusoidal function* can be written as $y = a \sin b(x - h) + k$ or $y = a \cos b(x - h) + k$. We will examine how the values of each constant a, b, h, and k transform the graph of the parent function.

In Chapter 1 we saw that the graph of $g(x) = a \cdot f(x)$ is a vertical stretch (if $|a| > 1$) or shrink (if $0 < |a| < 1$) of the graph of $f(x)$. If $a < 0$, the graph is also reflected across the x-axis. When the output of a sinusoidal function is multiplied by a constant, the vertical stretch or shrink affects the function's *amplitude*.

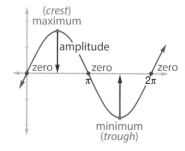

(crest) maximum
amplitude
zero   zero   zero
π 2π
minimum (trough)

DEFINITION

The **amplitude** of a sinusoid is one-half the difference of the function's maximum and minimum values. The amplitude of $y = a \sin x$ and $y = a \cos x$ is $|a|$.

Example 1   Graphing a Vertical Stretch or Shrink

State the amplitude of $g(x) = -\frac{1}{2} \sin x$. Then describe how $g(x)$ is obtained by transforming the parent function $f(x) = \sin x$ and graph the function over $[-2\pi, 2\pi]$.

Answer

amplitude $= |a| = \left| -\frac{1}{2} \right| = \frac{1}{2}$

The graph of $f(x)$ is vertically shrunk by a factor of $\frac{1}{2}$ and reflected across the x-axis.

$f(x) = \sin x$	$(0, 0)$	$\left(\frac{\pi}{2}, 1 \right)$	$(\pi, 0)$	$\left(\frac{3\pi}{2}, -1 \right)$	$(2\pi, 0)$
$g(x) = -\frac{1}{2} \sin x$	$(0, 0)$	$\left(\frac{\pi}{2}, -\frac{1}{2} \right)$	$(\pi, 0)$	$\left(\frac{3\pi}{2}, \frac{1}{2} \right)$	$(2\pi, 0)$

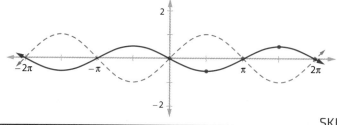

SKILL ✔ EXERCISE 11

Recall that the graph of $g(x) = f(bx)$ is a horizontal stretch (if $0 < |b| < 1$) or shrink (if $|b| > 1$) of the graph of $f(x)$ by a factor of $\frac{1}{|b|}$. Similarly, the constant b in $y = a \sin bx$ and $y = a \cos bx$ changes the period of these functions to $\frac{2\pi}{|b|}$. When b is negative, either $\sin(-x) = -\sin x$ or $\cos(-x) = \cos x$ can be applied to produce an equivalent function where b is positive.

DEFINITION

The **period** p of a periodic function is the horizontal length of one cycle. The period of $y = \sin bx$ and $y = \cos bx$ is $\frac{2\pi}{|b|}$.

TIP

The period of a sinusoid can be measured as the distance between adjacent maximum points or adjacent minimum points. This distance is often called the *wavelength*.

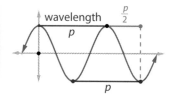

wavelength $\frac{p}{2}$
p
p

Example 2 Graphing a Horizontal Stretch or Shrink

State the amplitude and period of $h(x) = 3 \cos(-2x)$. Then describe how $h(x)$ is obtained by transforming the parent function $f(x) = \cos x$ and graph $h(x)$ over $[-2\pi, 2\pi]$.

Answer

Since cosine is an even function, $g(x) = 3\cos(-2x) = 3\cos 2x$.

amplitude: $|a| = |3| = 3$ period: $p = \dfrac{2\pi}{|b|} = \dfrac{2\pi}{|2|} = \pi$

The graph of $f(x)$ is horizontally shrunk by a factor of $\frac{1}{2}$ and vertically stretched by a factor of 3.

$y_1 = \cos x$	$(0, 1)$	$\left(\frac{\pi}{2}, 0\right)$	$(\pi, -1)$	$\left(\frac{3\pi}{2}, 0\right)$	$(2\pi, 1)$
$y_2 = \cos 2x$	$(0, 1)$	$\left(\frac{\pi}{4}, 0\right)$	$\left(\frac{\pi}{2}, -1\right)$	$\left(\frac{3\pi}{4}, 0\right)$	$(\pi, 1)$
$y_3 = 3\cos 2x$	$(0, 3)$	$\left(\frac{\pi}{4}, 0\right)$	$\left(\frac{\pi}{2}, -3\right)$	$\left(\frac{3\pi}{4}, 0\right)$	$(\pi, 3)$

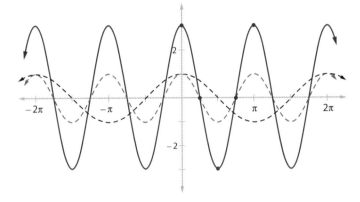

SKILL ✓ **EXERCISE 15**

Wave phenomena are modeled by sinusoids. The *frequency* (f) of a sinusoid is the reciprocal of the period: $f = \frac{1}{p} = \frac{|b|}{2\pi}$. The frequency for the cosine function in Example 2 is $\frac{1}{p} = \frac{1}{\pi} \approx 0.32$. This implies the graph completes 1 cycle over any x-interval of length π, or about 0.32 of a cycle per every unit of x. In many applications, frequencies are measured in *hertz* (Hz), or cycles per second. The loudness of a sound, which is measured in decibels, is related to the amplitude of the sound wave. The frequency of a sound wave is heard as its pitch.

The term *hertz* formally replaced cycles per second in 1960 in honor of the German physicist Heinrich Hertz, who in 1888 became the first person to transmit and receive radio waves, thus confirming their existence.

Example 3 Using Frequency

Humans can generally hear sound frequencies from 20 Hz to 20 kHz. Write a sine function modeling a 110 Hz note (A_2) played with an amplitude of 60 dB.

Answer

$a = \pm 60$

$|b| = 2\pi f = 2\pi(110) = 220\pi$

$\quad b = \pm 220\pi$

$f(x) = 60 \sin 220\pi x$

1. amplitude: $|a| = 60$

2. Use $f = \dfrac{1}{p} = \dfrac{|b|}{2\pi}$ to find the value of b.

3. Write an equation in the form $f(x) = a \sin bx$, choosing positive values for a and b.

SKILL ✓ **EXERCISE 17**

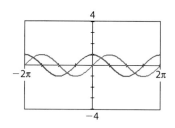

In previous chapters you have seen how $g(x) = f(x - h) + k$ is a translation of $f(x)$ by $|h|$ units right (if $h > 0$) or left (if $h < 0$) and $|k|$ units up (if $k > 0$) or down (if $k < 0$). The horizontal translation of a sinusoid is called its *phase shift*. Notice that translating the graph of $f(x) = \cos x$ right $\frac{\pi}{2}$ units produces $g(x) = \cos\left(x - \frac{\pi}{2}\right) = \sin x$. Translating the graph of $g(x) = \sin x$ left $\frac{\pi}{2}$ units produces $f(x) = \sin\left(x + \frac{\pi}{2}\right) = \cos x$.

When the sinusoid is written in the form $y = a \sin(bx + c) + k$ or $y = a \cos(bx + c) + k$, factoring out b yields $y = a \sin b\left(x + \frac{c}{b}\right) + k$ or $y = a \cos b\left(x + \frac{c}{b}\right) + k$, where $h = -\frac{c}{b}$ is the horizontal phase shift and k is the vertical shift.

Example 4 Graphing a Translated Sinusoid

State the amplitude, period, and phase shift of $g(x) = \sin\left(\frac{x}{2} + \frac{\pi}{4}\right) + 2$. Then describe how $g(x)$ is obtained by transforming the parent function $f(x) = \sin x$ and graph $g(x)$ over $[-2\pi, 4\pi]$.

Answer

Factor out the coefficient of x: $g(x) = \sin\left(\frac{x}{2} + \frac{\pi}{4}\right) + 2 = \sin \frac{1}{2}\left(x + \frac{\pi}{2}\right) + 2$.

amplitude: $|a| = |1| = 1$ $\qquad$ period: $p = \dfrac{2\pi}{|b|} = \dfrac{2\pi}{\left|\frac{1}{2}\right|} = 4\pi$ $\qquad$ phase shift: $h = -\dfrac{c}{b} = -\dfrac{\frac{\pi}{4}}{\frac{1}{2}} = -\dfrac{\pi}{2}$

The graph of $f(x)$ is horizontally stretched by a factor of 2, and then translated $\frac{\pi}{2}$ units left and 2 units up.

$y_1 = \sin x$	$(0, 0)$	$\left(\frac{\pi}{2}, 1\right)$	$(\pi, 0)$	$\left(\frac{3\pi}{2}, -1\right)$	$(2\pi, 0)$
$y_2 = \sin \frac{1}{2}x$	$(0, 0)$	$(\pi, 1)$	$(2\pi, 0)$	$(3\pi, -1)$	$(4\pi, 0)$
$y_3 = \sin \frac{1}{2}\left(x - \left(-\frac{\pi}{2}\right)\right) + 2$	$\left(-\frac{\pi}{2}, 2\right)$	$\left(\frac{\pi}{2}, 3\right)$	$\left(\frac{3\pi}{2}, 2\right)$	$\left(\frac{5\pi}{2}, 1\right)$	$\left(\frac{7\pi}{2}, 2\right)$

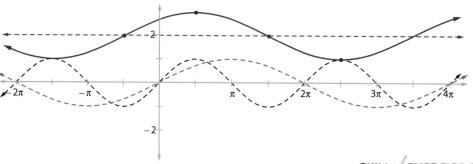

SKILL ✓ **EXERCISE 27**

The *midline* of a sinusoid is the horizontal line halfway between the maximum and minimum values of the function, $y = \frac{max - min}{2}$. The midline of the basic sinusoidal functions is the x-axis. The midline of a translated sinusoid is $y = k$. Since one cycle of $f(x) = \sin x$ is completed over $0 \leq x \leq 2\pi$, the corresponding cycle of $g(x) = a \sin(bx + c) + k$ is completed over $0 \leq bx + c \leq 2\pi$ or $-\frac{c}{b} \leq x \leq \frac{2\pi}{b} - \frac{c}{b}$. In Example 4, the midline is $y = 2$ and the function completes one cycle over $0 \leq \frac{x}{2} + \frac{\pi}{4} \leq 2\pi$ or $-\frac{\pi}{2} \leq x \leq \frac{7\pi}{2}$.

Characteristics of Sinusoidal Functions

functions of the form $f(x) = a \sin b(x - h) + k$ or
$f(x) = a \cos b(x - h) + k$ (where $a \neq 0$ and $b \neq 0$)

amplitude: $\lvert a \rvert$	period: $p = \frac{2\pi}{\lvert b \rvert}$	frequency: $f = \frac{1}{p} = \frac{\lvert b \rvert}{2\pi}$
phase shift: h	vertical shift: k	midline: $y = k$

When written as $f(x) = a \sin(bx + c) + k$ or
$f(x) = a \cos(bx + c) + k$, the phase shift $h = -\frac{c}{b}$.

Example 5   Writing the Equation of a Sinusoid

Write an equation of a sine function passing through $(-3, 0)$ with a period of 5 and an amplitude of 2.

Answer

Let $a = 2$.

Let $b = \frac{2\pi}{5}$.

Let $h = -3$.

$\therefore f(x) = 2 \sin \frac{2\pi}{5}(x + 3)$ or

$f(x) = 2 \sin \left(\frac{2\pi}{5} x + \frac{6\pi}{5} \right)$

Check

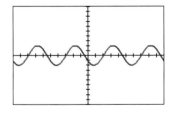

1. amplitude: $\lvert a \rvert = 2$, so $a = \pm 2$

2. period: $p = \frac{2\pi}{\lvert b \rvert} = 5$, so $\lvert b \rvert = \frac{2\pi}{5}$

3. The graph of $f(x) = 2 \sin \frac{2\pi}{5} x$ passes through $(0, 0)$, so the graph needs to be shifted 3 units left.

4. Write the equation.

5. Graph the function and check that it fulfills the requirements. Can you see why $g(x) = -2 \sin \frac{2\pi}{5}(x + 3)$ and $h(x) = 2 \sin \frac{2\pi}{5}(x - 2)$ are two of many other sine functions that also fulfill the requirements?

SKILL ✓ **EXERCISE 29**

Carl Hertz, the son of a nephew of Heinrich Hertz, was instrumental in developing medical ultrasound equipment and procedures. This technology is used by doctors in diagnosing and treating patients, and is now a standard part of prenatal care. The resulting sonograms vividly illustrate that life begins before birth (Jer. 1:4–5).

Sinusoidal functions frequently model periodic phenomena in God's creation.

Example 6 Modeling Data with a Periodic Function

Write a function modeling the illumination of the moon during 2018 if a full moon (100% illumination) occurred on January 2, 2018, and the next new moon (0% illumination) occurred on January 17, 2018. Then use the model to predict the percentage of the moon illuminated on July 9, the 190th day of that year.

Answer

maximum at (2, 1.00) and minimum at (17, 0.00)

1. Letting x represent the day of the year and y represent the illumination of the moon, express the data as ordered pairs.

$a = \frac{1}{2}(1.00 - 0.00) = \frac{1}{2}$

2. Use $a = \frac{1}{2}(y_{max} - y_{min})$ to determine the value of a.

$k = \frac{1}{2}(1.00 + 0.00) = \frac{1}{2}$

3. Use $k = \frac{1}{2}(y_{max} + y_{min})$ to determine the value of k.

$p = 2|x_{max} - x_{min}|$
$= 2|2 - 17| = 30$

4. Determine the period of the function using the fact that the horizontal distance between consecutive maximum and minimum points is half a cycle.

$|b| = \frac{2\pi}{p} = \frac{2\pi}{30}$; Let $b = \frac{\pi}{15}$.

5. Use $p = \frac{2\pi}{|b|}$ to determine the value of b.

$h = 2$

6. Since the first maximum point of $f(x) = \frac{1}{2}\cos\frac{\pi}{15}x + \frac{1}{2}$ is at (0, 1), the graph needs to be shifted right by 2 units.

$f(x) = \frac{1}{2}\cos\frac{\pi}{15}(x - 2) + \frac{1}{2}$

7. Write the equation of the modeling function.

$f(x) \approx 0.45$ or $\approx 45\%$

8. Evaluate $f(190)$ to predict the illumination percentage of the moon on July 9, 2018.

SKILL ✓ EXERCISE 37

A. Exercises

Use the 16 special values from the unit circle to state the exact coordinates of each illustrated point on the graph.

1.

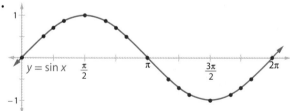

2.

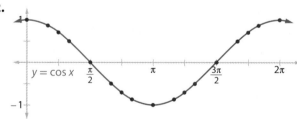

State the amplitude and period of each function.

3. $y = \frac{1}{4} \cos x$

4. $y = -3 \sin 2x$

5. $y = -2 \cos 4\pi x$

6. $y = \frac{7}{3} \cos \frac{2x}{3}$

7. Describe the graph of $g(x)$ as a transformation of $f(x) = \sin x$.

   a. $g(x) = 3 \sin x$

   b. $g(x) = -4 \sin \frac{x}{2}$

   c. $g(x) = \sin(-2x)$

8. Describe the graph of $g(x)$ as a transformation of $f(x) = \cos x$.

   a. $g(x) = \cos 0.25x$

   b. $g(x) = -\frac{1}{3} \cos 2x$

   c. $g(x) = 4 \cos(-x)$

9. Find the amplitude, period, and frequency of each function and explain what the frequency means.

   a. $g(x) = \sin 4x$

   b. $r(x) = -5 \cos 6\pi x$

   c. $v(x) = -\sin \frac{3\pi}{2} x$

State the amplitude, period, and any phase shift or vertical shift for each function. Then graph the function over [–2π, 2π].

10. $f(x) = 4 \sin x$

11. $g(x) = -\frac{1}{2} \cos x$

12. $h(x) = \cos x - 2$

13. $k(x) = \sin\left(x - \frac{\pi}{2}\right)$

14. $f(x) = \sin\left(x + \frac{\pi}{4}\right) + 3$

15. $g(x) = 2 \cos 3x$

16. The instantaneous voltage (V_i) of an alternating current generator can be modeled by $V_i = V_m \sin(\omega t)$ where V_m is the maximum voltage and ω is the angular speed of the generator's rotor in radians per second.

   a. What is the period of the function if the maximum voltage is 186.6 volts and the angular speed is 377 $\frac{\text{radians}}{\text{sec}}$?

   b. What is the frequency of the function in Hz?

17. An elephant call can start with a low rumble at 25 Hz and progress to a roar pitched at 470 Hz with an amplitude of 105 dB. Write a sine function that models the final sound wave.

> **B. Exercises**

State the amplitude, period, and any phase shift or vertical shift for each function. Then graph the function over [–2π, 2π].

18. $h(x) = -2 \sin \frac{1}{2} x$

19. $h(x) = 1.5 \cos \frac{2x}{3}$

20. $f(x) = \cos 3x + 2$

21. $f(x) = 2 \sin(x + \pi)$

State the amplitude, period, phase shift, and vertical shift for each function. Then describe the function's transformation from the parent function $f(x) = \sin x$ or $f(x) = \cos x$. Confirm your answer by using technology to graph the function and its parent function.

22. $g(x) = 2 \cos 5x - 1$

23. $h(x) = \sin\left(3x - \frac{\pi}{2}\right) + 3$

24. $r(x) = 2 \cos(\pi - 2x)$

Graph two periods of each function.

25. $f(x) = -2 \cos\left(x - \frac{\pi}{2}\right)$

26. $g(x) = 3 \sin\left(2x + \frac{\pi}{2}\right)$

27. $h(x) = -3 \sin(2x - \pi) + 2$

28. $k(x) = 2 \cos(4x - \pi) - 3$

Write a sine function with the given characteristics.

29. amplitude: 1, period: $\frac{\pi}{2}$, phase shift: $\frac{\pi}{8}$, translated 3 units up

30. amplitude: 4, period: 5π, passing through $(3, 0)$

Write a cosine function with the given characteristics.

31. amplitude: 3, period: π, phase shift: $-\frac{\pi}{6}$, translated 4 units up

32. passing through a relative maximum at $\left(\frac{1}{4}, \frac{5}{2}\right)$ and a relative minimum at $\left(\frac{5}{4}, \frac{3}{2}\right)$

Write a sine function rule for each graph.

33.

34.

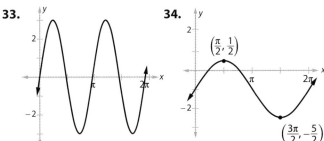

Write a cosine function rule for each graph.

35.

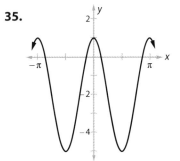

36.

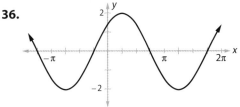

37. The blood pressure of a person with hypertension is modeled in millimeters of mercury (mm Hg) by a function of time (in minutes):
$p(t) = 125 + 35 \sin 2\pi t$.

  a. Use technology to graph two periods of the function. State the person's highest and lowest blood pressure.

  b. State the function's amplitude and its vertical shift.

  c. Find the function's period. How many times does the person's heart beat in one minute?

38. The world's tallest observation wheel (as of 2016) has a height of 550 ft and a diameter of 520 ft. Riders board and depart its glass observation cabins while the wheel takes approximately 30 min to complete one revolution.

  a. Derive a function $h(t)$ that models the height of an observation cabin as a function of the time (in minutes) after a rider enters at the bottom of the wheel.

  b. How high would a passenger be after 5 min?

  c. How much time would elapse before the passenger returned to that height?

> **C. Exercises**

39. Discuss: Write three sine function rules for $g(x)$.

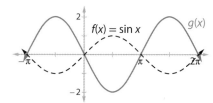

40. Discuss: Write two cosine function rules and two sine function rules for $g(x)$.

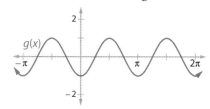

41. Turnagain Arm, a waterway in northwestern Alaska, boasts one of the world's largest bore tides. The water depth can be modeled by a sinusoidal function of time with a period of 12 hr 24 min. On a certain day a high tide of 25.87 ft occurs at 4:00 AM after the previous evening's low tide of 5.47 ft.

  a. At what time did the previous evening's low tide occur, and when will the next low tide occur?

  b. Write a sinusoidal function $d(t)$ that models the depth of the water that day.

  c. Estimate the depth of the water at 3:00 PM that day.

  d. When was the depth of the water 15.67 ft that day?

42. The table lists the average high temperatures on the 15th of each month in Minneapolis, Minnesota.

Month	1	2	3	4	5	6
High (°F)	21	28	40	57	70	79
Month	7	8	9	10	11	12
High (°F)	84	81	71	59	40	26

  a. Write a sinusoidal function $h(t)$ that models the high temperature as a function of time.

  b. Use technology to graph the data and your model. Which month has the largest residual?

  c. Use the function to estimate the high temperature on April 30.

Taylor polynomial approximations are used in calculus to estimate trigonometric functions. For exercises 43–44, complete the following steps to explore each approximation.
Note that $n!$ = n factorial = $n(n-1)(n-2)\ldots1$.

  a. Use technology to graph the trigonometric function as Y_1 and the given Taylor polynomial approximation as Y_2 over $[-2\pi, 2\pi]$. In what interval does the approximation appear to be a good model for the function?

  b. Define the residual function $Y_3 = Y_1 - Y_2$, then examine a table of values with Tstep = 0.1 to find the interval for which $|Y_3| \le 0.01$.

43. $f(x) = \sin x \approx x - \dfrac{x^3}{3!} + \dfrac{x^5}{5!}$

44. $f(x) = \cos x \approx 1 - \dfrac{x^2}{2!} + \dfrac{x^4}{4!}$

45. Write a polynomial function with roots of multiplicity 2 at −3 and at 4. [3.1]

Find the degree of each function if $P(x)$ is a quadratic function and $Q(x)$ is a cubic function. [1.7, 2.4]

46. $P(x) + Q(x)$ **47.** $P(x) \cdot Q(x)$ **48.** $\dfrac{Q(x)}{P(x)}$

49. When is the sum of two quadratic functions not quadratic?

50. Identify any vertical asymptote(s) for each reciprocal function. [2.5]

  a. $f(x) = \dfrac{1}{x + 3}$ **b.** $h(x) = \dfrac{1}{x^2 + 5x - 14}$

  c. $g(x) = \dfrac{1}{x^2 + 1}$

51. Which of the following is irrational? [4.3]

  A. $\tan \dfrac{\pi}{4}$ **D.** $\sin \dfrac{7\pi}{6}$

  B. $\cos \dfrac{\pi}{6}$ **E.** none of these

  C. $\tan \dfrac{3\pi}{2}$

52. Which of the following is not true if $\sin \theta = \dfrac{9}{41}$ and $\tan \theta > 0$? [4.3]

  A. $\csc \theta = \dfrac{41}{9}$ **D.** $\cos \theta > \dfrac{1}{2}$

  B. $\tan \theta = \dfrac{9}{40}$ **E.** These are all true.

  C. $\csc \theta > \sec \theta$

53. Find $\cos(-\theta) + \sec \theta$ if $\cos \theta = 0.8$. [4.3]

  A. 0   **D.** 2.05

  B. 0.45   **E.** none of these

  C. 1.6

54. For which angle θ is $\sin \theta > 0$ and $\tan \theta < 0$?

  A. 88°   **D.** 345°

  B. 146°   **E.** none of these

  C. 225°

4.5 Graphing Other Trigonometric Functions

The distance between an observer and a drone flying overhead can be modeled with a reciprocal trigonometric function.

After completing this section, you will be able to

- graph the tangent function and its transformations.
- graph the reciprocal trigonometric functions and their transformations.
- write function rules for transformations of tangent and reciprocal functions.

The tangent, cotangent, cosecant, and secant functions can be expressed as quotients using the sine and cosine functions. Whenever the expression in the denominator is 0, the function is undefined and the graph contains a vertical asymptote. After examining the graphs of tangent functions, the graphs of cotangent, cosecant, and secant functions will be considered as reciprocals of the basic sine, cosine, and tangent functions.

$$\tan x = \frac{\sin x}{\cos x} \qquad \cot x = \frac{\cos x}{\sin x} \qquad \sec x = \frac{1}{\cos x} \qquad \csc x = \frac{1}{\sin x}$$

Since these are periodic functions with either $\cos x$ or $\sin x$ in the denominator, they will have an infinite number of discontinuities. Consider completing the Technology Corner at the end of Section 4.3 to produce animated graphs of these functions.

Using key values from the unit circle, we can sketch a graph of the tangent function. Since $f(x) = \tan x = \frac{\sin x}{\cos x}$, its graph has vertical asymptotes where $\cos x = 0$ (at every odd multiple of $\frac{\pi}{2}$) and x-intercepts where $\sin x = 0$ (at every multiple of π). Note also that the function evaluates to 1 or −1 at odd multiples of $\frac{\pi}{4}$, and that the function increases from −∞ to ∞ within each interval defined by consecutive asymptotes.

x	0	$\frac{\pi}{4}$	$\frac{\pi}{2}$	$\frac{3\pi}{4}$	π	$\frac{5\pi}{4}$	$\frac{3\pi}{2}$	$\frac{7\pi}{4}$	2π
$\tan x$	0	1	*	−1	0	1	*	−1	0

* undefined

$f(x) = \tan x$	
vertical asymptotes: $x = (2n + 1)\frac{\pi}{2}, n \in \mathbb{Z}$.	
$D = \{x \mid x \neq (2n + 1)\frac{\pi}{2}, n \in \mathbb{Z}\}$ and $R = \mathbb{R}$ period: π	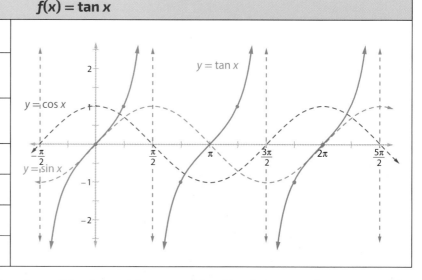
end behavior: $\lim\limits_{x \to \pm\infty} f(x)$ does not exist; y-values oscillate between −∞ and ∞.	
symmetry: origin (odd function)	
y-intercept: $(0, 0)$	
zeros: $x = n\pi, n \in \mathbb{Z}$	
relative max/min: none	

The graphs of functions of the form $g(x) = a \tan b(x - h) + k$ are transformations of the parent function $f(x) = \tan x$. While amplitude is not defined for tangent functions, their graphs are stretched or shrunk vertically by a factor of $|a|$ and reflected in the x-axis if $a < 0$. Since b causes a horizontal stretch ($|b| < 0$) or shrink ($|b| > 0$), the period is $\frac{\pi}{|b|}$. The constants h and k cause horizontal and vertical shifts as in sinusoids.

Example 1 Graphing a Tangent Function

State the period of $g(x) = \tan \frac{x}{2}$. Then describe how $g(x)$ is obtained by transforming the parent function $f(x) = \tan x$ and sketch three periods of $g(x)$.

Answer

period $= \frac{\pi}{|b|} = \frac{\pi}{\left|\frac{1}{2}\right|} = 2\pi$

The graph is horizontally stretched by a factor of 2.

$f(x) = \tan x$	VA: $x = -\frac{\pi}{2}$	$\left(-\frac{\pi}{4}, -1\right)$	$(0, 0)$	$\left(\frac{\pi}{4}, 1\right)$	VA: $x = \frac{\pi}{2}$
$g(x) = \tan \frac{x}{2}$	VA: $x = -\pi$	$\left(-\frac{\pi}{2}, -1\right)$	$(0, 0)$	$\left(\frac{\pi}{2}, 1\right)$	VA: $x = \pi$

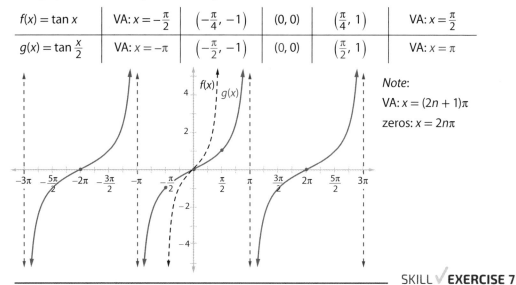

Note:

VA: $x = (2n + 1)\pi$

zeros: $x = 2n\pi$

SKILL ✔ **EXERCISE 7**

While one cycle of $f(x) = \tan x$ is completed over $-\frac{\pi}{2} \le x \le \frac{\pi}{2}$, the corresponding cycle of $g(x) = \tan \frac{x}{2}$ in Example 1 is completed over $-\frac{\pi}{2} \le \frac{x}{2} \le \frac{\pi}{2}$ or $-\pi \le x \le \pi$.

Using key values from the unit circle, we can also sketch a graph of the cotangent function $f(x) = \cot x = \frac{\cos x}{\sin x}$. The graph has vertical asymptotes where $\sin x = 0$ (at every multiple of π) and x-intercepts where $\cos x = 0$ (at every odd multiple of $\frac{\pi}{2}$). Note that $\cot x = \tan x = \pm 1$ at odd multiples of $\frac{\pi}{4}$. Note that the function decreases from $-\infty$ to ∞ within each interval defined by consecutive asymptotes.

x	0	$\frac{\pi}{4}$	$\frac{\pi}{2}$	$\frac{3\pi}{4}$	π	$\frac{5\pi}{4}$	$\frac{3\pi}{2}$	$\frac{7\pi}{4}$	2π
$\cot x$	*	1	0	-1	*	1	0	-1	*

* undefined

$f(x) = \cot x$	
vertical asymptotes: $x = n\pi$, $n \in \mathbb{Z}$	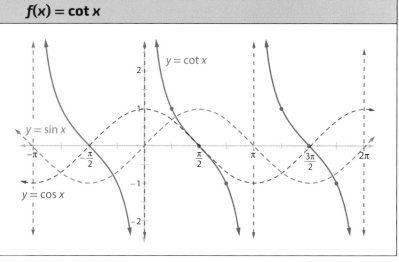
$D = \{x \mid x \ne n\pi, n \in \mathbb{Z}\}$ and $R = \mathbb{R}$; period: π	
end behavior: $\lim\limits_{x \to \pm\infty} f(x)$ does not exist; y-values oscillate between ∞ and $-\infty$.	
symmetry: origin (odd function)	
y-intercept: none	
zeros: $x = (2n + 1)\frac{\pi}{2}$, $n \in \mathbb{Z}$	
relative max/min: none	

Example 2 Graphing a Cotangent Function

State the period and phase shift of $g(x) = -2 \cot\left(x + \frac{\pi}{4}\right)$. Then describe how $g(x)$ is obtained by transforming the parent function $f(x) = \cot x$ and sketch the graph of $g(x)$ over $[-2\pi, 2\pi]$.

Answer

$\text{period} = \frac{\pi}{|b|} = \frac{\pi}{|1|} = \pi$; $\text{phase shift} = h = -\frac{\pi}{4}$

The graph is shifted $\frac{\pi}{4}$ units left, reflected in the y-axis and stretched vertically by a factor of 2.

$y_1 = \cot x$	VA: $x = 0$	$\left(\frac{\pi}{4}, 1\right)$	$\left(\frac{\pi}{2}, 0\right)$	$\left(\frac{3\pi}{4}, -1\right)$	VA: $x = \pi$
$y_2 = \cot\left(x + \frac{\pi}{4}\right)$	VA: $x = -\frac{\pi}{4}$	$(0, 1)$	$\left(\frac{\pi}{4}, 0\right)$	$\left(\frac{\pi}{2}, -1\right)$	VA: $x = \frac{3\pi}{4}$
$y_3 = -2 \cot\left(x + \frac{\pi}{4}\right)$	VA: $x = -\frac{\pi}{4}$	$(0, -2)$	$\left(\frac{\pi}{4}, 0\right)$	$\left(\frac{\pi}{2}, 2\right)$	VA: $x = \frac{3\pi}{4}$

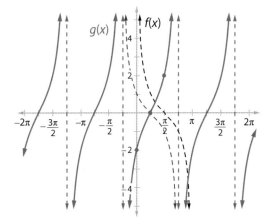

Note:

VA: $x = n\pi - \frac{\pi}{4}$

zeros: $x = (2n + 1)\frac{\pi}{2} - \frac{\pi}{4}$

$= n\pi + \frac{\pi}{4}$

SKILL ✓ **EXERCISE 23**

Since one cycle of $f(x) = \cot x$ is completed over $0 \leq x \leq \pi$, the corresponding cycle of $g(x) = -2 \cot\left(x + \frac{\pi}{4}\right)$ in Example 2 is completed over $0 \leq x + \frac{\pi}{4} \leq \pi$ or $-\frac{\pi}{4} \leq x \leq \frac{3\pi}{4}$.

Understanding general principles relating the graphs of $f(x)$ and its reciprocal function $g(x) = \frac{1}{f(x)}$ can help you graph secant, cosecant, and cotangent functions. Analyzing the graphs of $f(x) = x^2 - 4$ and its reciprocal $g(x) = \frac{1}{f(x)} = \frac{1}{x^2 - 4}$ reveals several key relationships.

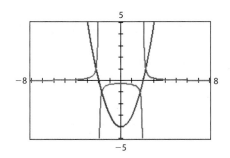

- If $f(x) = 0$, then $\frac{1}{f(x)}$ is undefined and $g(x)$ has a vertical asymptote.

- As $f(x) \to 0^+, \frac{1}{f(x)} \to \infty$, and as $f(x) \to 0^-, \frac{1}{f(x)} \to -\infty$.

- As $f(x) \to \infty, \frac{1}{f(x)} \to 0^+$, and as $f(x) \to -\infty, \frac{1}{f(x)} \to 0^-$.

- If $f(x) = 1$, then $\frac{1}{f(x)} = 1$, and if $f(x) = -1$, then $\frac{1}{f(x)} = -1$.

- If $f(x) > 1$, then $0 < \frac{1}{f(x)} < 1$, and if $0 < f(x) < 1$, then $\frac{1}{f(x)} > 1$.

- If $f(x) < -1$, then $-1 < \frac{1}{f(x)} < 0$, and if $-1 < f(x) < 0$, then $\frac{1}{f(x)} < -1$.

You can see how these principles apply to $f(x) = \tan x$ and $g(x) = \cot x = \dfrac{1}{\tan x}$. Since $y = \csc x = \dfrac{1}{\sin x}$ and $y = \sec x = \dfrac{1}{\cos x}$, their graphs can be drawn as reciprocals of the basic sinusoids. The relative maximums of the related sinusoid (its crests) become relative minimums of the reciprocal function and the relative minimums of the sinusoid (its troughs) become the relative maximums of the reciprocal function. Note also that if $f(x) = \pm\dfrac{1}{2}$, then $\dfrac{1}{f(x)} = \pm 2$.

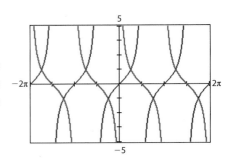

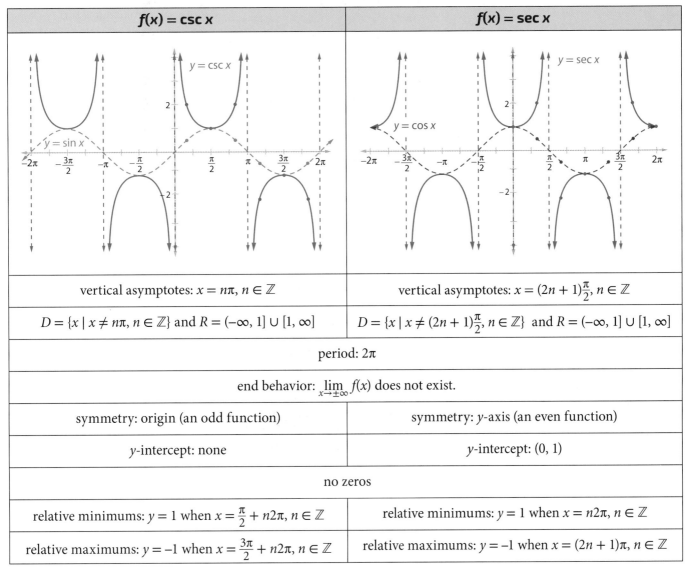

$f(x) = \csc x$	$f(x) = \sec x$
vertical asymptotes: $x = n\pi$, $n \in \mathbb{Z}$	vertical asymptotes: $x = (2n+1)\dfrac{\pi}{2}$, $n \in \mathbb{Z}$
$D = \{x \mid x \neq n\pi, n \in \mathbb{Z}\}$ and $R = (-\infty, 1] \cup [1, \infty]$	$D = \{x \mid x \neq (2n+1)\dfrac{\pi}{2}, n \in \mathbb{Z}\}$ and $R = (-\infty, 1] \cup [1, \infty]$
period: 2π	
end behavior: $\lim\limits_{x \to \pm\infty} f(x)$ does not exist.	
symmetry: origin (an odd function)	symmetry: y-axis (an even function)
y-intercept: none	y-intercept: $(0, 1)$
no zeros	
relative minimums: $y = 1$ when $x = \dfrac{\pi}{2} + n2\pi$, $n \in \mathbb{Z}$	relative minimums: $y = 1$ when $x = n2\pi$, $n \in \mathbb{Z}$
relative maximums: $y = -1$ when $x = \dfrac{3\pi}{2} + n2\pi$, $n \in \mathbb{Z}$	relative maximums: $y = -1$ when $x = (2n+1)\pi$, $n \in \mathbb{Z}$

Graphing a related basic trig function can help you draw the graphs of tranformed reciprocal functions of the form $g(x) = a \csc b(x - h) + k$ or $g(x) = a \sec b(x - h) + k$.

Example 3   Graphing a Cosecant Function

Sketch a graph of $g(x) = 2 \csc x$ over $[-2\pi, 2\pi]$. Then state the period, domain, and range of the function.

Answer

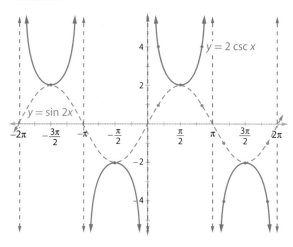

1. Graph $y = 2 \sin x$ over $[-2\pi, 2\pi]$.

2. Draw vertical asymptotes where $y = 2 \sin x = 0$ (at $x = n\pi$).

3. Plot relative minimums and maximums of $g(x) = 2\left(\dfrac{1}{\sin x}\right)$ at crests and troughs of $y = 2 \sin x$.

4. When $\sin x = \pm\dfrac{1}{2}$ (at $x = \dfrac{\pi}{6}, \dfrac{5\pi}{6}, \dfrac{7\pi}{6}, \dfrac{11\pi}{6}, \ldots$), $g(x) = 2\left(\dfrac{1}{\sin x}\right) = \pm 4$. Plotting these points shows how quickly $g(x) \to \pm\infty$ as $\sin x \to 0$.

5. Sketch the graph of $g(x) = 2 \csc x$. Note that the graph is a vertical stretch of $f(x) = \csc x$ by a factor of 2.

6. State the period, domain, and range.

The period is 2π.
$D = \left\{ x \mid x \neq (2n + 1)\dfrac{\pi}{2} \right\}; R = (-\infty, -2] \cup [2, \infty)$

SKILL ✓ **EXERCISE 9**

Example 4   Graphing a Secant Function

State the period and phase shift of $g(x) = \sec\left(\dfrac{2}{3}x - \dfrac{\pi}{6}\right)$ and describe how $g(x)$ is obtained by transforming the parent function $f(x) = \sec x$. Sketch a graph illustrating two periods of $g(x)$ and verify your graph using technology.

Answer

$g(x) = \sec\left(\dfrac{2}{3}x - \dfrac{\pi}{6}\right) = \sec\dfrac{2}{3}\left(x - \dfrac{\pi}{4}\right)$

1. Factor out the coefficient of x.

$\text{period} = \dfrac{2\pi}{\left|\frac{2}{3}\right|} = 3\pi$; phase shift: $h = \dfrac{\frac{\pi}{6}}{\frac{2}{3}} = \dfrac{\pi}{4}$

2. Find the period and phase shift using $p = \dfrac{2\pi}{|b|}$ and $h = \dfrac{c}{b}$.

The graph of $f(x)$ is stretched horizontally by a factor of $\dfrac{3}{2}$ and shifted $\dfrac{\pi}{4}$ units right.

3. Describe the transformations.

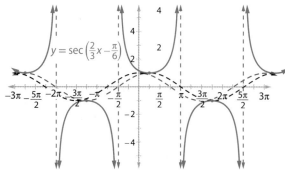

4. Graph $y = \cos\left(\dfrac{2}{3}x - \dfrac{\pi}{6}\right)$ over $[-3\pi, 3\pi]$ by shifting the graph of $y = \cos\dfrac{2}{3}x$ to the right by $\dfrac{\pi}{4}$ units.

5. Graph $g(x) = \sec\left(\dfrac{2}{3}x - \dfrac{\pi}{6}\right)$.

   a. Vertical asymptotes of $g(x)$ occur at zeros of the related sinusoid.

   b. Relative minimums and maximums of $g(x)$ occur at the crests and troughs of the related sinusoid, respectively.

CONTINUED ➡

Check

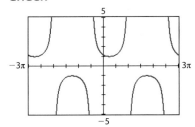

6. Graph $Y_1 = 1/\cos(2x/3 - \pi/6)$.

SKILL ✔ **EXERCISE 27**

Ernst Chladni, the Father of Acoustics, found that sound could be visualized by sprinkling sand on a metal plate and then bowing the plate with a violin bow. The sand moves to the areas on the plate that vibrate the least (the nodes), forming different patterns at different frequencies. Some violin makers still utilize Chladni patterns when designing their instruments.

Since one cycle of $f(x) = \sec x$ is defined by the vertical asymptotes at $-\frac{\pi}{2}$ and $\frac{3\pi}{2}$, the vertical asymptotes defining the corresponding cycle of $g(x) = \sec\left(\frac{2}{3}x - \frac{\pi}{6}\right)$ in Example 4 are found by solving $\frac{2}{3}x - \frac{\pi}{6} = -\frac{\pi}{2}$ and $\frac{2}{3}x - \frac{\pi}{6} = \frac{3\pi}{2}$ to get $x = -\frac{\pi}{2}$ and $x = \frac{5\pi}{2}$.

❯ A. Exercises

Use the special values from the unit circle to state the exact coordinates of each point on the graph.

1. $y = \tan x$

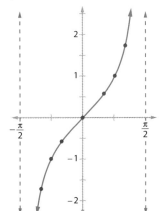

2. $y = \cot x$

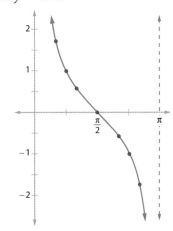

3. $y = \csc x$

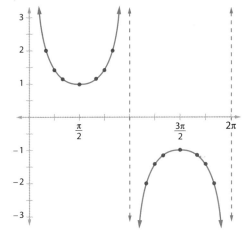

4. $y = \sec x$

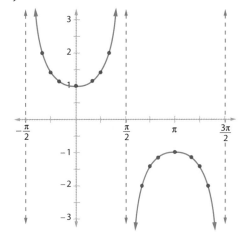

5. State the period, vertical asymptotes, and zeros of each function's graph.

    a. sine   **b.** cosine   **c.** tangent

    d. cotangent   **e.** cosecant   **f.** secant

Sketch a graph of each function over $[-2\pi, 2\pi]$.

6. $y = \csc \frac{x}{2}$ **7.** $y = \frac{1}{2} \tan x$

8. $y = \cot \left(x - \frac{\pi}{4} \right)$ **9.** $y = \sec \pi x$

Select all the functions that match each description.

A. $y = \sin x$ **C.** $y = \tan x$ **E.** $y = \csc x$

B. $y = \cos x$ **D.** $y = \cot x$ **F.** $y = \sec x$

10. has no zeros

11. has a period of π

12. has vertical asymptotes where $\sin \theta = 0$

13. has zeros at odd multiples of $\frac{\pi}{2}$

14. has zeros where $y = \csc x$ has vertical asymptotes

▶ B. Exercises

Without using technology, match each function with its graph.

15. $y = \tan 2x$ **16.** $y = 2 \tan x$

17. $y = \csc 2x$ **18.** $y = 2 \sec \frac{x}{2}$

19. $y = \csc (x - \pi)$ **20.** $y = \tan \left(x - \frac{\pi}{2} \right)$

A.
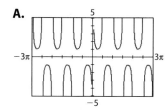

D.
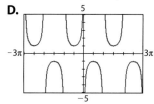

B.
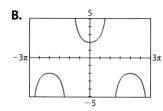

E.
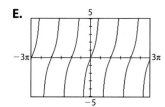

C.
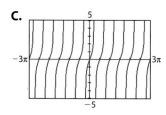

F.
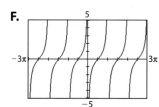

Sketch the graph of each function from -2π to 2π.

21. $y = -\frac{1}{2} \cot x$ **22.** $y = 2 \cot \frac{x}{2}$

23. $y = 2 \tan \frac{x}{2}$ **24.** $y = \csc \left(x - \frac{\pi}{2} \right)$

25. $y = 2 \sec (x + \pi)$ **26.** $y = -2 \csc x + 3$

Describe the graph of each function $g(x)$ as a transformation of its parent function.

27. $g(x) = 4 \csc (x + 2) - 8$

28. $g(x) = 5 \tan 3\left(x - \frac{\pi}{3} \right)$

29. $g(x) = -\frac{1}{3} \cot \left(\pi x + \frac{\pi}{3} \right)$

30. $g(x) = -0.2 \sec \left(\frac{x}{5} - \frac{\pi}{2} \right) + 0.6$

Write a rule for $g(x)$, the described transformation of $f(x)$.

31. The function $f(x) = \sec x$ is vertically stretched by 7 and horizontally shrunk so its period is π.

32. The function $f(x) = \tan x$ is horizontally shrunk so its period is $\frac{\pi}{3}$, shifted 2 units left, and vertically shrunk by a factor of $\frac{1}{4}$.

33. The function $f(x) = \sec x$ is horizontally shrunk so its period is 1, vertically stretched by a factor of 6, and shifted 4 units down.

34. Analyze: Which parent trigonometric function has asymptotes wherever $f(x) = \sec x$ has an asymptote? Explain your reasoning.

35. Analyze: Which parent trigonometric function has zeros where $f(x) = \sec x$ has an asymptote? Explain your reasoning.

36. Analyze: State the value of $g(x) = \tan x$ for any value of x where the graph of $f(x) = \csc x$ has a vertical asymptote. Explain your reasoning.

37. When Rebecca boards a glass elevator on the second floor of a building, the angle of depression as she views her niece standing on the first floor 20 ft from the base of the elevator is 35°.

    a. Write a function that models the elevator's distance above the first floor in terms of Rebecca's angle of depression.

    b. Find the elevator's height above ground level (to the nearest foot).

    c. From what height (to the nearest foot) and what floor will Rebecca be viewing her niece when the angle of depression is 71°? Assume each story in the building has the same height.

38. A drone performs a low-altitude airdrop of medical supplies at 80 ft and passes directly over a marker (M) in the drop zone.

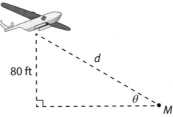

a. Write a function that models the distance from the marker to the drone in terms of the angle of elevation from the marker.

b. Graph the function from 0° to 90° and describe how the distance changes over this interval.

c. Find the distance when the drone is sighted at a 45° angle of elevation.

> **C. Exercises**

39. Analyze: Write function rules describing two different transformations of $f(x) = \sin x$ that result in $g(x) = \cos x$.

40. Analyze: Write function rules describing two different transformations of $f(x) = \tan x$ that result in $g(x) = \cot x$.

41. Prove: Use the figure to show that $\tan \theta$ is also the y-coordinate of the intersection of the angle's terminal side and the tangent drawn to the unit circle at $(1, 0)$.

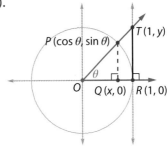

CUMULATIVE REVIEW

Identify any asymptotes and state each function's domain and range. [2.5]

42. $f(x) = \dfrac{1}{x^4}$

43. $f(x) = \dfrac{1}{(x + 1)^3}$

44. Find the radian measure of θ or the related arc length in a circle with the given radius. [4.1]

a. $r = 6$ cm, $s = 8\pi$ cm, $\theta = ?$

b. $r = 4$ ft, $\theta = \dfrac{\pi}{6}$, $s = ?$

45. Write an expression for all angles coterminal with $\theta = \dfrac{\pi}{5}$. Then state one positive and one negative coterminal angle. [4.1]

46. Evaluate the six trigonometric functions for $\angle B$. [4.2]

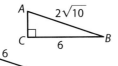

47. Find x to the nearest tenth. [4.2]

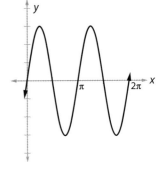

48. Find the angular speed (to the nearest radian per second) of the brush head of a sonic toothbrush that rotates at 30,000 rpm. [4.1]

A. 1000 radians/sec
B. 314 radians/sec
C. 500 radians/sec
D. 3142 radians/sec
E. none of these

49. A cosine function has a maximum value of –2 and an amplitude of 5. What is its minimum value? [4.4]

A. –7
B. –9
C. –10
D. –12
E. none of these

50. What is the frequency of $y = -2 \sin \left(\dfrac{x}{3}\right)$? [4.4]

A. $\dfrac{1}{6\pi}$
B. 3π
C. 6π
D. $\dfrac{1}{3}$
E. none of these

51. Which equation is represented by the graph? [4.4]

A. $y = 3 \sin x$
B. $y = 3 \sin \dfrac{x}{2}$
C. $y = 3 \sin 2x$
D. $y = \sin 2x$
E. none of these

The Utility and Value of Mathematics

How can it be that mathematics, a product of human thought independent of experience, is so admirably adapted to the objects of reality?

• • •

The eternal mystery of the world is its comprehensibility.

—*Albert Einstein*

Complex numbers provide an interesting example of the connection between pure mathematical theory and real-world applications. The Swiss mathematician Leonhard Euler developed complex number theory in the seventeenth century as a result of his study of polynomial equations with nonreal solutions. He described these abstract solutions as imaginary and represented them using i for $\sqrt{-1}$. Initially there were no practical applications for this field of mathematics. Even now students ask, "When are we ever going to use this?" Over time, complex numbers were applied to circuit analysis in electrical engineering, fractal design in geometry, and the theory of quantum mechanics in physics.

The ability of mathematics to accurately model such a variety of real-world applications often baffles modern mathematicians, many of whom believe that math is solely a product of human thought and do not recognize God as the ultimate source of mathematical truth. Mathematicians with a biblical worldview should be able to provide a clear explanation. As stated by James Nickel, "The mind of man, with its mathematical capabilities, and the physical world, with its observable mathematical order, *cohere* because of a common Creator. Einstein's eternal mystery has a solution. The biblical revelation of the Creator God is the unifying factor that reconciles what is irreconcilable in the humanistic context."

Conic sections provide another famous example of abstract mathematical theory being applied later to solve a practical problem. The ancient Greeks studied conics as early as 350 BC, resulting in its deductive presentation in the work of Apollonius around 200 BC. Archimedes applied conic theory in his development of catapults, delaying Rome's conquest of Syracuse for many years. However, the greatest application of conic section theory did not occur until the early seventeenth century, when Kepler presented his Copernican model of the universe based on elliptical orbits and his three planetary laws. Conic sec-

tions are the basis for studying the parabolic terrestrial motion of projectiles, the elliptical orbits of planets and some comets, and the hyperbolic path of several other celestial bodies. Sir Isaac Newton unified terrestrial and celestial motion with his mathematical description of universal gravitation.

Nikolai Lobachevsky, the nineteenth-century Russian founder of a non-Euclidean geometry, observed that "there is no branch of mathematics, however abstract, which may not someday be applied to the phenomena of the real world." Interestingly, his non-Euclidean geometry later became the basis for Albert Einstein's twentieth-century theory of relativity. Special relativity quickly proved valuable in the new fields of atomic and nuclear physics. Coupled with new mathematical measuring techniques, Einstein's general relativity has more recently provided explanations for pulsars and black holes. Classic experiments involving the sun's deflection of light and the gravitational redshift of light have confirmed the accuracy of Einstein's curved spacetime theory. Modern applications of general relativity involve high-precision measurements of both time and global positioning.

These examples demonstrate the utility and value of mathematics, as well as the importance of a biblical worldview in understanding the usefulness of mathematics. The popular math-puzzle writer Martin Gardner noted that "all mathematicians share . . . a sense of amazement over the infinite depth and the mysterious beauty and usefulness of mathematics." Without acknowledging that God is both the creator of the universe and the source of our ability to describe it, mathematicians will always be mystified by math's usefulness.

Exercises

1. What did Einstein say that mathematics was a product of?

2. List three modern applications of complex numbers.

3. Identify the common source of the physical universe and the human mind.

4. Explain why secular mathematicians are often surprised at the ability of mathematics to accurately model so many aspects of the physical universe.

5. Name the abstract mathematical topic that was used in the development of each application.
   a. fractal geometry design
   b. Kepler's three laws of planetary motion
   c. Einstein's theory of relativity

6. Who unified terrestrial and celestial motion with his work on universal gravitation?

7. Name the conic section used to model the motion of the following.
   a. planetary orbits
   b. terrestrial projectiles such as cannonballs

8. In what fields of physics has special relativity proved especially valuable?

9. Which classic experiments have confirmed the accuracy of Einstein's curved spacetime theory?

10. **Discuss:** Explain the usefulness of studying and developing abstract mathematical theories. Include several examples.

Inverse trigonometric functions are used to find the angle formed by the sides and the base of a pile of sand.

After completing this section, you will be able to

- define and graph inverse trig functions.
- evaluate inverse trig functions.
- evaluate compositions of trig and inverse trig functions.

In Section 4.2 inverse trigonometric functions were defined in terms of acute angles in right triangles. These definitions need to be expanded to include any angle θ and the real numbers. Since the graph of each trigonometric function fails the Horizontal Line Test, these functions are not one-to-one, and their inverses are not functions unless their domains are restricted.

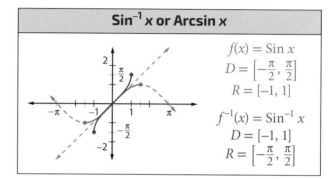

Sin^{-1} x or Arcsin x

$f(x) = \text{Sin } x$
$D = \left[-\frac{\pi}{2}, \frac{\pi}{2}\right]$
$R = [-1, 1]$

$f^{-1}(x) = \text{Sin}^{-1} x$
$D = [-1, 1]$
$R = \left[-\frac{\pi}{2}, \frac{\pi}{2}\right]$

Restricting the domain of $y = \sin x$ to $\left[-\frac{\pi}{2}, \frac{\pi}{2}\right]$ defines $f(x) = \text{Sin } x$, a one-to-one function with $R = [-1, 1]$. The capital letter indicates that the function's domain has been restricted. This function's inverse, $f^{-1}(x) = \text{Sin}^{-1}x$, or $f^{-1}(x) = \text{Arcsin } x$, is a function that returns a single angle or arc length within the interval $\left[-\frac{\pi}{2}, \frac{\pi}{2}\right]$. This value is the *principal value* of the inverse sine and is the value returned by a calculator when the $\sin^{-1}$ function is used. As with other inverse functions, the graphs of $f(x)$ and $f^{-1}(x)$ are reflections in the line $y = x$.

Example 1   Evaluating Inverse Sine Functions

Evaluate each expression in radians and degrees. State exact values if possible.

a. $\text{Sin}^{-1}\left(-\frac{1}{2}\right)$ **b.** Arcsin 0.75 **c.** $\text{Sin}^{-1} \pi$

Answer

a.

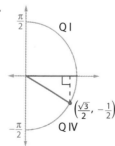

$$\text{Sin}^{-1}\left(-\frac{1}{2}\right) = -\frac{\pi}{6} \text{ or } -30°$$

1. Since the range of the Sin^{-1} function is $\left[-\frac{\pi}{2}, \frac{\pi}{2}\right]$, locate the point on the right side of the unit circle with a y-coordinate of $-\frac{1}{2}$.

2. Use the reference angle $\alpha = 30°$ to state the principal value.

CONTINUED ➡

b.

```
sin⁻¹(.75)
             0.848062079
sin⁻¹(.75)
             48.59037789
```

Use your calculator's sin⁻¹ function ([2nd], [SIN]) for x-values not associated with special angles on the unit circle.
Recall that the mode of the calculator determines whether the result is in degrees or radians.

Arcsin 0.75 ≈ 0.848 or 48.6°

---

c. $\text{Sin}^{-1}\,\pi$ is not defined.

The domain of $y = \text{Sin}^{-1}$ is [–1, 1} and $\pi > 1$.

SKILL ✔ **EXERCISE 7**

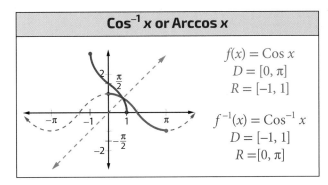

Cos⁻¹ x or Arccos x

$f(x) = \text{Cos}\,x$
$D = [0, \pi]$
$R = [-1, 1]$

$f^{-1}(x) = \text{Cos}^{-1}\,x$
$D = [-1, 1]$
$R = [0, \pi]$

Restricting the domain of $y = \cos x$ to $[0, \pi]$ defines $f(x) = \text{Cos}\,x$, a one-to-one function with $R = [-1, 1]$. This function's inverse, $f^{-1}(x) = \text{Cos}^{-1}\,x$ or $f^{-1}(x) = \text{Arccos}\,x$, is a function that returns a single angle or arc length within $[0, \pi]$. This principal value of the inverse cosine relation is the value returned by a calculator when its cos⁻¹ function is used.

Example 2   Evaluating Inverse Cosine Functions

Evaluate each expression in radians and degrees. State exact values if possible.

a. $\text{Cos}^{-1}\left(-\frac{\sqrt{2}}{2}\right)$

b. Arccos 0

c. $\text{Cos}^{-1}\frac{1}{4}$

Answer

a.

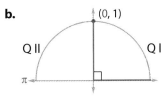

$$\text{Cos}^{-1}-\frac{\sqrt{2}}{2} = \frac{3\pi}{4} \text{ or } 135°$$

1. Since the range of the Cos⁻¹ function is [0, π], locate the point on the top half of the unit circle with an x-coordinate of $-\frac{\sqrt{2}}{2}$.

2. Use the reference angle $\alpha = 45°$ to state the principal value.

---

b.

(0, 1)

Q II   Q I

$$\text{Cos}^{-1}\,0 = \frac{\pi}{2} \text{ or } 90°$$

1. Locate the point on the top half of the unit circle with an x-coordinate of 0.

2. Use the quadrantal angle to state the principal value.

CONTINUED ➡

c.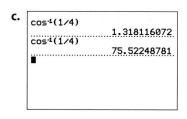

Use your calculator's $\cos^{-1}$ function ([2nd], [COS]) for x-values not associated with special angles on the unit circle.

Switch modes to find radian and degree measures.

$\text{Arccos } \dfrac{1}{4} \approx 1.318 \text{ or } 75.5°$

SKILL ✓ **EXERCISE 9**

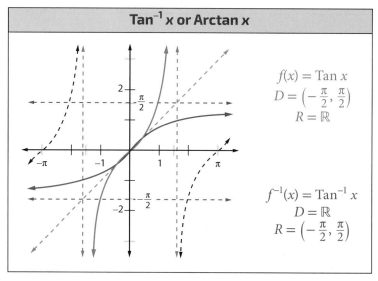

Tan⁻¹ x or Arctan x

$f(x) = \text{Tan } x$
$D = \left(-\dfrac{\pi}{2}, \dfrac{\pi}{2}\right)$
$R = \mathbb{R}$

$f^{-1}(x) = \text{Tan}^{-1} x$
$D = \mathbb{R}$
$R = \left(-\dfrac{\pi}{2}, \dfrac{\pi}{2}\right)$

Since $y = \tan x$ is undefined at $-\dfrac{\pi}{2}$ and $\dfrac{\pi}{2}$, the function is restricted to $\left(-\dfrac{\pi}{2}, \dfrac{\pi}{2}\right)$ to define $f(x) = \text{Tan } x$, a one-to-one function with $R = \mathbb{R}$. This function's inverse, $f^{-1}(x) = \text{Tan}^{-1} x$, or $f^{-1}(x) = \text{Arctan } x$, is a function that returns a single angle or arc length within $\left(-\dfrac{\pi}{2}, \dfrac{\pi}{2}\right)$. This principal value of the inverse tangent relation is returned by a calculator when its $\tan^{-1}$ function is used.

Example 3   Evaluating Inverse Tangent Functions

Evaluate each expression in radians and degrees. State exact values if possible.

a. $\text{Tan}^{-1} 1$ **b.** $\text{Arctan} \left(-\sqrt{3}\right)$ **c.** $\text{Tan}^{-1} 1.3764$

Answer

a.

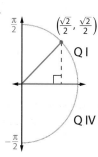

$\text{Tan}^{-1} 1 = \dfrac{\pi}{4} \text{ or } 45°$

1. Since the range of the Tan^{-1} function is $\left(-\dfrac{\pi}{2}, \dfrac{\pi}{2}\right)$, locate the point on the right side of the unit circle where $\dfrac{y}{x} = 1$.

2. Use the reference angle $\alpha = 45°$ to state the principal value.

The first known astronomical instrument was a gnomon, a simple vertical rod that allowed an observer to trace the shadow cast by the sun. The time of day, true north, and other compass points could then be determined. The sun's angle of elevation could also be found, using $\theta = \text{Tan}^{-1}$ $\left(\dfrac{\text{gnomon's height}}{\text{shadow's length}}\right)$.

CONTINUED ➡

b.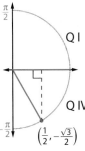

$\text{Arctan}\left(-\sqrt{3}\right) = -\frac{\pi}{3}$ or $-60°$

1. Locate the point on the right side of the unit circle where $\frac{y}{x} = -\sqrt{3}$.

2. Use the reference angle $\alpha = 60°$ to state the principal value.

c.
```
tan⁻¹(1.3764)
          0.9424840423
tan⁻¹(1.3764)
           54.00035788
```

$\text{Arctan } 1.3764 \approx 0.9425$ or $54°$

Use your calculator's $\tan^{-1}$ function (,) for x-values not associated with special angles on the unit circle.
Switch modes to find the angle in radians and degrees.

——————————————————— SKILL ✔ **EXERCISE 11**

Representing inverse trigonometric functions Sin^{-1}, Cos^{-1}, and Tan^{-1} as Arcsin, Arccos, and Arctan emphasizes that the result is the length of an arc on a unit circle (the radian measure) or an angle (measured in degrees). The inverse functions for the three reciprocal trigonometric functions are explored in exercises 38–40.

Since the trigonometric functions and their related inverse functions are not true inverses of each other, we must be careful when evaluating compositions involving a trigonometric function and its related inverse trigonometric function. While $\sin(\text{Sin}^{-1} x) = x$ for all $x \in [-1, 1]$ and $\text{Sin}^{-1}(\sin x) = x$ for all $x \in \left[-\frac{\pi}{2}, \frac{\pi}{2}\right]$, the expression $\text{Sin}^{-1}(\sin x)$ indicates a principal value when $x < -\frac{\pi}{2}$ or $x > \frac{\pi}{2}$. Similar cautions apply to $\text{Tan}^{-1}(\tan x)$ when $x < -\frac{\pi}{2}$ or $x > \frac{\pi}{2}$ and $\text{Cos}^{-1}(\cos x)$ when $x < 0$ or $x > \pi$.

TIP 💡

Some texts define the inverse trigonometric functions without capital letters, with the assumption of restricted domains for sine, cosine, and tangent functions.

Example 4   Evaluating Compositions

Evaluate each expression.

a. $\sin\left(\text{Sin}^{-1}\frac{1}{2}\right)$

b. $\text{Tan}^{-1}(\tan(-45°))$

c. $\text{Arccos}\left(\cos\frac{5\pi}{3}\right)$

Answer

a. $\sin\left(\text{Sin}^{-1}\frac{1}{2}\right) = \sin\frac{\pi}{6} = \frac{1}{2}$

The expression represents the sine of the angle within $\left[-\frac{\pi}{2}, \frac{\pi}{2}\right]$ with a sine of $\frac{1}{2}$.

b. $\text{Tan}^{-1}(\tan(-45°)) = \text{Tan}^{-1}(-1) = -45°$

Since $x = -45°$ is within the domain of the Tan^{-1} function, $\text{Tan}^{-1}(\tan x) = x$.

c. $\text{Arccos}\left(\cos\frac{5\pi}{3}\right) = \text{Arccos}\frac{1}{2} = \frac{\pi}{3}$

Since $\frac{5\pi}{3}$ is not in the domain of the Arccos function, the answer represents the principal value with the same cosine as $\frac{5\pi}{3}$.

——————————————————— SKILL ✔ **EXERCISE 25**

A reference triangle can be used to evaluate expressions involving compositions of trigonometric functions and other inverse trigonometric functions.

Example 5   Evaluating Compositions

Evaluate $\sin\left(\text{Cos}^{-1}\left(-\frac{3}{4}\right)\right)$.

Answer

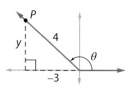

$(-3)^2 + y^2 = 4^2$
$y = \sqrt{16 - 9} = \sqrt{7}$

$\therefore \sin\left(\text{Cos}^{-1}\left(-\frac{3}{4}\right)\right) = \sin\theta = \frac{\sqrt{7}}{4}$

1. Since the range of the Cos^{-1} function is $[0, \pi]$, draw a Q II reference triangle illustrating $\theta = \text{Cos}^{-1}\left(-\frac{3}{4}\right)$.

2. Calculate the y-coordinate of the illustrated point. Use the positive root since θ is in Q II.

3. Use $\sin\theta = \frac{y}{r}$ to evaluate the expression.

SKILL ✓ **EXERCISE 31**

This method allows similar functions composed of trigonometric and inverse trigonometric functions to be expressed algebraically, which is useful in calculus.

Example 6   Evaluating Compositions

Express each function algebraically.

a. $f(t) = \cos\left(\text{Cos}^{-1} t\right)$ **b.** $g(t) = \sin\left(\text{Cos}^{-1} t\right)$ **c.** $h(t) = \tan\left(\text{Cos}^{-1} t\right)$

Answer

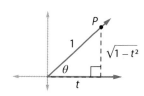

a. $f(t) = \cos\left(\text{Cos}^{-1} t\right) = \cos\theta = t$

b. $g(t) = \sin\left(\text{Cos}^{-1} t\right) = \sin\theta = \sqrt{1 - t^2}$

c. $h(t) = \tan\left(\text{Cos}^{-1} t\right) = \tan\theta = \frac{\sqrt{1 - t^2}}{t}$

1. Draw a Q I reference triangle illustrating $\theta = \text{Cos}^{-1} t$ when $t > 0$ and find an expression for the y-coordinate of P.

   If $t < 0$, the reference triangle is in Q II, and $y > 0$.

2. Express each function algebraically.

SKILL ✓ **EXERCISE 39**

To show King Hezekiah that his prayer for healing had been answered, God moved the sun's shadow backward on a sundial (2 Kings 20:8–11).

A. Exercises

Graph each function and state its domain and range.

1. $y = \text{Sin } x$ **2.** $y = \text{Sin}^{-1} x$ **3.** $y = \text{Cos } x$

4. $y = \text{Cos}^{-1} x$ **5.** $y = \text{Tan } x$ **6.** $y = \text{Tan}^{-1} x$

Evaluate each expression in radians and degrees.

7. $\text{Sin}^{-1} \dfrac{\sqrt{3}}{2}$ **8.** $\text{Cos}^{-1} \dfrac{1}{2}$

9. $\text{Arccos} \left(-\dfrac{1}{2}\right)$ **10.** $\text{Arcsin} \left(-\dfrac{\sqrt{2}}{2}\right)$

11. $\text{Tan}^{-1} (-1)$ **12.** $\text{Arctan} \dfrac{\sqrt{3}}{3}$

Use a calculator to evaluate each expression in radians and in degrees.

13. $\text{Sin}^{-1} 0.3420$ **14.** $\text{Tan}^{-1} 1.732$

15. $\text{Cos}^{-1} (-0.7138)$ **16.** $\text{Sin}^{-1} (-1.125)$

B. Exercises

State the interval over which each equation is true.

17. $\sin (\text{Sin}^{-1} x) = x$ **18.** $\text{Arcsin} (\sin x) = x$

19. $\text{Cos}^{-1} (\cos x) = x$ **20.** $\tan (\text{Tan}^{-1} x) = x$

Find the exact value for each expression without using a calculator.

21. $\text{Cos}^{-1} \left(\cos \dfrac{5\pi}{6} \right)$ **22.** $\text{Arctan} \left(\tan \left(-\dfrac{\pi}{4}\right) \right)$

23. $\text{Arcsin} \left(\sin \dfrac{2\pi}{3} \right)$ **24.** $\text{Cos}^{-1} \left(\cos \left(-\dfrac{\pi}{6}\right) \right)$

25. $\cos \left(\text{Arccos} \dfrac{3}{4} \right)$ **26.** $\sin \left(\text{Sin}^{-1} \dfrac{5}{4} \right)$

27. $\sin \left(\text{Cos}^{-1} \dfrac{\sqrt{2}}{2} \right)$ **28.** $\text{Tan}^{-1} \left(\cos \dfrac{3\pi}{2} \right)$

29. $\sin \left(\text{Arctan} \dfrac{4}{3} \right)$ **30.** $\tan \left(\text{Cos}^{-1} \dfrac{2}{3} \right)$

31. $\cos \left(\text{Sin}^{-1} \left(-\dfrac{\sqrt{5}}{3} \right) \right)$ **32.** $\csc \left(\text{Cos}^{-1} \left(-\dfrac{5}{8}\right) \right)$

Express each function algebraically.

33. $f(t) = \cos (\text{Sin}^{-1} t)$ **34.** $g(t) = \sin (\text{Tan}^{-1} t)$

35. $h(t) = \sec (\text{Cos}^{-1} t)$

36. Granular substances forming cone-shaped piles often reach their maximum angle of repose θ when they are poured onto a horizontal surface.

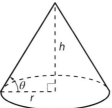

   a. Derive a formula for θ in terms of the cone's height h and radius r.

   b. Find the degree measure of the angle of repose for a 7 in. tall poured pile of sand with a diameter of 2 ft.

37. A missionary projects a video onto an 18 ft tall screen that is mounted on a wall so its lower edge is 10 ft above the floor. The viewing angle θ of the screen depends on the viewer's distance d from the wall. Assume that the eye level of the viewer is 4 ft above the floor.

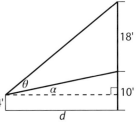

   a. Calculate the viewing angle (to the nearest tenth of a degree) for a viewer 30 ft from the wall and for a second viewer 40 ft from the wall.

   b. Write an equation expressing the viewing angle θ in terms of the viewer's distance from the wall.

   c. Use technology to graph the function and find the maximum viewing angle and the distance from the wall that provides it.

   d. Use technology to find any distances where the viewing angle is 17°.

C. Exercises

State a restricted domain that makes each reciprocal function one-to-one. Then graph the function and its inverse function on the same set of axes.

38. $f(x) = \text{Sec } x$ **39.** $g(x) = \text{Csc } x$

40. $h(x) = \text{Cot } x$

41. Prove: $\text{Csc}^{-1} t = \text{Sin}^{-1} \dfrac{1}{t}$ (*Hint:* Let $\text{Csc}^{-1} x = \theta$.)

42. Evaluate each expression (in radians).

   a. $\text{Sec}^{-1} 2$

   b. $\text{Csc}^{-1} 0.4$

   c. $\text{Cot}^{-1} -2.819$

43. The slope of the tangent to a curve, called the *derivative* in calculus, represents the instantaneous rate of change.

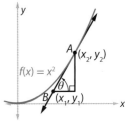

   a. If line l is tangent to $f(x)$ at A, write an equation expressing $\tan \theta$ in terms of the coordinates of A and B.

   b. Which characteristic of line l is represented by $\tan \theta$?

   c. Write the equation of the tangent to $y = x^2$ at $x = 3$ if $\tan \theta = 6$.

   d. Find θ to the nearest tenth of a degree.

44. Write the slope-intercept form equation of the line passing through the points $(-4, 5)$ and $(8, 11)$. [1.2]

Write the function rule for each composition when $f(x) = x^2 + 2x + 1$ and $g(x) = 2x + 1$. [1.8]

45. $(f \circ g)(x)$ **46.** $(g \circ f)(x)$

47. Draw a $-330°$ angle in standard position. [4.1]

48. Express θ as a function of x. [4.2]

49. State the equation of the midline of a sine function with a relative maximum at $(-1, 12)$ and a relative minimum at $(2, -6)$. [4.4]

50. What is the general form of $f(x) = \frac{5}{7}x - \frac{1}{4}$? [1.2]

A. $28x + 20y = 7$ **D.** $20x + 28y = 7$
B. $28x - 20y = 7$ **E.** $20x - 28y = -7$
C. $20x - 28y = 7$

51. Which of the following represents θ as a function of x? [4.1]

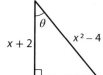

A. $\theta = \sin^{-1}\left(\dfrac{x + 2}{x^2 - 4}\right)$

B. $\theta = \sin^{-1}\left(\dfrac{1}{x + 2}\right)$ where $x \neq \pm 2$

C. $\theta = \cos^{-1}\dfrac{x + 2}{x^2 - 4}$

D. $\theta = \cos^{-1}\left(\dfrac{1}{x - 2}\right)$ where $x \neq \pm 2$

E. none of these

52. Determine the period and phase shift of $f(x) = -2 \sin\left(4x - \frac{\pi}{3}\right) - 3$. [4.4]

A. $p = \frac{\pi}{3}, h = 4$ **D.** $p = \frac{\pi}{2}, h = \frac{\pi}{12}$
B. $p = 4, h = -\frac{\pi}{12}$ **E.** none of these
C. $p = \frac{\pi}{4}, h = -3$

53. Which of the following is true for the graph of $f(x) = \cot x$? [4.5]

A. vertical asymptotes at $x = n\frac{\pi}{2}, n \in \mathbb{Z}$

B. symmetric with respect to the y-axis

C. zeros at $x = (2n + 1)\pi, n \in \mathbb{Z}$

D. y-intercept at $(0, 1)$

E. none of these

4.7 Analyzing Combinations of Sinusoidal Functions

Shock absorbers are designed to dampen the oscillation of a vehicle.

In Chapter 2, we saw that the sum of polynomial functions is a polynomial function. Graphing technology can be used to explore whether the sum of two sinusoids is a sinusoid. Notice that the graph of $f(x) = \sin x + \cos x$ appears to be a sinusoid with a period of 2π, zeros where $\sin x$ and $\cos x$ have opposite values, and relative maximums of $\sqrt{2}$ at $x = \frac{\pi}{4} \pm n2\pi$, $n \in \mathbb{Z}$.

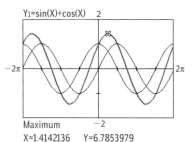

The sum (or difference) of two sinusoids may not be a sinusoid and frequently has a different period than either of the original sinusoids. Wave phenomena, such as the music of an orchestra, are often combinations of two or more simpler waves. The French mathematician Joseph Fourier (1768–1830) realized that even the most complex waveform could be decomposed into its sinusoidal components.

After completing this section, you will be able to

- analyze sums, products, and compositions of sinusoids and other functions.
- analyze damped oscillations.
- create and apply models of damped harmonic motion.

Example 1 Analyzing the Sum of Two Sinusoids

Determine the period of $f(x) = g(x) + h(x)$. Then use technology to graph two periods of $f(x)$. Does $f(x)$ appear to be a sinusoid?

a. $g(x) = \sin \frac{2}{3}x$ and $h(x) = -2 \cos x$

b. $g(x) = \sin \pi x$ and $h(x) = \frac{1}{2} \cos \left(\pi x - \frac{\pi}{3} \right)$

Answer

1. The period of $g(x)$ is 3π, and the period of $h(x)$ is 2π. The period of $f(x)$ is 6π, the least common multiple of the periods of $g(x)$ and $h(x)$.

2. Graph $f(x) = \sin \frac{2}{3}x - 2 \cos x$ over $[-6\pi, 6\pi]$.

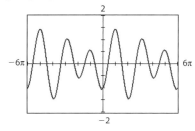

3. The function is not a sinusoid.

1. Since the period of both $g(x)$ and $h(x)$ is 2, the period of $f(x)$ is also 2.

2. Graph $f(x) = \sin \pi x + \frac{1}{2} \cos \left(\pi x - \frac{\pi}{3} \right)$ over $[-4, 4]$.

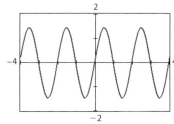

3. The function appears to be a sinusoid.

SKILL ✓ **EXERCISE 3**

KEYWORD SEARCH

Fourier series 🔍

Jules Lissajous studied compound vibrations by attaching small mirrors to two tuning forks with perpendicular planes of vibration. A light beam passed from one mirror to the other and then on to a screen, forming visual patterns. These "Lissajous figures" are still studied in modern physics classes.

It can be shown that the sum (or difference) of sinusoids with the same period is a sinusoid with that same period. While the sum (or difference) of sinusoids with different periods is not a sinusoid, the resulting function is periodic when the ratio of the addends' periods is rational.

The fact that trigonometric functions are periodic distinguishes them from algebraic, exponential, and logarithmic functions. Combinations of these functions with sinusoidal functions may or may not be periodic.

Consider the sum (or difference) of a polynomial function $p(x)$ and a sinusoidal function. Recall that the graph of $t(x) = a \sin b(x - h)$ or $t(x) = a \cos b(x - h)$ oscillates between $y = \pm a$. Therefore, the graph of $f(x) = p(x) + t(x)$ oscillates between the bounds of $y = p(x) \pm a$.

Example 2 Analyzing a Sum of Polynomial and Sinusoidal Functions

State equations for the bounds of $f(x) = x + 2 \sin 2x$. Then graph $f(x)$ and its bounding equations. Is $f(x)$ a periodic function?

Answer

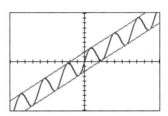

1. Since the value of $2 \sin 2x$ oscillates between ± 2, $f(x)$ oscillates between $y = x + 2$ and $y = x - 2$.

2. Graph $f(x)$ and its bounds.

3. The function $f(x)$ is not periodic since its value does not repeat over a regular interval.

SKILL ✓ EXERCISE 9

The basic sine and cosine functions are frequently composed with basic power functions. Note that $\sin^2 x$ is shortened notation for $(\sin x)^2$ and is different from $\sin x^2$.

Example 3 Analyzing Compositions of a Power and a Sinusoidal Function

Graph each composition of $g(x) = x^2$ and $h(x) = \cos x$. Does $f(x)$ appear to be periodic? If so, state its period.

a. $f(x) = h(g(x)) = \cos x^2$

b. $f(x) = g(h(x)) = \cos^2 x$

Answer

1.
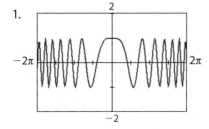

2. The function is not periodic. Note that some graphing calculators have difficulty displaying waves with high frequency.

1.
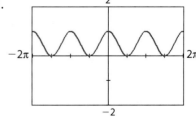

2. The function appears to have a period of π.

SKILL ✓ EXERCISE 15

When $t(x) = \sin bx$ or $t(x) = \cos bx$ is multiplied by another function $g(x)$, the graph of the product oscillates between $y = \pm g(x)$. You have already seen how the leading constant, a, determines the amplitude of a sinusoid so that $f(x) = 2 \sin x$ oscillates between the bounds of $y = 2$ and $y = -2$. Notice that the graph of $f(x) = x \sin 5x$, the product of $g(x) = x$ and $t(x) = \sin 5x$, is a sine wave with varying amplitude that oscillates between $y = \pm x$.

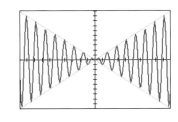

DEFINITIONS

A **damped sinusoid** is a function of the form $f(x) = g(x) \sin bx$ or $f(x) = g(x) \cos bx$. When $g(x)$ reduces the amplitude of the sinusoid model, $g(x)$ is called the **damping factor**, and $f(x)$ has a **damped oscillation**.

The function $f(x) = x \sin 5x$ is damped over $(-\infty, 0]$ with $g(x) = x$ as the damping factor.

Example 4   Analyzing Damped Sinusoids

State the damping factor and equations for the bounds of each function. Then use technology to graph the function and state the interval where a damping effect occurs.

a. $f(x) = \frac{x^2}{5} \sin 3x$

b. $f(x) = \frac{6}{x} \sin 9x$

Answer

1. damping factor: $\frac{x^2}{5}$

   bounds: $y = \pm\frac{x^2}{5}$

2.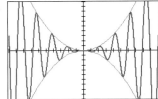

3. $f(x)$ is damped over $(-\infty, 0]$.

1. damping factor: $\frac{6}{x}$

   bounds: $y = \pm\frac{6}{x}$

2.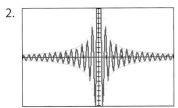

3. $f(x)$ is damped over $(0, \infty)$.

SKILL ✓ **EXERCISE 17**

When a mass suspended from a spring is pulled down and released, it moves above and below its resting (or equilibrium) position. In the ideal case of no friction, the oscillations would continue with the same amplitude, and *simple harmonic motion* would result. The height above or below the equilibrium position over time t is modeled by the function $y = -a \cos bt$ where $a > 0$ represents the maximum distance from the equilibrium position.

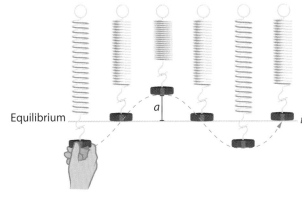

The *damped harmonic motion* that occurs when friction reduces the displacement of an oscillating object can be modeled by $f(t) = ae^{-ct} \cos bt$ or $f(t) = ae^{-ct} \sin bt$ ($c > 0$), where a is the maximum displacement. Greater values of c, the *damping constant*, indicate a faster decrease in the amplitude of oscillations. The damped function is not periodic since its amplitude varies, but the function's frequency can be used to find b using a *pseudoperiod*:

$$p = \frac{1}{f} = \frac{2\pi}{|b|}.$$

Example 5 Modeling Damped Harmonic Motion

A robot that explores tunnels uses springs connected to a steel plate as a shock absorber to protect the robot's electronics in the event of an explosion. In a laboratory test, the steel plate's initial displacement was 5 cm, the damping constant was 0.6, and the plate oscillated with a frequency of 2 Hz. Write a function modeling the plate's damped harmonic motion beginning at maximum displacement. Then use technology to graph the function and determine when the plate's displacement is within ±1 cm.

Answer

$d(t) = ae^{-ct} \cos bt$

1. Substitute values for a, c, and b into the general sinusoid equation that models damped harmonic motion where the maximum displacement occurs when $t = 0$.

   maximum displacement: $a = 5$

$d(t) = 5e^{-0.6t} \cos 4\pi t$

   damping constant: $c = 0.6$

   frequency: $f = 2$ Hz; so $p = \frac{1}{f} = \frac{1}{2} = \frac{2\pi}{|b|}$; $b = 4\pi$

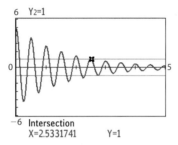

2. Graph $Y_1 = 5e^{-0.6x} \cos 4\pi x$, $Y_2 = 1$, and $Y_3 = -1$.

The displacement is within ±1 cm after ≈ 2.53 sec.

3. A careful examination of the graph indicates that the last intersection of $d(t)$ with $y = \pm 1$ occurs at ≈ 2.53 sec.

SKILL ✔ EXERCISE 39

⟩ A. Exercises

Determine the period of $f(x) = g(x) + h(x)$ and state whether $f(x)$ is a sinusoid. Then use technology to graph two periods of $f(x)$.

1. $g(x) = \sin x$; $h(x) = 2 \cos x$

2. $g(x) = \sin 2x$; $h(x) = -\cos x$

3. $g(x) = \cos \frac{\pi}{2}x$; $h(x) = \sin \pi x + 1$

4. $g(x) = \cos(3x + \pi)$; $h(x) = -2 \sin 3x$

5. $g(x) = 3 \sin \frac{x}{2} + 1$; $h(x) = -2 \cos \frac{x}{2}$

6. $g(x) = 2 \cos x - 1$; $h(x) = -\sin(2x - 1)$

State equations for the bounds of each function. Then graph the function and its bounds. Is the function periodic?

7. $y = x - 3 \sin x$

8. $y = \cos 3x - \frac{1}{2}x$

9. $y = (x^2 - 6) + 3 \cos 4x$

10. $y = \frac{x^2}{4} \sin 4x$

Use technology to graph each function. Does the function appear to be periodic? If so, state its period.

11. $y = 3 \sin x \cdot \cos x$

12. $y = |\sin x|$

13. $y = x \cdot \cos x$

14. $y = \cos x^3$

15. $y = \cos^3 x$

16. $y = \sin x + \cos \pi x$

State the damping factor for each function. Then graph the function and its bounds and state the interval where a damping effect occurs.

17. $y = \frac{x}{2} \sin 2x$

18. $y = \frac{12}{x} \cos x$

19. $y = 3^{-0.25x} \sin \frac{7x}{2}$

20. $y = e^{0.3x} \cos \pi x$

⟩ B. Exercises

Determine the period of each function and state whether the function is a sinusoid. Then use technology to graph two periods of $f(x)$.

21. $f(x) = \sin \pi x - 2 \cos \pi x + \frac{1}{2} \sin \left(\pi x - \frac{\pi}{2} \right)$

22. $f(x) = \cos(2x - \pi) + 3 \sin \frac{x}{2} - \sin \frac{x}{3}$

Choose the best description for each function in exercises 23–30.

A. a non-periodic function

B. a periodic function

C. a sinusoid

23. $y = \sin x + 3 \cos x$

24. $y = \sin x + \cos 2x$

25. $y = x + \cos 5x$

26. $y = x \cos 5x$

27. a sum of sinusoids with the same period

28. a sum of sinusoids whose periods have a common multiple

29. a product of an exponential function and a sinusoid

30. a sum of a sinusoid and a non-constant polynomial function

Match each function with its graph without using technology.

31. $y = x \cos 3x$

32. $y = x + \cos 3x$

33. $y = 3 \cos x + \sin x$

34. $y = \cos 3x + 2 \sin x$

35. $y = 3 \sin \pi x + 2 \cos x$

A.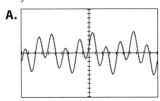

D.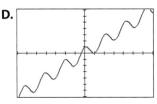

B.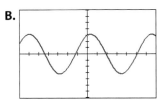

E.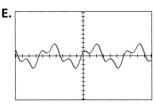

C.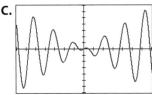

Write an equation for each damped sine function.

36. damping factor of e^{-2x}; pseudoperiod of π; phase shift of $\frac{\pi}{4}$ units left

37. bounds of $y = \pm 0.2x^2$; pseudoperiod of 2; phase shift of π units right

38. Tyler hit a bump on his motorcycle, initiating damped harmonic motion of the front wheel at 3 Hz with an initial displacement of 5 cm and a damping constant of 0.7.

  a. Write a function that models the displacement of the front wheel.

  b. Use a graph of the function to find how much time (to the nearest hundredth of a second) elapses before the front wheel oscillates with a displacement less than 1 cm.

39. The motion of a point on a plucked violin string can be modeled by $f(x) = ae^{-2.05x} \cos bx$, where a is the initial displacement from the string's resting position in centimeters. A musician displaces a violin string by 0.9 cm, causing damped vibrations at 49 Hz. Determine the displacement of the string one second after it has been plucked.

❭ C. Exercises

40. Explore: Graph $f(x) = \sin^2 x + \cos^2 x$ and write the equation suggested by the graph.

41. Explore: Graph the product of $g(x) = \sec x$ and $h(x) = \cos x$ and write the equation suggested by the graph. What does the graph reveal about these two functions?

42. Explore: Graph the product of $g(x) = \tan x$ and $h(x) = \cos x$ and write the equation suggested by the graph.

Use technology to graph each sum of sinusoids. Then use the graph to estimate the altitude and the phase shift to the nearest hundredth and rewrite the sum as a single sinusoid with the given form. Verify your equation by graphing the single sinusoid in the same window as the sum.

43. $f(x) = \sin x + \cos x = a \cos b(x - h)$

44. $f(x) = 2 \cos \pi x - 3 \sin \pi x = a \sin b(x - h)$

45. Find the inverse of $f(x) = \frac{2}{3}x - 5$. [1.8]

46. Convert $\frac{12\pi}{7}$ radians to degrees. [4.1]

47. If θ is an angle in standard position whose terminal side passes through $(-7, 2)$, find the exact value of $\sin \theta$. [4.3]

48. State the quadrant and reference angle for $\theta = 1000°$. [4.3]

State the zeros of each function. [4.5]

49. $f(x) = \sin x$ [4.4]

50. $g(x) = \cos x$ [4.4]

51. Which function is equivalent to $f(x) = 9 \cdot 3^{2x}$? [3.1]

    A. $g(x) = 3^{2x + 2}$ **D.** $g(x) = 81^x$

    B. $g(x) = 3^{4x}$ **E.** none of these

    C. $g(x) = 27^{2x}$

52. Which expression is equivalent to $\log \frac{x^2}{y^4}$? [3.3]

    A. $\log 2x - \log 4y$ **D.** $\log (x^2 - y^4)$

    B. $2 \log x + 4 \log y$ **E.** none of these

    C. $2 \log x - 4 \log y$

53. Which function is equivalent to $f(x) = \sec \left(\frac{\pi}{2} - x\right)$? [4.5]

    A. $g(x) = \sin x$ **D.** $g(x) = \csc x$

    B. $g(x) = \cos x$ **E.** $g(x) = \sec x$

    C. $g(x) = \cot x$

54. Evaluate $\text{Sin}^{-1} \left(-\frac{\sqrt{2}}{2}\right)$. [4.6]

    A. $\frac{\pi}{4}$

    B. $\frac{7\pi}{4}$ **D.** $-\frac{3\pi}{4}$

    C. $-\frac{\pi}{4}$ **E.** none of these

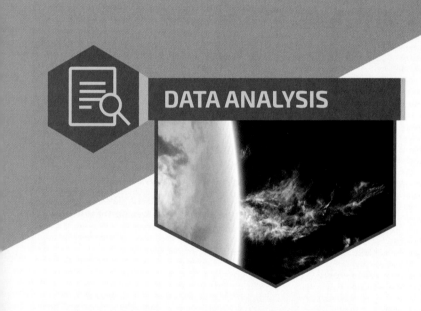

DATA ANALYSIS

Year	Average Daily Number of Sunspots
1980	149.1
1982	114.8
1984	43.5
1986	11.0
1988	100.9
1990	145.1
1992	93.5
1994	31.0
1996	8.4
1998	61.6
2000	123.3

Sunspots and Solar Flares

Sunspot data from the World Data Center SILSO, Royal Observatory of Belgium, Brussels

At about 6300°F, sunspots are dark and relatively cool areas on the sun's surface (average temperature about 10,000°F). They usually appear in pairs having opposite magnetic poles. Solar flares associated with these sunspots are huge eruptions from built-up magnetic energy in the solar atmosphere. These explosions can bombard the earth's atmosphere with magnetic power, interfering with satellite communications and creating radiation haz-ards for astronauts. Some believe that solar flares can also influence our weather.

1. Use technology to complete a scatterplot of the average daily sunspot data where x represents the number of years since 1980. What degree polynomial function would appear to fit the data? Why would this polynomial function be an inappropriate model for predictions outside the data set?

2. Consider modeling the data with a sinusoid. Using your scatterplot, estimate the following characteristics of such a model.

    a. period   **b.** range

    c. midline   **d.** amplitude

3. Within the context of the data, explain what each of the values in exercise 2 means.

4. Use technology to complete a sinusoidal regression and state the resulting sine function. You may be prompted to enter a number of *iterations* (attempts for the calculator to get the best fit) and a guess for the function's period.

5. State the following characteristics of the sine function that models the data.

    a. period   **b.** midline

    c. amplitude   **d.** range

    e. phase shift

6. Use your sinusoidal model to make predictions.

    a. Predict the average daily number of sunspots in 2010.

    b. Would you expect the number of sunspots in 2011 to be higher or lower than in 2010?

    c. Compare your results to the recorded numbers of 15.6 in 2010 and 50.1 in 2011. How does this reflect on the accuracy of the model?

According to NASA, worldwide temperatures have been consistently rising since 1980. There is much debate over whether climate change is primarily caused by natural events such as solar flares and volcanic eruptions or by human activity. Many in the scientific community believe that the burning of fossil fuels such as coal and petroleum releases significant amounts of carbon dioxide and may affect the climate. Others are skeptical that human activity can significantly change the global climate. Mathematical modeling is a valuable tool for those on either side of the issue, but a person's worldview also plays a significant role in the way he responds to mathematical models.

7. Does our mathematical model for the average number of sunspots support the claim that they are a significant factor in the recent rise in the earth's temperatures?

8. List several considerations that should be taken into account when analyzing our model.

9. Perform an Internet search to compile a list of factors that can affect the earth's climate. Discuss your results.

10. Many factors affect climate change, and some of these factors may still be unknown. Our response to this issue should be both analytical and biblical. Explain how Genesis 8:20–22, Genesis 1:27–28, Mark 12:31, and Psalm 46:2–3 should shape our view of climate change.

Chapter 4 Review

1. Convert to degrees, minutes, seconds (DMS) or decimal degrees (DD). [4.1]
   a. 168.32° to DMS
   b. 29°37′15.6″ to DD

2. Convert each degree measure to radians. [4.1]
   a. 2°
   b. −65°
   c. 13.59°

3. Convert each radian measure to degrees. [4.1]
   a. $-\frac{\pi}{10}$
   b. $-\frac{5\pi}{12}$
   c. 2.8

4. Represent a watercraft's bearing of 289°21′8″ relative to a buoy as a standard position angle in DD form. [4.1]

5. Write an expression for all angles coterminal with $\alpha = -175°$. Then specify one positive and one negative coterminal angle. [4.1]

6. Vienna's Giant Ferris Wheel has 15 gondolas and a diameter of approximately 61 m. Find the arc length between consecutive gondolas. Then find the area of the related sector. [4.1]

7. A washing machine's spin cycle has a maximum speed of 1300 rpm. Find the angular speed in radians per second. [4.1]

8. If the 156 ft long blade of a wind turbine rotates at a maximum speed of 16.9 rpm, find the maximum linear speed of the blade's tip (to the nearest foot per second). [4.1]

Find the exact values of the six trigonometric ratios for each angle. [4.2]

9. ∠A
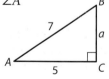

10. β
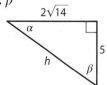

Find the other five trigonometric ratios for each angle θ. Round to the nearest ten thousandth. [4.2]

11. $\tan \theta = 0.6$

12. $\csc \theta = \frac{21}{19}$

13. Find d (to the nearest tenth). [4.2]
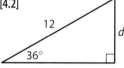

14. Find α (to the nearest tenth of a degree). [4.2]
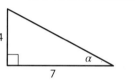

15. Solve △ABC, rounding angle measures to the nearest minute. [4.2]
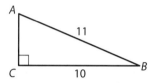

16. A runaway ramp is used by trucks in the event of brake failure. Calculate the vertical and horizontal distance traveled by a truck on a ramp with a 10% grade (a 5.71° angle of elevation) if the stopping distance after entry was 327 ft. [4.2]

17. Find the exact values for the six trigonometric functions of an angle in standard position whose terminal ray passes through (5, −6). [4.3]

18. Sketch $\theta = 315°$ and a reference triangle. Then state the measure of its reference angle α. [4.3]

19. Use a reference triangle to find the exact value of $\tan 210°$. [4.3]

20. If $\cos \theta = -\frac{5}{13}$ and $\sin \theta > 0$, find $\csc \theta$ and $\cot \theta$. [4.3]

Use the unit circle to evaluate the six trigonometric functions for each angle. [4.3]

21. $\theta = 0°$

22. $\theta = \frac{5\pi}{4}$

230   CHAPTER 4 TRIGONOMETRIC FUNCTIONS

23. Use the periodic nature of trigonometric functions to evaluate each expression. [4.3]

a. $\sin -\dfrac{55\pi}{4}$ **b.** $\cos \dfrac{32\pi}{3}$

State the amplitude, period, and any phase shift or vertical shift for each function. Then graph the function over [–2π, 2π] [4.4]

24. $y = -3 \cos\left(\dfrac{x}{2}\right)$ **25.** $y = \dfrac{1}{2} \sin x + 2$

26. $y = 2 \cos \left(x - \dfrac{\pi}{3}\right)$ **27.** $y = \sin (2x + \pi) - 1$

28. Write a sine function rule for the graph. [4.4]

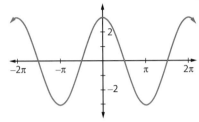

29. Write a function rule for a cosine function with a relative minimum at $(0, -6)$ and a period and amplitude of 2. [4.4]

30. The loudest animal is the pistol (or snapping) shrimp, whose snapping claw shoots out a high-speed jet of water generating an air bubble that implodes at a noise level of 200 dB. Write a sine function that models the initial behavior of the sound wave over time if the frequency is 200 kHz. [4.4]

Identify the period, vertical asymptotes, and zeros of each function. [4.5]

31. $f(x) = \sec x$ **32.** $g(x) = \cot 2x$

Sketch the graph of each function over [–2π, 2π]. [4.5]

33. $y = \csc \left(x - \dfrac{\pi}{4}\right)$ **34.** $y = -2 \tan \dfrac{x}{2}$

35. Describe the graph of $g(x) = -2 \tan \left(\dfrac{x}{2} - \pi\right)$ as a transformation of $f(x) = \tan x$. [4.5]

36. Write a function rule for a secant function with a period of $\dfrac{\pi}{3}$ and a phase shift of $\dfrac{\pi}{2}$ units left that has been stretched vertically by a factor of 5. [4.5]

37. Match each inverse trigonometric function with its graph. [4.6]

a. $y = \mathrm{Sin}^{-1} x$ **b.** $y = \mathrm{Cos}^{-1} x$ **c.** $y = \mathrm{Tan}^{-1} x$

I.

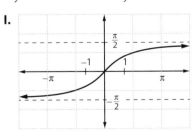

II.

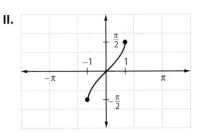

III.

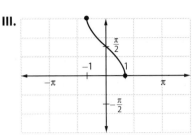

Evaluate each expression in radians and degrees without using technology. [4.6]

38. $\mathrm{Sin}^{-1}\left(-\dfrac{1}{2}\right)$ **39.** $\mathrm{Cos}^{-1}\left(-\dfrac{\sqrt{2}}{2}\right)$

40. $\mathrm{Tan}^{-1} \sqrt{3}$

41. Use a calculator to evaluate each expression in radians and degrees. [4.6]

a. $\mathrm{Sin}^{-1} 0.5976$ **b.** $\mathrm{Cos}^{-1} -1.7138$

c. $\mathrm{Tan}^{-1} 1.1918$

42. Find the exact value of each composition without using a calculator. [4.6]

a. $\sin (\mathrm{Sin}^{-1} 1)$ **b.** $\mathrm{Cos}^{-1} \left(\cos \left(-\dfrac{5\pi}{4}\right)\right)$

43. Find the exact value of each expression without using a calculator. [4.6]

a. $\mathrm{Sin}^{-1} \left(\cos \dfrac{2\pi}{3}\right)$ **b.** $\sec \left(\mathrm{Tan}^{-1}\left(-\dfrac{\sqrt{5}}{2}\right)\right)$

44. Express $f(t) = \tan (\mathrm{Sin}^{-1} t)$ algebraically. [4.6]

Determine the period of f(x) and state whether f(x) is a sinusoid. Then use technology to graph two periods of f(x). [4.7]

45. $f(x) = 3 \cos x - \sin x$

46. $f(x) = 2 \cos 4x + 2 \cos 6x$

State equations for any bounds of f(x). Then graph the function and its bounds. Is the function periodic? [4.7]

47. $f(x) = \dfrac{x^2}{3} - 2 \sin \pi x$ **48.** $f(x) = \sin^5 x$

State the damping factor and equations for the bounds of each function. Then use technology to graph the function and its bounds, and state the interval where a damping effect occurs. [4.7]

49. $y = \dfrac{x^2}{15} \sin x$ **50.** $y = 3.5e^{-0.12x} \sin 2x$

51. Write an equation for a damped sinusoid with a damping factor of $e^{-0.5x}$, a pseudoperiod of $\dfrac{\pi}{2}$, and a phase shift of $\dfrac{\pi}{4}$ to the right. [4.7]

5 Trigonometric Identities and Equations

BIBLICAL PERSPECTIVE OF MATHEMATICS

The beautiful unity of mathematics throughout its many diverse applications is evidence of God's creation of both the consistent underlying structure of the physical universe and our ability to describe this structure mathematically.

HISTORICAL CONNECTION

Joseph Fourier's study of heat in the eighteenth century led to the discovery of the power of infinite trigonometric series, harmonic analysis, and eventually the unification of theories of sound and light.

DATA ANALYSIS

Though Ptolemy studied the refraction of light, Willebrord Snell discovered the trigonometric equation that correctly models its refraction. Snell's law played a vital role in the development of fiber-optic networks in the 1970s.

5.1 Fundamental Identities

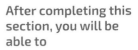

Identities can be used to simplify trigonometric equations that represent voltages across capacitors in an AC generator.

The majority of equations encountered in mathematics are *conditional equations*, equations that are true only for certain values of the variable. Solving a conditional equation, such as $5x + 3 = 13$, involves finding its *solution(s)*, any value of the variable for which the equation is true. Occasionally we encounter *false equations*, such as $x + 3 = x - 2$, that have no solutions. Other equations, such as $x^0 = 1$ or $(a + b)^2 = a^2 + 2ab + b^2$, are true for all values of the variables for which the expressions on each side of the equal sign are defined.

> ### DEFINITION
> An **identity** is an equation that is true for all values in the domain of the variable.

Just like theorems in geometry, identities need to be proved before they are accepted as true. In this chapter, you will learn how to use fundamental trigonometric identities to evaluate trigonometric functions, simplify trigonometric expressions, develop other identities, and solve trigonometric equations.

You already know several trigonometric identities that follow directly from the definitions of trigonometric functions.

Reciprocal Identities			Quotient Identities
$\csc \theta = \dfrac{1}{\sin \theta}$ $\quad \sec \theta = \dfrac{1}{\cos \theta}$		$\cot \theta = \dfrac{1}{\tan \theta}$	$\tan \theta = \dfrac{\sin \theta}{\cos \theta}$
$\sin \theta = \dfrac{1}{\csc \theta}$ $\quad \cos \theta = \dfrac{1}{\sec \theta}$		$\tan \theta = \dfrac{1}{\cot \theta}$	$\cot \theta = \dfrac{\cos \theta}{\sin \theta}$

The first reciprocal identity can be verified using the definitions $\sin \theta = \dfrac{y}{r}$ and $\csc \theta = \dfrac{r}{y}$.

$$\frac{1}{\sin \theta} = \frac{1}{\frac{y}{r}} = \frac{r}{y} = \csc \theta$$

The other reciprocal identities and quotient identities can be similarly proven.

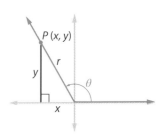

Several other basic trigonometric identities are derived using the Pythagorean Theorem.

$$x^2 + y^2 = r^2 \qquad \text{Pythagorean Theorem}$$

$$\frac{x^2}{r^2} + \frac{y^2}{r^2} = \frac{r^2}{r^2} \qquad \text{Divide each term by } r^2.$$

$$\left(\frac{x}{r}\right)^2 + \left(\frac{y}{r}\right)^2 = 1 \qquad \text{Simplify.}$$

$$\cos^2 \theta + \sin^2 \theta = 1 \qquad \text{Substitute using the definitions of sine and cosine.}$$

Two other versions of this basic Pythagorean identity can also be derived by dividing each term by either $\sin^2 \theta$ or $\cos^2 \theta$.

After completing this section, you will be able to

- state and verify the fundamental trig identities.
- use identities to evaluate other trig functions.
- simplify and rewrite trig expressions.

TIP

Powers of trig functions such as $(\sin \theta)^2$ are notated as $\sin^2 \theta$.

Pythagorean Identities		
$\cos^2 \theta + \sin^2 \theta = 1$	$1 + \tan^2 \theta = \sec^2 \theta$	$\cot^2 \theta + 1 = \csc^2 \theta$

Example 1   Using Identities to Evaluate Other Trig Functions

If $\csc \theta = \frac{4}{3}$ and $\cos \theta < 0$, find the other five trigonometric functions of θ.

Answer

$\sin \theta = \dfrac{1}{\csc \theta} = \dfrac{1}{\frac{4}{3}} = \dfrac{3}{4}$

1. Use a reciprocal identity to find $\sin \theta$.

$\cos^2 \theta + \sin^2 \theta = 1$
$\quad\cos^2 \theta = 1 - \sin^2 \theta$
$\quad\quad\cos \theta = \pm\sqrt{1 - \left(\frac{3}{4}\right)^2} = -\dfrac{\sqrt{7}}{4}$

2. Use a Pythagorean identity to find $\cos \theta$. Note that θ terminates in Quadrant II since $\sin \theta > 0$ and $\cos \theta < 0$.

$\tan \theta = \dfrac{\sin \theta}{\cos \theta} = \dfrac{\frac{3}{4}}{-\frac{\sqrt{7}}{4}} = -\dfrac{3}{\sqrt{7}} = -\dfrac{3\sqrt{7}}{7}$

3. Use a quotient identity to find $\tan \theta$.

$\sec \theta = \dfrac{1}{\cos \theta} = \dfrac{1}{-\frac{\sqrt{7}}{4}} = -\dfrac{4}{\sqrt{7}} = -\dfrac{4\sqrt{7}}{7}$

4. Use reciprocal identities to find $\sec \theta$ and $\cot \theta$.

$\cot \theta = \dfrac{1}{\tan \theta} = \dfrac{1}{-\frac{3\sqrt{7}}{7}} = -\dfrac{7}{3\sqrt{7}} = -\dfrac{\sqrt{7}}{3}$

SKILL ✔ **EXERCISE 5**

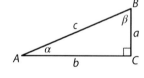

In Section 4.2 we illustrated how a right triangle can be used to show that the trigonometric function of an angle is equal to the *cofunction* of the angle's complement. Note that $\sin A = \frac{a}{c} = \cos B$ and $\cos A = \frac{b}{c} = \sin B$. It can also be shown that $\tan A = \cot B$ and $\sec A = \csc B$. Identities developed in Section 5.4 will provide simple proofs for the extension of these identities to non-acute angles and real numbers.

Cofunction Identities		
$\sin \theta = \cos\left(\frac{\pi}{2} - \theta\right)$	$\tan \theta = \cot\left(\frac{\pi}{2} - \theta\right)$	$\sec \theta = \csc\left(\frac{\pi}{2} - \theta\right)$
$\cos \theta = \sin\left(\frac{\pi}{2} - \theta\right)$	$\cot \theta = \tan\left(\frac{\pi}{2} - \theta\right)$	$\csc \theta = \sec\left(\frac{\pi}{2} - \theta\right)$

In Section 4.3, the unit circle was used to show that cosine is an even function and that sine is an odd function. The other even/odd trigonometric identities can be verified by expressing the functions in terms of sine and cosine.

Even/Odd Identities		
$\sin(-\theta) = -\sin \theta$	$\cos(-\theta) = \cos \theta$	$\tan(-\theta) = -\tan \theta$
$\csc(-\theta) = -\csc \theta$	$\sec(-\theta) = \sec \theta$	$\cot(-\theta) = -\cot \theta$

Example 2   Using Cofunction and Even/Odd Identities

If $\cot \theta = 2.25$, find $\tan \left(\theta - \frac{\pi}{2}\right)$.

Answer

$$\tan \left(\theta - \frac{\pi}{2}\right) = \tan \left[-\left(\frac{\pi}{2} - \theta\right)\right]$$
$$= -\tan \left(\frac{\pi}{2} - \theta\right)$$
$$= -\cot \theta$$
$$= -2.25$$

1. Factor and apply the fact that cotangent is an odd function.

2. Apply a cofunction identity and substitute.

SKILL ✓ EXERCISE 11

In Chapter 4, the unit circle and the graphs of the trigonometric functions illustrated the periodicity of trigonometric functions. This characteristic of each function can also be expressed as an identity. These identities can be used to evaluate functions outside of the interval $[0, 2\pi)$.

Periodic Identities $n \in \mathbb{Z}$		
$\sin (\theta + n2\pi) = \sin \theta$	$\sec (\theta + n2\pi) = \sec \theta$	$\tan (\theta + n\pi) = \tan \theta$
$\cos (\theta + n2\pi) = \cos \theta$	$\csc (\theta + n2\pi) = \csc \theta$	$\cot (\theta + n\pi) = \cot \theta$

The unity of mathematics was recognized by physicist Richard Feynman in his 1964 lecture series on the laws of the physical universe: "Nature uses only the longest threads to weave her patterns, so each small piece of her fabric reveals the organization of the entire tapestry."

The fundamental identities are frequently used to simplify complicated trigonometric expressions. Since the two sides of an identity are equal, one side of an identity may be substituted for the other. It is often helpful to rewrite the expression in terms of sine and cosine. Other typical substitutions involve various forms of the Pythagorean identities. For example, $\sin^2 \theta$ can be substituted for $1 - \cos^2 \theta$.

Example 3   Simplifying by Expressing in Terms of Sine and Cosine

Simplify $\tan \theta - \sec \theta \csc \theta$.

Answer

$$\tan \theta - \sec \theta \csc \theta$$
$$= \frac{\sin \theta}{\cos \theta} - \frac{1}{\cos \theta} \cdot \frac{1}{\sin \theta}$$

1. Use reciprocal and quotient identities to rewrite the expression in terms of sine and cosine.

$$= \frac{\sin^2 \theta}{\cos \theta \sin \theta} - \frac{1}{\cos \theta \sin \theta}$$

2. Combine fractions using the least common denominator.

$$= \frac{\sin^2 \theta - 1}{\cos \theta \sin \theta}$$

$$= \frac{(1 - \cos^2 \theta) - 1}{\cos \theta \sin \theta}$$

3. Simplify the numerator using another form of the basic Pythagorean identity $\sin^2 \theta = 1 - \cos^2 \theta$.

$$= \frac{-\cos^2 \theta}{\cos \theta \sin \theta}$$

$$= -\frac{\cos \theta}{\sin \theta} = -\cot \theta$$

4. Cancel the common factor and express in terms of a single trigonometric function.

Check

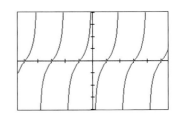

5. The graphs of $Y_1 = \tan(X) - 1/(\cos(X)*\sin(X))$ and $Y_2 = -\cot(X)$ appear to be identical.

SKILL ✓ EXERCISE 17

Algebraic manipulations such as factoring are frequently used to simplify an expression.

Example 4   Simplifying by Factoring

Simplify $\cos^2 x \sin\left(\frac{\pi}{2} - x\right) + \cos x \sin^2 x$.

Answer

$\cos^2 x \sin\left(\frac{\pi}{2} - x\right) + \cos x \sin^2 x$ 1. Substitute using $\sin\left(\frac{\pi}{2} - x\right) = \cos x$.

$= \cos^2 x (\cos x) + \cos x \sin^2 x$

$= \cos x (\cos^2 x + \sin^2 x)$ 2. Factor $\cos x$ from each term.

$= \cos x (1)$ 3. Substitute using the basic Pythagorean identity
$= \cos x$ and simplify.

Check

4. Values for
$Y_1 = \cos(X)^2 * \sin(\pi/2 - X) + \cos(X) * \sin(X)^2$ and
$Y_2 = \cos(X)$ appear to be identical.

X	Y1	Y2		
0	1	1		
0.2618	0.9659	0.9659		
0.5236	0.866	0.866		
0.7854	0.7071	0.7071		
1.0472	0.5	0.5		
1.309	0.2588	0.2588		
1.5708	0	0		
1.8326	-0.259	-0.259		
2.0944	-0.5	-0.5		
2.3562	-0.707	-0.707		
2.618	-0.866	-0.866		

X=0

SKILL ✔ EXERCISE 19

While we may be able to support our simplification graphically or numerically, neither of these methods can be used as a proof since every possible value cannot be verified by these methods. Finding just one member of the domains where the expressions do not have the same value would prove our simplification to be incorrect.

The combining of fractions plays an important part in the simplification of many expressions.

Example 5   Simplifying by Combining Fractions

Simplify $\dfrac{\cos \theta}{\sin \theta} - \dfrac{\sin \theta}{1 - \cos \theta}$.

Answer

$\dfrac{\cos \theta}{\sin \theta} - \dfrac{\sin \theta}{1 - \cos \theta}$ 1. Combine fractions using the least common denominator.

$= \dfrac{\cos \theta}{\sin \theta} \cdot \dfrac{1 - \cos \theta}{1 - \cos \theta} - \dfrac{\sin \theta}{1 - \cos \theta} \cdot \dfrac{\sin \theta}{\sin \theta}$

$= \dfrac{\cos \theta - \cos^2 \theta - \sin^2 \theta}{\sin \theta (1 - \cos \theta)}$

$= \dfrac{\cos \theta - (\cos^2 \theta + \sin^2 \theta)}{\sin \theta (1 - \cos \theta)}$ 2. Factor -1 from the last two terms of the numerator and apply the basic Pythagorean identity.

$= \dfrac{\cos \theta - 1}{\sin \theta (1 - \cos \theta)}$

$= \dfrac{-(1 - \cos \theta)}{\sin \theta (1 - \cos \theta)}$ 3. Factor -1 from the numerator and simplify.

$= -\dfrac{1}{\sin \theta} = -\csc \theta$

SKILL ✔ EXERCISE 29

In calculus, it is often desirable to rewrite trigonometric expressions in an equivalent form without fractions. This can be accomplished by using a product of conjugates: $(a + b)(a - b) = a^2 - b^2$.

Example 6 Rewriting as an Expression without Fractions

Rewrite $\dfrac{1}{1-\sin x}$ as an equivalent expression without fractions.

Answer

$\dfrac{1}{1-\sin x} = \dfrac{1}{1-\sin x} \cdot \dfrac{1+\sin x}{1+\sin x}$

$\qquad = \dfrac{1+\sin x}{1-\sin^2 x}$

1. Multiply the numerator and denominator by $1+\sin x$.

$\qquad = \dfrac{1+\sin x}{\cos^2 x}$

2. Substitute for the denominator using a form of the basic Pythagorean identity $\cos^2 x = 1 - \sin^2 x$.

$\qquad = \dfrac{1}{\cos^2 x} + \dfrac{\sin x}{\cos^2 x}$

3. Write the fraction as a sum.

$\qquad = \dfrac{1}{\cos^2 x} + \dfrac{\sin x}{\cos x} \cdot \dfrac{1}{\cos x}$

$\qquad = \sec^2 x + \tan x \sec x$

4. Use reciprocal and quotient identities to eliminate the fractions.

SKILL ✓ **EXERCISE 33**

A. Exercises

1. Use the image to prove each identity.

a. $\sec \theta = \dfrac{1}{\cos \theta}$

b. $\cot \theta = \dfrac{\cos \theta}{\sin \theta}$

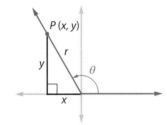

2. Derive each Pythagorean identity by dividing each term of $\sin^2 \theta + \cos^2 \theta = 1$ by the appropriate quantity.

a. $\cot^2 \theta + 1 = \csc^2 \theta$ **b.** $1 + \tan^2 \theta = \sec^2 \theta$

3. Use $\triangle ABC$ to prove each cofunction identity.

a. $\tan\left(\dfrac{\pi}{2} - \theta\right) = \cot \theta$

b. $\sec\left(\dfrac{\pi}{2} - \theta\right) = \csc \theta$

4. Verify each identity.

a. $\tan(-x) = -\tan(x)$ **b.** $\csc(-x) = -\csc x$

Use identities to find the value of each expression.

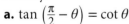

5. If $\sec \theta = 3$ and $\sin \theta > 0$, find $\sin \theta$ and $\tan \theta$.

6. If $\csc \theta = \dfrac{13}{5}$ and $\cos \theta < 0$, find $\tan \theta$ and $\sec \theta$.

7. If $\tan \theta = -\dfrac{15}{8}$ and $\cos \theta < 0$, find $\sec \theta$ and $\cos \theta$.

8. If $\cos \theta = \dfrac{1}{4}$ and $\tan \theta < 0$, find $\csc \theta$ and $\cot \theta$.

9. Which of the following is an equivalent form of the basic Pythagorean identity? List all correct answers.

A. $\sin^2 x = \cos^2 x - 1$ **C.** $\cos^2 x = \sin^2 x - 1$

B. $\sin^2 x = 1 - \cos^2 x$ **D.** $-\cos^2 x = \sin^2 x - 1$

10. Which of the following are equivalent forms of a Pythagorean identity? List all correct answers.

A. $\sec^2 x - \tan^2 x = 1$ **C.** $\cot^2 x - \csc^2 x = 1$

B. $\tan^2 x = -1 - \sec^2 x$ **D.** $\cot^2 x = \csc^2 x - 1$

Evaluate each expression.

11. $\sin\left(\dfrac{\pi}{2} - \theta\right)$ if $\cos \theta = 0.27$

12. $\csc\left(\dfrac{\pi}{2} - \theta\right)$ if $\sec \theta = -1.28$

13. $\cos\left(\theta - \dfrac{\pi}{2}\right)$ if $\sin \theta = 0.35$

14. $\tan\left(\theta - \dfrac{\pi}{2}\right)$ if $\cot \theta = -1.64$

Simplify each expression.

15. $\dfrac{\sin \theta - \cos \theta}{\sin \theta} + \cot \theta$

16. $\dfrac{\tan \theta \cos \theta}{\sin \theta}$

17. $\sin \theta \sec \theta - \sin \theta \csc \theta - \tan \theta$

18. $\dfrac{\sec \theta}{\cos \theta} - \dfrac{\tan \theta}{\cot \theta}$

B. Exercises

Simplify by factoring.

19. $\tan^3 x - \cot\left(\dfrac{\pi}{2} - x\right)\sec^2 x$

20. $\sin x - \sin^3 x$

21. $\tan x - \sin x \sec^3 x$

22. $\dfrac{\cos \theta}{\sec \theta + \tan \theta}$

5.1 FUNDAMENTAL IDENTITIES   237

Match each expression to its equivalent expression. Answers may be used more than once or not at all.

23. $\csc x \cos\left(\frac{\pi}{2} - x\right)$

24. $\sin x \cot x$

25. $\cos x \sec(-x)$

26. $\csc x \sin\left(\frac{\pi}{2} - x\right)$

A. 0
B. 1
C. –1
D. $\cos x$
E. $\cot x$
F. none of these

Simplify the expression. Then support your answer graphically.

27. $\dfrac{1 + \cot^2 \theta}{\cot^2 \theta}$

28. $\sin \theta + \cos \theta \cot \theta$

Simplify each expression.

29. $\dfrac{\sin x}{1 + \cos x} + \dfrac{1 + \cos x}{\sin x}$

30. $\cot x - \dfrac{\csc^2 x}{\cot x}$

31. $\dfrac{\cos x}{\sec x + 1} + \dfrac{\cos x}{\sec x - 1}$

32. $\dfrac{1}{\csc x - 1} + \dfrac{1}{\csc x + 1}$

Rewrite each expression without fractions.

33. $\dfrac{\cos x}{\sec x - \tan x}$

34. $\dfrac{\cot^2 x}{\csc x + 1}$

35. $\dfrac{\tan^2 x \sin x}{\sec x - 1}$

36. $\dfrac{\cos x \cot x}{\sin x + 1}$

》 C. Exercises

Use the properties of the natural log to rewrite each expression as an integer or a single natural logarithm. Support your answers graphically.

37. $\ln |\csc x| - \ln |\sin x|$

38. $\ln (\cos^2 x) + \ln (\cot^2 x + 1)$

Write the function rule for $f(g(x))$ and then use a Pythagorean identity to simplify.

39. $f(x) = \sqrt{49 - x^2}$
    $g(x) = 7 \cos \theta$

40. $f(x) = \sqrt{4x^2 + 25}$
    $g(x) = \frac{5}{2} \tan \theta$

41. In electronics, an RLC circuit contains a resistor (R), an inductor (L), and a capacitor (C) connected in series across an AC-voltage source. The voltage drop across the capacitor can be modeled by the function $v(t) = V_c \sin\left(\omega t - \frac{\pi}{2}\right)$, where V_c is the maximum voltage of the capacitor and ω is the angular frequency. Write a simplified equation for the function.

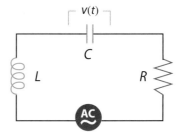

42. The vertical component of the instantaneous velocity of a golf ball that has traveled x ft horizontally after being struck with an initial velocity of v ft/sec at an angle θ above the horizontal can be modeled by the function $v_y(x) = \dfrac{v^2 \tan \theta \cos^2 \theta - 32x}{v \cos \theta}$.

a. Rewrite the function as the sum or difference of two terms.

b. Is the function linear, quadratic, or neither?

Simplify. [Algebra]

43. $\dfrac{3x^2 - 11x - 4}{2x^2 - 11x + 12}$

44. $\dfrac{4a^2 - 20a + 25}{4a^2 - 25}$

45. $\dfrac{1}{x+2} + \dfrac{3}{2x}$

46. Solve $\dfrac{1}{x+2} + \dfrac{3}{2x} = 1$. [Appendix 2]

47. State two ways an extraneous root can be introduced when solving a rational equation. [2.6]

48. State the exact value of each expression. [4.3]

    a. sin 30°   **b.** tan 135°   **c.** cos 210°

49. Find the value of x rounded to the nearest hundredth. [4.2]

    A. 5.66   **D.** 6.99

    B. 6.03   **E.** none of

    C. 6.68   these

50. Which model best fits growth that eventually slows and approaches a maximum value? [3.5]

    A. exponential   **C.** logarithmic

    B. linear   **D.** logistic

51. Which model best fits a rapid initial growth with a slower growth over time? [3.5]

    A. exponential   **C.** logarithmic

    B. linear   **D.** logistic

52. Find the value of $i + i^2 + i^3 + \cdots + i^{25}$. [Appendix 5]

    A. i **C.** 1   **E.** 0

    B. $-i$ **D.** -1

Joseph Fourier accompanied Napoleon Bonaparte on his Egyptian campaign during which the Rosetta Stone was discovered.

After completing this section, you will be able to

- determine whether an equation is an identity.
- verify trig identities.

Building on the work of Leonhard Euler, Joseph Fourier made significant contributions to the study of trigonometric series. A Fourier series represents a periodic function as the sum of simple sine waves.

In Section 5.1, fundamental identities were used to simplify or rewrite trigonometric expressions. This section focuses on *verifying identities*, showing that both sides of an equation are equal for all values of the variable for which the expressions are defined. Graphing both sides of an equation or examining a table of values can help you decide whether an equation might be an identity.

Example 1   Identifying an Equation That Is Not an Identity

Determine which equation is not an identity.

a. $\dfrac{\tan^2\theta + 1}{\tan^2\theta} = \sec^2\theta$ **b.** $\dfrac{\tan^2\theta + 1}{\tan^2\theta} = \csc^2\theta$

Answer

a.
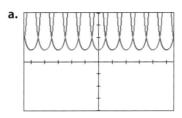

The graphs of $Y_1 = (\tan^2 X + 1)/\tan^2 X$ and $Y_2 = 1/\cos^2 X$ clearly do not coincide, so the equation is not an identity.

b.
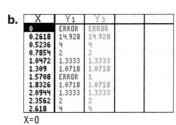

The values of $Y_1 = (\tan^2 X + 1)/\tan^2 X$ and $Y_3 = 1/\sin^2 X$ appear to be identical wherever both expressions are defined.
The fact that $Y_1\left(\dfrac{\pi}{2}\right)$ is undefined while $Y_3\left(\dfrac{\pi}{2}\right) = 1$ does not prevent the equation in part *b* from being an identity.

SKILL ✓ **EXERCISES 1, 3**

Finding just one instance where all the expressions are defined and have different values is sufficient to prove that an equation is not an identity. Using a graph or table of values can indicate the possibility that an equation is an identity, but these methods cannot prove the equation true for all values in its domain.

While you can solve equations by following specific steps, you will see and practice general strategies that can help prove identities. Since an identity cannot be assumed to be true until it has been proved, you cannot apply properties of equality to add or multiply both sides by the same quantity. Instead, begin with one side of the identity and transform it with a sequence of reversible steps using previously proven identities and algebraic manipulations until it matches the other side of the equation. The next example proves that the equation from Example 1*b* is an identity.

Example 2 Using Fundamental Identities

Verify $\dfrac{\tan^2\theta+1}{\tan^2\theta}=\csc^2\theta.$

Answer

$\dfrac{\tan^2\theta+1}{\tan^2\theta}=\dfrac{\sec^2\theta}{\tan^2\theta}$

1. Begin with the more complicated side and substitute using a Pythagorean identity.

$=\dfrac{\frac{1}{\cos^2\theta}}{\frac{\sin^2\theta}{\cos^2\theta}}$

2. Apply reciprocal and quotient identities to express the functions in terms of sine and cosine only.

$=\dfrac{1}{\cancel{\cos^2\theta}}\cdot\dfrac{\cancel{\cos^2\theta}}{\sin^2\theta}$

3. Simplify the complex fraction.

$=\dfrac{1}{\sin^2\theta}$

$=\csc^2\theta$

4. Rewrite the expression using a reciprocal identity.

Check

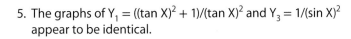

5. The graphs of $Y_1=((\tan X)^2+1)/(\tan X)^2$ and $Y_3=1/(\sin X)^2$ appear to be identical.

———————————————————— SKILL ✔ **EXERCISE 7**

There are often several ways to verify a particular identity. Notice that rewriting the left side of the identity in Example 1 as a sum of fractions produces a shorter proof.

$$\frac{\tan^2\theta+1}{\tan^2\theta}=\frac{\tan^2\theta}{\tan^2\theta}+\frac{1}{\tan^2\theta}=1+\cot^2\theta=\csc^2\theta$$

The proof begins with one side of the equation and lists a series of expressions that are easily seen to be equivalent, ending with the other side of the equation. Adding or subtracting fractions using their least common denominator frequently simplifies the more complicated side.

Example 3 Combining Fractions

Verify $2\sec^2 x=\dfrac{1}{\sin x+1}-\dfrac{1}{\sin x-1}.$

Answer

$\dfrac{1}{\sin x+1}-\dfrac{1}{\sin x-1}=\dfrac{(\sin x-1)-(\sin x+1)}{(\sin x+1)(\sin x-1)}$

1. Subtract the fractions on the right side of the equation.

$=\dfrac{-2}{\sin^2 x-1}$

2. Simplify.

$=\dfrac{2}{1-\sin^2 x}$

$=\dfrac{2}{\cos^2 x}$

3. Substitute using an alternate form of the basic Pythagorean identity.

$=2\sec^2 x$

4. Rewrite the expression using a reciprocal identity.

———————————————————— SKILL ✔ **EXERCISE 17**

Factoring expressions containing powers of trigonometric functions frequently helps simplify the more complicated side.

Example 4 Using Factoring

Verify $\sec^4 \theta - \sec^2 \theta = \tan^4 \theta + \tan^2 \theta$.

Answer

$$\tan^4 \theta + \tan^2 \theta = \tan^2 \theta \, (\tan^2 \theta + 1)$$
$$= (\sec^2 \theta - 1)(\sec^2 \theta)$$
$$= \sec^4 \theta - \sec^2 \theta$$

1. Factor the expression.
2. Substitute using two forms of the Pythagorean identity, $\tan^2 \theta + 1 = \sec^2 \theta$.
3. Distribute.

SKILL ✔ **EXERCISE 11**

Utilizing the product of conjugates pattern, $(a - b)(a + b) = a^2 - b^2$, can help simplify fractions with sums or differences in the denominator and set up a substitution using a Pythagorean identity.

Example 5 Using the Product of Conjugates

Verify $\dfrac{\cot x}{\csc x + 1} = \sec x - \tan x$.

Answer

$$\frac{\cot x}{\csc x + 1} = \frac{\cot x}{\csc x + 1} \cdot \frac{\csc x - 1}{\csc x - 1}$$
$$= \frac{\cot x \, (\csc x - 1)}{\csc^2 x - 1}$$
$$= \frac{\cot x \, (\csc x - 1)}{\cot^2 x}$$
$$= \frac{\csc x - 1}{\cot x}$$
$$= \frac{\dfrac{1}{\sin x} - 1}{\dfrac{\cos x}{\sin x}}$$
$$= \left(\frac{1}{\sin x} - 1 \right) \frac{\sin x}{\cos x}$$
$$= \frac{1}{\cos x} - \frac{\sin x}{\cos x}$$
$$= \sec x - \tan x$$

1. Multiply the numerator and denominator of the left side by the denominator's conjugate.

2. Substitute using a Pythagorean identity and simplify.

3. Rewrite in terms of sine and cosine and simplify the resulting complex fraction.

4. Use reciprocal and quotient identities to rewrite the expression in the form of the right side of the identity.

SKILL ✔ **EXERCISE 23**

Notice how rewriting the expression in terms of sine and cosine functions helped in the simplification of Example 5. When you struggle to transform one side into the other, you can also try working separately on each side to transform both sides into a common equivalent expression. Remember that the properties of equality cannot be used since the equation has not yet been proved to be true. A more formal proof could then be written starting with either side being transformed into the other.

One of the great benefits of studying mathematics is that it helps you learn to reason from basic principles to specific applications—a skill that is often required for living out biblical principles in a fallen world.

Example 6 Working on Both Sides

Verify $\dfrac{1-\sin t}{\sin t}=\dfrac{\cot^2 t}{1+\csc t}$.

Answer

Simplifying the Left Side	$\dfrac{1-\sin t}{\sin t}=\dfrac{\cot^2 t}{1+\csc t}$	Simplifying the Right Side
1. Rewrite as a difference of fractions.	$\dfrac{1}{\sin t}-\dfrac{\sin t}{\sin t}=\dfrac{\csc^2 t-1}{1+\csc t}$	1. Substitute using a Pythagorean identity.
2. Simplify by substituting using reciprocal and quotient identities.	$\csc t-1=\dfrac{(\csc t-1)(\csc t+1)}{1+\csc t}$ $=\csc t-1$	2. Factor the numerator and simplify.

——————————————————— SKILL ✓ **EXERCISE 13**

In order to make certain computations easier in calculus, an expression involving powers of trigonometric functions can be written as a more complicated expression involving sums. Example 7 demonstrates how one such identity can be derived.

Example 7 Rewriting a Power of a Trigonometric Function

Verify $\sin^5 x = \sin x\,(1-2\cos^2 x + \cos^4 x)$.

Answer

$\sin^5 x = \sin x \sin^2 x \sin^2 x$ $= \sin x\,(1-\cos^2 x)(1-\cos^2 x)$	1. Factor and apply a form of the basic Pythagorean identity.
$= \sin x\,(1-2\cos^2 x + \cos^4 x)$	2. Expand the product of binomials.

——————————————————— SKILL ✓ **EXERCISE 15**

We have illustrated how to discern when an equation is not an identity and several strategies that can be used to verify identities. If you are not sure which method of proof will work best, begin by applying one or more of these strategies. While your initial attempt may not be successful, it can provide valuable insights that will lead you to a correct solution.

Strategies for Verifying Identities

1. Begin by trying to transform one side, usually the more complicated side, into the other side.

2. Substitute using previously proven trigonometric identities.
   a. Use various forms of the Pythagorean identities.
   b. Express other trigonometric functions in terms of sine and cosine.

3. Simplify algebraically.
   a. Factor monomial terms, the difference of squares, or trinomials.
   b. Combine, separate, or simplify terms.
   c. Multiply using the Distributive Property, FOIL, or the product of conjugates.

4. Consider working on both sides separately to reach another equivalent expression.

A. Exercises

Use technology to graph each side of the equation and determine whether it appears to be or is not an identity.

1. $\cos x + \sin x \tan x = \csc x$

2. $\dfrac{\cot^2 x}{\csc x} = \cos x \cot x$

Use technology to make a table of values for each side of the equation and determine whether it appears to be or is not an identity.

3. $\tan^2 x \csc^2 x - \tan^2 x = 1$

4. $\cos^2 x - \sin x = \sin^2 x - \sin x - 1$

Verify each identity.

5. $\csc x \sin x = 1$

6. $\sin^2 x - \cos^2 x = 2 \sin^2 x - 1$

7. $\sec \theta - \sin \theta \tan \theta = \cos \theta$

8. $(\csc^2 \theta - 1) \sin^2 \theta = \cos^2 \theta$

9. $(1 - \cos x)(1 + \sec x) = \sec x - \cos x$

10. $\sin^2 x + \sin^2 \left(\dfrac{\pi}{2} - x\right) = 1$

11. $\cos \theta - \cos \theta \sin^2 \theta = \cos^3 \theta$

12. $\cot \theta \sec^2 \theta - \cot \theta = \tan \theta$

13. $\dfrac{\sin^2 x - 1}{\sin x} = -\cot x \cos x$

14. $\dfrac{(1 - \sec \theta)(1 + \sec \theta)}{\sin \theta} = -\tan \theta \sec \theta$

15. $\cos^4 x = 1 - 2 \sin^2 x + \sin^4 x$

16. $\sec^4 x \tan x = \sec^2 x (\tan x + \tan^3 x)$

B. Exercises

Verify each identity.

17. $\csc \theta - \cot \theta = \dfrac{\sin \theta}{1 + \cos \theta}$

18. $\dfrac{\csc x + 1}{\cot x} - \dfrac{\cot x}{\csc x - 1} = 0$

19. $\dfrac{1 + \cos \theta}{\sin \theta} + \dfrac{\sin \theta}{1 + \cos \theta} = 2 \csc \theta$

20. $\dfrac{\tan^2 \theta}{\csc \theta} + \dfrac{\cot^2 \theta}{\sec \theta} = \dfrac{\sin^5 \theta + \cos^5 \theta}{\sin^2 \theta \cos^2 \theta}$

21. $\dfrac{\sec^2 x - 3 \sec x + 2}{\sec^2 x - 1} = \dfrac{\sec x - 2}{\sec x + 1}$

22. $\sec^4 \theta + \sec^2 \theta \tan^2 \theta - 2 \tan^4 \theta = 3 \sec^2 \theta - 2$

23. $\dfrac{1 - \cos x}{1 + \cos x} = (\csc x - \cot x)^2$

24. $\dfrac{\cos x}{1 - \sin x} = \sec x + \tan x$

25. $\dfrac{\cot x}{\csc x + 1} = \sec x - \tan x$

26. $\dfrac{1}{\sec \theta + 1} + \dfrac{1}{\sec \theta - 1} = 2 \cos \theta \csc^2 \theta$

27. $\csc^4 \theta - \cot^4 \theta = \csc^2 \theta + \cot^2 \theta$

28. $\tan \theta - \dfrac{\sin^2 \theta}{\csc \theta \cos \theta} = \dfrac{\sec^2 \theta - 1}{\sec^2 \theta \tan \theta}$

29. $\csc^4 x = (\cot^2 x + 1) \csc^2 x$

30. $\cos^2 x \sin^5 x = \sin x (\cos^2 x - 2 \cos^4 x + \cos^6 x)$

Graph each side of the equation to determine whether it appears to be an identity. Then either verify the identity or provide a specific counterexample showing algebraically that the equation is not an identity.

31. $\dfrac{1}{1 - \sin x} + \dfrac{1}{1 + \sin x} = 2 \sec^2 x$

32. $\dfrac{\sin x \cot x + 2 \sin x - \cot x - 2}{\cot x + 2} = \sin x - 1$

33. $\dfrac{\csc x + \cot x}{\csc x - \cot x} = \dfrac{(\cos x + 1)^2}{\sin^2 x}$

34. $\dfrac{\dfrac{1}{\cos x} + 1}{\dfrac{1}{\cos x} - 1} = \cos^2 x + 2 \cos x \csc x + \csc^2 x$

C. Exercises

Verify each identity.

35. $\sqrt{\dfrac{\sec x + 1}{\sec x - 1}} = \left|\dfrac{\sec x + 1}{\tan x}\right|$

36. $\sqrt{\dfrac{\csc x - 1}{\csc x + 1}} = \left|\dfrac{\csc x - 1}{\cot x}\right|$

37. $\dfrac{\cos \theta}{\csc \theta - \sin \theta} - \dfrac{\sin \theta}{\sec \theta + \cos \theta} = \dfrac{\tan \theta}{1 + \cos^2 \theta}$

38. $\dfrac{2 \cot x}{1 - \cot^2 x} + \dfrac{1}{2 \sin^2 x - 1} = \dfrac{\sin x + \cos x}{\sin x - \cos x}$

Use the following definitions of hyperbolic trigonometric functions to prove the identities in exercises 39–42.

$\sinh x = \dfrac{1}{2}(e^x - e^{-x})$ $\qquad$ $\operatorname{csch} x = \dfrac{1}{\sinh x}$

$\cosh x = \dfrac{1}{2}(e^x + e^{-x})$ $\qquad$ $\operatorname{sech} x = \dfrac{1}{\cosh x}$

$\tanh x = \dfrac{\sinh x}{\cosh x}$ $\qquad$ $\coth x = \dfrac{1}{\tanh x}$

39. $\cosh^2 x - \sinh^2 x = 1$

40. $\coth^2 x - \operatorname{csch}^2 x = 1$

41. $\operatorname{sech}(-x) = \operatorname{sech} x$

42. $\operatorname{csch}(-x) = -\operatorname{csch} x$

43. Find the inverse of $f(x) = \frac{x}{x+3}$. [1.8]

44. Solve $\ln 3 = -2 + \ln x$. [3.4]

45. State the exact value of each expression. [4.3]

    a. $\tan 30°$ **b.** $\cos -135°$ **c.** $\sin -300°$

46. Express $\dfrac{1}{\sin^2 \theta} - \dfrac{1}{\sin \theta \cos \theta}$ as a single fraction. [5.1]

Express each function in terms of sine or cosine and then simplify. [5.1]

47. $\tan \theta + \sec \theta$

48. $\dfrac{\tan \theta \csc \theta}{\sec \theta}$

49. Which term describes the difference between the actual y-value of a data point and the y-value predicted by the regression equation? [1.9]

    A. coefficient of determination

    B. regression

    C. residual

    D. correlation

    E. none of these

50. Which expression represents the height of a utility pole if a 52 ft cable (guy-wire) attached to the top of the pole is anchored at a 47° angle to the ground? [4.2]

    A. $\sin 47°$

    B. $\cos 47°$

    C. $52 \sin 47°$

    D. $52 \cos 47°$

    E. $52 \tan 47°$

51. Find the value of $\sin \left(\text{Tan}^{-1} \frac{3}{4} \right)$. [4.6]

    A. $\frac{4}{3}$ **B.** $\frac{3}{4}$ **C.** $\frac{4}{5}$ **D.** $\frac{3}{5}$ **E.** $\frac{5}{3}$

52. Without using technology, determine which function has a wave with varying amplitude. [4.7]

    A. $y = x^2 \sin x$

    B. $y = \sin x^2$

    C. $y = \sin (3x + \pi)$

    D. $y = 3 \sin x$

    E. $y = \sin^2 \frac{x}{2}$

The standing wave produced by this machine clearly demonstrates the wave's nodes, points that do not experience any displacement.

After completing this section, you will be able to

• solve trig equations using algebraic techniques and trig identities.

Trigonometric identities are equations that are true for all values of the variable for which the expressions are defined. They are verified by transforming either or both sides independently until the expressions are identical. *Conditional trigonometric equations* may be true for certain values in the domains of the expressions but are not true for all values in their domains. Trigonometric equations are solved using standard algebraic practices such as applying properties of equality, collecting like terms, and factoring along with trigonometric identities. The goal is to isolate the trigonometric function on one side of the equation.

Example 1 Isolating the Trigonometric Function

Solve $2 \sin \theta + 1 = 0$.

Answer

$$2 \sin \theta + 1 = 0$$
$$2 \sin \theta = -1$$
$$\sin \theta = -\frac{1}{2}$$

1. Use the properties of equality to isolate $\sin x$ on the left side of the equation.

$$\theta = \frac{7\pi}{6}, \frac{11\pi}{6}$$

2. Use the unit circle to find the values of θ within $[0, 2\pi)$ for which $\sin \theta = -\frac{1}{2}$.

$$\theta = \frac{7\pi}{6} + n2\pi, \frac{11\pi}{6} + n2\pi$$
where $n \in \mathbb{Z}$

3. Since the period of the sine function is 2π, adding multiples of 2π produces all solutions to the equation.

Check

4. Find the zeros of $y = 2 \sin x + 1$ to verify your solution.

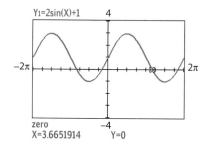

Y₁=2sin(X)+1   4

-2π 2π

zero -4
X=3.6651914   Y=0

SKILL ✔ **EXERCISE 1**

Since trigonometric functions are periodic, most trigonometric equations will have an infinite number of solutions. The *general solution* lists all the solutions to the equation. Frequently we are interested only in *primary solutions*, those within $[0, 2\pi)$.

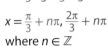

Example 2 Solving by Taking Roots

State primary and general solutions for $6 - \tan^2 x = \tan^2 x$.

Answer

$6 - \tan^2 x = \tan^2 x$
$6 = 2\tan^2 x$
$3 = \tan^2 x$
$\pm\sqrt{3} = \tan x$

1. Isolate tan x on the right side.
   Be sure to list both the positive and the negative square roots.

$x = \dfrac{\pi}{3}, \dfrac{2\pi}{3}, \dfrac{4\pi}{3}, \dfrac{5\pi}{3}$

2. Use the unit circle to find the primary solutions.

$x = \dfrac{\pi}{3} + n\pi, \dfrac{2\pi}{3} + n\pi$
where $n \in \mathbb{Z}$

3. Since the tangent function is periodic with a period of π, adding multiples of π to the primary solutions in Q I and Q II produces the general solution.

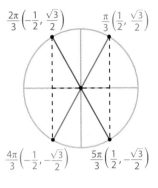

SKILL ✓ **EXERCISE 5**

Sometimes it is not possible to isolate a trigonometric function on one side of the equation. We can often solve trigonometric equations in quadratic form by factoring and applying the Zero Product Property.

Example 3 Solving by Factoring

Find the general solution for each equation.

a. $\sin^2 x + \cos x + 1 = 0$ **b.** $2\tan x \sin x = \sqrt{2}\tan x$

Answer

a.
$\sin^2 x + \cos x + 1 = 0$
$(1 - \cos^2 x) + \cos x + 1 = 0$
$-\cos^2 x + \cos x + 2 = 0$
$\cos^2 x - \cos x - 2 = 0$

1. Substitute using a Pythagorean identity and rewrite the equation as a quadratic in cos x.

$(\cos x + 1)(\cos x - 2) = 0$

2. Factor. You can think of the equation as $u^2 - u - 2 = 0$ with $u = \cos x$.

$\cos x = -1$ or $\cos x = 2$

3. Solve for cos x using the Zero Product Property.

$x = \pi$

4. Identify any primary solutions. Note that the range of the cosine function, $[-1, 1]$, implies that there are no real solutions to $\cos x = 2$.

$x = \pi + n2\pi = (2n + 1)\pi$
where $n \in \mathbb{Z}$

5. Write the general solution.

Check

6. Confirm graphically by finding zeros of $y = \sin^2 x + \cos x + 1$.

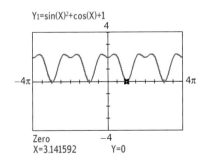

CONTINUED ➡

b. $2 \tan x \sin x = \sqrt{2} \tan x$ 1. Collect all terms on one side and factor.

$2 \tan x \sin x - \sqrt{2} \tan x = 0$

$\tan x (2 \sin x - \sqrt{2}) = 0$

$\tan x = 0$ or $\sin x = \dfrac{\sqrt{2}}{2}$ 2. Apply the Zero Product Property.

$x = 0, \pi \qquad x = \dfrac{\pi}{4}, \dfrac{3\pi}{4}$ 3. Identify any primary solutions.

$x = n\pi, \dfrac{\pi}{4} + n2\pi, \dfrac{3\pi}{4} + n2\pi$ 4. Write the general solution.
where $n \in \mathbb{Z}$

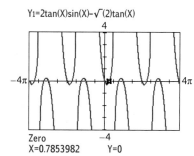
Y₁=2tan(X)sin(X)−√(2)tan(X)

Zero
X=0.7853982   Y=0

Check   5. Confirm graphically by finding zeros of
$y = 2 \tan x \sin x - \sqrt{2} \tan x$.

SKILL ✓ EXERCISE 9

Recall that dividing both sides of any equation by an expression containing a variable introduces the possibility of losing solutions to the equation. Dividing both sides of the equation in Example 3b by $\tan x$ would eliminate the solutions of $x = n\pi$ when both sides of the equation are unknowingly divided by 0.

You must check for extraneous solutions when both sides of an equation are multiplied by a trigonometric function or when both sides are squared.

Example 4   Checking for Extraneous Solutions

Find all primary solutions to each equation.

a. $3 \csc x - \sin x = 2$ **b.** $\cos x + \sin x = 1$

Answer

a. $3 \csc x - \sin x = 2$ 1. Substitute using the reciprocal identity for cosecant.

$\dfrac{3}{\sin x} - \sin x = 2$

$3 - \sin^2 x = 2 \sin x$ 2. Eliminate fractions by multiplying both sides by $\sin x$.

$\sin^2 x + 2 \sin x - 3 = 0$ 3. Solve the quadratic by factoring.

$(\sin x - 1)(\sin x + 3) = 0$

$\sin x - 1 = 0$ or $\sin x + 3 = 0$

$\sin x = 1$ or $\sin x = -3$ Note that the range of sine, $[-1, 1]$, implies that there are no real solutions to $\sin x = -3$.

$x = \dfrac{\pi}{2}$

Check

$3 \csc \dfrac{\pi}{2} - \sin \dfrac{\pi}{2} = 3(1) - 1 = 2$ 4. Substitute to check that $\dfrac{\pi}{2}$ is not extraneous.

> **TIP**
>
> Solutions can also be checked on a graphing calculator by finding the intersections of Y_1 (the expression on the left) and Y_2 (the expression on the right).

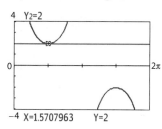
Y₂=2

X=1.5707963   Y=2

CONTINUED ➡

248   CHAPTER 5 TRIGONOMETRIC IDENTITIES AND EQUATIONS

b. $\cos x + \sin x = 1$

$\sin x = 1 - \cos x$

$\sin^2 x = 1 - 2\cos x + \cos^2 x$

$(1 - \cos^2 x) = 1 - 2\cos x + \cos^2 x$

1. Since factoring cannot separate $\sin x$ and $\cos x$, solve for $\sin x$ and square both sides to allow a substitution using the Pythagorean identity.

$2\cos^2 x - 2\cos x = 0$

$2\cos x(\cos x - 1) = 0$

$\cos x = 0$ or $\cos x = 1$

$x = 0, \dfrac{\pi}{2}, \dfrac{3\pi}{2}$

2. Solve for x.

Check

$\cos 0 + \sin 0 = 1 + 0 = 1$

$\cos \dfrac{\pi}{2} + \sin \dfrac{\pi}{2} = 0 + 1 = 1$

$\cos \dfrac{3\pi}{2} + \sin \dfrac{3\pi}{2} = 0 + (-1) \neq 1$

3. Substitute to check for extraneous roots.

$\therefore x = 0, \dfrac{\pi}{2}$

4. Exclude any extraneous solutions.

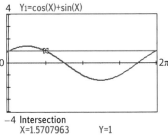

SKILL ✔ **EXERCISES 11, 13**

Recall that a calculator's inverse trigonometric functions return the principal value within $[0, \pi)$ for $\cos^{-1}$, $\left[-\dfrac{\pi}{2}, \dfrac{\pi}{2}\right]$ for $\sin^{-1}$, and $\left(-\dfrac{\pi}{2}, \dfrac{\pi}{2}\right)$ for $\tan^{-1}$. These values are used to determine the primary solutions found in other quadrants.

In 1593 King Henry IV of France summoned François Viète to respond to a Dutch ambassador's mathematical challenge. When presented with an equation of the forty-fifth degree, Viète used trigonometry to immediately provide one solution and then added twenty-two more solutions the following day.

Example 5 Using a Calculator When Solving Equations

Find the primary solutions for $3\sin^2 x - 5\sin x - 2 = 0$ (to the nearest hundredth).

Answer

$3\sin^2 x - 5\sin x - 2 = 0$

$(3\sin x + 1)(\sin x - 2) = 0$

$\sin x = -\dfrac{1}{3}$ or $\sin x = 2$

1. Factor and apply the Zero Product Property.

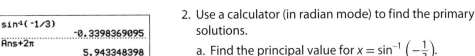

2. Use a calculator (in radian mode) to find the primary solutions.

   a. Find the principal value for $x = \sin^{-1}\left(-\dfrac{1}{3}\right)$. Note that it is not a primary solution.

   b. Add 2π to find the primary solution in Q IV.

   c. Add π to the reference angle $\alpha = \left|\sin^{-1}\left(-\dfrac{1}{3}\right)\right|$ to find the primary solution in Q III.

   d. There are no solutions for $\sin x = 2$.

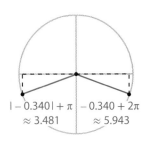

$|-0.340| + \pi$ $-0.340 + 2\pi$
≈ 3.481 ≈ 5.943

$x \approx 3.48, 5.94$

3. List decimal approximations of primary solutions.

Check

4. Find the 2 zeros of $y = 3\sin^2 x - 5\sin x - 2$ in $[0, 2\pi)$ to verify your solutions.

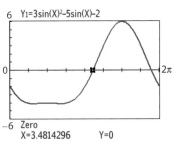

SKILL ✔ **EXERCISE 33**

When solving an equation containing a function of a multiple angle, such as cos kx, first solve for the multiple angle kx and then divide the result by k.

The tones for each number on a phone are composed of sinusoids. The receiving device uses a trigonometric equation known as a Fourier transform to identify the frequencies of the tone and the button that was pressed.

Example 6 Solving a Multiple Angle Equation

Find the general and primary solutions for $2 \cos 3x = \sqrt{3}$.

Answer

$2 \cos 3x = \sqrt{3}$

$\cos 3x = \dfrac{\sqrt{3}}{2}$

$3x = \dfrac{\pi}{6}$ and $\dfrac{11\pi}{6}$

$3x = \dfrac{\pi}{6} + n2\pi, \dfrac{11\pi}{6} + n2\pi, n \in \mathbb{Z}$

$x = \dfrac{\pi}{18} + \dfrac{2n}{3}\pi, \dfrac{11\pi}{18} + \dfrac{2n}{3}\pi, n \in \mathbb{Z}$

$n = 0; x = \dfrac{\pi}{18}, \dfrac{11\pi}{18}$

$n = 1; x = \dfrac{\pi}{18} + \dfrac{2}{3}\pi = \dfrac{13\pi}{18}$

$\qquad x = \dfrac{11\pi}{18} + \dfrac{2}{3}\pi = \dfrac{23\pi}{18}$

$n = 2; x = \dfrac{\pi}{18} + \dfrac{4}{3}\pi = \dfrac{25\pi}{18}$

$\qquad x = \dfrac{11\pi}{18} + \dfrac{4}{3}\pi = \dfrac{35\pi}{18}$

$x = \dfrac{\pi}{18}, \dfrac{11\pi}{18}, \dfrac{13\pi}{18}, \dfrac{23\pi}{18}, \dfrac{25\pi}{18}, \dfrac{35\pi}{18}$

1. Find the general solution for $3x$.
   a. Isolate cos $3x$.
   b. Use the unit circle to find primary solutions of $3x$.
   c. Write general solutions for $3x$.

2. Find the general solution for x by dividing both sides by 3.

3. Use $n = 0$, 1, and 2 to generate primary solutions within $[0, 2\pi)$.
   Note that if $n = 3$, $x = \dfrac{\pi}{18} + 2\pi$ and $x = \dfrac{11\pi}{18} + 2\pi$ are outside of $[0, 2\pi)$. In general, $n \in [0, k - 1]$.

SKILL ✓ **EXERCISE 29**

❯ A. Exercises

Find the primary solutions of each equation by isolating the trigonometric function.

1. $\sin x + 1 = 0$
2. $2 \cos x = \sqrt{3}$
3. $\cot x + 1 = 0$
4. $\tan x - \sqrt{3} = 0$

Find the primary solutions of each equation by taking roots.

5. $\sin^2 x - 3 = -3 \sin^2 x$
6. $2 \cos^2 x - 3 = -2 \cos^2 x$
7. $2 \sin^2 x - 1 = 0$

Use factoring to find the primary solutions of each equation.

8. $2 \cos^2 x - \sqrt{2} \cos x = 0$
9. $\cot^2 x - \sqrt{3} \cot x = 0$
10. $\tan x - \tan^2 x = 0$

Find the primary solutions of each equation. Be sure to check for extraneous solutions.

11. $1 - \sin x = \cos x$
12. $2 \sin x = 4 \csc x + 7$
13. $2 \cos x + 2 \sec x = 5$
14. $\cot x - 1 = \csc x$

Use inverse trigonometric functions to find all primary solutions (to the nearest hundredth).

15. $4 \sin x \cos x = \sin x$
16. $3 \sin^2 x + 2 \sin x - 1 = 0$

Find the primary solutions of each multiple angle equation.

17. $2 \sin 2x - 1 = 0$
18. $\sqrt{3} \tan \dfrac{x}{2} = -1$

❯ B. Exercises

Find the general solutions of each equation.

19. $\tan^2 x - 1 = 0$
20. $2 \cos^2 x + 3 \cos x + 1 = 0$
21. $\sec x - 2 \cos x = 1$
22. $\cos^2 x - 3 \sin x = 3$
23. $\tan x - 3 \cot x = 0$
24. $\dfrac{\cot^2 x}{\csc x} + \sin x = 2$
25. $2 - 2 \sin^2 x = \cos x + 1$
26. $2 \cos x + 2 \sec x = 5$
27. $\dfrac{\sin x}{1 + \cos x} + \dfrac{1 + \cos x}{\sin x} = -4$

28. $8 \sin^4 x - 2 \sin^2 x - 3 = 0$

29. $\sin^2 3x = 0$

30. $\cos \frac{x}{2} = \frac{1}{2}$

31. $\dfrac{\sin x}{1 - \cos x} = \dfrac{\cos x}{1 + \sin x}$

32. $\cos^2 4x + \cos 4x = 0$

Find the primary solutions of each equation. Round each radian measure to the nearest hundredth.

33. $\dfrac{3}{1 + 3 \sin x} = 1$

34. $5 \cos x = 6 \sin^2 x$

35. $3 \sin^2 x = 2 \cos x \sin x$

36. $2 \csc^2 x - \cot x - 5 = 0$

37. A soccer ball is kicked from the ground at an angle of θ above the horizontal with an initial speed of $v_0 = 85$ ft/sec. Use the formula for the range of a projectile, $d = \dfrac{{v_0}^2 \sin 2\theta}{32}$, to calculate θ (to the nearest tenth of a degree) if the balls lands 210 ft away.

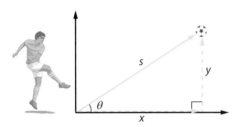

> ## C. Exercises

Find the primary solutions of each equation. Round decimal approximations to the nearest hundredth.

38. $8 \cos^2 x + 14 \cos x - 15 = 0$

39. $\tan^2 x + 8 \tan x - 4 = 0$

40. $\tan^2 x - \sin^2 x = \tan^2 x \sin^2 x$

41. $\tan^3 x + \tan^2 x - 3 \tan x - 3 = 0$

42. Standing waves result from a combination of waves with the same frequency and amplitude that are traveling at the same speed in opposite directions. A standing wave can be modeled with the function $y = (2A_0 \sin kx) \cos \omega t$. A *node* of a standing wave occurs where its amplitude $2A_0 \sin kx = 0$. Find the position x of the function's first 5 nodes in terms of the wavelength λ if $k = \frac{2\pi}{\lambda}$.

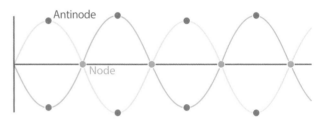

CUMULATIVE REVIEW

Solve each equation.

43. $2x^2 - 5x + 1 = 0$ [1.6]

44. $3 = \dfrac{x}{x + 1} + \dfrac{5}{x}$ [1.6]

45. $e^{-2x} = 3$ [3.4]

46. $2x^{-5} = \dfrac{1}{16}$ [3.4]

47. $\sqrt{x - 5} + 3 = 7$ [2.1]

48. Simplify $\dfrac{1}{\sec \left(x - \frac{\pi}{2} \right)}$. [5.1]

49. What is the period of the sum of $f(x) = \sin 2x$ and $g(x) = 3 \cos 2x$? [4.7]

 A. 1   **C.** π **E.** cannot be
 B. 2   **D.** 2π determined

50. Simplify $\cos^3 \theta + \sin^2 \theta \cos \theta$. [5.1]

 A. $\tan \theta$ **C.** $\sin \theta$ **E.** $\csc \theta$
 B. $\sec \theta$ **D.** $\cos \theta$

51. Which expression is equivalent to $\dfrac{\tan^2 x}{1 + \tan^2 x}$? [5.2]

 A. $\sin x$ **D.** $\sin^2 x \cos^2 x$
 B. $\sin^2 x$ **E.** none of these
 C. $\sin^2 x \cos x$

52. Which expression is equivalent to $\dfrac{\sin x}{1 - \cos x}$? [5.2]

 A. $\sin x - \tan x$ **D.** $\csc x + \cot x$
 B. $\sin x + \tan x$ **E.** none of these
 C. $\csc x - \tan x$

The Unity and Beauty of Mathematics

Mathematics compares the most diverse phenomena and discovers the secret analogies that unite them.
—Joseph Fourier (French mathematician and physicist)

Mathematics, rightly viewed, possesses not only truth, but supreme beauty.
—Bertrand Russell (British philosopher and mathematician)

The integers 0 and 1 are quite different from the irrational numbers π and e. The imaginary number i is from another mathematical world. Euler's identity $e^{i\pi} + 1 = 0$ combines these five foundational constants and the three fundamental operations of addition, multiplication, and exponentiation in one of the most beautiful equations in mathematics. The poet Dana Gioia stated that "beauty is the pleasure we get in recognizing the particular manifestation of a broader, universal order." The unity of mathematics across its extreme diversity is one of its most beautiful characteristics.

While π and e are both irrational numbers, each can be expressed as an infinite sum involving only integers.

$$\pi = 4 - \frac{4}{3} + \frac{4}{5} - \frac{4}{7} + \frac{4}{9} - \frac{4}{11} + \cdots \text{ and}$$

$$e = 2 + \frac{1}{2} + \frac{1}{2 \cdot 3} + \frac{1}{2 \cdot 3 \cdot 4} + \frac{1}{2 \cdot 3 \cdot 4 \cdot 5} + \cdots.$$

The number π was used in the solution to the Basel problem, which sought the sum of the reciprocals of all the perfect squares. This problem baffled mathematicians for nearly one hundred years, but Leonard Euler earned his reputation as a world-class mathematician in 1735 by proving that

$$1 + \frac{1}{4} + \frac{1}{9} + \frac{1}{16} + \frac{1}{25} + \cdots = \frac{\pi^2}{6}.$$

The seemingly unrelated constants π and e also appear together in the most important probability distribution function, the normal distribution, whose graph is the bell curve.

James Nickel describes several examples of "unity in diversity": "Basic trigonometric functions relate to the right triangle, music, and the electromagnetic spectrum. The Fibonacci sequence unifies many diverse aspects of creation. The spiral, the hexagon, and the pentagram are just a few of the other beautiful and inherent relationships in creation." Fibonacci discovered that the golden ratio, described much earlier by Euclid, could be estimated to any desired degree of accuracy using a sequence of ratios of successive terms of the Fibonacci sequence: $\frac{3}{2}, \frac{5}{3}, \frac{8}{5}, \frac{13}{8}, \frac{21}{13}, \ldots$. The golden ratio is symbolized by ϕ (phi) and is expressed exactly as $\frac{1 + \sqrt{5}}{2}$, the positive irrational solution to $x^2 - x - 1 = 0$.

The coordinate geometry of René Descartes unified symbolic algebra and the Euclidean geometry that was developed centuries earlier. The various conic sections described in ancient Greece by Apollonius were later represented with second-degree algebraic equations in two variables. While this important connection between geometric figures and abstract algebra is often described by secular mathematicians as "mysterious," this beautiful unity should cause Christian mathematicians to praise the Creator God.

In the nineteenth century, the foundation of Euclidean geometry was shaken by the development of two diverse non-Euclidean geometries. The brilliant German mathematician Carl Gauss applied non-Euclidean theory to the geometric nature of physical space but did not publish his discoveries, perhaps fearing the controversy they would create. In the twentieth century Felix Klein unified the geometries with his beautiful development of projective geometry. As Morris Kline wrote, "It is possible to erect projective geometry on an axiomatic basis in such a way that the theorems of the other three geometries result as specialized theorems of projective geometry. In other words, the contents of all four geometries are now incorporated in one harmonious whole." Later, Einstein's algebraic relativity formulas fulfilled Gauss's vision by applying non-Euclidean geometry to physical space in yet another example of the beautiful unity of algebra and geometry.

Sets, including geometric sets of points and algebraic sets of numbers, are an essential unifying concept in mathematics. Computers use an iterative equation and complex numbers to produce the amazing Mandelbrot set, an infinitely detailed graph in fractal geometry. Astrophysicist Jason Lisle observed that the fractal's beautifully organized shapes have been "built into mathematics by the Creator of mathematics." Zooming in on the different spirals surrounding the original Mandelbrot set reveals miniature "baby" versions similar to the original. Mathematicians have described portions of the graph with names such as *seahorse valley*, *triple spiral valley*, *elephant valley*, and

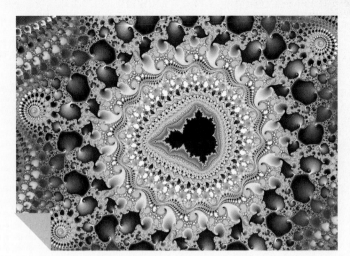

The Mandelbrot fractal is a complex plane visualization of the divergent nature of a set of complex numbers.

scepter valley. Analyzing the stems, branches, and bulbs of the Mandelbrot set results in common natural number sequences, including the Fibonacci sequence!

Exercises

1. State Euler's identity and list the fundamental mathematical operations used.

2. Match each constant in Euler's identity with its related foundational concept.

   a. 0   **I.** additive identity

   b. 1   **II.** complex numbers

   c. π **III.** multiplicative identity

   d. e **IV.** natural logarithms

   e. i **V.** radian measure

3. State the exact sum for each infinite series.

   a. $4 - \frac{4}{3} + \frac{4}{5} - \frac{4}{7} + \frac{4}{9} - \frac{4}{11} + \cdots$

   b. $2 + \frac{1}{2} + \frac{1}{2 \cdot 3} + \frac{1}{2 \cdot 3 \cdot 4} + \frac{1}{2 \cdot 3 \cdot 4 \cdot 5} + \cdots$

   c. $1 + \frac{1}{4} + \frac{1}{9} + \frac{1}{16} + \frac{1}{25} + \cdots$

4. State the sixth term for the golden ratio sequence given in the text. Then state its decimal value rounded to the nearest thousandth.

5. Solve $x^2 - x - 1 = 0$ using the quadratic formula. Then use a calculator to find a decimal approximation for the golden ratio (rounded to the nearest millionth).

6. Which mathematician's foundational work in applying abstract non-Euclidean theory to physical space led to Einstein's algebraic relativity formulas?

7. State two examples of ancient Greek geometry being later unified with algebraic descriptions.

8. **Discuss:** How does the Mandelbrot set illustrate the beautiful unity of complex numbers and fractal geometry?

9. **Discuss:** From a biblical perspective, explain why mathematics displays such beautiful unity despite its diverse applications.

5.4 Sum and Difference Identities

This RLC circuit has a resistor, an inductor, and a capacitor connected in series.

After completing this section, you will be able to

- derive sum and difference identities.
- use sum and difference identities to evaluate functions, verify identities, and solve equations.

The unit circle and relationships within 45-45-90 and 30-60-90 triangles enable us to state exact values for trigonometric functions of multiples of $\frac{\pi}{4}$ and $\frac{\pi}{6}$. In this section, you will derive identities for the sine, cosine, and tangent of a sum or difference of angles. These identities will allow you to calculate other exact trigonometric function values, verify other identities, and solve more trigonometric equations.

A counterexample proves that $\cos(\alpha - \beta) \neq \cos\alpha - \cos\beta$.

$$\cos(90° - 60°) \overset{?}{=} \cos 90° - \cos 60°$$

$$\cos 30° \overset{?}{=} 0 - \frac{1}{2}$$

$$\frac{\sqrt{3}}{2} \neq -\frac{1}{2}$$

An identity for $\cos(\alpha - \beta)$ can be derived from the unit circle where angles α, β, and $\alpha - \beta$ are drawn in standard position. The terminal sides of these angles intersect the unit circle at A $(\cos\alpha, \sin\alpha)$, B $(\cos\beta, \sin\beta)$, and C $(\cos(\alpha - \beta), \sin(\alpha - \beta))$, respectively. Since $m\angle AOB = \alpha - \beta$, $\overline{AB} \cong \overline{CD}$ and their lengths can be found using the distance formula.

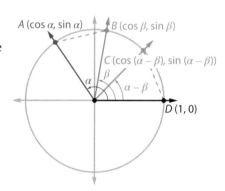

$$CD = AB$$
$$\sqrt{[\cos(\alpha - \beta) - 1]^2 + [\sin(\alpha - \beta) - 0]^2} = \sqrt{(\cos\alpha - \cos\beta)^2 + (\sin\alpha - \sin\beta)^2}$$

Square both sides to remove the radicals and expand the squared binomials.

$$\cos^2(\alpha - \beta) - 2\cos(\alpha - \beta) + 1 + \sin^2(\alpha - \beta)$$
$$= \cos^2\alpha - 2\cos\alpha\cos\beta + \cos^2\beta + \sin^2\alpha - 2\sin\alpha\sin\beta + \sin^2\beta$$

Rearrange the terms and use the Pythagorean identity $\sin^2 x + \cos^2 x = 1$ to simplify.

$$[\cos^2(\alpha - \beta) + \sin^2(\alpha - \beta)] - 2\cos(\alpha - \beta) + 1$$
$$= [\cos^2\alpha + \sin^2\alpha] - 2\cos\alpha\cos\beta - 2\sin\alpha\sin\beta + [\cos^2\beta + \sin^2\beta]$$

$$(1) - 2\cos(\alpha - \beta) + 1 = (1) - 2\cos\alpha\cos\beta - 2\sin\alpha\sin\beta + (1)$$

Subtract 2 from each side and then divide both sides by –2.

$$-2\cos(\alpha - \beta) = -2\cos\alpha\cos\beta - 2\sin\alpha\sin\beta$$
$$\cos(\alpha - \beta) = \cos\alpha\cos\beta + \sin\alpha\sin\beta$$

The identity for the cosine of a sum of two angles is derived using this identity and the odd/even identities for sine and cosine.

$\cos(\alpha + \beta) = \cos[\alpha - (-\beta)]$	1. Apply the definition of subtraction.
$\cos(\alpha + \beta) = \cos\alpha\cos(-\beta) + \sin\alpha\sin(-\beta)$	2. Apply the identity for cosine of a difference.
$\cos(\alpha + \beta) = \cos\alpha\cos\beta - \sin\alpha\sin\beta$	3. Substitute, using $\cos(-\theta) = \cos\theta$ and $\sin(-\theta) = -\sin\theta$.

The identity for the cosine of a difference also provides a simple proof for two important cofunction identities. The remaining cofunction identities can be proved using the results of Example 1.

Example 1   Proving Cofunction Identities

Prove the following cofunction identities.

a. $\cos\left(\frac{\pi}{2} - \theta\right) = \sin\theta$ **b.** $\sin\left(\frac{\pi}{2} - \theta\right) = \cos\theta$

Answer

a. $\cos\left(\frac{\pi}{2} - \theta\right) = \cos\frac{\pi}{2}\cos\theta + \sin\frac{\pi}{2}\sin\theta$ 1. Apply the cosine of a difference identity.

$\qquad = (0)\cos\theta + (1)\sin\theta$ 2. Evaluate and simplify.
$\qquad = \sin\theta$

b. $\sin\left(\frac{\pi}{2} - \theta\right) = \cos\left[\frac{\pi}{2} - \left(\frac{\pi}{2} - \theta\right)\right]$ 1. Apply the previous cofunction identity.

$\qquad = \cos(0 + \theta)$ 2. Simplify.
$\qquad = \cos\theta$

SKILL ✓ **EXERCISE 15**

These cofunction identities are used to derive the sine of a difference identity.

$$\sin(\alpha - \beta) = \cos\left[\frac{\pi}{2} - (\alpha - \beta)\right]$$

$$= \cos\left[\left(\frac{\pi}{2} - \alpha\right) + \beta\right]$$

$$= \cos\left(\frac{\pi}{2} - \alpha\right)\cos\beta - \sin\left(\frac{\pi}{2} - \alpha\right)\sin\beta$$

$$= \sin\alpha\cos\beta - \cos\alpha\sin\beta$$

The derivations of identities for the sine of a sum, the tangent of a difference, and the tangent of a sum are left as exercises. Because the formats of the sum and difference identities for each function are so similar, the identities are often combined using the $\pm$ (plus or minus) and $\mp$ (minus or plus) symbols, and read either along the top or along the bottom of each symbol.

Ptolemy used sum and difference identities to construct his table of chords in the second century AD. He used the fact that the product of the diagonals of an inscribed quadrilateral equals the sum of the products of the opposite sides (Ptolemy's Theorem) to prove these identities.

Sum and Difference Identities
$\cos(\alpha \pm \beta) = \cos\alpha\cos\beta \mp \sin\alpha\sin\beta$
$\sin(\alpha \pm \beta) = \sin\alpha\cos\beta \pm \cos\alpha\sin\beta$
$\tan(\alpha \pm \beta) = \dfrac{\tan\alpha \pm \tan\beta}{1 \mp \tan\alpha\tan\beta}$

These identities can help find exact trigonometric values for many angles other than multiples of $\frac{\pi}{4}$ and $\frac{\pi}{6}$.

Example 2 Evaluating a Sum or Difference

Find the exact value of each trigonometric expression.

a. $\sin \dfrac{7\pi}{12}$　　　　　　　　　　　　　　**b.** $\tan 15°$

Answer

```
(√6+√2)/4
              0.9659258263
sin(7π/12)
              0.9659258263
2-√3
              0.2679491924
tan(15°)
              0.2679491924
■
```

*A calculator can be used
to verify your answers.*

a. $\sin \dfrac{7\pi}{12} = \sin\left(\dfrac{4\pi}{12} + \dfrac{3\pi}{12}\right)$

$= \sin\left(\dfrac{\pi}{3} + \dfrac{\pi}{4}\right)$

$= \sin\dfrac{\pi}{3}\cos\dfrac{\pi}{4} + \cos\dfrac{\pi}{3}\sin\dfrac{\pi}{4}$

$= \left(\dfrac{\sqrt{3}}{2}\right)\left(\dfrac{\sqrt{2}}{2}\right) + \left(\dfrac{1}{2}\right)\left(\dfrac{\sqrt{2}}{2}\right)$

$= \dfrac{\sqrt{6} + \sqrt{2}}{4}$

b. $\tan 15° = \tan(45° - 30°)$

$= \dfrac{\tan 45° - \tan 30°}{1 + \tan 45° \tan 30°}$

$= \dfrac{1 - \dfrac{\sqrt{3}}{3}}{1 + (1)\left(\dfrac{\sqrt{3}}{3}\right)} \cdot \dfrac{\dfrac{3}{1}}{\dfrac{3}{1}}$

$= \dfrac{3 - \sqrt{3}}{3 + \sqrt{3}} \cdot \dfrac{3 - \sqrt{3}}{3 - \sqrt{3}}$

$= \dfrac{9 - 6\sqrt{3} + 3}{9 - 3}$

$= 2 - \sqrt{3}$

SKILL ✔ **EXERCISES 7, 11**

At times we can evaluate a trigonometric function of a sum or difference of angles without finding decimal approximations of the angles themselves.

Example 3 Evaluating a Sum or Difference

Find the exact value for each expression if α is in Q III with $\cos\alpha = -\dfrac{5}{13}$ and β is in Q II with $\sin\beta = \dfrac{3}{5}$.

a. $\cos(\alpha + \beta)$　　　　　　　**b.** $\sin(\alpha - \beta)$

Answer

$\left(-\dfrac{5}{13}\right)^2 + \sin^2\alpha = 1$　　　$\cos^2\beta + \left(\dfrac{3}{5}\right)^2 = 1$　　　1. Use $\cos^2 x + \sin^2 x = 1$ and the quadrant to find $\sin\alpha$ and $\cos\beta$. *Note:* Sketches of reference triangles could also be used to find these values.

$\sin^2\alpha = \dfrac{144}{169}$　　　　　　$\cos^2\beta = \dfrac{16}{25}$

$\sin\alpha = -\dfrac{12}{13}$　　　　　　$\cos\beta = -\dfrac{4}{5}$

$(\sin x < 0 \text{ in Q III})$　　　　$(\cos x < 0 \text{ in Q II})$

a. $\cos(\alpha + \beta) = \cos\alpha\cos\beta - \sin\alpha\sin\beta$

$= \left(-\dfrac{5}{13}\right)\left(-\dfrac{4}{5}\right) - \left(-\dfrac{12}{13}\right)\left(\dfrac{3}{5}\right)$

$= \dfrac{20}{65} + \dfrac{36}{65} = \dfrac{56}{65}$

2. Apply the cosine of a sum identity.

b. $\sin(\alpha - \beta) = \sin\alpha\cos\beta - \cos\alpha\sin\beta$

$= \left(-\dfrac{12}{13}\right)\left(-\dfrac{4}{5}\right) - \left(-\dfrac{5}{13}\right)\left(\dfrac{3}{5}\right)$

$= \dfrac{48}{65} + \dfrac{15}{65} = \dfrac{63}{65}$

3. Apply the sine of a difference identity.

SKILL ✔ **EXERCISE 17**

Example 4 Rewriting as an Algebraic Expression

Rewrite $\cos\left(\text{Tan}^{-1}\frac{3}{4} - \text{Sin}^{-1} x\right)$ as an algebraic expression.

Answer

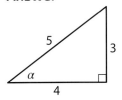

1. Draw reference triangles for $\alpha = \text{Tan}^{-1}\frac{3}{4}$ and $\beta = \text{Sin}^{-1} x$.

$\cos(\alpha - \beta) = \cos\alpha\cos\beta + \sin\alpha\sin\beta$

2. Rewrite the expression in terms of α and β and apply the cosine of a difference identity.

$= \left(\frac{4}{5}\right)\left(\sqrt{1-x^2}\right) + \left(\frac{3}{5}\right)(x)$

3. Use the reference triangles to rewrite each trig function as an algebraic expression.

$= \frac{4\sqrt{1-x^2}}{5} + \frac{3x}{5} = \frac{4\sqrt{1-x^2} + 3x}{5}$

4. Simplify.

SKILL ✓ **EXERCISE 21**

The sum and difference identities are also useful in proving other identities. Methods similar to those used in Example 2a can be used to prove other cofunction and periodic identities listed in Section 5.1. A *reduction identity* simplifies a trigonometric function of a sum or difference where one of the angles is a quadrantal angle.

Example 5 Verifying Reduction Identities

Verify each reduction identity.

a. $\sin\left(x - \frac{\pi}{2}\right) = -\cos x$

b. $\tan(270° + \theta) = -\cot\theta$

Answer

a. $\sin\left(x - \frac{\pi}{2}\right)$

$= \sin x \cos\frac{\pi}{2} - \cos x \sin\frac{\pi}{2}$

$= \sin x \cdot (0) - \cos x \cdot (1)$

$= -\cos x$

b. $\tan(270° + \theta) = \frac{\sin(270° + \theta)}{\cos(270° + \theta)}$

$= \frac{\sin 270° \cos\theta + \cos 270° \sin\theta}{\cos 270° \cos\theta - \sin 270° \sin\theta}$

$= \frac{(-1)\cos\theta + (0)\sin\theta}{(0)\cos\theta - (-1)\sin\theta}$

$= \frac{-\cos\theta}{\sin\theta} = -\cot\theta$

SKILL ✓ **EXERCISE 29**

TIP

Express $\tan(\theta + 270°)$ as $\frac{\sin(270° + \theta)}{\cos(270° + \theta)}$ since $\frac{\tan\theta - \tan 270°}{1 + \tan\theta \tan 270°}$ produces undefined values.

The sum and difference identities extend our ability to solve trigonometric equations.

Example 6   Solving a Trigonometric Equation

Find primary solutions for $\sin\left(x+\frac{\pi}{4}\right)=\cos\left(x-\frac{3\pi}{4}\right)+1$.

Answer

$$\sin x \cos\frac{\pi}{4}+\cos x \sin\frac{\pi}{4}=\cos x \cos\frac{3\pi}{4}+\sin x \sin\frac{3\pi}{4}+1$$

1. Apply the sine of a sum identity and the cosine of a difference identity.

$$(\sin x)\left(\frac{\sqrt{2}}{2}\right)+(\cos x)\left(\frac{\sqrt{2}}{2}\right)=(\cos x)\left(-\frac{\sqrt{2}}{2}\right)+(\sin x)\left(\frac{\sqrt{2}}{2}\right)+1$$

$$\sqrt{2}\cos x=1$$

2. Simplify.

$$\cos x=\frac{\sqrt{2}}{2}$$

$$x=\frac{\pi}{4},\frac{7\pi}{4}$$

3. List solutions within $[0, 2\pi)$.

SKILL ✓ EXERCISE 37

A. Exercises

Use the sum and difference identities to find the exact value of each expression.

1. $\cos\left(\frac{5\pi}{6}+\frac{\pi}{4}\right)$

2. $\sin\left(\frac{\pi}{6}+\frac{\pi}{4}\right)$

3. $\tan\left(\frac{5\pi}{6}-\frac{\pi}{4}\right)$

Use a sum or difference identity to write each expression in terms of a single trigonometric function.

4. $\sin\frac{5\pi}{3}\cos\frac{\pi}{4}-\cos\frac{5\pi}{3}\sin\frac{\pi}{4}$

5. $\cos\frac{5\pi}{4}\cos\frac{\pi}{3}+\sin\frac{5\pi}{4}\sin\frac{\pi}{3}$

6. $\dfrac{\tan\frac{\pi}{4}+\tan\frac{\pi}{6}}{1-\tan\frac{\pi}{4}\tan\frac{\pi}{6}}$

Use a sum identity to find the exact value of each expression.

7. $\cos 105°$

8. $\sin\frac{11\pi}{12}$

9. $\cos\frac{17\pi}{12}$

10. $\tan\frac{5\pi}{12}$

Use a difference identity to find the exact value of each expression.

11. $\sin\frac{\pi}{12}$

12. $\cos(15°)$

13. $\tan 165°$

14. $\cos\left(-\frac{11\pi}{12}\right)$

15. Use the cofunction identities proved in Example 1 to verify each cofunction identity below.

    a. $\tan\left(\frac{\pi}{2}-\theta\right)=\cot\theta$ **b.** $\csc\left(\frac{\pi}{2}-\theta\right)=\sec\theta$

16. Show that $\sin\left(\frac{\pi}{2}+\frac{\pi}{3}\right)\neq\sin\frac{\pi}{2}+\sin\frac{\pi}{3}$.

B. Exercises

Find the exact value for each expression if α is in Q I with $\sin\alpha=\frac{7}{25}$ and β is in Q II with $\cos\beta=-\frac{5}{13}$.

17. $\sin(\alpha+\beta)$

18. $\cos(\alpha-\beta)$

Find the exact value for each expression if α is in Q III with $\cos\alpha=-\frac{2}{3}$ and β is in Q IV with $\sin\beta=-\frac{4}{5}$.

19. $\cos(\alpha+\beta)$

20. $\tan(\alpha+\beta)$

Rewrite each trigonometric expression as an algebraic expression.

21. $\sin\left(\text{Cos}^{-1}x+\text{Tan}^{-1}\frac{\sqrt{3}}{3}\right)$

22. $\cos\left(\text{Cos}^{-1}\frac{\sqrt{3}}{2}-\text{Tan}^{-1}x\right)$

23. $\sin(\text{Arcsin }x+\text{Arccos }x)$

24. $\tan(\text{Sin}^{-1}x+\text{Tan}^{-1}x)$

25. Derive the sine of a sum identity from the sine of a difference identity.

26. Verify the tangent of a sum identity:

$$\tan(\alpha+\beta)=\frac{\tan\alpha+\tan\beta}{1-\tan\alpha\tan\beta}.$$

27. Verify the tangent of a difference identity:

$$\tan(\alpha-\beta)=\frac{\tan\alpha-\tan\beta}{1+\tan\alpha\tan\beta}.$$

28. Use a sum identity to verify each periodic identity.

    a. $\cos(\theta+2\pi)=\cos\theta$

    b. $\sin(\theta+2\pi)=\sin\theta$

    c. $\tan(\theta+\pi)=\tan\theta$

29. Use difference identities to verify the reduction identities for the supplement of an angle.

a. $\sin(\pi - \theta) = \sin\theta$

b. $\cos(\pi - \theta) = -\cos\theta$

c. $\tan(\pi - \theta) = -\tan\theta$

Verify each identity.

30. $\tan\left(x - \frac{\pi}{2}\right) = -\cot x$

31. $\sin\left(\frac{\pi}{2} - \theta\right) = \sin\left(\frac{\pi}{2} + \theta\right)$

32. $\cos(\pi - \alpha) = \cos(\pi + \alpha)$

33. $[\cos(\alpha - \beta)][\cos(\alpha + \beta)] = \cos^2\alpha - \sin^2\beta$

34. $\dfrac{\sin(\alpha - \beta)}{\sin(\alpha + \beta)} = \dfrac{\tan\alpha - \tan\beta}{\tan\alpha + \tan\beta}$

35. $\dfrac{\cos(\alpha - \beta)}{\cos(\alpha + \beta)} = \dfrac{\cot\alpha + \tan\beta}{\cot\alpha - \tan\beta}$

Find the primary solutions for each equation.

36. $\sin(\pi + x) = 1 - \sin(\pi + x)$

37. $\cos\left(x + \frac{\pi}{2}\right) = \sin^2 x$

38. $\sin\left(x - \frac{\pi}{6}\right) + \sin\left(x + \frac{7\pi}{6}\right) = \frac{1}{2}$

39. $\tan(x + \pi) = \sin(\pi - x)$

40. In an RLC circuit, the voltage across the inductor is modeled by $v_L = I_m X_L \sin\left(\omega t + \frac{\pi}{2}\right)$. Show that $v_L = V_L \cos\omega t$ is an equivalent model when the maximum voltage across an inductor is $V_L = I_m X_L$.

> **C. Exercises**

41. Use a sum identity to prove each double-angle identity.

a. $\sin 2\theta = 2\sin\theta\cos\theta$

b. $\cos 2\theta = \cos^2\theta - \sin^2\theta$

c. $\tan 2\theta = \dfrac{2\tan\theta}{1 - \tan^2\theta}$

42. Given $y_1 = m_1 x + b_1$ and $y_2 = m_2 x + b_2$ where $m_2 > m_1$ and both are positive, $\tan\alpha = m_2$ and $\tan\beta = m_1$.

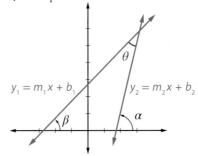

a. Express $\tan\theta$ in terms of m_1 and m_2.

b. Use the formula to find (to the nearest degree) the measure of the acute angle between $y_1 = x + 4$ and $y_2 = 4x - 10$.

43. A standing (or stationary) wave is formed when two waves having the same frequency, amplitude, and wavelength travel in opposite directions. Verify that the sum of the waves $y_1 = A_0 \sin(kx - \omega t)$ and $y_2 = A_0 \sin(kx + \omega t)$ is the standing wave $y = (2A_0 \sin kx)\cos\omega t$.

44. A function's difference quotient, $\dfrac{f(x + h) - f(x)}{h}$, is the slope of the secant line through two points of the function's graph. In calculus, it is used to examine the function's rate of change. Verify the difference quotient for the sine and cosine functions.

a. $\dfrac{\sin(x + h) - \sin x}{h}$

$= \sin x\left(\dfrac{\cos h - 1}{h}\right) + \cos x\left(\dfrac{\sin h}{h}\right)$

b. $\dfrac{\cos(x + h) - \cos x}{h}$

$= \cos x\left(\dfrac{\cos h - 1}{h}\right) - \sin x\left(\dfrac{\sin h}{h}\right)$

45. Evaluate each expression. [3.2]

   a. $\log_2 32$ **b.** $2\log_3 9$

   c. $\log 0.001$ **d.** $\ln \sqrt[3]{e}$

Write each function rule if $f(x) = 2x + 3$ and $g(x) = 2x^2 + x - 3$. [1.7]

46. $(f + g)(x)$ and $(f - g)(x)$

47. $fg(x)$

48. $\dfrac{f}{g}(x)$

49. $(f \circ g)(x)$ and $(g \circ f)(x)$

50. Use synthetic division to divide $4x^3 - 3x^2 - 15x - 18$ by $x - 3$. [2.3]

51. Which of the following is true of $f(x)$ and $g(x)$ if they are inverse functions? [1.8]

   a. $(fg)(x) = (gf)(x) = \frac{1}{x}$

   b. $(f + g)(x) = (g + f)(x) = -x$

   c. $(f \circ g)(x) = (g \circ f)(x) = x$

   d. Their graphs are reflections in the x-axis.

   e. Their graphs are reflections in the y-axis.

52. Which is not a possible zero of $f(x) = 9x^4 - 16x^3 + 24x^2 - 16$? [2.4]

   A. 2   **C.** $\dfrac{3}{8}$ **E.** $\dfrac{1}{9}$

   B. 4   **D.** $-\dfrac{4}{3}$

53. Which function is equivalent to $\cos\theta \cot\theta + \sin\theta$? [5.1]

   A. $\tan\theta$ **C.** $\sin\theta$ **E.** $\csc\theta$

   B. $\sec\theta$ **D.** $\cos\theta$

54. Find all primary solutions for $\cos\theta \cot\theta = 2\cos\theta$. [5.3]

   A. $\theta = 0, \pi$ **D.** both A and B

   B. $\theta \approx 0.464, \approx 3.605$ **E.** both B and C

   C. $\theta = \dfrac{\pi}{2}, \dfrac{3\pi}{2}$

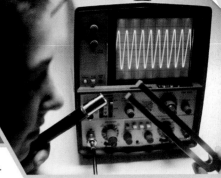

5.5 Multiple Angle Identities

The sinusoidal sound wave of a tuning fork can be viewed on an oscilloscope.

The sum identities examined in the last section are used to develop several other identities that aid in evaluating trigonometric expressions, proving even more identities, and solving trigonometric equations. The *double-angle identities* are derived by replacing α and β with θ.

$$\cos 2\theta = \cos(\theta + \theta)$$ 1. Substitute $(\theta + \theta)$ for 2θ.

$$= \cos\theta\cos\theta - \sin\theta\sin\theta$$ 2. Apply the cosine of a sum identity.

$$= \cos^2\theta - \sin^2\theta$$ 3. Simplify.

Alternate forms of this identity that use a single trigonometric function are derived by applying the Pythagorean identity. Similar derivations of the double-angle identities for sine and cosine are left as exercises.

Double-Angle Identities	
$\cos 2\theta = \cos^2\theta - \sin^2\theta$ $= 2\cos^2\theta - 1$ $= 1 - 2\sin^2\theta$	$\sin 2\theta = 2\sin\theta\cos\theta$ $\tan 2\theta = \dfrac{2\tan\theta}{1 - \tan^2\theta}$

Example 1 Applying Double-Angle Identities

If $\tan\theta = \frac{3}{2}$ and $\pi < \theta < \frac{3\pi}{2}$, find exact values for $\cos 2\theta$, $\sin 2\theta$, and $\tan 2\theta$.

Answer

$r = \sqrt{(-2)^2 + (-3)^2} = \sqrt{13}$

$\cos\theta = \dfrac{-2}{\sqrt{13}}$; $\sin\theta = \dfrac{-3}{\sqrt{13}}$ 1. Use a reference triangle to determine the ratios for $\cos\theta$ and $\sin\theta$.

$\cos 2\theta = 2\cos^2\theta - 1 = 2\left(\dfrac{-2}{\sqrt{13}}\right)^2 - 1 = -\dfrac{5}{13}$ 2. Apply double-angle identities.

$\sin 2\theta = 2\sin\theta\cos\theta = 2\left(\dfrac{-3}{\sqrt{13}}\right)\left(\dfrac{-2}{\sqrt{13}}\right) = \dfrac{12}{13}$

$\tan 2\theta = \dfrac{2\tan\theta}{1 - \tan^2\theta} = \dfrac{2\left(\frac{3}{2}\right)}{1 - \left(\frac{3}{2}\right)^2} = \dfrac{3}{-\frac{5}{4}} = -\dfrac{12}{5}$

 SKILL ✓ EXERCISE 3

The sum and double-angle identities can be used to derive other multiple-angle identities, such as $\sin 3\theta$, $\cos 4\theta$, and $\tan 6\theta$.

After completing this section, you will be able to

- derive and apply multiple-angle, power-reducing, and half-angle identities.
- solve equations using trig identities.
- derive and apply product-to-sum and sum-to-product identities.

A *hypocycloid* is a curve traced by a point on a circle as it rolls without slipping inside a circle of larger radius. An *astroid* is a hypocycloid where the ratio of the two radii is $4 : 1$. The trigonometric triple angle identity may be used to derive the formula for an astroid.

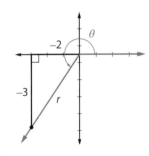

Example 2   Deriving a Triple-Angle Identity

Express $\sin 3\theta$ in terms of $\sin \theta$.

Answer

$\sin 3\theta = \sin(2\theta + \theta)$

$\qquad = \sin 2\theta \cos \theta + \cos 2\theta \sin \theta$

1. Express 3θ as a sum and apply the sine of a sum identity.

$\qquad = (2 \sin \theta \cos \theta) \cos \theta + (1 - 2 \sin^2 \theta) \sin \theta$

$\qquad = 2 \sin \theta \cos^2 \theta + \sin \theta - 2 \sin^3 \theta$

2. Substitute using double-angle identities and simplify.

$\qquad = 2 \sin \theta (1 - \sin^2 \theta) + \sin \theta - 2 \sin^3 \theta$

$\qquad = 2 \sin \theta - 2 \sin^3 \theta + \sin \theta - 2 \sin^3 \theta$

$\qquad = -4 \sin^3 \theta + 3 \sin \theta$

3. Substitute using a Pythagorean identity and simplify.

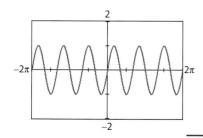

Check

The graphs of $Y_1 = \sin(3X)$ and $Y_2 = -4(\sin(X))^3 + 3 \sin(X)$ appear to be identical.

SKILL ✓ **EXERCISE 17**

Power-reducing identities are derived from double-angle identities. For example, solving $\cos 2\theta = 1 - 2 \sin^2 \theta$ for $\sin^2 \theta$ produces $\sin^2 \theta = \dfrac{1 - \cos 2\theta}{2}$.

Power-Reducing Identities		
$\sin^2 \theta = \dfrac{1 - \cos 2\theta}{2}$	$\cos^2 \theta = \dfrac{1 + \cos 2\theta}{2}$	$\tan^2 \theta = \dfrac{1 - \cos 2\theta}{1 + \cos 2\theta}$

Example 3   Reducing a Power

Express $\sin^4 \theta$ in terms with no power greater than 1.

Answer

$\sin^4 \theta = (\sin^2 \theta)^2$

1. Express x^4 as $(x^2)^2$.

$\qquad = \left(\dfrac{1 - \cos 2\theta}{2}\right)^2$

$\qquad = \dfrac{1 - 2 \cos 2\theta + \cos^2 2\theta}{4}$

2. Apply the sine power-reducing identity and expand the power.

$\qquad = \dfrac{1}{4} - \dfrac{1}{2} \cos 2\theta + \dfrac{1}{4}\left(\dfrac{1 + \cos 2(2\theta)}{2}\right)$

$\qquad = \dfrac{1}{4} - \dfrac{1}{2} \cos 2\theta + \dfrac{1}{8} + \dfrac{1}{8} \cos 4\theta$

$\qquad = \dfrac{1}{8}(3 - 4 \cos 2\theta + \cos 4\theta)$

3. Apply the cosine power-reducing identity and simplify.

SKILL ✓ **EXERCISE 21**

Half-angle identities are derived by replacing θ with $\dfrac{\theta}{2}$ in the power-reducing identities and taking the square root of both sides. The sign of the square root is determined by the quadrant in which $\dfrac{\theta}{2}$ lies.

$$\sin^2 \dfrac{\theta}{2} = \dfrac{1 - \cos 2\left(\dfrac{\theta}{2}\right)}{2}$$

$$\sin \dfrac{\theta}{2} = \pm\sqrt{\dfrac{1 - \cos \theta}{2}}$$

A hypocycloid where the ratio of the radii is 2 : 1 converts circular motion into linear motion. In the nineteenth century, this kind of hypocycloid was a proposed solution to converting the linear motion of a steam engine into circular motion. Hypocycloids are used today to design optimal gear shapes.

Half-Angle Identities

$$\sin \frac{\theta}{2} = \pm\sqrt{\frac{1-\cos\theta}{2}}$$

$$\cos \frac{\theta}{2} = \pm\sqrt{\frac{1+\cos\theta}{2}}$$

$$\tan \frac{\theta}{2} = \pm\sqrt{\frac{1-\cos\theta}{1+\cos\theta}}$$
$$= \frac{1-\cos\theta}{\sin\theta}$$
$$= \frac{\sin\theta}{1+\cos\theta}$$

Example 4 Applying Half-Angle Identities

Find the exact value of each expression.

a. $\sin \frac{\pi}{8}$ **b.** $\cos \frac{7\pi}{12}$ **c.** $\tan \frac{5\pi}{12}$

Answer

a. $\sin \frac{\pi}{8}$

$= \sin \frac{\left(\frac{\pi}{4}\right)}{2}$

$= \pm\sqrt{\frac{1-\cos\frac{\pi}{4}}{2}}$

$= \sqrt{\frac{1-\left(\frac{\sqrt{2}}{2}\right)}{2}}$

$= \sqrt{\frac{2-\sqrt{2}}{4}}$

$= \frac{\sqrt{2-\sqrt{2}}}{2}$

b. $\cos \frac{7\pi}{12}$

$= \cos \frac{\left(\frac{7\pi}{6}\right)}{2}$

$= \pm\sqrt{\frac{1+\cos\frac{7\pi}{6}}{2}}$

$= -\sqrt{\frac{1+\left(-\frac{\sqrt{3}}{2}\right)}{2}}$

$= -\sqrt{\frac{2-\sqrt{3}}{4}}$

$= -\frac{\sqrt{2-\sqrt{3}}}{2}$

c. $\tan \frac{5\pi}{12}$

$= \tan \frac{\left(\frac{5\pi}{6}\right)}{2}$

$= \frac{1-\cos\frac{5\pi}{6}}{\sin\frac{5\pi}{6}}$

$= \frac{1-\left(-\frac{\sqrt{3}}{2}\right)}{\left(\frac{1}{2}\right)}$

$= 2+\sqrt{3}$

1. Rewrite the angle as half of a special angle.

2. Apply a half-angle identity. Note that $\sin \frac{\pi}{8} > 0$ since it is in Q I, and $\cos \frac{7\pi}{12} < 0$ since it is in Q II.

3. Simplify.

SKILL ✓ EXERCISE 9

TIP 💡

Evaluating $\cos \frac{7\pi}{12}$ as
$\cos\left(\frac{3\pi}{12} + \frac{4\pi}{12}\right)$
produces $\frac{\sqrt{2}-\sqrt{6}}{4}$.
Your calculator can be used to verify that
this and $\frac{\sqrt{2-\sqrt{3}}}{2}$ are
equivalent expressions
for $\cos \frac{7\pi}{12}$.

```
cos(7π/12)
                -0.2588190451
-√2-√3 /2
                -0.2588190451
(√2-√6)/4
                -0.2588190451
■
```

These identities provide additional tools for solving trigonometric equations.

Example 5 Solving Equations with a Double-Angle Identity

Find primary solutions for $\sin 2x = \cos x$.

Answer

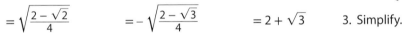

$\sin 2x = \cos x$

$2\sin x \cos x = \cos x$

1. Use a double-angle identity to substitute for $\sin 2x$.

$2\sin x \cos x - \cos x = 0$

$\cos x (2\sin x - 1) = 0$

$\cos x = 0$ or $\sin x = \frac{1}{2}$

$x = \frac{\pi}{2}, \frac{3\pi}{2}, \frac{\pi}{6}, \frac{5\pi}{6}$

2. Collect the terms on one side, factor, and solve using the Zero Product Property.

SKILL ✓ EXERCISE 13

Example 6 Solving Equations with a Half-Angle Identity

Find the general solution for $\cos \frac{x}{2} = \sin x$.

Answer

$$\cos \frac{x}{2} = \sin x$$

$$\left(\pm \sqrt{\frac{1 + \cos x}{2}} \right)^2 = \sin^2 x$$

$$\frac{1 + \cos x}{2} = \sin^2 x$$

$$1 + \cos x = 2(1 - \cos^2 x)$$

$$2 \cos^2 x + \cos x - 1 = 0$$

$$(2 \cos x - 1)(\cos x + 1) = 0$$

$$\cos x = \frac{1}{2} \quad \text{or} \quad \cos x = -1$$

$$x = \frac{\pi}{3}, \frac{5\pi}{3}, \frac{7\pi}{3}, \frac{11\pi}{3} \quad \text{or} \quad x = \pi, 3\pi$$

$$\cos \frac{\pi}{6} = \sin \frac{\pi}{3} \qquad \cos \frac{5\pi}{6} = \sin \frac{5\pi}{3}$$

$$\cos \frac{7\pi}{6} \neq \sin \frac{7\pi}{3} \qquad \cos \frac{11\pi}{6} \neq \sin \frac{11\pi}{3}$$

$$\cos \frac{\pi}{2} = \sin \pi \qquad \cos \frac{3\pi}{2} = \sin 3\pi$$

$$x = \frac{\pi}{3} + n4\pi, \frac{5\pi}{3} + n4\pi, (2n+1)\pi; n \in \mathbb{Z}$$

Check

1. Use a half-angle identity to substitute for $\cos \frac{x}{2}$ and square both sides.
   Recall that this step may introduce extraneous solutions.

2. Use a Pythagorean identity to express the equation as a quadratic in terms of $\cos x$. Then collect the terms on one side and factor.

3. Since $\cos \frac{x}{2}$ has period $p = \frac{2\pi}{\left|\frac{1}{2}\right|} = 4\pi$, list all solutions within $[0, 4\pi)$.

4. Substitute each answer into the original equation to identify the extraneous solutions $\frac{7\pi}{3}$ and $\frac{11\pi}{3}$.

5. State the general solution.

6. Use technology to verify the solution.

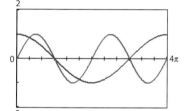

SKILL ✓ EXERCISE 25

Product-to-sum and sum-to-product identities are used to rewrite and evaluate certain trigonometric expressions. Each of the following product-to-sum identities can be verified by applying the sum and difference identities to simplify the right side of the equation.

Product-to-Sum Identities	
$\sin \alpha \sin \beta = \frac{1}{2}[\cos(\alpha - \beta) - \cos(\alpha + \beta)]$	$\sin \alpha \cos \beta = \frac{1}{2}[\sin(\alpha + \beta) + \sin(\alpha - \beta)]$
$\cos \alpha \cos \beta = \frac{1}{2}[\cos(\alpha - \beta) + \cos(\alpha + \beta)]$	$\cos \alpha \sin \beta = \frac{1}{2}[\sin(\alpha + \beta) - \sin(\alpha - \beta)]$

Example 7   Expressing a Product as a Sum

Rewrite $\sin 4x \cos 3x$ as a sum or difference.

Answer

$\sin 4x \cos 3x = \frac{1}{2}[\sin (4x + 3x) - \sin (4x - 3x)]$ 1. Apply the appropriate product-to-sum identity.

$\qquad\qquad = \frac{1}{2}[\sin 7x - \sin x]$ 2. Simplify.

$\qquad\qquad = \frac{1}{2} \sin 7x - \frac{1}{2} \sin x$

 SKILL ✓ **EXERCISE 31**

The Spirograph®, a geometric drawing toy developed in the 1960s, made generating cycloidal curves easy and fun. This toy aptly demonstrates our ability to appreciate mathematical beauty even without fully understanding the underlying mathematics.

Sum-to-Product Identities	
$\sin \alpha + \sin \beta = 2 \sin \dfrac{\alpha + \beta}{2} \cos \dfrac{\alpha - \beta}{2}$	$\cos \alpha + \cos \beta = 2 \cos \dfrac{\alpha + \beta}{2} \cos \dfrac{\alpha - \beta}{2}$
$\sin \alpha - \sin \beta = 2 \cos \dfrac{\alpha + \beta}{2} \sin \dfrac{\alpha - \beta}{2}$	$\cos \alpha - \cos \beta = -2 \sin \dfrac{\alpha + \beta}{2} \sin \dfrac{\alpha - \beta}{2}$

Notice how the first sum-to-product identity is verified using the appropriate product-to-sum identity to simplify the right side of the equation.

$$2 \sin \frac{\alpha + \beta}{2} \cos \frac{\alpha - \beta}{2} = 2\left\{ \frac{1}{2}\left[\sin \left(\frac{\alpha + \beta}{2} + \frac{\alpha - \beta}{2} \right) + \sin \left(\frac{\alpha + \beta}{2} - \frac{\alpha - \beta}{2} \right) \right] \right\}$$

$$= \sin \left(\frac{2\alpha}{2} \right) + \sin \left(\frac{2\beta}{2} \right)$$

$$= \sin \alpha + \sin \beta$$

Example 8   Evaluating a Sum

Find the exact value of $\cos \frac{13\pi}{12} - \cos \frac{5\pi}{12}$.

Answer

$\cos \dfrac{13\pi}{12} - \cos \dfrac{5\pi}{12} = -2 \sin \dfrac{\frac{13\pi}{12} + \frac{5\pi}{12}}{2} \sin \dfrac{\frac{13\pi}{12} - \frac{5\pi}{12}}{2}$ 1. Apply the appropriate sum-to-product identity.

$\qquad\qquad = -2 \sin \dfrac{3\pi}{4} \sin \dfrac{\pi}{3}$ 2. Simplify.

$\qquad\qquad = -2\left(\dfrac{\sqrt{2}}{2} \right)\left(\dfrac{\sqrt{3}}{2} \right) = -\dfrac{\sqrt{6}}{2}$

SKILL ✓ **EXERCISE 35**

Example 9 Solving an Equation with a Sum-to-Product Identity

Find the general solution for $\sin 3x - \sin 5x = 0$.

Answer

$$\sin 3x - \sin 5x = 0$$
$$2 \cos \frac{3x + 5x}{2} \sin \frac{3x - 5x}{2} = 0$$
$$2 \cos 4x \sin (-x) = 0$$

1. Apply the appropriate sum-to-product identity.

$\cos 4x = 0 \quad$ or $\quad \sin (-x) = 0$
$$\sin x = 0$$
$$4x = \frac{\pi}{2} + n\pi \qquad x = n\pi$$
$$x = \frac{\pi}{8} + \frac{n\pi}{4}$$

2. Solve using the Zero Factor Property.

Check

3. Identify the zeros of the graph of $y = \sin 3x - \sin 5x$.

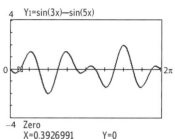

SKILL ✔ **EXERCISE 39**

》 A. Exercises

1. Derive each double-angle identity.
  a. $\sin 2\theta$ **b.** $\tan 2\theta$

2. Use $\cos 2\theta = \cos^2 \theta - \sin^2 \theta$ to derive each identity.
  a. $\cos 2\theta = 2 \cos^2 \theta - 1$ **b.** $\cos 2\theta = 1 - 2 \sin^2 \theta$

Find the exact values of cos 2θ, sin 2θ, and tan 2θ using the given information.

3. $\cos \theta = -\frac{3}{5}$ and $\frac{\pi}{2} < \theta < \pi$

4. $\sin \theta = -\frac{2}{3}$ and $270° < \theta < 360°$

5. $\tan \theta = \frac{\sqrt{3}}{3}$ and $180° < \theta < 270°$

6. $\sin \theta = \frac{5}{13}$ and $\frac{\pi}{2} < \theta < \pi$

7. Derive each power-reducing identity.
  a. $\cos^2 \theta$ **b.** $\tan^2 \theta$

8. Derive each half-angle identity.
  a. $\cos \frac{\theta}{2} = \pm \sqrt{\frac{1 + \cos \theta}{2}}$ **b.** $\tan \frac{\theta}{2} = \pm \sqrt{\frac{1 - \cos \theta}{1 + \cos \theta}}$

Use a half-angle identity to find the exact value of each expression.

9. $\sin \frac{\pi}{8}$ **10.** $\tan \frac{7\pi}{8}$

11. $\cos 112.5°$ **12.** $\cos \frac{5\pi}{12}$

Find the primary solutions of each equation.

13. $\sin 2x = \sin x$

14. $\sin 2x + \cos x = 0$

15. $\cos 2x + \cos x + 1 = 0$

16. $2 \sin^2 x + 2 \sin x + \cos 2x = 2$

》 B. Exercises

Derive each multiple-angle identity.

17. Express $\cos 3\theta$ in terms of $\cos \theta$.

18. Express $\tan 3\theta$ in terms of $\tan \theta$.

19. Express $\cos 4\theta$ in terms of $\cos \theta$.

20. Verify that $\sin 4\theta = 4 \cos^3 \theta \sin \theta - 4 \sin^3 \theta \cos \theta$.

Use power-reducing identities to rewrite each expression in terms with no power greater than 1.

21. $\sin^3 \theta$ **22.** $\cos^4 \theta$

23. $\tan^4 \theta$ **24.** $\sin^2 \theta \cos^2 \theta$

Find the general solutions of each equation. Verify your answers graphically.

25. $2 \cos \frac{x}{2} - 1 = \cos x$ **26.** $\sin \frac{x}{2} = \cos x$

27. $\sin^2 \frac{x}{2} - \sin^2 x = 0$ **28.** $\tan \frac{x}{2} = \tan^2 \frac{x}{2}$

29. Verify each product-to-sum identity.
  a. $\sin \alpha \cos \beta = \frac{1}{2}[\sin (\alpha + \beta) + \sin (\alpha - \beta)]$
  b. $\sin \alpha \sin \beta = \frac{1}{2}[\cos (\alpha - \beta) - \cos (\alpha + \beta)]$

30. Verify each sum-to-product identity.
  a. $\cos \alpha - \cos \beta = -2 \sin \frac{\alpha + \beta}{2} \sin \frac{\alpha - \beta}{2}$
  b. $\sin \alpha - \sin \beta = 2 \cos \frac{\alpha + \beta}{2} \sin \frac{\alpha - \beta}{2}$

Rewrite each expression as a sum or difference.

31. $\cos 3x \cos 2x$

32. $\cos 9x \sin (-5x)$

33. $\sin (a - b) \cos (a + b)$

Find the exact value of the expression.

34. $\cos 75° - \cos 15°$

35. $\sin 105° - \sin 15°$

36. $\sin \frac{3\pi}{4} + \sin \frac{\pi}{4}$

37. A musical instrument can be tuned by listening to the combined sound of a tuning fork and the instrument and eliminating any "beat" caused by slightly different frequencies. If the sound waves produced by the instrument and the tuning fork are modeled by $y_1 = A_0 \cos 2\pi f_1 t$ and $y_2 = A_0 \cos 2\pi f_2 t$, respectively, express the resultant wave $y = y_1 + y_2$ as a product.

Find the general solution of each equation. Verify your answers graphically.

38. $\cos 3\theta - \cos \theta = 0$

39. $\sin \theta - \sin 3\theta = 0$

40. $\dfrac{\sin \theta}{\cos 3\theta - \cos \theta} = 1$

Verify each identity.

41. $2 \sin^2 x - 1 = \sin^4 x - \cos^4 x$

42. $\csc 2x = \dfrac{1 + \tan^2 x}{2 \tan x}$

43. $\dfrac{\sin 3x}{\sin x} - \dfrac{\cos 3x}{\cos x} = 2$

44. $\cos^3 x - \sin^3 x = (\cos x - \sin x)\left(1 + \frac{1}{2}\sin 2x\right)$

C. Exercises

45. Use half-angle identities to find the exact value of each expression.

 a. $\cos \dfrac{\pi}{12}$ **b.** $\cos \dfrac{\pi}{24}$

46. Express $\sin 5\theta$ in terms of $\sin \theta$.

47. Given $\tan \dfrac{\theta}{2} = \pm\sqrt{\dfrac{1 - \cos \theta}{1 + \cos \theta}}$, derive $\tan \dfrac{\theta}{2} = \dfrac{1 - \cos \theta}{\sin \theta}$.

 a. Show that $\tan \dfrac{\theta}{2} = \pm\left|\dfrac{1 - \cos \theta}{\sin \theta}\right|$.

 b. What is the range of $f(x) = 1 - \cos \theta$?

 c. Graph $\sin \theta$ and $\tan \dfrac{\theta}{2}$ in the same window and compare the signs of the functions.

 d. Use the answers to parts b and c to explain why $\pm\left|\dfrac{1 - \cos \theta}{\sin \theta}\right| = \dfrac{1 - \cos \theta}{\sin \theta}$.

48. Solve $\cos 3x + \cos x = \cos 2x$.

CUMULATIVE REVIEW

49. State the slope and the x- and y-intercepts of $3x - 2y = -12$. [1.2]

50. Find the standard form equation of the line perpendicular to $2x + 5y = 9$ going through $(4, 6)$. [1.2]

51. Given $\triangle ABC$ where $m\angle C = 90°$, $a = 8$, and $b = 15$, find c. [4.2]

52. Find the area of isosceles $\triangle XYZ$ if $m\angle Z = 70°$. [4.2]

53. State the period and frequency of $f(x) = 3 \cos (-\pi x) + 5$. [4.4]

54. Write the equation of a cosine function with an amplitude of 3, a period of π, and a relative maximum at $(0, 4)$. [4.4]

55. If $P(x) \div (x - 7)$ has a remainder of 0, what can we conclude? [2.3]

 A. $P(7) = 0$ **D.** both B and C
 B. $P(-7) = 0$ **E.** both A and C
 C. $x - 7$ is a factor of $P(x)$.

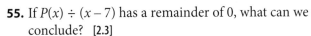

56. Find $\tan \theta$ if $\sin \theta = -\frac{3}{5}$ and $\cos \theta > 0$. [4.3]

 A. $\frac{4}{5}$ **C.** $\frac{3}{4}$ **E.** $-\frac{4}{3}$

 B. $\frac{4}{3}$ **D.** $-\frac{3}{4}$

57. Find $\sin \theta$ if $\sec \theta = -\frac{8}{5}$ and $\tan \theta < 0$. [5.1]

 A. $\frac{\sqrt{15}}{4}$ **C.** $\frac{3}{8}$ **E.** $\frac{39}{64}$

 B. $\frac{\sqrt{39}}{8}$ **D.** $\frac{\sqrt{255}}{16}$

58. Find the exact value of $\sin 105°$. [5.4]

 A. $\frac{\sqrt{3}}{2}$ **C.** $\frac{\sqrt{6} - \sqrt{2}}{4}$ **E.** $\frac{6 - \sqrt{2}}{4}$

 B. $\frac{\sqrt{3}}{4}$ **D.** $\frac{\sqrt{6} + \sqrt{2}}{4}$

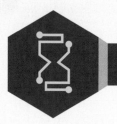
HARMONIC ANALYSIS

A host of eminent eighteenth-century mathematicians tried to describe the motion of a vibrating string and failed. In 1753 Daniel Bernoulli proposed a solution to the vibrating string problem consisting of an infinite trigonometric series. Leonhard Euler, the most respected mathematics authority of the time, declared him wrong, but in 1807 Bernoulli's solution was definitively proved by Joseph Fourier.

Fourier, who had considered becoming a Benedictine monk in his younger years, spoke of math revealing "an unchangeable order which presides over all natural causes." He was convinced that all complex natural processes are subject to a few simple laws which may be discerned through careful observation and experimentation. Motivated particularly by the success of Isaac Newton's universal laws of motion and gravity, Fourier sought universal laws for heat. His explorations led to the development of what is today called the *Fourier series*. He demonstrated that any function could be described by an infinite trigonometric series—even functions that are discontinuous and not "well behaved." The study of functions that can be represented by the Fourier series is called harmonic analysis.

Fourier's proposal, that simple sine functions could be combined to describe functions of wildly varying properties, seemed so counterintuitive that it took over a quarter of a century to convince the skeptics. During this process, even

the definition of a mathematical function was revised and functions with no possible graphical representation were discovered.

By the middle of the nineteenth century, scientists such as Michael Faraday were beginning to explore the wavelike qualities of electromagnetism. In 1873 James Clerk Maxwell combined the well-known experimentally derived results of Faraday's law and Ampere's law into a set of eight complex mathematical equations that explained how electric and magnetic fields work. He determined that electromagnetic waves travel at the same speed as light—and therefore these waves and visible light were actually two cases of the same phenomenon.

In 1886, seven years after Maxwell's death, Heinrich Hertz first proved the existence of the radio waves predicted by Maxwell. The Italian inventor Guglielmo Marconi then created a commercially successful wireless telegraph. Wireless telegraph operators began to be deployed aboard large cruise liners in the early 1900s. The ship that rescued survivors of the *Titanic* disaster in 1912 was summoned by onboard wireless operators employed by the Marconi Company.

Though some would trace the origins of harmonic analysis back to Pythagoras's musical theories or Ptolemy's planetary cycles and epicycles, its real power was not realized until Fourier discovered the efficacy of an infinite trigonometric series to describe natural phenomena. In her book *The Evolution of Applied Harmonic Analysis: Models of the Real World*, Elena Prestini provides examples of current applications of harmonic analysis in signal processing, computerized music, radio astronomy, and magnetic resonance imaging (MRI). In the preface to this book, Ronald Bracewell states, "Why exact mathematics, a product of the human mind, should have proved so useful in science and technology, remains a mystery."

COMPREHENSION CHECK

1. Which problem baffled many prominent eighteenth-century mathematicians but was solved by Daniel Bernoulli?

2. Who eventually proved Bernoulli's solution to be correct?

3. Who combined previous experimental results into eight equations describing electrical and magnetic fields?

4. What prediction of electromagnetic theory did Heinrich Hertz prove in 1886?

5. Name two current applications of harmonic analysis.

6. **Discuss:** Explain the worldview indicated by the quote from Ronald Bracewell.

5.6 Law of Sines

Pilots study trigonometry as an aid to navigation.

After completing this section, you will be able to
- prove the Law of Sines.
- solve triangles using the Law of Sines.
- identify the number of possible solutions for a triangle.

In Section 4.2 we solved right triangles. In the last two sections of this chapter, you will learn how to solve *oblique* triangles, those that do not contain a right angle. The *Law of Sines* is used to solve the unique triangle determined by the measures of two angles and the included side (ASA) or the measure of two angles and a side opposite one of the angles (AAS). It is also used to find any possible solutions when you know the measures of two sides and an angle opposite one of the known sides (SSA).

▌ LAW OF SINES

For $\triangle ABC$ with sides of length a, b, and c opposite angles A, B, and C, respectively,

$$\frac{a}{\sin A} = \frac{b}{\sin B} = \frac{c}{\sin C}.$$

To derive this identity, consider the acute and obtuse cases of $\triangle ABC$ with its altitude from B. In both triangles, $\sin A = \frac{h}{c}$ and $h = c \sin A$. In the acute triangle $\sin C = \frac{h}{a}$, and in the obtuse triangle $\sin (\pi - C) = \frac{h}{a}$. But $\sin (\pi - \theta) = \sin \theta$, so $\sin C = \frac{h}{a}$ and $h = a \sin C$ in both cases.

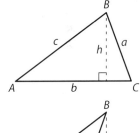

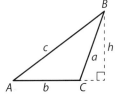

Therefore $c \sin A = a \sin C$, and $\dfrac{c}{\sin C} = \dfrac{a}{\sin A}$.

Similar reasoning with altitudes drawn from A produces $\dfrac{c}{\sin C} = \dfrac{b}{\sin B}$.

By the Transitive Property, $\dfrac{a}{\sin A} = \dfrac{b}{\sin B} = \dfrac{c}{\sin C}$.

Because the reciprocals of equal ratios are equal, the Law of Sines can also be written as

$$\frac{\sin A}{a} = \frac{\sin B}{b} = \frac{\sin C}{c}.$$

When two angles of a triangle are known, the third angle can be quickly determined. A known side length and the Law of Sines can then be used to find the other two side lengths.

Example 1   Solving the AAS Case

Solve $\triangle ABC$ if $A = 34°$, $B = 76°$, and $a = 9$ cm. Round lengths to the nearest tenth.

Answer

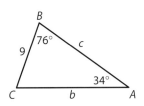

1. Make a sketch of the triangle.

$C = 180° - A - B$

$= 180 - 34 - 76 = 70°$

2. Determine C.

CONTINUED ➡

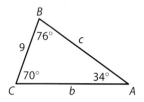

$$\frac{b}{\sin B} = \frac{a}{\sin A}$$

$$\frac{b}{\sin 76°} = \frac{9}{\sin 34°}$$

$$b = \frac{9 \sin 76°}{\sin 34°} \approx 15.6 \text{ cm}$$

$$\frac{c}{\sin C} = \frac{a}{\sin A}$$

$$\frac{c}{\sin 70°} = \frac{9}{\sin 34°}$$

$$c = \frac{9 \sin 70°}{\sin 34°} \approx 15.1 \text{ cm}$$

3. Substitute into the portion of the Law of Sines involving an unknown side length and the known side length.

4. Solve for b.

5. Substitute into the portion of the Law of Sines involving the other unknown side length and the given side length.

SKILL ✓ EXERCISE 9

Example 2 Solving the ASA Case

Johan and Wesley stand 360 ft apart on a level football field to observe the flight of a rocket from opposite sides. If Johan records a 72° angle of elevation to the apex of the flight path and Wesley records an 81° angle of elevation, determine the distance from the rocket to each observer and the height of the rocket's flight.

Answer

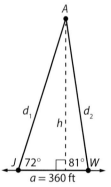

1. Make and label a sketch.

$$A = 180 - 72 - 81 = 27°$$

2. Determine A.

$$\frac{d_1}{\sin W} = \frac{a}{\sin A} \qquad \frac{d_2}{\sin J} = \frac{a}{\sin A}$$

$$d_1 = \frac{a \sin W}{\sin A} \qquad d_2 = \frac{a \sin J}{\sin A}$$

$$= (360 \text{ ft}) \frac{\sin 81°}{\sin 27°} \qquad = (360 \text{ ft}) \frac{\sin 72°}{\sin 27°}$$

$$\approx 783 \text{ ft} \qquad \approx 754 \text{ ft}$$

3. Use the Law of Sines to find the distance to A from each observer.

$$\sin J = \frac{h}{d_1},$$

so $h = d_1 \sin J \approx 783 \sin 72° \approx 745 \text{ ft}$

4. Use right-triangle trigonometry to find the height of the rocket's flight.

SKILL ✓ EXERCISE 7

Regiomontanus stated the Law of Sines in his major work, *On Triangles*, written in 1464. The geometric proof uses inscribed triangles and demonstrates that the ratio of each side length to the sine of the opposite angle equals twice the radius of the circumscribed circle. (See exercises 41–42.)

Two side lengths and the measure of an angle opposite one of those sides (SSA) do not determine a unique triangle. Since these measures may describe one, two, or no possible triangles, SSA is known as the *ambiguous case*. Examine the following possibilities when given $\angle A$ and lengths a and b.

The Ambiguous Case: SSA		
Obtuse or Right ∠A	**Acute ∠A ($h = b \sin A$)**	
One Triangle	**One Triangle**	
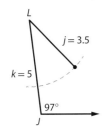 $a > b$	$a \geq b$	$a = h$
No Triangle	**Two Triangles**	**No Triangle**
$a \leq b$	$h < a < b$	$a < h$

When examining the ambiguous case, make a sketch similar to the illustrated possibilities with the angle, its adjacent side as the side above the horizontal ray, its opposite side, and the possible height h when the angle is acute.

Example 3 Determining the Number of Possible Triangles for SSA

Determine the number of possible triangles in each case.

a. $\triangle JKL$ if $j = 3.5$, $k = 5$, and $J = 97°$

b. $\triangle XYZ$ if $x = 4$, $z = 5$, and $Z = 55°$

c. $\triangle EFG$ if $f = 5$, $g = 2.5$, and $G = 30°$

Answer

a. Sketch obtuse ∠J, side k, and side j.

Since $j \leq k$, there is no possible $\triangle JKL$.

b. Sketch acute ∠Z, side x, and side z.

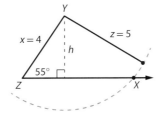

Since $z \geq x$, there is only one $\triangle XYZ$.

c. Sketch acute ∠G, side f, and side g.

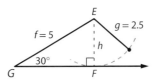

$h = f \sin G$
  $= 5 \sin 30° = 2.5$

Since $g = h$, there is only one $\triangle FGH$.

SKILL ✓ **EXERCISES 17, 19**

Attempting to use the Law of Sines to solve $\triangle JKL$ in Example 3a quickly reveals that no solution is possible.

$$\frac{\sin K}{5} = \frac{\sin 97°}{3.5}; \therefore \sin K = \frac{5 \sin 97°}{3.5} \approx 1.4, \text{ but } \sin K \text{ must be within } [-1, 1].$$

The Law of Sines can also show that there is only one possible $\triangle XYZ$ in Example 3*b*.

$$\frac{\sin X}{4} = \frac{\sin 55°}{5}, \therefore \sin X = \frac{4 \sin 55°}{5} \approx 0.6553 \text{ and}$$

$X \approx 41°$ or $\approx 139°$ (an acute angle and its supplement have the same sine value). But $\triangle XYZ$ cannot have $Z = 55°$ and $X = 139°$ since $55° + 139° > 180°$. Example 4 illustrates how the Law of Sines is applied when there are two possible triangles.

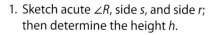

Example 4   Solving the Ambiguous Case

Solve $\triangle RST$ if $r = 3$ in., $s = 5$ in., and $R = 26°$.

Answer

$h = s \sin R = 5 \sin 26° \approx 2.192$

1. Sketch acute $\angle R$, side s, and side r; then determine the height h.

Since $h < r < s$, there are 2 possible triangles.

2. Determine the number of possible triangles.

using $\frac{\sin S}{s} = \frac{\sin R}{r}$:

$$\frac{\sin S}{5} = \frac{\sin 26°}{3}$$

$$\sin S = \frac{5(\sin 26°)}{3} \approx 0.7306$$

$$S \approx 46.9° \text{ or}$$

$$S \approx 180 - 46.9 = 133.1°$$

3. Apply the Law of Sines to find the two possible measures for S.

   The calculator's $\sin^{-1}$ function returns the principal value in Q I, which is also the reference angle used to find the obtuse angle (in Q II) with the same sine value, its supplement.

If $S \approx 46.9°$...

$$T \approx 180 - 26 - 46.9$$
$$= 107.1°$$

If $S \approx 133.1°$...

$$T \approx 180 - 26 - 133.1$$
$$= 20.9°$$

4. Solve both possible triangles.

   a. Find possible measures of T.

$$\frac{t}{\sin 107.1°} = \frac{3}{\sin 26°}$$

$$t \approx \frac{3 \sin 107.1°}{\sin 26°} \approx 6.5 \text{ in.}$$

$$\frac{t}{\sin 20.9°} = \frac{3}{\sin 26°}$$

$$t \approx \frac{3 \sin 20.9°}{\sin 26°} \approx 2.4 \text{ in.}$$

   b. Use $\frac{t}{\sin T} = \frac{r}{\sin R}$ to find the possible values for t.

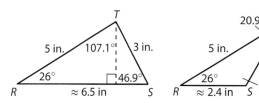

SKILL ✓ **EXERCISE 21**

You have seen how the Law of Sines can be applied to solve a unique triangle determined by two angle measures and a side length (AAS or ASA) and how it can be used to find all possible solutions for the ambiguous case (SSA). Section 5.7 shows how the Law of Cosines is used to solve the unique triangle described by three side lengths (SSS) or by the measures of two sides and the included angle (SAS). Recall from GEOMETRY that any two angles of a triangle determine the third angle (AA implies AAA) and an infinite number of similar triangles.

TECHNOLOGY CORNER (INTERACTIVE GEOMETRY SOFTWARE)

Interactive geometry software such as The Geometer's Sketchpad® or Geogebra® can be used to explore the Law of Sines and other trigonometric relationships. Use technology to complete the following steps.

1. Open a new file and construct $\triangle ABC$.

2. Measure each side length and each angle.

3. Calculate the ratio of each side length and the sine of the angle opposite that side.

4. Construct the triangle's circumcenter, D, by finding the intersection of perpendicular lines drawn through the midpoints of two sides. Then construct the circumscribed circle.

5. Measure the radius of the circle and calculate its diameter.

6. Compare the ratios to the diameter of the circle.

7. Drag the vertices to change the triangle's shape. Does $\dfrac{a}{\sin A} = \dfrac{b}{\sin B} = \dfrac{c}{\sin C} = 2r$ in all cases?

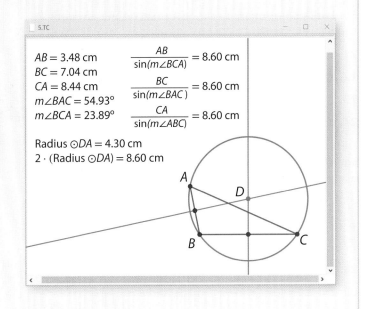

A. Exercises

1. Identify each case as ASA, AAS, or SSA.
   a. $a = 5$, $B = 48°$, $A = 68°$
   b. $a = 7$, $c = 2$, $\angle C = 12°$
   c. $R = 12°$, $S = 106°$, $t = 10$
   d. $x = 2$, $y = 5$, $X = 15°$

2. Identify each case as ASA, AAS, SSA, or SAS.
   a. $a = 9$, $A = 57°$, $c = 12$
   b. $A = 70°$, $c = 16$, $C = 37°$
   c. $j = 3$, $k = 7$, $L = 40°$
   d. $p = 7$, $\angle Q = 26°$, $\angle R = 42°$

Solve each triangle. Round answers to the nearest tenth.

3.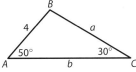

4.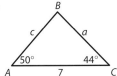

5.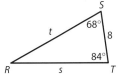

6.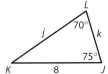

Sketch and solve each triangle. Round answers to the nearest tenth.

7. $\triangle ABC$ with $A = 52°$, $B = 49°$, and $c = 16$

8. $\triangle ABC$ with $C = 43°$, $B = 61°$, and $b = 9$

9. $\triangle DEF$ with $D = 23°$, $F = 42°$, and $d = 7$

10. $\triangle PQR$ with $Q = 26°$, $R = 51°$, and $p = 9$

Solve each triangle. (These SSA cases each have one solution.) Round answers to the nearest tenth.

11.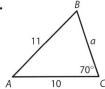

12.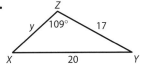

13. $\triangle LMN$ with $m = 18$, $n = 9$, and $M = 82°$

14. $\triangle ABC$ with $a = 11$, $b = 8$, and $A = 46°$

B. Exercises

Determine the number of possible triangles that satisfy the given information.

15. $\triangle ABC$ with $A = 78°$, $B = 46°$, and $c = 11$

16. $\triangle ABC$ with $A = 124°$, $a = 8$, and $b = 10$

17. $\triangle ABC$ with $A = 124°$, $a = 13$, and $c = 10$

18. $\triangle FGH$ with $F = 61°$, $f = 10$, and $g = 8$

5.6 LAW OF SINES   273

19. $\triangle FGH$ with $F = 61°$, $f = 8$, and $g = 10$

20. $\triangle FGH$ with $F = 61°$, $f = 9$, and $g = 10$

Find both solutions for each SSA case. Round answers to the nearest tenth.

21. $\triangle ABC$ with $A = 17°$, $a = 3$, and $b = 6$

22. $\triangle ABC$ with $B = 32°$, $b = 6$, and $c = 8$

23. $\triangle FGH$ with $H = 46°$, $g = 6$, and $h = 5$

24. $\triangle LMN$ with $L = 60°$, $l = 8$, and $m = 9$

Determine the number of solutions for each case, then solve each possible triangle. Round answers to the nearest tenth.

25. $\triangle ABC$ with $A = 12°$, $C = 89°$, and $a = 9$

26. $\triangle ABC$ with $B = 82°$, $b = 12$, and $c = 6$

27. $\triangle ABC$ with $B = 80°$, $a = 6$, and $b = 2$

28. $\triangle ABC$ with $C = 15°$, $a = 14$, and $c = 12$

29. $\triangle DEF$ with $E = 67°$, $d = 1.2$, and $e = 4$

30. $\triangle GHK$ with $K = 100°$, $g = 8$, and $k = 6$

31. $\triangle PQR$ with $Q = 33°$, $p = 8$, and $q = 4.4$

32. $\triangle SUV$ with $S = 62°$, $V = 95°$, and $u = 9$

33. Prove: Copy the acute and obtuse cases of $\triangle ABC$ used in the proof of the Law of Sines on page 269. Then draw the altitude from A in each triangle and show that $\dfrac{c}{\sin C} = \dfrac{b}{\sin B}$.

34. If a regular octagon has sides 4.2 cm long, use the Law of Sines to find the distance from its center to a vertex.

35. The Georgetown Lighthouse is 17.8 mi northeast of the lighthouse on Cape Romain. If the Georgetown light keeper noticed a boat in distress at $37°30'$ from the shoreline between the lighthouses, and the Cape Romain light keeper noticed the same boat at $17°15'$ from the same shoreline, find the boat's distance from each lighthouse.

36. To avoid thunderstorms, a pilot flies 70 mi on a path $15°$ north of the direct route from Atlanta, GA, to Charlotte, NC. How many degrees south must he turn from his current heading if the plane is now 178 mi from its destination?

> **C. Exercises**

37. Calculate the height of a tree if Kenneth measures a $20°$ angle of elevation from the ground to the top of the tree and Andrew measures a $33°$ angle of elevation when standing on the opposite side of the tree 300 ft from Kenny.

38. Find the height of a windmill if the afternoon sun shining at a $55°$ angle of elevation casts a 21.9 ft shadow directly down the $10°$ slope on which the windmill stands.

39. Fire tower 2 is located 19 km from fire tower 1 at a bearing of $96°$. A fire is located at a bearing of $157°$ from tower 1 and $202°$ from tower 2. Find the distance of the fire from each tower.

40. A 120 ft water tower is set on a vertical cliff next to a river so that the angle of depression from the top of the tower to a boat dock on the opposite side of the river is $29°15'$ and the angle of depression from the base of the tower to the dock is $17°22'$. Determine the width of the river and the height of the cliff.

41. Prove: Use acute $\triangle ABC$ and circumscribed $\odot M$ to prove that $\dfrac{a}{\sin A} = \dfrac{b}{\sin B} = \dfrac{c}{\sin C} = 2r$.

a. Explain why $m\angle B = \frac{1}{2}m\angle AMC$.

b. Explain why $m\angle B = \theta$.

c. Use $\triangle AMN$ to express $\sin B$ in terms of r and b.

d. Show that $\dfrac{a}{\sin A} = \dfrac{b}{\sin B} = \dfrac{c}{\sin C} = 2r$.

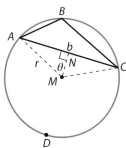

42. Prove: Use obtuse $\triangle ABC$ and circumscribed $\odot M$ to prove $\dfrac{a}{\sin A} = \dfrac{b}{\sin B} = \dfrac{c}{\sin C} = 2r$.

a. Find $m\angle B$ in terms of $m\angle AMC$. Hint: Use $\overset{\frown}{AC}$.

b. Express $m\angle B$ in terms of θ.

c. Use $\triangle AMN$ to express $\sin B$ in terms of r and b.

d. Show that $\dfrac{a}{\sin A} = \dfrac{b}{\sin B} = \dfrac{c}{\sin C} = 2r$.

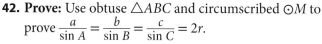

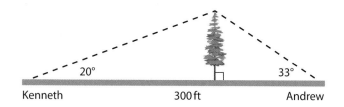

Simplify each expression. [5.1]

43. $\sin^2 \theta \csc \theta \tan \left(\frac{\pi}{2} - \theta \right)$

44. $\dfrac{\cot x + \tan x}{\sec^2 x}$

45. Verify $\tan \theta \sin \theta + \cos \theta = \sec \theta$. [5.2]

46. State the primary solutions for $3 \sin x = \cos x$ (to the nearest hundredth). [5.3]

47. State the primary solutions for $\sin x \tan x = \sin x$. [5.3]

48. Find the exact value of $\cos 15°$. [5.4]

49. Solve $\dfrac{2b}{ab + c} = 4$ for b. [2.6]

A. $b = \dfrac{2c}{2a - 1}$

D. $b = \dfrac{c}{a - 1}$

B. $b = \dfrac{2c}{1 - 2a}$

E. none of these

C. $b = \dfrac{c}{2a - 1}$

50. If $\log_b 5 = x$ and $\log_b 4 = y$, what is $\log_b 100$? [3.3]

A. $x^2 + y$

D. $2xy$

B. $x^2 y$

E. none of these

C. $2x + y$

51. Describe the measure of central $\angle C$ that subtends an arc whose length is half the circle's diameter. [4.1]

A. $m\angle C = 1$

D. $m\angle C > 90°$

B. $m\angle C = \dfrac{\pi}{4}$

E. cannot be determined

C. $m\angle C = 90°$

52. A carpenter braces a wall with a 6 ft board that extends from the floor to a point that is 4 ft 6 in. high on the wall. Which expression represents the angle between the brace and the floor? [4.2]

A. $\sin \dfrac{4.6}{6}$

D. $\cos^{-1} \dfrac{4.5}{6}$

B. $\cos \dfrac{4.5}{6}$

E. $\sin^{-1} \dfrac{4.5}{6}$

C. $\sin^{-1} \dfrac{4.6}{6}$

Using Heron's formula is the easiest method for calculating areas of triangular lots.

After completing this section, you will be able to

- prove the Law of Cosines.
- solve triangles using the Law of Cosines.
- find the area of oblique triangles.

Before calculators were widely available, the Law of Tangents was often used instead of the Law of Cosines since it required less use of logarithmic tables. Now that calculators are commonplace, the Law of Tangents is rarely included in textbooks.

While the Law of Sines is used to solve triangles when given ASA, AAS, or SSA, the Law of Cosines is used when you know the lengths of all three sides (SSS) or the measures of two sides and the included angle (SAS).

The Law of Cosines can be derived by placing $\triangle ABC$ so that A is at the origin and $\overline{AB}$ is on the positive x-axis. Draw the altitude from C to the x-axis as illustrated and note that the coordinates of C are $x = b \cos A$ and $y = b \sin A$. Then apply the Pythagorean Theorem.

$$
\begin{aligned}
a^2 &= (c - x)^2 + y^2 \\
&= c^2 - 2cx + x^2 + y^2 \\
&= c^2 - 2c(b \cos A) + (b \cos A)^2 + (b \sin A)^2 \\
&= c^2 - 2cb \cos A + b^2(\cos^2 A + \sin^2 A) \\
&= c^2 - 2cb \cos A + b^2 \\
&= b^2 + c^2 - 2bc \cos A
\end{aligned}
$$

Similar proofs that place B and C at the origin produce two other forms of this identity.

LAW OF COSINES

For $\triangle ABC$ with side lengths a, b, and c opposite angles A, B, and C, respectively,
$$a^2 = b^2 + c^2 - 2bc \cos A,$$
$$b^2 = a^2 + c^2 - 2ac \cos B, \text{ and}$$
$$c^2 = a^2 + b^2 - 2ab \cos C.$$

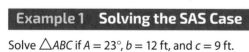

Example 1   Solving the SAS Case

Solve $\triangle ABC$ if $A = 23°$, $b = 12$ ft, and $c = 9$ ft.

Answer

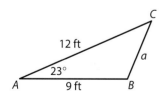

$a^2 = b^2 + c^2 - 2bc \cos A$
$\quad = 12^2 + 9^2 - 2(12)(9)(\cos 23°)$
$a^2 \approx 26.17$
$\quad a \approx 5.1$

1. Sketch $\triangle ABC$.

2. Find a by applying the Law of Cosines.

$\dfrac{\sin C}{9} \approx \dfrac{\sin 23°}{5.1}$

$\sin C \approx \dfrac{9 \sin 23°}{5.1} \approx 0.6874$

$\quad C \approx 43.4°$

3. Use $\dfrac{\sin C}{c} = \dfrac{\sin A}{a}$ to find the smaller of the two remaining angles, which must be acute.

$B \approx 180 - 23 - 43.4 = 113.6°$

4. Determine the measure of $\angle B$.

SKILL ✓ **EXERCISE 1**

Instead of using the Law of Sines to find the smaller angle in step 3 above, the Law of Cosines can be used to find either angle. Solving $a^2 = b^2 + c^2 - 2bc \cos A$ for $\cos A$ is helpful in this case and when solving the SSS case.

$$2bc \cos A = b^2 + c^2 - a^2$$

$$\cos A = \frac{b^2 + c^2 - a^2}{2bc}$$

Similarly, $\cos B = \dfrac{a^2 + c^2 - b^2}{2ac}$ and $\cos C = \dfrac{a^2 + b^2 - c^2}{2ab}$.

Example 2 Solving the SSS Case

Solve $\triangle FDG$ if $f = 8$, $d = 4$, and $g = 10$.

Answer

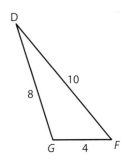

1. Sketch the triangle.

$$\cos G = \frac{f^2 + d^2 - g^2}{2fd}$$
$$= \frac{8^2 + 4^2 - 10^2}{2(8)(4)}$$
$$= -0.3125$$
$$G \approx 108.2°$$

2. Since you are given lengths for three sides of the triangle (SSS), use the Law of Cosines to find the measure of the angle opposite the largest side.

using $\dfrac{\sin F}{f} = \dfrac{\sin G}{g}$,

$$\frac{\sin F}{8} \approx \frac{\sin 108.2°}{10}$$

$$\sin F \approx \frac{8 \sin 108.2°}{10} \approx 0.7599$$

$$F \approx 49.5°$$

3. Find a second angle using either the Law of Cosines or the Law of Sines.

$D \approx 180 - 108.2 - 49.5 = 22.3°$

4. Find the measure of $\angle D$ by subtraction.

SKILL ✓ EXERCISE 3

TIP 💡

Many problems can be solved by making a sketch of an oblique triangle, labeling the known parts, and then applying the Law of Sines or the Law of Cosines to solve for the desired parts of the triangular model.

Initially finding the largest angle with the Law of Cosines guarantees that the other two angles must be acute.

Example 3 Triangulating a Location

An emergency call is made 5.6 mi from one cell tower and 2.7 mi from a second cell tower located 4 mi south of the first. State the two possible headings from the second cell tower for the location of the emergency call.

Answer

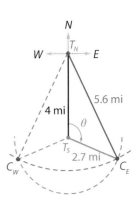

1. Sketch the locations of the towers and the two points 5.6 mi from the northern tower T_N and 2.7 mi from the southern tower T_S.

$$\cos \theta = \frac{4^2 + 2.7^2 - 5.6^2}{2(4)(2.7)} \approx -0.3736$$
$$\theta \approx 111.9°$$

2. Use the Law of Cosines to find θ, the heading to the point southeast of the towers.

$360 - 111.9 = 248.1°$

3. Determine the heading to the second point that is southwest of the towers.

SKILL ✓ EXERCISE 29

The distance from a third cell tower that is not on the same north-south line as the first two would be used to determine the exact location of the emergency call.

Formulas can be derived for the area of a triangle in terms of two side lengths and the measure of the included angle (SAS). When $\angle C$ and sides a and b are known, $\sin C = \frac{h}{a}$ and $h = a \sin C$. Substituting for h in $Area = \frac{1}{2}bh$ produces the formula $Area = \frac{1}{2}ab \sin C$. Similar reasoning can be applied to derive any of the three forms of this equation.

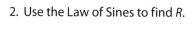

SAS Triangle Area Formulas		
$Area = \frac{1}{2}ab \sin C$	$Area = \frac{1}{2}bc \sin A$	$A = \frac{1}{2}ac \sin B$

When the given information involves SAA, AAS, or ASA, use the Law of Sines to find the additional side or angle before applying an SAS triangle area formula.

Example 4 Applying the SAS Triangle Area Formula

Find the area of $\triangle PQR$.

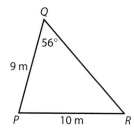

Answer

Since $q > r$, there is only one possible triangle.

1. Determine the number of possible triangles.

$\frac{\sin R}{9} = \frac{\sin 56°}{10}$

2. Use the Law of Sines to find R.

$\sin R = \frac{9 \sin 56°}{10} \approx 0.7461$

$R \approx 48.3°$

$P \approx 180 - 56 - 48.3 = 75.7°$

3. Find P.

$A = \frac{1}{2}rq \sin P$

4. Apply the SAS triangle area formula.

$\approx \frac{1}{2}(9)(10) \sin 75.7° \approx 43.6 \text{ m}^2$

SKILL ✓ **EXERCISE 13**

To find the area when all three side lengths of a triangle are known (SSS), you could use the Law of Cosines to find an angle and then apply an SAS triangle area formula. Heron's formula provides a quick alternative.

HERON'S FORMULA

The area of a triangle having sides of length a, b, and c is given by
$Area = \sqrt{s(s-a)(s-b)(s-c)}$ where the triangle's *semiperimeter* $s = \frac{1}{2}(a + b + c)$.

A proof of the formula uses an algebraic expression for sin C that is derived from a Pythagorean identity, the Law of Cosines, and some clever algebraic manipulations.

$$\sin C = \sqrt{1 - \cos^2 C} = \sqrt{1 - \left(\frac{a^2 + b^2 - c^2}{2ab}\right)^2} = \frac{\sqrt{4a^2b^2 - (a^2 + b^2 - c^2)^2}}{2ab}$$

substituting into $Area = \frac{1}{2}ab \sin C$:

$$Area = \frac{1}{2}ab \frac{\sqrt{4a^2b^2 - (a^2 + b^2 - c^2)^2}}{2ab}$$

$$= \frac{1}{4}\sqrt{4a^2b^2 - (a^2 + b^2 - c^2)^2}$$

$$= \frac{1}{4}\sqrt{[2ab - (a^2 + b^2 - c^2)][2ab + (a^2 + b^2 - c^2)]}$$

$$= \frac{1}{4}\sqrt{[c^2 - (a^2 - 2ab + b^2)][(a^2 + 2ab + b^2) - c^2]}$$

$$= \frac{1}{4}\sqrt{[c^2 - (a - b)^2][(a + b)^2 - c^2]}$$

$$= \sqrt{\frac{(c - (a - b))(c + (a - b))((a + b) - c)((a + b) + c)}{16}}$$

$$= \sqrt{\frac{(c + b - a)}{2} \cdot \frac{(c + a - b)}{2} \cdot \frac{(a + b - c)}{2} \cdot \frac{(a + b + c)}{2}}$$

noting that $2s = a + b + c$:

$$Area = \sqrt{\frac{(c + b - a - a + a)}{2} \cdot \frac{(c + a - b - b + b)}{2} \cdot \frac{(a + b - c - c + c)}{2} \cdot \frac{(a + b + c)}{2}}$$

$$= \sqrt{\frac{(2s - 2a)}{2} \cdot \frac{(2s - 2b)}{2} \cdot \frac{(2s - 2c)}{2} \cdot \frac{(2s)}{2}}$$

$$= \sqrt{s(s - a)(s - b)(s - c)}$$

Thankfully, the application of Heron's formula is much easier than its proof!

More than 10,000 civil aviation bird strikes are reported each year in the United States. The Law of Cosines can be used to explore the effects of glancing blows when an aircraft strikes a bird in flight.

Example 5 Applying Heron's Formula

A developer desires to purchase a triangular lot with 1100 ft of frontage on Main Street, 820 ft of frontage on Acadia Drive, and 638 ft of frontage on Rutherford Road. Calculate the acreage of the lot. (1 acre = 43,560 ft^2)

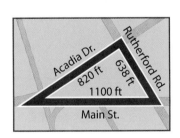

Answer

$s = \frac{1}{2}(1100 + 820 + 638) = 1279$ ft   1. Determine the lot's semiperimeter.

$Area = \sqrt{1279(1279 - 1100)(1279 - 820)(1279 - 638)}$ 2. Apply Heron's formula.
$\approx 259{,}536$ ft^2

$259{,}536 \text{ ft}^2\left(\frac{1 \text{ acre}}{43{,}560 \text{ ft}^2}\right) \approx 5.96$ acres   3. Convert to acres.

SKILL ✔ **EXERCISE 15**

A. Exercises

Solve each triangle. Round answers to the nearest tenth.

1.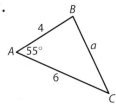

2.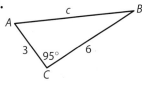

3.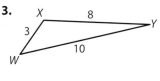

4.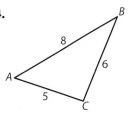

Solve each △ABC. Round answers to the nearest tenth.

5. $a = 9$, $b = 13$, and $C = 28°$

6. $b = 26$, $c = 18$, and $A = 64°$

7. $a = 52$, $b = 47$, and $c = 64$

8. $a = 35$, $b = 22$, and $c = 25$

Solve each △XYZ. Round measures to the nearest tenth.

9. $x = 6$, $y = 10$, and $Z = 60°$

10. $y = 31$, $z = 20$, and $X = 42.5°$

11. $x = 11$, $y = 9$, and $z = 14$

12. $x = 17$, $y = 21.2$, and $z = 13$

Find the area of each triangle.

13.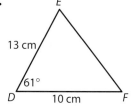

14.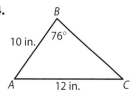

15. Find the area of △PQR using Heron's formula.

16. Find the area of △PQR using the Law of Cosines and the SAS triangle area formula.

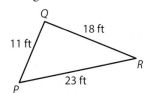

17. Use the given measurements to find the indicated distance across the swamp.

18. An investor knows the lengths of two sides of a triangular lot, but thick woods prevent her from measuring the third side. If she measures θ as $87°$, calculate the length of the third side (to the nearest foot).

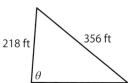

B. Exercises

Use the Law of Sines or the Law of Cosines to solve each △ABC. Round measures to the nearest tenth.

19. $a = 7$, $b = 9$, $c = 10$

20. $A = 57°$, $B = 31°$, $b = 9$

21. $A = 24°$, $C = 103°$, $b = 8$

22. $C = 38°$, $a = 13$, $b = 9$

23. $C = 43°$, $a = 12$, $c = 9$

24. $a = 17.4$, $b = 15$, $c = 24.2$

Find the area of each triangle (to the nearest tenth).

25. △ABC with $a = 9$ cm, $b = 14$ cm, and $C = 36°$

26. △PQR with $p = 27$ m, $q = 31$ m, and $r = 40$ m

27. △XYZ with $x = 38$ in., $y = 21$ in., and $z = 47$ in.

28. △DEF with $D = 31°$, $f = 12$ m, $d = 6.2$ m

29. Find the length of the diagonals of a parallelogram with adjacent sides of 10 cm and 7.2 cm if the measure of its acute angles is $56°$.

30. A baseball diamond is a square with sides measuring 90 ft. Find the distance of the fielder's throw to third base after catching a ball hit 360 ft from home plate to straightaway center field (directly over second base).

31. A surveyor is positioned 418 ft from one end of a proposed mountain tunnel and 371 ft from the other end. If he measures a $69°$ angle between the sight lines to the ends of the tunnel, how long will the tunnel be?

32. A radio antenna sits at the edge of a 200 ft tall cliff. A fisherman on the sea below the cliff records a $21°$ angle of elevation to the top of the antenna while a friend at the bottom of the antenna records a $10°$ angle of depression to the fisherman. What is the height of the antenna?

33. A boat is located 5 km from one buoy and 14 km from a second buoy anchored 10 km east of the first buoy. Find the boat's two possible bearings from the first buoy.

34. The Flatiron Building in New York City is famous for its triangular shape. Find the area of its base if its sides measure 190 ft, 173 ft, and 87 ft.

35. Offices at the tip of the Flatiron Building (described in exercise 34) are much sought after because they offer spectacular views. Calculate the measure of the smallest angle formed by the building's outer walls.

36. Given $\triangle ABC$, find x.

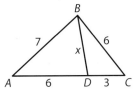

37. Prove: Copy the figure and use it to derive the Law of Cosines, $c^2 = a^2 + b^2 - 2ab \cos C$.

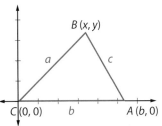

38. Prove: Copy the figure and use it to derive the Law of Cosines, $b^2 = a^2 + c^2 - 2ac \cos B$.

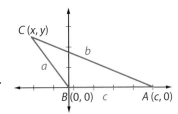

› **C. Exercises**

39. The illustrated rectangular shipping box is 3 ft wide, 4 ft long, and 2 ft high. Find the measure of $\angle CAB$.

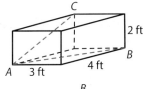

40. Cyclic quadrilaterals can be inscribed in a circle and have supplementary opposite angles. Find the lengths of the diagonals BD and AC of cyclic quadrilateral $ABCD$.

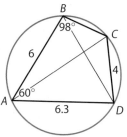

41. While the Law of Sines is commonly used to solve the SSA case, an alternative solution applies the Law of Cosines and solves the resulting quadratic equation. Use the Law of Cosines to find side c in $\triangle ABC$ if $a = 9$, $b = 12$, and $B = 60°$.

42. Find the exact value of a in $\triangle ABC$ with $A = 60°$,
$$c = \frac{1}{\sqrt{6} + \sqrt{2}}, \text{ and } b = \frac{1}{\sqrt{6} - \sqrt{2}}.$$

CUMULATIVE REVIEW

43. Determine the account balance of a $10,000 investment compounded monthly at 5% interest for 7 yr. [3.1]

44. Evaluate $\log_2 \frac{1}{16}$ [3.2]

45. Solve $3^{2x+3} = 5^{2x}$. [3.4]

46. Determine if each equation is an identity. If not, explain. [2.1, 5.1]

   a. $\sqrt{x^2} = x$ **b.** $\sqrt[3]{x^3} = x$

47. Solve $\sqrt{2x+3} - 1 = \sqrt{3x-5}$. [2.1]

48. State the period of $f(x) = g(x) + h(x)$ if $g(x) = \sin 3x$ and $h(x) = 2 \cos 3x$. [4.7]

49. Find $\cos \theta$. [4.2]

   A. $\frac{3}{7}$ **D.** $\frac{\sqrt{58}}{7}$

   B. $\frac{7}{3}$ **E.** $\frac{4\sqrt{10}}{7}$

   C. $\frac{2\sqrt{10}}{7}$

50. Which value of x produces a relative minimum for $g(x) = 2 \sin 2x$? [4.4]

   A. $\frac{\pi}{4}$ **C.** $\frac{\pi}{2}$ **E.** π

   B. $\frac{3\pi}{8}$ **D.** $\frac{3\pi}{4}$

51. Determine the number of possible triangles that exist for $\triangle ABC$ with $A = 60°$, $a = 7$, and $b = 8$. [5.6]

   A. 0   **C.** 2   **E.** > 3

   B. 1   **D.** 3

52. Which expression represents YZ in $\triangle XYZ$? [5.6]

   A. $YZ = \frac{33 \sin 56°}{\sin 27°}$

   B. $YZ = \frac{33 \sin 27°}{\sin 56°}$

   C. $YZ = \frac{33 \sin 97°}{\sin 56°}$

   D. $YZ = \frac{33 \sin 56°}{\sin 97°}$

   E. cannot be determined

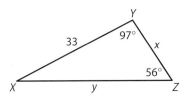

Refraction, Reflection, and Fiber Optics

Ancient scientists recognized that light generally travels in a straight line but its path bends (or *refracts*) as it crosses a boundary from one medium into another. A classic experiment compares the angle of incidence θ_i, which is measured from the *normal* (the line drawn perpendicular to the boundary),

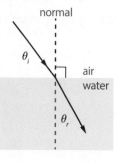

to the angle of refraction θ_r, which is also measured from the normal. Ptolemy is attributed with compiling the following table of data (ca. AD 140) for light crossing the boundary from air into water.

θ_i	10°	20°	30°	40°	50°	60°	70°	80°
θ_r	8.0°	15.5°	22.5°	29.0°	35.0°	40.5°	45.5°	50.0°

1. Examine the data and describe a general relationship between the angles as they pass from air (a less dense medium) to water (a denser medium).

2. Use technology to perform a quadratic regression on the data. State the quadratic function that models the data. What is the correlation coefficient?

Inaccuracies in the actual angles of refraction and the high correlation from the regression suggest that Ptolemy may have modified or created data to fit a quadratic model. In 1621 the Dutch astronomer and mathematician Willebrord Snell provided a more accurate model for the refraction of light.

Snell's law: $n_i \sin \theta_i = n_r \sin \theta_r$ where n is an experimentally determined constant for each medium, called the *index of refraction*.

The refractive index for a vacuum is defined as 1, and every other medium has $n > 1$. Since the refractive index of air ≈ 1.003, it is often rounded to 1. Water has a refractive index of 1.33.

3. Find each angle of refraction θ_r (to the nearest tenth of a degree) when light travels from air into water with the given angle of incidence.

   a. $\theta_i = 40°$ **b.** $\theta_i = 80°$

4. Find each angle of refraction θ_r (to the nearest tenth of a degree) when light travels from water (denser) into air (less dense) with the given angle of incidence.

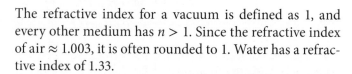
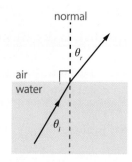

   a. $\theta_i = 40°$

   b. $\theta_i = 45°$

5. When light travels from a medium with a higher refractive index (denser) into a medium of lower index (less dense), does it bend toward or away from the normal?

6. Find each angle of incidence θ_i (to the nearest tenth of a degree) that produces the given angle of refraction when light travels from water into air.

   a. $\theta_r = 80°$ **b.** $\theta_r = 90°$

7. Explain why Snell's law cannot predict an angle of refraction into air for an incident light ray in water with $\theta_i = 50°$.

When light travels from a medium with a higher refractive index into a medium with a lower refractive index, the *critical angle* is the angle of incidence that produces a 90° angle of refraction. The critical angle θ_c for light rays leaving water and entering air is found by solving $n_{water} \sin \theta_c = n_{air} \sin 90°$. An incident light ray in water at

$$\theta_c = \sin^{-1} \frac{n_{air}}{n_{water}} = \sin^{-1} \frac{1}{1.33} \approx 48.8°$$ is refracted along the water-air boundary, 90° from the normal.

Incident light rays whose angle of incidence is larger than the critical angle are not refracted but are instead reflected back into the originating medium. In the case of a stream of water surrounded by air, light projected into the stream with $\theta_i > 48°$ will be reflected at the water-air boundary and travel within the path of the water. This phenomenon, known as total internal reflection, was used to create spectacular luminous fountains that amazed visitors at the Universal Exposition in Paris in 1889.

Today, total internal reflection helps to transmit gigabits of data per second through fiber-optic cables—tiny glass strands clad with materials having a lower index of refraction. The first transatlantic fiber-optic cable became operational in 1988. The critical angle θ_c of an optical fiber is calculated using Snell's law and the refractive indices of the fiber's core and cladding.

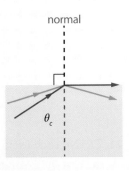

8. Find the critical angle for each fiber-optic cable.
   a. core with $n_1 = 1.5$ and cladding with $n_2 = 1.485$
   b. core with $n_1 = 1.52$ and cladding with $n_2 = 1.45$

9. Derive a formula for the critical angle of a fiber-optic cable whose core has a refractive index of n_1 and whose cladding has a refractive index of n_2.

"And God said, Let there be light: and there was light. And God saw the light, that it was good" (Gen. 1:3–4). Life on the earth depends on light. Our knowledge has also led to amazing applications of light, such as laser beams and fiber optics. We save money and reduce recovery time by using lasers in medical procedures. We transmit digital information over the Internet at tremendous speeds. It is appropriate to praise the Creator for His good creation. In fact, the consistency of light reflects God's goodness and faithfulness as the Father of Lights, who shows no variation (James 1:17).

Chapter 5 Review

1. Use the basic Pythagorean identity to derive $\tan^2\theta + 1 = \sec^2\theta$. [5.1]

2. If $\sec\theta = \frac{3}{2}$ and $\sin\theta < 0$, find $\sin\theta$ and $\tan\theta$.

3. Use the even/odd identity to evaluate each expression. [5.1]

   a. If $\sin x = 0.866$, find $\sin(-x)$.

   b. If $\cos x = 0.5$, find $\sec(-x)$.

4. Use a cofunction identity to complete the following. [5.1]

   a. Rewrite $\cos\frac{5\pi}{12}$ in terms of sine.

   b. Find $\cot\left(\theta - \frac{\pi}{2}\right)$ if $\tan\theta = \sqrt{2} - 1$.

Write each expression in terms of a single trigonometric function. [5.1]

5. $\sin^2 x - \cos^2 x \sin^2 x$

6. $\dfrac{1 + \cot^2\theta}{\cot^2\theta}$

7. $\cos x + \tan x \sin x$

8. $\dfrac{\sin\theta}{\csc\theta + 1} + \dfrac{\sin\theta}{\csc\theta - 1}$

Verify each identity. [5.2]

9. $\dfrac{\cos x}{1 + \sin x} - \dfrac{\cos x}{1 - \sin x} = -2\tan x$

10. $\tan^2\theta \sec^2\theta - \tan^2\theta = \tan^4\theta$

11. $\dfrac{\sin\theta}{1 + \cos\theta} = \dfrac{1 - \cos\theta}{\sin\theta}$

12. $(\sec\theta - \tan\theta)^2 = \dfrac{1 - \sin\theta}{1 + \sin\theta}$

13. $\tan^5 x = \tan x - 2\tan x \sec^2 x + \tan x \sec^4 x$

Find all primary solutions of each equation. [5.3]

14. $2\cos\theta + 1 = 0$

15. $4\sin^2\theta = 3$

16. $2\cot x \sin x - \sqrt{3}\cot x = 2\sin x - \sqrt{3}$

17. $4\cos^2 x = 7\cos x + 2$ (to the nearest hundredth)

18. $2\sin 2x + \sqrt{3} = 0$

Find the general solution for each equation. [5.3]

19. $\tan x + 1 = \sec x$

20. $4\tan^2 x + 5\tan x = 6$ (to the nearest hundredth)

21. Derive each identity. [5.4]

   a. Use the cosine of a difference identity to derive the cosine of a sum identity.

   b. Prove the cofunction identity $\cos\left(\frac{\pi}{2} - x\right) = \sin x$.

   c. Derive the sine of the sum of two angles.

Find the exact value of each expression. [5.4]

22. $\sin\left(\frac{5\pi}{6} - \frac{\pi}{4}\right)$ 23. $\cos\frac{11\pi}{12}$ 24. $\tan\frac{5\pi}{12}$

25. Find the exact value of $\sin(\alpha + \beta)$ if α and β are in Q II with $\sin\alpha = \frac{1}{3}$ and $\cos\beta = -\frac{3}{4}$. [5.4]

26. Rewrite $\sin\left(\operatorname{Tan}^{-1}\frac{4}{3} - \operatorname{Cos}^{-1} x\right)$ as an algebraic expression. [5.4]

27. Verify $\tan(\pi - \theta) = -\tan x$. [5.4]

28. Find all primary solutions of
   $\sin\left(x - \frac{\pi}{6}\right) = \cos\left(x + \frac{\pi}{3}\right) + 1$. [5.4]

29. Derive the following identities. [5.5]

   a. Derive $\cos 2x = 2\cos^2 x - 1$.

   b. Then derive the identity for $\cos^2 x$.

   c. Then derive the identity for $\cos\frac{x}{2}$.

Find the exact value of each expression if $\tan\theta = -\frac{3}{4}$ and $\frac{\pi}{2} \le \theta < \pi$. [5.5]

30. Find $\sin 2\theta$, $\cos 2\theta$, and $\tan 2\theta$.

31. Find $\sin\frac{\theta}{2}$, $\cos\frac{\theta}{2}$, and $\tan\frac{\theta}{2}$.

Find the exact value of each expression. [5.5]

32. $\cos\frac{7\pi}{12}$ 33. $\sin\frac{\pi}{12}\cos\frac{13\pi}{12}$

Find the general solution for each equation. [5.5]

34. $\sin 2x + \sin x = 0$

35. $\cos\frac{x}{2} = \sin x$

36. $\dfrac{\sin\theta}{\sin 3\theta - \sin\theta} = 1$

Verify each identity. [5.5]

37. $\sin 3x + \sin x = 2\sin 2x \cos x$

38. $\dfrac{\sin 2x}{1 + \cos 2x} = \dfrac{1 - \cos 2x}{\sin 2x}$

Solve each triangle. Round answers to the nearest tenth. [5.6–5.7]

39. $\triangle ABC$: $B = 25°$, $C = 70°$, $a = 8$

40. $\triangle PQR$: $P = 42°$, $r = 9$, $q = 7$

41. $\triangle WXY$: $Y = 42°$, $y = 2$, $w = 5$

42. $\triangle MNO$: $M = 50°$, $N = 36°$, $n = 6$

43. $\triangle PQR$: $p = 4$, $q = 7$, $r = 10$

44. $\triangle JKL$: $K = 110°$, $j = 7$, $k = 10$

45. $\triangle ABC$: $B = 13°$, $b = 6$, $c = 10$

Find the area of each triangle. [5.7]

46.

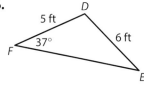

47.

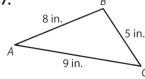

48. A jungle pilot flies 100 mi west and then makes a 20° adjustment to the north to avoid a storm. After he has flown for 70 mi on the adjusted course, how far is he from the original airstrip? [5.7]

49. Grace and Marie both observe a camera-equipped drone hovering over a community event. Find the height of the drone if they are standing 200 ft apart and measure angles of elevation from the ground to the drone as 25° and 12° when the drone is directly between them. [5.6]

50. A lost hiker is 2 km from the trailhead and 5 km from a ranger station 4 km due east of the trailhead. Find the hiker's two possible bearings from the trailhead. [5.7]

6 Vectors, Polar Graphs, and Complex Numbers

BIBLICAL PERSPECTIVE OF MATHEMATICS

Which types of reasoning are used to discover and verify mathematical truths?

HISTORICAL CONNECTION

While vectors and polar coordinates are often presented before operations with complex numbers, the development of vectors lagged behind the development of complex numbers by about 200 years.

DATA ANALYSIS

While some mathematicians studied operations thought to exist solely in the mind of man, these operations led to fractals, which are used to describe natural patterns occurring all around us and even inside of us.

Vectors in the Plane

Vector diagrams are used extensively in kinematics, the study of motion.

Quantities that can be measured using real numbers are *scalar* quantities. Both a mass of 20 kg and a volume of 250 cm^3 are scalar quantities. Other quantities that are described by both a number and a direction, such as a force applied to an object, its acceleration, or its velocity, are *vector* quantities. A 20 mph wind from the southeast or a 10 lb force pulling up on an object are vector quantities.

These quantities can be modeled with directed line segments called *vectors*. The vector with an *initial point* (or *tail*) at $P(x_1, y_1)$ and a *terminal point* (or *head*) at $Q(x_2, y_2)$ is notated $\overrightarrow{PQ}$ because it has the length of $\overline{PQ}$ and the direction of $\overrightarrow{PQ}$.

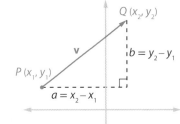

Vectors can also be named in printed text by a bold lowercase letter such as **v**, or in handwritten text by $\vec{v}$.

Vectors are frequently broken down into their horizontal and vertical *components*.
$$\mathbf{v} = \langle a, b \rangle \text{ where } a = x_2 - x_1 \text{ and } b = y_2 - y_1$$
This notation allows vectors anywhere in the plane to be translated to an equal vector in *standard position*, one having its initial point at the origin. Two vectors are equal if they have the same magnitude and direction. When expressed in terms of their components, $\mathbf{u} = \langle u_1, u_2 \rangle$ and $\mathbf{v} = \langle v_1, v_2 \rangle$ are equal if and only if $u_1 = v_1$ and $u_2 = v_2$.

After completing this section, you will be able to

- describe vectors in the coordinate plane.
- perform vector operations of addition, subtraction, and scalar multiplication.
- write a vector as a linear combination of unit vectors.
- solve real-world problems using vectors.

Example 1   Expressing a Vector in Component Form

Given $P(4, 2)$ and $Q(1, -2)$, express $\overrightarrow{PQ}$ in component form and draw an equal vector **v** in standard position.

Answer

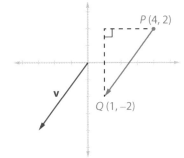

$$a = x_2 - x_1$$
$$= 1 - 4 = -3$$
$$b = y_2 - y_1$$
$$= -2 - 2 = -4$$
$$\overrightarrow{PQ} = \langle -3, -4 \rangle$$

1. Draw $\overrightarrow{PQ}$.

2. Express $\overrightarrow{PQ}$ in terms of its horizontal and vertical components.

3. Sketch **v** with its tail at the origin and its head at $(-3, -4)$.

SKILL ✓ **EXERCISE 1**

The distance formula can be used to find the *magnitude* (length) of a vector. Expressing a vector in component form simplifies the calculation and allows the vector's direction to be found using the reference angle α when the vector is placed in standard position. Unless stated otherwise, the direction of a vector is measured in terms of θ, the directed angle from the positive *x*-axis.

Magnitude and Direction of $\vec{v} = \langle a, b \rangle$			
Magnitude	Reference Angle	Direction (θ degrees from the positive x-axis)	
$|\mathbf{v}| = \sqrt{a^2 + b^2}$	$\alpha = \text{Tan}^{-1}\left|\dfrac{b}{a}\right|$	Q I: $\theta = \alpha$	Q II: $\theta = 180° - \alpha$
		Q III: $\theta = 180° + \alpha$	Q IV: $\theta = 360° - \alpha$

Example 2 Finding the Magnitude and Direction of a Vector

State the magnitude and direction of $\overrightarrow{PQ}$ in Example 1.

Answer

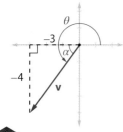

$\left|\overrightarrow{PQ}\right| = \sqrt{a^2 + b^2}$

$\qquad = \sqrt{(-3)^2 + (-4)^2}$

$\qquad = \sqrt{25} = 5$

1. Apply the formula for a vector's magnitude using $\overrightarrow{PQ} = \langle -3, -4 \rangle$.

$\alpha = \text{Tan}^{-1}\left|\dfrac{b}{a}\right|$

$\qquad = \text{Tan}^{-1}\left|\dfrac{-4}{-3}\right| \approx 53.1°$

2. Find the reference angle when the vector is placed in standard position.

Q III implies that
$\theta \approx 180° + 53.1° = 233.1°.$

3. Express the direction as a directed angle from the positive x-axis.

The Norwegian cartographer Caspar Wessel was neither a mathematician nor a scientist, yet in 1699 he became the first to publish the head-to-tail method of adding vectors.

SKILL ✓ EXERCISE 5

The sum of two vectors can be found by placing the tail of the second at the head of the first and drawing the *resultant vector* from the tail of the first to the head of the second. When the vectors are expressed in component form, their sum is found by adding the corresponding components.

▌DEFINITION

The **vector sum**, or the **resultant vector**, of $\mathbf{u} = \langle u_1, u_2 \rangle$ and $\mathbf{v} = \langle v_1, v_2 \rangle$ is
$\mathbf{r} = \mathbf{u} + \mathbf{v} = \langle u_1 + v_1, u_2 + v_2 \rangle.$

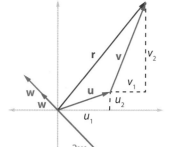

The product of a real number k (a *scalar*) and a vector $\mathbf{w}$ is defined as a vector with magnitude $k|\mathbf{w}|$. This resulting vector has the same direction as vector $\mathbf{w}$ when $k > 0$, but the direction is reversed when $k < 0$. Section 6.2 discusses the *dot product,* one of two ways to define the product of two vectors.

▌DEFINITION

The **scalar product** of the real number k and $\mathbf{w} = \langle w_1, w_2 \rangle$ is $k\mathbf{w} = \langle kw_1, kw_2 \rangle.$

Vector subtraction is defined as the addition of the opposite of a vector.

$\mathbf{u} - \mathbf{v} = \mathbf{u} + (-1)\mathbf{v} = \langle u_1 + (-1)v_1, u_2 + (-1)v_2 \rangle$
$\qquad\qquad = \langle u_1 - v_1, u_2 - v_2 \rangle$

The sum of a vector and its opposite vector is the *zero vector,* $\mathbf{0} = \langle 0, 0 \rangle$, which has a length of 0 and no direction.

Example 3 Performing Vector Operations

Given $\mathbf{u} = \langle -2, 1 \rangle$ and $\mathbf{v} = \langle 6, 3 \rangle$, find each resultant vector algebraically and geometrically.

a. $\mathbf{u} + \mathbf{v}$ **b.** $\frac{1}{3}\mathbf{v} - 2\mathbf{u}$

Answer

a. $\mathbf{r} = \langle -2 + 6, 1 + 3 \rangle = \langle 4, 4 \rangle$

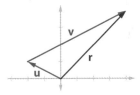

1. Add the corresponding components.
2. Draw $\mathbf{u}$ in standard position, then place the tail of $\mathbf{v}$ at the head of $\mathbf{u}$. Draw the resultant $\mathbf{r}$ from the tail of $\mathbf{u}$ to the head of $\mathbf{v}$.

b. $\mathbf{r} = \frac{1}{3}\langle 6, 3 \rangle - 2\langle -2, 1 \rangle$

$= \langle 2, 1 \rangle + \langle 4, -2 \rangle = \langle 6, -1 \rangle$

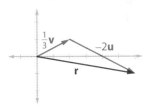

1. Apply the definitions of scalar product and vector addition.
2. Draw $\frac{1}{3}\mathbf{v}$ in standard position, then place the tail of $-2\mathbf{u}$ at the head of $\frac{1}{3}\mathbf{v}$. Draw the resultant $\mathbf{r}$ from the tail of $\frac{1}{3}\mathbf{v}$ to the head of $-2\mathbf{v}$.

SKILL ✓ **EXERCISE 9**

DEFINITION

Any vector $\mathbf{u}$ with magnitude $|\mathbf{u}| = 1$ is a **unit vector**. The *unit vector in the direction of $\mathbf{v}$* is found by dividing $\mathbf{v}$ by its magnitude: $\mathbf{u} = \dfrac{\mathbf{v}}{|\mathbf{v}|} = \dfrac{1}{|\mathbf{v}|}\mathbf{v}$.

Example 4 Finding a Unit Vector

Find the unit vector in the direction of $\mathbf{v} = \langle 3, -5 \rangle$ and verify that it has a length of 1.

Answer

$|\mathbf{v}| = \sqrt{3^2 + (-5)^2} = \sqrt{34}$

1. Find the magnitude of $\mathbf{v}$.

$\mathbf{u} = \dfrac{1}{|\mathbf{v}|}\mathbf{v} = \left(\dfrac{1}{\sqrt{34}}\right)\langle 3, -5 \rangle$

2. Find $\mathbf{u}$, the unit vector in the direction of $\mathbf{v}$.

$= \left\langle \dfrac{3}{\sqrt{34}}, -\dfrac{5}{\sqrt{34}} \right\rangle = \left\langle \dfrac{3\sqrt{34}}{34}, -\dfrac{5\sqrt{34}}{34} \right\rangle$

$|\mathbf{u}| = \sqrt{\left(\dfrac{3}{\sqrt{34}}\right)^2 + \left(-\dfrac{5}{\sqrt{34}}\right)^2}$

3. Verify that the length of the unit vector is 1.

$= \sqrt{\dfrac{9}{34} + \dfrac{25}{34}} = \sqrt{\dfrac{34}{34}} = 1$

SKILL ✓ **EXERCISE 17**

The *standard unit vectors* $\mathbf{i} = \langle 1, 0 \rangle$ and $\mathbf{j} = \langle 0, 1 \rangle$ can be used to write a vector $\mathbf{v}$ as a *linear combination* of its horizontal and vertical components.

$\mathbf{v} = \langle a, b \rangle$
$= a\langle 1, 0 \rangle + b\langle 0, 1 \rangle$
$= a\mathbf{i} + b\mathbf{j}$

Example 5 Expressing a Vector in Terms of Standard Unit Vectors

Write $\vec{PQ}$ with initial point $P\,(-2, 5)$ and terminal point $Q\,(9, -7)$ as a linear combination of standard unit vectors.

Answer

$$\vec{PQ} = \langle x_Q - x_P, y_Q - y_P \rangle$$
$$= \langle 9 - (-2), -7 - 5 \rangle = \langle 11, -12 \rangle$$

$$\vec{PQ} = 11\mathbf{i} - 12\mathbf{j}$$

1. Find the component form of $\vec{PQ}$.

2. Write $\vec{PQ}$ as a linear combination of $\mathbf{i}$ and $\mathbf{j}$.

SKILL ✔ **EXERCISE 15**

A vector expressed in terms of its magnitude $|\mathbf{v}|$ and its directed angle θ from the positive x-axis can be *resolved* into its horizontal and vertical components with the following formula.

$$\mathbf{v} = \langle a, b \rangle = \langle |\mathbf{v}| \cos \theta, |\mathbf{v}| \sin \theta \rangle$$

Example 6 Resolving a Vector into Horizontal and Vertical Components

State the component form of a vector representing the velocity of a plane flying 30° west of north at 400 knots. Then express the vector as a linear combination of standard unit vectors.

Answer

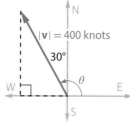

1. Draw and label a sketch.

$\theta = 90° + 30° = 120°$

2. Express the plane's direction with θ, the directed angle from the positive x-axis.

$\mathbf{v} = \langle 400 \cos 120°, 400 \sin 120° \rangle$
$$= \left\langle 400\left(-\frac{1}{2}\right), 400\left(\frac{\sqrt{3}}{2}\right) \right\rangle$$
$$= \langle -200, 200\sqrt{3} \rangle \approx \langle -200, 346.4 \rangle$$

3. Use $\mathbf{v} = \langle |\mathbf{v}| \cos \theta, |\mathbf{v}| \sin \theta \rangle$ to state the vector in component form.

$\mathbf{v} \approx -200\mathbf{i} + 346.4\mathbf{j}$

4. Express $\mathbf{v}$ as a linear combination of $\mathbf{i}$ and $\mathbf{j}$.

SKILL ✔ **EXERCISE 21**

"No one can deny the vast improvement that has taken place, in recent years, in our conceptions of physical processes; and few will deny that a large part of this improvement has been due to the ideas introduced with the advent of vector methods of thought."

– *Joseph Coffin*
(*from his 1909 book Vector Analysis*)

An object's velocity vector represents its speed and direction. The velocity of an object is relative to its frame of reference. A blimp's air speed (relative to the air around it) may be 20 mi/hr, but its ground speed (relative to the earth) when flying into a 15 mi/hr headwind is only $20 + (-15) = 5$ mi/hr. The resulting ground velocity of a vessel in moving air (or water) is the sum of its velocity in still air (or still water) and the velocity of the medium through which it travels.

Example 7   Applying Velocity Vectors

Leigh Anne wants to swim straight across a 300 m wide river flowing at 0.4 m/sec. At what angle upstream (to the nearest degree) should she head if she can swim 1.5 m/sec in still water? How long will it take her to cross the river?

Answer

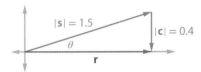

1. Draw vectors representing the swimmer's velocity headed slightly into the current (at θ), the current's velocity headed straight downriver (at 270°), and the resultant velocity heading directly across the river (at 0°).

$\theta = \text{Sin}^{-1}\dfrac{0.4}{1.5} \approx 15°$

$|\mathbf{r}| = \sqrt{1.5^2 - 0.4^2} \approx 1.45$ m/sec

2. Since the vector diagram forms a right triangle, determine θ and $|\mathbf{r}|$ using right-triangle trigonometry.

$t \approx \dfrac{300 \text{ m}}{1.45 \text{ m/sec}} \approx 207.5$ sec

3. Use rate × time = distance to find the time it takes to cross the river.

SKILL ✓ **EXERCISE 31**

Since forces have both magnitude and direction, they are represented by vectors. The weight of an object is the force gravity exerts on the object and is directed downward, toward the center of the earth. When the sum of all the forces (*net force*) on an object is 0, the object is at rest or has a constant velocity and is said to be at *equilibrium*.

Example 8   Applying Force Vectors

A 10 lb sign hangs motionless from two ropes, each at an angle of 60° above the horizontal. Find the tension in each rope.

Answer

1. Draw vectors in standard position representing the three forces acting on the sign.

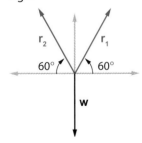

2. Since the sign is at equilibrium, draw a diagram showing $\mathbf{r_1} + \mathbf{r_2} + \mathbf{w} = \mathbf{0}$. The head of the last vector coincides with the tail of the first.

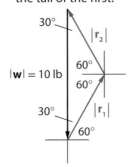

3. Use the Law of Sines to find $|\mathbf{r_1}|$.
Note that $|\mathbf{r_2}| = |\mathbf{r_1}|$ since the triangle has two congruent angles.

$\dfrac{|\mathbf{r_1}|}{\sin 30°} = \dfrac{10}{\sin 120°}$

$|\mathbf{r_1}| = \dfrac{10 \sin 30°}{\sin 120°}$

$= \dfrac{10\left(\frac{1}{2}\right)}{\frac{\sqrt{3}}{2}}$

$= \dfrac{10\sqrt{3}}{3} \approx 5.8$

Each rope exerts ≈ 5.8 lb of force on the sign.

SKILL ✓ **EXERCISE 37**

A. Exercises

Draw each vector $\vec{PQ}$. Then express $\vec{PQ}$ in component form and draw an equal vector $\vec{v}$ in standard position.

1. $P(-5, 1)$ and $Q(1, 4)$
2. $P(4, -1)$ and $Q(2, -5)$
3. $P(5, -1)$ and $Q(2, 3)$
4. $P(-4, 1)$ and $Q(-1, -2)$

Find the magnitude and direction of each vector.

5. $\mathbf{u} = \langle 4, 4 \rangle$
6. $\mathbf{v} = \langle -2, 6 \rangle$
7. $\mathbf{w} = \langle 5, -6 \rangle$
8. $\mathbf{z} = \langle -3, -8 \rangle$

Given $\mathbf{p} = \langle 4, 2 \rangle$ and $\mathbf{q} = \langle -3, 1 \rangle$, find each resultant vector algebraically and geometrically.

9. $\frac{1}{2}\mathbf{p} + \mathbf{q}$
10. $\mathbf{p} + 2\mathbf{q}$
11. $-2\mathbf{p} - \mathbf{q}$
12. $-\frac{1}{2}\mathbf{p} - 2\mathbf{q}$

Given $\mathbf{u} = \langle -7, 10 \rangle$, $\mathbf{v} = \langle 4, -3 \rangle$, and $\mathbf{w} = \langle -5, 8 \rangle$, write each resultant vector in component form and as a linear combination of standard unit vectors i and j.

13. $\mathbf{w} + \frac{1}{2}\mathbf{v}$
14. $\mathbf{u} + \mathbf{v} - \mathbf{w}$
15. $3\mathbf{v} - \frac{1}{2}\mathbf{u} + 2\mathbf{w}$
16. $2\mathbf{u} - 5\mathbf{w} - \frac{3}{2}\mathbf{v}$

B. Exercises

Find the unit vector in the direction of v.

17. $\mathbf{v} = \langle 4, -3 \rangle$
18. $\mathbf{v} = \langle -4, 1 \rangle$
19. $\mathbf{v} = \langle 3, 2 \rangle$
20. $\mathbf{v} = \langle 2, -6 \rangle$

State the component form of each vector.

21. $|\mathbf{v}| = 5; \theta = 20°$
22. $|\mathbf{u}| = 4\sqrt{3}; \theta = \frac{\pi}{6}$
23. $|\mathbf{w}| = 4$ in the direction of $\langle 2, -5 \rangle$
24. $|\mathbf{w}| = 9$ in the direction of $\langle -7, 15 \rangle$

State the component form of a vector modeling each quantity.

25. a train traveling 60° east of north at 50 mi/hr
26. a 22 mi/hr wind from the southeast
27. a westbound car accelerating at 800 ft/sec^2
28. the weight of a 3 lb bird feeder
29. a firework ascending 500 ft straight up
30. a 150 lb force exerted at 20° above the horizontal

When completing the following exercises, round angles to the nearest degree and lengths to the nearest tenth.

31. A helicopter flies 50 mi due south before turning and flying 80 mi due west. How far and at which bearing must the pilot fly to return to his point of origin?

32. A boy who swims at a speed of 3 mi/hr attempts to swim due east, directly across a river. The river's current flows due south at a speed of 4 mi/hr. Find the boy's resultant velocity as measured from the shore.

33. An airplane flies due north 125 mi from Newark to Albany, then to Detroit, 450 mi due west. What is the plane's distance and bearing from its starting point?

34. A boat sails 60 mi due east from the island of Unus to the island of Dosland, then 25 mi due south to Tres Island. What is the boat's distance and bearing from Unus?

35. A 1 lb mailbox and platform are supported by a horizontal force of 0.5 lb and a diagonal force. What is the magnitude and direction of the diagonal force?

36. A 20 lb sign hangs motionless from two chains, each at a 45° angle to the sign. Find the tension in each chain.

C. Exercises

37. A plane flies with an air speed of 200 mi/hr at a bearing of 225° through a 50 mi/hr wind from the south. What is the plane's velocity relative to the ground?

38. A wide river flows due south with a current of 10 knots. A boat crosses the river traveling upstream at a bearing of 60° and a speed of 30 knots. Find the resultant bearing and ground speed of the boat.

39. A pilot plots his course from Fernwood to Glendale at a bearing of 295°. If a 40 mi/hr wind is blowing from 60° east of north, at what compass heading and air speed does the pilot need to fly to maintain a ground speed of 350 mi/hr?

40. A boat leaves port and sails 50 mi due west to avoid a storm, then turns to a compass heading of 200° and proceeds 120 mi to its destination. How far and at what bearing should the boat travel when headed directly back to its original port?

An object resting on a ramp has three forces acting on it: its weight pulling down toward the center of the earth; the force of static friction acting parallel to the ramp; and the normal force, the force exerted by the ramp perpendicular to its surface.

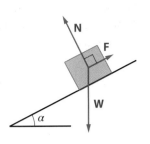

41. Determine the magnitude of the frictional force and the normal force when a 20 lb box of nails rests on a 30° ramp.

42. Find a seesaw's angle of incline if a 50 lb child rests on a tilted seesaw and the normal force is 40 lb.

43. A problem involving the sum of vectors can also be solved using equations generated by examining the components of the vectors. Complete steps *a–e* to solve the problem from Example 8:
A 10 lb sign hangs motionless from two ropes, each at an angle of 60° above the horizontal. Find the tension in each rope.

a. Draw the three forces acting on the sign as vectors in standard position.

b. Write each vector in terms of its horizontal and vertical components.

c. Using the fact that the net force is 0, write equations for the *x*- and *y*-components.

d. Solve the *x*-component equation and interpret the result.

e. Solve the *y*-component equation and interpret the result.

CUMULATIVE REVIEW

44. Convert 1.22 radians to the nearest degree. **[4.1]**

45. Convert 40° to radian measure. Express your answer in terms of π and as a decimal approximation rounded to the nearest thousandth. **[4.1]**

Find *A* in △*ABC* (to the nearest degree). [5.7]

46.

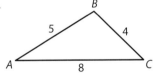

47. $b = 5$, $a = 8$, $C = 40°$

48. Graph $f(x) = 2 \cos 2x$ over $[0, 2\pi]$. **[4.4]**

49. Describe how $g(x) = -3 \cos \frac{x}{2} + 1$ is obtained by transforming the parent function $f(x) = \cos x$. **[4.4]**

50. Which expression is equivalent to i^{-4}? **[Appendix]**
  A. 1
  B. −1
  C. *i*
  D. −*i*
  E. none of these

51. Evaluate $\log_5 5^x$. **[3.2]**
  A. 1
  B. 25
  C. 3125
  D. *x*
  E. none of these

52. Which expression represents $m\angle E$? **[5.7]**
  A. $\text{Cos}^{-1} \frac{2}{3}$
  B. $\text{Cos}^{-1} \left(-\frac{1}{3}\right)$
  C. $\text{Cos}^{-1} \frac{5}{9}$
  D. $\text{Cos}^{-1} \left(-\frac{2}{3}\right)$
  E. none of these

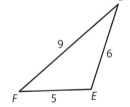

53. Which expressions represent the measure of the smallest angle in △*ABC*? List all correct answers. **[5.6]**
  A. $\text{Sin}^{-1} \frac{4}{7}$
  B. $\text{Sin}^{-1} \frac{20}{31}$
  C. $\text{Sin}^{-1} \frac{4 \sin A}{7}$
  D. $\text{Sin}^{-1} \frac{20 \sin C}{31}$
  E. none of these

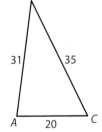

6.2 Dot Products

In physics, work is defined not as the amount of effort expended, but as the dot product of the displacement vector and the amount of force in that direction.

After completing this section, you will be able to

- calculate the dot product of two vectors.
- find the angle between two vectors.
- calculate projections of vectors.
- solve real-world problems requiring the decomposition of a vector.

Well-developed reasoning skills help you make complex decisions based on scriptural principles. Studying proofs can help you develop these skills.

In Section 6.1 you saw that the sum or difference of two vectors is another vector and that the result of multiplying a vector by a scalar (a real number) is a vector. This section explores the *dot product* of two vectors, a multiplication of two vectors that results in a scalar.

DEFINITION

The **dot product** of two vectors $\mathbf{u}$ and $\mathbf{v}$ is $\mathbf{u} \cdot \mathbf{v} = |\mathbf{u}|\,|\mathbf{v}| \cos \theta$, where θ is the angle between $\mathbf{u}$ and $\mathbf{v}$ when the vectors are placed in standard position ($0 \leq \theta \leq 180$).

Example 1   Finding a Dot Product

Find $\mathbf{u} \cdot \mathbf{v}$ if $|\mathbf{u}| = 6$ and $|\mathbf{v}| = 4$.

Answer

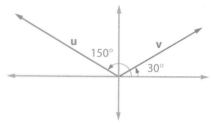

$\theta = |150° - 30°| = 120°$

$\mathbf{u} \cdot \mathbf{v} = |\mathbf{u}|\,|\mathbf{v}| \cos \theta$

$\qquad = 6 \cdot 4 \cos 120°$

$\qquad = 24\left(-\frac{1}{2}\right) = -12$

1. Find θ, the angle between $\mathbf{u}$ and $\mathbf{v}$.
2. Substitute into the definition of a dot product.
3. Simplify.

SKILL ✓ EXERCISE 5

The dot product can also be expressed in terms of the vector's horizontal and vertical components.

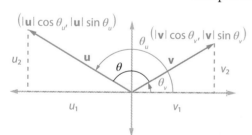

Use $\mathbf{u} = \langle u_1, u_2 \rangle$ where $u_1 = |\mathbf{u}| \cos \theta_u$ and $u_2 = |\mathbf{u}| \sin \theta_u$ and $\mathbf{v} = \langle v_1, v_2 \rangle$ where $v_1 = |\mathbf{v}| \cos \theta_v$ and $v_2 = |\mathbf{v}| \sin \theta_v$.

Then $\mathbf{u} \cdot \mathbf{v} = |\mathbf{u}|\,|\mathbf{v}| \cos (\theta_u - \theta_v)$

$\qquad = |\mathbf{u}|\,|\mathbf{v}| (\cos \theta_u \cos \theta_v + \sin \theta_u \sin \theta_v)$

$\qquad = |\mathbf{u}| \cos \theta_u\, |\mathbf{v}| \cos \theta_v + |\mathbf{u}| \sin \theta_u\, |\mathbf{v}| \sin \theta_v$

$\qquad = u_1 v_1 + u_2 v_2.$

Therefore, if $\mathbf{u} = \langle u_1, u_2 \rangle$ and $\mathbf{v} = \langle v_1, v_2 \rangle$, then $\mathbf{u} \cdot \mathbf{v} = u_1 v_1 + u_2 v_2.$

Example 2 Finding Dot Products Using Components

Find each dot product, given $\mathbf{p} = \langle 0, 3 \rangle$, $\mathbf{q} = \langle 2, 4 \rangle$, $\mathbf{r} = \langle -2, 1 \rangle$, and $\mathbf{s} = \langle 1, -3 \rangle$.

a. $\mathbf{p} \cdot \mathbf{q}$ **b.** $\mathbf{q} \cdot \mathbf{r}$ **c.** $\mathbf{s} \cdot \mathbf{r}$

Answer

Apply the dot product formula that uses vector components:
$\mathbf{u} \cdot \mathbf{v} = \langle u_1, u_2 \rangle \cdot \langle v_1, v_2 \rangle = u_1 v_1 + u_2 v_2$.

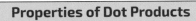

a. $\mathbf{p} \cdot \mathbf{q} = \langle 0, 3 \rangle \cdot \langle 2, 4 \rangle$
$= 0(2) + 3(4)$
$= 0 + 12 = 12$

b. $\mathbf{q} \cdot \mathbf{r} = \langle 2, 4 \rangle \cdot \langle -2, 1 \rangle$
$= 2(-2) + 4(1)$
$= -4 + 4 = 0$

c. $\mathbf{s} \cdot \mathbf{r} = \langle 1, -3 \rangle \cdot \langle -2, 1 \rangle$
$= 1(-2) + (-3)(1)$
$= -2 - 3 = -5$

SKILL ✔ **EXERCISE 7**

It is helpful to know the following properties of dot products. The proofs of the first and last properties are shown below. Proofs of the other properties are left as exercises.

Properties of Dot Products
Let u, v, and w be vectors and let k be a scalar.
1. $\mathbf{u} \cdot \mathbf{v} = \mathbf{v} \cdot \mathbf{u}$ 3. $k(\mathbf{u} \cdot \mathbf{v}) = k\mathbf{u} \cdot \mathbf{v}$ or $\mathbf{u} \cdot k\mathbf{v}$ 5. $\mathbf{u} \cdot \mathbf{u} = |\mathbf{u}|^2$
2. $\mathbf{u} \cdot (\mathbf{v} + \mathbf{w}) = \mathbf{u} \cdot \mathbf{v} + \mathbf{u} \cdot \mathbf{w}$ 4. $\mathbf{0} \cdot \mathbf{v} = 0$

Let $\mathbf{u} = \langle u_1, u_2 \rangle$ and $\mathbf{v} = \langle v_1, v_2 \rangle$.

$\mathbf{u} \cdot \mathbf{v} = u_1 v_1 + u_2 v_2$ and $\mathbf{u} \cdot \mathbf{u} = u_1 u_1 + u_2 u_2$
$\qquad\quad = v_1 u_1 + v_2 u_2$ $= u_1^2 + u_2^2$
$\qquad\quad = \mathbf{v} \cdot \mathbf{u}$ $= \left(\sqrt{u_1^2 + u_2^2} \right)^2$
$\qquad\qquad\qquad\qquad\qquad\qquad\qquad\qquad\qquad\;\; = |\mathbf{u}|^2$

Notice that this fifth property provides another way to express the magnitude of a vector.

$$|\mathbf{u}| = \sqrt{\mathbf{u} \cdot \mathbf{u}} = \sqrt{u_1^2 + u_2^2}$$

The angle θ between two vectors can be found using their dot product.
Since $\mathbf{u} \cdot \mathbf{v} = |\mathbf{u}|\,|\mathbf{v}| \cos \theta$, it follows that $\cos \theta = \dfrac{\mathbf{u} \cdot \mathbf{v}}{|\mathbf{u}|\,|\mathbf{v}|}$.

Example 3 Finding the Angle Between Two Vectors

Find the angle between each pair of vectors.

a. $\mathbf{p} = \langle 0, 3 \rangle$ and $\mathbf{q} = \langle 2, 4 \rangle$ **b.** $\mathbf{r} = \langle -2, 1 \rangle$ and $\mathbf{s} = \langle 1, -3 \rangle$

Answer

Use $\cos \theta = \dfrac{\mathbf{u} \cdot \mathbf{v}}{|\mathbf{u}|\,|\mathbf{v}|}$.

a. $\mathbf{p} \cdot \mathbf{q} = 0(2) + 3(4) = 12$

$|\mathbf{p}| = \sqrt{0^2 + 3^2} = 3$

$|\mathbf{q}| = \sqrt{2^2 + 4^2} = \sqrt{20}$

$\cos \theta = \dfrac{12}{3\sqrt{20}} \approx 0.8944$

$\theta \approx \cos^{-1} 0.8944$
$\quad \approx 26.6°$
$\quad$ or 0.46 radians

b. $\mathbf{r} \cdot \mathbf{s} = -2(1) + 1(-3) = -5$

$|\mathbf{r}| = \sqrt{(-2)^2 + 1^2} = \sqrt{5}$

$|\mathbf{s}| = \sqrt{1^2 + (-3)^2} = \sqrt{10}$

$\cos \theta = \dfrac{-5}{\sqrt{5} \cdot \sqrt{10}} \approx -0.7071$

$\theta \approx \cos^{-1}(-0.7071)$
$\quad \approx 135.0°$
$\quad$ or 2.36 radians

1. Find the dot product of the vectors and their magnitudes.

2. Substitute and use the $\cos^{-1}$ function to find θ.

SKILL ✔ **EXERCISES 11, 13**

Considering that $\mathbf{u} \cdot \mathbf{v} = |\mathbf{u}|\,|\mathbf{v}| \cos\theta$ and that $|\mathbf{u}|$ and $|\mathbf{v}|$ are always positive, the possible values of $\cos\theta$ are used to see that the dot product must be positive when $0° \leq \theta < 90°$, equal to 0 when $\theta = 90°$, and negative when $90° < \theta \leq 180°$. This reasoning shows that vectors $\mathbf{q}$ and $\mathbf{r}$ in Example 2 are perpendicular.

▌DEFINITION

Two vectors $\mathbf{u}$ and $\mathbf{v}$ are **orthogonal** if and only if $\mathbf{u} \cdot \mathbf{v} = 0$.

The terms *orthogonal* and *perpendicular* have the same meaning except in the case of the zero vector, $\mathbf{0}$. While the zero vector is orthogonal with any other vector (since $\mathbf{0} \cdot \mathbf{v} = 0$), it has no direction and cannot be perpendicular to another vector.

Example 4   Finding and Verifying Orthogonal Vectors

If $\mathbf{v} = \langle v_1, v_2 \rangle$ is orthogonal to $\mathbf{u} = \langle -6, 4 \rangle$, find the ratio of v_2 to v_1. Then find a general expression for all orthogonal vectors and verify that it is perpendicular to $\mathbf{u}$.

Answer

$\mathbf{u} \cdot \mathbf{v} = -6v_1 + 4v_2 = 0$ 1. Set $\mathbf{u} \cdot \mathbf{v} = 0$.

$\qquad\qquad 4v_2 = 6v_1$ 2. Solve for $\dfrac{v_2}{v_1}$.

$\qquad\qquad \dfrac{v_2}{v_1} = \dfrac{3}{2}$

$\therefore \mathbf{v} = k\langle 2, 3 \rangle = \langle 2k, 3k \rangle$ 3. Any scalar multiple of $\langle 2, 3 \rangle$ will have $\dfrac{v_2}{v_1} = \dfrac{3}{2}$.
$\qquad$ where $k \in \mathbb{R}$

$\mathbf{u} \cdot \mathbf{v} = -6(2k) + 4(3k) = 0$ 4. Use the dot product to show that $\mathbf{u}$ and the general expression for $\mathbf{v}$ are orthogonal.

SKILL ✓ **EXERCISE 17**

In Section 6.1 you saw how to resolve (or decompose) a vector into its horizontal and vertical components. However, in many applications it is helpful to resolve a vector, $\mathbf{u}$, into two orthogonal *component vectors*, one of which is parallel to another vector, $\mathbf{v}$.

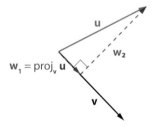

To resolve the vector $\mathbf{u}$ into $\mathbf{w}_1$ (its component in the direction of vector $\mathbf{v}$) and $\mathbf{w}_2$ (another orthogonal component), draw a perpendicular segment from the head of $\mathbf{u}$ to the line containing $\mathbf{v}$. Then draw the component vectors $\mathbf{w}_1$ and $\mathbf{w}_2$ such that $\mathbf{u} = \mathbf{w}_1 + \mathbf{w}_2$. The vector $\mathbf{w}_1$ is the *projection of u onto v*, notated as $\text{proj}_\mathbf{v}\,\mathbf{u}$. The dot product is used to express $\mathbf{w}_1 = \text{proj}_\mathbf{v}\,\mathbf{u}$ as a scalar multiple of $\mathbf{v}$.

$\mathbf{u} \cdot \mathbf{v} = (\mathbf{w}_1 + \mathbf{w}_2) \cdot \mathbf{v}$ Substitute, using $\mathbf{u} = \mathbf{w}_1 + \mathbf{w}_2$.

$\qquad = (\mathbf{w}_1 \cdot \mathbf{v}) + (\mathbf{w}_2 \cdot \mathbf{v})$ Distribute the dot product over vector addition.

$\qquad = \mathbf{w}_1 \cdot \mathbf{v} + 0$ Vectors $\mathbf{w}_2$ and $\mathbf{v}$ are orthogonal.

$\qquad = k\mathbf{v} \cdot \mathbf{v}$ Express $\mathbf{w}_1$ as a scalar multiple of $\mathbf{v}$, using $\mathbf{w}_1 = k\mathbf{v}$.

$\mathbf{u} \cdot \mathbf{v} = k|\mathbf{v}|^2$ Apply the fifth dot product property.

$\qquad k = \dfrac{\mathbf{u} \cdot \mathbf{v}}{|\mathbf{v}|^2}$ Solve for k.

$\therefore \mathbf{w}_1 = \text{proj}_\mathbf{v}\,\mathbf{u} = \left(\dfrac{\mathbf{u} \cdot \mathbf{v}}{|\mathbf{v}|^2} \right)\mathbf{v}$

The component that is orthogonal to $\mathbf{v}$ can then be found using $\mathbf{w}_2 = \mathbf{u} - \text{proj}_\mathbf{v}\,\mathbf{u}$.

Example 5 Finding a Projection and Its Orthogonal Component

Find the projection of $\mathbf{u} = \langle -4, 3 \rangle$ onto $\mathbf{v} = \langle 5, 2 \rangle$.
Then find the orthogonal component $\mathbf{w_2}$ such that
$\mathbf{u} = \text{proj}_{\mathbf{v}} \mathbf{u} + \mathbf{w_2}$.

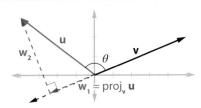

Answer

$\text{proj}_{\mathbf{v}} \mathbf{u} = \left(\dfrac{\langle -4, 3 \rangle \cdot \langle 5, 2 \rangle}{|\langle 5, 2 \rangle|^2} \right) \langle 5, 2 \rangle$

$= \dfrac{-4(5) + 3(2)}{\left(\sqrt{5^2 + 2^2} \right)^2} \langle 5, 2 \rangle$

$= -\dfrac{14}{29} \langle 5, 2 \rangle = \left\langle -\dfrac{70}{29}, -\dfrac{28}{29} \right\rangle$

$\mathbf{w_2} = \langle -4, 3 \rangle - \left\langle -\dfrac{70}{29}, -\dfrac{28}{29} \right\rangle$

$= \left\langle -\dfrac{116}{29} + \dfrac{70}{29}, \dfrac{87}{29} + \dfrac{28}{29} \right\rangle = \left\langle -\dfrac{46}{29}, \dfrac{115}{29} \right\rangle$

1. Find $\mathbf{w_1} = \text{proj}_{\mathbf{v}} \mathbf{u} = \left(\dfrac{\mathbf{u} \cdot \mathbf{v}}{|\mathbf{v}|^2} \right) \mathbf{v}$.

   The fact that the projection is in the opposite direction of $\mathbf{v}$ is indicated by the negative scalar $\dfrac{\mathbf{u} \cdot \mathbf{v}}{|\mathbf{v}|^2} = -\dfrac{14}{29}$.

2. Find $\mathbf{w_2} = \mathbf{u} - \mathbf{w_1}$.

Check

$\left\langle -\dfrac{70}{29}, -\dfrac{28}{29} \right\rangle \cdot \left\langle -\dfrac{46}{29}, \dfrac{115}{29} \right\rangle$

$= -\dfrac{70}{29}\left(-\dfrac{46}{29} \right) + \left(-\dfrac{28}{29} \right)\left(\dfrac{115}{29} \right) = \dfrac{3220 - 3220}{29^2} = 0$

3. Use the dot product to confirm that $\text{proj}_{\mathbf{v}} \mathbf{u}$ and $\mathbf{w_2}$ are orthogonal.

SKILL ✔ **EXERCISE 27**

Notice that $\text{proj}_{\mathbf{v}} \mathbf{u} = \left(\dfrac{\mathbf{u} \cdot \mathbf{v}}{|\mathbf{v}|^2} \right)\mathbf{v}$ is in the same direction as $\mathbf{v}$ when the dot product $\mathbf{u} \cdot \mathbf{v}$ is positive ($0° \le \theta < 90°$) and that $\text{proj}_{\mathbf{v}} \mathbf{u}$ is in the opposite direction from $\mathbf{v}$ when the dot product is negative ($90° < \theta \le 180°$).

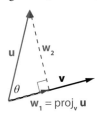

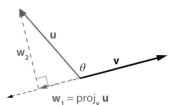

$\cos \theta = \dfrac{|\mathbf{w_1}|}{|\mathbf{u}|}$, so

$|\mathbf{u}| \cos \theta = |\mathbf{w_1}|$

$\cos(180° - \theta) = -\cos\theta = \dfrac{|\mathbf{w_1}|}{|\mathbf{u}|}$

$|\mathbf{u}| \cos \theta = -|\mathbf{w_1}|$

The right-triangle trigonometry demonstrated above shows that $|\mathbf{u}| \cos \theta$ provides the directed magnitude of $\text{proj}_{\mathbf{v}} \mathbf{u}$. Interpret positive values as being in the same direction as $\mathbf{v}$ and negative values as being in the opposite direction from $\mathbf{v}$.

Example 6   Using a Projection

Determine the downhill component of a 150 lb skier's weight that pulls the skier down a hill with a slope of 30°.

Answer

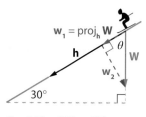

$\theta = 90° - 30° = 60°$

$\text{proj}_\mathbf{h} \, \mathbf{W} = \mathbf{w_1} = |\mathbf{W}| \cos \theta$

$\quad\quad\quad\quad = |150| \cos 60°$

$\quad\quad\quad\quad = 150\left(\frac{1}{2}\right) = 75 \text{ lb}$

1. Sketch a downhill vector **h**, the force vector **W** representing the skier's weight, $\mathbf{w_1} = \text{proj}_\mathbf{h} \, \mathbf{W}$, and the perpendicular component $\mathbf{w_2}$.

2. Determine θ, the angle between **W** and **h**.

3. Find the magnitude of the projection of **W** onto **h**.

SKILL ✓ **EXERCISE 31**

Vector projections are used to calculate the amount of work done by a constant force as it moves an object from point A to point B. The amount of work done is defined as the product of the component of the force that is parallel to the object's motion and the distance that the object is moved. The typical unit of work in both the British Imperial System and the US customary system is the foot-pound (ft-lb). In the International System of Units, a newton meter (N·m), also called a joule (J), is commonly used.

$$W = \left| \text{proj}_{\overrightarrow{AB}} \, \mathbf{F} \right| \left| \overrightarrow{AB} \right| \quad\quad \text{definition of work}$$

$$= |\mathbf{F}| \cos \theta \left| \overrightarrow{AB} \right| \quad\quad \text{definition of } \text{proj}_{\overrightarrow{AB}} \, \mathbf{F}$$

$$= |\mathbf{F}| \left| \overrightarrow{AB} \right| \cos \theta \quad\quad \text{commutative property}$$

$$W = \mathbf{F} \cdot \overrightarrow{AB} \quad\quad\quad\quad \text{definition of dot product}$$

Example 7   Finding Work

Find the amount of work done by Rebecca as she moves a wagon 300 m down the beach, pulling with 20 N of force on the handle, which is 35° above the horizontal.

Answer

$W = \mathbf{F} \cdot \overrightarrow{AB} = |\mathbf{F}| \left| \overrightarrow{AB} \right| \cos \theta$

$\quad\quad = (20 \text{ N})(300 \text{ m}) \cos 35°$

$\quad\quad \approx 4915 \text{ N·m or } 4915 \text{ J}$

Find the dot product of the vectors representing the applied force and the distance moved.

SKILL ✓ **EXERCISE 37**

A. Exercises

1. If $\mathbf{r} \cdot \mathbf{s} = 0$, the vectors are said to be _____ and the angle between the vectors (assuming $\mathbf{r} \neq \mathbf{0}$ and $\mathbf{s} \neq \mathbf{0}$) measures _____.

2. Describe the angle measure between vectors $\mathbf{r}$ and $\mathbf{s}$ in each case.

    a. $\mathbf{r} \cdot \mathbf{s} > 0$ **b.** $\mathbf{r} \cdot \mathbf{s} < 0$

Find $\mathbf{u} \cdot \mathbf{v}$, given the magnitudes and the angle θ between the vectors.

3. $|\mathbf{u}| = 2$, $|\mathbf{v}| = 3$, $\theta = 135°$

4. $|\mathbf{u}| = 10$, $|\mathbf{v}| = 5$, $\theta = 180°$

Find the dot product of each pair of vectors.

5.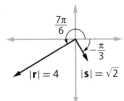

6.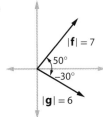

Find each dot product. Then state whether the angle between the vectors is $> 90°$, $< 90°$, or $= 90°$.

7. $\langle 2, 3 \rangle \cdot \langle 5, 7 \rangle$ 8. $\langle -1, -4 \rangle \cdot \langle 2, -3 \rangle$

9. $\langle 4, 8 \rangle \cdot \langle 4, -2 \rangle$ 10. $\langle -4, 6 \rangle \cdot \langle 6, -9 \rangle$

11. $\left\langle 6, \frac{1}{2} \right\rangle \cdot \left\langle \frac{1}{3}, -12 \right\rangle$ 12. $\left\langle \frac{3}{5}, \frac{-4}{7} \right\rangle \cdot \left\langle \frac{5}{6}, \frac{7}{8} \right\rangle$

Use a dot product to find the angle between each pair of vectors (to the nearest tenth of a degree).

13. $\mathbf{u} = \langle 1, 4 \rangle$, $\mathbf{v} = \langle -3, -2 \rangle$

14. $\mathbf{r} = \langle 7, 6 \rangle$, $\mathbf{s} = \langle 2, 9 \rangle$

15. $\mathbf{a} = \langle 5, -8 \rangle$, $\mathbf{b} = \langle 9, 1 \rangle$

16. $\mathbf{f} = \langle -3, 2 \rangle$, $\mathbf{g} = \langle -5, -6 \rangle$

B. Exercises

If $\langle v_1, v_2 \rangle$ is orthogonal to the given vector, find the ratio of v_2 to v_1. Then find a general expression that represents all the orthogonal vectors.

17. $\langle 10, -2 \rangle$ 18. $\langle -3, 8 \rangle$

19. $\left\langle \frac{1}{3}, \frac{5}{6} \right\rangle$ 20. $\left\langle -2, -\frac{3}{4} \right\rangle$

21. If $\mathbf{v} = \langle v_1, v_2 \rangle$ is orthogonal to $\mathbf{u} = \langle u_1, u_2 \rangle$, find the ratio of $\frac{v_2}{v_1}$ in terms of u_1 and u_2. Then find a general expression in terms of u_1 and u_2 for all vectors that are orthogonal to $\mathbf{u}$.

Prove each property of dot products using $\vec{\mathbf{u}} = \langle u_1, u_2 \rangle$, $\vec{\mathbf{v}} = \langle v_1, v_2 \rangle$, $\vec{\mathbf{w}} = \langle w_1, w_2 \rangle$, $\vec{\mathbf{0}} = \langle 0, 0 \rangle$, and scalar k.

22. $\mathbf{0} \cdot \mathbf{v} = 0$

23. $k(\mathbf{u} \cdot \mathbf{v}) = k\mathbf{u} \cdot \mathbf{v}$

24. $k(\mathbf{u} \cdot \mathbf{v}) = \mathbf{u} \cdot k\mathbf{v}$

25. $\mathbf{u} \cdot (\mathbf{v} + \mathbf{w}) = \mathbf{u} \cdot \mathbf{v} + \mathbf{u} \cdot \mathbf{w}$

Find the projection of $\mathbf{u}$ onto $\mathbf{v}$. Then find $\mathbf{w_2}$ so that $\text{proj}_\mathbf{v}\, \mathbf{u} + \mathbf{w_2} = \mathbf{u}$.

26. $\mathbf{u} = \langle 3, 8 \rangle$, $\mathbf{v} = \langle 1, 2 \rangle$ 27. $\mathbf{u} = \langle -2, 3 \rangle$, $\mathbf{v} = \langle 1, 4 \rangle$

28. $\mathbf{u} = \langle 4, 1 \rangle$, $\mathbf{v} = \langle 3, 5 \rangle$ 29. $\mathbf{u} = \langle 1, -5 \rangle$, $\mathbf{v} = \langle -2, 3 \rangle$

30. A 200 lb cart is resting on a hill with a slope of $20°$.

    a. Determine the downhill component of the cart's weight that is pulling it down the hill.

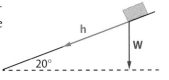

    b. Determine the component of the cart's weight that pushes into the hill perpendicular to the hill's surface.

31. A 50 lb box of gadgets rests on a ramp with a $40°$ incline.

    a. Determine the component of the box's weight that pulls it down the ramp.

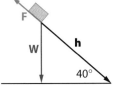

    b. What is the magnitude of the frictional force, $\mathbf{F}$, that prevents the box from sliding down the ramp?

32. As a worker pulls a pallet truck through the warehouse at a constant velocity, the horizontal component of the force he exerts on the handle is equal in magnitude to the 25 N force of friction resisting the forward motion of the truck. With what force is he pulling when the handle is at each degree measure above the horizontal?

    a. $60°$

    b. $45°$

    c. $30°$

33. Mr. Jones pushes his lawnmower with a 75 lb force directed along its handle, which makes a $38°$ angle with the ground.

    a. Determine the component of his push that is directed parallel to the ground.

    b. Determine the component of his push that is directed perpendicular to the ground.

34. How much work is done by lifting a 100 lb weight set up 6 ft?

35. How much work is done by lifting an object up 15 m with a force of 30 N?

36. How much work is done by pulling a sled for 100 m with a force of 70 N on a rope at a 30° angle above the ground?

37. How many foot-pounds of work does Bill do when he pushes an apple cart 50 yd with a force of 35 lb along a handle that is fixed at 25° above the horizontal of the cart?

❯ C. Exercises

38. Analyze: If $\mathbf{n} = \langle 20, 40 \rangle$ represents the number of soccer shorts and jerseys that need to be purchased and $\mathbf{p} = \langle 25, 35 \rangle$ represents the respective costs in dollars, calculate $\mathbf{n} \cdot \mathbf{p}$ and interpret its meaning.

39. Analyze: Given $\mathbf{r}$ with magnitude x at α and $\mathbf{s}$ with magnitude y at β, state the range of possible values for $\mathbf{r} \cdot \mathbf{s}$. Then describe the conditions that generate the maximum and minimum values.

Find the magnitude and argument of each vector and compute the dot product using $\mathbf{u} \cdot \mathbf{v} = |\mathbf{u}|\,|\mathbf{v}| \cos \theta$. Then verify your result by computing the dot product using vector components.

40. $\mathbf{u} = \langle 5, 5 \rangle$, $\mathbf{v} = \langle -2, -2 \rangle$

41. $\mathbf{u} = \langle 0, 4 \rangle$, $\mathbf{v} = \left\langle 2\sqrt{3}, 2 \right\rangle$

Given the vertices of $\triangle ABC$, use dot products to determine the measure of its angles (to the nearest tenth of a degree).

42. $A\,(1, 2)$, $B\,(4, 6)$, and $C\,(5, 3)$

43. $A\,(3, -2)$, $B\,(0, 4)$, and $C\,(-6, 5)$

CUMULATIVE REVIEW

Solve. [2.6]

44. $\dfrac{x+1}{5-x} = \dfrac{x}{x-5}$

45. $\dfrac{2x^2 + 9x - 35}{x^2 - 10x + 1} = 3$

46. Find the distance between $(5, -2)$ and $(-5, -7)$. [1.2]

47. Find the midpoint between $(-1, 6)$ and $(7, -3)$. [1.2]

48. Find the length of a diameter of the circle that is centered at $(2, 0)$ and contains the point $(6, 3)$. [1.2]

49. Find the center and length of a radius of the circle whose diameter has endpoints $(-2, 0)$ and $(8, 6)$. [1.2]

50. Convert $y = \log_2 x$ to exponential form. [3.2]
   A. $x = y^2$ **C.** $y = 2^x$ **E.** $x = 2y$
   B. $y = x^2$ **D.** $x = 2^y$

51. What are the primary solutions for $2 \sin x = 1$? [5.3]
   A. $\dfrac{\pi}{3}, \dfrac{2\pi}{3}$ **C.** $\dfrac{\pi}{6}, \dfrac{5\pi}{6}$ **E.** $\dfrac{\pi}{6}, -\dfrac{\pi}{6}$
   B. $\dfrac{\pi}{4}, \dfrac{3\pi}{4}$ **D.** $\dfrac{\pi}{6}, \dfrac{7\pi}{6}$

52. What is the magnitude and direction of $\mathbf{v} = \langle -5, 5 \rangle$? [6.1]
   A. $50; 45°$ **C.** $25; 135°$ **E.** $5\sqrt{2}; 135°$
   B. $5\sqrt{2}; 45°$ **D.** $2\sqrt{5}; 135°$

53. Which functions have a period of π? List all correct answers. [4.5]
   A. $y = \sin x$ **C.** $y = \tan x$ **E.** $y = \csc x$
   B. $y = \cos x$ **D.** $y = \cot x$ **F.** $y = \sec x$

BIBLICAL PERSPECTIVE OF MATHEMATICS

Truth and Mathematical Proof

There exists . . . a world which is the collection of mathematical truths, to which we have access only through our intellects, just as there is the world of physical reality; the one and the other independent of us, both of divine creation.

—Charles Hermite (nineteenth-century French mathematician)

Philippians 4:8 admonishes Christians to meditate on those things that are true. But our society values truth less and less. In fact, the Oxford Dictionaries 2016 word of the year was *post-truth*, "relating to or denoting circumstances in which objective facts are less influential in shaping public opinion than appeals to emotion and personal belief." This de-emphasis of truth contrasts with the position taken by great scientists like Galileo, who stated, "I value the discovery of a single even insignificant truth more highly than all the argumentation on the highest questions which fails to reach a truth." Sadly, many modern mathematicians fail to see mathematics as the reflection of an underlying transcendent truth originating with God. In 1940 Edward Kasner and James Newman wrote, "We have overcome the notion that mathematical truths have an existence independent and apart from our own minds. . . . [Mathematics] is man's own handiwork, subject only to the limitations imposed by the laws of thought."

Mathematicians continually seek to discover and verify new aspects of mathematical truth through inductive and deductive reasoning. Mathematical concepts are frequently discovered intuitively when the exploration of specific examples leads to general conclusions. These inductive conclusions are later verified using the logic of deductive reasoning. While some mathematicians such as Archimedes are known for both discovering and proving results, many such as Euclid are famous for the deductive organization and expansion of the discoveries of others. But even Euclid's work accepted many propositions as true without proof, and many major branches of mathematics progressed without logical development. Philip Jourdain wrote, "It is a curious fact that mathematicians have so often arrived at truth by a sort of instinct."

During the explosion of new mathematics in the Renaissance, mathematicians verified each other's inductive discoveries through deductive proof whenever possible. Pierre de Fermat, a seventeenth-century French lawyer and amateur mathematician, corresponded with René

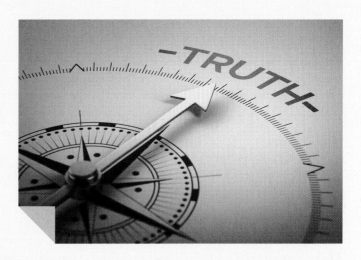

Descartes on calculus, Blaise Pascal on probability, and Marin Mersenne on prime numbers. Fermat is best known for several number theory contentions that he stated without deductive proof. Many mathematicians labored to prove or disprove his statements. Joseph-Louis Lagrange and Leonhard Euler each proved several of his conjectures, but Euler also disproved one of them. Fermat's Last Theorem, his most famous conjecture, eluded proof until the end of the twentieth century, after having gained recognition as the mathematical problem with the greatest number of published incorrect proofs. Carl Gauss observed, "It is characteristic of higher arithmetic that many of the most beautiful theorems can be discovered by induction with the greatest of ease but have proofs that lie anywhere but near at hand and are often found only after many fruitless investigations with the aid of deep analysis and lucky combinations."

Considering this difficulty, it is important to note that the truth of a mathematical statement is not dependent on the existence of a deductive proof. For instance, the famous Goldbach Conjecture (that all positive even integers greater than two can be expressed as the sum of two primes) has yet to be proved deductively, though the inductive evidence in favor of this statement is overwhelming. A computer search in April 2012 verified the conjecture for all even integers less than 4×10^{18}. Such a technique does not provide a satisfactory proof since the search cannot extend to infinity.

Kurt Gödel's incompleteness theorems rattled the mathematical world in 1931. As Larry Zimmerman explains, Gödel demonstrated that it is impossible to "bridge the abyss from finite to infinite, that the consistency of any deductive system which encompasses all of arithmetic can never be proved. Even more astounding, he showed that no set of axioms would be sufficient to account for the mathematical truth in any one branch of mathematics." Mathematicians should not be surprised when they discover truths that they cannot verify deductively. These truths along with mathematical truths that remain to be discovered are all part of transcendent mathematical truth.

Exercises

1. Verify the Goldbach Conjecture for each positive even integer.
   - **a.** 4
   - **b.** 8
   - **c.** 10
   - **d.** 16
   - **e.** 30

2. Which Bible verse admonishes Christians to think on things that are true?

3. State whether inductive or deductive reasoning is being described.
   - **a.** drawing a general principle from specific examples
   - **b.** proving a statement by applying previously proven principles in a logical step-by-step sequence
   - **c.** frequently used by mathematicians when discovering new truths
   - **d.** used by mathematicians to prove new discoveries

4. Which amateur mathematician is famous for stating number theory conjectures?

5. Who disproved one of those conjectures and proved several others?

6. Which theorem has had the greatest number of published incorrect proofs?

7. Who demonstrated in 1931 that not all mathematical truth can be proved?

8. One of Fermat's conjectures stated that $2^{2^n} + 1$ is prime when n is a counting number.
   - **a.** Show that the conjecture is true for $n = 2$.
   - **b.** Use a calculator and divide by 641 to show that the conjecture is false for $n = 5$.

9. **Discuss:** How does the term *conjecture* relate to the types of mathematical reasoning?

10. **Discuss:** Describe transcendent mathematical truth.

11. **Discuss:** Explain how we can know that transcendent mathematical truth exists.

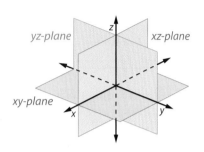

The bearing, ground speed, and angle of inclination of an aircraft in flight can be described by a three-dimensional vector.

The perpendicular *x*- and *y*-axes of the Cartesian plane allow each point in the plane to be described by a unique ordered pair. Similarly, three perpendicular axes allow each point in space to be uniquely described by an ordered triple, $P(x, y, z)$. The *z*-axis of our three-dimensional coordinate system passes through the origin of the *xy*-plane and is perpendicular to both the *x*- and *y*-axes. The *xy*-plane, the *yz*-plane, and the *xz*-plane divide space into eight regions called *octants*.

After completing this section, you will be able to

- represent three-dimensional vectors graphically and algebraically.
- perform three-dimensional vector operations.
- find the angle between two vectors in space.
- solve real-world problems involving three-dimensional vectors.

Example 1   Plotting a Point in Space

Plot the point $P(3, 4, 5)$.

Answer

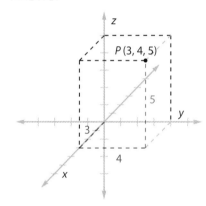

1. Sketch a 3D coordinate system.
2. Locate the point (3, 4) in the *xy*-plane and plot the point 5 units up (parallel to the *z*-axis).

SKILL ✔ **EXERCISE 5**

The distance between two points in space and the midpoint of the segment connecting them can be developed by extending the method used in two dimensions to three dimensions.

3D DISTANCE AND MIDPOINT FORMULAS

Given two points in space $P(x_1, y_1, z_1)$ and $Q(x_2, y_2, z_2)$,

the distance PQ is $d = \sqrt{(x_2 - x_1)^2 + (y_2 - y_1)^2 + (z_2 - z_1)^2}$,

and the midpoint of $\overline{PQ}$ is $M\left(\dfrac{x_1 + x_2}{2}, \dfrac{y_1 + y_2}{2}, \dfrac{z_1 + z_2}{2}\right)$.

TIP

Our 3D coordinate system is "right-handed" since the thumb of the right hand points in the direction of the positive *z*-axis when its fingers curve from the positive *x*-axis to the positive *y*-axis.

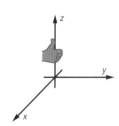

Example 2 Finding the Length and Midpoint of a Segment in Space

Find the length and the midpoint of the segment from A $(3, 0, -2)$ to B $(-1, -4, 6)$.

Answer

Length

$$d = \sqrt{(x_2 - x_1)^2 + (y_2 - y_1)^2 + (z_2 - z_1)^2}$$
$$= \sqrt{(-1-3)^2 + (-4-0)^2 + [6-(-2)]^2}$$
$$= \sqrt{(-4)^2 + (-4)^2 + 8^2} = \sqrt{96}$$
$$= 4\sqrt{6} \approx 9.80$$

Midpoint

$$\left(\frac{x_1 + x_2}{2}, \frac{y_1 + y_2}{2}, \frac{z_1 + z_2}{2}\right)$$
$$= \left(\frac{3 + (-1)}{2}, \frac{0 + (-4)}{2}, \frac{-2 + 6}{2}\right)$$
$$= (1, -2, 2)$$

SKILL ✓ **EXERCISE 11**

Many vector quantities, such as forces, velocities, and accelerations, are not confined to a plane. These three-dimensional vectors are often expressed in terms of their components. For example, $\overrightarrow{AB}$ from A (x_1, y_1, z_1) to B (x_2, y_2, z_2) is expressed in component form as
$$\mathbf{v} = \langle v_1, v_2, v_3 \rangle = \langle x_2 - x_1, y_2 - y_1, z_2 - z_1 \rangle.$$

Since $\overrightarrow{AB}$ is equal to the standard position $\mathbf{v}$, its length is $|\mathbf{v}| = \sqrt{v_1^2 + v_2^2 + v_3^2}$ and its direction can be described using the unit vector $\frac{\mathbf{v}}{|\mathbf{v}|}$.

Example 3 Describing a 3D Vector

Given A $(5, 1, -1)$ and B $(3, 6, 2)$, express $\overrightarrow{AB}$ in component form. Then find its length and a unit vector in the direction of $\overrightarrow{AB}$.

Answer

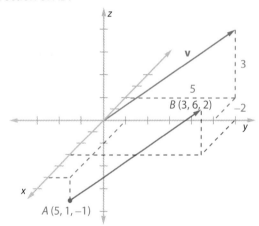

$\mathbf{v} = \langle 3 - 5, 6 - 1, 2 - (-1) \rangle$
$\quad = \langle -2, 5, 3 \rangle$

$|\mathbf{v}| = \sqrt{(-2)^2 + 5^2 + 3^2}$
$\quad = \sqrt{38} \approx 6.16$

$\mathbf{u} = \frac{1}{|\mathbf{v}|}\mathbf{v} = \frac{1}{\sqrt{38}}\langle -2, 5, 3 \rangle$

$\quad = \left\langle -\frac{2\sqrt{38}}{38}, \frac{5\sqrt{38}}{38}, \frac{3\sqrt{38}}{38} \right\rangle$

1. Express $\overrightarrow{AB}$ in component form using $\langle v_1, v_2, v_3 \rangle = \langle x_2 - x_1, y_2 - y_1, z_2 - z_1 \rangle$.

2. Find its length using $|\mathbf{v}| = \sqrt{v_1^2 + v_2^2 + v_3^2}$.

3. Divide the component form of the vector by its length.

SKILL ✓ **EXERCISE 19**

The Irish mathematician William Hamilton was the first to develop a method that extended vector operations with complex numbers into three dimensions. Quaternions, as Hamilton called them, are not commutative under multiplication.

The last step in the example above utilizes the fact that the properties of vectors extend from two dimensions to any number of dimensions.

VECTORS IN SPACE

Let k be a scalar, $\mathbf{v} = \langle v_1, v_2, v_3 \rangle$, $\mathbf{w} = \langle w_1, w_2, w_3 \rangle$, and θ be the angle between $\mathbf{v}$ and $\mathbf{w}$.

equality	$\mathbf{v} = \mathbf{w}$ if and only if $v_1 = w_1$, $v_2 = w_2$, and $v_3 = w_3$
vector addition	$\mathbf{v} + \mathbf{w} = \langle v_1 + w_1, v_2 + w_2, v_3 + w_3 \rangle$
scalar multiplication	$k\mathbf{v} = \langle kv_1, kv_2, kv_3 \rangle$
vector subtraction	$\mathbf{v} - \mathbf{w} = \mathbf{v} + (-\mathbf{w}) = \langle v_1 - w_1, v_2 - w_2, v_3 - w_3 \rangle$
zero vector	$\mathbf{0} = \langle 0, 0, 0 \rangle$
dot product	$\mathbf{v} \cdot \mathbf{w} = \lvert \mathbf{v} \rvert\, \lvert \mathbf{w} \rvert \cos \theta = v_1 w_1 + v_2 w_2 + v_3 w_3$

Example 4 Operations with 3D Vectors

Use $\mathbf{p} = \langle -5, 2, 0 \rangle$, $\mathbf{q} = \langle 1, -3, -2 \rangle$, and $\mathbf{r} = \langle 6, 4, -3 \rangle$ to complete each vector operation.

a. $2\mathbf{p} + \mathbf{q}$ **b.** $\frac{1}{2}\mathbf{r} - 3\mathbf{q}$ **c.** $\mathbf{q} \cdot \mathbf{r}$

Answer

a. $2\mathbf{p} + \mathbf{q} = 2\langle -5, 2, 0 \rangle + \langle 1, -3, -2 \rangle$
$\phantom{2\mathbf{p} + \mathbf{q}} = \langle -10, 4, 0 \rangle + \langle 1, -3, -2 \rangle$
$\phantom{2\mathbf{p} + \mathbf{q}} = \langle -9, 1, -2 \rangle$

1. Substitute.
   Complete the scalar multiplication.
   Complete the vector addition.

b. $\frac{1}{2}\mathbf{r} - 3\mathbf{q} = \frac{1}{2}\langle 6, 4, -3 \rangle - 3\langle 1, -3, -2 \rangle$
$\phantom{\frac{1}{2}\mathbf{r} - 3\mathbf{q}} = \left\langle 3, 2, -\frac{3}{2} \right\rangle + \langle -3, 9, 6 \rangle$
$\phantom{\frac{1}{2}\mathbf{r} - 3\mathbf{q}} = \left\langle 0, 11, \frac{9}{2} \right\rangle$

2. Substitute.
   Complete the scalar multiplication.
   Note that the vector subtraction is done by adding the opposite.

c. $\mathbf{q} \cdot \mathbf{r} = \langle 1, -3, -2 \rangle \cdot \langle 6, 4, -3 \rangle$
$\phantom{\mathbf{q} \cdot \mathbf{r}} = 1(6) + (-3)(4) + (-2)(-3)$
$\phantom{\mathbf{q} \cdot \mathbf{r}} = 6 - 12 + 6 = 0$

3. Find the dot product.

SKILL ✔ **EXERCISES 25, 27**

The fact that multiplication was not commutative in Hamilton's algebraic system of quaternions was as surprising to mathematicians as the alternative geometries being developed at that same time. However, we should not assume that any mathematical model completely describes God's infinitely complex creation.

Just as in a plane, $\mathbf{v} \cdot \mathbf{w} = \lvert \mathbf{v} \rvert\, \lvert \mathbf{w} \rvert \cos \theta$ can be rearranged to find θ, the measure of the angle formed by $\mathbf{v}$ and $\mathbf{w}$ when placed in standard position: $\cos \theta = \dfrac{\mathbf{v} \cdot \mathbf{w}}{\lvert \mathbf{v} \rvert\, \lvert \mathbf{w} \rvert}$. Note that vectors, such as $\mathbf{q}$ and $\mathbf{r}$ in Example 4, are orthogonal if and only if the dot product is equal to 0. A positive dot product implies $0° \leq \theta < 90°$, and a negative dot product implies $90° < \theta \leq 180°$.

Example 5   Finding the Angle Between Two 3D Vectors

Find the measure of the angle between $\mathbf{p} = \langle -5, 2, 0 \rangle$ and $\mathbf{q} = \langle 1, -3, -2 \rangle$.

Answer

Use $\cos \theta = \dfrac{\mathbf{p} \cdot \mathbf{q}}{|\mathbf{p}|\,|\mathbf{q}|}$.

$\mathbf{p} \cdot \mathbf{q} = -5(1) + 2(-3) + 0(-2) = -11$

$|\mathbf{p}| = \sqrt{(-5)^2 + 2^2 + 0^2} = \sqrt{29}$

$|\mathbf{q}| = \sqrt{1^2 + (-3)^2 + (-2)^2} = \sqrt{14}$

$\cos \theta = \dfrac{-11}{\sqrt{29} \cdot \sqrt{14}}$

$\theta = \text{Cos}^{-1}\left(\dfrac{-11}{\sqrt{29} \cdot \sqrt{14}}\right)$

$\approx 123°$ or 2.15 radians

1. Find the dot product of the vectors and their magnitudes.

2. Substitute and use the Cos^{-1} function to find θ.

——————— SKILL ✔ **EXERCISE 29**

Three-dimensional vectors are used in many practical applications.

Example 6   Applying 3D Vectors

An airplane taking off at a heading of 180° has an air velocity vector directed 20° above horizontal and an airspeed of 225 knots. There is a 40-knot wind from the southwest. Find a vector that represents the plane's velocity relative to the point of takeoff.

Answer

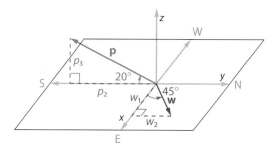

1. Sketch vectors representing the wind and the plane's velocity without the wind.

   Letting the positive x-axis represent due east implies the wind is blowing at 45° in the xy-plane and the vector for the plane's heading is directly above the negative y-axis.

$\mathbf{w} = \langle |\mathbf{w}| \cos 45°, |\mathbf{w}| \sin 45°, 0 \rangle$
$= \langle 40 \cos 45°, 40 \sin 45°, 0 \rangle$
$\approx \langle 28.3, 28.3, 0 \rangle$

2. Resolve $\mathbf{w}$ into $\langle w_1, w_2, 0 \rangle$ using $\cos 45° = \dfrac{|w_1|}{|\mathbf{w}|}$ and $\sin 45° = \dfrac{|w_2|}{|\mathbf{w}|}$.

$\mathbf{p} = \langle 0, -|\mathbf{p}| \cos 20°, |\mathbf{p}| \sin 20° \rangle$
$= \langle 0, -225 \cos 20°, 225 \sin 20° \rangle$
$\approx \langle 0, -211.4, 77.0 \rangle$

3. Use right-triangle trigonometry to resolve $\mathbf{p}$ into $\langle 0, p_2, p_3 \rangle$ using $\cos 20° = \dfrac{|p_2|}{|\mathbf{p}|}$ and $\sin 20° = \dfrac{|p_3|}{|\mathbf{p}|}$.

$\mathbf{w} + \mathbf{p} \approx \langle 28.3, 28.3, 0 \rangle + \langle 0, -211.4, 77.0 \rangle$
$\mathbf{r} \approx \langle 28.3, -183.1, 77.0 \rangle$

4. Add the vectors.

——————— SKILL ✔ **EXERCISE 35**

Exercises 38–40 explore the interpretation of the component form of the resultant vector in Example 6.

A. Exercises

1. State the octant or plane in which each point is located.

   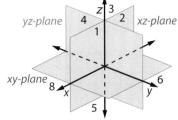

   a. $(5, 7, -10)$
   b. $(2, -9, -4)$
   c. $(-3, -7, 5)$
   d. $(0, -6, 4)$
   e. $(-9, -12, -4)$
   f. $(-11, 5, -2)$

Plot each point on a 3D coordinate system.

2. $(3, 3, 4)$
3. $(-3, 2, 3)$
4. $(2, -3, -2)$
5. $(-3, 3, -5)$

Graph each vector in standard position.

6. $\langle 3, 4, -2 \rangle$
7. $\langle -3, 5, 1 \rangle$
8. $\langle 3, 6, 1 \rangle$
9. $\langle 3, 0, 3 \rangle$

Find the length and the midpoint of $\overline{AB}$.

10. $A (2, 4, 5), B (2, 6, 1)$
11. $A (0, 7, -4), B (4, -1, -2)$
12. $A (0, 0, 4), B (3, 0, 0)$
13. $A (2, 4, 6), B (2x, 2y, 2z)$

14. An eagle is spotted at $(98, -47, 14)$ and a second eagle is seen at $(37, 122, 78)$. Find the distance between the eagles if the coordinates are stated in feet.

15. Lucas's drone is located at $(-1160, 538, 318)$ and Zoey's drone is located at $(455, -212, 270)$ on the same coordinate system. Find the distance between the drones if the coordinates are given in feet.

16. The coordinates of drone A are $(235, -102, 55)$ and the coordinates of drone B are $(-137, 68, 75)$. Find the coordinates of the midpoint between the drones.

17. A Navy airplane is located at $(346, 400, c)$ and an Air Force plane is at $(a, b, 3.5)$. Find the value of each variable if the coordinates of the midpoint between the two planes are $(279, 481, 2.5)$.

B. Exercises

Express $\overrightarrow{PQ}$ in component form. Then find its length and a unit vector in the direction of $\overrightarrow{PQ}$.

18. $P (7, 4, 2), Q (7, 9, 14)$
19. $P (1, 5, -8), Q (13, 9, -5)$
20. $P (-1, 5, 2), Q (-3, 2, -1)$
21. $P (-2, 6, -5), Q (3, -2, 4)$

Use $\mathbf{u} = \langle 2, -1, 1 \rangle$, $\mathbf{v} = \langle 4, -2, 3 \rangle$, and $\mathbf{w} = \langle 5, 2, -4 \rangle$ to complete each vector operation.

22. $\mathbf{v} + \mathbf{w}$
23. $\mathbf{u} - \mathbf{v}$
24. $\mathbf{v} - 2\mathbf{u}$
25. $2\mathbf{w} + 3\mathbf{u}$
26. $\mathbf{u} \cdot \mathbf{v}$
27. $\mathbf{v} \cdot \mathbf{w}$

Find the angle between each pair of vectors (to the nearest degree).

28. $\mathbf{v} = \langle 1, 4, 2 \rangle$, $\mathbf{w} = \langle -2, 5, -3 \rangle$
29. $\mathbf{v} = \langle 3, 6, -1 \rangle$, $\mathbf{w} = \langle 4, 1, -7 \rangle$
30. $\mathbf{p} = \langle 3, 2, 4 \rangle$, $\mathbf{q} = \langle -3, -3, 1 \rangle$
31. $\mathbf{p} = \langle 5, 5, -1 \rangle$, $\mathbf{q} = \langle -9, -5, 15 \rangle$

In exercises 32–34, draw a three-dimensional vector modeling each quantity and express the vector in component form.

32. driving 45 mi/hr on a level road heading 70° east of north

33. taking off at 140 knots heading due west with a 15° angle of climb

34. hiking southwest up a mountain at 1.5 mi/hr with an angle of inclination of 17.5°

35. An airplane takes off headed due north with an air velocity vector directed 15° above horizontal and an airspeed of 150 knots. There is a 16-knot wind from the northeast. Find a vector that represents the plane's velocity relative to the point of takeoff.

36. A kicker attempting a field goal kicks the football due north at a speed of 83 mi/hr and an initial angle of inclination of 40° with a wind blowing to the southeast at 12 mi/hr. Find a vector that represents the football's resulting initial velocity relative to the point from which it was kicked. What is the football's initial resulting speed?

C. Exercises

37. A missile is fired southeast at an angle of 50° at a speed of 3000 mi/hr. There is a 22 mi/hr wind from the south. Find a vector that represents the missile's velocity relative to its launch point.

The airplane in Example 6 has a resultant velocity vector $r \approx \langle 28.3, -183.1, 77.0 \rangle$.

38. What is the plane's resultant ground speed?

39. At what bearing is the plane traveling during its take-off (to the nearest degree)?

40. What is the plane's resultant angle of inclination (to the nearest degree)?

CUMULATIVE REVIEW

41. Which quadrant contains the terminal side of each angle?   [4.1]

　a. $\frac{5\pi}{4}$ 　　　　　　　　　**b.** $-240°$

42. The terminal side of an angle $\theta \in [0, 2\pi)$ passes through the point $(-6, -2)$. Find its reference angle α and the angle θ (to the nearest tenth of a degree). [4.3]

43. Find the exact coordinates of point P.   [4.3]

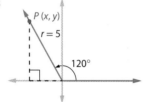

44. A triangular lot has sides of 450 ft and 570 ft. If the included angle is 100°, find the length of the third side to the nearest foot and the area of the lot to the nearest tenth of an acre (1 acre = 43,560 ft^2).   [5.7]

Use the definition of a circle and the distance formula to derive an equation for each described circle. [1.2]

45. centered at $(0, 0)$ with a radius of 8

46. centered at $(3, -4)$ with a radius of 5

47. Find the area of a circle whose diameter has end-points at $(4, 5)$ and $(-2, -3)$.   [1.2]

　A. $100 \ u^2$ 　　　　　　**D.** $50\pi \ u^2$

　B. $25 \ u^2$ 　　　　　　　**E.** The area cannot be

　C. $25\pi \ u^2$ 　　　　　　　　 determined.

48. Find an expression for the coordinates of A if the point lies on the unit circle.   [4.3]

　A. $(1, 1)$ 　　　　　　　　**D.** $(\tan\theta, \tan\theta)$

　B. $(\cos\theta, \sin\theta)$ 　　　　**E.** none of these

　C. $(\sin\theta, \cos\theta)$

49. Which angles are coterminal with $\frac{5\pi}{6}$? List all correct answers.   [4.3]

　A. $\frac{10\pi}{6}$ 　　**C.** $\frac{5\pi}{6} \pm 2\pi$ 　　**E.** none of these

　B. $\frac{17\pi}{6}$ 　　**D.** $-\frac{7\pi}{6}$

50. For which values of θ does $\tan\theta = 1$? List all correct answers.   [4.3]

　A. $\frac{\pi}{4}$ 　　**C.** $\frac{5\pi}{4}$ 　　**E.** all of these

　B. $\frac{3\pi}{4}$ 　　**D.** $\frac{7\pi}{4}$

Naval air traffic control systems employ polar coordinates.

Previously, you have graphed points and functions using rectangular coordinates (x, y) in the Cartesian coordinate system defined by the x- and y-axes, which intersect at the origin. Air traffic controllers, the Doppler radar shown in weather reports, flight plans, and sonar positioning systems on submarines all use a polar coordinate system. This system provides an alternative method of describing any position on a plane.

The *pole*, a fixed point O, serves as the origin for the polar coordinate system. The *polar axis* is an initial ray drawn from the pole in the direction of the positive x-axis. Any point P in the plane can be described by the *polar coordinates* (r, θ) where

 r is a directed distance from the pole O to the point P
 and θ is a directed angle from the polar axis.

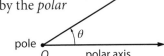

As usual, counterclockwise rotations are indicated by $\theta > 0$ and clockwise rotations are indicated by $\theta < 0$. When $r > 0$ the point lies on the terminal side of θ, but when $r < 0$ the point lies on the ray that is opposite the terminal side of θ. A *polar grid* can be used when graphing polar coordinates.

After completing this section, you will be able to

- graph points using polar coordinates.
- state multiple polar coordinates representing a point in the polar plane.
- find the distance between polar coordinates.
- convert between polar and rectangular coordinates.
- convert from a polar equation to a rectangular equation.

KEYWORD SEARCH

polar graph paper 🔍

Example 1 Plotting Points in the Polar Coordinate System

Graph each point described by its polar coordinates.

a. $A\left(4, \frac{\pi}{3}\right)$ **b.** $B\,(2, -120°)$ **c.** $C\left(-3, \frac{3\pi}{4}\right)$

Answer

a. Draw $\theta = \frac{\pi}{3}$ in Q I and plot A four units from O on the terminal side of θ.

b. Draw $\theta = -120°$ in Q III and plot B two units from O on the terminal side of θ.

c. Draw $\theta = \frac{3\pi}{4}$ in Q II and plot C three units from O on the ray opposite the terminal side of θ (in Q IV).

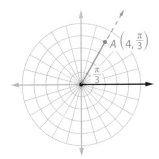

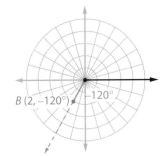

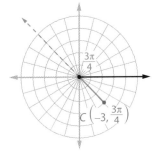

SKILL ✔ **EXERCISE 3**

In his *Method of Fluxions and Infinite Series* (published in 1736 but written much earlier), Isaac Newton used several different coordinate systems, including Cartesian and polar, to explore the properties of curves.

In the rectangular coordinate system each point is described by exactly one ordered pair, but this is not true in the polar coordinate system. Since there are an infinite number of coterminal angles, $P(r, \theta)$ can also be described by $(r, \theta + n2\pi)$ where $n \in \mathbb{Z}$. The point $P(r, \theta)$ can also be described by $(-r, \theta \pm \pi)$, or more generally $(-r, \theta + (2n + 1)\pi)$ where $n \in \mathbb{Z}$.

Example 2 Multiple Representations of a Point

Plot the point $P(3, 30°)$ and state four additional pairs of polar coordinates for P.

Answer

1. Draw $\theta = 30°$ in Q I and plot P three units from the pole on the terminal side of θ.

2. Keeping the same value for r, find $\theta \pm 360°$.

$(3, 30° + 360°)$
$= (3, 390°)$

$(3, 30° - 360°)$
$= (3, -330°)$

3. Using the opposite value for r, find $\theta \pm 180°$.

$(-3, 30° + 180°)$
$= (-3, 210°)$

$(-3, 30° - 180°)$
$= (-3, -150°)$

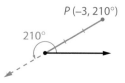
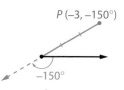

SKILL ✓ EXERCISE 9

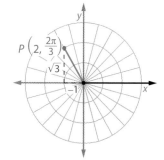

To understand the relationship between the polar and rectangular systems, superimpose them so that the pole coincides with the origin and the polar axis lies on the positive x-axis. Sketching the reference triangle related to $P(r, \theta)$ shows that

$$r^2 = x^2 + y^2, \cos \theta = \frac{x}{r}, \text{ and } \sin \theta = \frac{y}{r}.$$

Rearranging the last two equations produces formulas for x and y in terms of r and θ:
$x = r \cos \theta$ and $y = r \sin \theta$ so that $(x, y) = (r \cos \theta, r \sin \theta)$.

Example 3 Converting to Rectangular Coordinates

Convert the polar coordinates $\left(2, \frac{2\pi}{3}\right)$ to rectangular coordinates.

Answer

$(x, y) = (2 \cos \frac{2\pi}{3}, 2 \sin \frac{2\pi}{3})$

$= \left(2\left(-\frac{1}{2}\right), 2\left(\frac{\sqrt{3}}{2}\right)\right)$

$= (-1, \sqrt{3}) \approx (-1, 1.73)$

1. Substitute into $(x, y) = (r \cos \theta, r \sin \theta)$.

2. Simplify.

SKILL ✓ EXERCISE 13

When converting from rectangular coordinates to polar coordinates, find the reference angle $\alpha = \text{Tan}^{-1}\left|\frac{y}{x}\right|$, then use the appropriate formula from Section 6.1 to find $\theta \in [0, 360°)$ or $[0, 2\pi)$. Other polar coordinates for the point can then be found.

Example 4   Converting to Polar Coordinates

Find polar coordinates for $P(-5, -12)$ where $r > 0$ and $\theta \in [0, 360°)$.

Answer

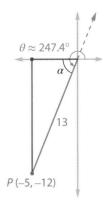

$r^2 = (-5)^2 + (-12)^2 = 169$

$r = \pm 13$

1. Substitute the known rectangular values to find possible values for r.

$\alpha = \text{Tan}^{-1}\left|\dfrac{-12}{-5}\right| \approx 67°$

$\theta \approx 67° + 180° = 247°$

2. Find the reference angle $\alpha = \text{Tan}^{-1}\left|\dfrac{y}{x}\right|$ and use the fact that P is in Q III to determine $\theta \in [0, 360°)$.

$P(13, 247°)$

3. Express P with coordinates where $r > 0$ and $\theta \in [0°, 360°)$.

SKILL ✔ **EXERCISE 19**

The distance between two points described by polar coordinates can be found using

$$d = \sqrt{r_1^2 + r_2^2 - 2r_1 r_2 \cos(\theta_2 - \theta_1)}.$$

This *polar distance formula* is derived and further investigated in exercise 44.

Example 5   Finding the Distance Between Polar Coordinates

The radar on a battleship detects ships at (15 mi, 140°) and (27 mi, 240°). Find the distance between these two ships.

Answer

1. Sketch a graph.

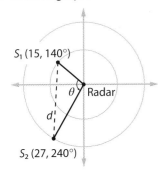

2. Apply the polar distance formula.

$$d = \sqrt{15^2 + 27^2 - 2(15)(27)\cos(240° - 140°)}$$
$$\approx 33.1 \text{ mi}$$

SKILL ✔ **EXERCISE 23**

To convert a rectangular equation to a polar equation, substitute $r \cos \theta$ for x and $r \sin \theta$ for y, then simplify the resulting equation.

Example 6   Converting to a Polar Equation

Write the equation of the line $x = 2$ in polar form where r is expressed in terms of θ.

Answer

$x = 2$

$r \cos \theta = 2$

1. Substitute $r \cos \theta$ for x.

$r = \dfrac{2}{\cos \theta}$

or $r = 2 \sec \theta$

2. Solve for r.

CONTINUED ➡

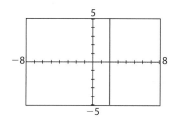

Check

3. Set your calculator to polar mode, select $\boxed{Y=}$, and enter 2/cos(θ) for r1 (using $\boxed{X,T,\Theta,n}$ for θ). Then $\boxed{GRAPH}$ the polar equation. See the Technology Corner for further instruction on graphing in polar mode.

SKILL ✓ **EXERCISE 27**

A polar equation can be converted to a rectangular equation by making similar substitutions. Algebraic manipulations may be required to set up substitutions involving the equations used to convert between rectangular and polar coordinates.

Example 7 Converting to a Rectangular Equation

Write each equation in rectangular form and describe its graph.

a. $r = 3$

b. $\theta = \dfrac{\pi}{6}$

Answer

a.
$$r = 3$$
$$r^2 = 9$$

1. Square both sides of the equation.

$$x^2 + y^2 = 9$$

2. Substitute $x^2 + y^2$ for r^2.

The graph is a circle centered at the origin with a radius of 3.

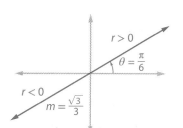

b.
$$\tan \theta = \tan \frac{\pi}{6}$$

1. Find the tangent of both sides of the equation.

$$\tan \theta = \frac{\sqrt{3}}{3}$$

$$\frac{y}{x} = \frac{\sqrt{3}}{3}$$

2. Substitute $\frac{y}{x}$ for $\tan \theta$.

$$y = \frac{\sqrt{3}}{3}x$$

3. Solve for y.

The graph is a line through the origin with a slope of $\dfrac{\sqrt{3}}{3} \approx 0.58$.

SKILL ✓ **EXERCISE 31**

Note that any point on the line $\theta = \frac{\pi}{6}$ in Q I has $r > 0$ and that any point on the line in Q IV has $r < 0$.

Example 8 Converting to a Rectangular Equation

Write $r = 4 \sin \theta$ in rectangular form.

Answer

$$r = 4 \sin \theta$$
$$r^2 = 4r \sin \theta$$

1. Multiply both sides by r to obtain recognizable forms.

$$x^2 + y^2 = 4y$$

2. Substitute using $r^2 = x^2 + y^2$ and $y = r \sin \theta$.

$$x^2 + y^2 - 4y = 0$$
$$x^2 + (y^2 - 4y + 4) = 4$$
$$x^2 + (y - 2)^2 = 4$$

3. Subtract $4y$ from each side; then complete the square.

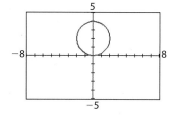

Check

4. Graphing $r = 4 \sin \theta$ in polar mode confirms that the graph is a circle centered at $(0, 2)$.

SKILL ✓ **EXERCISE 33**

Polar functions of r in terms of θ, like $r = 4 \sin \theta$ in Example 8, can be graphed on your calculator using polar mode. Press MODE and select POLAR and RADIAN.

Press Y= to display the polar function editor, which displays functions for r instead of y. Enter 4sin(θ) for r_1, using the X,T,Θ,n key for θ. Then select ZOOM, 6:ZStandard to graph the function. The circle will appear to be an ellipse since the window is not square.
Select WINDOW. Note the default settings of 0 for θmin and 2π for θmax. Reduce the default value of $\pi/24$ for θstep if the graph is not a smooth curve.

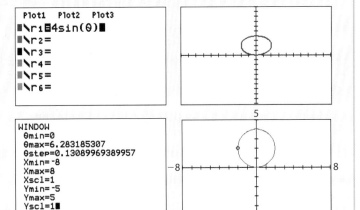

Use ZOOM, 5:ZSquare or enter −8 and 8 for Xmin and Xmax and −5 and 5 for Ymin and Ymax to obtain the graph next to Example 8.

Select the path icon, ⁙, from the graph options found to the left of r_1 on the Y= screen and press GRAPH. Notice that the graph is actually traced twice over [0, 2π].

⟩ A. Exercises

Graph each point described by its polar coordinates.

1. $A\left(3, \frac{\pi}{6}\right)$
2. $B\left(4, \frac{5\pi}{4}\right)$
3. $C\left(1, -60°\right)$
4. $D\left(3, -\frac{\pi}{4}\right)$
5. $E\left(-2, \frac{5\pi}{6}\right)$
6. $F\left(-3, \frac{5\pi}{3}\right)$

State all additional pairs of polar coordinates for each point where $\theta \in [-360°, 360°]$ or $\theta \in [-2\pi, 2\pi]$.

7. $G\left(2, 45°\right)$
8. $H\left(3, -120°\right)$
9. $I\left(-2, \pi\right)$
10. $J\left(3, -\frac{\pi}{3}\right)$

Convert the polar coordinates to rectangular coordinates.

11. $(-1, 180°)$
12. $(2, 30°)$
13. $(5, 45°)$
14. $\left(-2, -\frac{3\pi}{2}\right)$
15. $\left(3, \frac{2\pi}{3}\right)$
16. $\left(-1, \frac{11\pi}{6}\right)$

⟩ B. Exercises

Find the polar coordinates for each point where $r > 0$ and $\theta \in [0, 360°)$.

17. $P\left(2, 2\right)$
18. $Q\left(-3, -4\right)$
19. $R\left(-15, 8\right)$
20. $S\left(0, 1\right)$

Find the distance between the given polar coordinates (to the nearest tenth).

21. $(3, 40°), (1, 130°)$
22. $(-5, 315°), (3, 50°)$
23. $\left(3, \frac{\pi}{3}\right), \left(-1, \frac{\pi}{2}\right)$
24. $\left(4, \frac{5\pi}{12}\right), \left(6, \frac{5\pi}{4}\right)$

Transform each equation into polar form. Then verify your answer by using technology to graph the polar equation.

25. $y = 3$
26. $x + y = 3$
27. $2x - y = 4$
28. $x^2 + y^2 = 25$
29. $x^2 + 4y^2 = 16$
30. $y = x^2$

Graph each polar equation and describe the graph. Then transform the equation into rectangular form.

31. $r = 5 \sec \theta$
32. $r = -\csc \theta$
33. $r = -5$
34. $r = 8 \cos \theta$
35. $r = -6 \sin \theta$
36. $\theta = \frac{5\pi}{6}$

37. An airport control tower is tracking the locations of two planes flying at the same altitude. Find the distance between the planes if the first plane is located at (5 km, 155°) and the second is at (6 km, 35°).

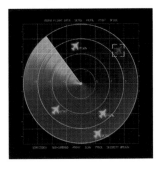

38. A ship's navigator observes ships at (3 nm, 70°) and (7 nm, 110°). Find the distance between the ships (nm = nautical mile).

39. **Explore:** Use technology to graph the four circles: $r = \pm 3 \sin \theta$ and $r = \pm 2 \cos \theta$.

   a. State the radius and center for $r = k \cos \theta$ in terms of k.

   b. State the radius and center for $r = k \sin \theta$ in terms of k.

> C. Exercises

Transform each equation into polar form. Verify your answer by using technology to graph the polar equation.

40. $(x - 2)^2 + (y + 1)^2 = 5$ 41. $xy = 4$

Graph each polar equation. Then transform the equation into rectangular form and describe the graph.

42. $r = 4 \sin \theta - 6 \cos \theta$

43. $r = 2 \cos \theta - 6 \sin \theta$

44. **Explore:** Investigate the polar distance formula.

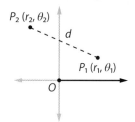

   a. Use the Law of Cosines to show that the distance between $P_1\,(r_1, \theta_1)$ and $P_2\,(r_2, \theta_2)$ is
   $$d = \sqrt{r_1^{\,2} + r_2^{\,2} - 2r_1\,r_2 \cos\,(\theta_2 - \theta_1)}.$$

   b. Simplify the formula in the case where $\theta_2 = \theta_1$.

   c. Simplify the formula in the case where $\theta_2 = \theta_1 + \pi$.

   d. Simplify the formula in the case where $\theta_2 = \theta_1 + \frac{\pi}{2}$.

CUMULATIVE REVIEW

Use the sum and difference identities to simplify each expression. [5.4]

45. $\sin\,(\pi \pm \theta)$ 46. $\cos\,(\pi \pm \theta)$

Graph each function over {0, 2π}. Then list any zeros of the function and any local maximum or minimum points within [0, 2π]. [4.4]

47. $y = 3 \sin x$ 48. $y = \cos 2x$

49. Find the general solution for $\cos 2\theta = 1$. [5.3]

50. Write simplified expressions for each power of i from i^0 to i^8. [Appendix 5]

51. If $\sin \theta = \frac{3}{5}$ and $\cos \theta = \frac{4}{5}$, what is $\tan \theta$? [4.2, 5.1]

   A. $\frac{3}{4}$ C. 5   E. $\frac{1}{2}$

   B. $\frac{4}{3}$ D. $-\frac{4}{3}$

52. Find θ to the nearest degree. [4.2]

   A. 22°   D. 68°

   B. 30°   E. none of these

   C. 60°

53. Evaluate $\mathrm{Tan}^{-1}\left(\tan \frac{3\pi}{4}\right)$. [4.6]

   A. 1   C. $\frac{\pi}{4}$ E. $\frac{3\pi}{4}$

   B. −1   D. $-\frac{\pi}{4}$

54. Which expression is equivalent to $\dfrac{\tan^2 x - \sin^2 x}{\sin^2 x\,\tan^2 x}$? [5.1]

   A. −1   D. $\cot^2 x$

   B. 1   E. none of these

   C. $\csc^2 x$

6.5 Graphs of Polar Equations

This peacock feather contains shapes that can be modeled with polar equations.

When you first learned to graph equations in the Cartesian coordinate system, you used a table of values to plot a sufficient number of points to illustrate the shape of the graph. You then used general characteristics of each type of graph to accurately sketch the graphs. By converting simple polar equations to rectangular form in the previous section, you saw that the graph of $r = k$ is a circle centered at the origin with radius k and that $\theta = k$ is a line making an angle of θ with the polar axis. The graphs of other polar equations can be found by making a table of values where r is dependent on θ. Each point is plotted as a directed distance r that varies while θ rotates around the pole.

After completing this section, you will be able to

- graph polar equations by plotting points.
- use symmetry, zeros, and maximum values to sketch polar graphs.
- graph and analyze common polar equations.

Example 1   Graphing a Spiral by Plotting Points

Graph $r = \theta$ where $\theta \geq 0$.

Answer

1. In order to plot a real number r, θ is expressed in radians rather than degrees. Round values for r to the nearest tenth.

θ	0	$\frac{\pi}{6}$	$\frac{\pi}{3}$	$\frac{\pi}{2}$	$\frac{2\pi}{3}$	$\frac{5\pi}{6}$	π
r	0	0.5	1.0	1.6	2.1	2.6	3.1

θ	$\frac{7\pi}{6}$	$\frac{4\pi}{3}$	$\frac{3\pi}{2}$	$\frac{5\pi}{3}$	$\frac{11\pi}{6}$	2π
r	3.7	4.2	4.7	5.2	5.8	6.3

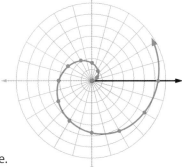

2. Plot the points and connect them with a smooth curve. This type of curve is known as an *Archimedean spiral*.

The study of Archimedes's treatise *On Spirals* during the seventeenth and eighteenth centuries encouraged the development of polar coordinate systems.

SKILL ✓ **EXERCISE 3**

When $\theta \leq 0$, the graph of $r = \theta$ is a reflection of the graph in Example 1 across the line $\theta = \frac{\pi}{2}$.

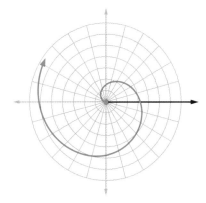

Example 2 Graphing a Circle by Plotting Points

Graph $r = 4 \cos \theta$.

Answer

1. Since $\cos \theta$ has a period of 2π, the entire graph can be drawn using $\theta \in [0, 2\pi]$.

θ	0	$\frac{\pi}{6}$	$\frac{\pi}{3}$	$\frac{\pi}{2}$	$\frac{2\pi}{3}$	$\frac{5\pi}{6}$	π
r	4	3.5	2	0	−2	−3.5	−4

θ	$\frac{7\pi}{6}$	$\frac{4\pi}{3}$	$\frac{3\pi}{2}$	$\frac{5\pi}{3}$	$\frac{11\pi}{6}$	2π
r	−3.5	−2	0	2	3.5	4

2. Plot the points and connect them with a smooth curve. Notice that the circle is actually graphed twice.

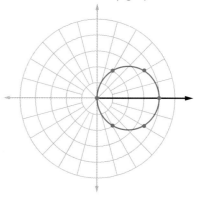

SKILL ✔ EXERCISE 5

Knowing whether the graph is symmetric with respect to the polar axis, the line $\theta = \frac{\pi}{2}$, or the pole reduces the number of points needed to determine the overall shape of the graph.

▌ TESTS FOR SYMMETRY IN POLAR GRAPHS

The graph of a polar equation has the described symmetry if either substitution for (r, θ) produces an equivalent equation.

The Polar Axis	The Line $\theta = \frac{\pi}{2}$	The Pole
$(r, -\theta)$ or $(-r, \pi - \theta)$	$(r, \pi - \theta)$ or $(-r, -\theta)$	$(r, \pi + \theta)$ or $(-r, \theta)$

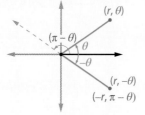 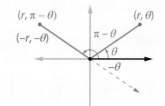 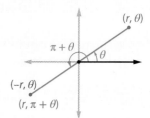

To show that the circle graphed in Example 2 is symmetric with respect to the polar axis, replace (r, θ) in $r = 4 \cos \theta$ with $(r, -\theta)$ and simplify using the fact that cosine is an even function:

$$r = 4 \cos(-\theta) = 4 \cos \theta.$$

The circle graphed in Section 6.4 Example 8 is shown to be symmetric with the line $\theta = \frac{\pi}{2}$ by replacing (r, θ) in $r = 4 \sin \theta$ with $(-r, -\theta)$ and using the fact that sine is an odd function:

$$-r = 4 \sin(-\theta) = 4(-\sin \theta) = -4 \sin \theta; \text{ so } r = 4 \sin \theta.$$

The odd/even identities can be used to verify the following quick tests for symmetry.

Quick Tests for Symmetry

The graph of $r = f(\cos \theta)$ is symmetric with respect to the polar axis.

The graph of $r = f(\sin \theta)$ is symmetric with respect to the line $\theta = \frac{\pi}{2}$.

Example 3 Using Symmetry to Graph a Limaçon

Graph $r = 3 + 2 \sin \theta$.

Answer

1. Since $r = f(\sin \theta)$, the graph is symmetric with respect to $\theta = \frac{\pi}{2}$. The function's period is 2π, so make a table of values using $\theta \in \left[-\frac{\pi}{2}, \frac{\pi}{2}\right]$.

θ	$-\frac{\pi}{2}$	$-\frac{\pi}{3}$	$-\frac{\pi}{6}$	0	$\frac{\pi}{6}$	$\frac{\pi}{3}$	$\frac{\pi}{2}$
r	1	1.3	2	3	4	4.7	5

2. Plot the points over $\left[-\frac{\pi}{2}, \frac{\pi}{2}\right]$ and connect them with a smooth curve.

3. Reflect the curve across the line $\theta = \frac{\pi}{2}$ to complete the graph. The result is a type of limaçon (**lim**-uh-sohn). (There are four types in all.)

KEYWORD SEARCH

animated limaçon image

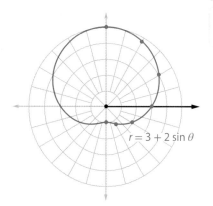

$r = 3 + 2 \sin \theta$

SKILL ✓ **EXERCISE 13**

It is helpful to identify values of θ for which $r = 0$ (where the graph intersects the pole). The fact that the sine and cosine functions range from −1 to 1 can help you identify points where the distance from the pole, $|r|$, is maximized.

Example 4 Using Maximum |r| to Graph a Rose

Graph $r = 4 \cos 2\theta$.

Answer

1. Since $r = f(\cos \theta)$, the graph is symmetric with respect to the polar axis.
2. zeros: when $2\theta = (2n + 1)\frac{\pi}{2}$ or $\theta = (2n + 1)\frac{\pi}{4}$
   maximum $|r|$: when $2\theta = n\pi$ or $\theta = n\frac{\pi}{2}$
3. Make a table of values for $\theta \in [0, \pi]$.

θ	0	$\frac{\pi}{6}$	$\frac{\pi}{4}$	$\frac{\pi}{3}$	$\frac{\pi}{2}$	$\frac{2\pi}{3}$	$\frac{3\pi}{4}$	$\frac{5\pi}{6}$	π
r	4	2	0	−2	−4	−2	0	2	4

4. Plot the points over $[0, \pi]$ and connect them with a smooth curve. Then reflect the curve across the polar axis. The resulting curve is called a rose and has 4 petals.

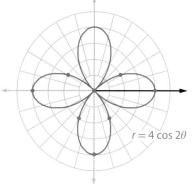

$r = 4 \cos 2\theta$

TIP

Notice how the polar graph of $r = 4 \cos 2\theta$ compares to the rectangular coordinate graph of $y = 4 \cos 2x$.

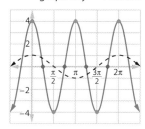

SKILL ✓ **EXERCISE 15**

After confirming that the graph in Example 4 is also symmetric with respect to the line $\theta = \frac{\pi}{2}$ and the pole, we could have used $\theta \in \left[0, \frac{\pi}{4}\right]$ and symmetry to draw the rest of the graph.

Although you can always graph polar equations by plotting points, recognizing the general form of the equation for common polar graphs is extremely helpful.

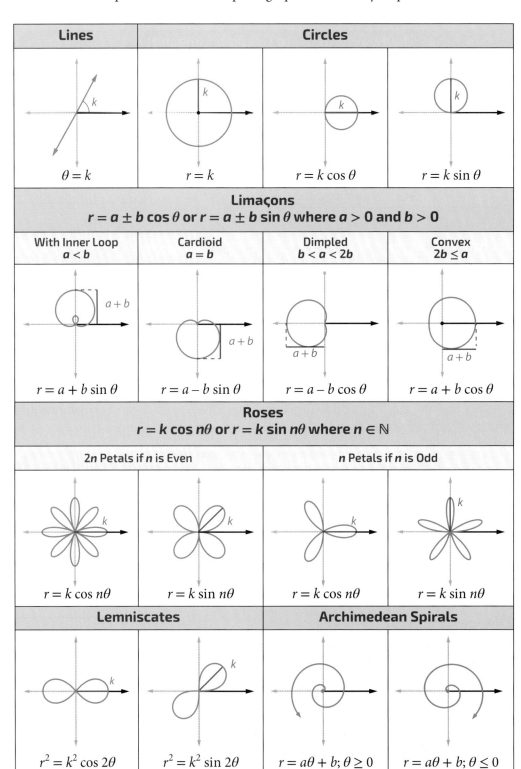

KEYWORD SEARCH

animated lemniscates 🔍

Example 5 Graphing a Cardioid

Sketch the graph of $r = 2 - 2\cos\theta$.

Answer

1. The general form $r = a - b\cos\theta$ where $a = b$ indicates the graph is a cardioid that is symmetric with respect to the polar axis.

2. Zeros occur when $\cos\theta = 1$ (when $\theta = 0, 2\pi$).

3. Maximum $|r|$ values occur when $\cos\theta = -1$ (when $\theta = \pi$).

4. Make a table of several key points.

θ	0	$\frac{\pi}{4}$	$\frac{\pi}{2}$	$\frac{3\pi}{4}$	π
r	0	0.6	2	3.4	4

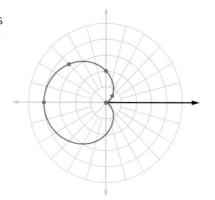

5. Plot the points and use symmetry to complete the sketch of the curve.

_____ SKILL ✔ **EXERCISE 23**

Microphone reception patterns are typically represented by a polar graph, often with overlays of different frequency response curves. The cardioid is a typical reception pattern for microphones designed for singers or announcers.

Example 4 illustrates that the graph of $r = k\cos n\theta$ or $r = k\sin n\theta$ is a rose with $2n$ petals when n is even. When n is odd the graph contains just n petals, each being traced twice over $[0, 2\pi]$.

Example 6 Graphing a Rose

Sketch the graph of $r = 3\sin 3\theta$.

Answer

1. The general form $r = k\sin n\theta$ where n is odd indicates the graph is a rose with three petals (traced twice from 0 to 2π) that is symmetric with respect to the line $\theta = \frac{\pi}{2}$.

2. Zeros occur when $3\theta = n\pi$ (when $\theta = 0, \frac{\pi}{3}, \frac{2\pi}{3}, \pi, \ldots$).

3. Maximum $|r|$ values occur at $3\theta = (2n + 1)\frac{\pi}{2}$ (when $\theta = \frac{\pi}{6}, \frac{\pi}{2}, \frac{5\pi}{6}, \ldots$).

4. Make a table of several key points.

θ	0	$\frac{\pi}{6}$	$\frac{\pi}{3}$	$\frac{\pi}{2}$	$\frac{2\pi}{3}$	$\frac{5\pi}{6}$	π
r	0	3	0	−3	0	3	0

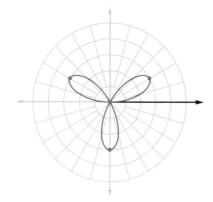

5. Plot the points and sketch the curve. The entire curve is plotted over $[0, \pi]$ and is traced again over $[\pi, 2\pi]$.

_____ SKILL ✔ **EXERCISE 25**

When $k > 0$, the first maximum $|r|$ value for $r = k\cos n\pi$ occurs on the polar axis (at $\theta = 0$), and the first maximum $|r|$ value for $r = k\sin n\theta$ occurs at $\theta = \frac{\pi}{2} \div n$.

The key characteristic of the equation for a lemniscate (**lem**-nis-keyt) is the squared radius. Taking the square root of both sides reveals that its domain is restricted.

Example 7 Graphing a Lemniscate

Sketch the polar graph of $r^2 = 16 \sin 2\theta$.

Answer

TIP

Notice how the polar graph of $r = 4\sqrt{\sin 2\theta}$ compares to the rectangular coordinate graph of $y = 4\sqrt{\sin 2x}$.

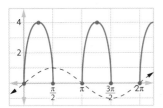

1. The general form indicates the graph is a lemniscate that is symmetric with respect to the pole and the line $\theta = \frac{\pi}{4}$.

   Note that $r = \pm 4\sqrt{\sin 2\theta}$ is not defined in $\left(\frac{\pi}{2}, \pi\right)$ or $\left(\frac{3\pi}{2}, 2\pi\right)$.

2. Zeros occur when $2\theta = n\pi$ (when $\theta = 0, \frac{\pi}{2}, \pi, \ldots$).

3. Maximum $|r|$ values for $r = \pm 4\sqrt{\sin 2\theta}$ occur when

   $\theta = (2n + 1)\frac{\pi}{2}$ is defined (when $\theta = \frac{\pi}{4}, \frac{5\pi}{4}, \ldots$).

4. Make a table of several key points.

θ	0	$\frac{\pi}{4}$	$\frac{\pi}{2}$
r	0	± 4	0

5. Plot the points and sketch the curve. Using positive and negative values of r causes the entire graph to be drawn with $\theta \in \left[0, \frac{\pi}{2}\right]$.

   It is then retraced using $\theta \in \left[\pi, \frac{3\pi}{2}\right]$.

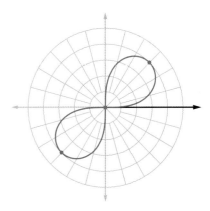

SKILL ✓ **EXERCISE 27**

❯ A. Exercises

1. Match each polar equation to the type of curve.

   a. $r = 3 \cos \theta$ **I.** Archimedean spiral

   b. $r = \sin 3\theta$ **II.** circle

   c. $r = 3\theta$ **III.** lemniscate

   d. $r^2 = 3 \cos 2\theta$ **IV.** rose

2. Identify the type of limaçon represented by each polar equation.

   a. $r = 3 - 3 \cos \theta$ **I.** cardioid

   b. $r = 3 + 2 \sin \theta$ **II.** convex limaçon

   c. $r = 3 + 4 \sin \theta$ **III.** dimpled limaçon

   d. $r = 3 - \cos \theta$ **IV.** limaçon with inner loop

Sketch the graph of each polar equation by plotting points. Then classify the curve.

3. $r = \frac{1}{2}\theta$ where $\theta \in [0, 3\pi]$

4. $r = \theta - 1$ where $\theta \in [-2\pi, 0]$

5. $r = 4 \sin \theta$

6. $r = -5 \cos \theta$

State whether a quick test for symmetry reveals the stated line of symmetry for each function.

7. with respect to the polar axis

   a. $r = 2 + 2 \cos \theta$ **b.** $r = -3 \sin \theta$

   c. $r = 4 \sin 2\theta$ **d.** $r^2 = 25 \cos 2\theta$

8. with respect to the line $\theta = \frac{\pi}{2}$

   a. $r = 2 + 2 \cos \theta$ **b.** $r = -3 \sin \theta$

   c. $r = 4 \sin 2\theta$ **d.** $r^2 = 25 \cos 2\theta$

List the values of $\theta \in [0, 2\pi]$ for which $r = 0$ and those for which $|r|$ has a maximum value.

9. $r = 2 + 2 \cos \theta$ 10. $r = -3 \sin \theta$

11. $r = 4 \sin 2\theta$ 12. $r^2 = 25 \cos 2\theta$

Classify each polar curve. Then use the results from exercises 7–12 and plot points as needed to graph each polar equation.

13. $r = 2 + 2 \cos \theta$ 14. $r = -3 \sin \theta$

15. $r = 4 \sin 2\theta$ 16. $r^2 = 25 \cos 2\theta$

State the number of petals in each polar rose and state the maximum value of $|r|$.

17. $r = 2 \cos 6\theta$ 18. $r = -6 \cos 7\theta$

B. Exercises

State whether a test reveals that the graph of the polar equation is symmetric with respect to each of the following.

a. the polar axis   **b.** the line $\theta = \frac{\pi}{2}$ **c.** the pole

19. $r = 1 + \cos\theta$

20. $r = 3 + 2\sin\theta$

21. $r = 5\sin 8\theta$

Classify each polar curve and then graph the equation.

22. $r = 4 - 4\sin\theta$ **23.** $r = 2 + 3\cos\theta$

24. $r = -3 + \sin\theta$ **25.** $r = 3\cos 5\theta$

26. $r = 2\cos 4\theta$ **27.** $r^2 = 9\cos 2\theta$

28. $r^2 = -16\sin 2\theta$ **29.** $r = 3\sin 5\theta$

30. $r = 2\cos 2\theta$ **31.** $r = -2\sin 3\theta$

32. $r = 3 - 3\cos\theta$ **33.** $r = 3 + 2\sin\theta$

Find the area enclosed by each polar curve.

34. $r = 7$ **35.** $r = -5\sin\theta$

C. Exercises

36. Explore: Use technology to graph $r = 3\cos\left(\frac{n}{2}\theta\right)$ for several odd values of $n \geq 3$. Explain how these graphs compare to previously graphed roses.

37. Explain: Why is it possible to classify circles of the form $r = \pm b\cos\theta$ or $r = \pm b\sin\theta$ as a rose?

38. Limaçons can be viewed as the sum (or difference) of two circles, $r_1 = \pm a$ and either $r_2 = b\sin\theta$ or $r_2 = b\cos\theta$. The relative magnitudes of a and b define the extent to which each function determines the shape of the limaçon. A similar effect occurs for the graphs of $r = a \pm b\sin n\theta$. Use technology to graph the following functions and explain how the values of a and b affect the petals of the related polar rose.

a. $r = 2 + 3\cos 2\theta$ **b.** $r = 2 + 2\sin 2\theta$

c. $r = 3 + 2\sin 2\theta$ **d.** $r = 3 + \cos 2\theta$

39. Microphone reception patterns are typically presented on a polar graph that has been rotated 90° where the microphone is at the origin, pointed at 0°. Different frequency response curves are often overlaid on the graph. Classify each polar graph and write an equation that models the microphone's response at each frequency.

a. 500 Hz

b. 1000 Hz

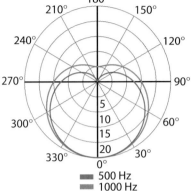

Explore: For exercises 40–41, complete the following steps to investigate the solving of each system of polar equations.

a. Use technology to graph both equations on the same polar grid. Then state the number of apparent points of intersection.

b. Use substitution to find the primary solutions of the system algebraically.

c. Graph each equation in function mode, where $y = r$ and $x = \theta$, and list any primary solutions of the system.

d. Return to polar mode and graph the equations simultaneously. Explain why some apparent points of intersection on the polar graphs are not solutions.

40. $r = 3\cos\theta$ **41.** $r = \sin\theta$
      $r = 1 + \cos\theta$ $r = 1 - \sin\theta$

Use $z_1 = 8 - 4i$ and $z_2 = 3 + i$ to evaluate each expression. [Appendix 5]

42. $z_1 + z_2$

43. $z_1 - z_2$

44. $z_1 \cdot z_2$

45. $z_1 \div z_2$

46. Factor over the set of complex numbers. [Appendix 5]

    a. $x^2 + 9$ **b.** $x^2 + ix + 12$

47. Solve $x^2 + 4 = 0$. [Appendix 5]

    a. by taking roots   **b.** by factoring

48. Simplify $(2 + 2i)^2$. [Appendix 5]

    A. 0   **C.** $-4i$ **E.** $-8i$

    B. $4i$ **D.** $8i$

49. Find the angle between $\mathbf{v} = \langle 2, 1, 3 \rangle$ and $\mathbf{w} = \langle -3, 4, -5 \rangle$ (to the nearest degree). [6.3]

    A. $50°$ **C.** $55°$ **E.** none of

    B. $130°$ **D.** $143°$ these

50. Convert the polar coordinates $\left(3\sqrt{2}, -\frac{\pi}{4}\right)$ to rectangular coordinates. [6.4]

    A. $(3, 3)$ **C.** $(-3, 3)$ **E.** none of

    B. $(3, -3)$ **D.** $(-3, -3)$ these

51. Convert the rectangular coordinates $\left(\sqrt{3}, 1\right)$ to polar coordinates. [6.4]

    A. $(1, 30°)$ **C.** $(2, 30°)$ **E.** none of

    B. $(1, 60°)$ **D.** $(2, 60°)$ these

COMPLEX NUMBERS

Impossible. Amphibian. Absurd. Useless. All these words were once used to describe imaginary numbers—by the very people who discovered them! In the sixteenth century, aversion to negative numbers was still the norm even among mathematicians, so the square roots of such numbers were really baffling. Mathematicians understood that any quadratic equation could be written as $ax^2 = bx + c$ and solved by finding the intersections of the parabola $f(x) = ax^2$ and the line $g(x) = bx + c$. When solved algebraically, a negative radicand indicated that the parabola and the line had no points of intersection. However, in the cubic equation $ax^3 + bx^2 = cx + d$ there had to be at least one point of intersection between the graph of $f(x) = ax^3 + bx^2$ and the line $g(x) = cx + d$. The pursuit of a general solution for cubic equations proved the necessity and usefulness of complex numbers.

Early in the sixteenth century Scipione del Ferro discovered the general solution to the depressed cubic, an equation of the form $x^3 + px = q$. It is not hard to show that a depressed cubic where $p > 0$ will always have just one real root, and finding one root was sufficient at that time. Soon, Niccolò Fontana (known as Tartaglia) found the general solution to cubic equations of the form $x^3 + px^2 = q$, and not long after, Gerolamo Cardano developed the method that extended del Ferro's solution to all cubics.

When a cubic with three real roots is evaluated using Cardano's formula, the solution requires manipulation of complex numbers. While Cardano called these cubics "irreducible," Rafael Bombelli had the novel thought that the resulting complex expression actually represents one of the real roots and became the first to demonstrate that complex numbers are subject to the normal rules of mathematical operation. Bombelli's willingness to explore algebraic operations with no obvious geometric interpretations unleashed the power of imaginary numbers. Even so, the search for geometric meaning continued.

In 1799 the Norwegian surveyor Caspar Wessel was the first to use vectors in the complex plane to geometrically represent operations with complex numbers. Wessel's methods received little attention outside of Denmark until 1831 when the highly respected Carl Gauss published the same methods. At that point Wessel's geometric representation of complex numbers, which is still used today, became generally accepted. Extending complex vector operations to three dimensions proved challenging. In 1843 the Irish mathematician William Hamilton discovered quaternions, an extension of complex numbers. A simpler system involving scalars and vectors was later developed by Josiah Gibbs and Oliver Heaviside. This system is the vector analysis still in use today.

Hamilton's quaternions, along with matrices and the complex numbers, are subsets of the *hypercomplex* numbers. Just as the study of conics proved useful in astronomy and infinite series were applied in electrical engineering, unexpected real-world applications of hypercomplex numbers have been discovered in medicine and computer graphics, including virtual reality. This remarkable ability of pure mathematics to model reality provides reasonable evidence of the underlying structure of the universe.

COMPREHENSION CHECK

1. What problem led to the development of imaginary numbers?

2. What is a depressed cubic, and who discovered its solution?

3. Who discovered a general solution for any cubic equation?

4. What was Rafael Bombelli's novel thought about the roots of cubic equations?

5. How did Caspar Wessel represent complex numbers geometrically?

6. Name at least two examples of "useless" mathematics being found to have important real-world applications. What does this imply about our world?

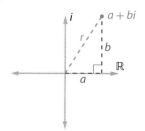

Fractal art generated by computers utilizes polar graphs of complex numbers.

After completing this section, you will be able to

- graph complex numbers.
- convert between the standard and polar forms of a complex number.
- find products, quotients, powers, and roots of complex numbers in polar form.

Any real number a can be illustrated by its graph on a real number line. Any complex number $a + bi$ can be illustrated by a point in the *complex plane* (as in an Argand diagram). The real component a is plotted along the horizontal *real axis* and the imaginary component bi is plotted along the vertical *imaginary axis* so that the complex number $a + bi$ is represented by the ordered pair (a, b).

Recall that the absolute value of a real number is defined as its distance from the origin. The absolute value of a complex number, $|a + bi|$, is also defined as the distance from the origin to the number's graph. The Pythagorean Theorem implies that $r = |a + bi| = \sqrt{a^2 + b^2}$.

Example 1 Graphing Complex Numbers

Plot each complex number in the complex plane and find its absolute value.

a. $3 - 3i$ **b.** $-\sqrt{3} + i$

Answer

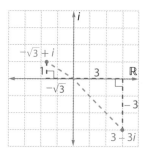

1. Plot each complex number.
2. Apply $|a + bi| = \sqrt{a^2 + b^2}$.

a. $r = \sqrt{3^2 + (-3)^2}$
$= \sqrt{18}$
$= 3\sqrt{2} \approx 4.24$

b. $r = \sqrt{(-\sqrt{3})^2 + 1^2}$
$= \sqrt{4}$
$= 2$

SKILL ✔ EXERCISE 1

Defining a directed angle θ from the positive real axis to the terminal ray through the graph of the complex number enables a complex number to be expressed in *polar (or trigonometric) form*. Right-triangle trigonometry indicates four key relationships.

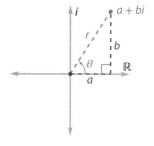

$$r = \sqrt{a^2 + b^2} \qquad a = r\cos\theta \qquad b = r\sin\theta \qquad \tan\theta = \frac{b}{a}$$

$$\therefore a + bi = r\cos\theta + i\,r\sin\theta$$
$$= r(\cos\theta + i\sin\theta), \text{ which is often abbreviated as } r\operatorname{cis}\theta.$$

▌ DEFINITIONS

A complex number in **standard** (or **rectangular**) **form**, $z = a + bi$, can be expressed in **polar** (or **trigonometric**) **form**, $z = r(\cos\theta + i\sin\theta)$ or $z = r\operatorname{cis}\theta$. The absolute value $r = \sqrt{a^2 + b^2}$ is also called the **modulus** (pl. *moduli*). The angle θ is the **argument** of the complex number.

While the standard form for $z = a + bi$ and its absolute value are unique, the existence of coterminal angles for the argument θ implies that its polar form, $z = r \operatorname{cis} \theta$, is not. Since the range of the Tan^{-1} function is $\left[-\frac{\pi}{2}, \frac{\pi}{2}\right]$, the following formulas express the argument θ within $[0, 2\pi)$.

$$\text{Q I: } \theta = \operatorname{Tan}^{-1}\frac{b}{a} \qquad \text{Q II \& Q III: } \theta = \pi + \operatorname{Tan}^{-1}\frac{b}{a} \qquad \text{Q IV: } \theta = 2\pi + \operatorname{Tan}^{-1}\frac{b}{a}$$

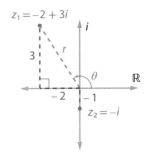

Example 2   Converting to Polar Form

Convert each complex number to polar form.

a. $z_1 = -2 + 3i$ **b.** $z_2 = -i$

Answer

a. $r = \sqrt{(-2)^2 + 3^2}$

$= \sqrt{13} \approx 3.61$

b. $r = \sqrt{0^2 + (-1)^2} = 1$

1. Determine the modulus.

$\theta = \pi + \operatorname{Tan}^{-1}\left(\frac{3}{-2}\right)$

$\approx \pi + (-0.98)$

≈ 2.16

Since $\operatorname{Tan}^{-1}\left(\frac{-1}{0}\right)$ is undefined, $\theta = \frac{\pi}{2}$ or $\frac{3\pi}{2}$.

2. Since z_1 is in Q II, use $\theta = \pi + \operatorname{Tan}^{-1}\frac{b}{a}$ to determine its argument within $[0, 2\pi)$.

$z_1 \approx 3.61 \operatorname{cis} 2.16$

$z_2 = 1 \operatorname{cis} \frac{3\pi}{2}$

3. Express in polar form.

SKILL ✓ **EXERCISE 7**

Example 3   Converting to Standard Form

Plot each complex number and convert to standard form.

a. $z_1 = 3 \operatorname{cis} \frac{\pi}{2}$ **b.** $z_2 = 4 \operatorname{cis} \frac{11\pi}{6}$

Answer

1. Use a polar grid to plot z_1 and z_2.

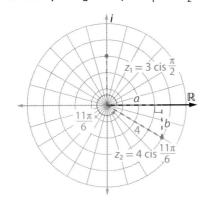

2. Evaluate $r(\cos\theta + i\sin\theta)$.

a. $z_1 = 3\left(\cos\frac{\pi}{2} + i\sin\frac{\pi}{2}\right)$

$= 3[0 + i(1)] = 3i$

b. $z_2 = 4\left(\cos\frac{11\pi}{6} + i\sin\frac{11\pi}{6}\right)$

$= 4\left[\frac{\sqrt{3}}{2} + i\left(-\frac{1}{2}\right)\right]$

$= 2\sqrt{3} - 2i$

$\approx 3.46 - 2i$

SKILL ✓ **EXERCISE 11**

Finding the product of two complex numbers in polar form involves finding the product of their moduli and summing their arguments. Finding a quotient involves finding the quotient of the moduli and the difference of the arguments.

PRODUCTS AND QUOTIENTS OF COMPLEX NUMBERS IN POLAR FORM

If $z_1 = r_1 \text{ cis } \theta_1$ and $z_2 = r_2 \text{ cis } \theta_2$, then

$$z_1 z_2 = r_1 r_2 \text{ cis } (\theta_1 + \theta_2) \text{ and } \frac{z_1}{z_2} = \frac{r_1 \text{ cis } \theta_1}{r_2 \text{ cis } \theta_2} = \frac{r_1}{r_2} \text{ cis } (\theta_1 - \theta_2).$$

The derivation of the product formula utilizes sum identities from Section 5.4.
Let $z_1 = r_1(\cos \theta_1 + i \sin \theta_1)$ and $z_2 = r_2(\cos \theta_2 + i \sin \theta_2)$.
Then $z_1 z_2 = r_1(\cos \theta_1 + i \sin \theta_1) \, r_2(\cos \theta_2 + i \sin \theta_2)$

$$
\begin{aligned}
&= r_1 r_2(\cos \theta_1 \cos \theta_2 + i \cos \theta_1 \sin \theta_2 + i \sin \theta_1 \cos \theta_2 + i^2 \sin \theta_1 \sin \theta_2) \\
&= r_1 r_2[(\cos \theta_1 \cos \theta_2 + i^2 \sin \theta_1 \sin \theta_2) + (i \cos \theta_1 \sin \theta_2 + i \sin \theta_1 \cos \theta_2)] \\
&= r_1 r_2[(\cos \theta_1 \cos \theta_2 - \sin \theta_1 \sin \theta_2) + i(\cos \theta_1 \sin \theta_2 + \sin \theta_1 \cos \theta_2)] \\
&= r_1 r_2[\cos (\theta_1 + \theta_2) + i \sin (\theta_1 + \theta_2)] \\
&= r_1 r_2 \text{ cis } (\theta_1 + \theta_2)
\end{aligned}
$$

The derivation of the quotient formula, completed in exercise 39, makes similar use of difference identities.

Example 4   Finding Products and Quotients in Polar Form

Find the product and quotient of $z_1 = 5 \text{ cis } \frac{4\pi}{3}$ and $z_2 = 2 \text{ cis } \frac{\pi}{6}$, expressing each in standard form.

a. $z_1 z_2$ **b.** $\frac{z_1}{z_2}$

Answer

a. $z_1 z_2 = 5 \cdot 2 \text{ cis } \left(\frac{4\pi}{3} + \frac{\pi}{6} \right)$ **b.** $\frac{z_1}{z_2} = \frac{5}{2} \text{ cis } \left(\frac{4\pi}{3} - \frac{\pi}{6} \right)$ 1. Apply the product or quotient formula.

$\qquad\qquad = 10 \text{ cis } \frac{3\pi}{2}$ $= \frac{5}{2} \text{ cis } \frac{7\pi}{6}$

$\qquad\qquad = 10(\cos \frac{3\pi}{2} + i \sin \frac{3\pi}{2})$ $= \frac{5}{2}(\cos \frac{7\pi}{6} + i \sin \frac{7\pi}{6})$ 2. Convert to standard form.

$\qquad\qquad = 10[0 + i(-1)]$ $= \frac{5}{2}\left(-\frac{\sqrt{3}}{2} + i\left(-\frac{1}{2}\right) \right)$

$\qquad\qquad = -10i$ $= -\frac{5\sqrt{3}}{4} - \frac{5}{4}i$

SKILL ✔ **EXERCISES 19, 21**

Finding a power or root of a complex number such as $(-1 + i)^7$ or $\sqrt[7]{-1 + i}$ is much easier in polar form. Consider the following powers of $z = r \text{ cis } \theta$ to develop a formula for the power of a complex number in polar form.

$$
\begin{aligned}
z^2 &= (r \text{ cis } \theta)(r \text{ cis } \theta) & z^3 &= z^2 z = (r^2 \text{ cis } 2\theta)(r \text{ cis } \theta) \\
&= r^2 \text{ cis } (\theta + \theta) & &= r^3 \text{ cis } (2\theta + \theta) \\
&= r^2 \text{ cis } 2\theta & &= r^3 \text{ cis } 3\theta
\end{aligned}
$$

Can you see why $z^4 = r^4 \text{ cis } 4\theta$? De Moivre's Theorem summarizes the general case for the nth power of a complex number.

DE MOIVRE'S THEOREM

If $z = r \text{ cis } \theta$, then $z^n = r^n \text{ cis } n\theta$, where $n \in \mathbb{Z}$.

A formal proof of De Moivre's Theorem requires mathematical induction, which will be studied in Chapter 9.

Example 5 Finding a Power of a Complex Number

Find $(-1 + i)^4$.

Answer

$r = \sqrt{(-1)^2 + 1^2} = \sqrt{2}$

1. Convert $z = -1 + i$ to polar form. Note that z lies in Q II of the complex plane.

$\theta = \pi + \text{Tan}^{-1}\left(\frac{1}{-1}\right) = \pi + \left(-\frac{\pi}{4}\right) = \frac{3\pi}{4}$

$z = \sqrt{2} \text{ cis } \frac{3\pi}{4}$

$(-1 + i)^4 = z^4 = \left[\sqrt{2} \text{ cis } \frac{3\pi}{4}\right]^4$

2. Apply De Moivre's Theorem to find the answer in polar form where the argument is within $[0, 2\pi)$.

$= \left(\sqrt{2}\right)^4 \text{ cis } 4\left(\frac{3\pi}{4}\right)$

$= 4 \text{ cis } 3\pi = 4 \text{ cis } \pi$

$= 4(\cos \pi + i \sin \pi)$

3. Express $4 \text{ cis } \pi$ in standard form.

$= 4[-1 + i(0)]$

$= -4$

SKILL ✓ **EXERCISE 23**

How many roots does a complex number have? The principal square root of 4 is 2, but –2 is also a square root of 4. The equation $x^6 = 64$ has two real roots, ± 2. The graph of $y = x^6 - 64$ illustrates those real roots as x-intercepts. Solving $x^6 - 64 = 0$ by factoring and applying the quadratic formula reveals all six complex roots of the equation that are guaranteed by the Fundamental Theorem of Algebra.

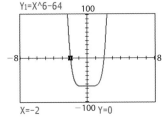

$(x^3 - 8)(x^3 + 8) = 0$

$(x - 2)(x^2 + 2x + 4)(x + 2)(x^2 - 2x + 4) = 0$

$x = \pm 2, -1 \pm i\sqrt{3}, 1 \pm i\sqrt{3}$

In general, there are n complex nth roots of any complex number.

▌ DEFINITIONS

The complex number $w = a + bi$ is an **nth root of the complex number** z if $w^n = z$. If $z = 1$, then w is an **nth root of unity**.

De Moivre's Theorem extends to other rational exponents besides integers. The following corollary uses the fact that $r^{\frac{1}{n}} = \sqrt[n]{r}$ to find the nth roots of a complex number.

▌ COROLLARY TO DE MOIVRE'S THEOREM

If $z = r \text{ cis } \theta$, then the n complex roots of z are $\sqrt[n]{r} \text{ cis } \frac{\theta + k2\pi}{n}$, where $k = 0, 1, 2, \ldots, n - 1$.

Example 6   Finding Roots of Unity

Find the eighth roots of unity.

Answer

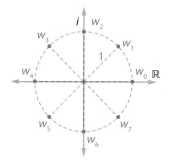

$z = 1 + 0i = 1 \operatorname{cis} 0$

1. Express $z = 1$ in polar form.

$w_k = \sqrt[8]{1} \operatorname{cis} \dfrac{0 + k2\pi}{8} = 1 \operatorname{cis}\left(0 + k\dfrac{\pi}{4}\right)$
where $k = 0, 1, 2, 3, \ldots, 7$

2. Apply the Corollary to De Moivre's Theorem.

$w_0 = \operatorname{cis} 0 = 1 + 0 = 1$ $w_4 = \operatorname{cis} \pi = -1 + 0 = -1$

3. Express each root in polar and in standard form.

$w_1 = \operatorname{cis} \dfrac{\pi}{4} = \dfrac{\sqrt{2}}{2} + \dfrac{\sqrt{2}}{2}i$ $w_5 = \operatorname{cis} \dfrac{5\pi}{4} = -\dfrac{\sqrt{2}}{2} - \dfrac{\sqrt{2}}{2}i$

$w_2 = \operatorname{cis} \dfrac{\pi}{2} = 0 + 1i = i$ $w_6 = \operatorname{cis} \dfrac{3\pi}{2} = 0 + (-1i) = -i$

$w_3 = \operatorname{cis} \dfrac{3\pi}{4} = -\dfrac{\sqrt{2}}{2} + \dfrac{\sqrt{2}}{2}i$ $w_7 = \operatorname{cis} \dfrac{7\pi}{4} = \dfrac{\sqrt{2}}{2} - \dfrac{\sqrt{2}}{2}i$

SKILL ✔ EXERCISE 27

The graphs of the complex roots of $z = r \operatorname{cis} \theta$ lie on the circle centered at the origin with a radius of $\sqrt[n]{r}$. The arguments of its successive roots differ by $\dfrac{2\pi}{n}$. These facts allow the polar form of other roots to be quickly determined once the *principal root* (the first root using $k = 0$) has been determined.

Example 7   Finding Roots of Complex Numbers

Find the fifth roots of $z = 32 \operatorname{cis} 50°$, expressing the roots in polar form.

Answer

$w_k = \sqrt[5]{32} \operatorname{cis} \dfrac{50° + k360°}{5}$

1. Apply the corollary to De Moivre's Theorem.

$= 2 \operatorname{cis} (10° + k72°)$
where $k = 0, 1, 2, 3, 4$

$w_0 = 2 \operatorname{cis} 10°$ $w_3 = 2 \operatorname{cis} 226°$
$w_1 = 2 \operatorname{cis} 82°$ $w_4 = 2 \operatorname{cis} 298°$
$w_2 = 2 \operatorname{cis} 154°$

2. State the principal root and then add $72°$ four times to find the remaining roots.

SKILL ✔ EXERCISE 33

A calculator can be used to find the standard form decimal approximations.

$w_0 \approx 1.97 + 0.35i$ $w_3 \approx -1.39 - 1.44i$

$w_1 \approx 0.28 + 1.98i$ $w_4 \approx 0.94 - 1.77i$

$w_2 \approx -1.80 + 0.88i$

A. Exercises

1. Graph each complex number in the complex plane.
   a. $z_1 = -4 + 2i$
   b. $z_2 = 2 + 3i$
   c. $z_3 = -1 - 2i$
   d. $z_4 = 5 - 5i$

2. Graph each complex number in the complex plane and determine its absolute value.
   a. $z_5 = 1 + 3i$
   b. $z_6 = 2 - 3i$
   c. $z_7 = 4i$
   d. $z_8 = -4 - 2i$

3. State the general formula for the argument θ of the complex number $z = a + bi$ located in the given quadrant.
   a. Q I
   b. Q II
   c. Q III
   d. Q IV

Convert each complex number to polar form.

4. $9 + 2i$

5. -7

6. $9i$

7. $-3 - 3i$

8. $-5 + 7i$

9. $\frac{\sqrt{3}}{4} - \frac{1}{4}i$

Plot each complex number in polar form and then convert to standard form.

10. $3 \text{ cis } \frac{4\pi}{3}$

11. $4 \text{ cis } \frac{\pi}{6}$

12. $2 \text{ cis } \frac{7\pi}{4}$

13. $2\sqrt{2} \text{ cis } \frac{3\pi}{4}$

B. Exercises

Find each product or quotient in polar form. Then express your answer in standard form.

14. $\left(7 \text{ cis } \frac{\pi}{3}\right)\left(2 \text{ cis } \frac{\pi}{6}\right)$

15. $(6 \text{ cis } 150°)(\text{cis } 210°)$

16. $\dfrac{9 \text{ cis } \frac{5\pi}{3}}{3 \text{ cis } \frac{\pi}{6}}$

17. $3 \text{ cis } 135° \div \frac{1}{2} \text{ cis } 45°$

Convert each number to polar form and then find the product $z_1 z_2$ in both polar form and standard form. Verify your answer by finding the product directly in standard form.

18. $z_1 = 1 + i; z_2 = 1 - i$

19. $z_1 = \sqrt{3} + i; z_2 = 2 - 2i$

Convert each number to polar form and then find the quotient $\frac{z_1}{z_2}$ in both polar and standard form. Verify your answer by finding the quotient directly in standard form.

20. $z_1 = 4 + 2i;$
    $z_2 = \sqrt{3} - i$

21. $z_1 = \sqrt{2} + \sqrt{2}i;$
    $z_2 = 3 - i$

Use De Moivre's Theorem to calculate each power. Express your answer in standard form.

22. $(1 + i)^3$

23. $\left(1 + \sqrt{3}\,i\right)^4$

24. $(-4 + 4i)^3$

25. $(3 + 2i)^8$

Find all nth roots for each complex number, expressing each root in both polar and standard form. Then graph the roots on the complex plane.

26. fourth roots of unity

27. fifth roots of unity

28. cube roots of $-i$

29. fourth roots of -3

Find all nth roots of each complex number in polar form. Label each principal root.

30. square roots of $49 \text{ cis } 50°$

31. cube roots of $125 \text{ cis } \frac{4\pi}{3}$

32. fourth roots of $81 \text{ cis } \frac{\pi}{2}$

33. fifth roots of $\text{cis } 65°$

Use the Corollary to De Moivre's Theorem to find all the roots for each equation. Write your answers in standard form.

34. $x^4 = 16$

35. $x^3 + i = 0$

36. $x^2 - 2i = 0$

37. $x^2 + 3i = 3$

C. Exercises

38. **Compare:** Expand $(3 + 2i)^8$ using the FOIL method and compare your answer to exercise 25. Which method do you prefer? Why?

39. **Prove:** Given $z_1 = r_1(\cos \theta_1 + i \sin \theta_1)$ and $z_2 = r_2(\cos \theta_2 + i \sin \theta_2)$, show that $\frac{z_1}{z_2} = \frac{r_1}{r_2}[\cos (\theta_1 - \theta_2) + i \sin (\theta_1 - \theta_2)]$.

Simplify.

40. $\dfrac{\left(3 \text{ cis } \frac{\pi}{3}\right)\left(5 \text{ cis } \frac{\pi}{6}\right)}{0.5 \text{ cis } \frac{\pi}{2}}$

41. Compute $\left[(-1 - i)\left(-4 + 4\sqrt{3}\,i\right)\right]^2$ in polar form. Then express the result in standard form.

42. Find the cube roots of $\left(25 \text{ cis } \frac{\pi}{6}\right)^2$ in polar form.

43. Find $(2 - 5i)^{100}$ in polar form.

44. State the magnitude and direction for $\mathbf{v} = \langle -5, 7 \rangle$. [6.1]

45. Find the angle between $\langle 4, -3 \rangle$ and $\langle -5, 7 \rangle$ (to the nearest degree). [6.2]

46. Find the unit vector that is orthogonal to $\mathbf{v} = \langle 7, -3 \rangle$. [6.2]

47. Given A $(-1, 2, 7)$ and B $(3, 7, 1)$, express $\overrightarrow{AB}$ in component form. Then find its length and a unit vector in the direction of $\overrightarrow{AB}$. [6.3]

48. Find the angle between $\langle 1, 4, -5 \rangle$ and $\langle -5, 3, 7 \rangle$ (to the nearest degree). [6.3]

49. Find the distance (to the nearest tenth) between the polar points $(-2, 20°)$, $(5, 280°)$. [6.4]

50. Which vectors are equal? Choose all correct answers. [6.1]

A. $\mathbf{w}$ and $\mathbf{q}$

B. $\mathbf{p}$ and $\mathbf{v}$

C. $\mathbf{q}$ and $\mathbf{z}$

D. $\mathbf{p}$ and $\mathbf{n}$

E. $\mathbf{z}$ and $\mathbf{n}$

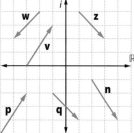

51. Find the angle between vectors $\mathbf{u} = \langle 3, 6 \rangle$ and $\mathbf{v} = \langle 2, -4 \rangle$ (to the nearest degree). [6.2]

A. 35°   C. 110°   E. none of
B. 63°   D. 127°   these

52. Which equation is represented by the graph? [6.5]

A. $r = 4 \cos 2\theta$

B. $r = 4 \sin 2\theta$

C. $r = 4 \cos 4\theta$

D. $r = 4 \sin 4\theta$

E. none of these

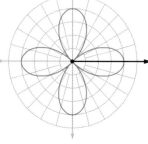

53. Which number cannot be the number of petals for a polar rose? [6.5]

A. 3   C. 9   E. none of
B. 6   D. 12   these

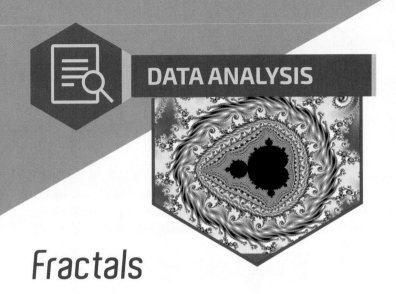

Fractals

In the 1970s the French American mathematician Benoit Mandelbrot (1924–2010) coined the term *fractal* to refer to sets that have fractured or rough edges. Mandelbrot formed beautifully complex self-similar curves (in which each part is a mini-image of the whole) using an iterative process and the relatively simple function $f(z) = z^2 + c$ where c is an imaginary number. The iterative process can be illustrated using $z_{n+1} = z_n^2 + c$ where $z_0 = 0$ and $c = 1$ (a real number).

$$z_1 = 0^2 + 1 = 1 \qquad z_4 = 5^2 + 1 = 26$$
$$z_2 = 1^2 + 1 = 2 \qquad z_5 = 26^2 + 1 = 677$$
$$z_3 = 2^2 + 1 = 5 \qquad z_6 = 677^2 + 1 = 458{,}330$$

Depending on the value of c, as the iterations increase, the points in the complex plane either "escape" to infinity (sometimes very quickly, sometimes more slowly) or are "captured" and remain within a certain distance of the origin. Examine the iterative process using $z_0 = 0$ and a complex number for c.

1. Let $c = i$ and compute z_1 thru z_6 (in terms of i). Does this point escape to infinity?

2. Let $c = 2i$ and compute z_1 thru z_5 (in terms of i). Does this point escape to infinity?

The Mandelbrot set consists of all the points in the complex plane that do not escape to infinity under $f(z) = z^2 + c$. Typically, the points in the set are colored black, while the coloring of other points depends on how quickly they escape to infinity. The most interesting patterns in the set are found near the boundary. It is here that we find self-similar patterns that continue infinitely. As long as you have the computing power to continue to magnify one portion of the curve, you will continue to find fascinating fractals. The study of fractals has contributed to our understanding of complex systems in which a small change in initial conditions creates huge consequential changes, such as weather patterns and the stock market. Fractals are also useful in modeling the human respiratory and circulatory systems.

3. Write and graph a function $r(x)$ representing the ratio of the surface area of a cube to its volume in terms of the cube's edge length x.

   a. Does the ratio increase or decrease as the cube gets bigger?

   b. Which type of function is this?

4. The lungs of a healthy human have a capacity of 305 in.³ and a total surface area of 1076 ft².

   a. Find the surface area-to-volume ratio (to the nearest in.⁻¹) for the lungs.

   b. Use the function from exercise 3 to determine the edge length of a cube having this same ratio.

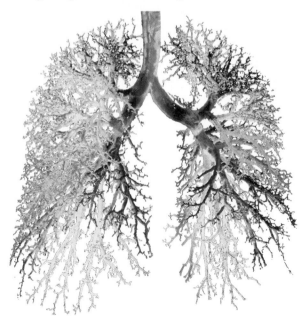

The circulatory system provides oxygen and nutrients to each of approximately 30 trillion cells in the human body. In order for these transfers to occur, every cell must be within approximately 100 microns of a capillary, the smallest type of blood vessel. Have you ever considered how many meters of blood vessels it takes to spread oxygen throughout your body?

5. Assuming the average adult body has a volume of 67 L and an average of 600 capillaries/mm^3 (averaging 1 mm long), calculate an estimate of how many kilometers of capillaries are in the human body. Then express your estimate in miles. (1 L = 1000 cm^3)

Systems in the human body are not the only places where we find fractal patterns. Your cell phone's antenna is shaped like a fractal to minimize space and weight while providing greater bandwidth and better reception. Recent patents using fractal patterns involve batteries, invisibility cloaking, and smart clothes. The twentieth-century mathematicians who first investigated the properties of fractal functions called them "pathological" and "monsters." Some believed they were exploring creations that had no possible natural connection and were solely from the mind of man. However, it turns out that we are surrounded by fractal patterns, and their benefits are now obvious.

6. **Discuss:** Consider the structural similarities between tree branches and lung bronchi. Someone with an evolutionary worldview might say these similarities are expected since the function of each system (respiration) is similar. How would you explain the similarities from a biblical worldview?

7. **Discuss:** Fractal mathematics captures some of the infinite complexities of creation. Chaos theory grew out of the study of fractals in which a minor change in initial conditions results in vastly different outcomes. Explain in your own words how fractal mathematics and chaos theory can be in harmony with an orderly creation.

KEYWORD SEARCH

fractals on TI-84 🔍

Chapter 6 Review

1. Given $P(-2, 5)$ and $Q(3, -4)$, write $\overrightarrow{PQ}$ in component form and as a linear combination of standard unit vectors. [6.1]

2. Find the magnitude and direction of $\mathbf{v} = \langle -4, 7 \rangle$. [6.1]

3. Given $\mathbf{v} = \langle 2, -1 \rangle$ and $\mathbf{w} = \langle 4, 2 \rangle$, find each resultant vector algebraically and geometrically. [6.1]

   a. $\mathbf{v} - \mathbf{w}$ b. $3\mathbf{v} + \frac{1}{2}\mathbf{w}$

4. Find the unit vector in the direction of each vector. [6.1]

   a. $\langle 7, -3 \rangle$ b. $\langle -20, 21 \rangle$

State the component form for each vector. [6.1]

5. $|\mathbf{v}| = 6; \theta = \frac{5\pi}{6}$ 6. a southbound car at 45 mi/hr

7. An airplane flies 920 mi due east from Kansas City, MO, to Washington, DC, and then 490 mi due north to Rochester, NY. What is the plane's distance and bearing from Kansas City? [6.1]

8. Find the normal and frictional forces acting on a 60 lb child sitting on a seesaw whose angle of incline is 25°. [6.1]

9. Find $\mathbf{u} \cdot \mathbf{v}$ if $|\mathbf{u}| = 5$, $|\mathbf{v}| = 8$, and the angle between the vectors is 30°. [6.2]

Find each dot product and state whether the angle between the vectors is > 90°, < 90°, or = 90°. [6.2]

10. $\langle 2, -3 \rangle \cdot \langle 7, 1 \rangle$ 11. $\langle -4, 7 \rangle \cdot \langle 14, 8 \rangle$

12. Use the dot product to find the angle between the vectors $\mathbf{u} = \langle 5, 3 \rangle$ and $\mathbf{v} = \langle -2, 7 \rangle$ (to the nearest tenth of a degree). [6.2]

13. If $\langle v_1, v_2 \rangle$ is orthogonal to $\langle 5, -3 \rangle$, find the ratio of v_2 to v_1. Then find a general expression that represents all the orthogonal vectors. [6.2]

14. Find the projection of $\mathbf{u} = \langle 7, 5 \rangle$ onto $\mathbf{v} = \langle -2, 6 \rangle$. Then find $\mathbf{w}_2$ so that $\text{proj}_\mathbf{v}\, \mathbf{u} + \mathbf{w}_2 = \mathbf{u}$. [6.2]

15. An 80 lb box of gadgets rests on a ramp with a 20° incline. [6.2]

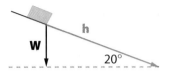

   a. Determine the component of the box's weight that pulls it down the ramp.

   b. What is the magnitude of the frictional force directed up along the ramp that prevents the box from sliding down the ramp?

16. Find the amount of work done by Jordan as he moves a cart 50 m, pulling with 30 N of force on the handle, which is 50° above the horizontal. [6.2]

17. Plot points $A(5, 1, -2)$ and $B(-2, 4, 3)$. [6.3]

18. Given $A(3, 1, -2)$ and $B(-4, 5, 3)$, find the length and midpoint of $\overline{AB}$. [6.3]

19. Given $P(2, 5, -3)$ and $Q(4, -1, 2)$, express $\overrightarrow{PQ}$ in component form, find its length, and find a unit vector in the direction of $\overrightarrow{PQ}$. [6.3]

Find each resultant if $\mathbf{u} = \langle 5, -1, 3 \rangle$, $\mathbf{v} = \langle -3, 4, 1 \rangle$, and $\mathbf{w} = \langle 8, 2, -2 \rangle$. [6.3]

20. $\mathbf{w} - \mathbf{u}$ 21. $2\mathbf{v} - 3\mathbf{u} + \frac{1}{2}\mathbf{w}$

Use a dot product to find the angle between the given vectors (to the nearest degree). [6.3]

22. $\mathbf{v} = \langle 2, 1, 5 \rangle$, $\mathbf{w} = \langle -2, -3, 7 \rangle$

23. $\mathbf{v} = \langle 4, 5, 1 \rangle$, $\mathbf{w} = \langle -2, 3, -7 \rangle$

24. An airplane takes off heading due south with a climb angle of 20° and an airspeed of 155 knots. There is a 25-knot wind from the northwest. Find a vector that represents the plane's velocity relative to its point of takeoff. [6.3]

25. Graph each point described by its polar coordinates: $A\left(2, -\frac{3\pi}{4}\right)$ and $B\left(-3, \frac{5\pi}{3}\right)$. [6.4]

26. State all the additional pairs of polar coordinates for $(3, 70°)$ if $-360° \leq \theta \leq 360°$. **[6.4]**

27. Convert between polar and rectangular coordinates. **[6.4]**

    a. $\left(-3, \frac{5\pi}{3}\right)$ to rectangular coordinates

    b. $(-2, 7)$ to polar coordinates

28. Find the distance (to the nearest tenth) between $\left(1, \frac{\pi}{2}\right)$ and $\left(4, \frac{5\pi}{4}\right)$. **[6.4]**

Transform each equation into polar form. Then verify your answer by using technology to graph the polar equation. [6.4]

29. $y = -3$

30. $3x + y = 5$

Transform each equation into rectangular form. Then describe the graph. [6.4]

31. $\theta = 45°$

32. $r = -8 \cos \theta$

33. Identify the type of curve represented by each polar equation. **[6.5]**

    a. $r = -2 \sin \theta$ **I.** line

    b. $r = 3 \cos 4\theta$ **II.** Archimedean spiral

    c. $\theta = \frac{4\pi}{3}$ **III.** circle

    d. $r = -2\theta$ **IV.** lemniscate

    e. $r^2 = 8 \sin 3\theta$ **V.** rose

    f. $r = 3$

34. Identify the type of limaçon represented by each polar equation. **[6.5]**

    a. $r = 2 + 3 \cos \theta$ **I.** cardioid

    b. $r = 3 - 2 \sin \theta$ **II.** dimpled limaçon

    c. $r = 2 + 2 \sin \theta$ **III.** convex limaçon

    d. $r = 2 - \cos \theta$ **IV.** limaçon with inner loop

35. Identify the type of symmetry in the graph of a polar equation if substituting either ordered pair for (r, θ) produces an equivalent equation. **[6.5]**

    a. $(r, \pi + \theta)$ or $(-r, \theta)$ **I.** the polar axis

    b. $(r, \pi - \theta)$ or $(-r, -\theta)$ **II.** the line $\theta = \frac{\pi}{2}$

    c. $(r, -\theta)$ or $(-r, \pi - \theta)$ **III.** the pole

Graph each polar equation. [6.5]

36. $r = 3 \sin 2\theta$

37. $r = 4 \cos 3\theta$

38. $r = 2 - 2 \sin \theta$

39. $r = 2 - 3 \cos \theta$

40. $r^2 = 9 \sin 2\theta$

41. Plot each complex number and express it in polar form. **[6.6]**

    a. $z_1 = 4 - 3i$ **b.** $z_2 = 4i$

42. Plot $b = 2$ cis 1.7 in polar form and express b in standard form. **[6.6]**

Find each product, quotient, or power in polar form. Then express the result in standard form. [6.6]

43. $\left(4 \text{ cis} \frac{2\pi}{3}\right)\left(-3 \text{ cis} \frac{5\pi}{6}\right)$

44. $\left(-3 \text{ cis} \frac{5\pi}{6}\right) \div \left(4 \text{ cis} \frac{2\pi}{3}\right)$

45. $(3 + 4i)^4$

46. $(1 - i)^3$

47. Find the cube roots of unity. Then graph the roots on the complex plane. **[6.6]**

48. Find the fourth roots of $-1 + 2i$, expressing your answers in polar form. **[6.6]**

7 Systems and Matrices

BIBLICAL PERSPECTIVE OF MATHEMATICS

Is it possible to prove the existence of God? After examining direct and indirect deductive proofs, you will analyze an indirect argument presented by Dr. Greg Bahnsen.

HISTORICAL CONNECTION

From astronomy to subatomic physics, matrices and determinants continue to play an important role in pure and applied mathematics.

DATA ANALYSIS

While secret codes and ciphers date to antiquity, the American mathematician Lester Hill first published a block cipher that used matrix operations for encryption in 1929.

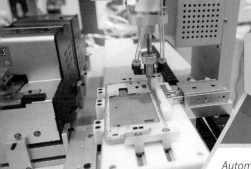

Automating the production of cell phones has helped meet the demand for popular smartphones.

Many problems in science and business can be modeled mathematically using a set of equations, each having more than one variable. A *system of equations* consists of several such equations that are solved simultaneously.

A linear equation can be written in the form $a_1x_1 + a_2x_2 + \cdots + a_nx_n = b$, where the real coefficients $a_1, a_2, \ldots, a_n$ are not all 0 and the constant b is real. Note the following examples.

Linear Equations	Nonlinear Equations
$2x + 3y = 7$	$4x^2 + y^2 = 16$
$5x - 6y + 3z = -37$	$xy = 12$
$x = 5$	$y = x^3 - 1$

When all of the equations are linear, the system is referred to as a system of linear equations. A *solution* to a system of equations in two variables is an ordered pair satisfying each equation in the system. The ordered pair $(5, -4)$ is a solution to the following system because the values $x = 5$ and $y = -4$ satisfy both equations.

Linear System	(5, –4) is a solution.
$2x + 3y = -2$	$2(5) + 3(-4) = -2$
$6x - y = 34$	$6(5) - (-4) = 34$

Recall from previous courses how the algebraic methods of substitution and elimination were used to find the solutions to a system. Substitution is frequently used to solve linear or nonlinear systems in two variables when an equation can be used to easily express one of the variables in terms of the other.

Example 1 Solving a Linear System by Substitution

Use substitution to solve the system.
$$2x - y = 8$$
$$x + 3y = -3$$

Answer

$x + 3y = -3$
    $x = -3 - 3y$
1. Solve the second equation for x.

$2(-3 - 3y) - y = 8$
    $-6 - 7y = 8$
        $-7y = 14$
            $y = -2$
2. Substitute the result into the first equation and solve for y.

$x = -3 - 3y$
    $= -3 - 3(-2) = 3$
3. Substitute $y = -2$ back into the equation from the first step to find the value of x.

$(3, -2)$
4. Write the solution as an ordered pair.

CONTINUED ➡

Check

$2(3) - (-2) = 8$

$(3) + 3(-2) = -3$

5. Substitute into the original equations to verify your solution.

SKILL ✔ **EXERCISE 3**

TIP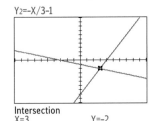

The answer can also be verified by finding the intersection of $Y_1 = 2X - 8$ and $Y_2 = -X/3 - 1$.

Using several variables and a system of equations can simplify the solution to many problems.

Example 2 Solving a Nonlinear System by Substitution

Find the dimensions of a rectangle whose perimeter is 48 ft and whose area is 108 ft².

Answer

$2x + 2y = 48$

$xy = 108$

1. Write equations for the perimeter and area where x = the rectangle's width and y = its length.

$x + y = 24$

$\quad y = 24 - x$

2. Solve the first equation for y.

$\quad x(24 - x) = 108$

$\quad -x^2 + 24x = 108$

$x^2 - 24x + 108 = 0$

$\quad (x - 6)(x - 18) = 0$

$\quad x = 6 \quad \text{or} \quad x = 18$

3. Substitute the result into the second equation and solve for x.

$6y = 108 \quad 18y = 108$

$\quad y = 18 \qquad y = 6$

4. Substitute both values back into one of the original equations and solve for y.

The rectangle is 6 ft by 18 ft.

5. Interpret the results.

Check

$2(6) + 2(18) = 48; 6(18) = 108$

6. Confirm the rectangle's perimeter and area.

SKILL ✔ **EXERCISE 7**

Linear systems of two or more equations are frequently solved by elimination. The key is to rewrite the equations as equivalent equations where the coefficients of one of the variables are opposites. The equations can then be added to eliminate that variable.

Example 3 Solving a Linear System by Elimination

Solve the system using elimination.

$6x - 5y = -43$

$7x + 2y = -11$

Answer

$2(6x - 5y = -43) \Rightarrow 12x - 10y = -86$

$5(7x + 2y = -11) \Rightarrow 35x + 10y = -55$

1. Multiply the first equation by 2 and the second by 5 to obtain opposite coefficients for y.

$\qquad\qquad\qquad 47x = -141$

$\qquad\qquad\qquad\quad x = -3$

2. Add the equations to eliminate the y-terms and solve for x.

$6(-3) - 5y = -43$

$\quad -18 - 5y = -43$

$\qquad\quad -5y = -25$

$\qquad\qquad y = 5$

3. Substitute $x = -3$ back into either original equation and solve for y.

$(-3, 5)$

4. Write the solution as an ordered pair.

CONTINUED ➡

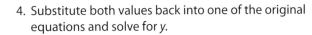

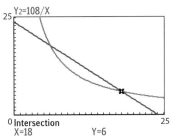

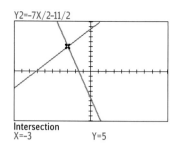

Y2=-7X/2-11/2

Intersection
X=-3   Y=5

Check

$7(-3) + 2(5) = -21 + 10 = -11$

5. Substitute into the other original equation to verify your solution.

SKILL ✔ **EXERCISE 11**

Graphical solutions for systems in two variables were also studied in Algebra. Exact solutions for many systems are difficult to obtain graphically. The use of technology enables this method to provide decimal approximations for solutions of systems when known algebraic methods cannot be employed.

Example 4   Solving a Nonlinear System Graphically

Use technology to solve the system graphically. $y = \log x$
$y = x^2 - 4x + 3$

Answer

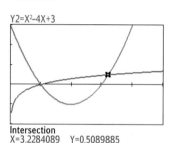

Y2=X²-4X+3

Intersection
X=3.2284089   Y=0.5089885

$(1, 0)$ and $\approx (3.23, 0.51)$

1. Graph $Y_1 = \log X$ and $Y_2 = X^2 - 4X + 3$ and find the two points of intersection.

Check

$\log (1) = 0$ and $(1)^2 - 4(1) + 3 = 0$

2. The first point $(1, 0)$ is easily verified. A calculator could be used to verify the decimal approximations for the second point.

SKILL ✔ **EXERCISE 17**

Examining the graphs of the equations in a system provides insight into the number of solutions. A unique solution to a system of linear equations in two variables represents the point of intersection of two lines with different slopes. Note how linear systems can also have an infinite number of solutions or no solution.

Types of Linear Systems in Two Variables			
Classification	independent consistent	dependent consistent	inconsistent
Solutions	one	an infinite number	no solution
Graphs	intersecting lines	coinciding lines	parallel lines

In general, consistent systems have one or more solutions, while inconsistent systems have no solution. The graphs of the equivalent equations in a dependent system coincide.

Example 5 Solving and Classifying Linear Systems in Two Variables

Solve each linear system algebraically and classify the system.

a. $2x + 3y = 6$

$y = -\frac{2}{3}x + 2$

b. $3x - 4y = -8$

$6x - 8y = 12$

Answers

a. Solve by substitution.

$$2x + 3\left(-\frac{2}{3}x + 2\right) = 6$$
$$2x - 2x + 6 = 6$$
$$6 = 6$$

Since the statement is true regardless of the value of x, there is an infinite number of solutions.

The solution to this dependent consistent system is a line:

$\{(x, y) \mid y = -\frac{2}{3}x + 2\}$.

b. Solve by elimination.

$$-2(3x - 4y = -8) \Rightarrow \begin{array}{r} -6x + 8y = 16 \\ 6x - 8y = 12 \\ \hline 0 = 28 \end{array}$$

The false statement indicates there is no solution.

The solution to this inconsistent system is the empty set, $\emptyset$.

—————————————————————— SKILL ✔ **EXERCISE 21**

Businesses use supply and demand curves to describe their willingness to produce more of a product and consumers' declining interest in purchasing the product as prices increase. The intersection of these two curves represents the equilibrium price, the point at which there is a stable price and quantity of goods in the marketplace.

Example 6 Finding the Equilibrium Price

A phone manufacturer has determined the supply and demand curves for a cell phone where p is the price (in dollars) and x is the supply (in thousands of phones).

supply: $p = 400 + 0.8x$
demand: $p = 1000 - 0.4x$

Find the equilibrium price and the number of phones that should be produced.

Answer

$$400 + 0.8x = 1000 - 0.4x$$
$$1.2x = 600$$
$$x = 500$$

1. Solve by substitution.

$p = 400 + 0.8(500) = 800$

The equilibrium price is $800 and 500,000 phones should be manufactured.

2. Interpret the results.

—————————————————————— SKILL ✔ **EXERCISE 29**

Algebraic solutions to systems of three linear equations typically eliminate the same variable from two different pairs of equations. The two resulting equations form a new system in two variables. After solving this smaller system, the values of the two variables are substituted into one of the original equations to find the value of the third variable.

Economic models are only as accurate as the data they are based on. For example, when gas prices were predicted to reach $6–$8 per gallon, a truck manufacturer replaced steel with lighter but more expensive aluminum in order to increase gas mileage. When gas prices actually declined, the equilibrium price shifted and the improved gas mileage did not result in the predicted higher demand.

Example 7 Solving a Three-Variable System

Solve the system.

$$-2x + 5y + 2z = 23$$
$$4x - y + 2z = -13$$
$$x - 3y + 6z = -17$$

Answer

$$
\begin{aligned}
& -2x + 5y + 2z = 23 \\
&2(x - 3y + 6z = -17) \Rightarrow \underline{2x - 6y + 12z = -34} \\
& \text{(a)} \qquad -y + 14z = -11
\end{aligned}
$$

1. Eliminate the x-term from the first and third equations by adding the first equation to 2 times the third equation.

$$
\begin{aligned}
&-4(x - 3y + 6z = -17) \Rightarrow -4x + 12y - 24z = 68 \\
& \underline{4x - y + 2z = -13} \\
& \text{(b)} \qquad 11y - 22z = 55
\end{aligned}
$$

2. Eliminate the x-term from the second and third equations by adding -4 times the third equation and the second equation.

$$
\begin{aligned}
&\phantom{\tfrac{1}{11}(11y-22z=55)\Rightarrow} -y + 14z = -11 \\
&\tfrac{1}{11}(11y - 22z = 55) \Rightarrow \underline{y - 2z = 5} \\
&\phantom{\tfrac{1}{11}(11y-22z=55)\Rightarrow} \qquad 12z = -6
\end{aligned}
$$

3. Solve the two-variable system formed by equations (a) and (b) using elimination.

$$z = -\frac{1}{2}$$
$$y - 2\left(-\frac{1}{2}\right) = 5$$
$$y = 4$$

$$x - 3(4) + 6\left(-\frac{1}{2}\right) = -17$$
$$x - 15 = -17$$
$$x = -2$$

4. Substitute the values of y and z into one of the original equations and solve for x.

$$\left(-2, 4, -\frac{1}{2}\right)$$

5. Write the solution as an ordered triple.

Check

$$-2(-2) + 5(4) + 2\left(-\frac{1}{2}\right) = 23$$
$$4(-2) - (4) + 2\left(-\frac{1}{2}\right) = -13$$

6. Substitute the coordinates into the other two equations to verify your solution.

SKILL ✓ **EXERCISE 31**

TIP

The process of substituting one or more values back into a previous equation to find the value of another variable is often called *back substitution*.

The graph of each linear equation in three variables represents a plane. The unique solution in Example 7 represents the point of intersection of three distinct planes in space. In order for a linear system to have a unique solution, there must be as many equations as variables.

Example 8 Solving a Dependent Three-Variable System

Solve the system.

$$2x + 3y - 7z = 8$$
$$6x + 8y - 11z = 4$$

Answer

$$
\begin{aligned}
&-3(2x + 3y - 7z = 8) \Rightarrow -6x - 9y + 21z = -24 \\
& \underline{6x + 8y - 11z = 4} \\
& \qquad -y + 10z = -20
\end{aligned}
$$

1. Eliminate x by multiplying the first equation by -3 and adding the result to the second equation.

There are infinitely many solutions to this dependent system.

2. Since there are no other equations, a second equation in y and z cannot be derived.

$$y = 10z + 20$$

3. Express y in terms of z.

CONTINUED ➡

$$2x + 3(10z + 20) - 7z = 8$$
$$2x + 23z + 60 = 8$$
$$2x = -23z - 52$$
$$x = -\frac{23}{2}z - 26$$

$$(x, y, z) = \left(-\frac{23}{2}t - 26, 10t + 20, t\right)$$

4. Substitute into either original equation to express x in terms of z.

5. The general solution can be expressed as an ordered triple where z is represented by the arbitrary parameter t.

SKILL ✓ **EXERCISE 35**

You can find particular solutions to the system in Example 8 by substituting any real number for t. For example, if $t = -2$, the solution is

$$\left(-\frac{23}{2}(-2) - 26, 10(-2) + 20, -2\right) = (-3, 0, -2).$$

The ordered triple $(-3, 0, -2)$ is just one of the points on the line in space formed by the intersection of the two planes.

A. Exercises

Identify any ordered pair that is a solution to the system. List all correct answers.

1. $3x - 2y = -4$
$2x + 3y = -7$
  A. $(1, -3)$
  B. $(-2, -1)$
  C. $\left(-1, \frac{1}{2}\right)$

2. $y = x^2 + 5x - 4$
$y = x + 1$
  A. $(-2, -1)$
  B. $(-5, -4)$
  C. $(1, 2)$

Use substitution to solve each system.

3. $2x - 5y = 3$
$x = -2y + 6$

4. $3x + 5y = 2$
$x + y = 2$

5. $2x + 4y = 3$
$4x - 7y = 6$

6. $3x + 2y = 3$
$4x + 5y = -10$

Use substitution to solve each system. Then verify your solution(s) graphically.

7. $y = 2x - 9$
$xy = 5$

8. $y = x^2 + 2x - 3$
$x - 2y = 4$

9. $y = 2x^2 + x - 2$
$y = -6x^2 - x + 4$

10. $4x - y = 20$
$y = x^3 - 4x^2 - 7x + 10$

Solve each system using elimination.

11. $x + 3y = 7$
$2x - 5y = -8$

12. $6x - 4y = 60$
$3x + 2y = 18$

13. $2x + 3y = -2$
$5x + 2y = 6$

14. $8x + 3y = 38.5$
$7x + 4y = 33$

15. $\frac{1}{2}x + \frac{1}{3}y = \frac{5}{6}$
$\frac{2}{3}x - y = -\frac{5}{2}$

16. $\frac{1}{2}x - 3y = \frac{13}{5}$
$\frac{4}{5}x + y = -\frac{14}{5}$

Solve each system using technology. Round answers to the nearest tenth if necessary.

17. $y = 3x^3 - 2x^2 - 4x + 2$
$y = 3x + 4$

18. $y = 2x^3 - 5x^2 - x + 6$
$y = -4x^2 + 3x + 5$

19. $y = \sqrt{2x + 5}$
$y = 3 \sin x$

20. $y = \log 10x$
$y = -2x^2 + 11x - 6$

B. Exercises

Solve each system. Then classify the system as independent consistent, dependent consistent, or inconsistent.

21. $0.6x + 2y = 3.66$
$1.3x - 0.5y = 2.13$

22. $5x + 2y = 20$
$\frac{15}{2}x + 3y = 30$

23. $2x + y = 3$
$4x + 2y = 7$

24. $x = \frac{7}{2} + \frac{1}{2}y$
$2x - y = 7$

25. Solve the system. (*Hint*: Let $a = \frac{1}{x}$ and $b = \frac{1}{y}$.)
$\frac{5}{x} - \frac{2}{y} = 6$
$\frac{3}{x} + \frac{4}{y} = 1$

Find the dimensions of a rectangle with the given perimeter and area.

26. perimeter of 52 m and area of 144 m^2

27. perimeter of 427 ft and area of 11,025 ft^2

Find the equilibrium price.

28. An airline determines the supply and demand curves for a flight where p is the price (in dollars) and x is the number of seats booked. Find the equilibrium price and the number of seats that should be provided.
supply: $p = 50 + 0.5x$
demand: $p = 950 - 2.5x$

29. An automobile manufacturer determines the supply and demand curves for a base model car where p is the price (in dollars) and x is the number of cars sold. Find the equilibrium price and the number of cars that should be produced.
supply: $p = 14{,}900 + 0.2x$
demand: $p = 32{,}120 - 0.3x$

Solve each system.

30. $2x + 3y + 4z = 3$
$3x - y - 5z = 10$
$5x - 2y - 3z = 5$

31. $2x + 3y - z = 9$
$4x - 5y - 6z = 1$
$5x + 2y - 3z = 8$

32. $x + 2y + 2z = -1$
$3x - 2y + z = -2$
$3y + 5z = -16$

33. $4x - 6y + 6z = -21$
$3x + 4y - z = -6$
$x - 2y + 4z = -8$

34. A two-equation system in three variables has a general solution of $(3t + 4, t - 6, t)$.

  a. Find particular solutions for $t = -1$ and $t = 2$.

  b. What value of t corresponds to the point with an x-coordinate of -8?

  c. What solution has an x-coordinate of 13?

Find a general solution for each system. Then state one particular solution and use it to verify your solution.

35. $x + 5y - z = 8$
$2x - 4y + 4z = 2$

36. $x - 2y + z = 7$
$5x - y + 3z = 1$

C. Exercises

37. Let $f(x) = ax + 4$, $g(x) = cx - 1$, $2f(x) + g(x) = 12x + 7$, and $f(x) - 3g(x) = -x + 7$. Find a and c.

38. Given $\triangle ABC$ with $A\,(-2, 5)$, $B\,(-6, 1)$, and $C\,(4, -1)$, find the intersection of side BC and the altitude from A.

39. Find all (x, y) within $[0, 2\pi)$ such that $2 \sin x + 4 \cos y = 4$ and $\sin x = 2 \cos y$.

40. Use the general equation for a circle, $x^2 + y^2 + Ax + By + C = 0$, to find A, B, and C for the circle passing through $(3, -6)$, $(-1, 2)$, and $(6, 3)$.

41. Explore: Solve the following system graphically. Then solve the system algebraically, listing all possible solutions. Reconcile the seeming contradiction caused by solving with different methods.
$3x + 2y = 6$
$xy = 12$

CUMULATIVE REVIEW

42. State the x-intercept, y-intercept, and slope of the line $5x + y = -10$. [1.2]

43. Find the slope of the line containing $(2, 7)$ and $(4, -5)$. [1.2]

Describe how the graph of $f(x) = x^2$ is transformed into the graph of $g(x)$. [1.3]

44. $g(x) = (x + 4)^2 - 3$

45. $g(x) = -|x - 3| + 1$

Find the zeros for each polynomial function, including the multiplicity of any repeated zeros. [2.2]

46. $p(x) = (x^2 - 25)(x^2 - 9)$

47. $p(x) = (x - 7)^4$

48. Which general form equation is equivalent to $y = \frac{2}{5}x - 3$? [1.2]

  A. $5x - 2y = 15$
  B. $-2x + 5y = 15$
  C. $2x - 5y = -15$
  D. $2x - 5y = 15$
  E. none of these

49. Find the area of the triangle. [5.7]

  A. 11 ft^2
  B. 20 ft^2
  C. 29.8 ft^2
  D. 12.9 ft^2
  E. none of these

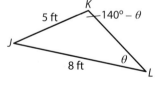

50. Find the midpoint of $\overline{AB}$ with $A\,(-3, 1, 2)$ and $B\,(7, -4, -2)$. [6.3]

  A. $(5, -\frac{5}{2}, -2)$
  B. $(2, -\frac{3}{2}, 0)$
  C. $(4, -3, 0)$
  D. $(11, -5, -4)$
  E. none of these

51. Which of the following equations passes a symmetry test for the polar axis? List all correct answers. [6.5]

  A $r = -\sin 3$
  B. $r = -5 \sin \theta$
  C. $r = 2 \sin 2\theta$
  D. $r^2 = 9 \cos 2\theta$
  E. none of these

Apps are available to help coaches record statistics for their teams.

Numerical data is often presented in a table or stored in the rows and columns of a spreadsheet. A *matrix* is a rectangular array of numbers and is designated with an upper-case letter. A matrix with m rows and n columns has *dimensions* of $m \times n$ (read "m by n"). Each number in the array is an *entry* (or *element*) of the matrix. The double-subscript notation a_{ij} denotes the entry in row i and column j of matrix A.

$$A = [a_{ij}] = \begin{bmatrix} a_{11} & a_{12} & a_{13} & \cdots & a_{1n} \\ a_{21} & a_{22} & a_{23} & \cdots & a_{2n} \\ a_{31} & a_{32} & a_{33} & \cdots & a_{3n} \\ \vdots & \vdots & \vdots & & \vdots \\ a_{m1} & a_{m2} & a_{m3} & \cdots & a_{mn} \end{bmatrix} \begin{matrix} \\ \\ \leftarrow \text{Row 3} \\ \\ \\ \end{matrix}$$

Column 2 ↓

> **After completing this section, you will be able to**
> - define *matrix* and related terms.
> - perform matrix operations.
> - compare and contrast the properties of matrices with the properties of real numbers.
> - use matrices to represent real-world data.

Example 1 Identifying Matrix Dimensions and Entries

State the dimensions of each matrix. Then state the value of the designated entry.

a. $A = \begin{bmatrix} 8 & -5 & 1 \\ 3 & 0 & 2 \end{bmatrix}$ **b.** $B = [-7 \quad 2]$ **c.** $C = \begin{bmatrix} 3 \\ -1 \\ 5 \end{bmatrix}$ **d.** $D = \begin{bmatrix} a & b & c \\ r & s & t \\ x & y & z \end{bmatrix}$

$a_{21} = ?$ $b_{12} = ?$ $c_{21} = ?$ $d_{32} = ?$

Answer

a. $2 \times 3; a_{21} = 3$ **b.** $1 \times 2; b_{12} = 2$ **c.** $3 \times 1; c_{21} = -1$ **d.** $3 \times 3; d_{32} = y$

SKILL ✓ **EXERCISE 1**

Benjamin Peirce, one of the earliest American mathematicians, included multiplication tables in matrix form for all complex associative algebras up to 6 dimensions in his 1870 text *Linear Associative Algebra*.

In Example 1, B is a *row matrix* and C is a *column matrix*. Because matrix D has the same number of rows and columns, it is a *square matrix* and is said to have an *order* of 3.

Two matrices $A = [a_{ij}]$ and $B = [b_{ij}]$ are *equal* if they have the same dimensions ($m \times n$) and their corresponding entries are equal, that is, $a_{ij} = b_{ij}$ for all $i = 1, 2, \ldots, m$ and $j = 1, 2, \ldots, n$.

The first basic matrix operation is *matrix addition*. Matrices are added by adding corresponding entries.

▍MATRIX ADDITION

If $A = [a_{ij}]$ and $B = [b_{ij}]$ are both $m \times n$ matrices, then $A + B = [a_{ij} + b_{ij}]$ for all $i = 1, 2, \ldots, m$ and $j = 1, 2, \ldots, n$.

Example 2 Matrix Addition

Find each sum if $A = \begin{bmatrix} 3 & -2 & 1 \\ -4 & 5 & 7 \end{bmatrix}$, $B = \begin{bmatrix} -11 & 0 & -4 \\ 5 & 9 & -3 \end{bmatrix}$, and $C = \begin{bmatrix} 1 & -4 \\ 0 & 3 \end{bmatrix}$.

a. $A + B$ **b.** $B + C$

Answer

a. $A + B = \begin{bmatrix} 3 - 11 & -2 + 0 & 1 - 4 \\ -4 + 5 & 5 + 9 & 7 - 3 \end{bmatrix}$

$= \begin{bmatrix} -8 & -2 & -3 \\ 1 & 14 & 4 \end{bmatrix}$

b. $B + C$ is undefined since the matrices do not have the same dimensions.

SKILL ✓ **EXERCISE 5**

The second basic matrix operation is *scalar multiplication*. To multiply a matrix A by a real number k, multiply each entry in A by k.

> **DEFINITION**
>
> The **scalar product** of the real number k and the $m \times n$ matrix $A = [a_{ij}]$ is $kA = [ka_{ij}]$, the $m \times n$ matrix obtained by multiplying each entry of A by k.

An $m \times n$ matrix with every entry equal to 0 is a *zero matrix*, *0*. This matrix is the *additive identity matrix* since $A + 0 = A$. Every $m \times n$ matrix A has an *additive inverse* (or *opposite*) *matrix*, designated as $-A$, where each entry is the opposite of the corresponding entry of A. Note that $-A = (-1)A$ and that $A + (-A) = -A + A = 0$.

Matrix subtraction is defined as the addition of the opposite matrix.

$$A - B = A + (-B) = [a_{ij}] + [-b_{ij}] = [a_{ij} - b_{ij}]$$

This means that matrix subtraction is defined only for matrices with the same dimensions and that corresponding entries are subtracted.

In his 1853 presidential address to the American Association for the Advancement of Science, Benjamin Peirce cautioned that mathematics should not become a toy or an idol, but should be used "for the benefit of mankind and the glory of his Creator."

Example 3 Scalar Multiplication and Subtraction

Find $2B - A$ if $A = \begin{bmatrix} -9 & 4 \\ 24 & 16 \end{bmatrix}$ and $B = \begin{bmatrix} 11 & 2 \\ -13 & -8 \end{bmatrix}$.

Answer

$2\begin{bmatrix} 11 & 2 \\ -13 & -8 \end{bmatrix} - \begin{bmatrix} -9 & 4 \\ 24 & 16 \end{bmatrix}$

Multiply each entry in B by 2, then add the opposite of each entry in A.

$= \begin{bmatrix} 22 & 4 \\ -26 & -16 \end{bmatrix} + \begin{bmatrix} 9 & -4 \\ -24 & -16 \end{bmatrix} = \begin{bmatrix} 31 & 0 \\ -50 & -32 \end{bmatrix}$

SKILL ✓ **EXERCISE 7**

Because matrices are arrays of real numbers, they share some of their properties.

Properties of Matrix Addition and Scalar Multiplication

The following properties apply to the $m \times n$ matrices
A, B, and C and real scalars g, h, and k.

Commutative Property of Matrix Addition	$A + B = B + A$
Associative Property of Matrix Addition	$(A + B) + C = A + (B + C)$
Commutative Property of Scalar Multiplication	$kA = Ak$
Associative Property of Scalar Multiplication	$(gh)A = g(hA)$
Distributive Properties	$k(A + B) = kA + kB$ and $(g + h)A = gA + hA$
Additive Identity Property	$A + 0 = A$
Additive Inverse Property	$A + (-A) = 0$
Scalar Identity Property	$1A = A$

The fact that matrix addition is commutative is easily demonstrated using the Commutative Property of Addition for real numbers.

$$A + B = [a_{ij} + b_{ij}] = [b_{ij} + a_{ij}] = B + A$$

Just as the subtraction of real numbers is not commutative, neither is the subtraction of matrices.

$$A - B \neq B - A; \text{ instead, } A - B = -(B - A)$$

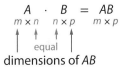

The multiplication of two matrices is defined only when the number of columns in the first matrix is equal to the number of rows in the second matrix. The product of $A_{m \times n}$ and $B_{n \times p}$ is an $m \times p$ matrix. Each entry c_{ij} in the product AB is the sum of the products of the entries in row i of A and corresponding entries in column j of B.

If $A_{2 \times 2} = \begin{bmatrix} a & b \\ c & d \end{bmatrix}$ and $B_{2 \times 3} = \begin{bmatrix} u & v & w \\ x & y & z \end{bmatrix}$, then the product AB is a 2×3 matrix with the following entries.

$$c_{11} = [a \quad b]\begin{bmatrix} u \\ x \end{bmatrix} \qquad c_{12} = [a \quad b]\begin{bmatrix} v \\ y \end{bmatrix} \qquad c_{13} = [a \quad b]\begin{bmatrix} w \\ z \end{bmatrix}$$
$$= au + bx \qquad\qquad = av + by \qquad\qquad = aw + bz$$

$$c_{21} = [c \quad d]\begin{bmatrix} u \\ x \end{bmatrix} \qquad c_{22} = [c \quad d]\begin{bmatrix} v \\ y \end{bmatrix} \qquad c_{23} = [c \quad d]\begin{bmatrix} w \\ z \end{bmatrix}$$
$$= cu + dx \qquad\qquad = cv + dy \qquad\qquad = cw + dz$$

The product BA is undefined since the number of columns in $B_{2 \times 3}$ is not equal to the number of rows in $A_{2 \times 2}$.

Example 4 Multiplying Matrices

Find AB if $A = \begin{bmatrix} 2 & -3 \\ 1 & 5 \end{bmatrix}$ and $B = \begin{bmatrix} 4 & 6 & 2 \\ -3 & 1 & -5 \end{bmatrix}$.

Answer

The product of $A_{2 \times 2}$ and $B_{2 \times 3}$ is a 2×3 matrix.

$$AB = \begin{bmatrix} 2(4) + (-3)(-3) & 2(6) + (-3)1 & 2(2) + (-3)(-5) \\ 1(4) + 5(-3) & 1(6) + 5(1) & 1(2) + 5(-5) \end{bmatrix} = \begin{bmatrix} 8 + 9 & 12 - 3 & 4 + 15 \\ 4 - 15 & 6 + 5 & 2 - 25 \end{bmatrix}$$

$$= \begin{bmatrix} 17 & 9 & 19 \\ -11 & 11 & -23 \end{bmatrix}$$

SKILL ✔ EXERCISE 13

Note the formal definition of matrix multiplication.

DEFINITION

The **matrix product** AB of the $m \times n$ matrix A and the $n \times p$ matrix B is the $m \times p$ matrix $AB = [c_{ij}]$ where $c_{ij} = a_{i1}b_{1j} + a_{i2}b_{2j} + \cdots + a_{in}b_{nj}$.

Example 5   Multiplying Matrices

If $A = \begin{bmatrix} 2 & 3 \\ -1 & 4 \\ 5 & -2 \end{bmatrix}$ and $B = \begin{bmatrix} -3 & 1 & 3 \\ 6 & -2 & -1 \end{bmatrix}$, state the dimensions and find each product.

a. AB

b. BA

Answer

a. $A_{3 \times 2} \cdot B_{2 \times 3}$ is a 3×3 matrix.

$$AB = \begin{bmatrix} 2 & 3 \\ -1 & 4 \\ 5 & -2 \end{bmatrix}\begin{bmatrix} -3 & 1 & 3 \\ 6 & -2 & -1 \end{bmatrix}$$

$$= \begin{bmatrix} -6+18 & 2+(-6) & 6+(-3) \\ 3+24 & -1+(-8) & -3+(-4) \\ -15+(-12) & 5+4 & 15+2 \end{bmatrix}$$

$$= \begin{bmatrix} 12 & -4 & 3 \\ 27 & -9 & -7 \\ -27 & 9 & 17 \end{bmatrix}$$

b. $B_{2 \times 3} \cdot A_{3 \times 2}$ is a 2×2 matrix.

$$BA = \begin{bmatrix} -3 & 1 & 3 \\ 6 & -2 & -1 \end{bmatrix}\begin{bmatrix} 2 & 3 \\ -1 & 4 \\ 5 & -2 \end{bmatrix}$$

$$= \begin{bmatrix} -6-1+15 & -9+4-6 \\ 12+2-5 & 18-8+2 \end{bmatrix}$$

$$= \begin{bmatrix} 8 & -11 \\ 9 & 12 \end{bmatrix}$$

SKILL ✓ EXERCISE 15

TIP

A graphing calculator can be used to check the products AB and BA.

```
[A][B]
        [ 12  -4   3 ]
        [ 27  -9  -7 ]
        [-27   9  17 ]
[B][A]
        [ 8 -11 ]
        [ 9  12 ]
```

See the Technology Corner on p. 358.

Noting that $AB \neq BA$ in Example 5 indicates that multiplication of matrices is not commutative. In fact, the dimensions of AB and BA are not the same.

$$I_n = \begin{bmatrix} 1 & 0 & 0 & \cdots & 0 \\ 0 & 1 & 0 & \cdots & 0 \\ 0 & 0 & 1 & \cdots & 0 \\ \vdots & \vdots & \vdots & & \vdots \\ 0 & 0 & 0 & \cdots & 1 \end{bmatrix}$$

While every matrix has an additive identity matrix 0, only square matrices have a *multiplicative identity matrix*, I, such that $AI = IA = A$. The multiplicative identity matrix of order n, I_n, is an $n \times n$ matrix with entries on the *main diagonal* (entries e_{ij} such that $i = j$) equal to 1 and all other entries equal to 0. Exercises 32–33 further investigate multiplicative identity matrices I_n. Section 7.5 discusses the *multiplicative inverse matrix*.

While matrix multiplication is generally not commutative, some of the other properties of real numbers do extend to matrix multiplication.

Properties of Matrix Multiplication	
Given matrices A, B, and C and scalar k; these properties apply if the products are defined.	
Associative Property of Matrix Multiplication	$(AB)C = A(BC)$
Associative Property of Scalar Multiplication	$k(AB) = (kA)B = A(kB)$
Left Distributive Property	$A(B + C) = AB + AC$
Right Distributive Property	$(B + C)A = BA + CA$
Multiplicative Identity for a Square Matrix of Order n	$AI_n = I_nA = A$

Because matrix multiplication is not commutative, $A(B + C) \neq (B + C)A$ and $AB + AC \neq BA + CA$.

Matrices provide several powerful techniques for solving systems of linear equations that will be explored in Sections 7.3–7.5. One of these methods involves writing the system as a matrix equation in the form of $AX = C$ where A is the *coefficient matrix* representing the coefficients when the equations are written in standard form, X is a column matrix containing the variables, and C is a column matrix containing the constants (the *constant matrix*). Notice how matrix multiplication is used to create a matrix equation that is equivalent to the following system of equations.

Solving vibration problems such as analyzing stress in bridges often involves the use of mass and stiffness matrices.

System of Equations in General Form

$$2x - 3y - 4z = -4$$
$$5x + 4y - z = -7$$
$$-8x + 0y + 3z = 0$$

Matrix Equation: $A \cdot X = C$

$$\begin{bmatrix} 2 & -3 & -4 \\ 5 & 4 & -1 \\ -8 & 0 & 3 \end{bmatrix} \begin{bmatrix} x \\ y \\ z \end{bmatrix} = \begin{bmatrix} -4 \\ -7 \\ 0 \end{bmatrix}$$

Example 6 Applying Matrices to Real-World Data

A high school basketball coach records individual statistics on a spreadsheet. The illustrated portion shows the shots made by his top 3 players during the first 10 games of the season. Write matrix S representing each player's made shots and matrix P representing the point value for each type of shot. Then write and evaluate a matrix expression representing the total points for each player.

	A	B	C	D
1			**Shots Made**	
2		2-Pointers	3-Pointers	Free Throws
3	Freeman	80	21	19
4	Gonzalez	59	15	12
5	Rodgers	55	5	9
6			**Point Value**	
7		2	3	1

Answer

$$S = \begin{bmatrix} 80 & 21 & 19 \\ 59 & 15 & 12 \\ 55 & 5 & 9 \end{bmatrix} ; P = \begin{bmatrix} 2 \\ 3 \\ 1 \end{bmatrix}$$

$$SP = \begin{bmatrix} 80 & 21 & 19 \\ 59 & 15 & 12 \\ 55 & 5 & 9 \end{bmatrix} \begin{bmatrix} 2 \\ 3 \\ 1 \end{bmatrix} = \begin{bmatrix} 160 + 63 + 19 \\ 118 + 45 + 12 \\ 110 + 15 + 9 \end{bmatrix} = \begin{bmatrix} 242 \\ 175 \\ 134 \end{bmatrix} \begin{matrix} \text{Freeman} \\ \text{Gonzalez} \\ \text{Rodgers} \end{matrix}$$

SKILL ✔ **EXERCISE 35**

A. Exercises

1. Given $A = \begin{bmatrix} 12 & 4 & -3 \\ 7 & 0 & 2 \\ 19 & -1 & 6 \\ 5 & -9 & 7 \end{bmatrix}$, state the following.

   a. dimensions of A

   b. value of a_{21}

   c. value of a_{12}

   d. element whose value is 2

   e. element whose value is –1

2. Given $B = \begin{bmatrix} 14 & 2 & 6 & -1 & 19 \\ 0 & -3 & 5 & 2 & 7 \\ 1 & 9 & 16 & -11 & 3 \end{bmatrix}$, state the following.

   a. dimensions of B

   b. value of b_{24}

   c. value of b_{31}

   d. element whose value is 0

   e. element whose value is 6

3. Let $D = \begin{bmatrix} 5 & -1 & 9 \\ 2 & 0 & -4 \end{bmatrix}$, $E = \begin{bmatrix} 0 & 1 \\ 1 & 0 \end{bmatrix}$,

and $F = \begin{bmatrix} 1 & 3 \\ -7 & 5 \\ -2 & 1 \end{bmatrix}$.

   a. Which matrix is a 2×3 matrix?

   b. Which matrix is a square matrix?

   c. Which two matrices could be added?

Find D if $A = \begin{bmatrix} 4 & -7 & 1 \\ -2 & 5 & 8 \end{bmatrix}$ and $B = \begin{bmatrix} -9 & -1 & 3 \\ 5 & 2 & -4 \end{bmatrix}$.

4. $D = A - B$ **5.** $D = A + B$

6. $D = 3A + 2B$ **7.** $D = 2A - 3B$

Perform the following matrix operations.

8. $\begin{bmatrix} 4 & -7 & 1 \\ -2 & 5 & 8 \end{bmatrix} + \begin{bmatrix} -9 & -1 & 3 \\ 5 & 2 & -4 \end{bmatrix}$

9. $\begin{bmatrix} 3 & -6 \\ 8 & -1 \end{bmatrix} - \begin{bmatrix} -4 & 9 \\ 6 & -13 \end{bmatrix}$

10. $-2 \begin{bmatrix} 8 \\ -7 \\ -3 \end{bmatrix} + 4 \begin{bmatrix} 2 \\ -6 \\ 7 \end{bmatrix}$

11. $\begin{bmatrix} 13 & -9 & 14 \\ 8 & 7 & -5 \end{bmatrix} - 3 \begin{bmatrix} 3 & 7 & -6 \\ 4 & \frac{1}{3} & 10 \end{bmatrix}$

State the dimensions of each matrix product, then find the product.

12. $\begin{bmatrix} 3 & -5 \\ 6 & 4 \end{bmatrix} \begin{bmatrix} -2 & 3 \\ 4 & 7 \end{bmatrix}$

13. $\begin{bmatrix} 3 & -1 & 4 \\ 5 & 0 & 2 \end{bmatrix} \begin{bmatrix} -3 & 2 & 6 \\ 0 & 2 & -4 \\ 1 & 4 & 2 \end{bmatrix}$

14. $\begin{bmatrix} 6 & -2 & 7 \end{bmatrix} \begin{bmatrix} 2 & 6 \\ 3 & -2 \\ -5 & 2 \end{bmatrix}$

15. $\begin{bmatrix} 3 & 2 & -1 & 6 \\ 2 & 2 & -2 & 4 \end{bmatrix} \begin{bmatrix} 2 \\ 5 \\ 6 \\ -1 \end{bmatrix}$

Write each linear system of equations as a matrix equation in the form $AX = C$.

16. $2x + 3y - 5z = 0$
    $-x + 2y + z = 4$
    $6x - y = -7$

17. $-3x + y + 2z = 1$
    $y = x + 2z$
    $3z = -6$

18. A class tracked the cookie sales of its two competing groups in a spreadsheet. Write matrix A representing sales from Group A and matrix B representing sales from Group B. Then write and evaluate a matrix expression representing the total boxes of each type of cookie sold by the class on each day.

◢	A	B	C	D	E	F	G
1			**Group A**			**Group B**	
2		Thur	Fri	Sat	Thur	Fri	Sat
3	Mint	14	37	79	14	31	79
4	Caramel	9	15	26	9	9	22
5	Peanut Butter	6	10	13	6	5	9
6	Toffee	8	11	9	8	14	16
7	Shortbread	1	4	7	1	5	7
8	S'more	3	12	18	3	4	17

B. Exercises

Given $A = \begin{bmatrix} 4 & -2 \\ 7 & 1 \end{bmatrix}$, $B = \begin{bmatrix} 5 & 1 \\ -4 & -1 \end{bmatrix}$, $C = \begin{bmatrix} 2 & -6 & 3 \end{bmatrix}$,

and $D = \begin{bmatrix} 4 \\ -3 \\ 8 \end{bmatrix}$, evaluate each matrix expression if possible. If not possible, explain why.

19. CD **20.** DB

21. AB **22.** BA

23. A^2 **24.** B^2

Multiply.

25. $\begin{bmatrix} 1 & 3 & 2 \\ 2 & -1 & 0 \\ 4 & 0 & 1 \end{bmatrix} \begin{bmatrix} -2 & 0 & 3 \\ 1 & 4 & 2 \\ 5 & 0 & -1 \end{bmatrix}$

26. $\begin{bmatrix} 0 & 2 & 1 \\ 4 & -1 & 6 \\ 3 & 5 & -2 \end{bmatrix} \begin{bmatrix} 4 & 5 & 3 \\ 0 & -2 & -4 \\ 2 & 1 & 6 \end{bmatrix}$

27. $\begin{bmatrix} 0 & 2 & -2 \\ -1 & 7 & -1 \\ 5 & 1 & 3 \end{bmatrix} \begin{bmatrix} 4 & 0 & -1 \\ 2 & 1 & 6 \\ 0 & 3 & 5 \end{bmatrix}$

28. $\begin{bmatrix} a & 0 & 0 \\ 0 & b & 0 \\ 0 & 0 & c \end{bmatrix} \begin{bmatrix} d & 0 & 0 \\ 0 & e & 0 \\ 0 & 0 & f \end{bmatrix}$

Use technology to find the following matrix products.

29. $\begin{bmatrix} 47 & 68 \\ -25 & 39 \end{bmatrix} \begin{bmatrix} 22 & -31 \\ 75 & 27 \end{bmatrix}$

30. $\begin{bmatrix} 239 & 332 \\ 112 & 159 \end{bmatrix} \begin{bmatrix} 99 & 51 \\ 187 & 307 \end{bmatrix}$

31. State the identity matrix for each order n.

   a. I_2 **b.** I_3

32. For each matrix, show that $AI = A$ and $IA = A$.

   a. $A = \begin{bmatrix} -2 & 5 \\ 9 & 6 \end{bmatrix}$ **b.** $A = \begin{bmatrix} a & b & c \\ r & s & t \\ u & v & w \end{bmatrix}$

33. Find the product AB if $A = \begin{bmatrix} 3 & 3 \\ 2 & 2 \end{bmatrix}$ and $B = \begin{bmatrix} -1 & 1 \\ 1 & -1 \end{bmatrix}$. Which property of real numbers is shown not to extend to matrix multiplication by this counterexample?

34. The spreadsheet shows seasonal data for three high school football teams. Write matrices S and P representing the scoring plays and the point values, respectively. Then write and evaluate a matrix expression representing the total points scored by each team.

⬜	A	B	C	D	E	F
1		**TD**	**FG**	**PAT**	**2PT-Conv**	**Safety**
2	Defenders	29	11	19	1	0
3	Eagles	22	7	14	0	0
4	Minutemen	37	9	26	1	1
5		**Point Values**				
6		6	3	1	2	2

35. Hunter purchases three types of smart home devices at wholesale prices and sells them at retail for a profit as shown on the spreadsheet. Write 1×3 matrices C and S representing the devices' wholesale costs and retail prices, respectively, and a 3×1 matrix N representing the number of each device sold. Then write and evaluate matrix expressions representing his total revenue R and total profit P.

⬜	A	B	C	D
1		**Smart Home Devices**		
2		Wholesale Cost	Retail Price	Number Sold
3	Smart Entrance	$120	$159	15
4	Leak Detector	$28	$35	29
5	Garage Door Tender	$85	$112	11

C. Exercises

36. Use $k = 3$, $A = \begin{bmatrix} 8 & -6 \\ 1 & 7 \end{bmatrix}$, and $B = \begin{bmatrix} -5 & 4 \\ 3 & 11 \end{bmatrix}$ to illustrate the Distributive Property of Scalar Multiplication over Matrix Addition.

37. Use $A = \begin{bmatrix} 1 & -3 \\ 4 & 2 \end{bmatrix}$, $B = \begin{bmatrix} 2 & 3 & 2 \\ 1 & 0 & 4 \end{bmatrix}$, and $C = \begin{bmatrix} 5 \\ -2 \\ 6 \end{bmatrix}$ to illustrate the Associative Property of Matrix Multiplication.

38. Write the linear system as a matrix equation in the form of $AX = C$. Then use $X = \begin{bmatrix} 6 \\ 3 \\ -2 \end{bmatrix}$ to show that $(6, 3, -2)$ is a solution to the system.

$3x - y + 4z = 7$
$2x - y + 6z = -3$
$-x + 2y - 3z = 6$

39. Analyze: Steven claims that $(A + B)(A - B) = A^2 - B^2$ since $(a + b)(a - b) = a^2 - b^2$ is true for real numbers.

   a. Use $A = \begin{bmatrix} 1 & 2 \\ 3 & -1 \end{bmatrix}$ and $B = \begin{bmatrix} 0 & 1 \\ 2 & -1 \end{bmatrix}$ to show that $(A + B)(A - B) \neq A^2 - B^2$.

   b. Expand $(A + B)(A - B)$ and explain why $(A + B)(A - B) \neq A^2 - B^2$.

40. Let $A = \begin{bmatrix} 0 & i \\ i & 0 \end{bmatrix}$.

   a. Find A^2, A^3, and A^4.

   b. Use the results above to find A^5, A^6, A^7, and A^8.

41. Matrix multiplication can be used to rotate figures in the Cartesian plane. Represent the figure with n vertices in an $n \times 2$ matrix where each row contains the coordinates of a vertex. Then right-multiply by the rotation matrix below to produce a matrix containing the coordinates of the image after a clockwise rotation by the angle α. Use R_α to find the vertices of each rotation of $\triangle ABC$. Then graph each image.

$$R_\alpha = \begin{bmatrix} \cos \alpha & -\sin \alpha \\ \sin \alpha & \cos \alpha \end{bmatrix}$$

   a. $\triangle DEF$, a $90°$ rotation

   b. $\triangle JKL$, a $180°$ rotation

   c. $\triangle PQR$, a $270°$ rotation

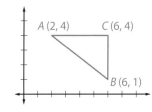

42. Find the zeros of $x^3 - 4x^2 + x + 6$. [2.3]

43. Prove $\frac{1}{2}\sec^2 x = \tan x \csc 2x$. [5.7]

Solve each system using substitution. Then verify graphically. [7.1]

44. $xy = 9$
$\quad\ y = 3x - 6$

45. $y = 2x^2 + 3x + 5$
$\quad\ y = x^2 + 3x + 6$

Solve each system using elimination. [7.1]

46. $x + 4y = 32$
$\quad\ -2x + 2y = 16$

47. $3x + 5y = 13$
$\quad\ -2x + 7y = 12$

48. Which ordered pair is a solution of $6x + 7y = 24$ and $x - 4y = 4$? [7.1]

A. $(0, -1)$

D. $(-4, -2)$

B. $(11, -6)$

E. none of these

C. $(4, 0)$

49. Find $\mathbf{u} \cdot \mathbf{v}$ if $\mathbf{u} = \langle 3, 1 \rangle$ and $\mathbf{v} = \langle 7, -2 \rangle$. [6.2]

A. 8

D. 23

B. 19

E. none of these

C. 1

50. Convert $z = 5 \operatorname{cis} \frac{5\pi}{4}$ to standard form. [6.6]

A. $-\frac{5\sqrt{2}}{2} + \frac{5\sqrt{2}}{2} i$

D. $-\frac{5\sqrt{2}}{2} - \frac{5\sqrt{2}}{2} i$

B. $\frac{5\sqrt{2}}{2} + \frac{5\sqrt{2}}{2} i$

E. none of these

C. $\frac{5\sqrt{2}}{2} - \frac{5\sqrt{2}}{2} i$

51. Which of the following describes the number of solutions for the system? [7.1]
$$-\frac{3x}{4} + \frac{y}{4} = \frac{1}{2}$$
$$-3x + y = 8$$

A. 0

D. infinitely many

B. 1

E. none of these

C. 2

Direct and Indirect Deductive Reasoning

No human investigation can be called real science if it cannot be demonstrated mathematically.

—Leonardo da Vinci

In stating that real science must be demonstrated mathematically, Leonardo da Vinci asserted that science should be supported by mathematical reasoning. He made this statement before the scientific laws of Galileo, Kepler, and Newton were supported by mathematical deductive reasoning. Scientific theories are often based on inductive reasoning, which draws general conclusions from specific examples and cannot guarantee the truth of the results. As science seeks to verify unproven theories, those theories that are based on mathematical reasoning are more reliable than those that are not. As Einstein declared, "It is mathematics that offers the exact natural sciences a certain measure of security which, without mathematics, they could not attain." The ability to verify mathematical concepts through various kinds of proofs has led to the universal acceptance of a large body of mathematical truth.

Mathematical proofs commonly use direct deductive reasoning, in which step-by-step logical reasoning establishes the truth of a statement. You did many direct proofs in Geometry. These proofs established the theorems that proved the many formulas and techniques you applied to real-world problems. While some direct proofs can be short and easy, others can be long and difficult. Andrew Wiles's proof of Fermat's Last Theorem is over 150 pages long and required seven years of research.

An indirect deductive proof assumes the negation of the statement that is to be proved and then applies logical reasoning to reach a contradiction. The contradiction shows that the negation is false and that the original statement must then be true. British mathematician G. H. Hardy described indirect proofs as "one of a mathematician's finest weapons," saying, "It is a far finer gambit than any chess gambit: a chess player may offer the sacrifice of a pawn or even a piece, but a mathematician offers *the game*" (the assumption that the negation might be true). Consider an indirect proof for there being no smallest rational number greater than 0. Start by assuming that there is a smallest rational number x greater than 0. But the rational number $\frac{x}{2}$ would be less than x and greater than 0.

Therefore the assumption that x is the smallest rational number greater than 0 is false, and the original statement must be true. This indirect reasoning proves there is no smallest rational number greater than 0. Examples of classic indirect proofs include proving that $\sqrt{2}$ is irrational and that the number of prime numbers is infinite.

Scripture often uses the word *prove* or *proof*. While these words often refer to a testing of God's chosen people or a particular person, other passages refer to a reasoned argument used to show the truthfulness of a fact. While these proofs can be inductive, the Holy Spirit can use direct and indirect deductive reasoning to strengthen our belief in spiritual truths and convince others of these truths (Acts 17:2; 18:4,19; 24:25; Heb. 5:14; 1 Pet. 3:15).

❯ Exercises

1. State whether the illustrated reasoning is deductive or inductive.

   a. $1^2 \geq 1,\ 2^2 \geq 2,\ 3^2 \geq 3,\ 4^2 \geq 4,\ 5^2 \geq 5$
   Therefore, $n^2 \geq n$ for all natural numbers n.

   b. For $n \in \mathbb{Z},\ n^2 + n = n(n + 1)$, the product of one odd and one even integer.
   Any even integer can be expressed as $2c$, with $c \in$ natural numbers.
   Therefore, $n^2 + n$ is divisible by 2.

2. Which type of deductive proof is the most common?

3. Use the figure to complete the proof of the Pythagorean Theorem.

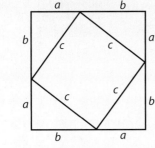

$$A_{Large\ Square} = A_{Small\ Square} + 4A_{Right\ Triangle}$$
$$(a + b)^2 = \underline{\hspace{1cm}} + 4(0.5ab)$$
$$\underline{\hspace{3cm}} = \underline{\hspace{3cm}}$$
$$a^2 + b^2 = c^2$$

4. Why is an indirect proof often called proof by contradiction?

5. Write the assumption that is the first step for each indirect proof.
  a. Prove that the set of prime numbers is infinite.
  b. Prove that $\sqrt{2}$ is irrational.

6. Read Acts 1:3. What is being proved?

7. What evidence is used as proof in Acts 1:3? (See also Matt. 28:16–17; Mark 16:14; Luke 24:33–37; John 20:19–20; and 1 Cor. 15:3–8.)

8. Discuss: Compare and contrast direct and indirect deductive proofs.

9. Discuss: Compare and contrast deductive proofs with the proof in Acts 1:3.

10. Discuss: Read the following excerpt from the Bahnsen-Stein debate. Identify the type of proof that Dr. Bahnsen employs and summarize his argument in your own words.

THE GREAT DEBATE: DOES GOD EXIST?
Dr. Gordon Stein (Atheist) v. Dr. Greg Bahnsen (Christian)

⟩ From Bahnsen's Opening Case

I suggest *we can prove the existence of God from the impossibility of the contrary. The transcendental proof for God's existence is that without Him it is impossible to prove anything*. . . . The atheist world view cannot allow for laws of logic, the uniformity of nature, the ability for the mind to understand the world, and moral absolutes. . . .

⟩ From Bahnsen's Closing Statement

Why should [Dr. Stein] feed the poor? He says they want to do that. I grant that. My argument has never been that atheists are the lousiest people in the world. That's not the point. Some Christians can be pretty lousy, too. But why is it that I can call atheists or Christians lousy when they act in the ways we're thinking of? [It's] because I have absolute standards of morality to judge. Dr. Stein does not.

Therefore, from a transcendental standpoint the atheistic view cannot account for this debate tonight; because this debate has assumed that we're going to use the laws of logic as standards of reasoning, or else we're irrational; that we're going to use laws of science. . . . It's assumed in a moral sense that we're not going to be dishonest and try to lie or just try to deceive you. . . .

How, in a material, naturalistic outlook on life and man his place in the world, can you account for the laws of logic, science, and morality?

The atheist world view cannot do it, and therefore I feel justified concluding . . . that the proof of the Christian God is the impossibility of the contrary. Without the Christian worldview this debate wouldn't make sense.

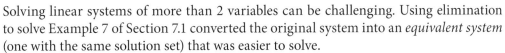

7.3 Gaussian Elimination

Solving linear systems of more than 2 variables can be challenging. Using elimination to solve Example 7 of Section 7.1 converted the original system into an *equivalent system* (one with the same solution set) that was easier to solve.

$$-2x + 5y + 2z = 23$$
$$4x - y + 2z = -13 \quad \Rightarrow$$
$$x - 3y + 6z = -17$$

$$x - 3y + 6z = -17$$
$$y - 2z = 5$$
$$z = -\frac{1}{2}$$

When a system with this inverted triangular form has all leading coefficients of 1, it is said to be in *row echelon form* (REF). The process of eliminating variables from the system to find an equivalent system in REF is called *Gaussian elimination*. While this process is similar to solving by elimination, a more formal notation illustrates how an equivalent system in REF is generated.

$$x - 3y + 6z = -17$$
$$4x - y + 2z = -13$$
$$-2x + 5y + 2z = 23$$

1. Interchange the first and third equations so the coefficient of the x-term in the first equation is 1.

$$x - 3y + 6z = -17$$
$$11y - 22z = 55$$
$$-y + 14z = -11$$

2. Replace the second equation with the sum of the second and -4 times the first to eliminate the x-term.

   Then replace the third equation with the sum of the third and 2 times the first to eliminate the x-term.

$$x - 3y + 6z = -17$$
$$y - 2z = 5$$
$$-y + 14z = -11$$

3. Divide each term in the second equation by 11.

$$x - 3y + 6z = -17$$
$$y - 2z = 5$$
$$12z = -6$$

4. Replace the third equation with the sum of the second and third equations to eliminate the y-term.

$$x - 3y + 6z = -17$$
$$y - 2z = 5$$
$$z = -\frac{1}{2}$$

5. Divide the last equation by 12 to get an equivalent REF system.

Once each equation in a linear system is written in standard form, Gaussian elimination uses operations that affect only the coefficients of the variables and the constant term. An *augmented matrix* keeps the coefficients and constants organized when converting the original system to an equivalent REF. Notice how an augmented matrix is made from the standard form equations by combining the system's coefficient matrix and its constant matrix.

$$\begin{array}{c} \text{System} \\ \begin{array}{r} -2x + 5y + 2z = 23 \\ 4x - y + 2z = -13 \\ x - 3y + 6z = -17 \end{array} \end{array} \Rightarrow \begin{array}{c} \text{Augmented Matrix} \\ \left[\begin{array}{rrr|r} -2 & 5 & 2 & 23 \\ 4 & -1 & 2 & -13 \\ 1 & -3 & 6 & -17 \end{array} \right] \end{array}$$

After completing this section, you will be able to

- list the elementary row operations.
- solve systems of equations using Gaussian elimination or Gauss-Jordan elimination.
- use matrices to model and solve real-world problems.

The German mathematician Carl Friedrich Gauss (1777–1855) helped develop the branch of mathematics called linear algebra.

Each operation that produced an equivalent system has a corresponding *elementary row operation* used to transform the augmented matrix into an equivalent REF matrix.

Elementary Row Operation

1. Interchange any two rows.

2. Multiply (or divide) each entry in a row by any nonzero number.

3. Add a multiple of one row to another row.

Notice how each step of the Gaussian elimination in Example 1 is notated using elementary row operations on the augmented matrix.

Example 1 Illustrating Gaussian Elimination with an Augmented Matrix

Illustrate the row operations used to convert the augmented matrix representing the system to an equivalent REF.

$$\begin{bmatrix} -2 & 5 & 2 & 23 \\ 4 & -1 & 2 & -13 \\ 1 & -3 & 6 & -17 \end{bmatrix}$$

Answer

$r_3 \Leftrightarrow r_1 \begin{bmatrix} 1 & -3 & 6 & -17 \\ 4 & -1 & 2 & -13 \\ -2 & 5 & 2 & 23 \end{bmatrix}$

1. Interchange the first and third rows.

$\begin{matrix} \\ -4r_1 + r_2 \Rightarrow r_2 \\ 2r_1 + r_3 \Rightarrow r_3 \end{matrix} \begin{bmatrix} 1 & -3 & 6 & -17 \\ 0 & 11 & -22 & 55 \\ 0 & -1 & 14 & -11 \end{bmatrix}$

2. Replace the second row with the sum of the second and -4 times the first.

   Then replace the third row with the sum of the third and 2 times the first.

$\frac{1}{11}r_2 \Rightarrow r_2 \begin{bmatrix} 1 & -3 & 6 & -17 \\ 0 & 1 & -2 & 5 \\ 0 & -1 & 14 & -11 \end{bmatrix}$

3. Divide all terms in the second row by 11.

$r_2 + r_3 \Rightarrow r_3 \begin{bmatrix} 1 & -3 & 6 & -17 \\ 0 & 1 & -2 & 5 \\ 0 & 0 & 12 & -6 \end{bmatrix}$

4. Replace the third row with the sum of the second and third rows.

$\frac{1}{12}r_2 \Rightarrow r_2 \begin{bmatrix} 1 & -3 & 6 & -17 \\ 0 & 1 & -2 & 5 \\ 0 & 0 & 1 & -\frac{1}{2} \end{bmatrix}$

5. Divide the last row by 12 to get an equivalent system in REF.

SKILL ✓ **EXERCISE 7**

Once the augmented matrix is in REF, the corresponding system is relatively easy to solve. Use the value of the last variable, $z = -\frac{1}{2}$, to back-substitute and find the value of the other variables as illustrated in Section 7.1.

Example 2   Using an Augmented Matrix and Gaussian Elimination

Write an augmented matrix representing the system.
Then use Gaussian elimination to find an equivalent
REF matrix and solve the system.

$$3x + 4y + 5z = -13$$
$$x - 2y = 14$$
$$2y + 10 = 4z + x$$

Answer

$$3x + 4y + 5z = -13$$
$$x - 2y + 0z = 14$$
$$-x + 2y - 4z = -10$$

$$\begin{bmatrix} 3 & 4 & 5 & | & -13 \\ 1 & -2 & 0 & | & 14 \\ -1 & 2 & -4 & | & -10 \end{bmatrix}$$

1. Write each equation in standard form before representing the system with an augmented matrix.

$$r_2 \Leftrightarrow r_1 \begin{bmatrix} 1 & -2 & 0 & | & 14 \\ 3 & 4 & 5 & | & -13 \\ -1 & 2 & -4 & | & -10 \end{bmatrix}$$

2. Interchange rows to make the leading coefficient of the first equation equal to 1.

$$\begin{matrix} \\ 3r_3 + r_2 \Rightarrow r_2 \\ r_1 + r_3 \Rightarrow r_3 \end{matrix} \begin{bmatrix} 1 & -2 & 0 & | & 14 \\ 0 & 10 & -7 & | & -43 \\ 0 & 0 & -4 & | & 4 \end{bmatrix}$$

3. Use elementary row operations to produce 0s under the leading 1 in the first column.

$$-\tfrac{1}{4}r_3 \Rightarrow r_3 \begin{bmatrix} 1 & -2 & 0 & | & 14 \\ 0 & 10 & -7 & | & -43 \\ 0 & 0 & 1 & | & -1 \end{bmatrix}$$

4. Divide row 3 by -4 to obtain a 1 along the major diagonal.

$$7r_3 + r_2 \Rightarrow r_2 \begin{bmatrix} 1 & -2 & 0 & | & 14 \\ 0 & 10 & 0 & | & -50 \\ 0 & 0 & 1 & | & -1 \end{bmatrix}$$

5. Since dividing row 2 by 10 would introduce fractions, add the multiple of row 3 that eliminates the z term in row 2.

$$\tfrac{1}{10}r_2 \Rightarrow r_2 \begin{bmatrix} 1 & -2 & 0 & | & 14 \\ 0 & 1 & 0 & | & -5 \\ 0 & 0 & 1 & | & -1 \end{bmatrix}$$

6. Divide the second row by 10 to finish converting to REF. The last row implies that $z = -1$ and the second row implies that $y = -5$.

$$1x - 2(-5) + 0 = 14$$
$$x = 4$$

7. Substitute $z = -1$ and $y = -5$ into the equation indicated by the first row to find x.

$$(4, -5, -1)$$

8. Write the solution as an ordered triple.

TIP

The REF of an augmented matrix is not unique. While the result using a calculator may differ from your work, the system's solution will be the same.

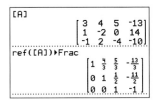

——————————————— SKILL ✔ **EXERCISE 23**

Performing the additional row operation of $2r_2 + r_1 \Rightarrow r_1$ on the last matrix in Example 2 produces a coefficient matrix equal to the multiplicative identity matrix I_3. The system's solution can then be read directly: $x = 4$, $y = -5$, and $z = -1$.

$$\begin{bmatrix} 1 & 0 & 0 & | & 4 \\ 0 & 1 & 0 & | & -5 \\ 0 & 0 & 1 & | & -1 \end{bmatrix}$$

A matrix is in *reduced row echelon form* (RREF) when the first nonzero element in each row is 1 and any other elements in that column are 0. Solving a system by applying elementary row operations to an augmented matrix until the unique RREF is found is called *Gauss-Jordan elimination*.

Example 3   Using Gauss-Jordan Elimination

Write an augmented matrix representing the system.
Then solve the system using Gauss-Jordan elimination.

$$2x + y - z = -7$$
$$-2x + 3y - 4z = -18$$
$$-x - 2y + 2z = 11$$

Answer

$$\begin{bmatrix} 2 & 1 & -1 & | & -7 \\ -2 & 3 & -4 & | & -18 \\ -1 & -2 & 2 & | & 11 \end{bmatrix}$$

1. Write an augmented matrix representing the system.

$$\begin{matrix} -r_3 \Rightarrow r_1 \\ r_1 + r_2 \Rightarrow r_2 \\ r_1 + 2r_3 \Rightarrow r_3 \end{matrix} \begin{bmatrix} 1 & 2 & -2 & | & -11 \\ 0 & 4 & -5 & | & -25 \\ 0 & -3 & 3 & | & 15 \end{bmatrix}$$

2. Use elementary row operations to make $e_{11} = 1$, $e_{21} = 0$, and $e_{31} = 0$.

CONTINUED ➡

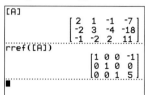
$$-\tfrac{1}{3}r_3 \Rightarrow r_2 \atop 3r_2 + 4r_3 \Rightarrow r_3 \begin{bmatrix} 1 & 2 & -2 & | & -11 \\ 0 & 1 & -1 & | & -5 \\ 0 & 0 & -3 & | & -15 \end{bmatrix}$$

3. Use elementary row operations to make $e_{22} = 1$. Notice how fractions can be avoided by combining multiples of two rows when making $e_{32} = 0$.

$$-\tfrac{1}{3}r_3 \Rightarrow r_3 \begin{bmatrix} 1 & 2 & -2 & | & -11 \\ 0 & 1 & -1 & | & -5 \\ 0 & 0 & 1 & | & 5 \end{bmatrix}$$

4. Finish converting to REF.

$$2r_3 + r_1 \Rightarrow r_1 \atop r_3 + r_2 \Rightarrow r_2 \begin{bmatrix} 1 & 2 & 0 & | & -1 \\ 0 & 1 & 0 & | & 0 \\ 0 & 0 & 1 & | & 5 \end{bmatrix}$$

5. Use elementary row operations to make $e_{13} = 0$ and $e_{23} = 0$.

$$-2r_2 + r_1 \Rightarrow r_1 \begin{bmatrix} 1 & 0 & 0 & | & -1 \\ 0 & 1 & 0 & | & 0 \\ 0 & 0 & 1 & | & 5 \end{bmatrix}$$

6. Finish converting to RREF.

$$(-1, 0, 5)$$

7. Write the solution as an ordered triple.

_____ SKILL ✓ **EXERCISE 27**

Consistent independent systems like those in Examples 1–3 produce a unique solution. A dependent consistent system has an infinite number of solutions that can be expressed using one or more arbitrary parameters.

Example 4 Finding a General Solution

Solve the system of linear equations.

$$\begin{aligned} x - 2y - 4z &= 2 \\ 3x - 10y - 4z &= -10 \\ -2x + 4y + 8z &= -4 \end{aligned}$$

Answer

$$\begin{bmatrix} 1 & -2 & -4 & | & 2 \\ 3 & -10 & -4 & | & -10 \\ -2 & 4 & 8 & | & -4 \end{bmatrix}$$

1. Write the system as an augmented matrix.

$$-3r_1 + r_2 \Rightarrow r_2 \atop 2r_1 + r_3 \Rightarrow r_3 \begin{bmatrix} 1 & -2 & -4 & | & 2 \\ 0 & -4 & 8 & | & -16 \\ 0 & 0 & 0 & | & 0 \end{bmatrix}$$

2. Use elementary row operations to convert to REF.

$$-\tfrac{1}{4}r_2 \Rightarrow r_2 \begin{bmatrix} 1 & -2 & -4 & | & 2 \\ 0 & 1 & -2 & | & 4 \\ 0 & 0 & 0 & | & 0 \end{bmatrix}$$

$$2r_2 + r_1 \Rightarrow r_1 \begin{bmatrix} 1 & 0 & -8 & | & 10 \\ 0 & 1 & -2 & | & 4 \\ 0 & 0 & 0 & | & 0 \end{bmatrix}$$

3. Convert to RREF.

$$\begin{aligned} x - 8z &= 10 & y - 2z &= 4 \\ x &= 8z + 10 & y &= 2z + 4 \end{aligned}$$

4. Use the equations from the first two rows to solve for x and y in terms of z.

$$(10 + 8t, 4 + 2t, t)$$

5. Write the general solution to the dependent system as an ordered triple where z is replaced by the arbitrary parameter t.

_____ SKILL ✓ **EXERCISE 31**

The system has an infinite number of solutions where every real value of t corresponds to an ordered triple that is a particular solution to the system. The particular solution corresponding to $t = 1$ is $(18, 6, 1)$, which can be checked in each equation of the original system.

An inconsistent system produces a row representing a false equation with all the coefficients being 0 but with a nonzero constant.

Example 5   Finding No Solution

Solve the system of linear equations.

$$3x - 4y + z = 7$$
$$-3x + 3z = -9$$
$$-x - 2y + 3z = -3$$

Answer

$$\begin{bmatrix} 3 & -4 & 1 & | & 7 \\ -3 & 0 & 3 & | & -9 \\ -1 & -2 & 3 & | & -3 \end{bmatrix}$$

1. Write the system as an augmented matrix.

$$-r_3 \Leftrightarrow r_1 \begin{bmatrix} 1 & 2 & -3 & | & 3 \\ -3 & 0 & 3 & | & -9 \\ 3 & -4 & 1 & | & 7 \end{bmatrix}$$

2. Use elementary row operations to convert to REF.

$$\begin{matrix} r_3 + r_2 \Rightarrow r_2 \\ -3r_1 + r_3 \Rightarrow r_3 \end{matrix} \begin{bmatrix} 1 & 2 & -3 & | & 3 \\ 0 & -4 & 4 & | & -2 \\ 0 & -10 & 10 & | & -2 \end{bmatrix}$$

$$\begin{matrix} -\frac{1}{4}r_2 \Rightarrow r_2 \\ \\ -\frac{1}{10}r_3 \Rightarrow r_3 \end{matrix} \begin{bmatrix} 1 & 2 & -3 & | & 3 \\ 0 & 1 & -1 & | & \frac{1}{2} \\ 0 & 1 & -1 & | & \frac{1}{5} \end{bmatrix}$$

$$-r_2 + r_3 \Rightarrow r_3 \begin{bmatrix} 1 & 2 & -3 & | & 3 \\ 0 & 1 & -1 & | & \frac{1}{2} \\ 0 & 0 & 0 & | & -\frac{3}{10} \end{bmatrix}$$

3. Note that the system is inconsistent since the last row represents a false equation:
$$0 + 0 + 0 = -\frac{3}{10}.$$

no solution (or $\varnothing$)

SKILL ✓ **EXERCISE 31**

In computer programming, Gauss-Jordan elimination is frequently used to find the multiplicative inverse of a square matrix. This procedure is illustrated in Section 7.4.

Many problems related to mixtures can be modeled by a system of equations. Once a system of equations is written, technology is frequently used to find the RREF of the related augmented matrix.

Example 6   Finding Profit

To raise funds, Sweet Valley Christian School sells boxes of varying combinations of candies, as shown. Find the profit from each type of candy if the school makes a profit of $6.60 on each bronze box, $8.35 on each silver box, and $15.15 on each gold box.

Box	Caramel	Almond	Truffle
Bronze	6	0	3
Silver	4	3	3
Gold	5	5	8

Answer

$$6c + 0a + 3t = 6.60$$
$$4c + 3a + 3t = 8.35$$
$$5c + 5a + 8t = 15.15$$

1. Write a system of equations representing the profit from each box. Use c, a, and t to represent the profit from each caramel, almond, and truffle candy, respectively.

CONTINUED ➡

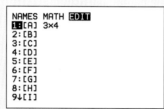

2. Create an augmented matrix representing the system and use technology to find its equivalent RREF.

There is a profit of $0.70 on each caramel candy, $1.05 on each almond candy, and $0.80 on each truffle candy.

3. Interpret the results.

SKILL ✓ EXERCISE 37

TECHNOLOGY CORNER (TI-84 PLUS FAMILY)

The MATRIX menu ([2nd], [x⁻¹]) can be used to complete many matrix operations, such as multiplying matrices, finding the equivalent row echelon form and reduced row echelon form, calculating the determinant, and finding inverse matrices.

To enter matrix A from Example 3, select the EDIT submenu from the MATRIX menu, select 1: [A], and then enter the dimensions and each individual element. Select QUIT ([2nd], [MODE]) to return to the home screen.

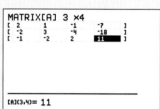

To find the row echelon form use [MATRIX], MATH, A:ref(, and then enter the matrix using [MATRIX], 1:[A] 3 × 4, [ENTER]. The reduced row echelon form can be found using the B:rref(command, one of many matrix operations found in the [MATRIX], MATH submenu.

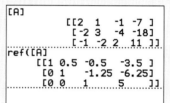

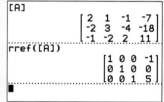

A. Exercises

Use back substitution to solve each system.

1. $5x + 3y = 2$
$y = 4$

2. $x + 3y - 4z = 1$
$2y + z = -5$
$z = -1$

Write each system of equations as an augmented matrix.

3. $3x - 4y = 6$
$2x + 5y = -19$

4. $2x + 4y - 3z = 9$
$3x - 2z = 9$
$4x - y = 18$

Write each system as an augmented matrix. Then complete the series of elementary row operations on both the system and the augmented matrix.

5. $2x + 5y = -16$
$x - y = 6$

   a. $r_1 \Leftrightarrow r_2$

   b. $-2r_1 + r_2 \Rightarrow r_2$

   c. $\frac{1}{7}r_2 \Rightarrow r_2$

6. $3x - 6y = 24$
$4x - 3y = 7$

   a. $\frac{1}{3}r_1 \Rightarrow r_1$

   b. $-4r_1 + r_2 \Rightarrow r_2$

   c. $\frac{1}{5}r_2 \Rightarrow r_2$

7. $x + y + z = 4$
$4x + 3y + z = 4$
$3x - y - 2z = -1$

   a. $-4r_1 + r_2 \Rightarrow r_2$
      $-3r_1 + r_3 \Rightarrow r_3$

   b. $-r_2 \Rightarrow r_2$

   c. $4r_2 + r_3 \Rightarrow r_3$

   d. $\frac{1}{7}r_3 \Rightarrow r_3$

8. $x - y - z = 9$
$2x + y + 3z = 1$
$5x - 6y + 4z = 8$

   a. $-2r_1 + r_2 \Rightarrow r_2$
      $-5r_1 + r_3 \Rightarrow r_3$

   b. $-r_3 \Leftrightarrow r_2$

   c. $-3r_2 + r_3 \Rightarrow r_3$

   d. $\frac{1}{32}r_3 \Rightarrow r_3$

Use the results of exercises 5–8 and back substitution to solve each system.

9. $2x + 5y = -16$
   $x - y = 6$

10. $3x - 6y = 24$
   $4x - 3y = 7$

11. $x + y + z = 4$
   $4x + 3y + z = 4$
   $3x - y - 2z = -1$

12. $x - y - z = 9$
   $2x + y + 3z = 1$
   $5x - 6y + 4z = 8$

Write the solution for the system represented by each matrix and classify the system as independent consistent, dependent consistent, or inconsistent.

13. $\begin{bmatrix} 1 & 2 & 3 & 5 \\ 0 & 1 & 2 & -1 \\ 0 & 0 & 1 & 4 \end{bmatrix}$

14. $\begin{bmatrix} 3 & 5 & 2 & -7 \\ 0 & -2 & 8 & 4 \\ 0 & 0 & 0 & 6 \end{bmatrix}$

15. $\begin{bmatrix} 2 & -3 & 1 & 3 \\ 0 & 1 & 3 & 2 \\ 0 & 0 & 0 & 0 \end{bmatrix}$

Write each matrix in equivalent row echelon form.

16. $\begin{bmatrix} 3 & 8 & -2 \\ 1 & 6 & -4 \end{bmatrix}$

17. $\begin{bmatrix} 2 & 7 & -4 \\ 4 & 5 & 10 \end{bmatrix}$

18. $\begin{bmatrix} 1 & 1 & -1 & 3 \\ 2 & 3 & 0 & -2 \\ 0 & 6 & 1 & -26 \end{bmatrix}$

Write each matrix in reduced row echelon form.

19. $\begin{bmatrix} 4 & 3 & -1 \\ 5 & 1 & 7 \end{bmatrix}$

20. $\begin{bmatrix} 1 & -2 & 1 & -7 \\ 3 & 1 & -2 & 12 \\ 4 & -3 & 4 & -8 \end{bmatrix}$

❯ B. Exercises

Solve each system using Gaussian elimination.

21. $3x + 5y = 9$
   $6x + 7y = 9$

22. $4x + y + 3z = 5$
   $2y + 5z = 6$
   $3z = 1$

23. $x - y - z = 10$
   $3x + 5z = 9$
   $4x - 9y = 23$

Use Gauss-Jordan elimination to solve each system. Classify any inconsistent or dependent systems.

24. $8x - 7y = -32$
   $4x + y = 2$

25. $15x + 2y = -15$
   $6x - 5y = 23$

26. $8x - y = 9$
   $2x - \frac{1}{4}y = 5$

27. $4x - 3y + 2z = -7$
   $6x + 2y + 3z = 9$
   $-8x + 3y - 5z = 3$

28. $3x - 2y - 5z = -9$
   $3x + 4y - 4z = 1$
   $-2x + 3y + 5z = 6$

29. $x - y - 17z = -2$
   $y + 4z = 2$
   $2x + 6y - 2z = 8$

30. $-2x + 3y + 5z = -1$
   $6x - 2y - 3z = 5$

31. $3x + 4y + 5z = 4$
   $x + 2y - 2z = 2$

Solve by using technology to find the reduced row echelon form of an augmented matrix.

32. $\frac{1}{8}x + \frac{1}{4}y = \frac{7}{5}$
   $\frac{1}{2}x - \frac{1}{5}y = -\frac{7}{8}$

33. $1.5x - 3.3y + 0.7z = 9.9$
   $0.2x + 4.1y - 1.3z = 10.5$
   $2.4x + 0.4y - 7.5z = 2.2$
   (Round to the nearest hundredth.)

34. $2x_1 + 3x_2 + x_3 + 2x_4 = 1$
   $4x_1 - x_2 + 3x_3 = 4$
   $-6x_1 + 4x_2 + 2x_3 + 3x_4 = -2$
   $-4x_1 - 2x_2 + 3x_3 + 2x_4 = 8$

35. $6x_1 + x_2 - 4x_3 - 5x_4 = 1$
   $2x_1 + 3x_2 - 2x_3 - 2x_4 = 6$
   $4x_1 - 2x_2 - 2x_3 - 3x_4 = -5$
   $4x_1 + 2x_2 - 3x_3 - 5x_4 = -1$

36. Auto Mart sells a full-strength antifreeze. Tom already has a brand that is a 50% antifreeze-water mixture. How many gallons of each should be mixed together to get 3 gal of a 70% antifreeze-water mixture?

37. Suzanne sells three different trail mixes at a local fair. Write and solve a system of equations to find the profit per cup for each ingredient.

Mix	Peanuts	Pretzels	Chocolate Pieces	Profit
Twisty	3 c	4 c	1 c	$5.40
Nutty	4 c	3 c	1 c	$5.90
Snack	1 c	2 c	0.5 c	$2.35

38. Joey sold the listed quantities of concessions at a local tournament and made $138.75, $106.25, and $188.75 in profits on Thursday, Friday, and Saturday, respectively. Write and solve a system of equations to find the profit per item for each type of concession.

Day	Popcorn	Drinks	Candy Bars
Thursday	30	60	15
Friday	25	40	20
Saturday	40	75	35

39. Josh has 72 quarters, dimes, and nickels, totaling $9.60. Write and solve a system of equations to find how many of each coin Josh has if he has 10 more quarters than dimes.

C. Exercises

Use row operations on an augmented matrix to solve each system.

40. $5x - 2y + 4z = -9$
$3x - 4y + 2z = -2$
$2x + 6y + 5z = -7$

41. $12x + 6y = 9$
$-2x + y = -\frac{3}{2}$
$4x + y = 4$

The equation of the parabola passing through three given points can be found by solving the system of equations created by substituting each point into $y = ax^2 + bx + c$.

Use matrices to find $f(x) = ax^2 + bx + c$, whose graph passes through the given points.

42. $(1, 2), (2, 5), (3, 14)$

43. $(-3, -8), (1, 4), (2, -3)$

44. A Christian school earned $150, $400, and $750, respectively, in the first three weeks of a paper drive. Find the quadratic function $f(x) = ax^2 + bx + c$ modeling the earnings during these weeks and use it to predict the fourth week's earnings.

CUMULATIVE REVIEW

45. Find the height of a building if a 6 ft tall observer 500 ft from the building views the top at a 52° angle of elevation. [4.2]

46. Write $y = 3x^2 - 7x + 1$ in vertex form. State the coordinates of the vertex and identify it as a maximum or minimum point. [1.6]

47. Write the equation of $g(x)$ as a transformation of $f(x) = \cos x$ with an amplitude of 3 and a period of $\frac{\pi}{2}$, having been translated $\frac{\pi}{3}$ units right. [4.4]

48. Convert $z = 2 - 2i$ to polar form. [6.4]

49. Convert the polar equation $r = \dfrac{\sin \theta}{\cos^2 \theta}$ to rectangular form. [6.6]

50. Find the measure of each angle (to the nearest tenth of a degree) in a triangle with sides $AC = 10$ cm, $BC = 9$ cm, and $AB = 14$ cm. [5.7]

51. Identify any solutions to the system. List all correct answers. [7.1]
$y = -x^2 + 2x - 15$
$y = 3x - 21$

A. $(2, -15)$ **C.** $(3, 30)$ **E.** none of
B. $(-2, 15)$ **D.** $(-3, -30)$ these

52. Use graphing technology to find any solutions to the system. List all correct answers [7.1]
$y = x^3 - x^2 - 2x$
$y = x^2 - 4x + 1$

A. $(-2, 1)$ **C.** $(1, -2)$ **E.** none of
B. $(1, 2)$ **D.** $(2, -1)$ these

53. Which of the following is true of matrix operations? List all correct answers. [7.2]

A. $A_{2 \times 3}$ times $B_{3 \times 2}$ is a 2×3 matrix.
B. $AI_n = I_n A$ **D.** $A(B + C) = AB + AC$
C. $AB = BA$ **E.** none of these

54. Find entry e_{23} in AB, given
$A = \begin{bmatrix} -4 & 1 \\ 2 & -3 \end{bmatrix}$ and $B = \begin{bmatrix} -3 & 2 & 6 \\ 1 & 0 & -2 \end{bmatrix}$. [7.2]

A. 8   **C.** 6   **E.** none of
B. 18   **D.** -6   these

7.4 Determinants

Gabriel Cramer (1704–52)

Many applications of matrices, including the solving of systems and the calculation of polygonal areas, use the *determinant* of a matrix. The determinant of a square matrix $A_{n \times n}$ is a real number denoted as $|A|$ or det (A). The determinant of a 1×1 matrix $A = [a]$ is equal to its only entry, a.

> **After completing this section, you will be able to**
> - calculate determinants.
> - use Cramer's rule to solve systems of equations.
> - use determinants to find polygonal areas.

DEFINITION

The **determinant of a 2×2 matrix** $A = \begin{bmatrix} a & b \\ c & d \end{bmatrix}$ is given by

$$|A| = \det(A) = \begin{vmatrix} a & b \\ c & d \end{vmatrix} = ad - cb.$$

The illustrated pattern emphasizes that the determinant of a 2×2 matrix is the difference of the products of the major and minor diagonals.

$$\begin{vmatrix} a & b \\ c & d \end{vmatrix} = ad - cb$$

Example 1   Finding the Determinant of a 2×2 Matrix

Find $|A|$ if $A = \begin{bmatrix} 6 & -2 \\ 5 & 8 \end{bmatrix}$.

Answer

$|A| = 6(8) - 5(-2) = 48 + 10 = 58$

SKILL ✓ EXERCISE 3

A pattern of products of diagonals can also be used to find the determinant of a 3×3 matrix. Begin by rewriting the first two columns to the right of the matrix.

$$\begin{bmatrix} a & b & c \\ d & e & f \\ g & h & i \end{bmatrix} \Rightarrow \begin{bmatrix} a & b & c \\ d & e & f \\ g & h & i \end{bmatrix} \begin{matrix} a & b \\ d & e \\ g & h \end{matrix}$$

Then find the sum of the products of each set of diagonals.

$$aei + bfg + cdh \qquad gec + hfa + idb$$

The determinant is the difference of the first and second sums.

> Determinants were actually developed before matrices, but as matrices were explored, their importance and usefulness surpassed determinants to the point that determinants are now defined in terms of square matrices.

DEFINITION

The **determinant of a 3×3 matrix** A is given by

$$\det(A) = |A| = \begin{vmatrix} a & b & c \\ d & e & f \\ g & h & i \end{vmatrix} = (aei + bfg + cdh) - (gec + hfa + idb).$$

Example 2 Finding the Determinant of a 3 × 3 Matrix

Find $|B|$ if $B = \begin{bmatrix} 2 & -3 & 4 \\ 0 & 5 & -1 \\ 4 & 6 & 1 \end{bmatrix}$.

Answer

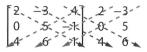

$|B| = [2(5)(1) + (-3)(-1)(4) + 4(0)(6)] - [4(5)(4) + 6(-1)(2) + 1(0)(-3)]$
$= [10 + 12 + 0] - [80 + (-12) + 0]$
$= 22 - 68 = -46$

Check

A graphing calculator or Internet app can be used to verify $|B|$.

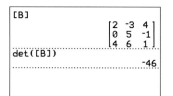

SKILL ✓ **EXERCISE 7**

Determinants of square matrices of an order higher than 3 require the use of *minors* and *cofactors*.

▎DEFINITIONS

The **minor** of entry a_{ij} in square matrix A, notated M_{ij}, is the determinant of the matrix formed by removing the ith row and jth column of A.
The **cofactor** C_{ij} of entry a_{ij} is $C_{ij} = (-1)^{i+j} M_{ij}$.

$$\begin{bmatrix} + & - & + & \cdots \\ - & + & - & \cdots \\ + & - & + & \cdots \\ \vdots & \vdots & \vdots & \end{bmatrix}$$

When finding cofactors, the sign of the minor is not changed in *even positions* (where $i + j$ is even) but is negated in *odd positions* (where $i + j$ is odd).

Example 3 Finding Minors and Cofactors

Find the minors and cofactors for each entry in row 1 of $B = \begin{bmatrix} 2 & -3 & 4 \\ 0 & 5 & -1 \\ 4 & 6 & 1 \end{bmatrix}$.

Answer

$M_{11} = \begin{vmatrix} 2 & -3 & 4 \\ 0 & 5 & -1 \\ 4 & 6 & 1 \end{vmatrix}$ $\qquad$ $M_{12} = \begin{vmatrix} 2 & -3 & 4 \\ 0 & 5 & -1 \\ 4 & 6 & 1 \end{vmatrix}$ $\qquad$ $M_{13} = \begin{vmatrix} 2 & -3 & 4 \\ 0 & 5 & -1 \\ 4 & 6 & 1 \end{vmatrix}$

$= 5(1) - 6(-1) = 11$ $\qquad$ $= 0(1) - 4(-1) = 4$ $\qquad$ $= 0(6) - 4(5) = -20$

Use the sign pattern and the minors to state the cofactors.

$C_{11} = (+1)M_{11} = 11$ $\qquad$ $C_{12} = (-1)M_{12} = -4$ $\qquad$ $C_{13} = (+1)M_{13} = -20$

SKILL ✓ **EXERCISE 11**

The use of minors and cofactors allows the determinant of a square matrix of order n to be defined inductively in terms of the determinants of square matrices of order $n - 1$.

DEFINITION

The **determinant of an $n \times n$ matrix** $A = [a_{ij}]$ (where $n \geq 2$) is the sum of the product of entries in any row or column and their respective cofactors. For example, expanding by the ith row:

$$\det(A) = |A| = a_{i1}C_{i1} + a_{i2}C_{i2} + \ldots + a_{in}C_{in}.$$

Example 4 Expanding by Cofactors

If $B = \begin{bmatrix} 2 & -3 & 4 \\ 0 & 5 & -1 \\ 4 & 6 & 1 \end{bmatrix}$ find $|B|$ expanding along each of the following.

a. row 1

b. column 1

Answers

$\begin{aligned} |B| &= b_{11}C_{11} + b_{12}C_{12} + b_{13}C_{13} \\ &= 2(11) + (-3)(-4) + 4(-20) \\ &= 22 + 12 - 80 = -46 \end{aligned}$

a. Use the entries in the first row and their cofactors found in Example 3.

$\begin{aligned} |B| &= b_{11}C_{11} + b_{21}C_{21} + b_{31}C_{31} \\ &= 2(M_{11}) - 0(M_{21}) + 4(M_{31}) \\ &= 2[5(1) - 6(-1)] + 4[-3(-1) - 5(4)] \\ &= 2(11) + 4(-17) = -46 \end{aligned}$

b. Notice that the sign from the cofactor's power of -1 is often applied to the entry before calculating the minor.

SKILL ✓ **EXERCISE 13**

Notice that the value of the determinant is the same no matter which row or column you use in the expansion. Expanding along a row or column with entries of 0 reduces the number of cofactors that need to be calculated since the product of an entry of 0 and its cofactor is always 0.

Example 5 Finding the Determinant of a 4 × 4 Matrix

Find $|D|$ if $D = \begin{bmatrix} 1 & 2 & 0 & -1 \\ -3 & 2 & 1 & 4 \\ -2 & -1 & 0 & 2 \\ 0 & 4 & 3 & 1 \end{bmatrix}$.

Answer

$|D| = 0C_{13} + 1C_{23} + 0C_{33} + 3C_{43}$

$= 1(-1)\begin{vmatrix} 1 & 2 & -1 \\ -2 & -1 & 2 \\ 0 & 4 & 1 \end{vmatrix} + 3(-1)\begin{vmatrix} 1 & 2 & -1 \\ -3 & 2 & 4 \\ -2 & -1 & 2 \end{vmatrix}$

1. Only two cofactors need to be calculated when expanding along the third column.

$|D| = -1[0 - 4(2 - 2) + (-1 + 4)] - 3[(4 + 4) - 2(-6 + 8) - (3 + 4)]$

2. Evaluate M_{23} along row 3 and M_{43} along row 1.

$= -1[0 + 3] - 3[8 - 4 - 7]$

$= -3 + 9 = 6$

3. Simplify.

SKILL ✓ **EXERCISE 21**

```
[C]
    [ 1   2   0  -1]
    [-3   2   1   4]
    [-2  -1   0   2]
    [ 0   4   3   1]
det([C])
                    6
■
```

While expansion by cofactors applies to square matrices of any order, technology is frequently used to calculate determinants beyond an order of 2 since the arithmetic often becomes laborious.

Determinants provide another method of solving systems of equations. Examine the following solution to the generalized system of linear equations in two variables.

$$ax + by = e$$
$$cx + dy = f$$

finding x by eliminating y:

$$d(ax + by = e) \Rightarrow \quad adx + bdy = ed$$
$$-b(cx + dy = f) \Rightarrow \quad -bcx - bdy = -fb$$
$$\overline{(ad - bc)x = de - bf}$$
$$x = \frac{ed - fb}{ad - bc}$$

finding y by eliminating x:

$$-c(ax + by = e) \Rightarrow \quad -acx - bcy = -ce$$
$$a(cx + dy = f) \Rightarrow \quad acx + ady = af$$
$$\overline{(ad - bc)y = af - ce}$$
$$y = \frac{af - ce}{ad - bc}$$

Recall that this system can be written as the matrix equation $AX = C$ where A is the coefficient matrix, X is a column matrix containing the variables, and C is a column matrix containing the constants.

$$\begin{bmatrix} a & b \\ c & d \end{bmatrix} \begin{bmatrix} x \\ y \end{bmatrix} = \begin{bmatrix} e \\ f \end{bmatrix}$$

Notice that the denominator of both x and y is the determinant of the coefficient matrix. The numerators can be expressed as $|A_x|$ where A_x is the matrix formed by replacing the first column in A with C, and $|A_y|$ where A_y is the matrix formed by replacing the second column in A with C.

$$x = \frac{|A_x|}{|A|} = \frac{\begin{vmatrix} e & b \\ f & d \end{vmatrix}}{\begin{vmatrix} a & b \\ c & d \end{vmatrix}} = \frac{ed - fb}{ad - bc} \text{ and } y = \frac{|A_y|}{|A|} = \frac{\begin{vmatrix} a & e \\ c & f \end{vmatrix}}{\begin{vmatrix} a & b \\ c & d \end{vmatrix}} = \frac{af - ce}{ad - bc}$$

Unique solutions to linear systems with more variables can be found in a similar manner using the theorem named after Gabriel Cramer (1704–52), who popularized the use of matrices and introduced this method of solving systems.

Real-world problems in engineering often include square matrices of an order greater than 1000. Understanding the math behind the formulas allows computer programmers to maximize efficiency and minimize errors.

CRAMER'S RULE

If a system of n linear equations in n variables has the coefficient matrix A with $|A| \neq 0$, its unique solution is given by

$$x_1 = \frac{|A_1|}{|A|}, x_2 = \frac{|A_2|}{|A|}, \ldots, x_n = \frac{|A_n|}{|A|}$$

where A_i is formed by replacing the ith column in A with a column of the system's constants.

Example 6   Using Cramer's Rule

Use Cramer's rule to solve the system of equations.

$$x + 3z = 2$$
$$3x - 2y = 6$$
$$2y - z = 8$$

Answer

$$\begin{bmatrix} 1 & 0 & 3 \\ 3 & -2 & 0 \\ 0 & 2 & -1 \end{bmatrix} \begin{bmatrix} x \\ y \\ z \end{bmatrix} = \begin{bmatrix} 2 \\ 6 \\ 8 \end{bmatrix}$$

1. Write the system as a matrix equation $AX = C$.

CONTINUED ➡

$|A| = \begin{vmatrix} 1 & 0 & 3 \\ 3 & -2 & 0 \\ 0 & 2 & -1 \end{vmatrix}$ $|A_x| = \begin{vmatrix} 2 & 0 & 3 \\ 6 & -2 & 0 \\ 8 & 2 & -1 \end{vmatrix}$ 2. Find $|A|, |A_x|, |A_y|,$ and $|A_z|$.

$= 0 - 2[0-9] - 1[-2-0]$ $\qquad = 2[2-0] - 0 + 3[12+16]$ a. using row 3 to find $|A|$

$= 18 + 2 = 20$ $\qquad\qquad = 4 + 84 = 88$ b. using row 1 to find $|A_x|$

$|A_y| = \begin{vmatrix} 1 & 2 & 3 \\ 3 & 6 & 0 \\ 0 & 8 & -1 \end{vmatrix}$ $|A_z| = \begin{vmatrix} 1 & 0 & 2 \\ 3 & -2 & 6 \\ 0 & 2 & 8 \end{vmatrix}$ c. using row 3 to find $|A_y|$

$= 0 - 8[0-9] - 1[6-6]$ $\qquad = 1[-16-12] - 0 + 2[6-0]$ d. using row 1 to find $|A_z|$

$= 72$ $\qquad\qquad = -28 + 12 = -16$

$x = \dfrac{|A_x|}{|A|}$ $\quad y = \dfrac{|A_y|}{|A|}$ $\quad z = \dfrac{|A_z|}{|A|}$ 3. Apply Cramer's rule.

$= \dfrac{88}{20} = 4.4$ $\quad = \dfrac{72}{20} = 3.6$ $\quad = \dfrac{-16}{20} = -0.8$

The solution is $(4.4, 3.6, -0.8)$.

———————————————————————— SKILL ✓ **EXERCISE 35**

If the determinant of the coefficient matrix is 0, the system does not have a unique solution and is either dependent or inconsistent. Cramer's rule does not produce the solution.

Example 7   Using Cramer's Rule

Apply Cramer's rule to each system of equations.

a. $3x + 8y = 5$
$\quad 6x + 16y = 7$

b. $3x + 8y = 5$
$\quad 6x + 16y = 10$

Answer

a. $|A| = \begin{vmatrix} 3 & 8 \\ 6 & 16 \end{vmatrix} = 0$

b. $|A| = \begin{vmatrix} 3 & 8 \\ 6 & 16 \end{vmatrix} = 0$

$|A_x| = \begin{vmatrix} 5 & 8 \\ 7 & 16 \end{vmatrix}$ $\quad |A_y| = \begin{vmatrix} 3 & 5 \\ 6 & 7 \end{vmatrix}$

$\qquad = 24$ $\qquad\qquad = -9$

$x = \dfrac{|A_x|}{|A|} = \dfrac{24}{0}$ $\quad y = \dfrac{|A_y|}{|A|} = \dfrac{-9}{0}$

undefined $\qquad\qquad$ undefined

Since the equations represent parallel lines, the system is inconsistent and its solution is $\varnothing$.

$|A_x| = \begin{vmatrix} 5 & 8 \\ 10 & 16 \end{vmatrix}$ $\quad |A_y| = \begin{vmatrix} 3 & 5 \\ 6 & 10 \end{vmatrix}$

$\qquad = 0$ $\qquad\qquad = 0$

$x = \dfrac{|A_x|}{|A|} = \dfrac{0}{0}$ $\quad y = \dfrac{|A_y|}{|A|} = \dfrac{0}{0}$

undefined $\qquad\qquad$ undefined

Since the equations represent the same line, the system is dependent, and its solution is $\{(x, y) \mid 3x + 8y = 5\}$.

———————————————————————— SKILL ✓ **EXERCISE 29**

Determinants can also be used to find the area of a triangle. Other polygonal areas can be estimated by dividing the region into several triangular areas.

▶ **AREA OF TRIANGLE**

The area of a triangle with vertices (x_1, y_1), (x_2, y_2), and (x_3, y_3) can be found using

$$Area = \pm\frac{1}{2}\begin{vmatrix} x_1 & y_1 & 1 \\ x_2 & y_2 & 1 \\ x_3 & y_3 & 1 \end{vmatrix}$$ where the area must be positive.

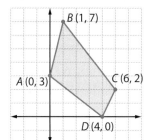

Example 8 Calculating the Area of a Polygonal Region

Use determinants to find the area of the shaded region.

Answer

$Area = Area_{\triangle ABC} + Area_{\triangle ADC}$

$Area_{\triangle ABC} = \pm\frac{1}{2}\begin{vmatrix} 0 & 3 & 1 \\ 1 & 7 & 1 \\ 6 & 2 & 1 \end{vmatrix}$

$= \pm\frac{1}{2}[-3(1-6) + 1(2-42)]$

$= \pm\frac{1}{2}[15 - 40] = \frac{25}{2}$

$Area_{\triangle ADC} = \pm\frac{1}{2}\begin{vmatrix} 0 & 3 & 1 \\ 4 & 0 & 1 \\ 6 & 2 & 1 \end{vmatrix}$

$= \pm\frac{1}{2}[-3(4-6) + 1(8-0)]$

$= \pm\frac{1}{2}[6 + 8] = 7$

$Area = 12.5 + 7 = 19.5 \ u^2$

1. Divide the area into two triangular areas.

2. Find the area of each triangle. Expanding along row 1 requires the calculation of only two minors.

3. Calculate the sum.

SKILL ✓ **EXERCISE 37**

> ## A. Exercises

Find the determinant of each matrix.

1. $[7]$

2. $[-2]$

3. $\begin{bmatrix} 8 & -3 \\ 5 & 9 \end{bmatrix}$

4. $\begin{bmatrix} -2 & -4 \\ -1 & -5 \end{bmatrix}$

5. $\begin{bmatrix} 11 & 7 \\ -13 & -9 \end{bmatrix}$

6. $\begin{bmatrix} \frac{1}{2} & 5 \\ 6 & 8 \end{bmatrix}$

Use the products of diagonals to find the determinant of each matrix.

7. $\begin{bmatrix} 2 & 1 & -4 \\ 3 & 2 & -5 \\ 6 & 2 & 1 \end{bmatrix}$

8. $\begin{bmatrix} 2 & -1 & 4 \\ 1 & 0 & -2 \\ 3 & 1 & 5 \end{bmatrix}$

9. $\begin{bmatrix} 1 & 0 & 2 \\ 1 & 0 & 3 \\ 0 & 1 & -2 \end{bmatrix}$

10. $\begin{bmatrix} 5 & -3 & 4 \\ 2 & 3 & -2 \\ 4 & -2 & 4 \end{bmatrix}$

Given $A = \begin{bmatrix} 2 & -1 & 3 \\ 4 & 2 & 1 \\ 1 & 3 & -2 \end{bmatrix}$**, find each minor and cofactor.**

11. in row 1

12. in column 2

Use cofactors from the given row or column to find the determinant of each matrix.

13. $\begin{bmatrix} 2 & -1 & 3 \\ 4 & 2 & 1 \\ 1 & 3 & -2 \end{bmatrix}$
row 1

14. $\begin{bmatrix} 5 & 1 & 3 \\ 2 & -1 & 0 \\ 1 & 7 & 6 \end{bmatrix}$
row 2

15. $\begin{bmatrix} -1 & 0 & -3 \\ 3 & 5 & -2 \\ 2 & 0 & 1 \end{bmatrix}$
column 2

16. $\begin{bmatrix} -6 & -2 & 4 \\ 1 & 7 & 3 \\ 2 & 5 & -1 \end{bmatrix}$
column 3

17. Use technology to find the determinant of each 3×3 matrix.

a. $A = \begin{bmatrix} 2 & -3 & 2 \\ 8 & 5 & 7 \\ -2 & 1 & 1 \end{bmatrix}$

b. $B = \begin{bmatrix} -8 & -1 & 3 \\ 1 & 6 & 5 \\ 4 & -5 & 2 \end{bmatrix}$

18. Use technology to find the determinant of each 4×4 matrix.

a. $A = \begin{bmatrix} 1 & 3 & 0 & -2 \\ 4 & 0 & 5 & 5 \\ 2 & -3 & -4 & 1 \\ 2 & 1 & -1 & 3 \end{bmatrix}$

b. $B = \begin{bmatrix} 9 & 0 & 2 & 3 \\ 11 & -4 & 1 & 6 \\ 3 & 1 & 7 & -1 \\ -1 & 5 & -2 & 8 \end{bmatrix}$

> ## B. Exercises

Use cofactors from the given row or column to find the determinant of each matrix.

19. $\begin{bmatrix} -2 & 3 & -1 \\ 1 & 2 & 3 \\ 4 & 0 & -1 \end{bmatrix}$
a. row 3
b. column 2

20. $\begin{bmatrix} 4 & -2 & 1 \\ 3 & 5 & 2 \\ -1 & 1 & -3 \end{bmatrix}$
a. row 3
b. column 1

21. $\begin{bmatrix} 2 & 0 & 3 & 1 \\ 1 & 2 & -2 & 3 \\ 0 & 3 & -1 & 2 \\ 0 & 4 & 3 & 1 \end{bmatrix}$
column 1

22. $\begin{bmatrix} 1 & 0 & 2 & 2 \\ -1 & 2 & 1 & 3 \\ 0 & 2 & 0 & 1 \\ -2 & 1 & 3 & 2 \end{bmatrix}$
row 3

Expand by cofactors to find the determinant of each matrix.

23. $\begin{bmatrix} 2 & -3 & 1 & 2 \\ 3 & 0 & -1 & 0 \\ -1 & 1 & 3 & 4 \\ 0 & 2 & -1 & -2 \end{bmatrix}$ 24. $\begin{bmatrix} 4 & 0 & 2 & 3 \\ 1 & 3 & -5 & 0 \\ -3 & 0 & -1 & 2 \\ -6 & 0 & -4 & -2 \end{bmatrix}$

Use Cramer's rule to solve each system of equations.

25. $2x + 2y = 10$
$4x - y = 5$

26. $3x - 2y = 3$
$-3x + 4y = -4$

27. $5x + 6y = -13$
$y = \frac{1}{3}x + \frac{4}{3}$

28. $y = -\frac{3}{2}x + 1$
$3x + 2y = -2$

29. $8x - 12y = 20$
$-6x + 9y = -15$

30. $6x - 2y = 11$
$14x + 5y = -13$

31. $x - y + 2z = 4$
$2x + y - z = -4$
$x + y + z = 3$

32. $2x - y - 3z = -4$
$3x + y - z = 2$
$-x + y + 2z = 3$

33. $2x - 3y + 4z = 16$
$-x + 4y - 10z = -13$
$4x + 6y - z = 8$

34. $3a - b - c = -5$
$21a - 3b + c = -7$
$-9a + 2b - 7c = 0$

Find the area of each triangle.

35. $\triangle ABC$ with A $(0, 2)$, B $(5, 6)$, and C $(10, 1)$.

36. $\triangle PQR$ with P $(-5, -3)$, Q $(1, 6)$, and R $(7, -2)$.

Use determinants to find the area of each shaded region.

37.

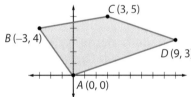

38.

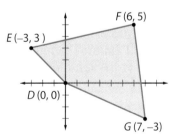

39. Three utility poles define a triangular area. If a utility worker standing at one of the poles walks 250 ft east and then 312 ft north, he arrives at the second pole. If instead he walks 140 ft west and 78 ft north, he arrives at the third pole. Find the area of the triangular region defined by the three poles.

40. Carter and Charlotte set up four 50 gal barrels for a disc golf practice field. Starting at the red barrel they walk 60 ft west and 320 ft north and set the green barrel. The blue barrel is set 600 ft north of the red barrel, and the yellow barrel is set 210 ft east and 50 ft south of the red barrel. Find the area of the region defined by the barrels in square feet and in acres (1 acre = 43,560 ft²).

> **C. Exercises**

41. Verify the formulas for determinants that use products of diagonals by using cofactors to derive the same result.

a. $A = \begin{bmatrix} a & b \\ c & d \end{bmatrix}$

b. $A = \begin{bmatrix} a & b & c \\ d & e & f \\ g & h & i \end{bmatrix}$

42. **Explore:** Investigate a method of determining whether three points are collinear.

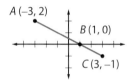

a. What is the result of applying the formula for the area of the triangle to points A, B, and C?

b. Will this result occur whenever the points are collinear? Explain your reasoning.

c. Are D $(-5, -4)$, E $(2, 1)$, and F $(6, 4)$ collinear? Explain your reasoning.

d. Are X $(14, 0)$, Y $(0, 6)$, and Z $(-7, 9)$ collinear? Explain your reasoning.

43. **Extend:** The results of exercise 42 imply that the equation of a line passing through distinct points P_1 (x_1, y_1) and P_2 (x_2, y_2) can be expressed as
$$\begin{vmatrix} x & y & 1 \\ x_1 & y_1 & 1 \\ x_2 & y_2 & 1 \end{vmatrix} = 0.$$
Use this equation to find the equation of the line passing through each pair of points.

a. $(0, 2)$ and $(3, 0)$

b. $(-3, 2)$ and $(3, -1)$

c. (a, k) and (b, k)

44. If the sides of a parallelogram are represented by $\mathbf{u} = \langle a, b \rangle$ and $\mathbf{v} = \langle c, d \rangle$, then its area is $\pm \begin{vmatrix} a & b \\ c & d \end{vmatrix}$.
Find the area of the parallelogram represented by each pair of vectors.

    a. $\mathbf{u} = \langle 4, -3 \rangle$ and $\mathbf{v} = \langle 3, 4 \rangle$

    b. $\mathbf{u} = \langle 3, 5 \rangle$ and $\mathbf{v} = \langle 7, 1 \rangle$

45. If the sides of a parallelepiped are represented by vectors $\mathbf{u}$, $\mathbf{v}$, and $\mathbf{w}$ as illustrated, its volume is

$$\pm \begin{vmatrix} u_1 & u_2 & u_3 \\ v_1 & v_2 & v_3 \\ w_1 & w_2 & w_3 \end{vmatrix}.$$

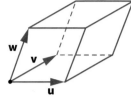

Find the volume of the parallelepiped represented by each set of vectors.

    a. $\mathbf{u} = \langle 4, 0, 0 \rangle$, $\mathbf{v} = \langle 0, 7, 0 \rangle$, $\mathbf{w} = \langle 0, 0, 5 \rangle$

    b. $\mathbf{u} = \langle 7, 1, 2 \rangle$, $\mathbf{v} = \langle 0, 5, 2 \rangle$, $\mathbf{w} = \langle 2, 0, 8 \rangle$

CUMULATIVE REVIEW

Solve each equation.

46. $5^{2x} = 129$ **[3.4]**

47. $\ln(-2x) = 8.5$ **[3.4]**

Graph each function.

48. $f(x) = 3 + \sqrt{x - 1}$ **[2.1]**

49. $g(x) = \dfrac{x+1}{x^2 - 4}$ **[2.5]**

50. Verify $\cos^4 x - \sin^4 x = \cos^2 x - \sin^2 x$.   **[5.2]**

51. Write the system as an augmented matrix.   **[7.3]**
$$2x + 3y - z = -6$$
$$3x - 2z = -1$$
$$4x - 2y = 2$$

52. Find the period of $y = \dfrac{3}{2} \cos \dfrac{\pi x}{3}$.   **[4.4]**

    A. $\dfrac{\pi}{3}$ **C.** $\dfrac{1}{6}$ **E.** none of these

    B. $\dfrac{3}{2}$ **D.** 6

53. Find $m\angle A$ (to the nearest degree) in a triangle with sides $AC = 12$ cm and $BC = 10$ cm and $m\angle B = 55°$. **[5.6]**

    A. $82°$ **C.** $35°$ **E.** none of
    B. $43°$ **D.** $39°$ these

54. Find entry e_{22} in AB if
$$A = \begin{bmatrix} d & e \\ f & g \end{bmatrix} \text{ and } B = \begin{bmatrix} t & v & w \\ x & y & z \end{bmatrix}. \quad \textbf{[7.2]}$$

    A. $dv + ey$ **C.** $fv + gy$ **E.** none of
    B. $ft + gx$ **D.** $fw + gz$ these

55. Find B so that the system is inconsistent.
$$2x + 7y = 6$$
$$6x + By = 6 \quad \textbf{[7.3]}$$

    A. 6 **C.** 14 **E.** none of
    B. 7 **D.** 21 these

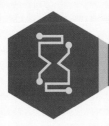

HISTORICAL CONNECTION

MATRICES AND DETERMINANTS

How many planets are in our solar system? The Italian astronomer Giuseppe Piazzi discovered a very small one on January 1, 1801. He recorded its position until the second week of February, when it was lost behind the sun. Piazzi appealed for help in determining the planet's orbit so that it could be reacquired. Many attempted this nearly impossible feat, but it was the 24-yr-old German mathematician Carl Gauss who accurately determined the planet's orbit by solving systems of equations involving more than 80 variables in three different coordinate systems. Using Gauss's results, the dwarf planet Ceres was reacquired nearly a year later on the first attempt. Gauss published his method in 1809 and it became the standard in astronomy.

In an 1888 textbook on geodesy, German surveyor Wilhelm Jordan published an improved version of Gauss's method, now known as Gauss-Jordan elimination. Many other mathematicians made contributions to the processes and notation used to solve systems, including Colin MacLaurin, Gabriel Cramer, and Augustin-Louis Cauchy. Arthur Cayley (1821–95) published the first comprehensive treatise on matrix theory in 1857. Working closely with Cayley was another British mathematician, James Joseph Sylvester (1814–97), who had given up on mathematics until he met Cayley while both of them were studying law.

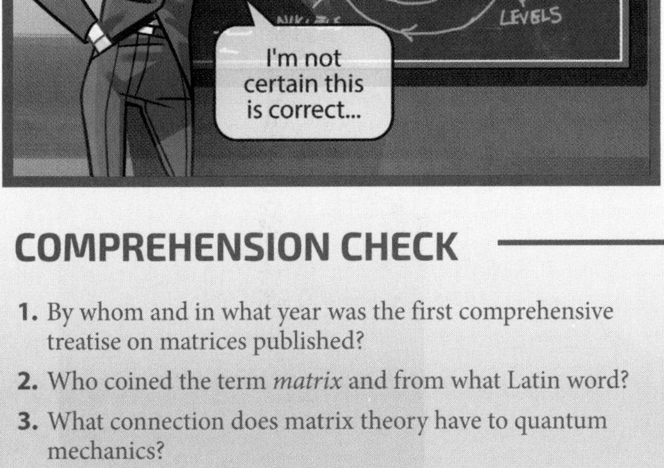
-ELECTRONS
LEVELS
I'm not certain this is correct...

When an influential British biologist stated that mathematics is "that study which knows nothing of observation, nothing of induction, nothing of experiment, nothing of causation," Sylvester replied, "I think no statement could have been made more opposite to the undoubted facts of the case, that mathematical analysis . . . affords a boundless scope for the exercise of the highest efforts of imagination and invention." Sylvester's emphasis on the role of creativity in mathematics is evidenced in his own work on matrices. In fact, he coined the term *matrix* from the Latin word for "womb." An Internet search for "Sylvester matrix" supplies many current research papers that extend Sylvester's work and provide practical applications over a century later.

Twentieth-century physicists wrestled with experimental results at the atomic level that could not be explained by Bohr's planetary atomic model. Werner Heisenberg (1901–76) was concerned that the use of models to portray unobservable physical phenomena was an obstacle to understanding. In 1925 he used matrices to develop a system that explained observed results without a physical representation. The merging of Heisenberg's matrix mechanics with Erwin Schrödinger's wave mechanics became quantum mechanics. It may seem unlikely that a mathematical concept could be useful in the vastness of space, on the surface of the earth, and in submicroscopic physics. Even Newton's laws, which work well in our everyday experience and in astronomy, are insufficient to explain experimental results at the atomic level. But determinants and matrices continue to play a crucial role in our understanding of our world at each of these levels.

COMPREHENSION CHECK

1. By whom and in what year was the first comprehensive treatise on matrices published?
2. Who coined the term *matrix* and from what Latin word?
3. What connection does matrix theory have to quantum mechanics?
4. **Discuss:** Both quotations in the third paragraph have some merit. What positive insights can you see in each person's view?

The Allies' ability to decode messages encrypted by Enigma cipher machines helped turn the tide of World War II.

After completing this section, you will be able to

- determine the inverse of a square matrix.
- solve systems of equations using inverse matrices.
- model and solve real-world problems using matrix equations.

The product of a nonzero real number a and its multiplicative inverse (or reciprocal) $a^{-1} = \frac{1}{a}$ is 1, the multiplicative identity. Similarly, many square matrices A have a unique *multiplicative inverse matrix* A^{-1}, defined so that the product of A and A^{-1} is the identity matrix of the same order, I_n.

$$a \cdot \frac{1}{a} = \frac{1}{a} \cdot a = 1 \text{ and } A \cdot A^{-1} = A^{-1} \cdot A = I_n$$

Example 1 Verifying Inverse Matrices

Show that $A = \begin{bmatrix} 2 & -1 \\ 5 & -3 \end{bmatrix}$ and $B = \begin{bmatrix} 3 & -1 \\ 5 & -2 \end{bmatrix}$ are inverse matrices.

Answer

$$AB = \begin{bmatrix} 2 & -1 \\ 5 & -3 \end{bmatrix}\begin{bmatrix} 3 & -1 \\ 5 & -2 \end{bmatrix} = \begin{bmatrix} 6-5 & -2+2 \\ 15-15 & -5+6 \end{bmatrix} = \begin{bmatrix} 1 & 0 \\ 0 & 1 \end{bmatrix} = I_2$$

$$BA = \begin{bmatrix} 3 & -1 \\ 5 & -2 \end{bmatrix}\begin{bmatrix} 2 & -1 \\ 5 & -3 \end{bmatrix} = \begin{bmatrix} 6-5 & -3+3 \\ 10-10 & -5+6 \end{bmatrix} = \begin{bmatrix} 1 & 0 \\ 0 & 1 \end{bmatrix} = I_2$$

Since $AB = BA = I$, A and B are inverse matrices ($B = A^{-1}$ and $A = B^{-1}$).

SKILL ✔ **EXERCISE 5**

Any matrix A for which A^{-1} exists is said to be *invertible* (or *nonsingular*) while a matrix for which no inverse exists is called *singular*. If $|A| = 0$, the matrix is singular. Notice that while matrix multiplication is not generally commutative, this property holds for the products of a matrix and its inverse.

The inverse of a 2×2 matrix can be found using a formula that includes its determinant.

> **TIP**
>
> Note that entries on the main diagonal are swapped, and entries on the minor diagonal are negated.

INVERSE OF A 2 × 2 MATRIX

If $A = \begin{bmatrix} a & b \\ c & d \end{bmatrix}$ and $|A| \neq 0$, then $A^{-1} = \frac{1}{|A|}\begin{bmatrix} d & -b \\ -c & a \end{bmatrix}$. If $|A| = 0$, then A is singular.

Example 2 Finding the Inverse of a 2 × 2 Matrix

Find the inverse of each matrix.

a. $A = \begin{bmatrix} 4 & 1 \\ 5 & 2 \end{bmatrix}$

b. $B = \begin{bmatrix} 4 & -2 \\ 6 & -3 \end{bmatrix}$

Answer

a. $|A| = 8 - 5 = 3$

1. Find the determinant of A.

$$A^{-1} = \frac{1}{3}\begin{bmatrix} 2 & -1 \\ -5 & 4 \end{bmatrix} = \begin{bmatrix} \frac{2}{3} & -\frac{1}{3} \\ -\frac{5}{3} & \frac{4}{3} \end{bmatrix}$$

2. Apply the formula for the inverse of a 2×2 matrix.

CONTINUED ➡

b. $|B| = -12 + 12 = 0$; B is singular.   Since $|B| = 0$, the matrix has no inverse.

SKILL ✓ **EXERCISE 9**

The reasoning that supports the formula for the inverse of a 2×2 matrix is illustrated by solving the systems generated by the matrix equation $AA^{-1} = I$. Using A from Example 2,

$$\begin{bmatrix} 4 & 1 \\ 5 & 2 \end{bmatrix}\begin{bmatrix} r & s \\ v & w \end{bmatrix} = \begin{bmatrix} 1 & 0 \\ 0 & 1 \end{bmatrix} \quad \text{implies} \quad \begin{array}{ll} 4r + v = 1 & 4s + w = 0 \\ 5r + 2v = 0 & 5s + 2w = 1. \end{array}$$

Since both systems have the same coefficient matrix, they can be solved simultaneously by augmenting the coefficient matrix with both constant column matrices to form $[A|I]$. Elementary row operations can then be used to transform this matrix to reduced row echelon form, $[I|A^{-1}]$.

$$\left[\begin{array}{cc|cc} 4 & 1 & 1 & 0 \\ 5 & 2 & 0 & 1 \end{array}\right]$$

$$-5r_1 + 4r_2 \Rightarrow r_2 \left[\begin{array}{cc|cc} 4 & 1 & 1 & 0 \\ 0 & 3 & -5 & 4 \end{array}\right]$$

$$\begin{array}{l} \frac{1}{4}r_1 \Rightarrow r_1 \\ \frac{1}{3}r_2 \Rightarrow r_2 \end{array} \left[\begin{array}{cc|cc} 1 & \frac{1}{4} & \frac{1}{4} & 0 \\ 0 & 1 & -\frac{5}{3} & \frac{4}{3} \end{array}\right]$$

$$-\frac{1}{4}r_2 + r_1 \Rightarrow r_1 \left[\begin{array}{cc|cc} 1 & 0 & \frac{2}{3} & -\frac{1}{3} \\ 0 & 1 & -\frac{5}{3} & \frac{4}{3} \end{array}\right]$$

This method can be extended to find the inverse of square matrices of an order higher than 2. As in 2×2 matrices, any $n \times n$ matrix is singular if its determinant is 0. When $\det(A) = 0$, the augmented matrix $[A|I]$ cannot be converted to $[I|A^{-1}]$.

Example 3   Finding the Inverse of a 3 × 3 Matrix

Find A^{-1} if $A = \begin{bmatrix} 1 & 0 & 2 \\ 2 & -1 & 1 \\ 1 & 1 & 1 \end{bmatrix}$.

Answer

$$[A|I] = \left[\begin{array}{ccc|ccc} 1 & 0 & 2 & 1 & 0 & 0 \\ 2 & -1 & 1 & 0 & 1 & 0 \\ 1 & 1 & 1 & 0 & 0 & 1 \end{array}\right]$$

$$\begin{array}{l} -2r_1 + r_2 \Rightarrow r_2 \\ -r_1 + r_3 \Rightarrow r_3 \end{array} \left[\begin{array}{ccc|ccc} 1 & 0 & 2 & 1 & 0 & 0 \\ 0 & -1 & -3 & -2 & 1 & 0 \\ 0 & 1 & -1 & -1 & 0 & 1 \end{array}\right]$$

$$\begin{array}{l} -r_2 \Rightarrow r_2 \\ r_2 + r_3 \Rightarrow r_3 \end{array} \left[\begin{array}{ccc|ccc} 1 & 0 & 2 & 1 & 0 & 0 \\ 0 & 1 & 3 & 2 & -1 & 0 \\ 0 & 0 & -4 & -3 & 1 & 1 \end{array}\right]$$

$$-\frac{1}{4}r_3 \Rightarrow r_3 \left[\begin{array}{ccc|ccc} 1 & 0 & 2 & 1 & 0 & 0 \\ 0 & 1 & 3 & 2 & -1 & 0 \\ 0 & 0 & 1 & \frac{3}{4} & -\frac{1}{4} & -\frac{1}{4} \end{array}\right]$$

$$\begin{array}{l} -2r_3 + r_1 \Rightarrow r_1 \\ -3r_3 + r_2 \Rightarrow r_2 \end{array} \left[\begin{array}{ccc|ccc} 1 & 0 & 0 & -\frac{1}{2} & \frac{1}{2} & \frac{1}{2} \\ 0 & 1 & 0 & -\frac{1}{4} & -\frac{1}{4} & \frac{3}{4} \\ 0 & 0 & 1 & \frac{3}{4} & -\frac{1}{4} & -\frac{1}{4} \end{array}\right]$$

$$A^{-1} = \begin{bmatrix} -\frac{1}{2} & \frac{1}{2} & \frac{1}{2} \\ -\frac{1}{4} & -\frac{1}{4} & \frac{3}{4} \\ \frac{3}{4} & -\frac{1}{4} & -\frac{1}{4} \end{bmatrix}$$

SKILL ✓ **EXERCISE 19**

Since the arithmetic involved in this technique can be tedious and formulas for the inverse of a square matrix of an order higher than 2 are quite complicated, technology is frequently used. The $\boxed{x^{-1}}$ key is used to find the inverse and the ▶Frac function from the $\boxed{\text{MATH}}$ menu is used to convert decimals to fractions.

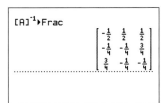

If a system of linear equations has the same number of independent equations as variables, its unique solution can be found using the matrix equation $AX = C$ where A is the square coefficient matrix, X is the variable matrix, and C is the constant column matrix. Notice how left-multiplying each side of the equation by A^{-1} produces the solution $X = A^{-1}C$.

$$AX = C$$
$$A^{-1}(AX) = A^{-1}C \quad \text{Multiplication Property of Equality}$$
$$(A^{-1}A)X = A^{-1}C \quad \text{Associative Property of Matrix Multiplication}$$
$$(I)X = A^{-1}C \quad \text{definition of multiplicative inverse}$$
$$X = A^{-1}C \quad \text{definition of multiplicative identity}$$

If the determinant of the coefficient matrix is 0, the system is either dependent or inconsistent and a matrix equation cannot be used to solve the system.

Example 4　Using an Inverse Matrix to Solve a 2 × 2 System

Solve the system using an inverse matrix.　$3x - 2y = 12$
$4x + 3y = -1$

Answer

$$\begin{bmatrix} 3 & -2 \\ 4 & 3 \end{bmatrix}\begin{bmatrix} x \\ y \end{bmatrix} = \begin{bmatrix} 12 \\ -1 \end{bmatrix}$$

1. Write the system as a matrix equation in the form $AX = C$.

$$A^{-1} = \frac{1}{17}\begin{bmatrix} 3 & 2 \\ -4 & 3 \end{bmatrix}$$

2. Use the formula to find the inverse of the 2 × 2 coefficient matrix.

$$X = A^{-1}C = \frac{1}{17}\begin{bmatrix} 3 & 2 \\ -4 & 3 \end{bmatrix}\begin{bmatrix} 12 \\ -1 \end{bmatrix}$$

3. Find the matrix product $X = A^{-1}C$.

$$= \frac{1}{17}\begin{bmatrix} 34 \\ -51 \end{bmatrix} = \begin{bmatrix} 2 \\ -3 \end{bmatrix}$$

The solution is the ordered pair (2, –3).

SKILL ✓ **EXERCISE 21**

Inverse matrices can greatly simplify the solution of real-life problems modeled by a system of linear equations.

Example 5　Using an Inverse Matrix to Solve a 3 × 3 System

Mr. Jones wants to invest a $100,000 inheritance in an aggressive-growth mutual fund with a projected return of 10% APY, a municipal bond fund with a projected return of 3% APY, and CDs with a 2% APY. How much should he invest in each fund if he hopes to earn $6300 and wants to invest as much in the mutual fund as he does in municipal bonds and CDs combined?

Answer

investment:　$g + b + c = 100{,}000$

return:　　$0.10g + 0.03b + 0.02c = 6300$

risk limit:　$g = b + c$

1. Write a system of equations modeling the scenario, letting c = the amount in CDs, b = the amount in bonds, and g = the amount in the growth mutual funds.

$$g + b + c = 100{,}000$$
$$10g + 3b + 2c = 630{,}000$$
$$g - b - c = 0$$

2. Write the equations in standard form. Multiplying the second equation by 100 eliminates the decimals.

$$\begin{bmatrix} 1 & 1 & 1 \\ 10 & 3 & 2 \\ 1 & -1 & -1 \end{bmatrix}\begin{bmatrix} g \\ b \\ c \end{bmatrix} = \begin{bmatrix} 100{,}000 \\ 630{,}000 \\ 0 \end{bmatrix}$$

3. Express the system as a matrix equation in the form of $AX = C$.

CONTINUED ➡

$[A]^{-1}[C]$

$$\begin{bmatrix} 50000 \\ 30000 \\ 20000 \end{bmatrix}$$

He should invest $50,000 in the aggressive-growth mutual fund, $30,000 in municipal bonds, and $20,000 in CDs.

4. Use a calculator to find $X = A^{-1}C$.

5. Interpret the result.

SKILL ✓ **EXERCISE 31**

Matrices and their inverses are used in cryptography to encrypt and decode messages. Each letter or character is assigned a number, as in the example below.

A	B	C	D	E	F	G	H	I	J	K	L	M
0	1	2	3	4	5	6	7	8	9	10	11	12
N	O	P	Q	R	S	T	U	V	W	X	Y	Z
13	14	15	16	17	18	19	20	21	22	23	24	25

Spaces between words are frequently omitted when the message is converted into numbers and partitioned into several $1 \times n$ row matrices. (In this example, $n = 3$.) Extra Xs may be added to the end of a message if necessary.

G	O	D	I	S	M	Y	J	O	Y	X	X
6	14	3	8	18	12	24	9	14	24	23	23

To encrypt a message, create an $m \times n$ uncoded matrix U by stacking the row matrices and then right-multiply by an invertible $n \times n$ encrypting matrix E to form the coded matrix C.

$$\begin{matrix} U & \cdot & E & = & C \end{matrix}$$

$$\begin{bmatrix} 6 & 14 & 3 \\ 8 & 18 & 12 \\ 24 & 9 & 14 \\ 24 & 23 & 23 \end{bmatrix} \begin{bmatrix} 1 & 3 & 3 \\ 1 & 4 & 3 \\ 1 & 3 & 4 \end{bmatrix} = \begin{bmatrix} 23 & 83 & 72 \\ 38 & 132 & 126 \\ 47 & 150 & 155 \\ 70 & 233 & 233 \end{bmatrix}$$

The message can then be sent as a string of values: 23, 83, 72, 38, 132, ... The recipient reconstructs the coded matrix and multiplies it by E^{-1}, the decoding matrix, to reveal the uncoded matrix: $CE^{-1} = (UE)E^{-1} = U(EE^{-1}) = U(I) = U$.

$$\begin{matrix} C & \cdot & E^{-1} & = & U \end{matrix}$$

$$\begin{bmatrix} 23 & 83 & 72 \\ 38 & 132 & 126 \\ 47 & 150 & 155 \\ 70 & 233 & 233 \end{bmatrix} \begin{bmatrix} 7 & -3 & -3 \\ -1 & 1 & 0 \\ -1 & 0 & 1 \end{bmatrix} = \begin{bmatrix} 6 & 14 & 3 \\ 8 & 18 & 12 \\ 24 & 9 & 14 \\ 24 & 23 & 23 \end{bmatrix}$$

The resulting string of numbers can then be converted back to the original message.

Encryption is a valuable tool for protecting information, but it can also be used maliciously. In 2017 the WannaCry virus infected over 300,000 computers, encrypting each user's files and demanding a bitcoin ransom. Several affected hospitals in the United Kingdom had to cancel operations and turn away patients.

A. Exercises

Use the determinant to decide whether each matrix is invertible or singular.

1. $\begin{bmatrix} 3 & -4 \\ -12 & 16 \end{bmatrix}$

2. $\begin{bmatrix} 10 & 90 \\ 4 & -36 \end{bmatrix}$

3. $\begin{bmatrix} -37 & 0 & 96 \\ 11 & 0 & 118 \\ 52 & 0 & 75 \end{bmatrix}$

4. $\begin{bmatrix} 5 & 2 & 14 \\ 1 & -2 & -2 \\ 6 & -4 & 4 \end{bmatrix}$

Determine whether *A* and *B* are inverse matrices.

5. $A = \begin{bmatrix} -2 & 3 \\ -3 & 4 \end{bmatrix}, B = \begin{bmatrix} 4 & -3 \\ 3 & -2 \end{bmatrix}$

6. $A = \begin{bmatrix} 0 & 1 \\ 1 & 0 \end{bmatrix}, B = \begin{bmatrix} 0 & 1 \\ 1 & 0 \end{bmatrix}$

7. $A = \begin{bmatrix} 1 & 0 & 2 \\ 2 & 1 & -2 \\ 1 & 0 & 1 \end{bmatrix}, B = \begin{bmatrix} -1 & 0 & 2 \\ 4 & 1 & -6 \\ 1 & 0 & -1 \end{bmatrix}$

8. $A = \begin{bmatrix} 0 & 1 & 1 \\ 2 & 1 & 1 \\ 1 & 2 & 0 \end{bmatrix}, B = \begin{bmatrix} 1 & 0 & 3 \\ 1 & 2 & 0 \\ 0 & -2 & -4 \end{bmatrix}$

Use the formula to find the inverse of each 2 × 2 matrix.

9. $\begin{bmatrix} 8 & 3 \\ 4 & 2 \end{bmatrix}$

10. $\begin{bmatrix} 3 & 7 \\ -5 & -9 \end{bmatrix}$

11. $\begin{bmatrix} 2 & 1 \\ 1 & \frac{2}{3} \end{bmatrix}$

12. $\begin{bmatrix} -\frac{5}{3} & \frac{4}{3} \\ -\frac{8}{3} & \frac{7}{3} \end{bmatrix}$

Use technology to find the inverse of each matrix. Express answers in fractional form.

13. $\begin{bmatrix} 16 & 4 \\ -7 & -2 \end{bmatrix}$

14. $\begin{bmatrix} 2 & 8 \\ -1 & 4 \end{bmatrix}$

15. $\begin{bmatrix} 7 & 0 & 4 \\ -5 & 1 & -2 \\ 2 & 2 & 3 \end{bmatrix}$

16. $\begin{bmatrix} 5 & -2 & 4 \\ 0 & 2 & 1 \\ 1 & 3 & 3 \end{bmatrix}$

B. Exercises

Use row operations on [A | I] to find the inverse of each matrix.

17. $\begin{bmatrix} 3 & 7 \\ 4 & 9 \end{bmatrix}$

18. $\begin{bmatrix} 2 & 4 \\ -3 & -1 \end{bmatrix}$

19. $\begin{bmatrix} 1 & 2 & 0 \\ 2 & 1 & -3 \\ 0 & 3 & 2 \end{bmatrix}$

20. $\begin{bmatrix} 3 & 5 & 6 \\ 1 & 2 & 2 \\ 2 & 4 & 5 \end{bmatrix}$

Write and solve a matrix equation to solve each system.

21. $x - 5y = -30$
    $2x - y = 3$

22. $2x + y = 8$
    $5x + 2y = 19$

23. $2x - 5y = -39$
    $x + 4y = 26$

24. $4x + 2y = -8$
    $x + 6y = 1$

Write and use technology to solve a matrix equation for each system. Express answers in fractional form.

25. $x + 3y - 4z = 41$
    $2x - y + 5z = 0$
    $4x + 2y + 4z = 44$

26. $2x + y + 3z = 10$
    $2x - 3y + 4z = 36$
    $-2x + 3y + 2z = 48$

27. $2x + 3y - z = 21$
    $x + y + 2z = 18$
    $x - 3y + 2z = 12$

28. $6y + 3z = 68$
    $4x + 5z = 92$
    $7x - 9y + 5z = 45$

29. The following systems cannot be solved by solving a related matrix equation. Classify each system and explain why its solution cannot be found using this method.

    a. $2x + y = 8$
    $4x + 2y = 16$

    b. $3a - 5b = 11$
    $-3a + 5b = 7$

Write a system of equations and solve the related matrix equation for each problem.

30. How old are Jenn and Dan if three times Jenn's age is the same as twice Dan's age and the sum of their ages is 60?

31. On Tuesday, Grayson filled up his ATV at $3.95/gal. On Friday, he filled up at $4.12/gal. Together the 5.7 gal of gasoline cost $22.94. How much gas did Grayson put into the tank each day?

32. Find two numbers whose sum is 20 if twice the first is 2 more than the opposite of the second.

33. Find three numbers whose sum is 35 if the least is 126 less than twice the greatest, and the sum of the least and the greatest is 6 times the other number.

34. Jackie wants to earn $500 in 1 yr by investing in a savings account earning 2% APY, a CD earning 3.5% APY, and a bond earning 4.7% APY. She plans on investing twice as much in the bond as she does in the CD and putting half of the amount invested in the CD and bond combined into savings. How much (to the nearest dollar) should Jackie deposit in each?

Use the encoding matrix *E* and the letter assignments from p. 373 to make a coded matrix for each message.

$$E = \begin{bmatrix} 1 & 2 & -1 \\ 0 & -2 & 1 \\ 1 & 1 & 0 \end{bmatrix}$$

35. PLEASE CALL

36. MEET ME AT NOON

▶ C. Exercises

37. Find B given A and AB.

$$A = \begin{bmatrix} 2 & 1 \\ 4 & -1 \end{bmatrix}, AB = \begin{bmatrix} 2 & 7 \\ 4 & 5 \end{bmatrix}$$

38. Find A given B and $(AB)^{-1}$.

$$B = \begin{bmatrix} 4 & 3 \\ 0 & -\frac{1}{4} \end{bmatrix}, (AB)^{-1} = \begin{bmatrix} -5 & 3 \\ 7 & -4 \end{bmatrix}$$

Decode each matrix that was encrypted using the letter assignments from the lesson and the encoding matrix

$$E = \begin{bmatrix} 1 & 2 & -1 \\ 0 & -2 & 1 \\ 1 & 1 & 0 \end{bmatrix}.$$

39. $C = \begin{bmatrix} 31 & 41 & -14 \\ 17 & -4 & 9 \\ 37 & 42 & -9 \end{bmatrix}$

40. $C = \begin{bmatrix} 8 & 1 & 3 \\ 18 & 6 & -1 \\ 19 & -1 & 1 \\ 12 & -4 & 6 \\ 36 & 43 & -10 \end{bmatrix}$

41. Verify the formula for the inverse of a 2×2 matrix by using row operations on $[A|I]$ to find the inverse of $A = \begin{bmatrix} a & b \\ c & d \end{bmatrix}$.

CUMULATIVE REVIEW

42. The quantity p varies jointly with q and r and inversely with t. If $p = 3q$ when $r = 4t$, find q when $p = 8$, $r = 12$, and $t = 20$. **[Algebra]**

43. Rewrite the expression $4 \sin \theta \cos \theta$ in terms of a single trigonometric function. **[5.5]**

44. Write an augmented matrix representing the system. **[7.3]**
$3x + y = 3$
$4x + 3z = -16$
$y - 2z = 14$

45. Sketch the graph of $p(x) = x^3 - x$. **[2.2]**

46. Solve the system. **[7.3]**
$5x + 2y - 3z = 9$
$4y + z = 19$
$z = 3$

47. If matrix A has a row of 0s, what is $|A|$? Explain your reasoning. **[7.4]**

48. Evaluate $\cos \frac{5\pi}{12}$. **[5.4]**

    A. $\dfrac{\sqrt{6} - \sqrt{2}}{4}$ **C.** $\dfrac{\sqrt{6} - \sqrt{2}}{2}$ **E.** none of these

    B. $\dfrac{\sqrt{6} + \sqrt{2}}{4}$ **D.** $\dfrac{\sqrt{3}}{4}$

49. Find the area of $\triangle ABC$ given $a = 3.2$ mi, $b = 4.8$ mi, and $m\angle C = 75°$. **[5.7]**

    A. 2 mi^2 **C.** 7.4 mi^2 **E.** none of

    B. 7.1 mi^2 **D.** 3 mi^2 these

50. Find $m\angle A$ (to the nearest degree). **[4.2]**

    A. 70°

    B. 20°

    C. 68°

    D. 22°

    E. none of these

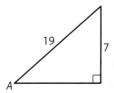

51. At which angle would the plots of consecutive 12th roots of a complex number differ on the polar coordinate plane? **[6.6]**

    A. $\dfrac{\pi}{6}$ **C.** $\dfrac{\pi}{3}$ **E.** none of

    B. $\dfrac{\pi}{12}$ **D.** $\dfrac{\pi}{24}$ these

7.6 Systems of Inequalities

After completing this section, you will be able to

- solve a system of inequalities in two variables.
- maximize or minimize an objective function for a set of linear constraints.
- model and solve real-world problems using linear programming.

Businesses examine supply and demand graphs to find the equilibrium price and the regions representing consumer surplus (a measure of consumer willingness to pay more for a product) and producer surplus (a measure of producer welfare). These regions can be described by a *system of inequalities.* Use the Internet keyword searches *consumer surplus* and *producer surplus* to find detailed definitions and descriptions of these business terms.

To solve a system of inequalities, graph each inequality and find the intersection of the graphs. Recall that the graph of each inequality's related equation (its *boundary*) is drawn as a dashed line for inequalities using > or <, or as a solid line for inequalities using ≤ or ≥. The set of points that satisfies all the inequalities is the system's solution.

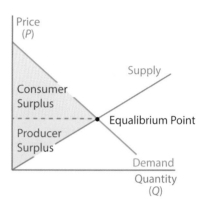

Example 1   Solving a System of Inequalities

Solve the system.

$$x - y \leq -2$$
$$y < -x^2 + 4$$

Answer

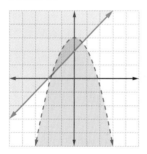

The solution is represented by the intersection of the two graphs.

1. Graph the linear inequality.

   a. Convert to slope-intercept form.
      $$-y \leq -x - 2$$
      $$y \geq x + 2$$

   b. Graph $y = x + 2$, using a solid line to indicate that the line is part of the solution.

   c. Using (0, 0) as a test point, $0 - 0 \leq -2$ indicates that the half-plane below the line is not the solution. Shade the half-plane above the line.

2. Graph the quadratic inequality.

   a. Reflect the graph of $y = x^2$ across the x-axis and shift the result 4 units up, using a dashed curve to indicate that the parabola is not part of the solution.

   b. Shade the region below the parabola.

_____ SKILL ✓ **EXERCISE 3**

It is often important to know the vertices of the solution region when solving a system of linear inequalities. You may need to solve a system of equations when the exact coordinates of a vertex are not apparent from the graph.

376   CHAPTER 7 SYSTEMS AND MATRICES

Example 2   Solving a System of Linear Inequalities

Solve the system and state the coordinates of each vertex of the solution region.

$$x \geq -3 \qquad x - y \leq 1$$
$$y \geq -1 \qquad 2x + 3y \leq 6$$

Answer

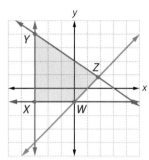

1. Graph each inequality and shade the common region.
   a. to the right of $x = -3$
   b. above $y = -1$
   c. above $y = x - 1$
   d. below $y = -\frac{2}{3}x + 2$

2. Vertices at $(0, -1)$, $(-3, -1)$, and $(-3, 4)$ can be determined from the graph.

$$\begin{bmatrix} 1 & -1 \\ 2 & 3 \end{bmatrix}\begin{bmatrix} x \\ y \end{bmatrix} = \begin{bmatrix} 1 \\ 6 \end{bmatrix}$$

$$X = A^{-1}C = \frac{1}{3 - (-2)}\begin{bmatrix} 3 & 1 \\ -2 & 1 \end{bmatrix}\begin{bmatrix} 1 \\ 6 \end{bmatrix}$$

$$= \frac{1}{5}\begin{bmatrix} 9 \\ 4 \end{bmatrix} = \begin{bmatrix} 1.8 \\ 0.8 \end{bmatrix}$$

3. Find the last vertex, Z, by solving the matrix equation $AX = C$ that represents the following system of linear equations.

$$x - y = 1$$
$$2x + 3y = 6$$

The coordinates of Z are $(1.8, 0.8)$.

SKILL ✔ **EXERCISE 21**

Optimization problems in management science strive to maximize or minimize the value of a quantity within given limitations, or *constraints*. In a two-dimensional *linear programming* problem, the quantity to be optimized is represented by a linear *objective function*, $f(x, y) = ax + by + c$, and the constraints are a system of linear inequalities. The solution to the system of constraints is known as the *feasible region*.

In such an optimization problem, any optimized value of the objective function occurs at a vertex of the feasible region.

Optimization models using linear programming grew out of George Dantzig's efforts to improve a deployment, training, and supply program for the Pentagon in 1946.

▌VERTEX PRINCIPLE OF LINEAR PROGRAMMING

If a maximum or minimum value of the objective function in a linear programming problem occurs, it occurs at one or more of the vertices of the feasible region.

Example 3   Solving a Linear Programming Problem

Maximize and minimize the objective function $f(x, y) = 5x + 2y$ under the given constraints.

$$x \geq 0 \qquad y \geq \frac{1}{2}x - 1$$
$$1 \leq y \leq 4 \qquad x + y \leq 8$$

Answer

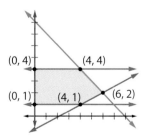

1. Graph each constraint to determine the feasible region.
   $x \geq 0$
   $1 \leq y \leq 4$
   $y \geq \frac{1}{2}x - 1$
   $x + y \leq 8$

2. Find the coordinates of the vertices.

CONTINUED ➡

(x, y)	$5x + 2y$	$f(x, y)$
$(0, 4)$	$5(0) + 2(4)$	8
$(0, 1)$	$5(0) + 2(1)$	2
$(4, 1)$	$5(4) + 2(1)$	22
$(6, 2)$	$5(6) + 2(2)$	34
$(4, 4)$	$5(4) + 2(4)$	28

3. Evaluate the objective function at each vertex to find the maximum and minimum values of $f(x, y)$.

maximum: $f(6, 2) = 34$
minimum: $f(0, 1) = 2$

SKILL ✓ EXERCISE 25

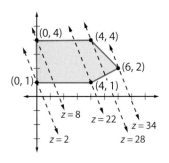

To understand why the Vertex Principle of Linear Programming works in Example 3, view the graphs of the objective function $f(x, y) = z = 5x + 2y$ as a family of parallel lines $y = -\frac{5}{2}x + \frac{z}{2}$. As the value of z increases from 0, the lines move away from the origin. The first line intersecting the feasible region does so at the vertex of the feasible region that generates the minimum value of $z = f(x, y)$ and the last line intersecting the region does so at the vertex that generates the maximum value of $z = f(x, y)$.

This reasoning also implies that when an optimal value occurs at two vertices of the feasible region, the objective function has that optimal value at any point on the connecting segment.

Businesses often seek to minimize costs and maximize profits within the market's constraints. While we will limit our study of linear programming problems to objective functions of two variables, the technique can be expanded to more complex problems involving many more variables.

Solving a Linear Programming Problem
1. Write an objective function for the quantity being maximized or minimized.
2. Write a system of inequalities modeling the constraints on the variables.
3. Graph the feasible region and find its vertices.
4. Substitute the coordinates of each vertex into the objective function to determine the maximum or minimum value.

Example 4 Maximizing Profit

Gaming Inc. manufactures the Vintage-X and the YnotPlay gaming consoles. The company budgets $150,000 for labor and $600,000 for components. The components cost $100 for each Vintage-X and $150 for each YnotPlay. Labor costs are $40 for each Vintage-X and $30 for each YnotPlay. If the profit for each Vintage-X is $45 and the profit for each YnotPlay is $60, how many of each console should be made to maximize profit? What is the maximum profit?

Answer

$P(x, y) = 45x + 60y$ where
x = the number of Vintage-X consoles and
y = the number of YnotPlay consoles.

1. Define the objective function representing profit.

$$x \geq 0$$
$$y \geq 0$$
$$100x + 150y \leq 600{,}000 \text{ (components)}$$
$$40x + 30y \leq 150{,}000 \text{ (labor)}$$

2. Write the system of inequalities representing the constraints.

CONTINUED ➡

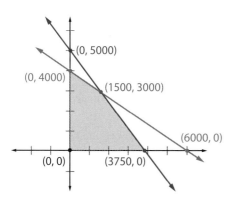

(0, 5000)
(0, 4000)
(1500, 3000)
(6000, 0)
(0, 0)
(3750, 0)

3. Graph the constraints, shade the feasible region, and find the vertices of the region.

4. Evaluate $P(x, y) = 45x + 60y$ at each vertex.

(x, y)	$P(x, y)$
$(0, 0)$	0
$(0, 4000)$	240,000
$(1500, 3000)$	247,500
$(3750, 0)$	168,750

A maximum profit of $247,500 can be achieved by producing 1500 Vintage-X consoles and 3000 YnotPlay consoles.

5. Interpret the results.

SKILL ✓ **EXERCISES 31–33**

TIP

The vertex formed by the component and labor constraints can be found graphically using $y = -\frac{2}{3}x + 4000$ and $y = -\frac{4}{3}x + 5000$.

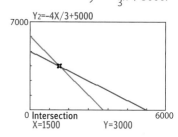

Y2=-4X/3+5000
7000

0   Intersection   6000
    X=1500   Y=3000

Example 5   Minimizing Cost

A transportation company wants to acquire at least 10 vehicles, including at least two 24-passenger minibuses, in order to accommodate at least 204 additional passengers. They can purchase a 15-passenger van for $60,000 and a 24-passenger minibus for $85,000. What is the minimum cost at which the company can expand their fleet to meet these needs?

Answer

$C(x, y) = 60x + 85y$ where $x =$ the number of vans and $y =$ the number of minibuses.

$$x \geq 0 \quad \text{(vans)}$$
$$y \geq 2 \quad \text{(minibuses)}$$
$$x + y \geq 10 \quad \text{(total vehicles)}$$
$$15x + 24y \geq 204 \quad \text{(passengers)}$$

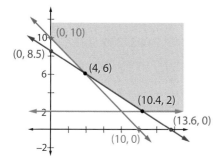

(0, 10)
(0, 8.5)
(4, 6)
(10.4, 2)
(13.6, 0)
(10, 0)

1. Define the objective function to represent cost in thousands of dollars.

2. Write the system of inequalities representing the constraints.

3. Graph the constraints, shade the feasible region, and find the vertices of the region.

4. Evaluate $C(x, y) = 60x + 85y$ at each vertex.

(x, y)	$C(x, y)$
$(0, 10)$	850
$(4, 6)$	750
$(10.4, 2)$	794

The company can purchase 4 vans and 6 minibuses for a minimum cost of $750,000.

Even the most carefully crafted models using the most accurate data cannot answer ethical questions raised when making business decisions. While mathematics may help determine whether something can be done, biblical principles should be applied to determine whether it should be done.

SKILL ✓ **EXERCISES 34–36**

The objective function clearly has no maximum value over the unbounded region in Example 5. Since the vertex with decimal coordinates does not produce a minimum value, nearby points in the feasible region with integral coordinates would also not generate the minimum cost.

A. Exercises

Solve each system.

1. $y < 3x + 3$
$y > -x + 2$

2. $x + 4y \geq -8$
$x - 3y < 9$

3. $y \geq (x + 2)^2 - 3$
$y < x + 2$

4. $y \geq x^2 - 4$
$y < -|x|$

5. $y \geq 2|x - 2| - 4$
$y > -(x - 1)^2 + 2$

6. $3x - 6y \leq -24$
$-2x + 4y \leq 2$

Write a system of inequalities representing each graph.

7.
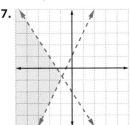

8.
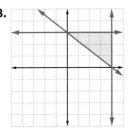

9.
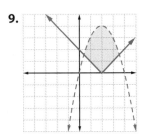

10.
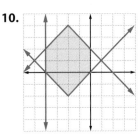

Solve the system and state the coordinates of each vertex of the solution region.

11. $-2 \leq x \leq 3$
$-1 \leq y \leq 2$

12. $y \geq 0$
$x \geq 0$
$3x + 5y \leq 15$

13. $x \geq 0$
$y \geq 0$
$y \leq 8 - x$
$y \leq \frac{1}{2}x + 5$

14. $0 \leq x \leq 2$
$x + y \geq 2$
$-x + y \leq 4$

Maximize and minimize the objective function under the given constraints.

15. $f(x, y) = -2x + 5y$
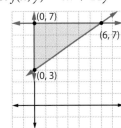

16. $f(x, y) = 8x + 11y$
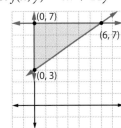

17. $f(x, y) = 8x + y - 3$
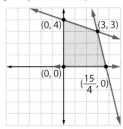

18. $f(x, y) = -3x + 4y + 1$
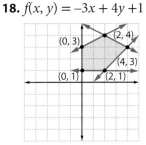

19. $f(x, y) = -6x + y$
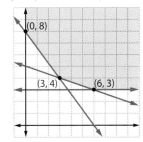

20. $f(x, y) = 3x + 2y + 5$
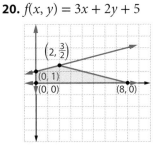

B. Exercises

Graph each system and find the vertices of the region representing the solution.

21. $x \geq -3$
$x + y \leq 7$
$2x - 3y \leq -6$
$6 \leq x + 3y \leq 21$

22. $x \geq 0$
$y \geq 0$
$2x + 3y \leq 8$
$-2x + y \geq -4$

23. $x \geq -1$
$x + 2y \leq 6$
$-2x + y \geq -2$
$6x + 2y \geq -6$

24. $y \geq 1$
$2x + 5y \leq 20$
$3x + 2y \geq 12$

Maximize and minimize the objective function under the given constraints.

25. $f(x, y) = 9x + 3y - 4$
$x \geq 0$
$y \geq 0$
$3x + 2y \leq 15$
$2x + 3y \leq 15$
$2x + y \geq 2$

26. $f(x, y) = 4x + 5y$
$x \leq 3$
$-2x + 3y \leq 18$
$6x + 5y \geq 30$

27. $f(x, y) = -4x + 4y$
$x \geq 1$
$y \geq x$
$y \leq 6$
$y \leq -2x + 12$

28. $f(x, y) = 2x + 2y$
$0 \leq x \leq 4$
$y \geq 0$
$2x + 2y \leq 12$
$x + 2y \leq 10$

29. $f(x, y) = 7x - 6y$
$x + y \leq 7$
$3x + y \leq 11$
$-x + 3y \geq 3$

30. $f(x, y) = -x + 6y$
$x \geq 0$
$y \geq 0$
$17x + 10y \leq 200$
$-3x + 5y \geq -15$
$4x + 5y \geq 20$

The juniors are baking coconut pies and macaroons for the Southwest Christian Academy bake-off. They have 51 c of shredded coconut and 21 c of sugar. Each coconut pie requires 0.5 c of sugar and 2 c of shredded coconut, and each batch of macaroons requires 3.5 c of sugar and 3 c of coconut. They can sell each coconut pie for $15 and each batch of coconut macaroons for $26, and they desire to maximize their revenue.

31. Write a revenue function and the system of constraints.

32. Graph the feasible region and find its vertices.

33. Determine the number of coconut pies and batches of coconut macaroons the juniors should make to maximize their revenue. What is the maximum revenue?

Due to higher-than-normal demand, Acme Inc. needs to assemble at least 3000 more gizmos each day. Regular employees can assemble 20 gizmos/day, while temporary employees can assemble 15. Management needs the ratio of temporary to regular employees to be at least 3 : 4 and at most 4 : 3. It costs $196/day to employ a regular assembler and $98/day to hire a temporary assembler.

34. Write a cost function for the additional assemblers and the system of constraints.

35. Graph the feasible region and find its vertices.

36. Determine the number of regular and temporary employees that will minimize the cost. How much will the additional employees cost?

> **C. Exercises**

Review the introduction to this section. The area under the demand curve and above the equilibrium price represents the consumer surplus. The area under the equilibrium price and above the supply curve represents the producer surplus.

Use a graph of the supply and demand curves to find the equilibrium price, the consumer surplus, and the producer surplus.

37. A martial arts center determines the supply and demand curves for enrollment where p is the price (in dollars) and x is the number of students enrolled.
supply: $p = 0.2x + 30$
demand: $p = -0.12x + 70$

38. Vons Sporting Goods determines the supply and demand curves for kayaks where p is the price (in dollars) and x is the number of kayaks sold.
supply: $p = 0.25x + 300$
demand: $p = -0.15x + 600$

Write and solve a system of inequalities for each problem.

39. Stephanie earns $10/hr working at an afterschool daycare and $15/hr working on Saturdays as a personal trainer. The gym is open 8:00 AM–4:00 PM, and Stephanie can work at most 15 hr/week in addition to her studies. How can Stephanie earn the most money and how much can she make?

40. A wireless carrier outlet obtains the Zphone 7 for $300 and the Zphone 8 for $500 and sells them for $475 and $775, respectively. Sales data predicts that the outlet will sell at most 200 Zphones per month and the budget allocates a maximum of $75,000 to acquire Zphones. Determine the outlet's maximum profit under these conditions and the number of each phone that should be ordered to obtain that profit.

41. Todd wants to increase his protein intake by adding protein powder to his pancake mix. He wants at least 60 g of protein and 90 g of carbohydrates in his breakfast. A serving of pancakes costs $0.75 and a serving of protein powder costs $1.00. How many servings of pancake mix and protein powder should Todd eat to achieve his nutritional goals at the lowest cost?

Per Serving	Protein (g)	Carbs (g)	Cost ($)
pancakes	10	45	$0.75
protein powder	30	15	$1.00

42. Use laws of logarithms to evaluate $\log \frac{a^2 b^3}{c}$ if $\log a = 2.3$, $\log b = 1.4$, and $\log c = 0.9$. **[3.3]**

43. Use a double-angle identity to rewrite the expression $10 \sin^2 \theta - 5$. **[5.5]**

44. State the number of petals and the maximum value of $|r|$ in the polar rose $r = 7 \sin 9\theta$. **[6.5]**

45. Convert $z = -4 - 6i$ to polar form. **[6.6]**

46. Solve the system by elimination. **[7.1]**

$4x - 6y = 24$
$5x + 6y = 30$

47. Find the inverse of $A = \begin{bmatrix} 0 & 3 \\ -2 & 7 \end{bmatrix}$. **[7.5]**

48. What is the force required to prevent a 234 lb dirt bike from rolling down a 40° incline (to the nearest tenth of a pound)? **[6.2]**

A. 150.4 lb   **C.** 225.8 lb   **E.** none of
B. 179.3 lb   **D.** 120.0 lb   these

49. Which of the following is an approximate polar form representation of $z = 10 - 8i$? **[6.6]**

A. 4.24 cis 5.61   **D.** 12.81 cis 5.61
B. 10.77 cis 7.18   **E.** none of these
C. 12.81 cis 6.95

50. Find the determinant of $A = \begin{bmatrix} 7 & -2 \\ 4 & -8 \end{bmatrix}$. **[7.4]**

A. 64   **C.** 62   **E.** none of
B. −48   **D.** 50   these

51. Solve $\log_4 (x^2 - x - 2) - \log_4 (x + 1) = 2$. **[3.4]**

A. $x = 14$ **C.** $x = 20$ **E.** none of
B. $x = 18$ **D.** $x = 12$ these

7.7 Partial Fractions

Polynomials were factored into a product of linear and irreducible quadratic factors in Chapter 2. You will now learn how to express a proper rational expression as a sum of simpler rational functions whose denominators are powers of linear or irreducible quadratic factors. This process of finding the *partial fraction decomposition* of a rational expression (the equivalent sum of *partial fractions*) is used in calculus when finding the area under the graph of a rational function.

If the rational expression can be factored into the form $\dfrac{px + q}{(x + a)(x + b)}$ with distinct linear factors in the denominator, the partial fraction decomposition has the form $\dfrac{A}{x + a} + \dfrac{B}{x + b}$.

> **After completing this section, you will be able to**
> - decompose rational expressions into partial fractions.

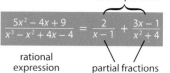

partial fraction decomposition

$$\underbrace{\dfrac{5x^2 - 4x + 9}{x^3 - x^2 + 4x - 4}}_{\text{rational expression}} = \underbrace{\dfrac{2}{x - 1} + \dfrac{3x - 1}{x^2 + 4}}_{\text{partial fractions}}$$

Example 1   Decomposing with Distinct Linear Factors

Find the partial fraction decomposition of $\dfrac{2x + 10}{x^2 - 2x - 8}$.

Answer

$\dfrac{2x + 10}{(x - 4)(x + 2)} = \dfrac{A}{x - 4} + \dfrac{B}{x + 2}$

1. When the denominator factors into distinct linear factors, the numerator of each partial fraction is a constant.

$\left[\dfrac{2x + 10}{(x - 4)(x + 2)} = \dfrac{A}{x - 4} + \dfrac{B}{x + 2}\right](x - 4)(x + 2)$

$2x + 10 = A(x + 2) + B(x - 4)$

2. Multiply the equation by the LCD to clear fractions.

$2x + 10 = Ax + 2A + Bx - 4B$
$2x + 10 = (A + B)x + (2A - 4B)$
$\therefore\ A + B = 2$
$\quad 2A - 4B = 10$

3. Rearrange the terms on the right side and equate the coefficients of like terms to form a system of equations.

$\begin{bmatrix} 1 & 1 \\ 2 & -4 \end{bmatrix}\begin{bmatrix} A \\ B \end{bmatrix} = \begin{bmatrix} 2 \\ 10 \end{bmatrix}$

$\begin{bmatrix} A \\ B \end{bmatrix} = -\dfrac{1}{6}\begin{bmatrix} -4 & -1 \\ -2 & 1 \end{bmatrix}\begin{bmatrix} 2 \\ 10 \end{bmatrix}$

$= -\dfrac{1}{6}\begin{bmatrix} -18 \\ 6 \end{bmatrix} = \begin{bmatrix} 3 \\ -1 \end{bmatrix}$

4. Solve the system by writing a matrix equation $CX = D$ and left-multiplying by the inverse of the coefficient matrix to produce $X = C^{-1}D$.

$\dfrac{2x + 10}{x^2 - 2x + 8} = \dfrac{3}{x - 4} - \dfrac{1}{x + 2}$

5. Write the partial fraction decomposition as a difference.

Check

$\dfrac{3}{(x - 4)} \cdot \dfrac{(x + 2)}{(x + 2)} - \dfrac{1}{(x + 2)} \cdot \dfrac{(x - 4)}{(x - 4)}$

$= \dfrac{(3x + 6) - (x - 4)}{(x - 4)(x + 2)} = \dfrac{2x + 10}{x^2 - 2x - 8}$

6. Combine the terms to verify the result.

SKILL ✔ **EXERCISE 7**

An alternative method of solving for A and B is frequently employed when there are no repeated factors. Substituting zeros of the original denominator into the equation after the fractions have been cleared produces equations that can be quickly solved for A and B.

$$\text{Use } 2x + 10 = A(x + 2) + B(x - 4).$$

letting $x = -2$:
$$2(-2) + 10 = A(-2 + 2) + B(-2 - 4)$$
$$6 = -6B$$
$$B = -1$$

letting $x = 4$:
$$2(4) + 10 = A(4 + 2) + B(4 - 4)$$
$$18 = 6A$$
$$A = 3$$

When a linear factor of the expression's denominator is repeated n times, include a partial fraction with a distinct constant numerator for each power of the factor from 1 to n.

$$\frac{px^2 + qx + r}{(x + a)^3} = \frac{A}{x + a} + \frac{B}{(x + a)^2} + \frac{C}{(x + a)^3}$$

Example 2   Decomposing with a Repeated Linear Factor

Find the partial fraction decomposition of $\dfrac{7x^2 - 21x + 16}{x^3 - 4x^2 + 4x}$.

Answer

$$\frac{7x^2 - 21x + 16}{x(x - 2)(x - 2)} = \frac{A}{x} + \frac{B}{x - 2} + \frac{C}{(x - 2)^2}$$

1. Include partial fractions with a distinct constant numerator for each power of the repeated linear factors.

$$\left[\frac{7x^2 - 21x + 16}{x(x - 2)^2} = \frac{A}{x} + \frac{B}{x - 2} + \frac{C}{(x - 2)^2}\right]x(x - 2)^2$$
$$7x^2 - 21x + 16 = A(x - 2)^2 + Bx(x - 2) + Cx$$

2. Multiply by the LCD to clear fractions.

$$= Ax^2 - 4Ax + 4A + Bx^2 - 2Bx + Cx$$
$$= (A + B)x^2 + (-4A - 2B + C)x + 4A$$
$$\therefore \ A + B = 7$$
$$-4A - 2B + C = -21$$
$$4A = 16$$

3. Rearrange the terms on the right side and equate the coefficients of like terms to form a system of equations.

3rd equation: $A = 4$

1st equation: $(4) + B = 7; B = 3$

2nd equation: $-4(4) - 2(3) + C = -21; C = 1$

4. Since the system is in triangular form, it can be solved quickly using back substitution.

$$\left[\frac{7x^2 - 21x + 16}{x^3 - 4x^2 + 4x} = \frac{4}{x} + \frac{3}{x - 2} + \frac{1}{(x - 2)^2}\right]$$

5. Write the partial fraction decomposition as a sum.

Check

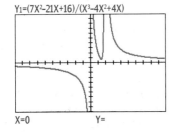

Y₁=(7X²−21X+16)/(X³−4X²+4X)

X=0   Y=

6. The graphs of $Y_1 = \dfrac{7x^2 - 21x + 16}{x(x - 2)^2}$ and
$Y_2 = \dfrac{4}{x} + \dfrac{3}{x - 2} + \dfrac{1}{(x - 2)^2}$ appear identical.

SKILL ✓ **EXERCISE 13**

An alternative solution involves substituting $x = 0$ and $x = 2$ into the results of Step 2 to find A and C.

$$7x^2 - 21x + 16 = A(x - 2)^2 + Bx(x - 2) + Cx$$

letting $x = 0$:
$$0 - 0 + 16 = 4A + 0 + 0$$
$$16 = 4A$$
$$A = 4$$

letting $x = 2$:
$$7(4) - 21(2) + 16 = 0 + 0 + 2C$$
$$2 = 2C$$
$$C = 1$$

Substituting these values and any other convenient value for x (such as $x = 1$) produces an equation that can then be solved to find B.

$$7(1) - 21(1) + 16 = 4(1) + B(-1) + 1(1)$$
$$2 = 5 - B$$
$$B = 3$$

When the original expression's denominator contains an irreducible quadratic factor, include a partial fraction with a linear numerator.

$$\frac{px^2 + qx + r}{(x + a)(x^2 + bx + c)} = \frac{A}{x + a} + \frac{Bx + C}{x^2 + bx + c}$$

Example 3 Decomposing with an Irreducible Quadratic Factor

Find the partial fraction decomposition of $\dfrac{5x^2 - 4x - 3}{x^3 + 1}$.

Answer

$$\frac{5x^2 - 4x - 3}{(x + 1)(x^2 - x + 1)} = \frac{A}{x + 1} + \frac{Bx + C}{x^2 - x + 1}$$

1. Include a partial fraction with a linear numerator and the irreducible quadratic denominator.

$$\left[\frac{5x^2 - 4x - 3}{(x + 1)(x^2 - x + 1)} = \frac{A}{x + 1} + \frac{Bx + C}{x^2 - x + 1}\right](x + 1)(x^2 - x + 1)$$

$$5x^2 - 4x - 3 = A(x^2 - x + 1) + (Bx + C)(x + 1)$$

2. Multiply by the LCD to clear fractions.

$$= (Ax^2 - Ax + A) + (Bx^2 + Bx + Cx + C)$$
$$= (A + B)x^2 + (-A + B + C)x + (A + C)$$

$$\therefore \ A + B = 5$$
$$-A + B + C = -4$$
$$A + C = -3$$

3. Rearrange the terms on the right side and equate the coefficients of like terms to form a system of equations.

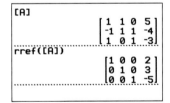

4. The resulting system can be quickly solved by using a calculator to find the equivalent RREF of the augmented matrix.

$$\frac{5x^2 - 4x - 3}{x^3 + 1} = \frac{2}{x + 1} + \frac{3x - 5}{x^2 - x + 1}$$

5. Write the partial fraction decomposition as a sum.

SKILL ✓ **EXERCISE 17**

The alternative method of substituting zeros of the original denominator does not work well when there is an irreducible quadratic factor since there are not enough convenient values of x.

When an irreducible quadratic factor of the expression's denominator is repeated n times, include a partial fraction with a distinct linear numerator for each power of the factor from 1 to n.

$$\frac{mx^3 + px^2 + qx + r}{\left(x^2 + bx + c\right)^2} = \frac{Ax + B}{x^2 + bx + c} + \frac{Cx + D}{\left(x^2 + bx + c\right)^2}$$

Example 4 Decomposing with a Repeated Irreducible Quadratic Factor

Find the partial fraction decomposition of $\dfrac{5x^4 + 21x^2 - x + 18}{x^5 + 6x^3 + 9x}$.

Answer

$\dfrac{5x^4 + 21x^2 - x + 18}{x\left(x^2 + 3\right)^2} = \dfrac{A}{x} + \dfrac{Bx + C}{x^2 + 3} + \dfrac{Dx + E}{\left(x^2 + 3\right)^2}$

1. Include partial fractions with a linear numerator for each power of the irreducible quadratic denominator.

$\left[\dfrac{5x^4 + 21x^2 - x + 18}{x\left(x^2 + 3\right)^2} = \dfrac{A}{x} + \dfrac{Bx + C}{x^2 + 3} + \dfrac{Dx + E}{\left(x^2 + 3\right)^2}\right]x(x^2 + 3)^2$

2. Multiply by the LCD to clear fractions.

$5x^4 + 21x^2 - 1x + 18$
$= A(x^2 + 3)^2 + (Bx + C)x(x^2 + 3) + (Dx + E)x$
$= (Ax^4 + 6Ax^2 + 9A) + (Bx^4 + Cx^3 + 3Bx^2 + 3Cx)$
$\qquad\qquad\qquad\qquad\qquad\qquad + (Dx^2 + Ex)$
$= (A + B)x^4 + Cx^3 + (6A + 3B + D)x^2 + (3C + E)x + 9A$
$\therefore\ A + B = 5$
$\quad C = 0$
$\quad 6A + 3B + D = 21$
$\quad 3C + E = -1$
$\quad 9A = 18$

3. Rearrange the terms on the right side and equate the coefficients of like terms to form a system of equations.

5th equation: $A = 2$

1st equation: $(2) + B = 5; B = 3$

3rd equation: $6(2) + 3(3) + D = 21; D = 0$

4th equation: $3(0) + E = -1; E = -1$

4. Solve the system using back substitution.

$\dfrac{5x^4 + 21x^2 - x + 18}{x^5 + 6x^3 + 9x} = \dfrac{2}{x} + \dfrac{3x}{x^2 + 3} - \dfrac{1}{\left(x^2 + 3\right)^2}$

5. Write the partial fraction decomposition as a sum.

— SKILL ✔ **EXERCISE 21**

Improper rational fractions such as $\dfrac{x^3}{x^2 - 1}$ can be decomposed by using polynomial division to obtain the quotient $x + \dfrac{x}{x^2 - 1}$. A remainder with a nonlinear denominator can then be decomposed into partial fractions using the techniques from this section.

$\dfrac{x}{x^2 - 1} = \dfrac{A}{x - 1} + \dfrac{B}{x + 1}$

$\left[\dfrac{x}{x^2 - 1} = \dfrac{A}{x - 1} + \dfrac{B}{x + 1}\right](x - 1)(x + 1)$

$x = A(x + 1) + B(x - 1)$
$\ = Ax + A + Bx - B$
$\ = (A + B)x + (A - B)$

$\therefore A + B = 1$
$A - B = 0; A = B$
and $A + (A) = 1$
$2A = 1$
$A = \dfrac{1}{2} = B$

$\therefore \dfrac{x}{x^2 - 1} = \dfrac{\frac{1}{2}}{x - 1} + \dfrac{\frac{1}{2}}{x + 1}$

$\qquad = \dfrac{1}{2(x - 1)} + \dfrac{1}{2(x + 1)}$

and

$\dfrac{x^3}{x^2 - 1} = x + \dfrac{1}{2(x - 1)} + \dfrac{1}{2(x + 1)}$

Partial Fraction Decomposition for Proper Rational Expressions

Denominator	Rational Expression	Partial Fractions
distinct linear factors	$\dfrac{px + q}{(x + a)(x + b)}$	$\dfrac{A}{x + a} + \dfrac{B}{x + b}$
repeated linear factors	$\dfrac{px^{n-1} + qx^{n-2} + \cdots + rx + s}{(x + a)^n}$	$\dfrac{A_1}{x + a} + \dfrac{A_2}{(x + a)^2} + \cdots + \dfrac{A_n}{(x + a)^n}$
distinct irreducible quadratic factors	$\dfrac{px^2 + qx + r}{(x + a)(x^2 + bx + c)}$	$\dfrac{A}{x + a} + \dfrac{Bx + C}{x^2 + bx + c}$
repeated irreducible quadratic factors	$\dfrac{mx^{n+1} + px^n + \cdots + qx + r}{(x^2 + bx + c)^n}$	$\dfrac{A_1 x + B_1}{x^2 + bx + c} + \dfrac{A_2 x + B_2}{(x^2 + bx + c)^2} + \cdots + \dfrac{A_n x + B_n}{(x^2 + bx + c)^n}$

》A. Exercises

Write the form for each partial fraction decomposition. Do not solve.

1. $\dfrac{5x - 30}{(x - 2)(x - 12)}$

2. $\dfrac{x^3 + 6x^2 + 3x + 3}{(x^2 + 6x + 3)^2}$

3. $\dfrac{5x^2 - 8x + 11}{(x - 1)(x^2 - 2x - 5)}$

4. $\dfrac{5x^3 - 2}{x^4}$

5. $\dfrac{2x + 23}{x^2 + x - 30}$

6. $\dfrac{3x - 7}{x^2 - 8x + 16}$

Write the partial fraction decomposition for each rational expression. Use a matrix equation to solve the generated system.

7. $\dfrac{7x + 11}{(x - 2)(x + 3)}$

8. $\dfrac{3x - 6}{(x + 4)(x + 1)}$

9. $\dfrac{20x - 17}{2x^2 - 7x - 4}$

10. $\dfrac{5x - 38}{3x^2 + 22x - 16}$

Write the partial fraction decomposition for each rational expression.

11. $\dfrac{4x + 3}{x^2}$

12. $\dfrac{1 - 3x}{x^2}$

13. $\dfrac{2x + 1}{(x - 1)^2}$

14. $\dfrac{4x + 11}{(x + 3)^2}$

15. $\dfrac{7x^2 + 9x + 5}{x(x + 1)^2}$

16. $\dfrac{2x^2 - 7x + 16}{x(x - 2)^2}$

》B. Exercises

Write the partial fraction decomposition for each rational expression. Use technology to solve the generated system with an augmented matrix.

17. $\dfrac{7x^2 - 3x + 14}{x^3 - 8}$

18. $\dfrac{4x^2 + 4x + 17}{(x - 1)(x^2 + x + 3)}$

19. $\dfrac{8x^2 + 55x + 12}{(x + 1)(x^2 + 8x + 2)}$

20. $\dfrac{3x^2 + 7x + 10}{(x + 2)(x^2 + 3x + 4)}$

Write the partial fraction decomposition for each rational expression. Use technology to confirm your solution graphically.

21. $\dfrac{5x^3 + 5x + 3}{(x^2 + 1)^2}$

22. $\dfrac{7x^3 - 14x - 1}{(x^2 - 2)^2}$

23. $\dfrac{5x^4 + 25x^2 + x + 27}{x(x^2 + 3)^2}$

24. $\dfrac{4x^4 + x^3 - 4x^2 - 2x + 4}{x(x^2 - 2)^2}$

Write the partial fraction decomposition for each rational expression.

25. $\dfrac{9x - 8}{9x^2 - 12x + 4}$

26. $\dfrac{23 - x}{x^2 - x - 20}$

27. $\dfrac{3x^2 + x - 2}{x^3 - 6x^2 + 7x - 2}$

28. $\dfrac{x^3 + 5x - 1}{x^4 + 4x^2 + 4}$

29. $\dfrac{5x - 23}{2x^2 - 17x + 30}$

30. $\dfrac{3x^2 - 2x + 2}{x^3 + x^2 - 10x - 6}$

31. $\dfrac{3x^2 - 24x + 32}{x^3 - 8x^2 + 16x}$

32. $\dfrac{10x^4 - 32x^2 + 2x + 27}{4x^5 - 12x^3 + 9x}$

》C. Exercises

Divide each improper rational expression and then find the partial fraction decomposition of the rational remainder. Write your answer as the sum of the quotient and the expanded remainder.

33. $\dfrac{4x^2 + 3}{x^2 - x}$

34. $\dfrac{2x^2 - x + 3}{x^2 + 3x}$

35. $\dfrac{x^3 - 8x + 11}{x^2 + 2x - 3}$

36. $\dfrac{3x^3 - 3x^2 - 33x - 19}{x^2 - x - 12}$

37. Analyze: Use technology to analyze $f(x) = \dfrac{4x+5}{x^2+5x}$.

   a. Find the partial fraction decomposition. Verify your answer by graphing the original expression as Y_1 and the sum of the partial fractions as Y_2.

   b. Graph the partial fractions separately as Y_3 and Y_4 along with Y_2, the graph of their sum. Do the three graphs coincide?

   c. Compare the asymptotes of each partial fraction and their sum.

38. Explore: Consider how a partial fraction decomposition can help evaluate the sum $\displaystyle\sum_{n=1}^{\infty} \dfrac{12}{16n^2+8n-3}$.

   a. Find the partial fraction decomposition of $\dfrac{12}{16n^2+8n-3}$.

   b. Use the partial fraction decomposition to list the sum of the first four terms in the series.

   c. Make a conjecture about what happens to the sum when the series is extended infinitely. Explain your reasoning.

CUMULATIVE REVIEW

39. Find the angle between the vectors $\mathbf{p} = \langle -1, 2 \rangle$ and $\mathbf{q} = \langle 3, -3 \rangle$ (to the nearest degree). **[6.2]**

40. State all equivalent polar coordinates for $(r, \theta) = \left(3, -\frac{\pi}{3}\right)$ if $-2\pi \le \theta \le 2\pi$. **[6.4]**

41. Find the inverse of $f(x) = 3e^x$. **[3.3]**

42. Verify that $A = \begin{bmatrix} 1 & -3 \\ 2 & 4 \end{bmatrix}$ and $B = \begin{bmatrix} \frac{2}{5} & \frac{3}{10} \\ -\frac{1}{5} & \frac{1}{10} \end{bmatrix}$ are inverse matrices. **[7.5]**

43. Without graphing, specify all asymptotes and the domain and range for each function. **[2.5]**

   a. $f(x) = \frac{1}{x}$

   b. $g(x) = \frac{1}{x^2}$

   c. $h(x) = \dfrac{x+1}{x^2+4x+3}$

44. What is the determinant of any identity matrix? **[7.4]**

45. Which of the following is *not* an equivalent pair of polar coordinates for $(r, \theta) = \left(-4, \frac{5\pi}{6}\right)$? **[6.4]**

   A. $\left(-4, -\frac{7\pi}{6}\right)$

   B. $\left(4, \frac{11\pi}{6}\right)$

   C. $\left(4, -\frac{\pi}{6}\right)$

   D. $\left(4, -\frac{2\pi}{3}\right)$

   E. none of these

46. Which of the following is the determinant of $\begin{bmatrix} -14 & 3.5 \\ -42 & -5.6 \end{bmatrix}$? **[7.4]**

   A. 225.4

   B. 68.6

   C. –225.4

   D. –68.6

   E. none of these

47. Which of the following is the approximate length of a in $\triangle ABC$ if $A = 47°$, $b = 86$, and $c = 79$? **[5.7]**

   A. 66

   B. 123

   C. 11

   D. 87

   E. 4370

48. Which points are vertices of the region defined by the given constraints? List all correct answers. **[7.6]**

$x \ge 0$

$y \ge 1$

$x + y \le 5$

   A. $(0, 0)$

   B. $(0, 5)$

   C. $(0, 1)$

   D. $(4, 1)$

   E. all of these

Cryptology

In 2017 over 147 million people had their personal data exposed to hackers due to a security breach at Equifax, a leading US credit reporting company. Governments and military forces have always been keenly interested in information security, but in the modern era of digital communications and online commerce, the secure storage and transmission of data is now extremely important to everyone. In 2001 the National Institute of Standards and Technology published the Advanced Encryption Standard, an algorithm that relies on the difficulty of factoring products of very large prime numbers to encrypt messages.

Cryptology includes both cryptography (creating and using ciphers) and cryptanalysis (breaking ciphers). Simple monoalphabetic ciphers pair a letter with a different letter or symbol based on a key. For example, the Caesar cipher key adds three to the original letter so that A becomes D, B becomes E, and so on. Even if the key is more complex, these ciphers are easily broken by analyzing how often each symbol occurs and comparing its frequency to the known frequency of occurrence of letters in normal usage.

In 1929 Lester Hill, a teacher at Hunter College in New York, published a polyalphabetic block cipher using an algebraic alphabet. While never widely used, the Hill cipher introduced mathematics into cryptology and is still commonly taught in undergraduate linear algebra and computer science classes. The Hill cipher pairs each letter of the alphabet with a whole number from 0 to 25.

A	B	C	D	E	F	G	H	I	J	K	L	M
0	1	2	3	4	5	6	7	8	9	10	11	12
N	O	P	Q	R	S	T	U	V	W	X	Y	Z
13	14	15	16	17	18	19	20	21	22	23	24	25

The plaintext message is then converted into an uncoded $m \times n$ matrix U and encrypted by right-multiplying by an $n \times n$ invertible matrix E as described in Section 7.5.

Additionally, each number in the coded matrix C can be replaced with its remainder when divided by 26 (known as modulus 26, or mod 26). This allows the message "SEND FOOD" to be sent as a string of letters.

$$
\begin{array}{ccccccc}
U & \cdot & E & = & C & \Rightarrow & C_{mod\,26}
\end{array}
$$

$$
\begin{bmatrix} 18 & 4 \\ 13 & 3 \\ 5 & 14 \\ 14 & 3 \end{bmatrix} \cdot \begin{bmatrix} 2 & 3 \\ 1 & 4 \end{bmatrix} = \begin{bmatrix} 40 & 70 \\ 29 & 51 \\ 24 & 71 \\ 31 & 54 \end{bmatrix} \Rightarrow \begin{bmatrix} 14 & 18 \\ 3 & 25 \\ 24 & 19 \\ 5 & 2 \end{bmatrix} = \text{OSDZYTFC}
$$

While the product CE^{-1} decodes matrix C, multiplying $C_{mod\,26}$ by E^{-1} does not. To decipher the message, the recipient recreates $C_{mod\,26}$ and multiplies by the mod 26 inverse of the encryption matrix, $E^{-1}_{mod\,26}$. Only matrices where $|E|$ mod 26 = 1, 3, 5, 7, 9, 11, 15, 17, 19, 21, 23, or 25 have a mod 26 inverse matrix.

1. Find $|E|$, $|E|_{mod\,26}$, and E^{-1} for $E = \begin{bmatrix} 2 & 3 \\ 1 & 4 \end{bmatrix}$.

To find $E^{-1}_{mod\,26}$, each fraction in E^{-1} must be converted into a whole number by multiplying the numerator by the modular multiplicative inverse of the denominator (listed in the table) and writing the result in mod 26. Since e_{12} in $E^{-1} = -\frac{3}{5}$, e_{12} in $E^{-1}_{mod\,26}$ is the remainder when $-3(21)$ is divided by 26.

$$e_{21} = -11$$

Convert a negative mod 26 value to an equivalent mod 26 whole number by adding 26 or a multiple of 26.

$$-11 \bmod 26$$
$$= (-11 + 26) \bmod 26$$
$$= 15 \bmod 26$$

denominator	1	3	5	7	9	11	15	17	19	21	23	25
mod 26 mult. inv.	1	9	21	15	3	19	7	23	11	5	17	25

2. Convert E^{-1} to $E^{-1}_{mod\,26}$.

3. Decode OSDZYTFC using $E^{-1}_{mod\,26}$.

If the mod 26 determinant of E shares a common factor with 26, $E^{-1}{}_{mod\,26}$ does not exist and a mod 26 encryption cannot be decoded.

Consider the 3×3 encryption matrix $E = \begin{bmatrix} 2 & 0 & 1 \\ 3 & 2 & 4 \\ 1 & 5 & 3 \end{bmatrix}$.

4. Find $|E|$ and the whole number $|E|$ mod 26.

5. Use $E_{3 \times 3}$ to find the alphabetic encryption of "ALL IS WELL."

6. Find the decrypting matrix $E^{-1}{}_{mod\,26}$.

7. Use $E^{-1}{}_{mod\,26}$ to decode your encrypted message from exercise 5.

8. Decode this message encrypted with $E_{3 \times 3}$: CALKKXTDLTUA.

Cryptology plays an essential role in preserving private information, intellectual property, and international security. Cryptology can also be controversial. Law enforcement agencies claim that the surge in encryption creates a major impediment to law enforcement as it is more difficult to access digitally stored information when investigating criminal activity. Tech companies and privacy advocates claim that providing "back doors" to law enforcement would violate the user's right to privacy. How much privacy should be relinquished in order to apprehend criminals?

9. Discuss: Which biblical principles should be considered in the cryptology debate between law enforcement and privacy advocates?

10. Discuss: Evaluate the following statement: "In criminal cases, law enforcement officials should be able to obtain a search warrant granting access to all information stored on related electronic devices."

Chapter 7 Review

Solve each system. Then classify each system as independent consistent, dependent consistent, or inconsistent. [7.1]

1. $3x - y = 1$
$5x + 2y = -24$

2. $2x + y = 15$
$4x + 2y = 19$

3. $5x - 3y = 10$
$1.5y - 2.5x = -5$

4. $2x + 5y = 14$
$3x - 2y = -17$

5. Find the dimensions of a rectangle whose perimeter is 156 ft and area is 1296 ft. [7.1]

6. A cell phone manufacturer has determined the supply and demand curves for a cell phone where p is the price (in dollars) and x is the supply in hundred thousands of phones. Find the equilibrium price and the number of phones that should be produced. [7.1]
supply: $p = 100x - 460$
demand: $p = 915 - 25x$

Solve each system. [7.1]

7. $2x - 4y + 5z = -7$
$5x + 3y + 2z = 1$
$7x - y + 3z = 6$

8. $3x + 2y - z = 9$
$9x - 2y + 2z = 3$

9. Given $A = \begin{bmatrix} 5 & 12 & -2 & 0 \\ 9 & 7 & 14 & 2 \\ -1 & 3 & 6 & 8 \end{bmatrix}$, state the following.
[7.2]

  a. dimensions of A

  b. value of a_{32}

  c. value of a_{23}

  d. element whose value is 2

  e. element whose value is –1

10. If $A = \begin{bmatrix} 5 & -2 & 10 \\ 1 & 7 & 9 \end{bmatrix}$ and $B = \begin{bmatrix} 3 & 1 & -5 \\ -4 & 6 & 2 \end{bmatrix}$,
find $D = 3A - 2B$. [7.2]

11. State the dimensions of each matrix product, or state *not defined*. [7.2]

  a. $A_{3 \times 2} \times B_{2 \times 3}$

  b. $A_{3 \times 2} \times C_{3 \times 2}$

  c. $D_{4 \times 1} \times E_{1 \times 2}$

  d. $F_{2 \times 2} \times G_{2 \times 5}$

Multiply. [7.2]

12. $\begin{bmatrix} 3 & 5 \\ -1 & 2 \end{bmatrix}\begin{bmatrix} 4 & 0 \\ 2 & -1 \end{bmatrix}$

13. $\begin{bmatrix} 6 & -2 & 1 \\ 3 & 4 & -2 \end{bmatrix}\begin{bmatrix} -5 & 4 \\ -1 & 3 \\ 6 & 3 \end{bmatrix}$

14. Write each 3 × 3 matrix. [7.2]

  a. multiplicative identity matrix

  b. additive identity matrix

15. The school athletic director needs to order tennis equipment for the new season. Write matrix $N_{2 \times 3}$ representing the team's needs and matrix C representing the costs. Then write and evaluate a matrix expression to find the cost for each group. [7.2]

Team Equipment Needs			
	Balls	**Rackets**	**Uniforms**
Boys	45	12	16
Girls	40	14	18
Cost			
Ball	**Racket**	**Uniform**	
$1.50	$42.00	$57.00	

16. Write $\begin{bmatrix} 2 & 5 & 4 \\ 3 & 6 & 3 \end{bmatrix}$ in equivalent REF. [7.3]

17. Write $\begin{bmatrix} 2 & 1 & 2 \\ 3 & -2 & 17 \end{bmatrix}$ in RREF. [7.3]

18. Solve using Gaussian elimination. [7.3]
$2x + 4y + 2z = -10$
$3x - 2y + 8z = 17$
$6x + 2y - 3z = 10$

Use Gauss-Jordan elimination to solve each system. Classify any inconsistent or dependent systems. [7.3]

19. $2x - 3y + z = 3$
$y + 3z = 2$
$-4x + 6y - 2z = -6$

20. $x + y + z = 7$
$3x + 4y = 6$
$2x + z = 2$

21. $x + 4y + 2z = 7$
$2x + 9y + 7z = 7$
$y + 3z = -5$

22. John sold the listed quantities of art pieces at a craft fair and made \$690, \$470, and \$1325 in profits on Thursday, Friday, and Saturday, respectively. Write and solve a system of equations to find the profit per item for each type of art piece. [7.3]

Day	Ornaments	Paintings	Prints
Thursday	12	1	4
Friday	10	0	8
Saturday	15	2	10

Find the determinant of each matrix using the product of the diagonals. [7.4]

23. $\begin{bmatrix} 7 & 9 \\ -3 & 2 \end{bmatrix}$

24. $\begin{bmatrix} 5 & -2 & 0 \\ 2 & -4 & 7 \\ -3 & 1 & 1 \end{bmatrix}$

25. Find the determinant of the matrix using minors and cofactors for each given row or column. [7.4]

$\begin{bmatrix} 1 & 2 & 0 \\ 3 & -1 & -2 \\ 1 & 3 & 2 \end{bmatrix}$
  a. row 1
  b. column 1

26. Evaluate the determinant of

$\begin{bmatrix} -1 & 1 & -4 & 2 \\ 2 & 0 & 0 & 3 \\ 5 & 3 & 1 & 0 \\ 0 & -2 & 3 & -2 \end{bmatrix}$ [7.4]

Solve each system using Cramer's rule. [7.4]

27. $2x - y = 13$
$4x + 2y = 6$

28. $2x - y = 1$
$x + 2z = -1$
$y + 3z = -1$

Find the area of each polygonal region. [7.4]

29. $\triangle ABC$ with $A(0, 0)$, $B(-2, 5)$, and $C(4, 3)$

30. quadrilateral $ABCD$

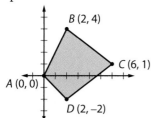

31. Determine whether each pair of matrices are inverse matrices. [7.5]

a. $A = \begin{bmatrix} 2 & -3 \\ -1 & 2 \end{bmatrix}$, $B = \begin{bmatrix} 2 & 3 \\ 1 & 2 \end{bmatrix}$

b. $C = \begin{bmatrix} 4 & 3 \\ 1 & 1 \end{bmatrix}$, $D = \begin{bmatrix} 1 & -3 \\ -1 & 3 \end{bmatrix}$

32. Use the formula to find the inverse of $A = \begin{bmatrix} -3 & 4 \\ -2 & 2 \end{bmatrix}$. [7.5]

33. Use row operations on $[A \,|\, I]$ to find the inverse of

$B = \begin{bmatrix} 2 & -1 & 3 \\ 6 & -1 & 9 \\ -4 & 3 & -11 \end{bmatrix}$. [7.5]

34. Use a matrix equation to solve the system. [7.5]
$2x + 5y = 4$
$-3x - 4y = 1$

35. Solve the system by writing and solving a matrix equation with technology. [7.5]
$3x + y - z = 16$
$x + y + 2z = 12$
$x - y + z = 8$

36. Write and solve a matrix equation to find three numbers whose sum is 4 if the difference of the first and the third is 1 more than twice the second, and the sum of the first two is 23 less than twice the third. [7.5]

37. Joseph wants to place \$42,000 for his children's college fund into a savings account earning 3.5% APY, a CD earning 4% APY, and a bond earning 5.5% APY. He wants to earn \$1700 in interest next year while investing twice as much in the CD as the other two investments. Write and solve a matrix equation to find the amount that should be placed in each investment. [7.5]

Solve each system of inequalities. [7.6]

38. $y < -x + 5$
$y < \frac{1}{2}x - 2$

39. $y < -3|x - 4| + 5$
$y > (x - 4)^2 - 5$

Graph each system and state the coordinates of the vertices of the solution region.

40. $1 \le y \le 2$
$x + 3y \le 10$
$-x + y \le 1$

41. $x - y \ge -3$
$2x + y \le 3$
$2x + 3y \ge -6$

42. Maximize and minimize $f(x, y) = 7x - 2y$ with the given constraints.
$x \le 5$ $2x + y \ge 6$
$y \le 4$ $x - y \le 3$

43. A grocer makes \$5.00 profit on the larger Tropical fruit basket and \$3.00 on the smaller Heartland basket. Research indicates the store will sell at most 60 fruit baskets and sales of the Heartland will be at least double the sales of the Tropical. This week the grocer has only 50 of the smaller baskets to use for the Heartland. Write the profit function and a system of constraints. Then graph the feasible region, find how many of each basket should be made to maximize the possible profit this week, and find the maximum profit.

Find the partial fraction decomposition for each rational expression. [7.7]

44. $\dfrac{3x - 7}{x^2 - 6x + 9}$

45. $\dfrac{7x - 32}{x^2 - 10x + 24}$

46. $\dfrac{2x^2 - x + 2}{4x^3 - 4x^2 + x}$

47. $\dfrac{5x^2 - 16x - 12}{(x - 2)(x^2 - 3x - 2)}$

48. $\dfrac{4x^4 + x^3 + 3x^2 + x + 2}{x^5 + 2x^3 + x}$

8 Analytic Geometry

HISTORICAL CONNECTION

Like most ideas in the history of mathematics, the advent of analytic geometry required prior advancements in other areas, such as symbolic notation and algebra. Unlike most other developments, the two individuals most responsible for the origin of analytic geometry were not professional mathematicians.

BIBLICAL PERSPECTIVE OF MATHEMATICS

All worldviews ultimately require faith in foundational axioms. Explore how counterexamples and existence proofs are related to a biblical worldview.

DATA ANALYSIS

Conic sections are used to represent the orbits of the planets and comets within our solar system, satellites of the earth, and even interstellar objects.

8.1 Conics and Parabolas

The Frederick Douglass–Susan B. Anthony Memorial Bridge in Rochester, NY, has a nearly parabolic triple arch that spans 433 ft.

After completing this section, you will be able to

- describe conics as a section of a conical surface.
- define a parabola as a locus of points.
- write the equation of a parabola.
- graph a parabola, given its equation.
- solve real-world problems related to parabolas.

Apollonius unified the classical Greek knowledge of *conic sections* in his eight-volume treatise, *Conics*. The combining of geometry and algebra into analytic geometry by René Descartes and Pierre Fermat in the seventeenth century laid the foundations for the use of conics in the modeling of projectile motion by Galileo and planetary orbits by Johannes Kepler. The analytic geometry of conic sections also paved the way for Isaac Newton and Gottfried Leibniz to develop the foundations of calculus. Since Christ "is before all things, and by him all things consist" (Col. 1:17), He is the controlling and unifying force in nature. We can expect to find wonderful order in His creation. Mathematics provides many models of Christ's creative order.

A conic section (or *conic*) is formed by the intersection of a plane with a *right circular conical surface*. A *conical surface* is the union of all lines (*elements*) through the points of a *generating curve* and the *vertex*, a point not in the plane of the curve. The vertex divides the surface into two *nappes*. The generating curve of a right circular conical surface is a circle, and the surface's axis (the line connecting the circle's center to the vertex) is perpendicular to the plane of the circle.

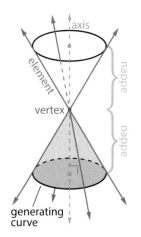

A plane can intersect this conical surface in seven ways. If the plane does not contain the vertex, the intersection is a circle, ellipse, parabola, or hyperbola. A *degenerate conic* (a point, a line, or two intersecting lines) is formed when the plane passes through the vertex.

Basic Conics			
Parabola	Ellipse	Circle	Hyperbola
The plane is parallel to an element of the conical surface.	The plane intersects one nappe and is not parallel to an element.	The plane is perpendicular to the axis of the conical surface.	The plane intersects both nappes of the conical surface.

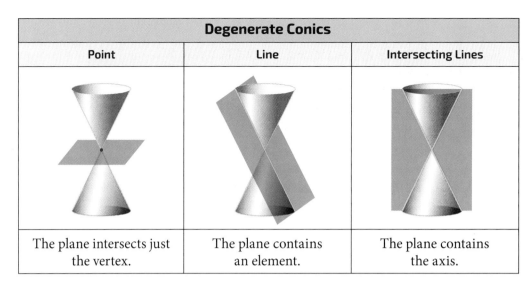

Degenerate Conics		
Point	**Line**	**Intersecting Lines**
The plane intersects just the vertex.	The plane contains an element.	The plane contains the axis.

KEYWORD SEARCH

interactive conic sections 🔍

In analytic geometry conic sections are also described algebraically with second-degree (quadratic) equations in the form of $Ax^2 + Bxy + Cy^2 + Dx + Ey + F = 0$. If $A = B = C = 0$, the equation is a first-degree (linear) equation representing one of the degenerate conics. If $B \neq 0$, the equation represents a rotation of one of the nondegenerate conic sections. The study of rotated conic sections will be introduced in Section 8.4. The values of D, E, and F translate the curve.

A conic can also be defined as a set of points that satisfy a certain condition, or a *locus* of points. A circle has been defined as the set of points in a plane that are equidistant from a given point. This definition was used to derive the standard equation for a circle, $(x - h)^2 + (y - k)^2 = r^2$. In this chapter we will define each basic conic section as a locus of points and derive standard equations representing them, beginning with parabolas.

In Section 1.6 you graphed quadratic functions of the form $y = ax^2 + bx + c$ using the vertex form $y = a(x - h)^2 + k$. These parabolas have a vertical axis of symmetry. We will see how a parabola's locus definition is used to derive other standard form equations for parabolas with either a vertical or a horizontal axis of symmetry.

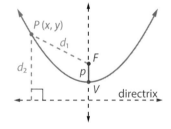

▌ DEFINITIONS

A **parabola** is the set of points in a plane that are equidistant from a fixed line (its **directrix**) and a fixed point (its **focus**) not on that line.

In orbital mechanics the parabola represents the path followed by a satellite which has reached escape velocity, that is, the minimum speed required to escape the gravitational pull of the attracting body.

The distance d_1 from any point $P(x, y)$ on the parabola to the focus F is equal to d_2, the point's perpendicular distance to the directrix.

The parabola's axis of symmetry passes through its focus and is perpendicular to its directrix. The parabola's vertex, V, is the midpoint of the segment on the axis connecting the focus and the directrix. If p represents the directed distance from the vertex to the focus, then $|p|$ is the parabola's *focal length*.

If the vertex of the parabola is at $V(h, k)$ and represents a minimum point, the parabola opens upward, $p > 0$, the focus is $F(h, k + p)$, and the directrix is the line $y = k - p$. An equation for the parabola in terms of h, k, and p can be derived using the fact that $d_1 = d_2$.

$$d_1 = d_2$$

$$\sqrt{(x-h)^2 + [y-(k+p)]^2} = \sqrt{(x-x)^2 + [y-(k-p)]^2}$$

Square both sides and simplify.

$$(x-h)^2 + [y-k-p]^2 = [y-k+p]^2$$

Apply the Associative Property to group y and k.

$$(x-h)^2 + [(y-k)-p]^2 = [(y-k)+p]^2$$

Expand, keeping $(x-h)^2$ and $(y-k)$ intact.

$$(x-h)^2 + (y-k)^2 - 2p(y-k) + p^2 = (y-k)^2 + 2p(y-k) + p^2$$

Subtract $(y-k)^2$ and p^2 from each side and solve for y.

$$(x-h)^2 - 2p(y-k) = 2p(y-k)$$
$$(x-h)^2 = 4p(y-k)$$
$$\frac{1}{4p}(x-h)^2 = y-k$$
$$y = \frac{1}{4p}(x-h)^2 + k$$

This equation is equivalent to the vertex form $y = a(x-h)^2 + k$ if $a = \frac{1}{4p}$ or $p = \frac{1}{4a}$.

Example 1   Analyzing and Graphing a Parabola

Graph $y = -\frac{1}{2}(x+3)^2 + 2$ and its vertex, focus, and directrix.

Answer

$V(-3, 2)$

$p = \dfrac{1}{4\left(-\frac{1}{2}\right)} = -\dfrac{1}{2}$

$F\left(-3, 2 - \frac{1}{2}\right) = (-3, 1.5)$

directrix: $y = 2 + \frac{1}{2}$ or $y = 2.5$

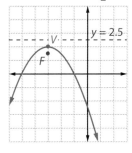

1. Identify (h, k) from the vertex form $y = a(x-h)^2 + k$.

2. Use $p = \frac{1}{4a}$ to find the directed focal length.

3. For parabolas with a vertical axis, the focus is $F(h, k+p)$, and the directrix is the line $y = k - p$.

4. Graph the parabola, using its vertex and $a = -\frac{1}{2}$. Then plot $F(-3, 1.5)$ and graph the directrix $y = 2.5$.

    Notice that the parabola opens toward its focus and away from its directrix.

SKILL ✔ **EXERCISES 7, 11**

A *chord of a curve* is a segment with both endpoints on the curve. The length of the chord through the parabola's focus and perpendicular to its axis defines the parabola's *focal width*, which is $|4p|$. The focal width of the parabola in Example 1 is $|4p| = \left|4\left(-\frac{1}{2}\right)\right| = 2$, the length of the chord with endpoints $(-4, 1.5)$ and $(-2, 1.5)$.

The inverse relation of a parabola of the form $y = \frac{1}{4p}x^2$ is $x = \frac{1}{4p}y^2$, a parabola with a horizontal axis and a vertex at the origin. If this parabola is translated so its vertex is at $V(h, k)$, its standard form equation is $x = \frac{1}{4p}(y-k)^2 + h$. This formula is derived in exercise 42.

Standard Form Equations of a Parabola	
with vertex $V(h, k)$ and focal length $\lvert p \rvert$ where $a = \frac{1}{4p}$	
$y = \frac{1}{4p}(x - h)^2 + k$	$x = \frac{1}{4p}(y - k)^2 + h$
focus: $F(h, k + p)$; axis: $x = h$; directrix: $y = k - p$	focus: $F(h + p, k)$; axis: $y = k$; directrix: $x = h - p$
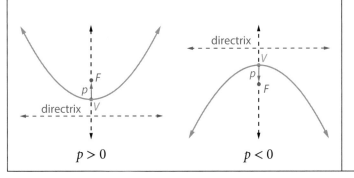	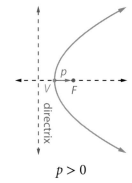 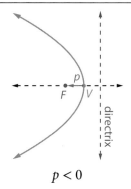

Example 2 Writing the Equation of a Parabola

Write the standard form equation of the parabola with focus $(-1, 2)$ and directrix $x = 3$.

Answer

$$V\left(\frac{-1 + 3}{2}, \frac{2 + 2}{2}\right) = (1, 2)$$
$$p = -2$$

$$a = \frac{1}{4(-2)} = -\frac{1}{8}$$

$$x = -\frac{1}{8}(y - 2)^2 + 1$$

Check

$$x - 1 = -\frac{1}{8}(y - 2)^2$$
$$-8(x - 1) = (y - 2)^2$$
$$y - 2 = \pm\sqrt{-8(x - 1)}$$
$$y = \pm\sqrt{-8(x - 1)} + 2$$

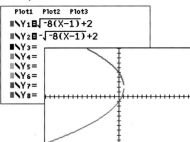

1. Plot the focus and draw the directrix.
2. Locate the vertex halfway between the focus and the directrix.
3. Sketch the parabola curving around the focus.
4. Use the sketch to determine p, and use $a = \frac{1}{4p}$ to find the value of a.
5. Substitute the values of a, k, and h into the standard form equation $x = a(y - k)^2 + h$.
6. Solve the equation for y.
7. Since the parabola is not a function, enter the two functions whose union forms the parabola, and graph them in a square window to avoid distortion. Your calculator may not plot the nearly vertical portions of the graphs.

Apollonius's definition of a parabola is a one-sentence paragraph of over 200 words. When manipulating formulas seems difficult, imagine trying to perform the same operations using only words, with no symbols at all.

SKILL ✔ EXERCISE 15

When the equation of a parabola is written in the *general form* for conics,

$$Ax^2 + Bxy + Cy^2 + Dx + Ey + F = 0,$$

parabolas with a vertical axis have the form $Ax^2 + Dx + Ey + F = 0$ (with $B = C = 0$), and parabolas with a horizontal axis have the form $Cy^2 + Dx + Ey + F = 0$ (with $A = B = 0$). Converting these equations to a standard form for parabolas frequently involves the process of completing a square.

Example 3 Analyzing and Graphing a Parabola

Graph $2y^2 - x + 4y - 1 = 0$ and its focus and directrix.

Answer

$x = 2y^2 + 4y - 1$

1. Since the equation has a y^2-term but no x^2-term, solve for x.

$x = 2(y^2 + 2y) - 1$

2. Complete the square for the y-terms.

$\quad = 2(y^2 + 2y + 1^2) - 1 - 2(1)$

$x = 2(y + 1)^2 - 3$

$p = \dfrac{1}{4(2)} = \dfrac{1}{8}$

3. Use $p = \dfrac{1}{4a}$ to find the directed focal length.

4. Use the vertex $V(-3, -1)$ and $a = 2$ to graph the parabola.

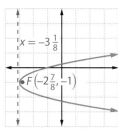

5. Plot the focus $\dfrac{1}{8}$ unit to the right of the vertex and the directrix $\dfrac{1}{8}$ unit to its left.

—————————————————— SKILL ✓ **EXERCISE 21**

A tangent to a conic intersects the conic at just one point. The tangent to a parabola at point P defines an isosceles triangle whose vertex is the parabola's focus F and base is $\overline{PA}$ where A is the intersection of the tangent and the parabola's axis. This property allows us to find the equation of the tangent drawn at a given point on the parabola.

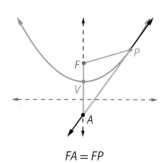

$FA = FP$

Example 4 Finding a Tangent to a Parabola

Find the equation of the line tangent to $y = -\dfrac{1}{2}x^2$ at $P(-2, -2)$.

Answer

$p = \dfrac{1}{4\left(-\frac{1}{2}\right)} = -\dfrac{1}{2}, \therefore F\left(0, -\dfrac{1}{2}\right)$

1. Note that the vertex is at the origin and use $p = \dfrac{1}{4a}$ to find the parabola's focus.

$FP = \sqrt{(-2 - 0)^2 + \left(-2 + \dfrac{1}{2}\right)^2}$

2. Find the distance from F to P.

$\quad = \sqrt{4 + \dfrac{9}{4}} = \sqrt{\dfrac{25}{4}} = \dfrac{5}{2}$

$A\left(0, -\dfrac{1}{2} + \dfrac{5}{2}\right) = (0, 2)$

3. Use $FA = FP$ to locate A on the parabola's axis.

$m = \dfrac{-2 - 2}{-2 - 0} = 2$

4. Find the slope of the tangent, using $P(-2, -2)$ and $A(0, 2)$.

$y = 2x + 2$

5. Use $y = mx + b$ to write the equation of the tangent.

—————————————————— SKILL ✓ **EXERCISE 25**

Satellite dishes, automobile headlights, and radio telescopes all take advantage of another property of parabolas. Signals emitted from a parabola's focus are reflected parallel to its axis, and all the signals entering the parabola parallel to the axis are reflected to the focus.

Example 5   Modeling with Parabolas

The "Heavenly Eye" radio telescope in Guizhou province, China, has a diameter of 500 m. The paraboloid reflects incoming radio waves to a receiver 140 m above the reflective surface. Write an equation modeling a cross section through the center of the telescope and use it to find the height of the reflective surface.

Answer

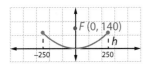

1. Sketch a cross section of the telescope and its focus. Place the vertex at the origin to simplify the problem and use $p = 140$. Since the diameter is 500 m, the parabola's domain is $[-250, 250]$.

$a = \dfrac{1}{4(140)} = \dfrac{1}{560}$

$y = \dfrac{1}{560}x^2$

2. Use $a = \dfrac{1}{4p}$ to find a, and then write the equation modeling the cross section.

$y = \dfrac{1}{560}(\pm 250)^2 \approx 111.6 \text{ m}$

3. Find y when $x = \pm 250$.

SKILL ✓ EXERCISE 33

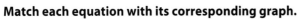

❯ A. Exercises

1. Match each description of the plane intersecting a right circular conical surface to its basic conic section.

   a. intersects both nappes of the conical surface
   b. parallel to an element of the conical surface
   c. intersects one nappe and is not parallel to an element
   d. perpendicular to the axis of the conical surface

   I. circle
   II. ellipse
   III. hyperbola
   IV. parabola

C.

D.

E.

F.

Match each equation with its corresponding graph.

2. $y = \frac{1}{2}x^2$

3. $x = -\frac{1}{2}y^2$

4. $x = \frac{1}{2}(y - 2)^2 + 1$

5. $y = -\frac{1}{4}(x + 1)^2 + 2$

A.

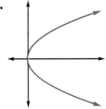

B.

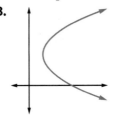

Graph each parabola and its vertex, focus, and directrix.

6. $y = \frac{1}{4}x^2$

7. $x = -\frac{1}{8}y^2$

8. $x = \frac{1}{12}(y - 4)^2$

9. $y = -\frac{1}{2}(x - 1)^2 + 6$

10. $x = -\frac{1}{4}(y - 3)^2 - 2$

11. $x = \frac{1}{16}(y - 2)^2 - 3$

12. $y = \frac{1}{6}(x - 2)^2 + 1$

13. $y = \frac{1}{8}(x - 2)^2 - 2$

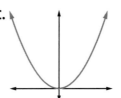
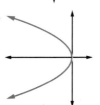
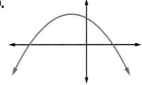
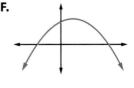

Write a standard form equation for each parabola with the given characteristics. Check your answer by using technology to graph the parabola.

14. $V(0, 0)$; $F(-4, 0)$

15. $V(4, -6)$; $F(4, -1)$

16. $V(-1, -6)$; directrix: $y = -5.5$

17. $V(5, 3)$; directrix: $x = 2$

18. $F(-1, 1)$; directrix: $y = 5$

19. $F\left(-\frac{3}{4}, -3\right)$; directrix: $x = -\frac{5}{4}$

B. Exercises

Write each equation in standard form. Then graph the parabola, its focus, and its directrix.

20. $y^2 - x - 8y + 18 = 0$ **21.** $x^2 - 10x + 8y + 9 = 0$

22. $y^2 + 2x - 2y - 6 = 0$ **23.** $x^2 + 8x - 4y + 20 = 0$

Write the equation of the tangent to the parabola at the given point P.

24. $x^2 = 4y$, $P(-2, 1)$ **25.** $x^2 + 2y = 0$, $P(4, -8)$

26. $x = \frac{1}{8}y^2$, $P(8, 8)$ **27.** $y^2 + 4x = 8$, $P(-7, -6)$

Use the vertex and the other point on the parabola to find *a*, then write the standard form equation of the parabola.

28.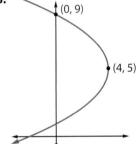

29.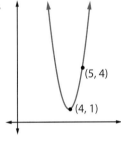

30. the parabola passing through $(5, -5)$ with a vertical axis and a vertex at $(-1, -2)$

31. the parabola passing through $(-2, 2)$ with a horizontal axis and a vertex at $(-4, 3)$

32. The 433 ft center span of the Frederick Douglass–Susan B. Anthony Memorial Bridge in Rochester, NY, is supported by triple arches that rise 70 ft above the highway. Write an equation of a parabola modeling the arches.

33. A parabolic satellite dish for a cable company has a diameter of 8 ft and a depth of 3 ft. Find the parabolic equation that models a cross section through the center of the satellite and determine the location of the receiver (its focal point).

34. A solar furnace uses a parabolic reflector to direct the light to the focal point. If the reflector is 10 m high and has a focal length of 3.2 m, find the depth of the reflector.

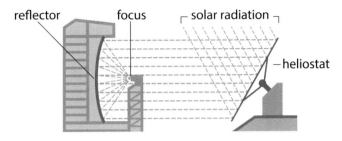

35. Which of the following statements are true? List all correct answers.

A. A tangent to a conic can intersect that conic at more than one point.

B. Conic sections are described algebraically with second-degree equations in the form of $Ax^2 + Bxy + Cy^2 + Dx + Ey + F = 0$.

C. A conic section is formed by the intersection of a line and a conical surface.

D. The focal width is the distance from the vertex to the focus.

E. Degenerate conics include a point, a line, and two intersecting lines.

C. Exercises

Graph the solution of each system of inequalities.

36. $y \le -(x - 5)^2 + 5$
$y \ge (x - 5)^2 - 3$

37. $y \le -2(x - 1)^2 + 5$
$x \le -(y - 1)^2 + 5$

38. $x^2 + y^2 \le 36$
$x \ge \frac{1}{2}y^2 - 8$
$3y - x^2 + 12 \ge 0$

39. $x^2 + 12x + y^2 + 10y \le -52$
$y^2 - x + 10y + 19 \ge 0$
$y^2 + x + 10y + 31 \ge 0$

Find the equation of each tangent to the parabola at the given point P.

40. $x^2 + 16x + 8y + 8 = 0$, $P(-4, 5)$

41. $y^2 - 4x - 4y - 12 = 0$, $P(5, 8)$

42. Derive: Sketch a parabola with vertex (h, k) and opening to the right. Label the focus and the directrix in terms of h, k, and p. Sketch $\overline{PF}$ from a point $P(x, y)$ on the curve to the focal point and $\overline{PD}$ representing the perpendicular distance from P to the directrix. Label the coordinates of D in terms of y, h, and p. Use the figure and the locus definition of a parabola to derive the standard form equation of a parabola with a horizontal axis: $x = \frac{1}{4p}(y - k)^2 + h$.

43. Prove: Prove that the triangle defined by the endpoints of the chord representing the focal width of a parabola and the point of intersection of the parabola's axis and directrix is an isosceles right triangle.

CUMULATIVE REVIEW

Write the equation for each circle. [1.2]

44. a circle centered at the origin with a radius of 8

45. a circle centered at $(-1, -3)$ and containing the point $(2, 1)$

Graph each circle. [1.2]

46. $x^2 + y^2 = 16$ **47.** $(x - 2)^2 + (y + 3)^2 = 4$

Write each quadratic function in vertex form. [1.6]

48. $f(x) = -3x^2 + 6x + 13$ **49.** $g(x) = 6x^2 + 48x + 90$

50. Which of the following is not a zero of the equation $f(x) = 2x^3 - 5x^2 - 11x - 4$? [2.4]

A. -1 **C.** $-\frac{1}{2}$ **E.** These are

B. 4 **D.** 1 all zeros.

51. Which values of x are zeros of $f(x) = 2x^2 + x - 10$? [2.4]

A. $-\frac{5}{2}, 2$ **C.** $-\frac{1}{4}, 2$ **E.** none of

B. $-2, \frac{5}{2}$ **D.** $-2, \frac{1}{4}$ these

52. Which function has an amplitude of 3, period of π, and phase shift of π? [4.4]

A. $f(x) = 3 \sin x + \pi$ **D.** $f(x) = 3 \sin 2x + \pi$

B. $f(x) = 3 \sin 2(x - \pi)$ **E.** none of these

C. $f(x) = 3 \sin (x - \pi)$

53. From the top of a 210 ft cliff, the angle of depression of a ship at sea is $4°$. Find the distance from the foot of the cliff to the ship (to the nearest foot). [4.2]

A. 209 ft   **C.** 3003 ft   **E.** none of

B. 15 ft   **D.** 50 ft   these

National Statuary Hall in the US Capitol functions as a whispering gallery.

A parabola has been defined as a set of points equidistant from a given point (its focus) and a given line (its directrix). The definition of an ellipse involves the distances from two given points. Ellipses are formed by intersections of one nappe of the conical surface and a plane that is not parallel to an element. Compare the locus definition of an ellipse to the definition of a parabola.

After completing this section, you will be able to

- define an ellipse.
- analyze and graph an ellipse, given its equation.
- write the equation of an ellipse.
- identify a circle as a special case of an ellipse.
- solve real-world problems related to ellipses.

▶ DEFINITION

An **ellipse** is the set of points $P(x, y)$ in a plane such that the sum of the distances from two fixed points (its foci) is constant.

An ellipse can be formed by attaching a string to the two foci and using a pencil to draw the points of the ellipse while keeping the string taut. The section of string on each side of the pencil illustrates the distance from a point to each focus, and the sum of both sections (the string's length) remains constant.

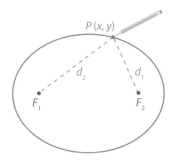

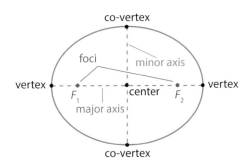

The first known reference to the now-familiar method of creating an ellipse by using two fixed points and a loop of string was made by the Greek mathematician Anthemius of Tralles in the sixth century.

The chord of the ellipse containing the foci (F_1 and F_2) is its *major axis* and the chord's midpoint is the *center* of the ellipse, typically notated as $C(h, k)$. The distance from the center to each focus is represented by c, the *focal distance*. The distance from the center to the ellipse's *vertices* (the endpoints of the major axis) is notated as a, the length of the *semimajor axis*. For an ellipse that is elongated horizontally, the major axis is horizontal, while an ellipse elongated vertically has a vertical major axis. The *minor axis* is the chord through the center and perpendicular to the major axis. Its endpoints are sometimes called *co-vertices*, and the distance between a co-vertex and the center is represented by b, the length of the *semiminor axis*.

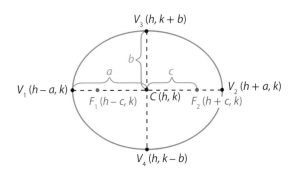

The sum of the distances from the foci to any point $P(x, y)$ on the ellipse, $d_1 + d_2$, can be determined using V_1 on the major axis. Since $V_1F_1 = a - c$ and $V_1F_2 = a + c$, the sum $d_1 + d_2 = (a - c) + (a + c) = 2a$. Therefore, the constant sum in the definition is the length of the major axis.

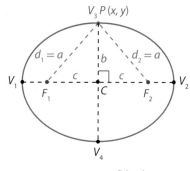

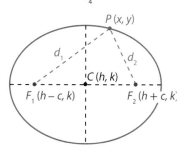

The relationships between a, b, and c can be determined by examining V_3 on the minor axis. Since the two right triangles formed are congruent and the sum of the distances from the foci is $2a$, the distance from V_3 to each focus is a. The Pythagorean Theorem indicates that $b^2 + c^2 = a^2$ or $c^2 = a^2 - b^2$. This implies $a > b$ and $a > c$.

The definition of an ellipse can be used to derive a standard form equation of an ellipse with a horizontal major axis centered at $C(h, k)$ whose foci $F(h \pm c, k)$ are c units from the center.

Applying the distance formula to any point $P(x, y)$ on the ellipse:
$$PF_1 + PF_2 = 2a.$$

$$\sqrt{[x - (h - c)]^2 + (y - k)^2} + \sqrt{[x - (h + c)]^2 + (y - k)^2} = 2a$$

Regroup the terms using the Associative Property of Addition.
$$\sqrt{[(x - h) + c]^2 + (y - k)^2} + \sqrt{[(x - h) - c]^2 + (y - k)^2} = 2a$$

Isolate a radical and square both sides.
$$\sqrt{[(x - h) + c]^2 + (y - k)^2} = 2a - \sqrt{[(x - h) - c]^2 + (y - k)^2}$$
$$[(x - h) + c]^2 + (y - k)^2 = 4a^2 - 4a\sqrt{[(x - h) - c]^2 + (y - k)^2} + [(x - h) - c]^2 + (y - k)^2$$

Subtract $(y - k)^2$ from both sides and expand the binomials outside the radicals.
$$(x - h)^2 + 2c(x - h) + c^2 = 4a^2 - 4a\sqrt{[(x - h) - c]^2 + (y - k)^2} + (x - h)^2 - 2c(x - h) + c^2$$

Isolate the radical term and simplify.
$$4a\sqrt{[(x - h) - c]^2 + (y - k)^2} = 4a^2 - 4c(x - h)$$
$$a\sqrt{[(x - h) - c]^2 + (y - k)^2} = a^2 - c(x - h)$$

Square both sides and expand the left side, keeping $(x - h)$ and $(y - k)$ intact.
$$a^2\{[(x - h) - c]^2 + (y - k)^2\} = a^4 - 2a^2c(x - h) + c^2(x - h)^2$$
$$a^2[(x - h)^2 - 2c(x - h) + c^2 + (y - k)^2] = a^4 - 2a^2c(x - h) + c^2(x - h)^2$$
$$a^2(x - h)^2 - 2a^2c(x - h) + a^2c^2 + a^2(y - k)^2 = a^4 - 2a^2c(x - h) + c^2(x - h)^2$$

Collect all terms containing x or y on the left side and the other terms on the right.
$$a^2(x - h)^2 - c^2(x - h)^2 + a^2(y - k)^2 = a^4 - a^2c^2$$

Factor $(x - h)^2$ from the first two terms on the left and a^2 on the right side.
$$(a^2 - c^2)(x - h)^2 + a^2(y - k)^2 = a^2(a^2 - c^2)$$

Since $b^2 + c^2 = a^2$, substitute using $b^2 = a^2 - c^2$.
$$b^2(x - h)^2 + a^2(y - k)^2 = a^2b^2$$

Finally, divide both sides by a^2b^2.
$$\frac{b^2(x - h)^2}{a^2b^2} + \frac{a^2(y - k)^2}{a^2b^2} = \frac{a^2b^2}{a^2b^2}$$
$$\frac{(x - h)^2}{a^2} + \frac{(y - k)^2}{b^2} = 1$$

An ellipse with a horizontal major axis, center at $(0, 0)$, and foci at $(\pm c, 0)$ has the standard form equation $\frac{x^2}{a^2} + \frac{y^2}{b^2} = 1$. Its inverse, $\frac{y^2}{a^2} + \frac{x^2}{b^2} = 1$, is an ellipse with a vertical major axis, center at $(0, 0)$, and foci at $(0, \pm c)$. Translations of these vertically elongated ellipses to a center at $C(h, k)$ could be written as $\frac{(y - k)^2}{a^2} + \frac{(x - h)^2}{b^2} = 1$ or in the standard form stated in the following table.

Standard Form Equations of an Ellipse
centered at $C(h, k)$ with $a > b$ and $c^2 = a^2 - b^2$

$\dfrac{(x-h)^2}{a^2} + \dfrac{(y-k)^2}{b^2} = 1$	$\dfrac{(x-h)^2}{b^2} + \dfrac{(y-k)^2}{a^2} = 1$

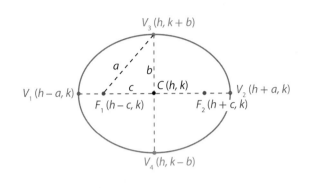

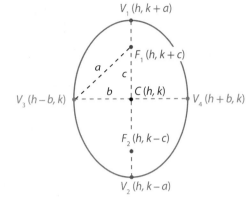

horizontal on $y = k$	**major axis**	vertical on $x = h$
$(h \pm a, k)$	**vertices**	$(h, k \pm a)$
vertical on $x = h$	**minor axis**	horizontal on $y = k$
$(h, k \pm b)$	**co-vertices**	$(h \pm b, k)$
$(h \pm c, k)$	**foci**	$(h, k \pm c)$

Example 1   Graphing an Ellipse

Graph each ellipse and its foci.

a. $\dfrac{(x+3)^2}{25} + \dfrac{(y-1)^2}{9} = 1$

b. $4x^2 + 3y^2 = 48$

Answer

a.

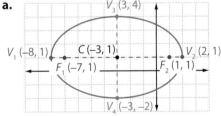

1. Identify and plot the center: $C(h, k) = (-3, 1)$.
2. Since $a^2 = 25$, use $a = 5$ to plot the vertices: $(-3 \pm 5, 1)$.
3. Since $b^2 = 9$, use $b = 3$ to plot the co-vertices: $(-3, 1 \pm 3)$.
4. Sketch the ellipse.
5. Since $c^2 = 25 - 9 = 16$, use $c = 4$ to plot the foci: $(-3 \pm 4, 1)$.

b. $\dfrac{4x^2}{48} + \dfrac{3y^2}{48} = \dfrac{48}{48}, \dfrac{x^2}{12} + \dfrac{y^2}{16} = 1$

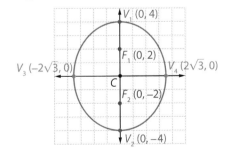

1. Convert to the standard form for an ellipse by dividing both sides by 48.
2. The ellipse has a vertical major axis and is centered at the origin.
3. Since $a^2 = 16$, use $a = 4$ to plot the vertices: $(0, \pm 4)$.
4. Since $b^2 = 12$, use $b \approx 3.5$ to plot the co-vertices: $(\pm 2\sqrt{3}, 0)$.
5. Sketch the ellipse.
6. Since $c^2 = 16 - 12 = 4$, use $c = 2$ to plot the foci: $(0, \pm 2)$.

SKILL ✓ **EXERCISE 7**

When the equation of an ellipse is written in general form for conics, convert the equation to a standard form for an ellipse to reveal the center and the lengths of the semimajor and semiminor axes. You will likely need to complete the square for both the x-terms and the y-terms.

Example 2 Converting to Standard Form

Convert $4x^2 + 16y^2 - 8x + 64y + 4 = 0$ to a standard form for an ellipse.

Answer

$$(4x^2 - 8x) + (16y^2 + 64y) = -4$$

1. Group the x-terms and the y-terms on the left side and the constant on the right.

$$4(x^2 - 2x) + 16(y^2 + 4y) = -4$$
$$4(x^2 - 2x + 1) + 16(y^2 + 4y + 4) = -4 + 4 + 64$$
$$4(x - 1)^2 + 16(y + 2)^2 = 64$$
$$\frac{(x - 1)^2}{16} + \frac{(y + 2)^2}{4} = 1$$

2. Complete the square for both variables.

3. Divide both sides by 64.

SKILL ✓ **EXERCISE 13**

You can also use characteristics of an ellipse to determine its standard form equation.

Example 3 Writing the Equation of an Ellipse

Write the equation of the ellipse with foci at $\left(2, \pm\sqrt{21}\right)$ and a minor axis that is 4 units long.

Answer

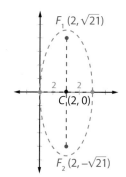

$c = \sqrt{21}; b = 2$

1. Use a sketch to determine the center $(2, 0)$ and the values of c and b.

$21 = a^2 - 4$
$25 = a^2$
$a = 5$

2. Use $c^2 = a^2 - b^2$ to find the value of a.

$$\frac{(x - 2)^2}{2^2} + \frac{(y - 0)^2}{5^2} = 1$$
$$\frac{(x - 2)^2}{4} + \frac{y^2}{25} = 1$$

3. Since the major axis is vertical, substitute into $\frac{(x - h)^2}{b^2} + \frac{(y - k)^2}{a^2} = 1$ and simplify.

SKILL ✓ **EXERCISE 17**

The equation for the ellipse in Example 3 can be written in the general form for conics, $Ax^2 + Bxy + Cy^2 + Dx + Ey + F = 0$ (by multiplying by 100 and simplifying) as $25x^2 + 4y^2 - 100x = 0$. From this form you can see that the ellipse has not been rotated (since $B = 0$) or translated vertically (since $E = 0$). The fact that A and C have the same sign (and therefore $AC > 0$) indicates that the equation represents an ellipse.

When $A = C$, the equation represents a circle, a special case of an ellipse where both foci are at the center. In this case $c = 0$ and $a = b = r$. Dividing the standard form equation of a circle $(x - h)^2 + (y - k)^2 = r^2$ by r^2 converts the equation into the standard form for an ellipse: $\frac{(x - h)^2}{r^2} + \frac{(y - k)^2}{r^2} = 1$.

Example 4 Describing a Circle in Terms of an Ellipse

Convert $x^2 + y^2 + 4x - 6y - 3 = 0$ to a standard form of an ellipse and graph the conic section.

Answer

$$(x^2 + 4x) + (y^2 - 6y) = 3$$
$$(x^2 + 4x + 4) + (y^2 - 6y + 9) = 3 + 4 + 9$$
$$(x + 2)^2 + (y - 3)^2 = 16$$

1. Complete the square for the x- and y-terms.

$$\frac{(x + 2)^2}{16} + \frac{(y - 3)^2}{16} = 1$$

2. Divide by 16 to write in the standard form of an ellipse.

$C(-2, 3); a = b = 4 = r$
$c^2 = 16 - 16 = 0$
$\therefore$ foci at $(-2 \pm 0, 3 \pm 0) = (-2, 3)$

3. Since $a = b$, the ellipse is a circle, and both foci are located at the center.

4. Graph the circle centered at $(-2, 3)$ with a radius of 4.

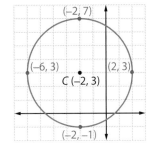

SKILL ✔ EXERCISE 25

An ellipse's amount of elongation from a circle is measured by its *eccentricity*, defined as $e = \frac{c}{a}$.

Example 5 Determining the Eccentricity of an Ellipse

Find the eccentricity of each ellipse.

a.

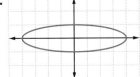

b.

TIP

Note that e is used for both the irrational number $e \approx 2.718$ and the eccentricity of a conic. The symbol's context is used to distinguish its meaning.

Answer

a. $a = 4, b = 1$

$c^2 = 4^2 - 1^2 = 15$

$c = \sqrt{15}$

$e = \frac{c}{a}$

$= \frac{\sqrt{15}}{4} \approx 0.968$

b. $a = 2, b = 1$

$c^2 = 2^2 - 1^2 = 3$

$c = \sqrt{3}$

$e = \frac{c}{a}$

$= \frac{\sqrt{3}}{2} \approx 0.866$

1. Find the lengths of the semimajor and semiminor axes.
2. Use $c^2 = a^2 - b^2$ to find the value of c.

3. Apply the definition of eccentricity.

SKILL ✔ EXERCISE 5

The more elongated ellipse has greater eccentricity since the foci's distance from the center, c, is greater and the foci are closer to the vertices. In any ellipse $0 \leq c < a$ and $0 \leq e < 1$. The eccentricity of a circle is 0 since $c = 0$.

Kepler's first law of planetary motion states that the orbit of a planet is an ellipse with the sun at one of the foci. The point at which an orbiting object is closest to the sun is the *perihelion*, while its farthest point from the sun is the *aphelion*. These distances are frequently measured in astronomical units (AU), which are multiples of the earth's average distance from the sun. The average eccentricity of the sun's planets is a nearly circular $e \approx 0.0601$.

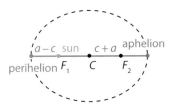

Example 6 **Modeling a Planet's Orbit**

Write an equation modeling the orbit of Mercury if its aphelion is 0.467 AU from the sun and its perihelion is 0.307 AU away. Then graph the ellipse using technology and find its eccentricity, the highest of any of the sun's planets.

Answer

$2a = 0.307 + 0.467 = 0.774$
$\quad a = 0.387$

1. Use the fact that the length of the major axis is the sum of the distances from the sun to the perihelion and the aphelion to find a.

$c = a - (a - c) = 0.387 - 0.307 = 0.08$

2. Determine the value of c by subtracting the perihelion distance from a.

$b^2 = a^2 - c^2 = 0.387^2 - 0.08^2 \approx 0.143$

3. Determine the value of b^2 using $c^2 = a^2 - b^2$.

$\dfrac{x^2}{0.387^2} + \dfrac{y^2}{0.143} \approx 1$

$\dfrac{x^2}{0.150} + \dfrac{y^2}{0.143} \approx 1$

4. Substitute into the standard form equation $\dfrac{x^2}{a^2} + \dfrac{y^2}{b^2} = 1$ and simplify.

$\dfrac{y^2}{0.143} \approx 1 - \dfrac{x^2}{0.150}$

$y^2 \approx 0.143\left(1 - \dfrac{x^2}{0.150}\right)$

$y \approx \pm\sqrt{0.143\left(1 - \dfrac{x^2}{0.150}\right)}$

5. Solve the equation for y.

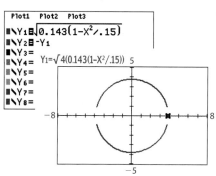

6. Graph the two functions that model the ellipse in a square window to avoid distortion. Remember that parts of the graphs may not display. Use TRACE or [TABLE] to verify points that are not displayed.

$e = \dfrac{c}{a} = \dfrac{0.08}{0.387} \approx 0.207$

7. Find the eccentricity of the orbit.

Kepler's laws are specifically stated in terms of planets orbiting the sun, but they also model the orbit of natural and manmade satellites about the earth and other planets.

SKILL ✓ EXERCISE 35

Rotating an ellipse about the major axis forms an ellipsoid in which signals emitted from one focus are reflected off the ellipsoid and pass through its other focus. Exercise 32 investigates how a lithotripter applies this property with ultra high frequency (UHF) shockwaves to break up kidney stones without surgery.

❯ **A. Exercises**

State the coordinates of the center and the length of the major and the minor axis for each ellipse.

1. $\dfrac{x^2}{9} + \dfrac{y^2}{25} = 1$

2. $\dfrac{(x-2)^2}{16} + (y+1)^2 = 1$

State the coordinates of the center, the vertices, and the co-vertices for each ellipse.

3. $\dfrac{x^2}{25} + \dfrac{y^2}{49} = 1$

4. $\dfrac{(x-3)^2}{36} + \dfrac{(y+5)^2}{9} = 1$

State the coordinates for the vertices and the foci for each ellipse, then calculate its eccentricity.

5. $\dfrac{(x+1)^2}{9} + \dfrac{(y-3)^2}{25} = 1$

6. $\dfrac{(x+6)^2}{12} + \dfrac{(y+2)^2}{4} = 1$

Graph each ellipse and its foci.

7. $\dfrac{x^2}{16} + \dfrac{y^2}{4} = 1$

8. $\dfrac{x^2}{4} + \dfrac{y^2}{9} = 1$

9. $(x+1)^2 + \dfrac{(y-5)^2}{4} = 1$

10. $\dfrac{(x-2)^2}{9} + \dfrac{(y-2)^2}{4} = 1$

Write each equation in standard form. Then identify the conic as an ellipse or a circle.

11. $16x^2 + 4y^2 = 64$

12. $x^2 + y^2 - 6x - 2y = -1$

13. $25x^2 + 9y^2 - 54y = 144$

14. $16x^2 + 9y^2 + 128x - 54y = -193$

Write the standard form equation of each described ellipse.

15. vertices: $(-3, 9)$, $(-3, 1)$
    co-vertices: $(-5, 5)$, $(-1, 5)$

16. vertices: $(7, -4)$, $(-3, -4)$
    co-vertices: $(2, -1)$, $(2, -7)$

17. vertices: $(-3, 2)$, $(11, 2)$
    length of minor axis: 4

18. co-vertices: $(-8, 3)$, $(-2, 3)$
    length of major axis: 12

19. co-vertices: $(-5, 1)$, $(1, 1)$
    foci: $(-2, 5)$, $(-2, -3)$

20. foci: $(-11, -2)$, $(5, -2)$
    length of major axis: 34

> **B. Exercises**

21. Write the standard form equation of an ellipse centered at the origin with an eccentricity of 0.6, a semi-major axis length of 5, and a horizontal major axis.

22. Write the standard form equation of an ellipse centered at $(4, 1)$ with an eccentricity of 0.28, a semi-major axis length of 25, and a vertical major axis.

Graph each ellipse and its foci. State the eccentricity of the ellipse.

23. $x^2 + 25y^2 = 100$

24. $4x^2 + y^2 = 16$

25. $x^2 + y^2 - 2x + 4y + 1 = 0$

26. $25x^2 + 16y^2 + 150x + 128y + 81 = 0$

27. $9x^2 + 36y^2 - 36x - 144y + 36 = 0$

28. $9x^2 + 81y^2 - 108x + 324y = 81$

Use technology to graph each conic.

29. $\dfrac{(x + 1)^2}{4} + \dfrac{(y - 2)^2}{9} = 1$

30. $(x - 4.2)^2 + (y + 1.6)^2 = 5.75$

31. A mirror frame is being cut so the opening is an 18 in. wide and 32 in. high ellipse. Write the standard form equation modeling the ellipse if it is centered at the origin. Then find the foci and the string length needed to draw the ellipse.

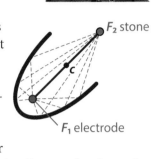

32. A lithotripter is a medical device used to break up kidney stones. Shock waves generated by an electrode at one focus of a half ellipsoidal chamber are reflected toward a kidney stone positioned at the second focus. If the semimajor axis measures 50 mm and the minor axis measures 15 mm, find the distance the electrode should be positioned from the kidney stone.

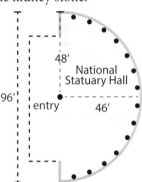

33. Due to its semi-elliptical design, National Statuary Hall in the US Capitol is known as a whispering gallery. If the room is 96 ft long and 46 ft wide, find the distance the foci are from the wall, and then find the eccentricity.

34. The earth travels around the sun in an elliptical path with the sun at one focus. The semimajor axis of the ellipse is about 1.49×10^8 km. If the eccentricity of its orbit is 0.017, find the perihelion and the aphelion.

35. If the orbit of Mars has a semimajor axis of 1.52 AU and an eccentricity of 0.0934, write a standard form equation modeling its orbit, and then find the perihelion and aphelion.

Graph without the aid of technology.

36. $f(x) = 3\sqrt{1 - x^2}$

37. $f(x) = \dfrac{2\sqrt{9 - x^2}}{3}$

> **C. Exercises**

Graph the solution to each system of inequalities.

38. $x^2 + y^2 - 6x - 2y + 1 \leq 0$
    $4x^2 + 25y^2 - 24x - 50y - 39 \leq 0$

39. $4x^2 + 9y^2 + 48x - 90y + 225 \leq 0$
    $x^2 + y^2 + 8x - 10y + 40 \geq 0$

40. Derive: Complete each step to derive the formula for the area of an ellipse: $A_{ellipse} = \pi ab$.

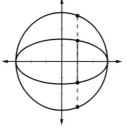

  a. Write the equation for the standard form of an ellipse centered at the origin and solve for y.

  b. Write the equation for the standard form of a circle centered at the origin with $r = a$ and solve for y.

  c. What is the ratio of corresponding vertical chords of the circle and the ellipse?

  d. Write a proportion using the fact that the areas of the ellipse and circle also have this ratio (Cavalieri's principle) and solve to derive the formula for the area of an ellipse.

41. Write a function that models the top curve of the window. Then use the formula for the area of an ellipse, $A_{ellipse} = \pi ab$, to find the area of the window to the nearest square inch.

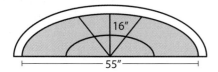

42. Prove: The focal width of an ellipse is defined as the length of the chord through a focus and perpendicular to the major axis. Show that the ellipse $\dfrac{x^2}{a^2} + \dfrac{y^2}{b^2} = 1$ has a focal width of
$$P_1 P_2 = 2\left(\frac{b^2}{a}\right).$$

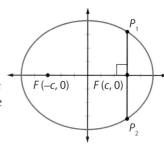

43. Prove: Sketch an ellipse with a vertical major axis centered at $C(h, k)$ with foci $F(h, k \pm c)$ and semimajor and semiminor axis lengths of a and b, respectively, where $c^2 = a^2 - b^2$. Then use the definition of an ellipse and the distances to any point $P(x, y)$ to derive its standard form equation.

CUMULATIVE REVIEW

Graph each function as a transformation of a parent function. [1.5]

44. $g(x) = \dfrac{1}{x-3}$

45. $h(x) = \dfrac{1}{2}|x + 2| - 2$

Graph the parabola, its focus, and its directrix. [8.1]

46. $y = \dfrac{1}{2}(x-2)^2 - 3$

47. $x = -\dfrac{1}{4}(y+1)^2 - 2$

State the maximum number of real zeros and relative extrema for each function. Then find the real zeros. [2.2]

48. $y = 4x^4 - 36x^3 + 32x^2$

49. $y = 5x^6 - 25x^5 - 70x^4$

50. Classify the graph of $r = 2\cos\theta$. [6.4]

  A. hyperbola

  B. parabola

  C. ellipse

  D. circle centered on the polar axis

  E. circle centered on $\theta = \dfrac{\pi}{2}$

51. Shawna makes an initial investment of $5000. How much does she have after 10 yr if the interest is 4.5% compounded continuously? [3.1]

  A. $7841.56

  B. $7764.85

  C. $5230.14

  D. $450,085.66

  E. none of these

52. A 52° central angle of a circle intercepts an arc whose length is 358 ft. What is the radius of the circle (to the nearest foot)? [4.1]

  A. 539 ft

  B. 788 ft

  C. 160 ft

  D. 394 ft

  E. none of these

53. Find xy if $x = \dfrac{\sqrt{3}u - v}{2}$ and $y = \dfrac{u + \sqrt{3}v}{2}$. [Algebra]

  A. $\dfrac{\sqrt{3}u^2 - 2uv - \sqrt{3}v^2}{4}$

  B. $\dfrac{\sqrt{3}u^2 + 2uv - \sqrt{3}v^2}{4}$

  C. $\dfrac{\sqrt{3}u^2 - 2uv + \sqrt{3}v^2}{4}$

  D. $\dfrac{\sqrt{3}u^2 + 2uv - \sqrt{3}v^2}{2}$

  E. none of these

Do you, Mr. Al Gebra, take Miss Geome Trie...

ANALYTIC GEOMETRY

Geometry has a rich history that is thousands of years old and includes observations by astronomers and mathematicians dating back to before the time of Moses. Analytic geometry, on the other hand, is not yet 400 yr old and was pioneered by a philosopher and a lawyer. René Descartes (1596–1650), the philosopher, was primarily concerned with geometry as a vehicle to demonstrate the validity of his method for discovering truth and published just one mathematical work. Pierre de Fermat (1607–65), the lawyer, was really more interested in number theory than geometry. Together these men are considered the cofounders of analytic geometry.

Descartes's *The Geometry* was the third appendix to his philosophical treatise, *Discourse on the Method*. According to Ian Maclean, professor emeritus at the Univerisity of Oxford, the work's publication in 1637 "marks the moment … at which geometry and algebra ceased being separate." While geometers had previously used algebra in a limited way, Descartes described how to convert any geometric problem into an algebraic equation or system of equations. Once solved, the answer could be reinterpreted with a geometric construction. The key to Descartes's method was a system of coordinates that allowed the easy location of any point in the plane

(analytic geometry is sometimes called *coordinate geometry*). The modern practices of using a lowercase letter to denote the length of a line, using the first letters of the alphabet to denote constants and the last letters to denote variables, and consistently using exponents all had their origins in *The Geometry*.

Only one of Fermat's many mathematical works was published in his lifetime ("Concerning the Comparison of Curved Lines with Straight Lines"), but through frequent written correspondence with French mathematician Marin Mersenne, his papers were widely circulated among mathematicians. One of Fermat's projects was restoring an ancient Greek manuscript on the loci of plane curves, written by Apollonius. This is apparently where Fermat developed the idea that all equations can be represented as curves in the plane. His algebraic representations of parabolas, hyperbolas, and spirals are still used today. In correspondence with French mathematician Gilles Personne de Roberval in 1636, Fermat detailed the results of his analytic geometry that were eventually published posthumously as "Introduction to Plane and Solid Loci."

Isaac Newton added an extensive appendix on analytic geometry in his *Opticks* (1704) that included 72 "species" of cubic equations, with a sketch of each. Euler's 1748 *Introduction to the Analysis of the Infinite* contained a "systematic treatise on analytic geometry in the sense of Fermat," according to mathematics historian Carl Boyer, who calls Euler's book "probably the most influential textbook of modern times." In the nineteenth century Julius Plucker devoted a lifetime of study to analytic geometry, paving the way for modern breakthroughs in specialized branches of this subject that originated with the work of Descartes and Fermat.

COMPREHENSION CHECK

1. List the cofounders of analytic geometry and the primary occupation of each.

2. Describe the motivation of each cofounder of analytic geometry.

3. Name three other scientist-mathematicians who made major contributions to analytic geometry.

4. In *Principles of Philosophy* Descartes claims, "in order to seek truth, it is necessary once in the course of our life, to doubt, as far as possible, of all things." Is this statement consistent with a biblical worldview? Why or why not?

The equation of a hyperbola can be written to model the possible positions of a lightning strike.

After completing this section, you will be able to

- define a hyperbola.
- analyze and graph a hyperbola.
- write the equation of a hyperbola.
- solve real-world problems related to hyperbolas.

Recall that parabolas and ellipses intersect a single nappe of a right circular conical surface, while a hyperbola intersects both nappes of the surface. Compare the definitions and characteristics of a hyperbola and an ellipse and note their similarities and differences.

> **DEFINITION**
>
> A **hyperbola** is the set of points $P(x, y)$ in a plane such that the difference of the distances from two fixed points (its foci) is constant.

A hyperbola consists of two disjoint, symmetrical curves called *branches*. The *vertices* are the intersections of each branch and the line containing its foci (F_1 and F_2). The segment connecting the vertices is the hyperbola's *transverse axis* and its midpoint is the hyperbola's *center*. The *conjugate axis* is a segment through the center and perpendicular to the transverse axis. While the conjugate axis does not intersect the hyperbola, the endpoints are the *co-vertices*.

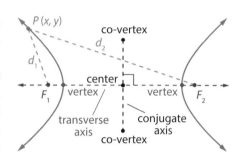

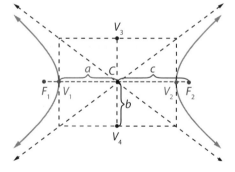

The characteristic distances a, b, and c are similar to those of the ellipse, but they are related differently. The hyperbola's *focal distance* is the distance from the center to each focus, c. The length of the *semitransverse axis* is the distance from the hyperbola's center to either vertex, a. The length of the *semiconjugate axis* is the distance from the center to each co-vertex, b, where $b^2 = c^2 - a^2$ (or $c^2 = a^2 + b^2$). This implies $c > a$, $c > b$, and that a may be greater than, less than, or equal to b. The vertices and co-vertices can be used to draw a rectangle whose diagonals are asymptotes of the hyperbola's branches.

The difference of the distances from the foci can be determined using V_1 on the transverse axis. Since $V_1F_2 = a + c$ and $V_1F_1 = c - a$, the difference is $(a + c) - (c - a) = 2a$, the length of the transverse axis. By definition, the difference is constant for any point on the hyperbola.

The definition of a hyperbola can then be used to derive a standard form equation for a hyperbola with a horizontal transverse axis centered at $C(h, k)$ whose foci $F(h \pm c, k)$ are c units from the center.

Applying the distance formula to the point $P(x, y)$ on the hyperbola:

$$PF_1 - PF_2 = 2a.$$

$$\sqrt{[x - (h - c)]^2 + (y - k)^2} - \sqrt{[x - (h + c)]^2 + (y - k)^2} = 2a$$

Regroup the terms, using the Associative Property of Addition.

$$\sqrt{[(x - h) + c]^2 + (y - k)^2} - \sqrt{[(x - h) - c]^2 + (y - k)^2} = 2a$$

Isolate a radical and square both sides.

$$\sqrt{[(x-h)+c]^2+(y-k)^2} = 2a + \sqrt{[(x-h)-c]^2+(y-k)^2}$$
$$[(x-h)+c]^2+(y-k)^2 = 4a^2 + 4a\sqrt{[(x-h)-c]^2+(y-k)^2} + [(x-h)-c]^2+(y-k)^2$$

Subtract $(y-k)^2$ from both sides and expand the binomials outside the radical.

$$(x-h)^2+2c(x-h)+c^2 = 4a^2 + 4a\sqrt{[(x-h)-c]^2+(y-k)^2} + (x-h)^2-2c(x-h)+c^2$$

Isolate the radical term and simplify, keeping $(x-h)$ and $(y-k)$ intact.

$$4c(x-h)-4a^2 = 4a\sqrt{[(x-h)-c]^2+(y-k)^2}$$
$$c(x-h)-a^2 = a\sqrt{[(x-h)-c]^2+(y-k)^2}$$

Square both sides and use the Distributive Property to expand the right side.

$$c^2(x-h)^2 - 2a^2c(x-h) + a^4 = a^2\{[(x-h)-c]^2+(y-k)^2\}$$
$$c^2(x-h)^2 - 2a^2c(x-h) + a^4 = a^2[(x-h)^2-2c(x-h)+c^2+(y-k)^2]$$
$$c^2(x-h)^2 - 2a^2c(x-h) + a^4 = a^2(x-h)^2 - 2a^2c(x-h) + a^2c^2 + a^2(y-k)^2$$

Collect all terms containing x or y on the left side and all other terms on the right.

$$c^2(x-h)^2 - a^2(x-h)^2 - a^2(y-k)^2 = a^2c^2 - a^4$$

Factor $(x-h)^2$ from the first two terms on the left and a^2 from the right side.

$$(c^2-a^2)(x-h)^2 - a^2(y-k)^2 = a^2(c^2-a^2)$$

Since $b^2 = c^2 - a^2$ in a hyperbola, substitute and divide both sides by a^2b^2.

$$b^2(x-h)^2 - a^2(y-k)^2 = a^2b^2$$
$$\frac{b^2(x-h)^2}{a^2b^2} - \frac{a^2(y-k)^2}{a^2b^2} = \frac{a^2b^2}{a^2b^2}$$
$$\frac{(x-h)^2}{a^2} - \frac{(y-k)^2}{b^2} = 1$$

In his seventeenth-century work "Introduction to Plane and Solid Loci," Fermat stated that a hyperbola was the locus of points represented by the second-degree equation "A in E aequetur Z plano" (or $xy = k^2$ in modern notation).

The central rectangle can be used to find the hyperbola's asymptotes. Consider the hyperbola $\frac{x^2}{a^2} - \frac{y^2}{b^2} = 1$, which is centered at the origin and has a horizontal transverse axis. Clearing fractions produces $b^2x^2 - a^2y^2 = a^2b^2$, and solving for y produces $y^2 = \frac{b^2(x^2-a^2)}{a^2}$ and $y = \pm\frac{b}{a}\sqrt{x^2-a^2}$. As $x \to \pm\infty$, the subtraction of a^2 becomes insignificant and $\sqrt{x^2-a^2} \to \sqrt{x^2}$ or x, but is never equal to x. Therefore, the hyperbola $y = \pm\frac{b}{a}\sqrt{x^2-a^2}$ approaches its asymptotes $y = \pm\frac{b}{a}x$, lines intersecting at the hyperbola's center $(0,0)$ with slopes of $\frac{b}{a}$ and $-\frac{b}{a}$.

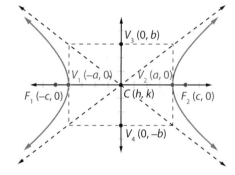

A similar derivation for the inverse hyperbola $\frac{y^2}{a^2} - \frac{x^2}{b^2} = 1$, which is centered at the origin with a vertical transverse axis, yields oblique asymptotes of $y = \pm\frac{a}{b}x$. When a hyperbola is translated, the asymptotes experience the same translation.

Notice that the signs of the squared terms in the standard form determine the orientation of the transverse axis.

Standard Form Equations of a Hyperbola
centered at $C(h, k)$ with $c^2 = a^2 + b^2$

$$\frac{(x-h)^2}{a^2} - \frac{(y-k)^2}{b^2} = 1 \qquad\qquad \frac{(y-k)^2}{a^2} - \frac{(x-h)^2}{b^2} = 1$$

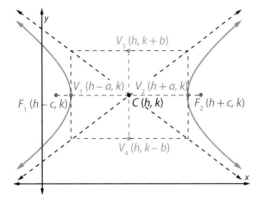
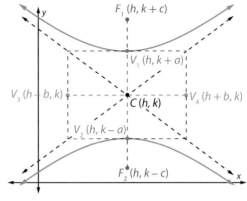

horizontal on $y = k$	**transverse axis**	vertical on $x = h$
$(h \pm a, k)$	**vertices**	$(h, k \pm a)$
vertical on $x = h$	**minor axis**	horizontal on $y = k$
$(h, k \pm b)$	**co-vertices**	$(h \pm b, k)$
$F(h \pm c, k)$	**foci**	$F(h, k \pm c)$
$y = \pm \frac{b}{a}(x - h) + k$	**asymptotes**	$y = \pm \frac{a}{b}(x - h) + k$

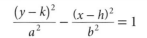
Example 1   Graphing a Hyperbola

Graph $\dfrac{x^2}{9} - \dfrac{(y-2)^2}{16} = 1$ and its foci. Then state the equations of its asymptotes.

Answer

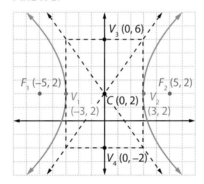

asymptotes: $y = \pm \frac{4}{3}(x - 0) + 2$ or

$\qquad\qquad y = \pm \frac{4}{3}x + 2$

1. Note that the hyperbola has a horizontal transverse axis at $y = 2$ since the x^2-term is positive.
2. Identify and plot the center: $C(0, 2)$.
3. Sketch the central rectangle using $a = 3$ and $b = 4$ and draw the asymptotes.
4. Plot the vertices: $(0 \pm 3, 2)$.
5. Sketch the hyperbola through its vertices and approaching its asymptotes.
6. Since $c^2 = 9 + 16 = 25$, use $c = 5$ to plot the foci: $(\pm 5, 2)$.
7. Substitute into $y = \pm \frac{b}{a}(x - h)^2 + k$ and simplify.

SKILL ✓ **EXERCISE 13**

Like an ellipse, the eccentricity of a hyperbola is defined as $e = \frac{c}{a}$. In any hyperbola $c > a$, so its eccentricity is always greater than 1. When e is close to 1, the foci are near the vertices and the branches are near the transverse axis. As e increases, the foci are farther from the vertices and the hyperbola's branches are wider. In Section 8.6 you will see that the eccentricity of any parabola is 1.

Notice how a conic's eccentricity (the measure of its deviation from a circle) increases as the intersecting plane deviates from being perpendicular to the axis of the conical surface.

Circle	Ellipse	Parabola	Hyperbola
$e = 0$	$0 \le e < 1$	$e = 1$	$e > 1$

Example 2   Analyzing a Hyperbola

Given the hyperbola $9x^2 - 4y^2 + 18x + 8y + 41 = 0$, identify its center, vertices, co-vertices, foci, eccentricity, and asymptotes.

Answer

$9(x^2 + 2x) - 4(y^2 - 2y) = -41$
$9(x^2 + 2x + 1) - 4(y^2 - 2y + 1) = -41 + 9 - 4$
$9(x + 1)^2 - 4(y - 1)^2 = -36$
$$\frac{(y - 1)^2}{9} - \frac{(x + 1)^2}{4} = 1$$

$C(-1, 1)$
$a = 3; b = 2$

vertices: $(-1, 1 \pm 3) = (-1, 4)$ and $(-1, -2)$
co-vertices: $(-1 \pm 2, 1) = (1, 1)$ and $(-3, 1)$
$c^2 = 9 + 4 = 13; c = \sqrt{13}$
$F\left(-1, 1 \pm \sqrt{13}\right) \approx (-1, 4.6)$ and $(-1, -2.6)$
$e = \frac{\sqrt{13}}{3} \approx 1.2$

$y = \pm\frac{3}{2}(x + 1) + 1$

$y = \frac{3}{2}x + \frac{5}{2}$ and $y = -\frac{3}{2}x - \frac{1}{2}$

Check

$(y - 1)^2 = 9\left(1 + \frac{(x + 1)^2}{4}\right)$

$y = 1 \pm 3\sqrt{1 + \frac{(x + 1)^2}{4}}$

1. Write the equation in standard form by completing the square for the x- and y-terms and dividing both sides by the constant, -36. Note that the hyperbola has a vertical transverse axis.

2. Use $\frac{(y - k)^2}{a^2} - \frac{(x - h)^2}{b^2} = 1$ to identify the center and the values of a and b.

3. Identify the vertices $(h, k \pm a)$ and co-vertices $(h \pm b, k)$.

4. Use $c^2 = a^2 + b^2$ to find c and identify the foci: $F(h, k \pm c)$.

5. Calculate the eccentricity using $e = \frac{c}{a}$.

6. Use $y = \pm\frac{a}{b}(x - h) + k$ to identify the asymptotes.

7. Solve the standard form equation for y and graph the two functions that form the hyperbola. Then graph the asymptotes.

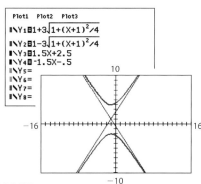

SKILL ✓ **EXERCISE 25**

To write the standard form equation of a hyperbola, determine its center and the lengths a and b. The standard form equation can then be changed to the general quadratic equation used for conics, $Ax^2 + Bxy + Cy^2 + Dx + Ey + F = 0$.

Example 3 Writing the Equation of a Hyperbola

Write a standard form equation for the hyperbola with vertices at (4, 1) and (4, 5) and an eccentricity of $\frac{3}{2}$. Then write an equivalent equation in the general quadratic form for conics.

Answer

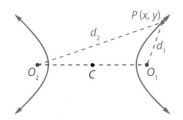

$C(h, k) = \left(\dfrac{4+4}{2}, \dfrac{1+5}{2}\right) = (4, 3)$

1. Sketch the hyperbola and find the center, the midpoint of the transverse axis.

$a = 2$

2. Use the center and vertices to find a.

$\dfrac{c}{2} = \dfrac{3}{2}; c = 3$

3. Use $e = \dfrac{c}{a}$ to find c and $c^2 = a^2 + b^2$ to find b.

$b^2 = c^2 - a^2 = 3^2 - 2^2 = 5; b = \sqrt{5}$

$\dfrac{(y-3)^2}{4} - \dfrac{(x-4)^2}{5} = 1$

4. Substitute into $\dfrac{(y-h)^2}{a^2} - \dfrac{(x-k)^2}{b^2} = 1$.

$5(y-3)^2 - 4(x-4)^2 = 20$
$5y^2 - 30y + 45 - 4x^2 + 32x - 64 = 20$
$-4x^2 + 5y^2 + 32x - 30y - 39 = 0$
$4x^2 - 5y^2 - 32x + 30y + 39 = 0$

5. Multiply both sides by the LCD and expand to convert to the general form for conics. Multiplying by -1 allows the lead coefficient to be positive, which is a common practice.

SKILL ✔ **EXERCISES 27, 33**

Note that $B = 0$ in the general form equation for Example 3, and that A and C have different signs ($AC < 0$). This indicates that the conic is a hyperbola with a horizontal or vertical transverse axis.

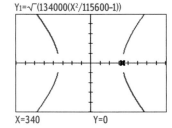

By examining the difference of the distances between a lightning strike and two observers (O_1 and O_2), the equation of a hyperbola can be written to model all possible positions of the strike, the points where this difference of distances $\Delta d = d_1 - d_2 = 2a$. Comparing this hyperbola with a second hyperbola derived from the positions of another set of observers allows the exact location to be found.

Example 4 Modeling the Possible Locations of a Lightning Strike

Eric observes a lightning strike and hears the thunder 2 sec earlier than Abby, who is standing 1 km due east of Eric. If sound travels at 340 m/sec, model the possible locations of the lightning strike by writing the equation of a hyperbola centered at the origin and with the observers at the foci.

Answer

Using $C(0, 0), c = 500$ m.

1. The observers are at the foci (± 500, 0).

$\Delta d = \left(340 \dfrac{m}{sec}\right)(2 \text{ sec}) = 680 \text{ m} = 2a$

2. Use $d = rt$ and the fact that the difference of the distances is $2a$ to find a and a^2.

$a = 340 \text{ m}; a^2 = 115{,}600$

$b^2 = 500^2 - 340^2 = 134{,}400$

3. Use $c^2 = a^2 + b^2$ to find b^2.

Y₁=√(134000(X²/115600−1))

$\dfrac{x^2}{115{,}600} - \dfrac{y^2}{134{,}400} = 1$

4. Substitute into $\dfrac{(x-k)^2}{a^2} - \dfrac{(y-h)^2}{b^2} = 1$.

$\dfrac{x^2}{115{,}600} - 1 = \dfrac{y^2}{134{,}400}$

$y = \pm\sqrt{134{,}400\left(\dfrac{x^2}{115{,}600} - 1\right)}$

5. Solve for y and use technology to plot the possible locations, which are any point on the hyperbola's branches.

X=340   Y=0

SKILL ✔ **EXERCISE 35**

Light rays headed toward one focus of a hyperbolic mirror are reflected to its other focus. In a Cassegrain reflecting telescope, a small hyperbolic mirror is positioned in front of a larger parabolic mirror along the same optical axis so that the paraboloid's focus and one of the hyperboloid's foci coincide. Signals reflected to the parabola's focus reflect off the hyperbolic mirror through a hole in the center of the primary mirror to the hyperbola's other focus.

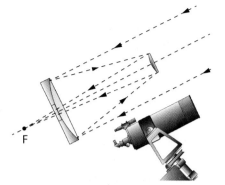

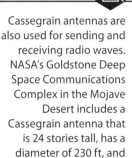

Cassegrain antennas are also used for sending and receiving radio waves. NASA's Goldstone Deep Space Communications Complex in the Mojave Desert includes a Cassegrain antenna that is 24 stories tall, has a diameter of 230 ft, and weighs 16 million lb.

A. Exercises

1. A hyperbola represents all the points in a plane such that the _____ of the distances from two fixed points is _____.

2. The _____ is the segment connecting the vertices of a hyperbola, while the _____ is the segment connecting its co-vertices.

3. Match each formula or expression with its description.

   I. length of the transverse axis

   II. length of the conjugate axis

   III. distance from the center to a focal point

   IV. equation of a hyperbola with a horizontal transverse axis

   V. equation of a hyperbola with a vertical transverse axis

   a. $\dfrac{(y-k)^2}{a^2} - \dfrac{(x-h)^2}{b^2} = 1$

   b. $\dfrac{(x-h)^2}{a^2} - \dfrac{(y-k)^2}{b^2} = 1$

   c. c

   d. $2a$

   e. $2b$

4. Which of the following is true for a hyperbola?

   A. The difference of the distances from any point on the hyperbola to the foci is $2a$.

   B. The distance from the center to a co-vertex is b.

   C. The distance from a vertex to a co-vertex is c.

   D. $c^2 = a^2 + b^2$

   E. All are true statements.

State the coordinates of the center and the lengths of the transverse and conjugate axes for each hyperbola.

5. $\dfrac{x^2}{144} - \dfrac{y^2}{25} = 1$

6. $\dfrac{(y+2)^2}{9} - \dfrac{(x+7)^2}{36} = 1$

State the coordinates of the center, the vertices, and the co-vertices for each hyperbola.

7. $\dfrac{y^2}{64} - \dfrac{x^2}{36} = 1$

8. $\dfrac{(x-1)^2}{16} - \dfrac{(y-5)^2}{36} = 1$

State the coordinates of the center, the vertices, and the foci for each hyperbola. Then calculate its eccentricity.

9. $\dfrac{y^2}{81} - \dfrac{x^2}{144} = 1$

10. $\dfrac{(x-2)^2}{64} - \dfrac{(y+4)^2}{225} = 1$

State the coordinates of the center, the vertices, and the equations of the asymptotes for each hyperbola.

11. $\dfrac{x^2}{9} - \dfrac{y^2}{16} = 1$

12. $\dfrac{(y-1)^2}{4} - \dfrac{(x+2)^2}{9} = 1$

Graph each hyperbola and its foci, stating the equations of its asymptotes.

13. $\dfrac{x^2}{4} - \dfrac{y^2}{9} = 1$

14. $\dfrac{x^2}{25} - \dfrac{y^2}{4} = 1$

15. $\dfrac{y^2}{16} - \dfrac{x^2}{4} = 1$

16. $y^2 - x^2 = 4$

17. $(y+2)^2 - (x-1)^2 = 1$

18. $x^2 - \dfrac{(y-2)^2}{9} = 1$

B. Exercises

Give the center, vertices, and equations of the asymptotes for each hyperbola. Then use technology to graph each hyperbola and its asymptotes.

19. $\dfrac{(x-3)^2}{9} - \dfrac{(y+2)^2}{25} = 1$

20. $\dfrac{(y+1)^2}{4} - \dfrac{(x-4)^2}{9} = 1$

Identify the center, vertices, foci, eccentricity, and asymptotes for each hyperbola.

21. $25(x-6)^2 - 9y^2 = 225$

22. $9(y+7)^2 - 16(x-12)^2 = 144$

23. $16x^2 - 25y^2 - 150y = 625$

24. $y^2 - 9x^2 + 4y - 18x = 14$

25. $4x^2 - y^2 - 40x + 4y = -92$

26. $4y^2 - 49x^2 + 24y - 294x = 601$

Write the standard form equation for each hyperbola with the given characteristics.

27. foci at $(\pm 5, 0)$ and $e = \frac{5}{3}$

28. foci at $(0, \pm 17)$ and $e = \frac{17}{15}$

29. centered at $(2, 4)$, a vertex at $(6, 4)$, and an asymptote $y = x + 2$

30. centered at $(-4, -3)$, a focus at $(-4, 2)$, and a vertex at $(-4, 1)$

Write a general form equation for each hyperbola with the given characteristics.

31. vertices at $(\pm 2, 0)$ and $e = \frac{\sqrt{29}}{2}$

32. vertices at $(-4, 0)$ and $(2, 0)$ and $e = \sqrt{5}$

33. vertices at $(7, 1)$ and $(7, 9)$ and $e = \frac{\sqrt{65}}{4}$

34. vertices at $(10, -21)$ and $(10, -15)$ and $e = \frac{\sqrt{13}}{3}$

35. Jayden hears the firing of a cannon 3 sec before Olivia. If Olivia is 2000 m south of Jayden and the sound traveled at 340 m/sec, write the equation of a hyperbola centered at the origin and modeling the possible locations of the cannon. Then use technology to plot the possible locations.

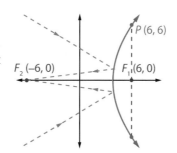

36. The focal width of a hyperbola is defined as the length of a chord through a focus and perpendicular to the line containing its foci. A proof similar to exercise 42 in Section 8.2 shows that the hyperbola $\frac{x^2}{a^2} - \frac{y^2}{b^2} = 1$ has a focal width of $2\left(\frac{b^2}{a}\right)$.

Use this fact to find the equation of a hyperbola modeling the illustrated mirror that reflects light rays headed toward its focus at $(0, 6)$ to its other focus at $(-6, 0)$ if its focal width is 12.

$F_2\,(-6, 0)$ $F_1\,(6, 0)$ $P\,(6, 6)$

> **C. Exercises**

37. State the center, vertices, and equations of the asymptotes for $\frac{(y + 1)^2}{5} - \frac{(x - 4)^2}{8} = 1$. Then use technology to graph the hyperbola and its asymptotes.

38. Graph each degenerate hyperbola.

   a. $x^2 - 4y^2 = 0$ **b.** $\frac{y^2}{16} - \frac{(x - 3)^2}{9} = 0$

Graph each hyperbolic inequality.

39. $\frac{x^2}{9} - \frac{(y - 1)^2}{4} \geq 1$ 40. $y^2 - x^2 < 9$

41. The LORAN (long range navigation) network was developed during World War II to guide ships and airplanes across the ocean. The difference in the times required to receive radio signals broadcasted simultaneously from a master station and each of two substations was used to determine two hyperbolic equations modeling the receiver's possible location. The vessel's exact location was then determined using an intersection of the two hyperbolas. Assume that transmitters located at $M\,(0, 0)$, $S_1\,(200\text{ km}, 0)$, and $S_2\,(0, 360\text{ km})$ simultaneously broadcast radio signals that travel at 300 km/sec.

   a. Write the equation of a hyperbola modeling a ship's possible locations if the signal from S_1 arrives at the ship 400 ms earlier than the signal from M. (1 ms $= 10^{-3}$ sec)

   b. Write the equation of a hyperbola modeling the ship's possible locations if the signal from S_2 arrives at the ship 500 ms earlier than the signal from M.

   c. Use graphing technology to find the coordinates of the ship (to the nearest km).

42. A Cassegrain telescope is constructed by placing a hyperbolic mirror 12 in. in front of a parabolic mirror with a focal length of 14 in. (see the figure on p. 417). If the surface of the hyperbolic mirror is modeled by $13x^2 - 36y^2 = 468$, how far behind the parabolic mirror are the reflected light rays focused?

43. **Prove:** Sketch a hyperbola centered at $C\,(h, k)$ and foci $(h, k \pm c)$ with semitransverse and semiconjugate axes with lengths of a and b, respectively, where $c^2 = a^2 + b^2$. Then use the definition of a hyperbola to derive its standard form equation.

Graph each conic and any foci.

44. $9x^2 + 16y^2 + 128y + 112 = 0$ [8.2]

45. $y^2 - 2x - 8y + 16 = 0$ [8.1]

Find each if $\theta \in \left[0, \frac{\pi}{2}\right]$. [4.6]

46. $\cot 2\theta = \dfrac{\sqrt{3}}{3}$

47. $\cot 2\theta = 0$

Use reference triangles and the half-angle formula to find the exact value of $\cos \theta$. [5.5]

48. $\cot 2\theta = \dfrac{5}{12}$

49. $\cot 2\theta = \dfrac{7}{24}$

50. Find x^2 if $x = \dfrac{\sqrt{3}\,u - v}{2}$. [Algebra]

A. $\dfrac{3u^2 - v^2}{4}$

D. $\dfrac{3u^2 - 2\sqrt{3}\,uv + v^2}{4}$

B. $\dfrac{2\sqrt{3}\,u^2 - 2\sqrt{3}\,uv + v^2}{4}$

E. none of these

C. $\dfrac{3u^2 + 2\sqrt{3}\,uv + v^2}{4}$

51. Find xy if $x = \dfrac{\sqrt{2}\,u - \sqrt{2}\,v}{2}$ and $y = \dfrac{\sqrt{2}\,u + \sqrt{2}\,v}{2}$. [Algebra]

A. $\dfrac{u^2 - \sqrt{2}\,uv + v^2}{2}$

D. $\dfrac{u^2 - \sqrt{2}\,uv - v^2}{2}$

B. $\dfrac{u^2 + \sqrt{2}\,uv + v^2}{2}$

E. none of these

C. $\dfrac{u^2 - v^2}{2}$

52. Solve $9^{x+1} = 27^{1-2x}$. [3.4]

A. $x = \dfrac{1}{8}$ **C.** $x = \dfrac{1}{4}$ **E.** $x = 4$

B. $x = -\dfrac{1}{8}$ **D.** $x = -\dfrac{1}{4}$

53. Solve $\log_4 2 + \log_4 x = 2$. [3.3]

A. $x = 2$ **C.** $x = 4$ **E.** $x = 16$

B. $x = \dfrac{1}{2}$ **D.** $x = 8$

TECHNOLOGY CORNER (DESMOS® GRAPHING CALCULATOR)

Many interactive graphing applications such as the Desmos online graphing calculator allow equations to be entered in a variety of forms and allow the use of sliders to define constants. These features enable the user to quickly graph a variety of rectangular and polar equations and can be extremely helpful when studying conic sections.

Notice how the hyperbola and asymptotes from Example 2 can be quickly verified using the general form equation of the hyperbola. The asymptotes and key points can also be easily plotted on the same graph. Click and hold the icon to the left of the equation to adjust the color and format of the graphs. This is especially helpful when checking graphs of rotated conics in Section 8.4.

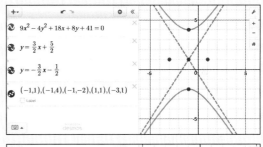

Enter parametric equations from Section 8.5 Example 1a as an ordered pair and define the bounds of the parameter's interval. The domain of the rectangular equation can be limited by writing the conjunction within curly braces, {}. Clicking the icon to the left of the equation turns that graph on and off.

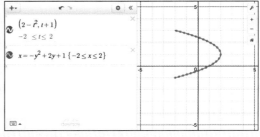

Polar equations for conics from Section 8.6 are easily explored. Use E to represent the eccentricity since e is reserved for the constant $e \approx 2.718$. Type pi or theta to enter these Greek letters.

Entering more than 2 variables in an equation prompts the user to define sliders that are used to quickly change the values of the other variables that act as constants, such as E and d. Clicking on the minimum or maximum value of the slider allows you to define those values and the step for that slider.

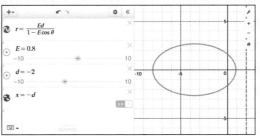

Saturn's axial tilt makes its rings take on the appearance of rotated ellipses.

After completing this section, you will be able to

- determine the angle of rotation and graph a rotated conic.
- write the equation of a rotated conic.
- classify conics using the discriminant test.

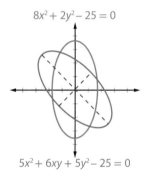

$8x^2 + 2y^2 - 25 = 0$

$5x^2 + 6xy + 5y^2 - 25 = 0$

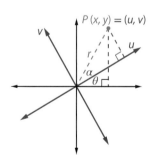

Recall that the equation of a conic section can be written using the general form of a quadratic (second-degree) equation: $Ax^2 + Bxy + Cy^2 + Dx + Ey + F = 0$. In prior sections, the axes of the conics were horizontal or vertical since $B = 0$. When $B = 0$ the conic is a parabola if there is no x^2- or y^2-term ($AC = 0$), a hyperbola if A and C have different signs ($AC < 0$), and an ellipse if A and C have the same sign ($AC > 0$), including the special case of a circle where $A = C$. Conics whose axes are rotated so they are not parallel to the x- or y-axis are represented by the general form equations which contain an xy-term where $B \neq 0$. This section introduces a method of quickly identifying any conic, given its general form equation.

The previous methods used to analyze conic sections can be employed if the x- and y-axes are rotated about the origin by an acute angle θ so that the new u- and v-axes are parallel to the axes of the conic section. The conic's equation in the new uv-coordinate plane is then $A'u^2 + C'v^2 + D'u + E'v + F' = 0$ where there is no uv-term ($B' = 0$).

The equations relating the (x, y) and (u, v) coordinates of any point P can be derived by examining the right triangles drawn to each axis. Note that $(u, v) = (r \cos \alpha, r \sin \alpha)$ and $(x, y) = (r \cos (\theta + \alpha), r \sin (\theta + \alpha))$

$$\therefore x = r(\cos \theta \cos \alpha - \sin \theta \sin \alpha) \quad \text{and} \quad y = r(\sin \theta \cos \alpha + \cos \theta \sin \alpha)$$
$$x = (r \cos \alpha) \cos \theta - (r \sin \alpha) \sin \theta \qquad y = (r \cos \alpha) \sin \theta + (r \sin \alpha) \cos \theta$$
$$x = u \cos \theta - v \sin \theta \qquad y = u \sin \theta + v \cos \theta$$

To determine θ, the angle of rotation that causes the x- and y-axes to be parallel to the conic's axes, substitute the *rotation formulas* into the general form of a conic. After expanding and regrouping the terms (see exercise 35), set the resulting coefficient of the uv term, B', equal to 0 and solve.

$$2(C - A) \sin \theta \cos \theta + B(\cos^2 \theta - \sin^2 \theta) = 0$$
$$(C - A) \sin 2\theta + B \cos 2\theta = 0$$
$$B \cos 2\theta = (A - C) \sin 2\theta$$
$$\cot 2\theta = \frac{A - C}{B}$$

Solving the system consisting of the two rotation formulas above (see exercise 36) produces equations for u and v.

$$u = x \cos \theta + y \sin \theta \quad \text{and} \quad v = y \cos \theta - x \sin \theta$$

> **ROTATION OF CONICS**
>
> A general quadratic equation $Ax^2 + Bxy + Cy^2 + Dx + Ey + F = 0$ where $B \neq 0$ can be rewritten as $A'u^2 + C'v^2 + D'u + E'v + F' = 0$ in the uv-plane by rotating the xy-plane by the acute angle θ such that $\cot 2\theta = \frac{A - C}{B}$.
>
> The equations in the uv-plane and the xy-plane are related using the following *rotation formulas*.
> $$x = u \cos \theta - v \sin \theta \quad \text{and} \quad y = u \sin \theta + v \cos \theta$$
> $$u = x \cos \theta + y \sin \theta \quad \text{and} \quad v = y \cos \theta - x \sin \theta$$

Example 1   Analyzing and Graphing a Rotated Conic

Given the equation $xy - 4 = 0$, find the angle θ that rotates the xy-plane so that there is no uv-term. Then write the general form equation in terms of the uv-plane and classify the conic. Finally, sketch a graph of the conic and any foci.

Answer

$A = 0, B = 1, C = 0$

$\cot 2\theta = \dfrac{0 - 0}{1} = 0; \, 2\theta = \dfrac{\pi}{2}; \, \theta = \dfrac{\pi}{4}$

$x = u \cos \dfrac{\pi}{4} - v \sin \dfrac{\pi}{4}$ and $y = u \sin \dfrac{\pi}{4} + v \cos \dfrac{\pi}{4}$

$x = \dfrac{\sqrt{2}}{2}u - \dfrac{\sqrt{2}}{2}v \qquad\qquad y = \dfrac{\sqrt{2}}{2}u + \dfrac{\sqrt{2}}{2}v$

1. Use $\cot 2\theta = \dfrac{A - C}{B}$ to determine the angle of rotation.

2. Determine the rotation formulas.

$$xy - 4 = 0$$

$$\left(\dfrac{\sqrt{2}}{2}u - \dfrac{\sqrt{2}}{2}v \right)\left(\dfrac{\sqrt{2}}{2}u + \dfrac{\sqrt{2}}{2}v \right) - 4 = 0$$

$$\dfrac{u^2}{2} - \dfrac{v^2}{2} - 4 = 0$$

$$u^2 - v^2 - 8 = 0$$

3. Rewrite the equation as a general quadratic in terms of u and v. Note that $A' > 0$ and $B' < 0$.

The equation represents a hyperbola.

$$u^2 - v^2 = 8$$

$$\dfrac{u^2}{8} - \dfrac{v^2}{8} = 1$$

4. Convert to the standard form for a hyperbola with a transverse axis along the u-axis.

$C\,(0, 0); a = 2\sqrt{2}; b = 2\sqrt{2}$

$c^2 = a^2 + b^2 = 8 + 8 = 16; c = 4$

$\therefore V'\,(\pm 2\sqrt{2}, 0)$, and $F'\,(\pm 4, 0)$

$V'\,(\pm 2\sqrt{2}, 0)$:

$x = (\pm 2\sqrt{2})\dfrac{\sqrt{2}}{2} - (0)\dfrac{\sqrt{2}}{2} = \pm 2$

$y = (\pm 2\sqrt{2})\dfrac{\sqrt{2}}{2} + (0)\dfrac{\sqrt{2}}{2} = \pm 2$

V: $(2, 2)$ and $(-2, -2)$

5. Identify the center, vertices, and foci in the uv-plane.

6. The rotation formulas
$x = u \cos \theta - v \sin \theta$ and
$y = u \sin \theta + v \cos \theta$
can be used to locate the vertices in the xy-plane.

7. Sketch the graph of the hyperbola.

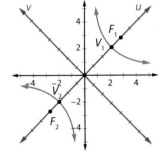

SKILL ✔ **EXERCISE 11**

The formulas for u and v in terms of x and y can be used to confirm that the asymptotes of the hyperbola rotated by $\theta = \dfrac{\pi}{4}$ in Example 1, $v = \pm u$, are the x-axis and y-axis.

$$u = x \cos \theta + y \sin \theta = \dfrac{\sqrt{2}}{2}x + \dfrac{\sqrt{2}}{2}y \quad \text{and} \quad v = -x \sin \theta + y \cos \theta = -\dfrac{\sqrt{2}}{2}x + \dfrac{\sqrt{2}}{2}y$$

Substituting into the asymptote $v = u$,

$$-\dfrac{\sqrt{2}}{2}x + \dfrac{\sqrt{2}}{2}y = \dfrac{\sqrt{2}}{2}x + \dfrac{\sqrt{2}}{2}y$$

$$0 = \sqrt{2}x$$

$$\text{or } x = 0.$$

Substituting into the asymptote $v = -u$,

$$-\dfrac{\sqrt{2}}{2}x + \dfrac{\sqrt{2}}{2}y = -\dfrac{\sqrt{2}}{2}x - \dfrac{\sqrt{2}}{2}y$$

$$\sqrt{2}y = 0$$

$$\text{or } y = 0.$$

Fermat's treatise on conics used substitutions to reduce more complicated second-degree equations to a standard form. These substitutions resulted in a transformation of the axes.

Example 2   Analyzing and Graphing a Rotated Conic

Given the equation $8x^2 + 12xy + 17y^2 = 20$, find the angle θ that rotates the xy-plane so that there is no uv-term. Then write the general form equation in terms of the uv-plane and classify the conic. Finally, sketch a graph of the conic.

Answer

$\cot 2\theta = \dfrac{8 - 17}{12} = -\dfrac{3}{4}$

$2\theta \approx 126.9°; \theta \approx 63.4°$

$\cos 2\theta = -\dfrac{3}{5}$

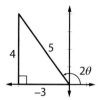

1. Since $\cot 2\theta = \dfrac{A - C}{B}$ does not produce an exact value for θ, use a reference triangle to find $\cos 2\theta$.

$\cos \theta = \sqrt{\dfrac{1 + \cos 2\theta}{2}} \qquad \sin \theta = \sqrt{\dfrac{1 - \cos 2\theta}{2}}$

$\quad = \sqrt{\dfrac{1 + \left(-\frac{3}{5}\right)}{2}} \qquad\qquad = \sqrt{\dfrac{1 - \left(-\frac{3}{5}\right)}{2}}$

$\quad = \sqrt{\dfrac{1}{5}} = \dfrac{1}{\sqrt{5}} \qquad\qquad = \sqrt{\dfrac{4}{5}} = \dfrac{2}{\sqrt{5}}$

2. Use half-angle identities to find $\cos \theta$ and $\sin \theta$ for the acute angle θ.

$x = u \cos \theta - v \sin \theta$ and $y = u \sin \theta + v \cos \theta$

$x = \dfrac{1}{\sqrt{5}}u - \dfrac{2}{\sqrt{5}}v \qquad y = \dfrac{2}{\sqrt{5}}u + \dfrac{1}{\sqrt{5}}v$

3. Determine the rotation formulas for the conic and substitute.

$$8x^2 + 12xy + 17y^2 = 20$$

$$8\left(\dfrac{u - 2v}{\sqrt{5}}\right)^2 + 12\left(\dfrac{u - 2v}{\sqrt{5}}\right)\left(\dfrac{2u + v}{\sqrt{5}}\right) + 17\left(\dfrac{2u + v}{\sqrt{5}}\right)^2 = 20$$

Then expand, multiply both sides by 5, and simplify.

$$8(u^2 - 4uv + 4v^2) + 12(2u^2 - 3uv - 2v^2) + 17(4u^2 + 4uv + v^2) = 100$$

$$(8 + 24 + 68)u^2 + (-32 - 36 + 68)uv + (32 - 24 + 17)v^2 = 100$$

$$100u^2 + 25v^2 = 100$$

$$4u^2 + v^2 - 4 = 0$$

The equation is an ellipse.

$\dfrac{u^2}{1} + \dfrac{v^2}{4} = 1$

4. A' and $B' > 0$

5. Convert to the standard form for an ellipse.

$a' = 2; b' = 1$

$(c')^2 = (a')^2 - (b')^2 = 4 - 1 = 3; c' = \sqrt{3} \approx 1.7$

$\therefore V'(0, \pm 2)$ and $F'\left(0, \pm\sqrt{3}\right)$

6. Rotate the axes by $\theta \approx 63.4°$ and graph an ellipse centered at the origin with its major axis on the v-axis.

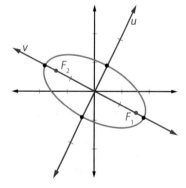

The formulas for u and v in terms of x and y can be used to write the equation of a rotated conic.

Example 3 Writing the Equation of a Rotated Parabola

After being rotated by $30°$, the equation for a parabola in the uv-plane is $v = -\frac{1}{4}u^2 + 3$. Write a general form equation for the parabola in the xy-plane. Then use technology to graph the parabola.

Answer

$u = x \cos 30° + y \sin 30°$ and $v = y \cos 30° - x \sin 30°$

$u = \frac{\sqrt{3}}{2}x + \frac{1}{2}y$ 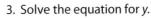 $v = \frac{\sqrt{3}}{2}y - \frac{1}{2}x$

$$-4v = u^2 - 12$$

$$-4\left(\frac{\sqrt{3}y - x}{2}\right) = \left(\frac{\sqrt{3}x + y}{2}\right)^2 - 12$$

$$-2\sqrt{3}y + 2x = \frac{3x^2 + 2\sqrt{3}xy + y^2}{4} - 12$$

$$-8\sqrt{3}y + 8x = 3x^2 + 2\sqrt{3}xy + y^2 - 48$$

$$3x^2 + 2\sqrt{3}xy + y^2 - 8x + 8\sqrt{3}y - 48 = 0$$

$$y^2 + 2\sqrt{3}xy + 8\sqrt{3}y + 3x^2 - 8x - 48 = 0$$

$$y^2 + (2\sqrt{3}x + 8\sqrt{3})y + (3x^2 - 8x - 48) = 0$$

$$y = \frac{-(2\sqrt{3}x + 8\sqrt{3}) \pm \sqrt{(2\sqrt{3}x + 8\sqrt{3})^2 - 4(3x^2 - 8x - 48)}}{2}$$

Check

Since $\tan 30° = \frac{\sqrt{3}}{3}$, the u-axis is at $y = \frac{\sqrt{3}}{3}x$, and the v-axis is at $y = -\sqrt{3}x$.

1. Express u and v in terms of x and y.

2. Multiply both sides of $v = -\frac{1}{4}u^2 + 3$ by -4 before substituting.

   Then expand and simplify.

3. Solve the equation for y.
   a. Express in quadratic form.
   b. Use the quadratic formula.

4. Graph both functions whose union forms the parabola.

5. Graph the u- and v-axes using the slope of the u-axis $= \tan\theta$ and $m_v = -\frac{1}{m_u}$.

TIP

The length and complexity of the expressions for Y1 and Y2 make them difficult to enter correctly. Use MATHPRINT mode if possible and carefully check the placement of parentheses.

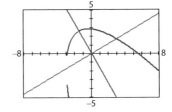

SKILL ✓ **EXERCISE 27**

The location of the focus or other characteristic points of the parabola in Example 3 can be found from their position in the uv-plane. Since $V'(0, 3)$ and $p = \frac{1}{4a} = -1$, the focus is $F'(0, 2)$ in the uv-plane.

using the rotation formulas:

$x = u \cos\theta - v \sin\theta$ and $y = u \sin\theta + v \cos\theta$

$x = (0)\frac{\sqrt{3}}{2} - (2)\frac{1}{2}$ $\qquad$ $y = (0)\frac{1}{2} + (2)\frac{\sqrt{3}}{2}$

Therefore, the parabola's focus is $F(-1, \sqrt{3})$ in the xy-plane.

When using the quadratic formula, $x = \frac{-b \pm \sqrt{b^2 - 4ac}}{2a}$, to solve a quadratic equation of the form $ax^2 + bx + c = 0$, the *discriminant*, $b^2 - 4ac$, is used to identify the type and number of roots. A similar expression $B^2 - 4AC$, which is also called the discriminant, can be used to identify the type of conic section represented by a general form quadratic equation in two variables.

For the parabola in Example 3, $B^2 - 4AC = \left(2\sqrt{3}\right)^2 - 4(3)(1) = 0$. Examining its general form in the uv-plane, $u^2 - 4v - 12 = 0$, the discriminant $(B')^2 - 4A'C' = (0)^2 - 4(1)(0) = 0$ as well. In fact, the discriminant of any conic is *invariant under rotation*, so that $B^2 - 4AC = (B')^2 - 4A'C'$. When the conic is rotated so there is no uv-term, $B' = 0$ and $B^2 - 4AC = -4A'C'$. Notice how the characteristics for conics with horizontal and vertical axes reviewed at the beginning of this section are special cases for the following general characteristics of conic sections.

Identifying a Conic by Its Discriminant			
The graph of a basic conic section whose equation is of the form $Ax^2 + Bxy + Cy^2 + Dx + Ey + F = 0$ can be classified using the value of the discriminant: $B^2 - 4AC$.			
Circle	Ellipse	Parabola	Hyperbola
$B^2 - 4AC < 0$ $B = 0$ and $A = C$	$B^2 - 4AC < 0$ $B \neq 0$ or $A \neq C$	$B^2 - 4AC = 0$	$B^2 - 4AC > 0$

Example 4 Using the Discriminant Test

Use the discriminant to classify each conic section.

a. $3x^2 + 9xy + 3y^2 - 10 = 0$
b. $3x^2 - 4xy + 3y^2 + 2x - 6y - 10 = 0$
c. $x^2 + 6y - 2x = 6xy - 9y^2 + 22$
d. $6x^2 + 6y^2 = 10 - 3x - 2y$

Answer

a. $3x^2 + 9xy + 3y^2 - 10 = 0$ Evaluate the discriminant.
$B^2 - 4AC = (9)^2 - 4(3)(3) = 45 > 0$
$\therefore$ a hyperbola

b. $3x^2 - 4xy + 3y^2 + 2x - 6y - 10 = 0$ Evaluate the discriminant.
$B^2 - 4AC = (-4)^2 - 4(3)(3) = -20 < 0$
$\therefore$ an ellipse (which is not a circle, since $B \neq 0$)

c. $x^2 + 6y - 2x = 6xy - 9y^2 + 22$ Express the equation in general form
$x^2 - 6xy + 9y^2 - 2x + 6y - 22 = 0$ before evaluating the discriminant.
$B^2 - 4AC = (-6)^2 - 4(1)(9) = 0$
$\therefore$ a parabola

d. $6x^2 + 6y^2 = 10 - 3x - 2y$ This is a special case of an ellipse.
$\therefore$ a circle, since $B = 0$ and $A = C$ $B^2 - 4AC = 0^2 - 4(6)(6) = -144 < 0$

SKILL ✓ **EXERCISE 5**

A. Exercises

State whether the conic is rotated. Then use the discriminant test to classify the graph as a circle, ellipse, parabola, or hyperbola.

1. $4x^2 - 9y^2 - 8x + 54y - 113 = 0$
2. $x^2 + xy + 2y^2 - 6 = 0$
3. $5x^2 + 5y^2 - 30x - 6y + 5 = 0$
4. $4x^2 + 9y^2 - 8x + 126y - 131 = 0$
5. $x^2 - 2xy + y^2 - 5x - 15y = 0$
6. $3x^2 - 12xy + 2y^2 - 144 = 0$

State the rotation formulas that will rotate each general quadratic equation to a *uv*-plane without a *uv*-term.

7. $xy = -2$
8. $2x^2 + xy + 2y^2 - 1 = 0$
9. $2x^2 + \sqrt{3}xy + y^2 + y + x = 0$
10. $3x - \sqrt{3}xy + y^2 + 5 = 0$

Find the angle of rotation of the *xy*-plane that causes the *u*- or *v*-axis to be parallel to the conic's axes. Then write the standard form equation in terms of *u* and *v* and sketch a graph of the conic and any foci.

11. $xy - 8 = 0$
12. $xy + 6 = 0$
13. $9x^2 - 6\sqrt{3}xy + 15y^2 - 288 = 0$
14. $15x^2 + 2\sqrt{3}xy + 13y^2 - 48 = 0$
15. $4x^2 - 12xy + 9y^2 - 9\sqrt{13}x - 6\sqrt{13}y = 0$
16. $x^2 + 2xy + y^2 + \dfrac{\sqrt{2}}{2}x - \dfrac{\sqrt{2}}{2}y = 0$

B. Exercises

Write a general form equation for each conic in terms of *x* and *y*, given its angle of rotation and equation in terms of *u* and *v*.

17. $\theta = \dfrac{\pi}{4};\ 2u^2 + v^2 = 9$
18. $\theta = \dfrac{\pi}{6};\ 3u = v^2$
19. $\theta = \dfrac{\pi}{3};\ 4u^2 - 3v^2 = 12$
20. $\theta = \dfrac{\pi}{4};\ \dfrac{u^2}{25} - \dfrac{v^2}{16} = 1$
21. $\theta = \dfrac{\pi}{6};\ \dfrac{u^2}{9} + \dfrac{v^2}{4} = 1$
22. $\theta = \dfrac{\pi}{3};\ \dfrac{u^2}{28} + \dfrac{v^2}{7} = 1$

Find the angle of rotation of the *xy*-plane that causes the *u*- or *v*-axis to be parallel to the conic's axes. Then write the standard form equation in terms of *u* and *v* and sketch a graph of the conic and any foci.

23. $6x^2 - 6xy + 14y^2 = 90$
24. $16x^2 + 24xy + 9y^2 + 30x - 40y = 0$
25. $3x^2 + 2\sqrt{3}xy + y^2 + 4x - 4\sqrt{3}y + 24 = 0$
26. $621x^2 + 290xy - 75y^2 = 2600$

Write a general form equation for each conic in terms of *x* and *y*, given its angle of rotation and equation in terms of *u* and *v*. Then use technology to graph the conic.

27. $\theta = \dfrac{\pi}{4},\ 3u^2 + v^2 = 4$
28. $\theta = 30°,\ v^2 = 6u$
29. $\theta = \dfrac{\pi}{4},\ \dfrac{u^2}{25} - v^2 = 1$
30. $\theta = 60°,\ \dfrac{u^2}{4} + \dfrac{v^2}{5} = 1$

Recall that a point is a degenerate ellipse, a line is a degenerate parabola, and two intersecting lines are a degenerate hyperbola. Use the discriminant test to classify each conic section. Then solve for *y* and describe the degenerate conic.

31. $4x^2 + 12xy + 9y^2 = 0$
32. $16x^2 - 25y^2 = 0$

33. A satellite dish with a parabolic cross section is represented (in feet) by the equation
$x^2 - 2xy + y^2 - 10\sqrt{2}x - 10\sqrt{2}y = 0.$

   a. Write a standard form equation for the parabola in terms of *u* and *v*.

   b. How far in front of the vertex should the receiver be located?

34. **Prove:** Show that a rotation has no effect on a circle with the equation $x^2 + y^2 = r^2$.

35. **Prove:** Substitute the rotation formulas $x = u \cos\theta - v \sin\theta$ and $y = u \sin\theta - v \cos\theta$ into the general quadratic equation $Ax^2 + Bxy + Cy^2 + Dx + Ey + F = 0$ and show that B', the coefficient of the *uv*-term, is $2(C - A)\sin\theta \cos\theta + B(\cos^2\theta - \sin^2\theta)$.

36. **Prove:** Solve the system of equations $x = u \cos\theta - v \sin\theta$ and $y = u \sin\theta + v \cos\theta$ to derive the rotation formulas expressing *u* and *v* in terms of *x* and *y*.

C. Exercises

Find the angle of rotation of the *xy*-plane that causes the *u*- or *v*-axis to be parallel to the conic's axes. Then write the standard form equation in terms of *u* and *v* and sketch a graph of the conic and any foci.

37. $4x^2 - 16xy + 16y^2 + 20\sqrt{5}y = 0$

38. $3x^2 + 6xy + 3y^2 + 3\sqrt{2}x + \sqrt{2}y = 0$

Write the general form equation for each conic in terms of *x* and *y*, given its angle of rotation and equation in terms of *u* and *v*. Then use technology to graph the conic.

39. $\theta = \frac{\pi}{6}$, $v = 4u^2 + 2u$

40. $\theta = \frac{\pi}{4}$, $\left(u - 2\sqrt{2}\right)^2 - \left(v - \sqrt{2}\right)^2 = 1$

41. Prove: Substitute the rotation formulas into general quadratic form for conics to find each coefficient of the rotated formula in the (u, v) plane having $B' = 0$: $A'u^2 + C'v^2 + D'u + E'v + F' = 0$.

42. Explain: Use the results of exercise 41 to explain why each expression is invariant under rotation.

    a. F **b.** $A + C$

CUMULATIVE REVIEW

43. Find the ordered pair for the parametric equations $x = 2t - 1$ and $y = t - 4$ when $t = 2$. [1.8]

44. Eliminate the parameter for the equations $x = t + 5$ and $y = 3t + 1$. [1.8]

Simplify. [5.1]

45. $2\cos^2\theta + 2\sin^2\theta$ **46.** $4\tan^2\theta - 4\sec^2\theta$

47. Write the standard form equation of each conic with its center not at the origin.

    a. a parabola with a vertical axis of symmetry [8.1]

    b. an ellipse with a horizontal major axis [8.2]

    c. a hyperbola with a horizontal transverse axis [8.3]

48. Express $3x^2 + 6y^2 + 18x - 24y + 33 = 0$ in standard form. [8.2]

49. What is the sum of the measures of the acute angles α and β if $\tan\alpha = \cot\beta$? [4.3]

    A. $45°$ **C.** $90°$ **E.** $180°$

    B. $60°$ **D.** $120°$

50. What is $\sin x \csc x + \sec x \tan x$ if $x = 30°$? [4.3, 5.1]

    A. $\frac{2}{3}$ **C.** 2 **E.** none of

    B. $\frac{5}{3}$ **D.** $\frac{\sqrt{3}}{2}$ these

51. What is $\dfrac{\sin^2\theta + \cos^2\theta + \tan\theta}{\sec^2\theta - \tan^2\theta}$ if $\theta = \frac{\pi}{4}$? [5.1]

    A. 0 **C.** 2 **E.** $-\dfrac{\sqrt{3}}{3}$

    B. -2 **D.** $\dfrac{\sqrt{3}}{3}$

52. Which set of polar coordinates represents the rectangular coordinates $(6, 8)$? [6.4]

    A. $(6\sin\theta, 8\cos\theta)$ **D.** $(10, 36.9°)$

    B. $(6\cos\theta, 8\sin\theta)$ **E.** $(10, 53.1°)$

    C. $(10\cos\theta, 10\sin\theta)$

Counterexamples and Existence Proofs

Some mathematics problems look simple, and you try them for a year or so, and then you try them for a hundred years, and it turns out that they're extremely hard to solve. There's no reason why these problems shouldn't be easy, and yet they turn out to be extremely intricate. Fermat's Last Theorem is the most beautiful example of this.

—Andrew Wiles (British mathematician who proved Fermat's Last Theorem)

A counterexample proves that a statement is false. The statement "there are no solutions to $a^2 + b^2 = c^2$ where a, b, and c are consecutive even integers" is easily disproved by doubling the most famous Pythagorean triple (3, 4, 5) to get the counterexample $6^2 + 8^2 = 10^2$. This example also provides an existence proof for the related statement "there is a solution to $a^2 + b^2 = c^2$ where a, b, and c are consecutive even integers."

Several special cases of the general equation $a^x + b^y = c^z$ in which all variables represent natural numbers have generated famous problems in mathematics. The first special case is the Pythagorean Theorem, in which $x = y = z = 2$. The equation $a^2 + b^2 = c^2$ has an infinite number of solutions (a, b, c), including the frequently occurring Pythagorean triples (3, 4, 5), (5, 12, 13), (7, 24, 25), and (8, 15, 17) and all their integral multiples.

Fermat's Last Theorem addresses a second special case, stating there are no solutions to $a^n + b^n = c^n$ where $n > 2$. While no counterexample could be found to this 1637 conjecture, its proof became the most famous unsolved problem in mathematics until it was finally proven in 1994 by Andrew Wiles.

Another special case states that "no solution exists to $a^x + b^y = c^z$ with unique x, y, and z where a, b, and c are relatively prime." At the beginning of the millennium, there were ten known counterexamples. The first five could be referred to as "small" solutions. The missing values for x are found in exercise 5. Notice that each of the five "large" solutions contains 2 as one of the exponents.

$$1 + 2^x = 3^2$$
$$2^5 + 7^2 = 3^x$$
$$7^x + 13^2 = 2^9$$
$$2^x + 17^3 = 71^2$$
$$3^x + 11^4 = 122^2$$

$$17^7 + 76{,}271^3 = 21{,}063{,}928^2$$
$$1414^3 + 2{,}213{,}459^2 = 65^7$$
$$43^8 + 96{,}222^3 = 30{,}042{,}907^2$$
$$33^8 + 1{,}549{,}034^2 = 15{,}613^3$$
$$9262^3 + 15{,}312{,}283^2 = 113^7$$

Andrew Beal, a Texas banker and number theory enthusiast, presented a related conjecture in 1993 after extensive computer testing. The Beal Conjecture states there are no solutions to $a^x + b^y = c^z$ where a, b, and c are *relatively prime* (share no common integral factor other than 1) for $x \geq 3$, $y \geq 3$, and $z \geq 3$. Currently, the American Mathematical Society is offering a $1,000,000 prize for either a correct proof or a counterexample for the Beal Conjecture.

Counterexamples are frequently used to disprove statements in other areas of reasoning. While these proofs may not be as definitive as those found in mathematics, counterexamples can be used to arrive at reasonable conclusions in many fields of study.

Consider the claim "there are no miracles." Instead of accepting the possibility of a miracle, many believe that people accidentally or intentionally misinterpret an explainable event as supernatural. To prove this statement to be false, many counterexamples have been cited. The resurrection of Christ provides the supreme counterexample.

For a Christian, experiencing the love of Christ and the guidance of the Holy Spirit provides a counterexample to the statement "there is no God." Anyone who has not seen the reality of God in his life may not accept these examples as proof. God wants us to accept His existence by faith (Heb. 11:6). Just as it is impossible to mathematically prove God's existence, it is also impossible to prove that there is no God.

❯ Exercises

1. What is the purpose of a counterexample?

2. Which type of statement can be proved by an example?

Consider $a^x + b^y = c^z$ where all variables represent natural numbers.

3. What additional condition is required by the Pythagorean Theorem?

4. What additional condition is required by Fermat's Last Theorem?

5. Find x in each "small solution" $a^x + b^y = c^z$, where a, b, and c are relatively prime.
   a. $1 + 2^x = 3^2$ **b.** $2^5 + 7^2 = 3^x$
   c. $7^x + 13^2 = 2^9$ **d.** $2^x + 17^3 = 71^2$
   e. $3^x + 11^4 = 122^2$

6. Explain why each equation is not a counterexample to the Beal Conjecture.
   a. $2^9 + 8^3 = 4^5$
   b. $19^4 + 38^3 = 57^3$
   c. $34^5 + 51^4 = 85^4$
   d. $1414^3 + 2{,}213{,}459^2 = 65^7$

7. How could you reasonably refute the statement "all men are lazy"?

8. Name and describe the common powerful counterexample frequently used in court to reasonably disprove the possibility that someone committed a crime at a given time and location.

9. The complexity of brain functionality required for vision would render it useless in any primitive form. What theory can be reasonably proven false with this counterexample?

10. How does our personal relationship with Christ relate to the statement "there is no God"?

11. **Discuss:** Christ appeared to Mary, the disciples, and many other witnesses after His resurrection. List several statements that these counterexamples disprove.

12. **Discuss:** How should the truths found in John 12:37 and Acts 1:3 affect how we share the gospel with others?

Parametric Representations

Parametric equations can be used to model the path of a kicked ball.

Parametric equations were introduced in Section 1.8. The introduction of the parameter t, a third variable representing time, provided a more complete model for the path of a projectile. The trajectory of a ball kicked at a speed of 40 ft/sec with an angle of elevation of approximately 53° can be modeled by $y = -\frac{1}{36}x^2 + \frac{4}{3}x$. However, this model provides no information regarding the times associated with the ball's flight. Expressing the horizontal displacement and height as functions of time allows the x- and y-coordinates to be determined at any time during the ball's flight. An arrowhead is drawn to indicate the curve's *orientation*, the order of the points as the parameter t increases.

$x(t) = 24t$ and $y(t) = -16t^2 + 32t$

t	0	$\frac{1}{2}$	1	$\frac{3}{2}$	2
x	0	12	24	36	48
y	0	12	16	12	0

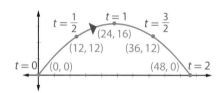

After completing this section, you will be able to

- graph curves represented by parametric equations.
- eliminate the parameter to rewrite parametric equations.
- write parametric equations for a curve.
- solve projectile motion problems using parametric equations.

▌ DEFINITIONS

A **parametric curve** is a set of ordered pairs (x, y) defined by the **parametric equations** $x = f(t)$ and $y = g(t)$ where $f(t)$ and $g(t)$ are continuous functions of t on the *parameter interval, I*.

If the parameter interval is not specified, the implied interval is all values of t that produce real-number values of x and y.

Example 1   Graphing Parametric Equations

Draw the curve described by each set of parametric equations.

a. $x = 2 - t^2$ and $y = t + 1; t \in [-2, 2]$

b. $x = 2 - \frac{t^2}{4}$ and $y = 1 - \frac{t}{2}$

Answer

a.

t	−2	−1	0	1	2
x	−2	1	2	1	−2
y	−1	0	1	2	3

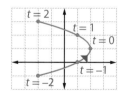

1. Evaluate x and y for several values of t within the interval.

2. Plot the resulting points and connect them with a smooth curve. Add an arrowhead to indicate the curve's orientation.

CONTINUED ➡

TIP

Set your calculator to parametric mode to verify the graphs.

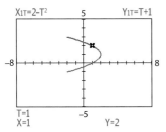

Use the trace function to find x- and y-values for each value of t and verify the orientation. (See Section 1.8.)

b.

t	-4	-2	0	2	4
x	-2	1	2	1	-2
y	3	2	1	0	-1

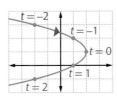

1. Evaluate $x = 2 - \frac{t^2}{4}$ and $y = 1 - \frac{t}{2}$ for several values of t.

2. Plot the resulting points and connect them with a smooth curve. Add an arrowhead to indicate the curve's orientation.

SKILL ✓ **EXERCISE 3**

Parametric equations can be used to represent curves that fail the Vertical Line Test and are not functions. Examples 1*a* and 1*b* define the same curve over different intervals and different orientations. Notice the first curve is traced more rapidly (in terms of t) than the second curve.

The parameter can be eliminated by solving either equation for t and substituting into the other equation. This process frequently simplifies the graphing process by revealing a familiar form of the curve's equation in terms of x and y (rectangular form). The domain may need to be restricted to ensure the same set of points is generated.

Example 2 Eliminating the Parameter

Given $x = 2 - t^2$ and $y = t + 1$ with $t \in [-2, 2]$, eliminate the parameter and restrict the domain to generate the same curve as in Example 1.

Answer

$y = t + 1$
$t = y - 1$
$x = 2 - (y - 1)^2$
$x = -(y - 1)^2 + 2$
$x = -y^2 + 2y + 1$

1. Solving for t in terms of y and substituting into the other equation confirms the graph of a parabola with vertex $(2, 1)$ that opens to the left.

$t^2 = 2 - x$ and $|t| \le 2$
$\quad 0 \le 2 - x \le 4$
$\quad -2 \le -x$ and $-x \le 2$
$\quad\quad x \le 2 \quad\quad x \ge -2$
$\therefore D = [-2, 2]$

2. Solve for t^2 in terms of x and examine its minimum value of 0 and maximum value of 4 from the interval $t \in [-2, 2]$ to find the appropriate restriction on the domain.

TIP

Solving for t in terms of x and substituting yields $y = \pm\sqrt{2 - x} + 1$, which can be used to graph the curve in function mode.

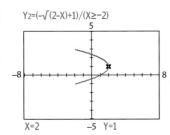

SKILL ✓ **EXERCISE 11**

The parameter does not always represent time. A Pythagorean identity is often used to eliminate parameters that represent angles.

Example 3 Eliminating the Parameter for an Ellipse

Given $x = 5 \cos \theta$ and $y = 3 \sin \theta$, eliminate the parameter and write the rectangular equation in standard form. Then sketch the graph.

Answer

$\cos \theta = \frac{x}{5}$ and $\sin \theta = \frac{y}{3}$

$\left(\frac{x}{5}\right)^2 + \left(\frac{y}{3}\right)^2 = 1$

$\frac{x^2}{25} + \frac{y^2}{9} = 1$

1. Solve for $\cos \theta$ and $\sin \theta$ and then substitute into $\cos^2 \theta + \sin^2 \theta = 1$.

CONTINUED ➡

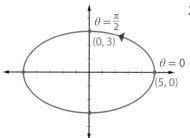

2. Sketch the resulting ellipse centered at the origin with a horizontal major axis where $a = 5$ and $b = 3$. Evaluating when $\theta = 0$ and $\frac{\pi}{2}$ produces $(5, 0)$ and $(0, 3)$, which indicates a counterclockwise orientation.

SKILL ✔ **EXERCISE 15**

How can you find a set of parametric equations for a given graph or rectangular equation? Recall from Example 1 that the parametric representations for a curve are not unique. The orientation and speed of the parametric curve depend on the definition of the parameter.

Example 4   Writing Parametric Equations for a Parabola

Use each parameter to write parametric equations for the graph of $y = x^2 - 1; x \in [-2, 2]$.

a. $t = x$ **b.** $t = \frac{x}{2} + 1$ **c.** $t = 1 - 3x$

Answer

a. using $t = x; t \in [-2, 2]$
   $y = t^2 - 1$

b. using $t = \frac{x}{2} + 1; t \in [0, 2]$
   $x = 2t - 2$
   $y = (2t - 2)^2 - 1$
   $= 4t^2 - 8t + 3$

c. using $t = 1 - 3x; t \in [-5, 7]$
   $x = \frac{1 - t}{3}$
   $y = \left(\frac{1-t}{3}\right)^2 - 1 = \frac{t^2 - 2t - 8}{9}$

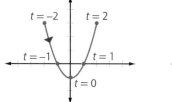

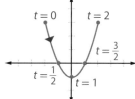

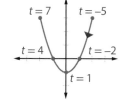

$x = t$ and $y = t^2 - 1$;
$t \in [-2, 2]$

$x = 2t - 2$ and
$y = 4t^2 - 8t + 3; t \in [0, 2]$

$x = \frac{1 - t}{3}$ and $y = \frac{t^2 - 2t - 8}{9}$;
$t \in [-5, 7]$

SKILL ✔ **EXERCISE 25**

Example 5   Writing Parametric Equations for a Hyperbola

Write a set of parametric equations for the hyperbola with vertices at $(1, 5)$ and $(1, -1)$ and foci at $(1, 7)$ and $(1, -3)$.

Answer

transverse axis on $x = 1$

$C\left(1, \frac{-1 + 5}{2}\right) = (1, 2)$

$a = 3; c = 5$

$b^2 = c^2 - a^2 = 25 - 9 = 16; b = 4$

$\therefore \frac{(y - 2)^2}{3^2} - \frac{(x - 1)^2}{4^2} = 1$

Since $\sec^2 \theta - \tan^2 \theta = 1$, let

$\sec \theta = \frac{y - 2}{3}$ and $\tan \theta = \frac{x - 1}{4}$.

$\therefore x = 1 + 4 \tan \theta$ and $y = 2 + 3 \sec \theta$

1. Write the standard form equation for the

   hyperbola: $\frac{(y - k)^2}{b^2} - \frac{(x - h)^2}{a^2} = 1$.

   Recall that $c^2 = a^2 + b^2$ in a hyperbola.

2. Use a Pythagorean identity to create parametric equations for x and y.

CONTINUED ➡

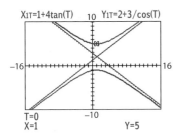

$X_{1T}=1+4\tan(T)$ 10 $Y_{1T}=2+3/\cos(T)$

-16 16

-10

T=0
X=1   Y=5

Architects use parametric equations to model the effects of earthquakes on structures in order to enhance public safety.

Check

3. Graph the equations in parametric mode using $\theta \in [0, 2\pi]$. Extending the interval for θ retraces the hyperbola.

SKILL ✓ **EXERCISE 29**

Parametric equations are frequently used to model motion within a plane. You have already seen how the parabolic path of a projectile can be modified. In general, the position of an object launched from an initial height h_0 at an angle of θ above the horizontal with an initial speed of v_0 after t seconds is modeled by the parametric equations

$$x = (v_0 \cos \theta)t \text{ and } y = -\frac{1}{2}gt^2 + (v_0 \sin \theta)t + h_0$$

where the acceleration due to gravity, g, is approximately 32 ft/sec² or 9.8 m/sec².

Example 6   Modeling 2D Motion with Parametric Equations

Julie throws a ball at a 1 ft wide circular dunk tank target 30 ft away whose center is 4 ft above the ground. She releases the ball from a height of 6 ft with a 10° angle of elevation and a speed of 50 ft/sec. Write a set of parametric equations modeling the ball's trajectory and determine whether the 4 in. diameter ball hits the target.

Answer

$x = (50 \cos 10°)t$ and
$y = -16t^2 + (50 \sin 10°)t + 6$

1. Write the parametric equations for projectile motion.

$30 = (50 \cos 10°)t_{30}$

$t_{30} = \dfrac{30}{50 \cos 10°} \approx 0.61$ sec

2. Determine the time it takes for the ball to reach a horizontal displacement of 30 ft.

$y = -16t_{30}^2 + (50 \sin 10°)t_{30} + 6$
   ≈ 5.35 ft or $\approx$ 5 ft 4 in.

3. Find the height of the ball at that time.

The balls misses the target by $\approx (16 - 6 - 2) \approx 8$ in.

4. The center of the ball (2 in. radii) passes $\approx$ 16 in. above the center of the target (6 in. radii).

Check

5. Graph the equations in parametric mode. Using the trace function with $t \approx 0.61$ confirms that the ball is too high.

SKILL ✓ **EXERCISE 35**

TIP

If $t \in [0, 1]$, the target can be represented by $x = 30$ and $y = 3.5 + t$.

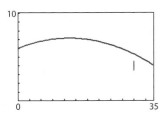

10

0   35

⟩ A. Exercises

Complete the table and draw the graph described by each set of parametric equations.

1. $x = t - 1$ and $y = t - 2$; $t \in [0, 4]$

t	0	1	2	3	4
x					
y					

2. $x = t^2 - 1$ and $y = t + 1$; $t \in [-2, 2]$

t	-2	-1	0	1	2
x					
y					

3. $x = t + 1$ and $y = t^2$; $t \in [-2, 2]$

t	-2	-1	0	1	2
x					
y					

4. $x = 4 \cos \theta$ and $y = 2 \sin \theta$; $\theta \in [0, 2\pi]$

θ	0	$\dfrac{\pi}{4}$	$\dfrac{\pi}{2}$	$\dfrac{3\pi}{4}$	π	$\dfrac{5\pi}{4}$	$\dfrac{3\pi}{2}$	$\dfrac{7\pi}{4}$	2π
x									
y									

Use a graphing calculator in parametric mode to graph each set of parametric equations. Then explore the graph with the trace function and describe the graph's orientation.

5. $x = 1 - t$ and $y = 3 + t; t \in [-5, 5]$

6. $x = 2t^2$ and $y = t; t \in [-2, 2]$

7. $x = 2 - t$ and $y = t^2; t \in [-3, 3]$

8. $x = 2 \cos t$ and $y = 20 \sin t; t \in [0, 2\pi]$

Eliminate the parameter and restrict the domain to find the rectangular equation generating the same curve as the parametric equations. Use graphing technology to verify your answer.

9. $x = 1 - t$ and $y = t; t \in [-2, 2]$

10. $x = t - 2$ and $y = 1 + 2t; t \in [-1, 2]$

11. $x = t - 1$ and $y = -t^2 + 4; t \in [-2, 2]$

12. $x = -t + 1$ and $y = t^2 - 5; t \in [-3, 3]$

13. $x = -1 + t^2$ and $y = t - 1; t \in [-2, 2]$

14. $x = 1 - t^2$ and $y = t - 2; t \in [-2, 2]$

⟩ B. Exercises

Eliminate the parameter $\theta \in [0, 2\pi]$ to write the standard form equation for each conic section. Then sketch the graph with its orientation.

15. $x = 3 \sin \theta$ and $y = 4 \cos \theta$

16. $x = 5 \cos \theta$ and $y = 2 \sin \theta$

17. $x = 3 \sin \theta$ and $y = 3 \cos \theta$

18. $x = 2 \sec \theta$ and $y = 2 \tan \theta$

19. $x = 3 \tan \theta$ and $y = \sec \theta$

20. $x = \cot \theta$ and $y = 2 \csc \theta$

Eliminate the parameter $\theta \in [0, 2\pi]$ to write a standard form equation for each conic.

21. $x = 2 \cos \theta + 1$ and $y = 4 \sin \theta + 3$

22. $x = 10 \cos \theta - 2$ and $y = 10 \sin \theta + 4$

23. $x = 6 \csc \theta - 4$ and $y = 5 \cot \theta - 8$

24. $x = 3 \sec \theta + 5$ and $y = 9 \tan \theta - 5$

Use the given parameter to write a set of parametric equations for each parabolic curve.

25. $y = x^2 + 1; x \in [-2, 2]$
$t = x + 1$

26. $y = x^2 - 3; x \in [-2, 2]$
$t = x - 2$

27. $y = 2x^2 - 3; x \in [-2, 1]$
$t = x + 4$

28. $y = -4x^2 + 7; x \in [-1, 2]$
$t = 2x - 6$

Write a set of parametric equations for each conic section.

29. a hyperbola with vertices at $(-2, -2)$ and $(-2, 4)$ and foci at $(-2, -4)$ and $(-2, 6)$

30. a hyperbola with vertices at $(-2, 3)$ and $(4, 3)$ and foci at $(-4, 3)$ and $(6, 3)$

31. an ellipse with vertices at $(1, -12)$ and $(1, 8)$ and foci at $(1, -8)$ and $(1, 4)$

32. an ellipse with vertices at $(-6, 3)$ and $(4, 3)$ and co-vertices at $(-1, 0)$ and $(-1, 6)$

33. A baseball player throws a ball with a 15° angle of elevation from a height of 6.5 ft at a speed of 70 ft/sec.

   a. Write a set of parametric equations modeling the ball's path.

   b. What is the height of the ball 1 sec after release?

   c. How far will the ball have traveled across the field after 1.2 sec?

34. A quarterback passes a football with a 12° angle of elevation from a height of 6.3 ft at a speed of 64 ft/sec. Write parametric equations modeling the ball's trajectory and determine the following. Explain your reasoning.

   a. Does a defensive player whose maximum vertical reach is 7.5 ft have the ability to block the pass if it takes 0.5 sec for the ball to reach his position?

   b. Will the football be catchable for a wide receiver 30 yd down the field?

35. Autumn hits her golf ball at 120 ft/sec with a 15° launch angle. Write and graph parametric equations modeling the ball's flight and determine the following.

   a. How long is the ball in flight, and how far does the ball travel down the fairway (to the nearest yard)?

   b. By how many feet does her drive clear the top of a 10 ft tree that is 70 ft away?

36. A kicked soccer ball leaves the ground at a 30° angle of elevation and an initial speed of 85 ft/sec. Write a set of parametric equations modeling the ball's path. Determine the amount of time (to the nearest hundredth of a second) the ball is in the air and the percentage of the length of the 100 yd soccer field it travels if it was kicked straight down the field.

C. Exercises

37. Eliminate the parameter to express each set of parametric equations in the standard rectangular form of a circle.

   a. $x = r \cos \theta$ and $y = r \sin \theta$

   b. $x = r \cos \theta + h$ and $y = r \sin \theta + k$

38. Write a set of parametric equations for the circle with the given center and radius.

   a. $C\,(0, 0);\ r = 7$ **b.** $C\,(3, -2);\ r = 6$

39. Describe the graph of the parametric equations $x = a \cos \theta$ and $y = b \sin \theta$ with both a and $b > 0$ (a) if $a = b$, (b) if $a < b$, and (c) if $a > b$. Explain your reasoning.

Write a set of parametric equations for each standard form of a conic.

40. $\dfrac{(x - h)^2}{a^2} + \dfrac{(y - k)^2}{b^2} = 1$ 41. $\dfrac{(x - h)^2}{a^2} - \dfrac{(y - k)^2}{b^2} = 1$

42. **Explore:** Analyze various launch angles for a field goal attempt taken 40 yd from a goal post whose horizontal crossbar is 10 ft high. Use parametric equations to find the height of a ball kicked with an initial speed of 70 ft/sec when it reaches the goal post if kicked with launch angles of 15°, 30°, 45°, and 60°. Which of these launch angles results in a field goal?

CUMULATIVE REVIEW

Write each polar equation in rectangular form and identify the conic. [6.6]

43. $r = 8$

44. $r \sin \theta = 5$

45. $r \sin \theta = r^2 \cos^2 \theta$

Identify each conic and then state the coordinates of its vertices and foci and its eccentricity.

46. $\dfrac{(x - 2)^2}{36} + \dfrac{y^2}{16} = 1$ [8.2]

47. $9x^2 - 4y^2 = 36$ [8.3]

48. $x + (y - 1)^2 = 3$ [8.1]

49. For which θ does $\cos \theta = -\dfrac{\sqrt{3}}{2}$? List all correct answers. [4.1]

   A. $\dfrac{\pi}{6}$ **C.** $\dfrac{5\pi}{6}$ **E.** 300°

   B. $\dfrac{2\pi}{3}$ **D.** 210°

50. What is the smallest positive value of x for which $y = \sin 2x$ has a relative minimum? [4.4]

   A. $\dfrac{\pi}{4}$ **C.** $\dfrac{3\pi}{4}$ **E.** $\dfrac{3\pi}{2}$

   B. $\dfrac{\pi}{2}$ **D.** π

51. Which equation represents a parabola with a vertex at (2, 6) and a focus at (2, 3)? [8.1]

   A. $y = \dfrac{1}{12}(x + 2)^2 + 6$ **D.** $y = -\dfrac{1}{12}(x + 2)^2 + 6$

   B. $y = \dfrac{1}{12}(x - 2)^2 + 6$ **E.** $y = -\dfrac{1}{12}(x - 2)^2 + 6$

   C. $y = \dfrac{1}{12}(x - 2)^2 - 6$

52. Use the discriminant test to classify the conic $4x^2 + 12xy = -9y^2 + 16$. [8.4]

   A. circle   **C.** parabola

   B. ellipse   **D.** hyperbola

8.6 Polar Equations of Conics

Engineers calculate the precise amount of thrust that generates the hyperbolic path used by spacecraft as they escape Earth's gravitational pull.

Earlier in this chapter a parabola was defined as the set of points equidistant from a given point (the focus) and a given line (the directrix). Ellipses and hyperbolas were defined as the set of points such that the sum or difference of the distances from two points (the foci) is constant. Defining parabolas, ellipses, and hyperbolas in terms of the distance from each point to a focus and to its related directrix provides a unified definition for these conics.

DEFINITIONS

A **conic section** is the set of points in a plane whose distances from a given line (its **directrix**) and a given point (its **focus**) not on that line have a constant ratio. This ratio, $\frac{PF}{PD} = e$, is the **eccentricity** of the conic.

> **After completing this section, you will be able to**
> - identify polar equations of conics in terms of eccentricity.
> - write and graph the polar equation of a conic, given its eccentricity and directrix.
> - analyze planetary orbits with polar conics.

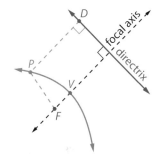

The line through the focus that is perpendicular to the directrix is the conic's *focal axis*, and any intersection of the conic and its focal axis is a *vertex*. If the center of a conic is located at the origin, the resulting rectangular equation is relatively simple. When representing a conic section by a polar equation, it is often simpler to position a focus at the pole (or origin) with the directrix perpendicular to or parallel to the polar axis. While a parabola has one focus and one directrix, either of the two focus-directrix pairs in an ellipse or a hyperbola can be used to define the conic.

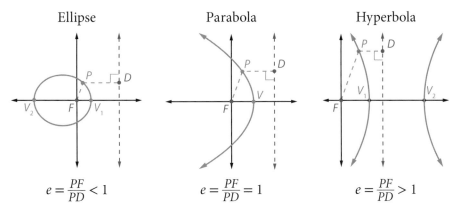

Ellipse $\quad e = \frac{PF}{PD} < 1$

Parabola $\quad e = \frac{PF}{PD} = 1$

Hyperbola $\quad e = \frac{PF}{PD} > 1$

To find a unified polar equation for conics, consider the point $P(r, \theta)$ on the conic whose focus is at the pole and whose directrix is d units to the right of the pole perpendicular to the polar axis. From the figure, note that $PF = r$ and $PD = d - r\cos\theta$. Solving $\frac{PF}{PD} = e$ for PF implies that $PF = e \cdot PD$. Substitute and solve for r.

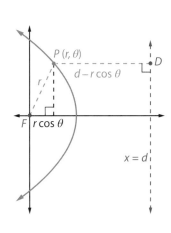

$$PF = e \cdot PD$$
$$r = e(d - r\cos\theta)$$
$$r = ed - er\cos\theta$$
$$r + er\cos\theta = ed$$
$$r(1 + e\cos\theta) = ed$$
$$r = \frac{ed}{1 + e\cos\theta}$$

Johan de Witt, a Dutch politician and mathematician, coined the word *directrix* in his seventeenth-century work *Elements of Linear Curves*. De Witt thought it unnecessary to use a three-dimensional object (cone) to define two-dimensional curves.

Similar derivations can be done when the directrix is d units to the left of the pole and when it is d units above or below the pole.

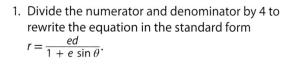

Polar Equations for Conics

standard orientations for any conic with a focus at the pole, $e > 0$, and $d > 0$

$r = \dfrac{ed}{1 + e \cos \theta}$	$r = \dfrac{ed}{1 - e \cos \theta}$	$r = \dfrac{ed}{1 + e \sin \theta}$	$r = \dfrac{ed}{1 - e \sin \theta}$
directrix: $x = d$	directrix: $x = -d$	directrix: $y = d$	directrix: $y = -d$

Explore the graphs of these conics as described in the Technology Corner on p. 419. Circles and degenerate conics cannot be represented by these polar equations. The type of conic and its orientation can be determined by analyzing its polar equation.

Example 1   Analyzing Polar Equations of Conics

Determine the eccentricity, type of conic, and directrix for each polar equation.

a. $r = \dfrac{6}{4 + 3 \sin \theta}$

b. $r = \dfrac{-9}{6 \cos \theta - 3}$

Answer

a. $r = \dfrac{6 \div 4}{(4 + 3 \sin \theta) \div 4}$

$r = \dfrac{1.5}{1 + 0.75 \sin \theta}$

1. Divide the numerator and denominator by 4 to rewrite the equation in the standard form $r = \dfrac{ed}{1 + e \sin \theta}$.

$e = 0.75;$ $ed = 1.5$
$d = \dfrac{1.5}{0.75} = 2$

2. Identify the eccentricity, e, and the distance of the directrix from the pole, d.

The conic is an ellipse with directrix $y = 2$.

3. Use the eccentricity, $e < 1$, and the standard form to identify the conic and locate the directrix.

Check

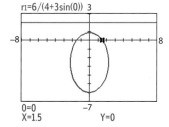

r1=6/(4+3sin(θ)) 3
-8 ... 8
0=0   -7
X=1.5   Y=0

4. Use technology to graph the ellipse and its directrix, $r = 2 \csc \theta$, in polar mode.

---

b. $r = \dfrac{-9 \div (-3)}{(6 \cos \theta - 3) \div (-3)}$

$r = \dfrac{3}{1 - 2 \cos \theta}$

1. Divide the numerator and denominator by -3 to rewrite the equation in the standard form $r = \dfrac{ed}{1 - e \cos \theta}$.

$e = 2;$ $ed = 3$
$d = \dfrac{3}{2} = 1.5$

2. Identify the eccentricity, e, and the distance of the directrix from the pole, d.

The conic is a hyperbola with directrix $x = -1.5$.

3. Use the eccentricity, $e > 1$, and the standard form to identify the conic and locate the directrix.

Check

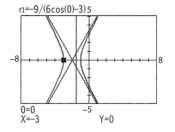

r1=-9/(6cos(θ)-3) 5
-8 ... 8
0=0   -5
X=-3   Y=0

4. Use technology to graph the hyperbola and its directrix, $r = -1.5 \sec \theta$, in polar mode.

SKILL ✔ **EXERCISE 3**

The characteristics of a conic can be used to write the polar equation of a conic.

Example 2 Writing the Polar Equation of a Conic

Write a polar equation for each conic section with a focus at the origin.

a. $e = 1$; directrix: $y = -3$

b. $e = \frac{1}{3}$; vertices at $(-4, 0)$ and $(2, 0)$

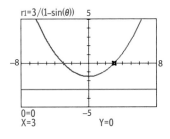

Answer

a. $r = \dfrac{(1)(3)}{1 - (1)\sin\theta}$, $\therefore r = \dfrac{3}{1 - \sin\theta}$

1. Substitute into the standard form $r = \dfrac{ed}{1 - e\sin\theta}$ where $d = 3$, since the directrix crosses the negative y-axis.

Check

2. Use technology to graph the parabola and its directrix, $r = -3\csc\theta$.

b. $C\left(\dfrac{-4+2}{2}, \dfrac{0+0}{2}\right) = (-1, 0)$

1. Since $e < 1$, the conic is an ellipse. Use the vertices to find its center.

$2 = \dfrac{\left(\frac{1}{3}\right)d}{1 + \left(\frac{1}{3}\right)\cos(0)} \cdot \dfrac{3}{3}$

2. Since the center is on the negative x-axis, the directrix has form $x = d$. Use the standard form $r = \dfrac{ed}{1 + e\cos\theta}$, $e = \frac{1}{3}$, and a point on the ellipse, $(r, \theta) = (2, 0)$, to find d.

$2 = \dfrac{d}{3 + 1}$; $d = 8$

$r = \dfrac{\frac{1}{3}(8)}{1 + \frac{1}{3}\cos\theta}$ or $r = \dfrac{8}{3 + \cos\theta}$

3. Substitute e and d into the standard form and simplify the complex fraction.

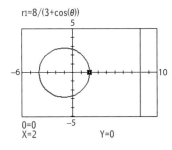

Check

4. Use technology to graph the ellipse and its directrix, $r = 8\sec\theta$.

SKILL ✓ **EXERCISE 15**

The relationships between the center, foci, vertices, and co-vertices learned in earlier sections of this chapter can be used to rewrite polar equations of conics as equivalent rectangular equations.

Example 3 Writing the Rectangular Equation of a Conic

Write a rectangular equation for the conic represented by $r = \dfrac{9}{4 + 5\cos\theta}$.

Answer

$r = \dfrac{9 \div 4}{(4 + 5\cos\theta) \div 4}$

$r = \dfrac{2.25}{1 + 1.25\cos\theta}$; $e = 1.25$

1. Rewrite the equation in the standard form $r = \dfrac{ed}{1 + e\cos\theta}$ and identify the eccentricity which indicates that the conic is a hyperbola with vertices on the polar axis.

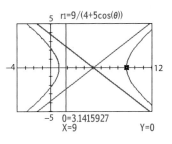

$r(0) = \dfrac{9}{4 + 5\cos(0)} = \dfrac{9}{4 + 5} = 1$

$r(\pi) = \dfrac{9}{4 + 5\cos(\pi)} = \dfrac{9}{4 - 5} = -9$

2. Evaluate the polar function at 0 and π to find the vertices in polar form.

	(r, θ)	(x, y)
V_1	$(1, 0)$	$(1, 0)$
V_2	$(-9, \pi)$	$(9, 0)$

3. Express the vertices using rectangular coordinates.

$V_1 : x = 1\cos 0 = 1$; $y = 1\sin 0 = 0$
$V_2 : x = -9\cos\pi = 9$; $y = -9\sin\pi = 0$

$C\left(\dfrac{1 + 9}{2}, \dfrac{0 + 0}{2}\right) = (5, 0)$; $c = 5$

4. Find the center (h, k) and use the fact that the focus is at the origin to find the value of c.

$a = \dfrac{c}{e} = \dfrac{5}{1.25} = 4$

$b^2 = c^2 - a^2 = 25 - 16 = 9$

5. Find the values of a and b^2 using $e = \frac{c}{a}$ and $c^2 = a^2 + b^2$.

CONTINUED ➡

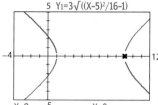

$$\frac{(x-5)^2}{16} - \frac{y^2}{9} = 1$$

Check

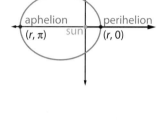

6. Write the standard rectangular form for a hyperbola with a horizontal transverse axis:
$$\frac{(x-h)^2}{a^2} - \frac{(y-k)^2}{b^2} = 1.$$

7. Graph the functions $y = \pm 3\sqrt{\frac{(x-5)^2}{16} - 1}$ and compare their graphs to the polar graph.

———— SKILL ✓ **EXERCISE 23**

The orbits of planets, comets, and satellites are frequently modeled by polar equations in which the much more massive central body is placed at the focus. This expresses the distance to the orbiting object as a function of the angle traveled from the polar axis.

Modeling an elliptical orbit with $r = \dfrac{ed}{1 + e\cos\theta}$ causes the perihelion (the point closest to the sun) to occur when $\theta = 0$ and the aphelion (the point farthest from the sun) to occur when $\theta = \pi$. The length of the major axis is the sum of the r-values for these two vertices:

$$2a = \frac{ed}{1 + e\cos 0} + \frac{ed}{1 + e\cos\pi} = \frac{ed}{1+e} + \frac{ed}{1-e} = \frac{ed(1-e) + ed(1+e)}{1-e^2} = \frac{2ed}{1-e^2}.$$
$$\therefore ed = a(1 - e^2).$$

The elliptical orbit can then be modeled in terms of the semimajor axis and the eccentricity:

$$r = \frac{a(1 - e^2)}{1 + e\cos\theta}.$$

Example 4 Modeling an Orbit with a Polar Equation

Write a polar equation modeling the orbit of Comet Borrelly, given its eccentricity of 0.624 and its semimajor axis of 3.61 AU. Then find the distances to its perihelion and aphelion.

Answer

$$r = \frac{3.61(1 - 0.624^2)}{1 + 0.624\cos\theta}$$

$$r(0) = \frac{3.61(1 - 0.624^2)}{1 + 0.624} \approx 1.36 \text{ AU}$$

$$r(\pi) = \frac{3.61(1 - 0.624^2)}{1 - 0.624} \approx 5.86 \text{ AU}$$

Check

$$1.36 + 5.86 = 2(3.61) = 7.22 \text{ AU}$$

1. Write the equation in the standard form
$$r = \frac{a(1 - e^2)}{1 + e\cos\theta}.$$

2. Evaluate $r(0)$ to determine the perihelion distance and $r(\pi)$ to determine the aphelion distance.

3. The sum of the perihelion and aphelion is the length of the major axis.

———— SKILL ✓ **EXERCISE 31**

The eccentricity of the hyperbolic path of Oumuamua, the first interstellar object ever observed, is 1.20. From its perihelion it is approximately 0.25 AU (23,700,000 mi) from the sun.

A. Exercises

Determine the eccentricity, type of conic, and directrix for each polar equation.

1. $r = \dfrac{4}{1 + \sin \theta}$

2. $r = \dfrac{27}{3 \cos \theta + 1}$

3. $r = \dfrac{18}{2 - 12 \cos \theta}$

4. $r = \dfrac{12}{2 \sin \theta + 8}$

5. $r = \dfrac{-6}{\cos \theta - 0.75}$

6. $r = \dfrac{49}{2 - 7 \sin \theta}$

7. $r = \dfrac{7}{5 - 3 \cos \theta}$

8. $r = \dfrac{10}{2 - 5 \sin \theta}$

Match each equation with its graph.

A.
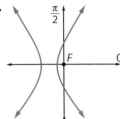

D.
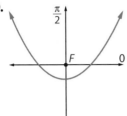

B.
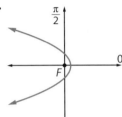

E.
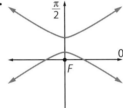

C.
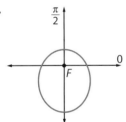

F.
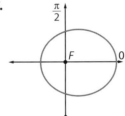

9. $r = \dfrac{2}{1 + 2 \sin \theta}$

10. $r = \dfrac{1}{1 + \cos \theta}$

11. $r = \dfrac{2.5}{1 - 0.5 \cos \theta}$

12. $r = \dfrac{4}{2 + \sin \theta}$

13. $r = \dfrac{5}{2 - 2 \sin \theta}$

14. $r = \dfrac{6}{3 - 6 \cos \theta}$

Write a polar equation for each conic section. Then classify the conic and verify your answer by using technology to graph the curve and its directrix.

15. $e = 1$; directrix: $y = 5$

16. $e = \frac{1}{2}$; directrix: $x = -3$

17. $e = 2$; directrix: $y = -1$

18. $e = \frac{5}{2}$; directrix: $x = 2$

B. Exercises

Write a polar equation for each conic section with a focus at the pole. Then use technology to graph the conic and its directrix.

19. $e = 0.5$; $V(x, y)$: $(-3, 0)$, $(1, 0)$

20. $e = \frac{3}{2}$; $V(x, y)$: $(3, 0)$, $(15, 0)$

21. $e = 2$; $V(r, \theta)$: $\left(2, \frac{\pi}{2}\right)$, $\left(-6, \frac{3\pi}{2}\right)$

22. $e = 1$; $V(r, \theta)$: $\left(\frac{5}{2}, \frac{3\pi}{2}\right)$

Write a rectangular equation for each conic.

23. $r = \dfrac{30}{4 + \sin \theta}$

24. $r = \dfrac{10}{2 - 3 \cos \theta}$

25. $r = \dfrac{4}{1 + \cos \theta}$

26. $r = \dfrac{5}{2 - 2 \sin \theta}$

27. $r = \dfrac{24}{1 - 3 \sin \theta}$

28. $r = \dfrac{42}{5 + 2 \cos \theta}$

29. Elliptical orbits can be modeled by $r = \dfrac{a(1 - e^2)}{1 + e \cos \theta}$. Use this equation to find expressions for the perihelion distance and the aphelion distance in terms of the semimajor axis and eccentricity.

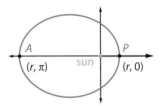

Write the equation modeling each planet's orbit, given its eccentricity and semimajor axis length. Then find its perihelion and aphelion distances.

30. Neptune: $e = 0.009$, $a = 30.06$ AU

31. Mars: $e = 0.093$, $a = 1.524$ AU

Write the polar form equation for each conic section.

32. $x^2 = 6y + 9$

33. $y^2 - 8x - 16 = 0$

34. $3(x + 2)^2 + 4y^2 = 48$

35. $\dfrac{(y - 5)^2}{16} - \dfrac{x^2}{9} = 1$

C. Exercises

36. Write the polar form equation for $\dfrac{x^2}{64} - \dfrac{y^2}{36} = 1$.

Make a sketch of the given directrix ($d > 0$) and the conic with its focus at the origin (similar to the last figure on p. 435). Then use the sketch and the definition of a conic to derive the standard form polar equation for the conic.

37. $x = -d$; $r = \dfrac{ed}{1 - e \cos \theta}$

38. $y = d$; $r = \dfrac{ed}{1 + e \sin \theta}$

39. $y = -d$; $r = \dfrac{ed}{1 - e \sin \theta}$

State the rotation formulas that will rotate each general quadratic equation to a *uv*-plane without a *uv*-term. [8.4]

40. $-x^2 + 2xy - y^2 + \sqrt{2}x + \sqrt{2}y + 144 = 0$

41. $3x^2 - 4\sqrt{3}xy + 7y^2 + 120 = 0$

42. Graph $(x - 4)^2 + \dfrac{(y - 1)^2}{25} = 1$ and its foci. Then state its eccentricity. [8.2]

State the next three terms of each sequence. [Algebra]

43. 5, 10, 15, 20…

44. 4, 16, 64, 256…

45. Find the first, second, and tenth term of the sequence $a_n = 4n$. [Algebra]

46. Which polar coordinate expression is equivalent to the rectangular coordinates $(1, \sqrt{3})$? [6.4]

    A. $(1, 30°)$ **C.** $(2, 30°)$ **E.** $(4, 30°)$

    B. $(1, 60°)$ **D.** $(2, 60°)$

47. Find AB if $A = \begin{bmatrix} 2 & 1 \\ 4 & -2 \end{bmatrix}$ and $B = \begin{bmatrix} 0 & -1 \\ 3 & 1 \end{bmatrix}$. [7.2]

    A. $\begin{bmatrix} 2 & -1 \\ 12 & -2 \end{bmatrix}$ **C.** $\begin{bmatrix} 3 & -1 \\ 12 & -6 \end{bmatrix}$ **E.** $\begin{bmatrix} 0 & -1 \\ 12 & -2 \end{bmatrix}$

    B. $\begin{bmatrix} 6 & 0 \\ 12 & 0 \end{bmatrix}$ **D.** $\begin{bmatrix} 3 & -1 \\ -6 & -6 \end{bmatrix}$

48. Find the domain for the graph of $x = t + 1$ and $y = 1 - t^2$ where $t \in [-2, 2]$. [8.5]

    A. $x \in [-2, 2]$ **C.** $x \in [-3, 1]$ **E.** $x \in \mathbb{R}$

    B. $x \in [-1, 3]$ **D.** $x \in [0, 4]$

49. Find the domain for the graph of $x = t^2 - 3$ and $y = t - 1$ where $t \in [-2, 2]$. [8.5]

    A. $x \in [-2, 2]$ **C.** $x \in [1, 7]$ **E.** $x \in [-3, 1]$

    B. $x \in [1, 9]$ **D.** $x \in [3, 7]$

DATA ANALYSIS

Conics in Space

In his State of the Union address on January 25, 1984, President Ronald Reagan directed NASA to construct an international space station (ISS). The first crew arrived in November 2000, and the ISS has been continuously occupied ever since. Reusable American space shuttles completed more than 30 missions delivering and assembling components of the space station. Rendezvousing and docking with a platform traveling at nearly 5 mi/sec requires careful planning.

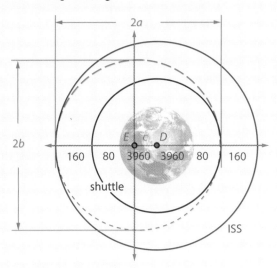

The diagram provides a simplified overview of how the properties of conic sections are used to complete a successful rendezvous. The shuttle initially assumes a circular orbit closer to the earth than the space station so that it can "catch up" to the station. The shuttle fires its rockets to complete half of an elliptical orbit (dashed line) that takes it to the orbit of the ISS.

The radius of the earth is 3960 mi. Assume that the ISS is in a circular orbit 240 mi above the surface of the earth, and the initial orbit of the shuttle is 80 mi above the surface of the earth. Let D represent the center of the earth and E represent the center of the elliptical orbit. Use E as the origin of your coordinate system and assume the orbits are coplanar.

1. State the coordinates of D.

2. Write standard form equations that model the circular orbits of the ISS and the shuttle.

3. Write a standard form equation modeling the elliptical orbit and state the orbit's eccentricity.

While the touchdown of Atlantis on July 21, 2011, marked the end of the space shuttle program, the essential role of conics in space exploration continues. In April 2018, NASA used a commercial rocket to launch the Transiting Exoplanet Survey Satellite (TESS) into an elliptical high-earth orbit. TESS is designed to conduct an exhaustive search for exoplanets, planets that orbit a star other than our sun.

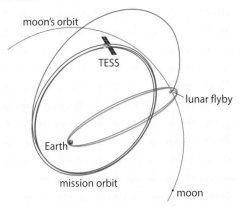

Its unique orbit requires a gravitational assist from a flyby of the moon that propels it into a hyperbolic trajectory toward its final orbit. To reach the precise path required for the flyby, TESS will make a series of "phasing" orbits whose apogee (farthest point from the earth) increases from about 150,000 mi to over 240,000 mi. Once established in its final orbit, TESS will complete one orbit every 13.7 days, two orbits for every one moon orbit. Combining this period with an orbital plane orthogonal to the moon's orbit virtually eliminates perturbations (orbital disruptions) caused by the moon's gravitational pull. The orbit is also designed so that each perigee (closest point to the earth) is well above the narrow band occupied by geostationary satellites. At each perigee TESS will download approximately 10 billion pixels of data to NASA's Pleiades supercomputer.

Assume that TESS's final elliptical orbit has an apogee of 235,960 mi and a focal length of 82,500 mi.

4. Write a standard form rectangular equation that models this orbit with an ellipse centered at the origin and Earth at the focus on the positive x-axis.

5. How close is TESS to Earth's surface at perigee?

6. Find the eccentricity of TESS's final elliptical orbit.

7. Write a polar equation modeling TESS's final orbit.

Scientists expect to identify tens of thousands of new exoplanets from this data. As more planets are discovered and the vastness of space becomes more apparent, many people question our place in the universe, or whether the human race is significant at all. Despair would be a logical conclusion in a godless universe. A biblical worldview, however, allows us to marvel and rejoice as the Creator God's majesty and power are increasingly displayed.

8. Psalm 8 records David's musings as he considered God's vast creation. Use Psalm 8 to list some appropriate biblical worldview responses to a vast universe.

9. Much of space exploration is driven by a desire to find life on other planets.

   a. The answer to what major question is being sought with this goal?

   b. What would finding life on another planet seem to indicate from a secular worldview?

10. In a 1995 television interview Stephen Hawking said, "The human race is just a chemical scum on a moderate-sized planet, orbiting around a very average star in the outer suburb of one among a hundred billion galaxies. We are so insignificant that I can't believe the whole universe exists for our benefit." Evaluate each part of this statement from a biblical worldview.

    a. The human race is a chemical scum.

    b. The earth is very small in a vast universe.

    c. The human race is insignificant.

    d. The universe exists for our benefit.

Chapter 8 Review

Graph the parabola and its vertex, focus, and directrix. [8.1]

1. $(x - 3)^2 = 8(y + 1)$ **2.** $y^2 = -4(x - 1)$

Write the equation of the parabola with the following characteristics. [8.1]

3. $V(3, -3)$; $F(3, -2.5)$

4. $F\left(\frac{5}{4}, 2\right)$; directrix: $x = \frac{3}{4}$

Graph the parabola and its focus and directrix. [8.1]

5. $-\frac{1}{4}x^2 - y + 3x - 5 = 0$ **6.** $-y^2 + 8x = 4y - 20$

7. Find the equation of the line tangent to $x^2 + 2y = 0$ at $(2, -2)$. [8.1]

8. The deck of the Hulme Arch Bridge in Manchester, England, is supported by cables attached to a parabolic arch that is 25 m high and that is 52 m wide at its base. Write a standard form equation that models the arch with one base at the origin and the other on the positive x-axis. [8.1]

9. Find the vertices, the foci, and the eccentricity for $\frac{x^2}{9} + \frac{y^2}{16} = 1$. Then graph the ellipse and its foci. [8.2]

Write each equation in the standard form for an ellipse. Then find its foci and eccentricity and graph the conic. [8.2]

10. $x^2 + y^2 - 2x + 4y = 4$

11. $x^2 + 4y^2 + 6x - 8y + 9 = 0$

Write the standard form equation of each described ellipse. [8.2]

12. vertices: $(7, -4)$, $(-3, -4)$
     co-vertices: $(2, -1)$, $(2, -7)$

13. co-vertices: $(-3, -3)$, $(7, -3)$
     foci: $(2, 9)$, $(2, -15)$

14. $C(0, 0)$, $e = 0.75$
     vertices: $(0, \pm4)$

15. $F(3, 3)$ and $(3, -5)$
     a minor axis length of 6

16. A whispering room is designed with a focus 2 ft from the northern wall and 16 ft from the southern wall. Write a standard form equation modeling the elliptical room, using the northern focus as the origin. Verify your equation by using technology to graph the ellipse. [8.2]

17. Graph $\frac{x^2}{9} - \frac{y^2}{4} = 1$ and state the equations of its asymptotes. [8.3]

18. State the center, vertices, and equations of the asymptotes for $\frac{(x - 4)^2}{16} - \frac{(y + 1)^2}{4} = 1$. [8.3]

State the center, vertices, co-vertices, foci, and eccentricity for each hyperbola. [8.3]

19. $16(y + 9)^2 - 9(x - 15)^2 = 144$

20. $y^2 - 4x^2 - 2y - 16x = 31$

Write a standard form equation for each hyperbola with the given characteristics. [8.3]

21. foci at $(0, \pm4)$; $e = \frac{4}{3}$

22. center at $(-1, 3)$, vertex at $(5, 3)$,
     an asymptote of $y = 2x + 5$

Write a general quadratic form equation for each hyperbola with the given characteristics. [8.3]

23. vertices at $(6, 1)$ and $(-4, 1)$; $e = \frac{\sqrt{34}}{5}$

24. vertices at $(5, -3)$ and $(5, 5)$; $e = \frac{\sqrt{5}}{2}$

25. Frank is 3000 ft due west of Rodger. Rodger hears a dynamite blast 1 sec before Frank hears it. If the sound traveled at 1126 ft/sec, model the possible locations of the blast with the equation of a hyperbola in which the locations of Frank and Rodger are foci on the horizontal axis. [8.3]

26. Determine whether each conic is rotated, then classify its graph as a hyperbola, parabola, ellipse, or circle. [8.4]
     a. $3x^2 - 2\sqrt{3}xy + y^2 + 8\sqrt{3}x + 8y - 8x - 8\sqrt{3}y + 96 = 0$
     b. $x^2 + 4y^2 - 4x + 40y + 96 = 0$
     c. $7x^2 + 2xy - 3y^2 + 5x + 11y - 7 = 0$

State the rotation formulas that will rotate the equation to the *uv*-plane without a *uv*-term. [8.4]

27. $x^2 + 8xy + y^2 + 9 = 0$

28. $13x^2 + 6\sqrt{3}xy + 7y^2 - 15x + 8y - 221 = 0$

Find the angle of rotation of the *xy*-plane that causes the *u*- or *v*-axis to be parallel to the conic's axis. Then write the standard form equation in terms of *u* and *v* and sketch a graph of the conic and any foci. [8.4]

29. $5x^2 + 26xy + 5y^2 - 72 = 0$

30. $3x^2 - 4\sqrt{3}xy + 7y^2 - 9 = 0$

31. $9x^2 + 12xy + 4y^2 + 8\sqrt{13}x + \sqrt{13}y + 13 = 0$

Write a general form equation for each conic in terms of *x* and *y*, given its angle of rotation and equation in terms of *u* and *v*. Then use technology to graph the conic. [8.4]

32. $v^2 - 4u = 0$; $\theta = 45°$ **33.** $u^2 + 4v^2 = 25$; $\theta = 30°$

34. Graph $x = t + 1$ and $y = t^2 - 2$; $t \in [-2, 2]$ and indicate the orientation. [8.5]

35. Given $x = 1 + t^2$ and $y = t + 2$; $t \in [-2, 2]$, eliminate the parameter and restrict the domain to find the rectangular equation generating the same curve. Use graphing technology to verify your answer. [8.5]

Eliminate the parameter for each conic and write the resulting equation in standard form. [8.5]

36. $x = 10 \sin \theta$ and $y = 10 \cos \theta$

37. $x = 8 \sin \theta + 5$ and $y = 3 \cos \theta - 2$

38. Write a set of parametric equations for $y = 2x^2 - 1$ where $x \in [-2, 2]$ given $t = x - 2$.

Write a set of parametric equations for each described conic. [8.5]

39. an ellipse with vertices at $(-3, 1)$ and $(9, 1)$ and a minor axis length of 4

40. a hyperbola with vertices at $(1, 10)$ and $(1, -6)$ and foci at $(1, 12)$ and $(1, -8)$

41. A quarterback throws a football from a height of 6.3 ft with a 20° angle of elevation and speed of 60 ft/sec. [8.5]

   a. Write a set of parametric equations modeling the ball's trajectory.

   b. Find the height of the ball 1.2 sec after release.

   c. How far has the ball traveled down the field after 1.4 sec?

Determine the eccentricity, type of conic, and directrix for each polar equation. [8.6]

42. $r = \dfrac{6}{2 + 3 \cos \theta}$ **43.** $r = \dfrac{5}{1 - 0.2 \sin \theta}$

Write a polar equation for each conic section. Then use technology to graph the conic and its directrix. [8.6]

44. $e = 1$; directrix: $x = -2$ **45.** $e = \frac{2}{3}$; directrix: $y = -3$

Write a polar equation for each conic section with a focus at the pole. Then use technology to graph the conic and its directrix. [8.6]

46. $e = 2$; $V_1 (-3, 0)$, $V_2 (-1, 0)$

47. $e = 1$; $V (0, 1)$

Write a rectangular equation for each conic. [8.6]

48. $r = \dfrac{6}{1 - \sin \theta}$ **49.** $r = \dfrac{3}{1 + 2 \cos \theta}$

50. Write a polar equation modeling the orbit of Venus, given its eccentricity of 0.007 and semimajor axis length of 0.723 AU. Then find its perihelion and aphelion distances. [8.6]

9 Sequences and Series

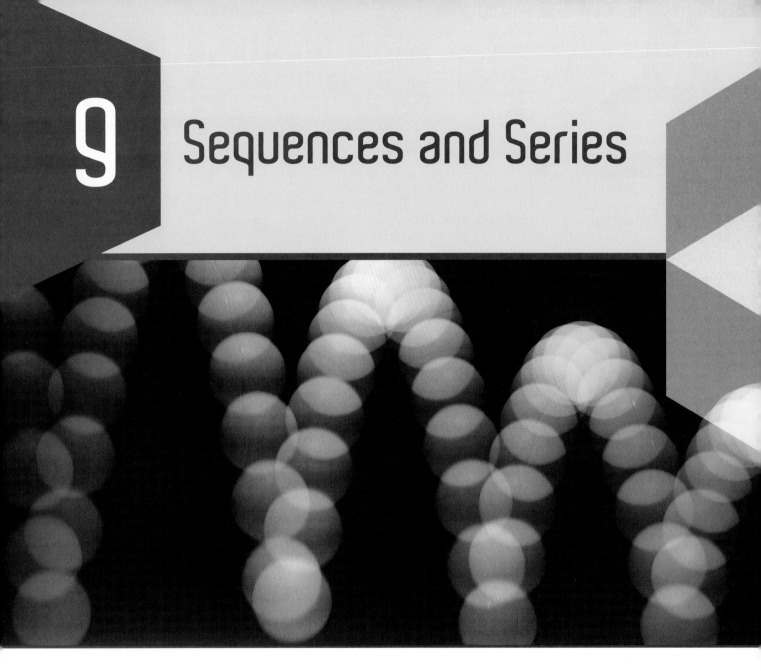

BIBLICAL PERSPECTIVE OF MATHEMATICS
From Siri® to chatbots to self-driving cars, artificial intelligence (AI) seems to be the unstoppable wave of the future. Bill Gates and Stephen Hawking have warned of its potential dangers. How does a biblical worldview inform our opinions of AI?

HISTORICAL CONNECTION
While Isaac Newton is credited with the Binomial Theorem and Blaise Pascal with his eponymous triangle, the first written expansion of a binomial can be traced to Euclid, and charts equivalent to Pascal's triangle can be found in a 1303 Chinese publication.

DATA ANALYSIS
Leonhard Euler's solution to a popular puzzle concerning bridges crossed while taking a stroll resulted in the birth of graph theory—the mathematics at the heart of navigation applications that provide optimal routing in near real time.

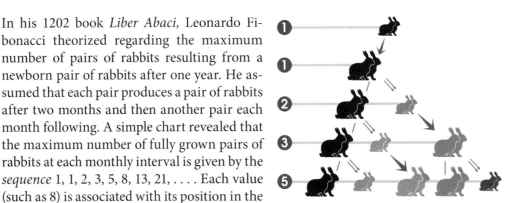

The Fibonacci sequence can be used to model a population of rabbits.

After completing this section, you will be able to

- represent sequences numerically, algebraically, and graphically.
- evaluate expressions containing factorial notation.
- determine whether a sequence is divergent or convergent.
- use sigma notation to find the sum of terms in a sequence.
- model and solve real-world problems using sequences.

The golden ratio can be represented using the Fibonacci sequence, $\lim\limits_{n \to \infty} \dfrac{a_n}{a_{n-1}} = \phi$ (phi). This number can frequently be found in God's creation.

KEYWORD SEARCH

Fibonacci sequence 🔍

In his 1202 book *Liber Abaci*, Leonardo Fibonacci theorized regarding the maximum number of pairs of rabbits resulting from a newborn pair of rabbits after one year. He assumed that each pair produces a pair of rabbits after two months and then another pair each month following. A simple chart revealed that the maximum number of fully grown pairs of rabbits at each monthly interval is given by the *sequence* 1, 1, 2, 3, 5, 8, 13, 21, ... Each value (such as 8) is associated with its position in the sequence (month 6). Unlike in a set, the order of elements is important in a sequence.

DEFINITIONS

An **infinite sequence** is a function whose domain is the natural numbers, $\mathbb{N}$, and whose range contains the function values $a_1, a_2, a_3, \ldots, a_n, \ldots$, which are the *terms* of the sequence. The nth term is called the *general term*. The domain of a **finite sequence** of n terms consists of the first n natural numbers.

Since functions are sets of ordered pairs, Fibonacci's sequence above is a shortened notation for $\{(1, 1), (2, 1), (3, 2), (4, 3), (5, 5), (6, 8), (7, 13), (8, 21), \ldots\}$, and $f(6) = a_6 = 8$. Set notation is rarely used since the simple list is more convenient.

Example 1 Writing the Terms of a Sequence

Find the first 4 terms and the tenth term of each sequence.

a. $a_n = 5n + 3$

b. $a_n = n^2 + 1$

c. $a_n = \dfrac{(-1)^{n-1}}{2n}$

Answer

a. $a_1 = 5(1) + 3 = 8$
$a_2 = 5(2) + 3 = 13$
$a_3 = 5(3) + 3 = 18$
$a_4 = 5(4) + 3 = 23$
$\vdots$
$a_{10} = 5(10) + 3 = 53$

b. $a_1 = (1)^2 + 1 = 2$
$a_2 = (2)^2 + 1 = 5$
$a_3 = (3)^2 + 1 = 10$
$a_4 = (4)^2 + 1 = 17$
$\vdots$
$a_{10} = (10)^2 + 1 = 101$

c. $a_1 = \dfrac{(-1)^{1-1}}{2(1)} = \dfrac{1}{2}$

$a_2 = \dfrac{(-1)^{2-1}}{2(2)} = -\dfrac{1}{4}$

$a_3 = \dfrac{(-1)^{3-1}}{2(3)} = \dfrac{1}{6}$

$a_4 = \dfrac{(-1)^{4-1}}{2(4)} = -\dfrac{1}{8}$
$\vdots$

$a_{10} = \dfrac{(-1)^{10-1}}{2(10)} = -\dfrac{1}{20}$

SKILL ✔ **EXERCISE 5**

Mathematicians frequently study the patterns found in sequences. Examining the relationship between successive terms and the position of each term can help determine the unlisted terms in a sequence. Stating an *explicit formula* for the nth term as a function of n clearly defines the sequence.

Example 2   Finding an Explicit Formula for a Sequence

Write an explicit formula for the value of a_n and use it to find the tenth term.

a. $17, 20, 23, 26, \ldots$ **b.** $-5, 10, -20, 40, \ldots$ **c.** $0, 3, 8, 15, \ldots$

Answer

a. Each successive term increases by 3.
$a_2 = 17 + 3$
$a_3 = (17 + 3) + 3$
$\quad = 17 + 2(3)$
$a_4 = [17 + 2(3)] + 3$
$\quad = 17 + 3(3)$
$\vdots$
$a_n = 17 + 3(n - 1)$
$\quad = 3n + 14$
$a_{10} = 3(10) + 14 = 44$

b. Each term is the product of the previous term and -2.
$a_2 = -5(-2)$
$a_3 = [-5(-2)](-2) = -5(-2)^2$
$a_4 = [-5(-2)^2](-2) = -5(-2)^3$
$\vdots$
$a_n = -5(-2)^{n-1}$
$a_{10} = -5(-2)^{10-1} = 2560$

c. Each term is 1 less than the square of its position.
$a_1 = 1^2 - 1$
$a_2 = 2^2 - 1$
$a_3 = 3^2 - 1$
$a_4 = 4^2 - 1$
$\vdots$
$a_n = n^2 - 1$
$a_{10} = 10^2 - 1 = 99$

SKILL ✔ **EXERCISE 15**

You may have noticed in Example 2c that the differences between consecutive terms are consecutive odd numbers. While this fact allows the next term to be determined, it does not easily lead to an explicit formula. A *recursive formula* for a sequence states the first term(s) and defines the remaining terms using the previous term(s).

Example 3   Writing the Terms of a Sequence

Write the first 6 terms of the sequence defined by $b_1 = 2$, $b_2 = 4$, $b_k = b_{k-1} + b_{k-2}$ where $k \geq 3$.

Answer

by definition:
$b_1 = 2$
$b_2 = 4$

using the recursive formula:
$b_3 = b_2 + b_1 = 4 + 2 = 6$
$b_4 = b_3 + b_2 = 6 + 4 = 10$
$b_5 = b_4 + b_3 = 10 + 6 = 16$
$b_6 = b_5 + b_4 = 16 + 10 = 26$

Therefore, the first 6 terms are:
2, 4, 6, 10, 16, 26.

SKILL ✔ **EXERCISE 7**

TIP

While any variable can be used to represent the sequence or the subscripts, $i, j, k,$ and n are frequently used for the subscripts. If the general term is b_k, the previous term is b_{k-1} and the next term is b_{k+1}.

Comparing consecutive terms is especially helpful when finding the pattern used in a recursive formula.

Example 4   Finding a Recursive Formula for a Sequence

Write a recursive formula for each sequence and use it to find a_5, a_6, and a_7.

a. 17, 20, 23, 26, . . .   **b.** −5, 10, −20, 40, . . .   **c.** 0, 3, 8, 15, . . .

Answer

a. After 17, each term increases by 3.

$a_1 = 17$, $a_n = a_{n-1} + 3$ where $n \geq 2$

$a_5 = 26 + 3 = 29$
$a_6 = 29 + 3 = 32$
$a_7 = 32 + 3 = 35$

b. After −5, each term is the product of the previous term and −2.

$a_1 = -5$, $a_n = -2a_{n-1}$ where $n \geq 2$

$a_5 = -2(40) = -80$
$a_6 = -2(-80) = 160$
$a_7 = -2(160) = -320$

c. After 0 and 3, the difference between a term and the preceding term is two more than the difference between the two previous terms.

$a_1 = 0$, $a_2 = 3$
$a_n = a_{n-1} + (a_{n-1} - a_{n-2}) + 2$
$= 2a_{n-1} - a_{n-2} + 2$, $n \geq 3$

$a_5 = 2(15) - (8) + 2 = 24$
$a_6 = 2(24) - (15) + 2 = 35$
$a_7 = 2(35) - (24) + 2 = 48$

SKILL ✓ **EXERCISE 19**

This TI-84 program quickly calculates a_{100} for the recursively defined sequence $a_1 = 1$, $a_n = a_{n-1} + (n - 1)$.

```
PROGRAM:RECURSEQ
:1→A
:For(N,2,100)
:A+N-1→A
:End
:Disp "TERM 100 IS ",A
:
```
```
prgmRECURSEQ
TERM 100 IS
                    4951
                    Done
■
```

Be aware that a listing of the first several terms is not sufficient to uniquely define a sequence. For example, 1, 2, 4, . . . can be the first three terms of either of the following sequences:

1, 2, 4, 8, 16, . . . with an explicit formula of $a_n = 2^n$ or
1, 2, 4, 7, 11, . . . with a recursive formula of $a_1 = 1$, $a_n = a_{n-1} + (n - 1)$, $n \geq 2$.

It is clearly easier to find a_{100} with an explicit formula. While using a recursive formula to find the value of this term would require the calculation of all previous terms of the sequence, a calculator or computer can be programmed to perform these calculations. Numerous relationships can only be modeled recursively.

Many sequences involve a special product called a *factorial*. Note the explicit formula used to define this product.

▌ **DEFINITION**

The product of *n* and every natural number less than *n* is notated **n!**, which is read as **n factorial**. Symbolically, $n! = n(n-1)(n-2)(n-3) \ldots (1)$. Note that 0! is defined as 1.

In some sequences it is convenient to use the set of whole numbers as the domain: a_0, a_1, a_2, a_3, ... A sequence of factorials can then be generated using the recursive definition $a_n = na_{n-1}$ with $a_0 = 1$.

$a_0 = 1$ $a_2 = 2(1) = 2$ $a_4 = 4(6) = 24$ $a_6 = 6(120) = 720$
$a_1 = 1(1) = 1$ $a_3 = 3(2) = 6$ $a_5 = 5(24) = 120$ ⋮

Example 5   Using Factorials to Find Terms of a Sequence

Given $a_n = \dfrac{2n!}{(n+1)^2}$, find a_0, a_1, a_2, a_3, and a_4.

Answer

$a_0 = \dfrac{2 \cdot 0!}{(0+1)^2}$ $a_1 = \dfrac{2 \cdot 1!}{(1+1)^2}$ $a_2 = \dfrac{2 \cdot 2!}{(2+1)^2}$ $a_3 = \dfrac{2 \cdot 3!}{(3+1)^2}$ $a_4 = \dfrac{2 \cdot 4!}{(4+1)^2}$

$= \dfrac{2(1)}{1^2} = 2$ $= \dfrac{2(1)}{2^2} = \dfrac{1}{2}$ $= \dfrac{2(2 \cdot 1)}{3^2} = \dfrac{4}{9}$ $= \dfrac{2(3 \cdot 2 \cdot 1)}{4^2} = \dfrac{3}{4}$ $= \dfrac{2(4 \cdot 3 \cdot 2 \cdot 1)}{5^2} = \dfrac{48}{25}$

SKILL ✓ **EXERCISE 11**

The end behavior of functions has been described using limits. If the values of a sequence approach a finite real number L as the position number approaches infinity, the sequence is *convergent* and $\lim\limits_{n\to\infty} a_n = L$ is the *limit of the sequence*. If not, the sequence is *divergent*. Note that finding the limit of rational sequences is similar to finding the horizontal asymptote of a rational function, which was described in Section 2.5.

Example 6 Finding the Limit of an Infinite Sequence

Determine whether each sequence converges or diverges and state the limit of any convergent sequences.

a. $a_n = \dfrac{5n-1}{n+1}$

b. $a_n = -2n + 4$

c. $a_n = 3(-1)^n$

Answer

a. converges; since
$$\lim_{n\to\infty} \frac{5n-1}{n+1} = 5$$

b. diverges; since
$$\lim_{n\to\infty} (-2n+4) = -\infty$$

c. diverges; The limit does not exist since the terms alternate between 3 and −3.

Check

The Technology Corner at the end of this section explains how the sequences can be graphed.

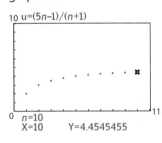

u=(5n−1)/(n+1)
n=10 X=10 Y=4.4545455

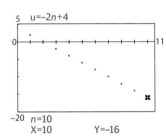

u=−2n+4
n=10 X=10 Y=−16

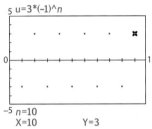

u=3*(−1)^n
n=10 X=10 Y=3

SKILL ✓ **EXERCISE 25**

A sum of the terms in a sequence is a *series*. The Greek capital letter sigma, Σ, is frequently used to represent a series.

> ▌ **DEFINITION**
>
> A **series** of a given sequence $a_1, a_2, a_3, a_4, \ldots$ can be represented in *summation* (or *sigma*) *notation* as
> $$\sum_{i=b}^{c} a_i = a_b + a_{b+1} + a_{b+2} + \cdots + a_c$$
> where the index (or counter) i has a lower bound of b and an upper bound of c. An *infinite series* has an upper bound of ∞.

TIP

This sigma notation is read as "The sum of a_i from $i = b$ to c."

Example 7 Evaluating Summation Notation

Evaluate $\displaystyle\sum_{i=3}^{7} (i^2 - 2i)$.

Answer

The bounds of the index indicate that the series is the sum of the terms from a_3 to a_7. Find each term by substituting the values 3, 4, 5, 6, and 7 for i, and then find the sum.

$$\sum_{i=3}^{7} (i^2 - 2i) = [3^2 - 2(3)] + [4^2 - 2(4)] + [5^2 - 2(5)] + [6^2 - 2(6)] + [7^2 - 2(7)]$$
$$= 3 + 8 + 15 + 24 + 35$$
$$= 85$$

SKILL ✓ **EXERCISE 29**

The sum of a sequence's first n terms, $\sum_{i=1}^{n} a_i$, is called the *nth partial sum* and is abbreviated as S_n.

Example 8   Evaluating Partial Sums

Given the sequence 2, 4, 6, 8, . . . , $2n$; find S_5, S_6, and S_7.

Answer

$S_5 = \sum_{i=1}^{5} a_i = 2 + 4 + 6 + 8 + 10 = 30$ 1. Find S_5 by adding the first 5 terms.

$S_6 = S_5 + a_6 = 30 + 12 = 42$ 2. Successive partial sums can be found by adding the next term.

$S_7 = S_6 + a_7 = 42 + 14 = 56$

SKILL ✔ EXERCISE 33

The series in Examples 7 and 8 are finite series. Can an infinite series be calculated when a person cannot add an infinite number of terms? Given a sequence of terms a_k, you can generate a related sequence of partial sums: S_1, S_2, S_3, . . . , S_n. If the sequence of partial sums converges to a real number S, then the infinite series $\sum_{i=1}^{\infty} a_i = S$ and the series is *convergent*. If the terms of the sequence a_i do not approach 0, the sequence of partial sums S_n approaches infinity and the series is *divergent*. Be careful to distinguish the limit of the sequence from the limit of the partial sums.

Example 9   Evaluating Infinite Series

Evaluate each infinite series and describe the series as convergent or divergent.

a. $3 + 3 + 3 + 3 + \cdots$ **b.** $0.3 + 0.03 + 0.003 + 0.0003 + \cdots$

Answer

a. Since $\lim_{i \to \infty} 3 = 3$, the sequence of partial sums 3, 6, 9, 12, 15, . . . has no finite limit.

Therefore, $\sum_{i=1}^{\infty} 3 = \infty$ and the series is divergent.

b. Note that $\lim_{n \to \infty} \dfrac{3}{10^n} = 0$ and that the sequence of partial sums 0.3, 0.33, 0.333, 0.3333, . . . approaches $0.\overline{3}$ or $\frac{1}{3}$.

Therefore, $\sum_{n=1}^{\infty} \dfrac{3}{10^n} = \dfrac{1}{3}$ and the series is convergent.

SKILL ✔ EXERCISE 37

❯ A. Exercises

1. Identify each expression.

   a. 2, 4, 6, 8, . . .   **I.** finite series

   b. $3 + 6 + 9 + 12 + \cdots + 30$ **II.** infinite series

   c. 1, 4, 7, . . . , 25   **III.** finite sequence

   d. $\sum_{i=1}^{15} 5i$ **IV.** infinite sequence

   e. $\sum_{i=9}^{\infty} 0.2^i$

Find the first 4 terms and the tenth term of each explicitly defined sequence.

2. $a_n = 2n - 5$ 3. $a_n = \dfrac{3}{(n^2 + 1)}$

4. $a_n = \dfrac{n(n-1)}{2}$ 5. $a_n = 1 + \dfrac{1}{n}$

Write the first 6 terms of each recursively defined sequence.

6. $a_1 = 4$; $a_n = 3(a_{n-1}) - 9$ where $n \geq 2$

7. $a_1 = 3$; $a_n = 2^{n-1}(a_{n-1})$ where $n \geq 2$

8. $a_1 = 1$, $a_2 = 4$; $a_n = (a_{n-1} - a_{n-2})^2$ where $n \geq 3$

9. $a_1 = 2$, $a_2 = 10$; $a_n = 3a_{n-1} + 2a_{n-2}$ where $n \geq 3$

Find a_0, a_1, a_2, a_3, and a_4 for each sequence.

10. $a_n = \dfrac{4}{n!}$

11. $a_n = \dfrac{3n!}{2n+1}$

12. $a_n = \dfrac{n!}{(n+2)!}$

13. $a_n = \dfrac{(-1)^n}{2n!}$

> ## B. Exercises

Write an explicit formula for the value of a_n and use it to find the tenth term.

14. $1, \sqrt{2}, \sqrt{3}, 2, \ldots$

15. $3, 5, 7, 9, \ldots$

16. $1, -1, 1, -1, \ldots$

17. $0, \frac{1}{2}, \frac{2}{3}, \frac{3}{4}, \ldots$

Write a recursive formula for each sequence and use it to find a_5, a_6, and a_7.

18. $3, 6, 9, 12, \ldots$

19. $3, 6, 9, 15, \ldots$

20. $3, 5, 8, 12, \ldots$

21. $8, 1.8, 1.18, 1.118, \ldots$

22. Assume a home's value appreciates by the same percentage each year. Write a sequence with a_0 representing the home's original value and a_1, a_2, a_3, and a_4 representing the value of the home (rounded to the nearest dollar) in each of the next 4 years. Then write a recursive formula for the sequence.

   a. $a_0 = \$225{,}000$; 5% APR

   b. $a_0 = \$380{,}000$; 7% APR

23. The Fibonacci sequence $1, 1, 2, 3, 5, 8, \ldots$ models the number of mature rabbit pairs after n months (assuming no rabbits die).

   a. Find the number of rabbit pairs after 1 yr and after 18 mo.

   b. Write the recursive formula for the Fibonacci sequence.

24. The golden rectangles commonly found in art and architecture have a length-to-width ratio that aproximates the golden ratio, ϕ. This ratio can be approximated by the converging sequence $b_n = \dfrac{a_n}{a_{n-1}}$ where a_n is the Fibonacci sequence with $n > 1$. Write the first 10 terms of b_n as fractions and then evaluate b_9 and b_{10} to three decimal places.

Determine whether each sequence converges or diverges and state the limit of any convergent sequences.

25. $1, \frac{1}{2}, \frac{1}{3}, \frac{1}{4}, \ldots$

26. $1, 1, 2, 3, 5, \ldots$

27. $a_1 = 4$, $a_n = a_{n-1} - 7$

28. $a_n = \dfrac{n-1}{n+1}$

Evaluate each finite series.

29. $\displaystyle\sum_{n=4}^{8} n^2$

30. $\displaystyle\sum_{k=2}^{4} (k^2 - 1)$

31. $\displaystyle\sum_{i=1}^{5} \dfrac{4}{i}$

32. $\displaystyle\sum_{j=0}^{5} i^j$, where $i = \sqrt{-1}$

Find the partial sums S_5, S_6, and S_7 for each sequence. Round answers to the hundred-thousandth place if necessary.

33. $a_n = \dfrac{1}{(n-1)!}$

34. $a_n = \dfrac{(-1)^{n-1}}{(n-1)!}$

35. $a_n = \dfrac{(-1)^n}{(n+1)!}$

36. $a_n = \dfrac{4(-1)^{n-1}}{2n-1}$

Evaluate each infinite series and describe it as convergent or divergent.

37. $\displaystyle\sum_{k=1}^{\infty} 2(0.1)^k$

38. $\displaystyle\sum_{k=1}^{\infty} \dfrac{k}{3}$

39. $\displaystyle\sum_{i=1}^{\infty} (-5i)$

40. $\displaystyle\sum_{i=1}^{\infty} 45(0.01)^i$

> ## C. Exercises

41. Express the number of seconds in 6 weeks in factorial notation.

42. Calculators determine sine and cosine values using the following infinite series:

$$\sin x = \sum_{k=0}^{n} \dfrac{(-1)^k x^{2k+1}}{(2k+1)!} \text{ and } \cos x = \sum_{k=0}^{n} \dfrac{(-1)^k x^{2k}}{(2k)!}.$$

Estimate each trigonometric value by finding the partial sums S_0, S_1, S_2, and S_3 (to five decimal places).

   a. $\sin \dfrac{\pi}{6}$

   c. $\cos \left(-\dfrac{\pi}{6}\right)$

   b. $\cos \dfrac{\pi}{4}$

   d. $\sin \left(-\dfrac{\pi}{3}\right)$

43. Use technology to graph $Y_1 = \sin x$ and $Y_2 = x - \dfrac{x^3}{3!} + \dfrac{x^5}{5!} - \dfrac{x^7}{7!}$. State the interval of x for which the two graphs appear to have identical values.

Write the slope-intercept form equation of each described line. [1.2]

44. passing through $(0, 3)$ and $(8, -2)$

45. passing through $(-1, 5)$ and perpendicular to the line containing $(0, 4)$ and $(-3, 5)$

Graph each exponential function and state its domain and range. Then classify the function as exponential growth or decay. [3.1]

46. $y = \frac{1}{2} \cdot 2^x$

47. $y = 9\left(\frac{1}{3}\right)^x$

48. Find a fourth-degree polynomial equation with roots of $3 - i$ and $5 + 2i$. [2.4]

49. Right $\triangle ABC$ has legs 6 cm and 10 cm long. Find the exact value of the sine, cosine, and tangent of the smaller acute $\angle A$. [4.2]

50. Which region(s) represent the solution of the system?
$-3x + 5y \leq 7$
$y \geq -2x^2 - 8x + 5$ [7.6]

A. region 1

B. region 4

C. region 5

D. regions 2 and 4

E. regions 3 and 5

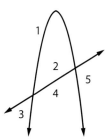

51. Find the partial fraction decomposition for $\dfrac{2x + 3}{x^2 + 3x + 2}$. [7.7]

A. $\dfrac{1}{x + 1} + \dfrac{1}{x + 2}$

B. $\dfrac{6}{x + 1} + \dfrac{1}{x + 2}$

C. $\dfrac{3}{x + 1} + \dfrac{2}{x + 2}$

D. $\dfrac{2}{x + 1} + \dfrac{3}{x + 2}$

E. none of these

52. Convert $x^2 + 3y^2 - 6x + 6y = 0$ to a standard form for an ellipse. [8.2]

A. $\dfrac{(x - 3)^2}{12} - \dfrac{(y + 1)^2}{4} = 1$

B. $\dfrac{(x - 3)^2}{12} + \dfrac{(y + 1)^2}{4} = 1$

C. $\dfrac{(x + 3)^2}{3} + \dfrac{(y + 1)^2}{4} = 1$

D. $\dfrac{(x - 3)^2}{3} + \dfrac{(y + 1)^2}{4} = 1$

E. none of these

53. Use the discriminant test to classify the conic $x^2 + y^2 - 6x + 8y + 7 = 0$. [8.4]

A. parabola

B. hyperbola

C. ellipse

D. circle

E. none of these

A sequence is a function whose domain contains natural numbers. It can be graphed in FUNCTION mode as a scatterplot using its explicit formula. It can also be graphed in SEQUENCE mode using either its recursive or explicit formula.

To graph a sequence while in FUNCTION mode, select option 5 from the LIST ([2nd], [STAT]) OPS menu. To store the first ten natural numbers in L_1, store seq(X, X, 1, 10, 1) in L_1, where the first X is the expression and the second X is the variable that starts at 1 and ends at 10 with a step of 1. The explicit formula for a sequence can then be used to store the first ten terms of the sequence in L_2. Given $a_n = \frac{2n-1}{4n}$, store $(2L_1-1) \div (4L_1)$ as L_2. The answer can be converted to fractions using 1:▶ from the [MATH] menu.

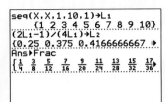

Clear any equations in the [Y=] editor and then use STAT PLOT ([2nd], [Y=]) to turn on Plot1 and [GRAPH] the scatterplot. [TRACE] can be used to identify the ordered pairs of the sequence. Notice how the graph illustrates the sequence as it approaches its $\lim\limits_{n \to \infty} \frac{2n-1}{4n} = 0.5$.

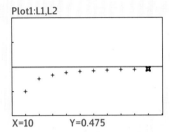

Selecting SEQUENCE mode allows the sequence to be entered using either its explicit or recursive formula. Press [Y=] and turn Plot1 off. To graph the Fibonacci sequence, enter 1 for nMin, then enter the recursive formula u(n)=u($n-1$)+u($n-2$) and the first term (or in this case a list of the first two initial terms) of the sequence for u(nMin). Enter the explicit formula for the linear sequence v(n)=4n+3. Note that v(nMin) is left blank when the sequence is defined explicitly. Use [WINDOW] to define nMax and other characteristics of the graphing window. [TRACE] can again be used to identify ordered pairs of the sequence. The sequences can also be viewed using TABLE ([2nd], [GRAPH]). Use the TBLSET menu ([2nd], [WINDOW]) to be sure that TblStart = 1 and ΔTbl = 1.

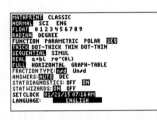

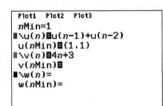

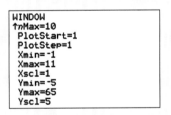

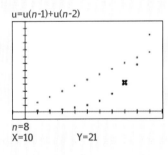

KEYWORD SEARCH

plot sequence desmos 🔍

Computer Proofs and Artificial Intelligence

[My proof] differs significantly from earlier approaches by making extensive use of computers.
—Thomas Hales (American mathematician who proved the Kepler Conjecture)

Over the last six decades computers have been very helpful in attacking famous unsolved problems in mathematics. For example, computers have supplied extensive inductive evidence that Goldbach's Conjecture and the Riemann Hypothesis are both true by confirming trillions of examples without finding a single counterexample. Computers have also played an instrumental role in providing deductive proofs for the Four-Color Problem and Kepler's Conjecture using a technique called enumeration of cases (or proof by exhaustion). This technique establishes the conclusion by dividing the problem into a finite number (often a very large number) of cases and proving each case separately.

According to the Four-Color Problem, first proposed in 1852, four colors at most are needed to color any separation of a plane into contiguous regions so that no two adjacent regions have the same color. The problem's proof by exhaustion in 1976 was controversial since it was the first major proof to heavily rely on computer assistance; the majority of its 1936 cases were checked by a computer rather than by hand. Another computer-assisted proof in 1996 reduced the number of cases to 633. The Four-Color Theorem was proved with generalized theorem-proving software in 2005. The field of automated theorem proving (ATP) is still growing in application and acceptability.

The Kepler Conjecture was first analyzed in the late-sixteenth century as a cannonball packing problem. It is now a mathematical theorem stating that the density of equal-sized spheres packed in space is never greater than $\frac{\pi}{3\sqrt{2}} \approx 74.05\%$. In the early 1990s Thomas Hales and Samuel Ferguson, one of Hales's graduate students at the University of Michigan, developed a proof by exhaustion that systematically applied linear programming methods to over 5000 different configurations of spheres. Hales used Mathematica® software to complete the symbolic math, and his work was verified by Ferguson using Maple® software. After independently writing key portions of the programs twice and checking the results on different types of computers, Hales declared their success

in an email to colleagues around the world in 1998. After a referee's panel declared it could not certify the correctness of the computer calculations in 2003, a collaborative project led by Hales sought to create a formal proof verified by automated proof-checking software. The project was completed in 2014 and the formal proof of the Kepler Conjecture was accepted by a leading research journal in 2017.

ATP is a subfield of artificial intelligence (AI). From playing chess and other games at higher and higher levels, AI has improved to the point that an IBM® computer named Watson defeated two champions from the popular game show *Jeopardy!* in 2011. *Forbes* magazine reported in 2013 that the technology is now being used to improve successful patient diagnosis rates in hospitals, where nurses using Watson as a resource take the AI program's advice 90% of the time. AI is now nearly ubiquitous with applications such as Apple's Siri® and GPS navigation.

In 2014 the world-renowned physicist Stephen Hawking told a BBC interviewer, "The development of full artificial intelligence could spell the end of the human race. It would take off on its own, and re-design itself at an ever-increasing rate . . . . Humans, who are limited by slow biological evolution, couldn't compete, and would be superseded."

In his 2017 magazine article entitled "A Christian View of Artificial Intelligence," Cody Volkers said, "Technology has always been about making life better for the human race. In its best forms, AI continues this tradition. But in its more dangerous iterations, AI aspires to attain omniscience, something reserved only for God." We should realize that real-world applications of AI rely on imperfect algorithms for sifting imperfect data sets which do not represent all the information related to the problem. It is crucial that humans understand that they are made in God's image, retain their own sense of humanity, and have the courage to overrule AI output. Despite the hype, computers don't think; they merely perform algorithms written by people who do think.

Exercises

1. Name two famous unproven math statements for which computers have provided extensive inductive evidence.

2. Name two famous math problems that were solved in the latter half of the twentieth century using deductive computer proofs.

3. Name and describe the type of proof used in solving these two famous math problems.

4. To verify the conjecture that there are no 4-digit numbers that are integral multiples of their "reversals" using the proof-by-exhaustion technique, how many cases would need to be checked?

5. Show that each number is a counterexample for the conjecture in exercise 4.

   a. 8172   b. 9801

6. A computer can verify that the other 4-digit numbers are not integral multiples of their reversals. Revise the conjecture in exercise 4 to state a theorem that is proved by enumeration of cases.

7. How are ATP and AI related?

8. Which two popular mathematic software packages were utilized by Hales and Ferguson in their proof of the Kepler Conjecture?

9. **Discuss:** Describe several ways that computers have advanced the quest for mathematical truth.

10. **Discuss:** In his 2017 article Cody Volkers continues, "Some AI pioneers believe they can create a machine with boundless potential for learning, a machine that can conquer all knowledge. This kind of AI would go beyond mere usefulness and amount to a modern Tower of Babel." How should a Christian view artificial intelligence?

The cost of drilling a well is modeled by an arithmetic series in exercise 38.

After completing this section, you will be able to

- represent arithmetic sequences using recursive and explicit formulas.
- find *n*th terms and arithmetic means of arithmetic sequences.
- find *n*th partial sums of arithmetic sequences.
- model and solve real-world problems using arithmetic sequences.

If $1000 is invested at 8% simple interest for 5 yr, it earns $400 in interest during that time. The $80 annual return can be seen in the sequence of annual balances: 1080, 1160, 1240, 1320, 1400. Notice that the difference between consecutive terms is the same.

DEFINITION

In an **arithmetic sequence**, the difference between any two consecutive terms is a constant, *d*, which is called the *common difference*.

This definition implies that the common difference can be found by subtracting any two consecutive terms and that arithmetic sequences can be described by the *recursive formula*
$$a_n = a_{n-1} + d.$$

Example 1 Identifying an Arithmetic Sequence

Determine whether each sequence is arithmetic. If so, state the common difference and list the next 3 terms. If not, explain why.

a. 9, 13, 17, 21, 25, . . . **b.** 2, 5, 10, 17, 26, . . .

Answer

a. arithmetic; $d = 4$;
$a_6 = 29; a_7 = 33; a_8 = 37$

b. not arithmetic; The differences are not constant: 3, 5, 7, 9, . . .

SKILL ✔ **EXERCISE 3**

Using an arithmetic sequence to model mortality rates was a key simplification that allowed early actuaries to easily compute the cost of an annuity.

The *explicit formula* for an arithmetic sequence can be derived using the recursive formula, which states that each term is found by adding *d* to the previous term.

$$a_1 = a_1$$
$$a_2 = a_1 + d$$
$$a_3 = a_1 + 2d$$

$$a_4 = a_1 + 3d$$
$$\vdots$$
$$a_n = a_1 + (n-1)d$$

Example 2 Finding and Applying Recursive and Explicit Formulas

Write both the recursive formula and a simplified explicit formula for each arithmetic sequence. Then find a_{20}.

a. 19, 16, 13, 10, 7, . . . **b.** ln 2, ln 6, ln 18, ln 54, . . .

Answer

a. $a_1 = 19; a_n = a_{n-1} - 3$

$a_n = 19 + (n-1)(-3)$
$a_n = -3n + 22$
$a_{20} = -3(20) + 22 = -38$

1. Use the common difference $d = -3$ to write the recursive formula.

2. Substitute into the explicit formula $a_n = a_1 + (n-1)d$ and simplify.

3. Substitute and simplify to find a_{20}.

CONTINUED ➡

b. $d = \ln 18 - \ln 6 = \ln \frac{18}{6} = \ln 3$ 1. Determine the common difference.

$a_1 = \ln 2; a_n = a_{n-1} + \ln 3$ 2. Write the recursive formula.

$a_n = \ln 2 + (n-1)(\ln 3)$ 3. Substitute into the explicit formula
$= n \ln 3 + \ln 2 - \ln 3$ $\quad a_n = a_1 + (n-1)d$ and simplify.

$a_n = n \ln 3 + \ln \frac{2}{3}$

$a_{20} = 20 \ln 3 + \ln \frac{2}{3}$ 4. Substitute and simplify to find a_{20}.

$\quad = \ln \frac{2 \cdot 3^{20}}{3} = \ln (2 \cdot 3^{19})$

_____ SKILL ✓ **EXERCISES 9, 13**

The graph of the sequence in Example 2a shows that the function is linear with a slope of −3, the common difference. In general, the explicit formula can also be stated as
$a_n = dn + a_0$ where $a_0 = a_1 - d$.

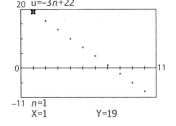

The fact that arithmetic sequences are linear with a slope of d can be used to derive a generalized explicit formula given any two terms (k, a_k) and (n, a_n).

$\dfrac{a_n - a_k}{n - k} = d$

$a_n - a_k = (n - k)d$

$\quad a_n = a_k + (n - k)d$

Arithmetic Sequences			
Recursive	**Explicit**		
$a_n = a_{n-1} + d$	$a_n = a_1 + (n-1)d$ (basic)	$a_n = a_k + (n-k)d$ (generalized)	$a_n = dn + a_0;$ $a_0 = a_1 - d$ (simplified)

Example 3 Writing and Using Explicit Formulas

Given the arithmetic sequence with $b_3 = 8$ and $b_7 = -6$, write a simplified explicit formula for b_n and then use the formula to find b_{20}.

Answer

$b_7 = b_3 + (7 - 3)d$ 1. Find d by substituting both terms into $b_n = b_k + (n - k)d$
$-6 = 8 + 4d$ $\quad$ and solving.
$-14 = 4d$
$d = -\dfrac{7}{2}$

$b_n = 8 + (n - 3)\left(-\dfrac{7}{2}\right)$ 2. Substitute d and $b_3 = 8$ (with $k = 3$) into $b_n = b_k + (n - k)d$
$b_n = 8 - \dfrac{7}{2}n + \dfrac{21}{2}$ $\quad$ and simplify.
$b_n = -\dfrac{7}{2}n + \dfrac{37}{2}$

$b_{20} = -\dfrac{7}{2}(20) + \dfrac{37}{2}$ 3. Evaluate the explicit formula to find b_{20}.

$\quad = -\dfrac{103}{2}$ or -51.5

_____ SKILL ✓ **EXERCISE 15**

The terms between two given terms of an arithmetic sequence are called *arithmetic means*.

Example 4 Finding Arithmetic Means

Write an arithmetic sequence with the following arithmetic means.

a. three arithmetic means
between 1.7 and 7.3

b. one arithmetic mean
between −8 and 15

Answer

a. Let $a_1 = 1.7$ and $a_5 = 7.3$.

$7.3 = 1.7 + (5 - 1)d$
$5.6 = 4d$
$d = 1.4$

$a_2 = 1.7 + 1.4 = 3.1$
$a_3 = 3.1 + 1.4 = 4.5$
$a_4 = 4.5 + 1.4 = 5.9$

1. The three arithmetic means are a_2, a_3, and a_4.
2. Substitute a_5 and a_1 into $a_n = a_1 + (n - 1)d$ and solve for d.
3. Use the recursive formula to find the three arithmetic means.
   Find $a_5 = 5.9 + 1.4 = 7.3$ to verify your work.

---

b. Let $a_1 = -8$ and $a_3 = 15$.

$15 = -8 + (3 - 1)d$
$23 = 2d$
$d = 11.5$

$a_2 = -8 + 11.5 = 3.5$

1. The arithmetic mean is a_2.
2. Substitute a_3 and a_1 into $a_n = a_1 + (n - 1)d$ and solve for d.
3. Use the recursive formula to find the arithmetic mean.
   Find $a_3 = 3.5 + 11.5 = 15$ to verify your work.

SKILL ✓ EXERCISE 19

Note that finding a single arithmetic mean between two numbers is the same as finding the average of the numbers: $\dfrac{-8 + 15}{2} = \dfrac{7}{2} = 3.5$.

The reciprocals of the terms of an arithmetic sequence form a *harmonic sequence*.

Example 5 Classifying a Sequence

Classify each sequence as arithmetic, harmonic, or neither. Then describe each as convergent or divergent.

a. $a_n = 7n - 2$

b. $2, 1, \dfrac{2}{3}, \dfrac{1}{2}, \dfrac{2}{5}, \ldots$

Answer

a. arithmetic

divergent

1. The explicit formula is linear.
2. Each term in the sequence 5, 12, 19, . . . is 7 more than the previous term.

---

b. harmonic

convergent

1. The term's reciprocals $\dfrac{1}{2}, 1, \dfrac{3}{2}, 2, \dfrac{5}{2}, \ldots$ form the arithmetic sequence $a_n = \dfrac{1}{2}n$.
2. $\lim\limits_{n \to \infty} \dfrac{2}{n} = 0$

SKILL ✓ EXERCISE 23

DEFINITION

An **arithmetic series** is a sum of the terms of an arithmetic sequence. The sum of the first n terms of $a_1, a_2, a_3, \ldots$ is the nth partial sum, $S_n = a_1 + a_2 + a_3 + \cdots + a_n$.

In 1852 the French clockmaker Jean-Baptiste Schwilgué designed and built a machine that could sum arithmetic sequences. The tool was useful for laying out a template to cut gear wheels for large tower clocks.

Given the arithmetic sequence $2, 4, 6, \ldots$, the 50th partial sum $S_{50} = 2 + 4 + 6 + \cdots + 100$ could be evaluated by completing each addition. A better approach is to derive and apply a general formula for S_n in any arithmetic sequence. The key is to use two expressions for $S_n = a_1 + a_2 + \cdots + a_{n-1} + a_n$, the first in terms of a_1 and the second in terms of a_n.

$S_n = a_1 + (a_1 + d) + (a_1 + 2d) + \cdots + [a_1 + (n-1)d]$ 1. Each term after a_1 is found by repeatedly adding d.

$S_n = a_n + (a_n - d) + (a_n - 2d) + \cdots + [a_n - (n-1)d]$ 2. Reverse the order of the terms, beginning with a_n, and repeatedly subtract d.

$S_n + S_n = (a_1 + a_n) + (a_1 + a_n) + \cdots + (a_1 + a_n)$ 3. Add the two equations for S_n.

$2S_n = n(a_1 + a_n)$ 4. There are n identical terms.

$S_n = \frac{n}{2}(a_1 + a_n)$ 5. Solve for S_n.

When a_n is not known, substitute using $a_n = a_1 + (n-1)d$ and simplify.

$$S_n = \frac{n}{2}[a_1 + (a_1 + (n-1)d)] = \frac{n}{2}[2a_1 + (n-1)d]$$

Arithmetic Series
$S_n = \frac{n}{2}(a_1 + a_n)$ or $S_n = \frac{n}{2}[2a_1 + (n-1)d]$

Example 6   Evaluating an Arithmetic Series

Evaluate each sum.

a. $2 + 4 + 6 + \cdots + 100$

b. $\sum\limits_{k=1}^{500}(11k - 6)$

Answer

a. $100 = 2 + (n-1)(2)$
$100 = 2n$
$n = 50$

   1. Determine the value of n using $a_n = a_1 + (n-1)d$.

$S_n = \frac{50}{2}(2 + 100)$
$= 25(102) = 2550$

   2. Substitute $a_1 = 2$, $a_n = 100$, and $n = 50$ into $S_n = \frac{n}{2}(a_1 + a_n)$ and simplify.

b. $a_1 = 11(1) - 6 = 5$
$d = 11$

   1. Recognize the linear expression, $11k - 6$, as the explicit formula for an arithmetic sequence, $a_k = dk + a_0$.

$S_{500} = \frac{500}{2}[2(5) + (500 - 1)11]$
$= 1{,}374{,}750$

   2. Substitute into $\frac{n}{2}[2a_1 + (n-1)d]$ and simplify.

SKILL ✓ **EXERCISE 27**

Example 7 Using a Partial Sum to Find the Explicit Formula

Write a simplified explicit formula for the arithmetic sequence with $a_1 = 10$ if $S_{100} = 10,900$.

Answer

$10,900 = \frac{100}{2}[2(10) + (100 - 1)d]$

$10,900 = 50(20 + 99d)$

$\quad 218 = 20 + 99d$

$\quad 198 = 99d$

$\quad\quad d = 2$

$a_n = 10 + (n - 1)2$

$a_n = 2n + 8$

1. Substitute into $S_n = \frac{n}{2}[2a_1 + (n - 1)d]$ and solve for d, the common difference.

2. Substitute into $a_n = a_1 + (n - 1)d$ and simplify.

SKILL ✓ **EXERCISE 35**

Example 8 Applying Arithmetic Sequences and Series

Mr. and Mrs. King decided to pay off their mortgage early by adding an extra $25 to their $800 mortgage payment in January and then increasing their additional payment by another $5 each successive month. Write a simplified explicit formula for the arithmetic sequence representing their payments. Then find the amount paid in December of the second year and the total amount paid during those 2 yr.

Answer

$a_1 = 825, d = 5$

$a_n = 825 + (n - 1)5$

$\quad = 5n + 820$

$a_{24} = 5(24) + 820 = \$940$

$S_{24} = \frac{24}{2}(825 + 940) = \$21,180$

1. Substitute values for a_1 and d into $a_n = a_1 + (n - 1)d$ and simplify.

2. In December of the second year, $n = 24$.

3. Substitute values for n, a_1, and a_n into $a_n = a_1 + (n - 1)d$ and simplify.

SKILL ✓ **EXERCISE 39**

> ### A. Exercises

1. Identify each formula related to arithmetic sequences.

a. $S_n = \dfrac{n(a_1 + a_n)}{2}$ **I.** recursive

b. $a_n - a_{n-1} = d$ **II.** basic explicit

c. $a_n = a_{n-1} + d$ **III.** generalized explicit

d. $a_n = a_k + (n - k)d$ **IV.** simplified explicit

e. $a_n = a_1 + (n - 1)d$ **V.** common difference

f. $a_n = dn + a_0$ **VI.** finite series

If the sequence is arithmetic, state the common difference and list the next 3 terms. If it is not arithmetic, explain why.

2. $-14, -10, -6, -2, 2, \ldots$ **3.** $66, 77, 88, 99, 110, \ldots$

4. $37, 28, 19, 10, 1, \ldots$ **5.** $28, 35, 43, 54, 67, \ldots$

Identify the common difference for each arithmetic sequence and then find the fifth term.

6. $a_n = a_{n-1} - 1, a_1 = 5$ **7.** $a_n = 6n - 8$

Write the recursive formula and a simplified explicit formula for each arithmetic sequence. Then find a_{20}.

8. $-1, -5, -9, \ldots$

9. $7, 19, 31, \ldots$

10. positive multiples of 8

11. odd natural numbers

12. $\ln 3, \ln 12, \ln 48, \ln 192, \ldots$

13. $\log 10, \log 1000, \log 100,000, \log 10,000,000, \ldots$

Write the simplified explicit formula for the following sequences, then find a_{20}.

14. $9, 13, 17, 21, \ldots$

15. a_n is arithmetic with $a_9 = 35$ and $a_{23} = -49$.

16. a_n is arithmetic with $a_7 = 52$ and $a_{15} = 90$.

17. $\frac{1}{5}, \frac{1}{12}, \frac{1}{19}, \frac{1}{26}, \ldots$

B. Exercises

Find the arithmetic means between the given terms.

18. $a_{18} = 9$ and $a_{21} = 30$

19. $a_{10} = 32$ and $a_{14} = 71$

20. $a_6 = 25.83$ and $a_8 = 94.05$

21. Prove that the single arithmetic mean x between a and b is the average of a and b.

Write the first 5 terms of each sequence. Then classify the sequence as arithmetic, harmonic, or neither and state whether it converges or diverges.

22. $a_1 = 11$, $a_n = a_{n-1} - 4$

23. $a_n = -2 + 3(n-1)$

24. $a_n = \dfrac{1}{3 + 2n}$

25. $a_1 = \dfrac{1}{2}$, $a_n = \dfrac{1}{\frac{1}{a_{n-1}} + 2}$

26. Classify each sequence as arithmetic or harmonic. Graph the first 10 terms and determine whether the sequence converges or diverges and state the limit of any convergent sequences.

a. $a_n = \dfrac{1}{5}n + 1$ **b.** $a_n = \dfrac{3}{n}$

c. $a_n = -\dfrac{6}{n-1}$ **d.** $a_n = -\dfrac{n}{3} + 2$

Evaluate each arithmetic series.

27. $100 + 95 + 90 + \cdots + 5$

28. $3 + 5 + 7 + \cdots + 31$

29. $\displaystyle\sum_{k=1}^{500} (2k + 3)$

30. $\displaystyle\sum_{j=1}^{60} \dfrac{j+6}{3}$

Use sigma notation to write each sum.

31. $5 + 9 + 13 + 17 + \cdots + 117$

32. $-3 - 6 - 9 - 12 - \cdots - 300$

Find the requested value for each arithmetic sequence.

33. Find d if $a_1 = 43$ and $a_{19} = -137$.

34. Find a_1 if $a_{25} = -1$ and $d = 14$.

35. Find a_{15} if $S_{15} = 30$ and $a_1 = 3$.

36. Find S_{10} if $a_{10} = 30$ and $a_{15} = 70$.

37. A church borrows $50,000 at 3% simple interest for 4 yr with one balloon payment at the end. Use a sequence to express the balance due at the end of each year.

38. A well-drilling company charges $2 for the first foot, $3 for the second foot, $4 for the third foot and so on. What is the cost of drilling a 75 ft well?

39. A construction crew designs a trapezoidal stone patio for a customer. If the first row requires 11 stones and each additional row requires two more stones, how many total stones will be needed for the patio if it will have 18 total rows?

40. Prove that $a_n = a_1 + (n-1)d$ simplifies to a linear function with slope of d and y-intercept $a_0 = a_1 - d$.

C. Exercises

41. Prove that the explicit formula for a general harmonic sequence, $a_n = \dfrac{b}{dn + c}$, simplifies to the reciprocal of a simplified arithmetic sequence.

Partial sums of the harmonic sequence $a_n = \dfrac{1}{n}$ have applications in many areas including music, physics, business, and theoretical mathematics.

42. Express the first 5 partial sums of $a_n = \dfrac{1}{n}$ in fractional form.

43. Use a graphing calculator to graph the sequence of partial sums for $a_n = \dfrac{1}{n}$ and use $\boxed{\text{TRACE}}$ to find the tenth partial sum (rounded to the nearest thousandth). Then graph a second sequence $v(n) = \ln(n)$ in the same window and use the graphs to support the conjecture that the sequence of partial sums diverges.

44. Use the "sum" and "seq" functions of a graphing calculator to find S_{10}, S_{100}, S_{400}, and S_{900} (rounded to the nearest thousandth).

Evaluate. [3.1]

45. $f(-2)$ when $f(x) = 4^x$

46. $p(4)$ when $p(x) = 3\left(\frac{2}{3}\right)^x$

47. Find a plane's resultant velocity and heading if it flies at a bearing of $75°$ with an air speed of 200 mi/hr and the wind is blowing from the north at 30 mi/hr. [6.1]

48. Graph the parabola $x = y^2 + 4y - 1$, its vertex, focus, and directrix. [8.1]

Find the first 4 terms and the tenth term of each explicitly defined sequence. [9.1]

49. $a_n = 7n - 2$

50. $a_n = \frac{n^2 - 2}{n}$

51. Classify the conic $13x^2 + 10xy + 13y^2 - 72 = 0$. [8.4]

    A. circle   **C.** parabola   **E.** none of

    B. ellipse   **D.** hyperbola   these

52. Classify the conic $r = \dfrac{-3}{2\cos\theta - 1}$. [8.6]

    A. circle   **C.** parabola   **E.** none of

    B. ellipse   **D.** hyperbola   these

53. Find a_{10} in the sequence $4, -8, 16, -32, \ldots$ [9.1]

    A. 1024   **C.** -2048 **E.** none of

    B. -1024 **D.** 4096   these

54. Find a_6 in the sequence
$a_1 = 2, a_2 = 4, a_n = a_{n-1} + a_{n-2}$. [9.1]

    A. 12   **C.** 26   **E.** none of

    B. 16   **D.** 64   these

Compound interest can multiply early investments toward your retirement.

If \$1000 is invested at 8% APR compounded yearly, the balance at the end of each of the next 5 yr can be represented by the sequence 1080.00, 1166.40, 1259.71, 1360.49, 1469.33. This sequence is not arithmetic because the difference between consecutive terms is not constant. However, the ratio of any two consecutive terms is approximately 1.08.

DEFINITION

In a **geometric sequence**, the quotient of any two consecutive terms is a constant, $r = \dfrac{a_{n+1}}{a_n}$, which is called the *common ratio*.

The definition shows that the common ratio can be found by dividing any term by its previous term and that a geometric sequence can be described by its recursive formula $a_n = a_{n-1}r$.

Example 1 Identifying a Geometric Sequence

Determine whether each sequence is geometric. If so, state the common ratio and list the next 3 terms. If not, explain why.

a. 1, 4, 9, 16, . . .

b. 36, −24, 16, $-\dfrac{32}{3}$, . . .

Answer

a. $\dfrac{a_2}{a_1} = 4; \dfrac{a_3}{a_2} = \dfrac{9}{4} = 2.25$

not geometric; The ratio of consecutive terms is not constant.

b. $\dfrac{a_2}{a_1} = \dfrac{-24}{36} = -\dfrac{2}{3}; \dfrac{a_3}{a_2} = \dfrac{16}{-24} = -\dfrac{2}{3}; \dfrac{a_4}{a_3} = \dfrac{-\frac{32}{3}}{16} = -\dfrac{2}{3}$

geometric $\left(\text{with a common ratio of } -\dfrac{2}{3}\right)$

$a_5 = a_4\left(-\dfrac{2}{3}\right) = -\dfrac{32}{3}\left(-\dfrac{2}{3}\right) = \dfrac{64}{9}$

$a_6 = a_5\left(-\dfrac{2}{3}\right) = \dfrac{64}{9}\left(-\dfrac{2}{3}\right) = -\dfrac{128}{27}$

$a_7 = a_6\left(-\dfrac{2}{3}\right) = -\dfrac{128}{27}\left(-\dfrac{2}{3}\right) = \dfrac{256}{81}$

SKILL ✓ **EXERCISE 3**

The explicit formula for a geometric sequence is derived from its recursive formula, which states that each term is found by multiplying the previous term by r.

$a_1 = a_1$
$a_2 = a_1 \cdot r$
$a_3 = a_1 \cdot r^2$

$a_4 = a_1 \cdot r^3$
$\vdots$
$a_n = a_1 \cdot r^{n-1}$

The mathematical knowledge that allows insurance companies to provide a cost-effective service for those desiring to wisely prepare for unforeseen events also enables governments to profit from lottery schemes that promise easy money at astronomical odds.

TIP

The sequence can be viewed using the TABLE function on your calculator.

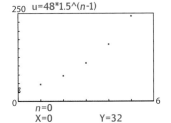

n	$u(n)$
0	32
1	48
2	72
3	108
4	162
5	243
6	364.5
7	546.75
8	820.13
9	1230.2
10	1845.3

$n=0$

Example 2   Finding and Applying Recursive and Explicit Formulas

Write the recursive formula and an explicit formula for each geometric sequence. Then find a_{10}.

a. 48, 72, 108, 162, . . .   **b.** $10^7, 10^4, 10^1, 10^{-2}, . . .$

Answer

a. $a_1 = 48, a_n = \dfrac{3}{2}a_{n-1}$

$a_n = 48\left(\dfrac{3}{2}\right)^{n-1}$

$a_{10} = 48\left(\dfrac{3}{2}\right)^{10-1} = \dfrac{3 \cdot 2^4 \cdot 3^9}{2^9} = \dfrac{3^{10}}{2^5}$

$\qquad = \dfrac{59,049}{32} \approx 1845.28$

1. Use the common ratio $r = \dfrac{72}{48} = \dfrac{3}{2}$ to write the recursive formula.

2. Substitute into the explicit formula $a_n = a_1 r^{n-1}$.

3. Substitute and simplify to find a_{10}.

b. $a_1 = 10^7, a_n = 10^{-3}a_{n-1}$

$a_n = 10^7\left(10^{-3}\right)^{n-1}$

$a_n = 10^7\left(10^{-3}\right)^{10-1}$

$\qquad = 10^7\left(10^{-27}\right) = 10^{-20}$

1. Use the common ratio $r = \dfrac{10^4}{10^7} = 10^{-3}$ to write the recursive formula.

2. Substitute into $a_n = a_1 r^{n-1}$.

3. Substitute and simplify to find a_{10}.

SKILL ✓ EXERCISE 7

250   u=48*1.5^(n-1)

0

$n=0$
X=0   Y=32   6

The graph of the sequence in Example 2a shows that the function contains points on the graph of the exponential function $f(x) = 48\left(\dfrac{3}{2}\right)^{x-1}$ or $f(x) = 32\left(\dfrac{3}{2}\right)^{x}$. Notice that the explicit formula $a_n = a_1 r^{n-1}$ can be rewritten as $a_n = a_0 r^n$ where $a_0 = \dfrac{a_1}{r}$.

Observing the pattern of obtaining a_n from a_k (where $k < n$) by repeated multiplications of r produces a more generalized explicit formula: $a_n = a_k r^{n-k}$.

Geometric Sequences			
Recursive	Explicit		
$a_n = a_{n-1} \cdot r$	$a_n = a_1 r^{n-1}$ (basic)	$a_n = a_k r^{n-k}$ (generalized)	$a_n = a_0 r^n;\ a_0 = \dfrac{a_1}{r}$ (simplified)

Example 3   Writing and Using Explicit Formulas

Given the geometric sequence with $a_3 = 6$ and $a_7 = 96$, write a simplified explicit formula for a_n and use the formula to find a_{10}.

Answer

$a_7 = a_3 r^{7-3}$

$96 = 6r^4$

$16 = r^4$

$r = \pm 2$

1. Find r by substituting both terms into $a_n = a_k r^{n-k}$ and solving. Note that there are two possible values for r in this case.

CONTINUED ➡

Case 1: $r = 2$

$a_n = 6(2)^{n-3}$

$a_n = 6(2)^n(2)^{-3}$

$a_n = \frac{3}{4}(2)^n$

2. Substitute $r = 2$ and $a_3 = 6$ (with $k = 3$) into $a_n = a_k r^{n-k}$ and simplify.

$a_{10} = \frac{3}{4}(2)^{10} = 768$

3. Evaluate the explicit formula to find a_{10}.

Case 2: $r = -2$

$a_n = 6(-2)^{n-3}$

$a_n = 6(-2)^n(-2)^{-3}$

$a_n = -\frac{3}{4}(-2)^n$

4. Substitute $r = -2$ and $a_3 = 6$ (with $k = 3$) into $a_n = a_k r^{n-k}$ and simplify.

$a_{10} = -\frac{3}{4}(-2)^{10} = -768$

5. Evaluate the explicit formula to find a_{10}.

SKILL ✔ **EXERCISE 11**

The terms between two given terms of a geometric sequence are called the *geometric means*. The geometric means between a_3 and a_7 in the sequence from Example 3 can be found using the recursive formula once r has been determined. If $r = 2$, the geometric means are 12, 24, and 48. If $r = -2$, they are -12, 24, and -48.

Example 4   Finding a Geometric Mean

Find the single geometric mean between 10 and 50.

Answer

Let $a_1 = 10$ and $a_3 = 50$.

1. The geometric mean is a_2.

$50 = 10r^{3-1}$

$5 = r^2$

$r = \pm\sqrt{5}$

2. Substitute a_3 and a_1 into $a_n = a_1 r^{n-1}$ and solve for r.

$a_2 = 10(\pm\sqrt{5}) = \pm10\sqrt{5}$

3. Use the recursive formula, $a_n = a_{n-1}r$, to find the geometric mean.

Check

4. Find $a_3 = \pm10\sqrt{5}(\pm\sqrt{5}) = 50$.

SKILL ✔ **EXERCISE 17**

Notice that the geometric mean between 10 and 50 is $\pm\sqrt{10 \cdot 50} = \pm10\sqrt{5}$. The fact that the geometric mean between two numbers a and c is $\pm\sqrt{ac}$ is used in geometry and proved in exercise 42.

▌**DEFINITION**

A **geometric series** is a sum of the terms of a geometric sequence. The sum of the first n terms of $a_1, a_2, a_3, \ldots$ is the nth partial sum, $S_n = a_1 + a_2 + a_3 + \cdots + a_n$.

For the geometric sequence $36, -24, 16, \ldots$, the seventh partial sum, $S_7 = 36 - 24 + 16 - \cdots + \frac{256}{81}$, could be evaluated by completing each addition. Instead, we will derive and apply a general formula for S_n in any geometric sequence by examining the sums S_n and $-rS_n$.

$$S_n = a_1 + a_1 r + a_1 r^2 + \cdots + a_1 r^{n-2} + a_1 r^{n-1}$$

1. Write S_n in terms of a_1 and multiples of r.

$$-rS_n = -a_1 r - a_1 r^2 - a_1 r^3 - \cdots - a_1 r^{n-1} - a_1 r^n$$

2. Multiply both sides by $-r$.

$$S_n - rS_n = a_1 - a_1 r^n$$

3. Add the equations. Note that most of the terms cancel.

$$S_n(1 - r) = a_1(1 - r^n)$$

4. Solve for S_n.

$$S_n = \frac{a_1(1 - r^n)}{1 - r}$$

When given the last term a_n instead of n, you can solve $a_n = a_1 r^{n-1}$ for n, a process that may require the use of logarithms. Alternately, substituting $a_n r$ for $a_1 r^n$ in step 3 above produces a second formula.

$$S_n - rS_n = a_1 - a_n r$$
$$S_n(1 - r) = a_1 - a_n r$$
$$S_n = \frac{a_1 - a_n r}{1 - r}$$

Finite Geometric Series

$$S_n = \frac{a_1(1 - r^n)}{1 - r} \text{ or } S_n = \frac{a_1 - a_n r}{1 - r}$$

Example 5 Evaluating Finite Geometric Series

Evaluate each geometric series.

a. $1458 + 486 + 162 + \cdots + 2$

b. $\displaystyle\sum_{k=3}^{10} \frac{3}{4}(2)^n$

Answer

a. $\dfrac{a_2}{a_1} = \dfrac{486}{1458} = \dfrac{1}{3} = r$

1. Determine the common ratio.

$$S_n = \frac{1458 - 2\left(\frac{1}{3}\right)}{1 - \frac{1}{3}} = 2186$$

2. Evaluate the sum using $S_n = \dfrac{a_1 - a_n r}{1 - r}$.

---

b. $a_1 = \dfrac{3}{4}(2)^3 = 6$

$r = 2$

$n = (10 - 3) + 1 = 8$

1. Recognize the sum as a geometric series and identify a_1, r, and n.

$$S_n = \frac{a_1(1 - r^n)}{1 - r} = \frac{6(1 - 2^8)}{1 - 2} = \frac{6(-255)}{-1} = 1530$$

2. Evaluate the sum using $S_n = \dfrac{a_1(1 - r^n)}{1 - r}$.

SKILL ✔ EXERCISE 19

Suppose a 25-yr-old invests $100 at the end of each month into an annuity that pays 6% APR compounded monthly (0.5% per month) until retiring at the age of 65. The value of each of these $40(12) = 480$ monthly investments at retirement can be determined using the compound interest formula. The total value of the annuity can be calculated as a geometric series with $a_1 = 100$, $r = 1.005$, and $n = 480$.

$$S_n = \frac{a_1(1 - r^n)}{1 - r} = \frac{100(1 - 1.005^{480})}{1 - 1.005} = \$199,149.07$$

Note that the contributions of $100(480) = \$48,000$ earned $151,149.07 in interest over 40 yr.

Payment	Amount	Value
1	100	$100(1.005)^{480}$
2	100	$100(1.005)^{479}$
3	100	$100(1.005)^{478}$
$\vdots$	$\vdots$	$\vdots$
478	100	$100(1.005)^2$
479	100	$100(1.005)^1$
480	100	100

FUTURE VALUE OF AN ANNUITY

The future value, *FV*, of an annuity consisting of *n* periodic payments of *P* with a periodic interest rate *i* is given by $FV = P\left[\dfrac{1 - (1 + i)^n}{1 - (1 + i)}\right]$ or $FV = P\left[\dfrac{(1 + i)^n - 1}{i}\right]$.

Example 6   Finding the Future Value of an Annuity

Find the future value and interest earned in an annuity with $500 quarterly payments after 45 yr if the account earns 8% APR compounded quarterly.

Answer

$i = \dfrac{0.08}{4} = 0.02; n = 45(4) = 180$

1. Determine the quarterly interest rate and number of payments.

$FV = 500\left[\dfrac{1.02^{180} - 1}{0.02}\right] = \$858,020.78$

2. Substitute into $FV = P\left[\dfrac{(1 + i)^n - 1}{i}\right]$ and evaluate.

$\$858,020.78 - \$90,000 = \$768,020.78$

3. Subtract the original contributions of 180($500) to determine the amount of interest earned.

——————————— SKILL ✓ **EXERCISE 37**

Recall from Section 9.1 that the sum of an infinite series is defined if the related sequence of partial sums $S_1, S_2, S_3, \ldots S_n$ converges to a real number S as $n \to \infty$. The sum of an infinite arithmetic series cannot be calculated since a_n does not approach 0 as $n \to \infty$ and the sequence of partial sums is divergent. Similar reasoning shows infinite geometric series with $|r| \geq 1$ cannot be evaluated. However, if $|r| < 1$, $r^n \to 0$ as $n \to \infty$ and

$S_n = \dfrac{a_1(1 - r^n)}{1 - r}$ converges to $S = \dfrac{a_1}{1 - r}$.

The nineteenth-century Norwegian mathematician Niels Abel referred to divergent series as "the work of the Devil" since they led to many contradictions and paradoxes.

Infinite Geometric Series
An infinite geometric series with $|r| < 1$ *converges* to $S = \dfrac{a_1}{1 - r}$. If $|r| \geq 1$, the series *diverges*.

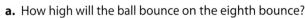

Example 7 Evaluating Infinite Geometric Series

Evaluate each infinite geometric series if possible.

a. $\sum_{k=1}^{\infty} 3(0.9)^k$ **b.** $\sum_{n=1}^{\infty} \left(\frac{e}{2}\right)^{n-1}$ **c.** $\frac{1}{2} - \frac{1}{4} + \frac{1}{8} - \frac{1}{16} + \cdots$

Answer

a. $S = \frac{3(0.9)^1}{1-(0.9)} = \frac{2.7}{0.1} = 27$ Since $|r| = |0.9| < 1$, substitute into $S = \frac{a_1}{1-r}$ and evaluate.

b. The sum does not exist.   The series is divergent since $|r| = \left|\frac{e}{2}\right| \approx 1.36 > 1$.

c. $S = \frac{\frac{1}{2}}{1-\left(-\frac{1}{2}\right)} = \frac{1}{2}\left(\frac{2}{3}\right) = \frac{1}{3}$ Since $|r| = \left|-\frac{1}{2}\right| < 1$, substitute into $S = \frac{a_1}{1-r}$ and evaluate.

SKILL ✔ **EXERCISE 23**

Geometric sequences and series can be used to model and solve real-world problems.

Example 8 Applying a Geometric Series

Suppose a rubber ball is dropped from a height of 20 ft and it rebounds to 80% of its previous height on each bounce.

a. How high will the ball bounce on the eighth bounce?

b. How far will the ball have traveled vertically before it finally comes to rest?

Answer

a. $b_1 = 20(0.8) = 16$ ft   1. Compute the height of the first 3 bounces.

$b_2 = 16(0.8) = 12.8$ ft

$b_3 = 12.8(0.8) = 10.24$ ft

$\vdots$

$b_n = 20(0.8)^n$ 2. Recognize that the heights can be represented as a geometric sequence with $a_0 = 20$ and $r = 0.8$.

$b_8 = 20(0.8)^8 \approx 3.36$ ft   3. Use the simplified explicit formula to find the height of the eighth bounce.

---

b. $\sum_{n=1}^{\infty} 20(0.8)^n = \frac{20(0.8)^1}{1-0.8} = \frac{16}{0.2} = 80$ 1. Model the sum of the heights with an infinite geometric series and evaluate the sum using $S = \frac{a_1}{1-r}$.

the total distance traveled   2. The ball falls from the initial height of 20 ft and then rises to and falls from each bounce's subsequent height.
$= 20 + 2(80) = 180$ ft

SKILL ✔ **EXERCISE 39**

A. Exercises

1. Identify each formula related to geometric sequences.

a. $S = \dfrac{a_1}{1 - r}$

b. $S_n = \dfrac{a_1(1 - r^n)}{1 - r}$

c. $a_n = r \cdot a_{n-1}$

d. $a_n = a_k r^{n-k}$

e. $a_n = a_1 r^{n-1}$

f. $\dfrac{a_n}{a_{n-1}} = r$

I. recursive

II. basic explicit

III. generalized explicit

IV. common ratio

V. finite series

VI. infinite series

If the sequence is geometric, state the common ratio and list the next 3 terms. If the sequence is not geometric, explain why.

2. $\dfrac{1}{8}, \dfrac{1}{2}, 2, 8, \ldots$

3. $0.053, 0.53, 5.3, 53, \ldots$

4. $-3, 9, -36, 81, \ldots$

5. $-\dfrac{8}{27}, \dfrac{4}{9}, -\dfrac{2}{3}, 1, \ldots$

6. Which of the following is an explicit formula for a geometric sequence? (Select all that apply.)

A. $a_n = 4^{n-1}$

B. $a_n = -5n^2$

C. $a_n = \left(\dfrac{2}{3}\right)^n$

D. $a_n = \dfrac{7n + 8}{19}$

Write the recursive formula and an explicit formula for each geometric sequence. Then find a_{10}.

7. $-7, 14, -28, 56, \ldots$

8. $625, -125, 25, -5, \ldots$

9. $4, 10, 25, 62.5, \ldots$

10. $\dfrac{1}{x}, \dfrac{1}{x^2}, \dfrac{1}{x^3}, \dfrac{1}{x^4}, \ldots$

Given the terms of a geometric sequence, write a simplified explicit formula for a_n. Then use the formula to find the specified term.

11. $a_3 = 3;\ a_8 = 9375;\ a_5$

12. $a_2 = 6;\ a_6 = 486;\ a_{10}$

13. $a_3 = 2;\ a_5 = \dfrac{1}{2};\ a_{12}$

14. $a_2 = 3;\ a_4 = 12;\ a_9$

Find the geometric means between the given terms.

15. $a_7 = -2$ and $a_{10} = 250$

16. $a_{19} = 3$ and $a_{23} = 768$

17. $a_{38} = 4$ and $a_{40} = 196$

18. $a_{29} = 13$ and $a_{32} = -832$

B. Exercises

Evaluate each finite geometric series.

19. $\displaystyle\sum_{n=1}^{16} 2^n$

20. $\displaystyle\sum_{n=1}^{15} 3\left(-\dfrac{1}{2}\right)^n$

21. $\displaystyle\sum_{n=1}^{1000} e^n$

22. $\displaystyle\sum_{n=1}^{14} 5(0.2)^{n-1}$

Evaluate each infinite geometric series or state that the series is divergent.

23. $4 + 1 + \dfrac{1}{4} + \cdots$

24. $1 - \dfrac{2}{5} + \dfrac{4}{25} - \cdots$

25. $\dfrac{1}{16} + \dfrac{1}{8} + \dfrac{1}{4} + \cdots$

26. $\displaystyle\sum_{n=1}^{\infty} 2\left(\dfrac{2}{5}\right)^{n-1}$

27. $\displaystyle\sum_{n=1}^{\infty} \left(\dfrac{1}{2}\right)^n$

28. $\displaystyle\sum_{n=1}^{\infty} 18\left(\dfrac{1}{3}\right)^n$

Find the requested value for each geometric sequence or series.

29. Find n if $a_2 = 36$, $r = 9$, and $a_n = 2916$.

30. Find n if $a_5 = -\dfrac{1}{3}$, $r = 6$, and $a_n = -432$.

31. Find n if $a_2 = 30$, $r = 6$, and $S_n = 215$.

32. Find r if $a_1 = 8$ and $S = \dfrac{32}{7}$.

33. A church borrows \$50,000 at 3% APR compounded annually with one balloon payment at the end of 4 yr. Write a sequence representing the balance due at the end of each year.

34. A logging company purchased a piece of equipment for \$269,000. If the depreciation rate is 30% per year, what will be the value of the equipment after 4 yr?

35. One job offers a beginning salary of \$46,500 with an annual raise of 3% while a second job starts at \$43,000 with a 5% raise each year. Find the annual salary and total amount earned (to the nearest dollar) for each job offer at the end of 6 yr.

36. A software engineer has earned \$1,340,825 over the last 12 yr at his current position. If his salary has increased by 4% each year, how much (to the nearest dollar) did he earn during his first year? during his twelfth year?

37. Calculate the amount of interest earned over 5 yr if you invest \$1000 at the beginning of each year in an annuity that earns 5% annually.

38. When he was born, Sam's parents began to deposit \$200 at the end of each month in a mutual fund for his college education. Estimate (to the nearest dollar) the fund's balance after 18 yr if the fund is projected to grow at an annual rate of 6%.

39. A rubber ball is thrown to a height of 80 ft and then rebounds to 50% of its previous height on each bounce.

a. Find the height of the fifth bounce.

b. Find the total distance the ball has traveled vertically when it hits the ground the sixth time.

c. Find the total distance the ball has traveled vertically when it finally comes to rest.

40. Use the basic explicit formula $a_n = a_1 r^{n-1}$ to derive the simplified explicit formula $a_n = a_0 r^n$.

❯ C. Exercises

41. Prove: If a_k is the kth term of a geometric sequence with a common ratio r, then $a_n = a_k r^{n-k}$.

42. Prove: The geometric mean between two numbers a and c is $\pm\sqrt{ac}$.

43. Prove: Show that $a_n{}^2$ is a geometric sequence if a_n is a geometric sequence.

44. Ada would like to retire in 35 yr with $1,000,000. How much should she deposit at the end of each month into an account paying 6% APR compounded monthly?

45. How many years will it take Bob to save $1,000,000 if he contributes $200 at the end of each month in an account that pays 4.8% APR compounded monthly?

46. Use technology to calculate the APR (to the nearest tenth of a percent) needed for $500 monthly payments into an annuity over 20 yr to grow to $1,000,000.

CUMULATIVE REVIEW

Write the first 6 terms of each recursively defined sequence. [9.1]

47. $a_1 = \frac{1}{9}$; $a_n = 3^{n-1}(a_{n-1})$ where $n \geq 2$

48. $a_1 = 1, a_2 = 3$; $a_n = 4a_{n-1} - a_{n-2}$ where $n \geq 3$

Determine whether each sequence is arithmetic. If so, state the common difference and list the next 3 terms. If not, explain why. [9.2]

49. $1, 10, 19, 28, 37, \ldots$ **50.** $39, 33, 26, 20, 14, \ldots$

Write a simplified polar equation for each conic section. Then classify the conic and verify your answer by using technology to graph the curve and its directrix. [8.6]

51. $e = 2.5$; directrix: $y = 3$

52. $e = \frac{1}{3}$; directrix: $x = -6$

53. Find A such that $\sin(A - \theta) = \cos\theta$. [5.4]

   A. π **C.** $\frac{\pi}{4}$ **E.** none of these

   B. $\frac{\pi}{2}$ **D.** 0

54. Find the direction of $\mathbf{z} = \langle 3, -7 \rangle$. [6.1]

   A. $\theta \approx 66.8°$ **C.** $\theta \approx 246.8°$ **E.** $\theta \approx 336.8°$

   B. $\theta \approx 113.2°$ **D.** $\theta \approx 293.2°$

55. Find the partial fraction decomposition for $\dfrac{2x+1}{x^2 - 2x + 1}$. [7.7]

   A. $\dfrac{2x}{x-1} + \dfrac{1}{(x-1)^2}$ **D.** $\dfrac{2}{x+1} + \dfrac{3}{(x+1)^2}$

   B. $\dfrac{3}{x-1} + \dfrac{2}{(x-1)^2}$ **E.** none of these

   C. $\dfrac{2}{x-1} + \dfrac{3}{(x-1)^2}$

56. Eliminate the parameter θ in $x = 4\sec\theta$ and $y = \frac{1}{4}\tan\theta$ to write a rectangular equation for the conic. [8.5]

   A. $\dfrac{x^2}{4} - \dfrac{y^2}{4} = 1$ **D.** $\dfrac{x^2}{16} - 16y^2 = 1$

   B. $\dfrac{x^2}{4} + 4y^2 = 1$ **E.** none of these

   C. $\dfrac{x^2}{16} - \dfrac{y^2}{16} = 1$

BINOMIAL EXPANSION AND PASCAL'S TRIANGLE

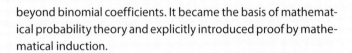

Consider Proposition 4 from Book II of Euclid's *Elements* (ca. 300 BC): When a segment is randomly divided, the square drawn on the whole segment is equal to the squares drawn on the pieces plus twice the rectangle formed by the pieces. Can you express this statement in modern algebraic notation? If the cut pieces have lengths of x and y, then $(x + y)^2 = x^2 + y^2 + 2xy$. Euclid used geometric figures to prove his propositions, including Proposition 7, which is equivalent to $(x - y)^2 = x^2 + y^2 - 2xy$ in modern notation. While Euclid did not address equations beyond those of degree two, this is the first written evidence of a binomial expansion.

Over 1000 yr later the Persian scholar al-Khwārizmī (ca. AD 800) used geometric figures to show how to solve second-degree equations and then explained how to multiply binomials that we would write as $(a + bx)(c + dx)$. The Persian mathematician and engineer al-Karajī (953–1029) created a table similar to Pascal's triangle with columns that listed binomial expansion coefficients up to $(a + b)^5$. The Chinese mathematician Zhu Shijie included a chart like Pascal's triangle in a 1303 publication and explained how to use it to solve equations up to degree 14. He referred to this method as "ancient," indicating it had been known in China for some time.

Several hundred years later, a chart similar to those found in Persian and Chinese documents was developed independently in Europe. Michael Stifel's *Arithmetica Integra* (1544) contained a version of Pascal's triangle in columnar form. Finally, in 1654, Blaise Pascal (1623–62) published his *Treatise on the Arithmetical Triangle*. This comprehensive work explained how to construct the triangle and explored several patterns and applications beyond binomial coefficients. It became the basis of mathematical probability theory and explicitly introduced proof by mathematical induction.

Pascal was a child prodigy born into a wealthy family and educated at home by his father. At the age of 15 he discovered a theorem of projective geometry that he called the "Theorem of the Mystic Hexagon," known today as Pascal's Theorem (the extended opposite sides of a hexagon formed by six random points on a conic will intersect in three collinear points). Pascal published a treatise on conic sections at 16 yr of age, and at the age of 22 he completed a 3-yr endeavor of inventing a calculating machine to aid his father in collecting taxes. This became the first commercially produced desktop calculating machine. Pascal also studied physics and was the first to publish a system of hydrostatics in *Treatise on the Equilibrium of Liquids*, which contains Pascal's principle of pressure. His later treatise on the measurement of the weight of the atmosphere led to the invention of the barometric altimeter.

With all of Pascal's privilege and accomplishments, you might never suspect the illnesses and pain he struggled with throughout his life, especially in his last few years. He devoted a large portion of his time to studying and writing on theology. In 1659 he wrote a 15-paragraph treatise entitled "Prayer, to Ask of God the Proper Use of Sickness," published in *Minor Works*. In the third paragraph he states, "I praise thee, my God, and I will bless thee all the days of my life, that it has pleased thee to reduce me to the incapacity of enjoying the sweets of health and the pleasures of the world."

COMPREHENSION CHECK

1. Express Euclid's Book II Proposition 7, the expansion of $(x - y)^2$, in words with no symbols. *Hint*: write all terms as positive so that $x^2 + y^2 = 2xy$.

2. Name two cultures where "Pascal's triangle" was used hundreds of years prior to Pascal.

3. What 1654 publication by Blaise Pascal introduced mathematical probability theory and proof by induction?

4. List several ways that Pascal's statement about his suffering reflects a biblical worldview.

The Binomial Theorem

After completing this section, you will be able to

- expand powers of a binomial using Pascal's triangle.
- expand powers of a binomial using the combinatorial notation of the Binomial Theorem.
- find probabilities within a binomial experiment.

This section is devoted to studying the series generated when expanding powers of a *binomial*, the sum of two unlike terms. As discussed in the Biblical Perspective of Mathematics feature in Chapter 6, many mathematical concepts are discovered intuitively by studying patterns found in specific examples. Examine the following expansions of powers of $(x + y)^n$.

$$(x + y)^0 = 1$$
$$(x + y)^1 = 1x + 1y$$
$$(x + y)^2 = 1x^2 + 2xy + 1y^2$$
$$(x + y)^3 = 1x^3 + 3x^2y + 3xy^2 + 1y^3$$
$$(x + y)^4 = 1x^4 + 4x^3y + 6x^2y^2 + 4xy^3 + 1y^4$$
$$(x + y)^5 = 1x^5 + 5x^4y + 10x^3y^2 + 10x^2y^3 + 5xy^4 + 1y^5$$

Notice the following patterns.

Each expansion contains $n + 1$ terms, each having a degree of n.

The exponents of x decrease by 1 from n in the first term to 0 in the last term.

The exponents of y increase by 1 from 0 in the first term to n in the last term.

The coefficients exhibit symmetry, with the first two coefficients being 1 and n.

Extracting the *binomial coefficients* produces Pascal's triangle, an array of numbers that can be used to determine the other coefficients for expansions of higher binomial powers. The top line containing 1 is row 0 since it corresponds to $(x + y)^0$. Row 1 contains the coefficients of $(x + y)^1$. The remaining rows begin and end with coefficients of 1, and the other coefficients are the sum of the two numbers above it in the previous row. Row n provides the coefficients for the corresponding expansion of $(x + y)^n$.

Pascal's Triangle	
1	row 0
1 1	row 1
1 2 1	row 2
1 3 3 1	row 3
1 4 6 4 1	row 4
1 5 10 10 5 1	row 5

KEYWORD SEARCH

Sierpinski in Pascal's Triangle 🔍

Example 1 Using Pascal's Triangle

Use Pascal's triangle to expand $(a + b)^6$.

Answer

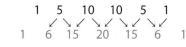

$$a^6 + 6a^5b + 15a^4b^2 + 20a^3b^3 + 15a^2b^4 + 6ab^5 + b^6$$

1. Derive row 6 of Pascal's triangle from row 5.

2. Use the descending powers of a, the ascending powers of b, and coefficients from row 6 of Pascal's triangle to expand the binomial power.

SKILL ✓ EXERCISE 1

To expand a binomial power of the form $(x - y)^n$, consider the equivalent expression $(x + (-y))^n$.

Example 2 Using Pascal's Triangle

Use Pascal's triangle to expand $(2x - y)^4$.

Answer

$1(2x)^4 + 4(2x)^3(-y) + 6(2x)^2(-y)^2 + 4(2x)(-y)^3 + 1(-y)^4$ 1. Expand the binomial power using row 4 of Pascal's triangle, descending powers of the first term, $2x$, and ascending powers of the second term.

$= 16x^4 - 32x^3y + 24x^2y^2 - 8xy^3 + y^4$ 2. Simplify each term. Notice that the signs of the terms alternate when expanding powers of $(x - y)^n$.

SKILL ✓ **EXERCISE 5**

Using Pascal's triangle to recursively determine the coefficients for the expansion of a binomial power can become tedious. Examining the coefficients in the expansion of $(x + y)^3$ can lead to a more efficient explicit process.

$$(x + y)^3 = (x + y)(x + y)(x + y) = x^3 + 3x^2y + 3xy^2 + y^3$$

There is only one x^3 term and it is the product of the x-term in each of the three factors. The expansion generates three separate terms of x^2y. Each is obtained using y from one of the factors and x from the other two factors. The three ways of choosing the factor that contributes the y (and by default, choosing the other two factors to contribute an x) is often notated as $_3C_1$ which can be read "3 choose 1." There are also three ways to select two factors to contribute a y (and by default, the one factor contributing an x) which generate the $_3C_2 = 3$ separate terms of xy^2. There is only one way to multiply a y from each factor, so there is only $_3C_3 = 1$ term of y^3.

The number of different ways to choose r out of n items is given by the formula $_nC_r = \dfrac{n!}{r!(n - r)!}$, where $_nC_r$ can be read "n choose r." The number of ways to choose 1 factor from the 3 factors above can be calculated using $_3C_1 = \dfrac{3!}{1!(3 - 1)!} = \dfrac{3 \cdot 2!}{1 \cdot 2!} = 3$. The expression $_nC_r$ is called a *combination* and may also be notated as $C(n, r)$ or $\binom{n}{r}$.

Example 3 Evaluating Combinations

Evaluate each combination.

a. $_6C_2$ **b.** $_6C_4$ **c.** $_nC_0$ **d.** $_nC_1$

Answer

a. $_6C_2 = \dfrac{6!}{2!(6 - 2)!}$ **b.** $_6C_4 = \dfrac{6!}{4!(6 - 4)!}$ **c.** $_nC_0 = \dfrac{n!}{0!(n - 0)!}$ **d.** $_nC_1 = \dfrac{n!}{1!(n - 1)!}$

$= \dfrac{6 \cdot 5 \cdot 4!}{2 \cdot 1 \cdot 4!} = 15$ $= \dfrac{6 \cdot 5 \cdot 4!}{4! \cdot 2 \cdot 1} = 15$ $= \dfrac{n!}{1 \cdot n!} = 1$ $= \dfrac{n \cdot (n - 1)!}{1 \cdot (n - 1)!} = n$

SKILL ✓ **EXERCISE 9**

TIP

Most calculators have an nCr function (found in the [MATH], PROB menu on the TI-84 Plus) that can be used to calculate combinations.

```
6 nCr 2
                    15
6 nCr 4
                    15
```

In the expansion of $(a + b)^6$ in Example 1, the coefficient of a^4b^2 is $_6C_2 = 15$ and the coefficient of a^2b^4 is $_6C_4 = 15$. The fact that $_6C_2 = _6C_4 = 15$ illustrates that $_nC_r = _nC_{n-r}$, which accounts for the symmetry in the expansion's coefficients.

In general, $_nC_r$ is the coefficient of $x^{n-r}y^r$ in the expansion of $(x + y)^n$.

▌THE BINOMIAL THEOREM

For any positive integer n,
$$(x + y)^n = {_nC_0}x^n + {_nC_1}x^{n-1}y + {_nC_2}x^{n-2}y^2 + {_nC_3}x^{n-3}y^3 + \cdots + {_nC_n}y^n$$
$$= \sum_{r=0}^{n} {_nC_r}x^{n-r}y^r \text{ where } {_nC_r} = \frac{n!}{r!(n-r)!}.$$

▬ Example 4   Applying the Binomial Theorem

Use the Binomial Theorem to expand $(c^3 + 2d)^4$.

Answer

```
4 nCr {0,1,2,3,4}
            {1 4 6 4 1}
```

1. The binomial coefficients can be found using the calculator's nCr function and a list of values for r. Enter 4 nCr {0,1,2,3,4}.

$(c^3)^4 + 4(c^3)^3(2d) + 6(c^3)^2(2d)^2$
$\qquad + 4(c^3)(2d)^3 + (2d)^4$

2. Use the list of coefficients, descending powers of c^3, and ascending powers of $2d$ to write the expansion.

$c^{12} + 8c^9d + 24c^6d^2 + 32c^3d^3 + 16d^4$

3. Simplify.

SKILL ✔ **EXERCISE 17**

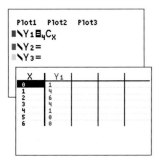
Using the explicit formula for $_nC_r$ to find the coefficient is especially helpful when determining a specific term in the expansion of a binomial power.

▬ Example 5   Finding Specific Terms of a Binomial Expansion

Given $(2x - 1)^8$, find the x^5 term and the seventh term of its expansion.

Answer

$_8C_3(2x)^5(-1)^3 = 56(32x^5)(-1) = -1792x^5$

1. The term containing x^5 has $r = 3$.

$_8C_6(2x)^2(-1)^6 = 28(4x^2)(1) = 112x^2$

2. Since r begins at 0, the seventh term has $r = 6$.

SKILL ✔ **EXERCISE 25**

The Binomial Theorem can be used to model probabilities associated with a *binomial experiment* consisting of n independent trials where each trial results in either a success or a failure. For example, rolling three dice looking for how many times a four results is a binomial experiment consisting of three trials where the probability of success is $p = \frac{1}{6}$ and the probability of failure is $q = 1 - p = \frac{5}{6}$.

▌DEFINITION

The **probability** of x successes in a binomial experiment with n independent trials is $P(x) = {_nC_x}p^xq^{n-x}$, where p is the probability of success and q, the probability of failure, is $1 - p$.

Example 6 Finding a Binomial Probability

Jeff randomly selects answers to 5 multiple-choice questions, each having 4 choices. Find the probability of each event.

a. He gets exactly 3 questions correct.

b. He gets at least 3 questions correct.

Answer

a. $p = \frac{1}{4}$; $q = \frac{3}{4}$

$_5C_3\left(\frac{1}{4}\right)^3\left(\frac{3}{4}\right)^2 = 10\left(\frac{1}{64}\right)\left(\frac{9}{16}\right) = \frac{45}{512}$
≈ 0.0879 or 8.79%

1. Determine the probability of a success and a failure for each question.

2. Determine the probability of exactly 3 successes in 5 independent trials.

b. $_5C_3\left(\frac{1}{4}\right)^3\left(\frac{3}{4}\right)^2 + _5C_4\left(\frac{1}{4}\right)^4\left(\frac{3}{4}\right)^1 + _5C_5\left(\frac{1}{4}\right)^5\left(\frac{3}{4}\right)^0$

$= 10\left(\frac{1}{64}\right)\left(\frac{9}{16}\right) + 5\left(\frac{1}{256}\right)\left(\frac{3}{4}\right) + 1\left(\frac{1}{1024}\right)(1)$

$= \frac{90}{1024} + \frac{15}{1024} + \frac{1}{1024} = \frac{53}{512}$

≈ 0.1035 or 10.35%

1. Find the sum of the probabilities of getting 3, 4, or all 5 correct.

SKILL ✔ **EXERCISE 33**

❯ A. Exercises

Use Pascal's triangle to expand each binomial power.

1. $(x + y)^4$
2. $(p - q)^3$
3. $(w + v)^8$
4. $(a - 4)^6$
5. $(3a - 1)^5$
6. $(x + 2y)^5$
7. $(2a - 3b)^4$
8. $(4m + 5n)^5$

Evaluate each pair of combinations without using technology.

9. $_6C_4$ and $_6C_2$
10. $_{10}C_7$ and $_{10}C_3$
11. $_5C_4$ and $_5C_1$
12. $_9C_9$ and $_9C_0$
13. $_nC_0$ and $_nC_n$
14. $_nC_1$ and $_nC_{n-1}$

❯ B. Exercises

Use the Binomial Theorem to expand each binomial.

15. $(a + b)^3$
16. $(x + 2)^5$
17. $(2c - 1)^3$
18. $(3m + 4n)^4$
19. $(4 + z)^5$
20. $(c + 10)^5$
21. $(2a - 3b)^4$
22. $(6v - 5w)^3$
23. $(5a + 4z)^5$
24. $(3c + 2d^2)^4$

Find the given term in the expansion of each binomial power.

25. seventh term in $(x + y)^8$
26. fifth term in $(a - 3b)^{10}$
27. m^4n^3 term in $(2m - 5n)^7$

28. v^5 term in $(4v + 2)^{11}$
29. c^8d^7 term in $(c - d)^{15}$
30. fourth term in $(5x - 3y)^9$
31. third term in $(w + 7)^{12}$
32. c^4d^3 term in $(6c + \frac{1}{3}d)^7$

Find each probability to the nearest tenth of a percent.

33. getting exactly 4 twos in 10 tosses of a die
34. getting exactly 2 threes in 12 tosses of a die
35. getting heads exactly 4 times in 8 tosses of a coin
36. getting tails exactly 3 times in 11 tosses of a coin
37. getting 5 or more correct on a 7-question multiple-choice quiz if random guessing is used on each of the 4-choice questions

Prove each statement involving combinations.

38. $_nC_r = _nC_{n-r}$
39. $_nC_2 + _{n+1}C_2 = n^2$

❯ C. Exercises

Expand each binomial.

40. $\left(\sqrt{3} + 5t\right)^4$
41. $\left(\sqrt{x} - 2\right)^5$
42. $\left(m^{\frac{2}{3}} + 2n^{\frac{4}{3}}\right)^3$
43. $\left(4i - \sqrt{7}\right)^4$

44. A coin is tossed 3 times.
   a. Find $P(0 \text{ heads})$ and $P(3 \text{ heads})$.
   b. Find $P(1 \text{ head})$ and $P(2 \text{ heads})$.
   c. Find the sum of the 4 probabilities above.

45. Four dice are rolled.

    a. Find $P(0 \text{ ones})$ and $P(4 \text{ ones})$.

    b. Find $P(1 \text{ one})$ and $P(3 \text{ ones})$.

    c. Find $P(2 \text{ ones})$.

    d. Find the sum of the 5 probabilities above.

46. Verify the rule for determining numbers in Pascal's triangle by proving that $_nC_r = {}_{n-1}C_{r-1} + {}_{n-1}C_r$.

Pascal's Triangle	
$1 \quad (n-1) \ldots {}_{n-1}C_{r-1} \quad {}_{n-1}C_r \ldots (n-1) \quad 1$	row $n-1$
$1 \qquad n \ldots\ldots\ldots\ldots {}_nC_r \ldots\ldots\ldots\ldots n \qquad 1$	row n

CUMULATIVE REVIEW

Express $\overrightarrow{PQ}$ in component form. Then find its length and a unit vector in the direction of $\overrightarrow{PQ}$. [6.3]

47. $P(2, 7, 5), Q(4, -4, 2)$ **48.** $P(-2, 3, 1), Q(8, -2, 1)$

If the sequence is geometric, state the common ratio and list the next 3 terms. If the sequence is not geometric, explain why. [9.3]

49. $1, 4, 9, 16, 25, \ldots$ **50.** $25, -10, 4, -\frac{8}{5}, \frac{16}{25}, \ldots$

Write both the recursive formula and an explicit formula for each geometric sequence. Then find a_{10}. [9.3]

51. $4, 6, 9, \frac{27}{2}, \ldots$ **52.** $729, -243, 81, -27, \ldots$

53. Find the value of $\frac{9!}{5!4!}$. [9.1]

    A. 220   **C.** 126   **E.** none of these

    B. 756   **D.** 3024

54. Find the maximum value of $f(x, y) = 2x + y$ under the given constraints.

$x \geq 0, y \geq 0, x + 2y \leq 8$, and $3x + y \leq 9$ [7.6]

    A. 16   **C.** 6   **E.** none of

    B. 7   **D.** 4   these

55. Find the sum of the first 4 terms if $a_1 = 5$ and $a_n = a_{n-1} - 2$. [9.2]

    A. 8   **C.** 13   **E.** none of

    B. 5   **D.** −3   these

56. Find an expression for the nth term of the following sequence: triangle, pentagon, heptagon, ... [9.2]

    A. $2(n+1)$-gon   **D.** $2(n-1)$-gon

    B. $(2n-1)$-gon   **E.** none of these

    C. $(2n+1)$-gon

9.5 Mathematical Induction

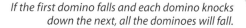

If the first domino falls and each domino knocks down the next, all the dominoes will fall.

Consider the statement: $n^2 - n + 11$ is prime for all natural numbers. This statement is true for:

$n = 1; 1^2 - 1 + 11 = 11$ (prime) $n = 5; 5^2 - 5 + 11 = 31$ (prime)
$n = 2; 2^2 - 2 + 11 = 13$ (prime) $n = 6; 6^2 - 6 + 11 = 41$ (prime)
$n = 3; 3^2 - 3 + 11 = 17$ (prime) $n = 7; 7^2 - 7 + 11 = 53$ (prime)
$n = 4; 4^2 - 4 + 11 = 23$ (prime) $n = 8; 8^2 - 8 + 11 = 67$ (prime)

Can we conclude that the statement is true for all natural numbers? No, in fact, we can prove that the statement is false by using the counterexample of $n = 11; 11^2 - 11 + 11 = 121$ (not prime). Showing that a statement is true for a few or even many values of n does not constitute a mathematical proof. In this section we will study *mathematical induction*, a common method of proving statements concerning natural numbers.

▌PRINCIPLE OF MATHEMATICAL INDUCTION

The proposition $P(n)$ is true for all natural numbers n if
(1) $P(1)$ is true (the *anchor step*), and
(2) $P(k + 1)$ is true when $P(k)$ is true (the *inductive step*).

In other words, you first show that the proposition is true when $n = 1$. Then you prove the induction step: if the proposition is true for k, it must be true for $k + 1$. The reasoning behind mathematical induction is similar to a sequence of falling dominoes. If the first domino falls ($P(1)$ is true), and if any falling domino knocks down the next domino ($P(k + 1)$ is true whenever $P(k)$ is true), then all the dominoes fall ($P(n)$ is true for all $\mathbb{N}$).

It may seem like the inductive step assumes the proposition that is being proved, but this step does not prove the proposition for any given value of n. Instead it shows only that every proposition follows from the previous proposition. It may help to write both the *inductive hypothesis*, $P(k)$, and the *inductive conclusion*, $P(k + 1)$, before attempting to prove the inductive step.

Example 1   Preparing for a Math Induction Proof

Consider the proposition $P(n)$: $\sum_{k=1}^{n} 8k = 8 + 16 + 24 + \cdots + 8n = 4n(n + 1)$ for all $n \in \mathbb{N}$.

a. Verify $P(1)$, the anchor step.

b. State the assumption of $P(k)$, the inductive hypothesis.

c. State $P(k + 1)$, the inductive conclusion.

Answer

a. $P(1)$: $8 = 4(1)(1 + 1) = 4(2) = 8$

b. $P(k)$: $8 + 16 + 24 + \cdots + 8k = 4k(k + 1)$

c. $P(k + 1)$: $8 + 16 + 24 + \cdots + 8k + 8(k + 1) = 4(k + 1)[(k + 1) + 1]$

SKILL ✓ **EXERCISE 5**

After completing this section, you will be able to

- use mathematical induction to prove statements involving natural numbers.
- prove and apply summation properties and formulas for sums of powers of integers.
- determine and prove a formula for the nth term of a sequence.

Fermat developed a form of proof similar to induction that he called "infinite descent." Use the Internet keyword search *Fermat infinite descent* to find more information and examples.

The inductive step for the statement in Example 1 is often stated in "if-then" form as "If $8 + 16 + 24 + \cdots + 8k = 4k(k+1)$, then $8 + 16 + 24 + \cdots + 8(k+1) = 4(k+1)(k+2)$."

Math induction can be used to prove theorems about sequences and series that we have already studied.

Example 2   Proving a Sequence's Explicit Formula

Prove the explicit formula $a_n = a_1 r^{n-1}$ for a geometric sequence.

Answer

$P(1): a_1 = a_1 r^{1-1} = a_1 r^0 = a_1$

1. Show that $P(n)$ is true when $n = 1$.

Assume $P(k): a_k = a_1 r^{k-1}$.

2. Begin the inductive step by assuming $P(k)$ is true for k.

3. Show that $P(k)$ implies $P(k+1)$.

$$a_k \cdot r = a_1 r^{k-1} \cdot r$$

  a. Since the sequence is geometric, multiply both sides by the common ratio r.

$$a_{k+1} = a_1 r^{k-1+1}$$

  b. Simplify using the recursive definition on the left side and a rule for exponents on the right side.

$$P(k+1): a_{k+1} = a_1 r^{(k+1)-1}$$

  c. Use the Commutative Property within the exponent to express the equation in the form of $P(k+1)$.

$$\therefore a_n = a_1 r^{n-1} \text{ for all } n \in \mathbb{N}$$

4. Conclude that $P(n)$ is true for all $n \in \mathbb{N}$.

SKILL ✔ **EXERCISE 19**

Many of the properties of operations of real numbers can be generalized using summation notation.

Properties of Summations	
a_i and b_i are sequences; c and p are constants.	
1. $\displaystyle\sum_{i=1}^{n} c = nc$ (repeated additions of c defined as multiplication)	2. $\displaystyle\sum_{i=1}^{n} ca_i = c \sum_{i=1}^{n} a_i$ (Distributive Property)
3. $\displaystyle\sum_{i=1}^{n} (a_i + b_i) = \sum_{i=1}^{n} a_i + \sum_{i=1}^{n} b_i$	4. $\displaystyle\sum_{i=1}^{n} a_i = \sum_{i=1}^{p} a_i + \sum_{i=p+1}^{n} a_i$ where $1 < p < n$.
(Commutative and Associative Properties of Addition)	

Mathematical induction can also be used to prove formulas for other frequently occurring summations.

Example 3   Proving a Summation Formula

Prove $\displaystyle\sum_{k=1}^{n} k = 1 + 2 + 3 + \cdots + n = \dfrac{n^2 + n}{2}$.

Answer

$P(1): \displaystyle\sum_{k=1}^{1} k = 1 = \dfrac{1^2 + 1}{2} = \dfrac{2}{2} = 1$

1. Show that $P(n): \displaystyle\sum_{k=1}^{n} k = \dfrac{n^2+n}{2}$ is true for $n = 1$.

Assume $P(k): 1 + 2 + 3 + \cdots + k = \dfrac{k^2 + k}{2}$.

2. Begin the inductive step by assuming $P(k)$ for any specific k value.

CONTINUED ➡

$$1 + 2 + 3 + \cdots + k + (k+1) = \frac{k^2 + k}{2} + (k+1)$$

$$= \frac{k^2 + k}{2} + \frac{2(k+1)}{2}$$

$$= \frac{(k^2 + k + 2k + 2)}{2}$$

$$= \frac{(k^2 + 2k + 1) + (k+1)}{2}$$

$$P(k+1): 1 + 2 + 3 + \cdots + (k+1) = \frac{(k+1)^2 + (k+1)}{2}$$

Conclude that $P(n)$ is true for all $n \in \mathbb{N}$.

3. Show that $P(k)$ implies $P(k+1)$.
   a. Add the next term $(k+1)$ to both sides.
   b. Obtain a common denominator on the right side.
   c. Add the fractions, then consider $P(k+1)$ below.
   d. Group in terms of $k + 1$.
   e. Factor the perfect square trinomial to achieve $P(k+1)$.
4. Apply the principle of math induction.

SKILL ✓ **EXERCISE 21**

Explicit formulas for sums of the first n powers of integers can be proved using math induction. The proofs of the other formulas in the table below are left as exercises.

Partial Sums of Powers of Integers	
1. $\displaystyle\sum_{k=1}^{n} k = \frac{n^2 + n}{2} = \frac{n(n+1)}{2}$	2. $\displaystyle\sum_{k=1}^{n} k^2 = \frac{n(n+1)(2n+1)}{6}$
3. $\displaystyle\sum_{k=1}^{n} k^3 = \frac{n^2(n+1)^2}{4}$	4. $\displaystyle\sum_{k=1}^{n} k^4 = \frac{n(n+1)(2n+1)(3n^2 + 3n - 1)}{30}$

The properties of summation and these formulas are used to evaluate partial sums of polynomial sequences. These techniques will also be used in the introduction to calculus found in Chapter 12.

Example 4 Using Properties to Evaluate Partial Sums

Evaluate.

a. $\displaystyle\sum_{k=1}^{17} (4k^2 - 9)$

b. $\displaystyle\sum_{k=8}^{20} k^3$

Answer

a. $\displaystyle\sum_{k=1}^{17} (4k^2 - 9) = 4\sum_{k=1}^{17} k^2 + \sum_{k=1}^{17} (-9)$

$$= 4\left(\frac{17(17+1)[2(17)+1]}{6}\right) + 17(-9)$$

$$= 4(1785) - 153 = 6987$$

b. $\displaystyle\sum_{k=8}^{20} k^3 = \sum_{k=1}^{20} k^3 - \sum_{k=1}^{7} k^3$

$$= \frac{20^2(20+1)^2}{4} - \frac{7^2(7+1)^2}{4}$$

$$= 44{,}100 - 784 = 43{,}316$$

SKILL ✓ **EXERCISES 13, 15**

You can prove many divisibility statements using math induction. Saying that 7 is a factor of an expression is equivalent to saying that the expression is equal to $7c$ where c is an integer. For example, saying 7 is a factor of -42 is equivalent to saying that $-42 = 7c$ where $c = -6$.

Example 5   Proving a Divisibility Statement with Math Induction

Prove that 5 is a factor of $6^{n-1} + 4$ for all $n \in \mathbb{N}$.

Answer

$P(1)$: $6^{1-1} + 4 = 1 + 4 = 5$
$\qquad\qquad\quad = 5c$ where $c = 1$

1. Verify the anchor step, $P(n)$ is true when $n = 1$.

Assume $P(k)$: $6^{k-1} + 4 = 5c$
$\qquad\qquad$ where c is an integer.
$\qquad\qquad \therefore 6^{k-1} = 5c - 4$

2. Write the inductive hypothesis and subtract 4 from both sides.

$6^{(k+1)-1} + 4 = 6^{k-1+1} + 4$
$\qquad\qquad\quad = 6(6^{k-1}) + 4$

3. Begin the statement of the inductive conclusion by substituting $k + 1$ for n and rearranging the exponential expression.

$\qquad\qquad\quad = 6(5c - 4) + 4$
$\qquad\qquad\quad = 30c - 20$

  a. Substitute using the result of the inductive hypothesis in step 2 and simplify.

$\qquad\qquad\quad = 5(6c - 4) = 5d$

  b. Factor and substitute the integer $d = 6c - 4$.

$P(k+1)$: $6^{(k+1)-1} = 5d$
$\qquad\qquad$ where d is an integer.

  c. Note that the inductive conclusion has been derived from the inductive hypothesis.

$\therefore$ 5 is a factor of $6^{n-1} + 4$
for all $n \in \mathbb{N}$.

4. Conclude that $P(n)$ is true for all $n \in \mathbb{N}$.

SKILL ✓ **EXERCISE 23**

You can also prove inequalities using math induction. Recall that an Addition Property of Inequality states that if $a \leq b$ and $c \leq d$, then $a + c \leq b + d$.

Example 6   Proving an Inequality with Math Induction

Prove that $n + 1 \leq 2^n$ for all $n \in \mathbb{N}$.

Answer

$P(1)$: $1 + 1 \leq 2^1$

1. Verify the anchor step.

Assume $P(k)$: $k + 1 \leq 2^k$.

2. Write the inductive hypothesis and reason to the inductive conclusion.

Since $1 \leq 2^k$ for $k \in \mathbb{N}$,
$(k + 1) + 1 \leq 2^k + 2^k$.

  a. Apply the Addition Property of Inequality that states if $a \leq b$ and $c \leq d$, then $a + c \leq b + d$, where $c = 1$ and $d = 2^k$ lead to the inductive conclusion.

$\qquad\qquad \leq 2 \cdot 2^k$
$\qquad\qquad \leq 2^{k+1}$

  b. Simplify the right side.

$P(k+1)$: $(k + 1) + 1 \leq 2^{k+1}$

  c. State the inductive conclusion.

$\therefore n + 1 \leq 2^n$ for all $n \in \mathbb{N}$

3. Conclude that $P(n)$ is true for all $n \in \mathbb{N}$.

SKILL ✓ **EXERCISE 27**

Math induction frequently allows us to prove results that we arrive at inductively.

Example 7 Finding and Proving a Partial-Sum Formula

Find an explicit formula for $\displaystyle\sum_{j=1}^{n} \frac{1}{j(j+1)}$.

Then use mathematical induction to verify the formula for all $n \in \mathbb{N}$.

Answer

$S_1 = \dfrac{1}{1(2)} = \dfrac{1}{2}$

$S_2 = \dfrac{1}{2} + \dfrac{1}{2(3)} = \dfrac{3}{6} + \dfrac{1}{6} = \dfrac{2}{3}$

$S_3 = \dfrac{2}{3} + \dfrac{1}{3(4)} = \dfrac{8}{12} + \dfrac{1}{12} = \dfrac{9}{12} = \dfrac{3}{4}$

$S_4 = \dfrac{3}{4} + \dfrac{1}{4(5)} = \dfrac{15}{20} + \dfrac{1}{20} = \dfrac{16}{20} = \dfrac{4}{5}$

1. Find the first several partial sums, looking for a pattern.

$S_n = \dfrac{n}{n+1}$

2. Write an explicit formula for S_n.

$P(n): \displaystyle\sum_{j=1}^{n} \frac{1}{j(j+1)} = \frac{n}{n+1}$

3. State the proposition $P(n)$.

$P(1): \dfrac{1}{1(2)} = \dfrac{1}{1+1}$ is true.

4. Verify the anchor step.

Assume $P(k): S_k = \dfrac{k}{k+1}$.

5. Write the inductive hypothesis, using S_k for the partial sum and reason to the inductive conclusion.

$S_k + \dfrac{1}{(k+1)[(k+1)+1]} = \dfrac{k}{k+1} + \dfrac{1}{(k+1)[(k+1)+1]}$

a. Add the $(k+1)$ term to both sides.

$S_{k+1} = \dfrac{k(k+2)}{(k+1)(k+2)} + \dfrac{1}{(k+1)(k+2)}$

b. Rename the left side and combine the fractions on the right side.

$= \dfrac{k^2 + 2k + 1}{(k+1)(k+2)}$

$= \dfrac{\cancel{(k+1)}(k+1)}{\cancel{(k+1)}(k+2)}$

c. Factor the numerator and cancel.

$P(k+1): S_{k+1} = \dfrac{(k+1)}{(k+1)+1}$

d. State the inductive conclusion.

$\displaystyle\sum_{j=1}^{n} \frac{1}{j(j+1)} = \frac{n}{n+1}$ for all $n \in \mathbb{N}$

6. Conclude that $P(n)$ is true for all $n \in \mathbb{N}$.

SKILL ✓ **EXERCISE 31**

A statement $P(n)$ may be false for $k = 1$ but true for all $n \geq j$ where $j > 1$. Extended mathematical induction is used to prove such a statement. The anchor step verifies $P(j)$ instead of $P(1)$ and the inductive step verifies all the other propositions as done previously.

Cornelius Van Til states in *A Survey of Christian Epistemology*, "If God is recognized as the only and the final explanation of any and every fact, neither the inductive nor the deductive method can any longer be used to the exclusion of the other. That this is the case can best be realized if we keep in mind that the God we contemplate is an absolute God."

Example 8 Applying Math Induction for Anchor $j > 1$

Use math induction to prove that any set of n coplanar points, no three of which are collinear, determines $\frac{n(n-1)}{2}$ line segments.

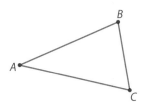

Answer

$P(3)$: 3 noncollinear points determine $\frac{3(3-1)}{2} = 3$ segments.

1. Since any set of noncollinear points has at least 3 points, verify the anchor step $P(3)$.

Assume $P(k)$: A set of k coplanar points, no three of which are collinear, determines $\frac{k(k-1)}{2}$ line segments.

2. Write the inductive hypothesis and reason to the inductive conclusion.

$P(k+1)$: $\frac{k(k-1)}{2} + k$

a. Adding another point that is not collinear with any two previous points allows k additional segments to be drawn, one to each of the previous k points.

$$= \frac{k^2 - k}{2} + \frac{2k}{2} = \frac{k^2 + k}{2}$$

b. Combine the fractions.

$$= \frac{(k+1)k}{2} = \frac{(k+1)[(k+1)-1]}{2}$$

c. Factor and rewrite the numerator to match $P(k+1)$.

$P(k+1)$: A set of $k+1$ coplanar points, no three of which are collinear, determines $\frac{(k+1)[(k+1)-1]}{2}$ line segments.

d. State the inductive conclusion.

Therefore n coplanar points, no three of which are collinear, determine $\frac{n(n-1)}{2}$ line segments.

3. Conclude that $P(n)$ is true for all integers $n \geq 3$.

SKILL ✓ **EXERCISE 35**

⟩ A. Exercises

1. Identify each part in a mathematical induction proof.

   a. $P(n)$ is true for all $n \in \mathbb{N}$.

   b. $P(k+1)$ is true when $P(k)$ is true.

   c. $P(k+1)$

   d. $P(k)$

   e. $P(1)$ is true.

   I. induction proposition

   II. anchor step

   III. inductive step

   IV. inductive hypothesis

   V. inductive conclusion

Find the smallest natural number n that provides a counterexample for each proposition $P(n)$.

2. $P(n)$: $5 + 8 + 11 + \cdots + (3n + 2) = \frac{n(n+9)}{2}$

3. $P(n)$: 3 is a factor of $n(n+1)$ for $n \geq 2$.

4. $P(n)$: $\left(1 + \frac{1}{n}\right)^n > n$

For each proposition $P(n)$ state the anchor step, the inductive hypothesis, and the inductive conclusion.

5. $8 + 10 + 12 + \cdots + 2(n+3) = n(n+7)$

6. $1 + 3 + 6 + \cdots + \frac{j(j+1)}{2} = \frac{n(n+1)(n+2)}{6}$

7. 3 is a factor of $7^n - 4^n$.

8. $3^n \geq 2n + 1$

State (do not prove) the "if-then" form of the inductive step for each proposition $P(n)$ for all $n \in \mathbb{N}$.

9. $1 + 5 + 9 + \cdots + (4n - 3) = 2n^2 - n$

10. 8 is a factor of $3^{2n} - 1$.

11. $3n < 2^n + 3$

If $\sum_{k=1}^{200} a_k = 20$, $\sum_{k=1}^{200} b_k = 67$, and $\sum_{k=1}^{200} c_k = 404$, use properties of summations to evaluate each sum.

12. $\sum_{k=1}^{200} 3a_k$

13. $\sum_{k=1}^{200} (4c_k + 3)$

14. $\sum_{k=4}^{200} 5b_k$ if $b_1 + b_2 + b_3 = 17$

Evaluate each partial sum.

15. $\sum_{k=1}^{20} k^4$

16. $\sum_{k=1}^{38} (3k^2 + 7k - 4)$

17. $\sum_{k=15}^{43} k^4$

▶ B. Exercises

Use math induction to prove each formula.

18. $P(n)$: given the arithmetic sequence a_n with common difference d, $a_n = a_1 + (n-1)d$

19. $P(n)$: given the geometric sequence a_n with common ratio r, $S_n = \dfrac{a_1(1 - r^n)}{1 - r}$

Use math induction to prove each summation formula.

20. $\sum_{k=1}^{n} k^2 = \dfrac{n(n+1)(2n+1)}{6}$

21. $\sum_{k=1}^{n} k^3 = \dfrac{n^2(n+1)^2}{4}$

Use math induction to prove each divisibility statement.

22. 2 is a factor of $n(n+1)$.

23. 6 is a factor of $n^3 - n + 12$.

24. 3 is a factor of $4^n - 1$.

25. 5 is a factor of $8^n - 3^n$.

Use math induction to prove each inequality.

26. $(n+1)^2 \geq n^2 + 1$ for all $n \in \mathbb{N}$

27. $2^n > n$ for all $n \in \mathbb{N}$

28. $\left(1 + \dfrac{1}{n}\right)^n < n$ for $n \geq 3$

29. $n! > 2^n$ for $n \geq 4$

Find an explicit formula for each partial sum. Then use math induction to prove your result.

30. $1 + 3 + 5 + 7 + 9 + \cdots + (2n - 1)$

31. $1 + 2 + 4 + 8 + \cdots + 2^{n-1}$

32. $\dfrac{1}{2} + \dfrac{1}{2^2} + \dfrac{1}{2^3} + \cdots + \dfrac{1}{2^n}$

33. Use the summation formulas to show that
$$\sum_{k=1}^{n} k^3 = \left(\sum_{k=1}^{n} k\right)^2.$$

34. A recreational league plans a round-robin volleyball tournament (each team plays every other team once).

    a. Write the sequence representing the total number of games played by n teams.

    b. Determine an explicit formula for a_n and explain your reasoning.

    c. State the inductive proposition $P(n)$ for your formula.

    d. Use math induction to prove $P(n)$.

    e. Use the explicit formula to determine the total number of games if 9 teams sign up.

35. A convex n-gon has n vertices.

    a. Write the sequence representing the sum of the interior angle degree measures in a convex n-gon.

    b. Determine the explicit formula for a_n and explain your reasoning.

    c. State the induction proposition $P(n)$ for your formula.

    d. Use math induction to prove $P(n)$.

    e. Use the explicit formula to find the sum of the interior angle degree measures in a convex decagon.

▶ C. Exercises

Use math induction to prove the following partial-sum formulas.

36. given the arithmetic sequence a_n with common difference d, $S_n = \dfrac{n(2a_1 + (n-1)d)}{2}$

37. $\sum_{k=1}^{n} k^4 = \dfrac{n(n+1)(2n+1)(3n^2 + 3n - 1)}{30}$

38. Find an explicit formula for
$S_n = \dfrac{1}{4} + \dfrac{1}{12} + \dfrac{1}{24} + \dfrac{1}{40} + \dfrac{1}{60} + \cdots + \dfrac{1}{2n(n+1)}.$
Then use math induction to prove your formula.

39. Use math induction to prove that $\cos n\pi = (-1)^n$.

40. While previous sections emphasized arithmetic and geometric sequences, this section includes quadratic and other polynomial sequences. Using technology, complete a regression to determine whether each sequence is arithmetic (linear), quadratic, geometric (exponential), or none of these. State the explicit formula for any sequence if the coefficient of determination, r^2, is 1.

    a. $\dfrac{5}{32}, \dfrac{1}{4}, \dfrac{2}{5}, \dfrac{16}{25}, \cdots$

    b. $\dfrac{3}{8}, \dfrac{5}{4}, \dfrac{19}{8}, \dfrac{15}{4}, \cdots$

    c. $\dfrac{1}{4}, \dfrac{3}{8}, \dfrac{1}{2}, \dfrac{5}{8}, \cdots$

    d. $\dfrac{5}{32}, \dfrac{51}{32}, \dfrac{185}{32}, \dfrac{479}{32}, \cdots$

41. A line is uniquely determined by two points, a parabola by three points, and a cubic function by four points. Use your calculator and a cubic regression to find the unique cubic explicit formula for each set of four points given in exercise 40.

a. $\dfrac{5}{32}, \dfrac{1}{4}, \dfrac{2}{5}, \dfrac{16}{25}, \ldots$

b. $\dfrac{3}{8}, \dfrac{5}{4}, \dfrac{19}{8}, \dfrac{15}{4}, \ldots$

c. $\dfrac{1}{4}, \dfrac{3}{8}, \dfrac{1}{2}, \dfrac{5}{8}, \ldots$

d. $\dfrac{5}{32}, \dfrac{51}{32}, \dfrac{185}{32}, \dfrac{479}{32}, \ldots$

42. Use mathematical induction to prove the Binomial Theorem.

CUMULATIVE REVIEW

Consider the following functions.

a. $f(x) = x^4 - 3x^2 + 2$ b. $g(x) = x^3 - x^2$

c. $h(x) = 2x^3 - x$ d. $k(x) = 2\cos\dfrac{x}{2}$

43. Classify each function as even, odd, or neither. [3.1]

44. Which function has a zero at $x = \sqrt{2}$? [2.6]

Determine whether A and B are inverse matrices. [7.5]

45. $A = \begin{bmatrix} -3 & -6 \\ 1 & 3 \end{bmatrix}$, $B = \begin{bmatrix} -1 & -2 \\ \frac{1}{3} & 1 \end{bmatrix}$

46. $A = \begin{bmatrix} -1 & 0 \\ -3 & 1 \end{bmatrix}$, $B = \begin{bmatrix} -1 & 0 \\ -3 & 1 \end{bmatrix}$

Find the geometric means between the given terms. [9.3]

47. $a_8 = 3$ and $a_{10} = 507$

48. $a_{38} = -5$ and $a_{41} = 3645$

49. Atlanta, Georgia, had a population of 416,474 in 2000. The city's population in 2010 was 418,981. Find the city's average annual rate of growth from 2000 to 2010. [3.5]

A. 1%   C. 0.6%   E. none of these

B. 6%   D. 0.06%

50. Which of the following represents the period, vertical asymptotes, and zeros of the cotangent function? [4.5]

A. 2π, none, $(2n+1)\dfrac{\pi}{2}$ D. π, $x = (2n+1)\dfrac{\pi}{2}$, $n\pi$

B. π, $x = n\pi$, $(2n+1)\dfrac{\pi}{2}$ E. none of these

C. 2π, $x = n\pi$, none

51. Write the partial fraction decomposition for the rational expression $\dfrac{5x-12}{x^2-6x+9}$. [7.7]

A. $\dfrac{5}{x-3} + \dfrac{3}{(x-3)^2}$ D. $\dfrac{4}{x-3} - \dfrac{1}{(x-3)^2}$

B. $\dfrac{4}{x-3} + \dfrac{1}{(x-3)^2}$ E. none of these

C. $\dfrac{5}{x-3} - \dfrac{3}{(x-3)^2}$

52. Find a_{98} in the sequence $-12, -15, -18, -21, \ldots$ [9.2]

A. -300 C. -306 E. none of these

B. -303 D. -309

Graph Theory and Networks

In 1736 Leonhard Euler published his solution to a well-known problem from Prussia: can the seven bridges in Königsberg all be crossed exactly one time in a single walk? Euler generalized the problem to a system of points and lines that could answer the question for any number of bridges and islands. This was the genesis of graph theory.

Consider the following 4 × 4 grid (or *network*). How many different paths are there from *A* to any given *node* (point of intersection) if you can only move to the right or down along the segments (or *edges*)? The figure shows the number of possible paths from *A* to each node.

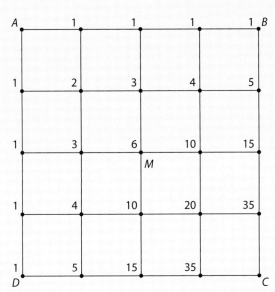

1. What pattern can be seen diagonally in the numbers on this figure?

2. Sketch the 6 possible paths to the middle node, *M*.

3. How many ways are there to go from *A* to *C*?

4. If you cannot pass through *M*, how many paths are there from *A* to *C*?

Graph theory led to the study of networks, a vital component of myriad real-world applications in many diverse fields. Navigation programs like Google Maps are especially helpful applications. Each location is a node (or vertex), and the roads are edges. In a *weighted* graph, the decisions become more difficult as each edge is assigned a nonnegative number indicating the time (or cost) required to traverse that segment. The goal is to find the shortest (or least expensive) route between two nodes—not simply the number of different ways to get there.

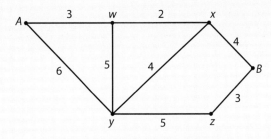

Finding the shortest path from *A* to *B* is a fairly simple task in this small network, but more complicated scenarios can be daunting. A basic algorithm to find the shortest distance between two locations on a weighted graph was published by E. W. Dijkstra in 1959.

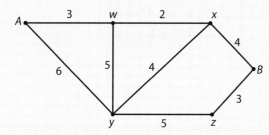

The iterative algorithm can be explained with a table. Begin by listing the vertices as a set of points that have not been visited. Then set the cost of the starting point to 0 and the cost of all other points as infinite. The first iteration begins by moving from the node with the least cost (A) to a set of visited nodes and then finding the cost to reach the connected vertices. (A to $w = 3$ and A to $y = 6$.) If these costs are less than the entry currently listed in that row, its cost and the "previous node" value are updated.

Not Visited: {$\cancel{A}$, $\cancel{w}$, x, y, z, B}		
Node	Cost (from A)	Previous Node
$\cancel{A}$	0	
$\cancel{w}$	$\cancel{\infty}$ 3	A
x	$\cancel{\infty}$ 5	w
y	$\cancel{\infty}$ 6	A
z	∞	
B	∞	
Visited: {A, w, }		

initial condition
1st iteration, 2nd iteration

The algorithm then starts over by moving the lowest-cost node in the not-visited set (w this time) to the visited set and finding the cost to reach each connected node (w to $x = 2$ so A to $x = 3 + 2 = 5$, and w to $y = 5$ so A to $y = 3 + 5 = 8$.) In the row for node x, replace ∞ with 5 and record w for its previous vertex. In the row for y leave 6 and A since $6 < 8$.

5. Copy the table and continue the iterations until the lowest cost to each node has been determined.
   a. List the lowest-cost route from A to B and state the route's cost.
   b. List the lowest-cost route from A to z and state the route's cost.

6. Make a table and use Dijkstra's algorithm to find the lowest-cost route from S to F in the following network and state its cost.

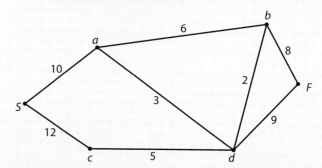

Modern mapping applications have improved upon Dijkstra's algorithm and are able to consider constantly changing conditions such as traffic volume, road construction, and weather delays. While the benefits of mapping programs are obvious, there are concerns about how the vast amounts of data may be used. If you've ever visited a restaurant or store and later received an unsolicited message on your phone asking you to rate the location, you may have wondered who was watching. The implications of big data are worth considering.

7. **Discuss:** Research the term *big data*.
   a. Define the term in your own words.
   b. From a biblical worldview, list several possible benefits and problems resulting from the use of big data.

Chapter 9 Review

1. Classify each as a finite sequence, infinite sequence, finite series, or infinite series.   [9.1]
   a. 1, 2, 3, 4, 5
   b. $2 + 6 + 18 + 54 + \cdots$

2. Find the first 4 terms and the tenth term of the explicitly defined sequence $a_n = \dfrac{n(n+1)}{4}$.   [9.1]

3. Given 1, 4, 9, 16, . . . , write an explicit formula for the value of a_n and use it to find the tenth term.   [9.1]

4. Write the first 6 terms of each recursively defined sequence.   [9.1]
   a. $a_1 = 3$; $a_n = (a_{n-1} - 1)^2$, where $n \geq 2$
   b. $a_1 = 5$; $a_n = \dfrac{1}{a_{n-1} + 2}$, where $n \geq 2$

5. Write a recursive formula for $1, \dfrac{1}{2}, \dfrac{1}{4}, \dfrac{1}{8}, \ldots$.
   Then use the formula to find a_5, a_6, and a_7.   [9.1]

6. Given $a_n = \dfrac{n!}{2^n}$, find a_0, a_1, a_2, a_3, and a_4.   [9.1]

7. Determine whether the sequence $a_n = \dfrac{2n+3}{n-2}$ converges or diverges and state the limit if it is convergent.   [9.1]

8. Evaluate $\displaystyle\sum_{k=6}^{7} 5k$.   [9.1]

9. Given $a_n = \dfrac{(n+1)!}{(n-1)!}$, find the partial sums S_5, S_6, and S_7.   [9.1]

10. Evaluate the infinite series $\displaystyle\sum_{i=1}^{\infty} 10(0.01)^i$ and classify it as convergent or divergent.   [9.1]

11. Determine whether $41, 26, 11, -4, -19, \ldots$ is an arithmetic sequence. If so, state the common difference and list the next 3 terms. If not, explain why.   [9.2]

12. Identify the common difference d for each arithmetic sequence and then find the fifth term.   [9.2]
   a. $a_1 = 2$, $a_n = a_{n-1} + 3$
   b. $a_n = -5n + 9$

13. Write the recursive and simplified explicit formulas for the sequence of whole numbers: 0, 1, 2, ... Then find a_{20}.   [9.2]

14. Given an arithmetic sequence with $a_1 = 20$ and $d = 39$, find a_{58}.   [9.2]

15. Find the arithmetic means between $a_5 = 54$ and $a_9 = 18$.   [9.2]

16. Write the simplified explicit formula for the sequence $\dfrac{1}{8}, \dfrac{1}{13}, \dfrac{1}{18}, \dfrac{1}{23}, \ldots$, then find a_{20}.   [9.2]

Evaluate each arithmetic series.   [9.2]

17. $\displaystyle\sum_{n=1}^{50} 4n$

18. $\displaystyle\sum_{k=1}^{30} \dfrac{1}{2}(k+3)$

19. Write a simplified explicit formula for the arithmetic sequence with $a_1 = 1$ if $S_{250} = 62,500$.   [9.2]

20. If you borrow $7595 from your parents to buy a used car, how many months will it take to pay back the loan if you pay $200 the first month and increase your payment by $3 each month?   [9.2]

Determine whether each sequence is geometric. If so, state the common ratio and list the next 3 terms. If not, explain why.   [9.3]

21. 2, 3, 4.5, 6, . .

22. $18, 6, 2, \dfrac{2}{3}, \ldots$

Write both the recursive and an explicit formula for each geometric sequence. Then find a_{10}.   [9.3]

23. 216, 72, 24, 8, . . .

24. $4, -6, 9, -\dfrac{27}{2}, \ldots$

25. Given a geometric sequence with $a_2 = \dfrac{5}{2}$ and $a_7 = 80$, write a simplified explicit formula for a_n. Then find a_{10}.   [9.3]

26. Find the geometric means between $a_8 = 16$ and $a_{11} = \dfrac{1}{4}$.   [9.3]

Evaluate each geometric series.   [9.3]

27. $\displaystyle\sum_{n=1}^{10} -2\left(\dfrac{3}{2}\right)^{n-1}$

28. $-\dfrac{1}{3} + \dfrac{1}{6} - \dfrac{1}{12} + \dfrac{1}{24}, \cdots$

29. Find the interest earned in an annuity with $3000 quarterly deposits for 15 yr if the account earns 3% APR compounded quarterly.   [9.3]

30. A rubber ball is thrown to a height of 50 ft and then rebounds to 75% of its previous height on each bounce. [9.3]

a. Find the height of the seventh bounce.

b. Find the total distance the ball has traveled vertically when it hits the ground the eighth time.

c. Find the total distance the ball has traveled vertically when it finally comes to rest.

Use Pascal's triangle to expand. [9.4]

31. $(a - 3)^5$ **32.** $(3m + 4n)^4$ **33.** $(2 - 2z)^6$

Evaluate. [9.4]

34. $_7C_3$ and $_7C_5$ **35.** $_4C_2$ and $_4C_4$

Use the Binomial Theorem to expand each binomial. [9.4]

36. $(3c + 1)^3$ **37.** $\left(\sqrt{2} - 3t\right)^4$

Find the given term in the expansion of each binomial power. [9.4]

38. $a^6 b^3$ term of $(3a - 2b)^9$

39. eighth term of $(w + 5)^{11}$

40. What is the probability (to the nearest tenth of a percent) of getting exactly 3 fours on 12 tosses of a die? [9.4]

For each proposition $P(n)$,
a. verify $P(1)$, the anchor step,
b. state the inductive hypothesis, $P(k)$, and
c. state the inductive conclusion, $P(k + 1)$. [9.5]

41. 4 is a factor of $9^n - 5^n$.

42. $2^2 + 4^2 + 6^2 + \cdots + (2n)^2 = \dfrac{2n(n + 1)(2n + 1)}{3}$

43. Given $\displaystyle\sum_{k=1}^{100} a_k = 18$, $\displaystyle\sum_{k=1}^{100} b_k = 54$, and $\displaystyle\sum_{k=1}^{100} c_k = 243$, use summation properties to evaluate each sum. [9.5]

a. $\displaystyle\sum_{k=1}^{100} 5a_k$ **b.** $\displaystyle\sum_{k=1}^{100} (2b_k + 3c_k)$

44. Evaluate each sum. [9.5]

a. $\displaystyle\sum_{k=1}^{15} (2k^3 - 2)$ **b.** $\displaystyle\sum_{k=6}^{20} k^4$

Use math induction to prove each statement. [9.5]

45. 2 is a factor of $n^2 + n + 4$.

46. 5 is a factor of $6^n - 1$.

47. $3^n > 3n$ for $n > 1$

48. $1^2 + 3^2 + 5^2 + \cdots + (2n - 1)^2 = \dfrac{n(2n - 1)(2n + 1)}{3}$

49. A convex n-gon has $\dfrac{n(n - 3)}{2}$ diagonals.

50. Find an explicit formula for $2 + 4 + 6 + \cdots + 2n$, and then verify the formula for all $n \in \mathbb{N}$. [9.5]

10 Descriptive Statistics

DATA ANALYSIS

If you test positive in a medical screening that correctly identifies people with a given condition ninety-eight percent of the time, how likely is it that you actually have the condition?

HISTORICAL CONNECTION

You may be surprised to learn that Florence Nightingale and the Crimean War played important roles in the development of descriptive statistics.

BIBLICAL PERSPECTIVE OF MATHEMATICS

In *Celestial Mechanics*, a foundational work on probability theory, Pierre-Simon de Laplace supported a Platonic view of the universe. Should a Christian endorse mathematical Platonism?

10.1 Counting Principles

After completing this section, you will be able to

- distinguish between independent and dependent events.
- solve counting problems using tree diagrams or the Fundamental Counting Principle.
- apply permutations and combinations to solve counting problems.

Counting techniques are extremely important in a study of probability and statistics. For example, there are several options for fall and spring sports. If the playing of a particular fall sport does not affect the playing of any particular spring sport, those sports are *independent* events. If the selection of a fall sport affects the selection of a spring sport, the choices are *dependent* events.

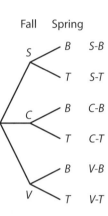

The tree diagram represents all the possibilities if soccer, cross-country, and volleyball are the fall sports and baseball and track are the spring sports. With 3 fall sports and 2 spring sports, there are 6 ways to choose a fall and a spring sport.

Tree diagrams can become cumbersome as the number of choices increases. The *Fundamental Counting Principle* summarizes the results and is usually used to determine the number of possible ways to complete a process.

▌FUNDAMENTAL COUNTING PRINCIPLE

In a multi-event process where there are m_1 possible outcomes for the first event, m_2 possible outcomes for the second event, and so on, there are $m_1 \cdot m_2 \cdot \ldots \cdot m_n$ total possible outcomes.

Example 1 Applying the Fundamental Counting Principle

A school fundraiser poster claims to offer 12 meal combinations. Participants can choose a fried chicken plate or a spaghetti plate as the main course; a dessert of chocolate cake, banana pudding, or pecan pie; and either tea or coffee to drink.

a. Use the Fundamental Counting Principle to determine whether the claim of offering 12 meal combinations is correct.

b. Are the choices of main course, dessert, and drink independent or dependent events?

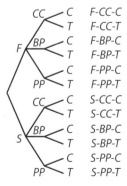

Answer

a. $2(3)(2) = 12$

The claim is correct.

There are 2 possible main courses, 3 possible desserts, and 2 possible beverages.

---

b. The choices are independent events.

Each choice does not affect the other choices.

Check

A tree diagram can be used to verify the number of possible outcomes.

SKILL ✔ **EXERCISE 5**

Example 2 Applying the Fundamental Counting Principle

A local deli offers triple-scoop ice-cream cones. For each case, find the number of different arrangements (distinct orders) of flavors and whether the arrangements are independent or dependent.

a. The deli has 5 flavors and the cone can contain repeated flavors.

b. The deli has 5 flavors and the cone cannot contain repeated flavors.

c. The deli has 28 flavors and the cone cannot contain repeated flavors.

Answer

a. $5(5)(5) = 125$
independent

There are 5 different choices for each scoop.

b. $5(4)(3) = 60$
dependent

There are 5 choices for the first scoop, 4 choices for the second scoop, and 3 choices for the third scoop.

c. $28(27)(26) = 19{,}656$
dependent

There are 28 choices for the first scoop, 27 choices for the second scoop, and 26 choices for the third scoop.

SKILL ✓ **EXERCISE 7**

Example 3 Applying the Fundamental Counting Principle

A computer programming team consists of 8 members.

a. How many ways can they line up for a yearbook photo?

b. How many ways can a president, vice president, and secretary be selected?

Answer

a. $8(7)(6)(5)(4)(3)(2)(1) = 40{,}320$

There are 8 choices for the first spot, 7 choices for the second, 6 choices for the third, and so on until there is only 1 choice left for the last spot.

b. $8(7)(6) = 336$

Any of the 8 can be selected as president, then 7 choices remain for vice president, and then 6 choices are left for secretary.

SKILL ✓ **EXERCISE 15**

TIP

The factorial function, found in the MATH, PROB submenu, can be used to calculate the answers to Example 3.

```
8!
                    40320
8!/(8-3)!
                      336
■
```

Applying the Fundamental Counting Principle to determine the number of possible arrangements of n objects produces $n(n - 1)(n - 2) \ldots 1 = n!$ arrangements, as seen in Example 3a. When arranging only r of the n objects, the ways of arranging the remaining $(n - r)$ objects are not included. The possible arrangements of 3 of the 8 computer programming team members in Example 3b can be calculated using $\frac{8!}{(8 - 3)!} = \frac{8(7)(6)\cancel{5!}}{\cancel{5!}} = 8(7)(6) = 336$.

▌DEFINITION

A **permutation** is an arrangement of objects in which order is important. The number of permutations of n objects taken r at a time is $_nP_r = \frac{n!}{(n - r)!}$.

The notation $_nP_r$ can be read as "arrange r out of n objects" or simply "n arrange r." Note that this definition implies $_nP_n = \frac{n!}{(n - n)!} = \frac{n!}{0!} = \frac{n!}{1} = n!$, as stated previously.

TIP

The nPr function, found in the MATH, PROB submenu, can be used to calculate permutations.

7 nPr 4
840

Example 4 Applying the Permutation Formula

How many 4-letter arrangements can be made from $\{a, b, c, d, e, f, g\}$ if letters cannot be repeated?

Answer

$$_7P_4 = \frac{7!}{(7-4)!} = \frac{7(6)(5)(4)\cancel{3!}}{\cancel{3!}}$$

$$= 7(6)(5)(4) = 840$$

Apply the formula $_nP_r = \frac{n!}{(n-r)!}$.

Note that $_7P_4$ is often read as "7 arrange 4."

SKILL ✓ **EXERCISE 17**

How many distinguishable arrangements can be made using the letters in the word *SCHOOL*? If the two *O*s were distinguishable (using O_1 and O_2), there would be $6! = 720$ arrangements; but this number includes otherwise undistinguishable arrangements such as $SCHO_1O_2L$ and $SCHO_2O_1L$. Dividing 720 by 2!, the number of ways O_1 and O_2 can be arranged, produces the correct number of distinguishable permutations—360.

DEFINITION

Given n objects with n_1 identical objects of one type, n_2 identical objects of a second type, and so on where $n = n_1 + n_2 + \cdots + n_k$, the number of **distinguishable permutations** is $\frac{n!}{n_1! n_2! \dots n_k!}$.

Example 5 Finding Permutations with Identical Objects

Find the number of permutations of the letters in each word.

a. *BUTTERFLY*

b. *CATERPILLAR*

Answer

a. $\frac{9!}{2!} = 181{,}440$

There are nine letters in *BUTTERFLY*.
All are distinguishable except the 2 *T*s.

b. $\frac{11!}{2!2!2!} = 4{,}989{,}600$

There are 11 letters in *CATERPILLAR*.
Three letters (*A*, *R*, and *L*) are each used twice.

SKILL ✓ **EXERCISE 23**

In permutations, order is important. Selections of objects where order is not important are called *combinations*. There are $3! = 6$ permutations of the three letters *abc*: *abc*, *acb*, *bac*, *bca*, *cab*, and *cba*. The number of ways to select r items from a group of n objects can be found by dividing its number of permutations by $r!$.

$$_nC_r = \frac{_nP_r}{r!} = \frac{\frac{n!}{(n-r)!}}{r!} = \frac{n!}{r!(n-r)!}$$

DEFINITION

A **combination** is a collection of objects in which order is not important. The number of combinations of n objects taken r at a time is written as $_nC_r = \frac{n!}{r!(n-r)!}$.

Some mathematicians were not in favor of using an exclamation point for factorial. British mathematician Augustus De Morgan called it a "barbarism" and suggested those who used it were expressing "surprise and admiration" that such results were to be found in mathematics.

The notation $_nC_r$ can be read as "choose r out of n objects" or simply "n choose r."

Example 6   Calculating Combinations

Calculate each combination.

a. $_8C_3$

b. $_{12}C_{12}$

Answer

a. $_8C_3 = \dfrac{8!}{3!(8-3)!}$

$= \dfrac{8(7)(6)5!}{3(2)5!}$

$= 8(7) = 56$

b. $_{12}C_{12} = \dfrac{12!}{12!(12-12)!}$

$= \dfrac{12!}{12!(1)}$

$= 1$

1. Substitute into $_nC_r = \dfrac{n!}{r!(n-r)!}$ and simplify.

Check

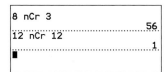

```
8 nCr 3
                              56
12 nCr 12
                               1
■
```

2. Use the nCr function from the MATH, PROB submenu to evaluate each expression.

SKILL ✔ **EXERCISE 13**

Example 7   Applying the Combination Formula

A committee of 2 women and 4 men will be selected from 10 students, of which 4 are women and 6 are men. How many different committees can be selected?

Answer

women: $_4C_2 = \dfrac{4!}{2!(4-2)!} = \dfrac{4!}{2!2!} = 6$

men: $_6C_4 = \dfrac{6!}{4!(6-4)!} = \dfrac{6!}{4!2!} = 15$

$6(15) = 90$ different committees

1. Calculate the number of combinations for each of the two independent events: selecting 2 of 4 women and selecting 4 of 6 men.

2. Apply the Fundamental Counting Principle to find the number of possible committees.

SKILL ✔ **EXERCISE 27**

Counting Formulas	
Fundamental Counting Principle	In a multi-event process where there are m_1 possible outcomes for the first event, m_2 possible outcomes for the second event, and so on, there are $m_1 \cdot m_2 \cdot \ldots \cdot m_n$ total possible outcomes.
permutations	$_nP_r = \dfrac{n!}{(n-r)!}$ ways to arrange r out of n objects
distinguishable permutations	Given n objects with n_1 identical objects of one type, n_2 identical objects of a second type, and so on where $n = n_1 + n_2 + \cdots + n_k$, the number of distinguishable permutations is $\dfrac{n!}{n_1! n_2! \ldots n_k!}$.
combinations	$_nC_r = \dfrac{n!}{r!(n-r)!}$ ways to choose r out of n objects

A. Exercises

1. Events whose possible outcomes are affected by other events are said to be _____, while events whose possible outcomes have no effect on each other are called _____.

2. Selections of objects in which order is not important are called _____, while arrangements of objects in which order is important are _____.

A bag contains four cards numbered 1 through 4. Isaiah draws a card from the bag, records the first digit, and then draws a second card and records the second digit. Use a tree diagram to determine how many two-digit numbers are possible in each case below. Then state whether the two draws are independent or dependent.

3. Isaiah does not replace the first card before drawing the second card.

4. Isaiah replaces the first card before drawing the second card.

Apply the Fundamental Counting Principle to answer the following questions.

5. Downtown Catering Service offers box lunches that include a sandwich, a bag of chips, a fruit, and a cookie. How many different box lunches are possible if customers can choose from 4 kinds of sandwiches, 5 types of chips, 3 different fruits, and 6 kinds of cookies?

6. How many different credit card numbers are possible if a company's card numbers are 15 digits long and start with either 34 or 37?

7. How many different ways can 7 out of 9 different chocolates be distributed to 7 students?

8. How many different license plates can be made containing 3 letters followed by 4 numbers?

Evaluate each expression without using technology, and then check your answer with technology.

9. $_9P_3$

10. $_8P_4$

11. $_{14}P_3$

12. $_{12}C_9$

13. $_7C_5$

14. $_{100}C_{98}$

Use the appropriate counting technique.

15. How many ways are there to arrange 6 books on a bookshelf?

16. Jessica has chosen 3 possible paint colors, 6 possible rugs, and 2 possible sets of curtains for her dining room. How many different ways can she redecorate the room?

17. Josh's family is planning a Holy Land tour but only has time to see 6 out of 9 historic sites outside of the Jerusalem area. How many different itineraries can be planned for those sites?

18. If there are 20 rising seniors vying to be a class officer, how many different ways can a president, vice president, and secretary/treasurer be selected?

19. How many different 5-person committees can be chosen from a group of 24 people?

20. Out of the first 100 people who enter a new grocery store, 2 people will be selected to win a $500 shopping spree. How many different pairs of shoppers could win the prizes?

B. Exercises

Determine how many ways the letters in each word can be arranged.

21. *LEOPARD*

22. *CALENDAR*

23. *BALLOON*

24. A bag of marbles contains 3 blue, 5 red, 4 yellow, and 3 green marbles. In how many different ways can all the marbles be lined up in a row?

25. Three couples have tickets in the same row for a football game. Determine the different seating arrangements in each case.
    a. They don't mind who sits next to whom.
    b. Each couple sits together.

26. Coach Grant has 15 boys on his baseball team.
    a. How many groups of 9 starting players can he have?
    b. How many different 9-person batting orders can he make?

27. There are 18 boys and 22 girls in the church youth group. How many different banquet committees can be formed with the given conditions?
    a. 2 boys and 3 girls
    b. 2 boys and 2 girls
    c. 2 boys and 2 or 3 girls

28. The 1947 North American Number Plan (NANP) standardized area codes and phone numbers. Originally the 3-digit area code was of the form NPX where N could be any number 2 through 9, P could be only 0 or 1, and X could be any digit 0 through 9.
    a. How many different area codes were possible with the original format?

b. In 1995 the area code numbering plan was updated to the form NXX. How many different codes of this form are possible?

c. When the second and third digits of an area code are the same, that code is called an easily recognizable code (ERC). ERCs designate special services, e.g. 888 for toll-free service. How many ERCs are available?

d. Codes of the form N11 are used as service codes instead of area codes. How many of these codes are there? Give a common example of one of these codes.

e. Area codes of the form N9X are reserved as expansion codes and will be used when the current 10-digit number formatting needs to be expanded. How many expansion codes are there?

29. How many different 4- to 6-character passcodes are possible using letters, the digits 0–9, or the symbols # or $?

   a. if no character is repeated

   b. if characters can be repeated

30. If 8 sprinters compete in a semifinal heat, how many possible groups of 2, 3, or 4 runners could advance to the final from this race?

31. Simplify each permutation.

   a. $_nP_n$ **b.** $_nP_{n-r}$

   c. $_nP_1$ **d.** $_nP_0$

32. Simplify each combination.

   a. $_nC_n$ **b.** $_nC_{n-r}$

   c. $_nC_1$ **d.** $_nC_0$

❯ C. Exercises

33. The high school choir consists of 8 seniors, 6 juniors, 5 sophomores, and 3 freshmen. In how many ways can 8 choir members be selected so that there are 2 students from each grade represented?

34. Jesse needs to read 3 novels and 2 biographies from a summer reading list that includes 10 novels and 7 biographies.

   a. How many different combinations of books can Jesse read to fulfill the requirement?

   b. In how many different orders can Jesse read 5 books from the list to fulfill the requirement?

35. The information technology department is exploring minimum security requirements for 6-character passwords used within their company. Determine the number of different possible passwords for each set of requirements.

   a. One character must be a number 0 through 9, and the rest are lowercase letters.

   b. One character must be a number, one an uppercase letter, and the rest are lowercase letters.

   c. One character must be a number, one an uppercase letter, another is 1 of 10 special characters, and the rest are lowercase letters.

   d. Why is a password containing lowercase and uppercase letters, numbers, and symbols safer?

36. Since the two illustrated circular arrangements are considered to be identical, the number of circular arrangements differs from the number of linear arrangements of the same items. Consider linear and circular arrangements of the letters A, B, C, D, and E to derive an expression for the number of circular arrangements of n items.

   a. How many different linear arrangements are possible for the 5 letters?

   b. List all the linear arrangements that are identical to ABCDE when the letters are arranged in a circle.

   c. How many linear arrangements are equivalent to each circular arrangement of the 5 letters?

   d. How many different circular arrangements can be made with the 5 letters?

   e. Describe how the number of circular arrangements of n items can be found if there are l linear arrangements.

37. Prove: Show that $n(_{n-1}C_{r-1}) = (n-r+1)_nC_{r-1}$.

38. Complete the following steps to determine the number of distinguishable permutations of the letters in the word *MALL*.

   a. How many ways are there to select 2 of the 4 positions in which to place the *L*s?

   b. After placing the 2 *L*s, how many ways are there to select a position for the *M*?

   c. Finally, how many ways are there to select the position for the *A*?

   d. Use the Fundamental Counting Principle to calculate the total number of ways the 4 letters can be arranged.

39. Complete the following steps to determine the number of distinguishable permutations of the letters in the word *SUCCESS*.

a. How many ways are there to select the positions in which to place the *S*s?

b. After placing the *S*s, how many ways are there to select the positions for the *C*s?

c. How many ways are there to then place the *U*? and then the *E*?

d. Use the Fundamental Counting Principle to calculate the total number of ways to place all the letters.

40. Prove: Use the reasoning illustrated in exercises 38–39 to show that $\frac{n!}{a!b!c! \ldots z!}$ is the number of distinguishable permutations of n objects with a identical objects of one type, b identical objects of a second type, and so on where $n = a + b + c + \cdots + z$.

a. Write an expression for the number of ways to select positions for the first a objects.

b. Write an expression for the number of ways to then place the next b objects.

c. Write an expression for the number of ways to place the next $c, \ldots, z$ objects.

d. Use the Fundamental Counting Principle to calculate the total number of ways to place all the letters.

CUMULATIVE REVIEW

Classify each rational function as proper or improper. Then identify all asymptotes and any point discontinuities. [2.5]

41. $f(x) = \dfrac{x+1}{x^2 - 7x + 12}$

42. $h(x) = \dfrac{x^3 + 2x}{x^2 - 1}$

43. Write the general form for the partial fraction decomposition of $\dfrac{x^2}{x^3 + x^2}$. Do not solve. [7.7]

44. Find the partial fraction decomposition of $\dfrac{9x - 24}{x^2 - 3x - 10}$. [7.7]

Use the Binomial Theorem to expand each binomial. [9.4]

45. $(c + d)^3$

46. $(3x - 1)^3$

47. Convert $z = -3 + 4i$ to polar form. [6.6]

A. 5 cis 0.93

B. 5 cis −0.93

C. 5 cis 2.21

D. 5 cis −2.21

E. −5 cis −2.21

48. Which of the following is true for an ellipse with vertices $(0, -2)$ and $(10, -2)$ and eccentricity of 0.75? List all correct answers. [8.2]

A. $a = 10$

B. $a = 5$

C. $c = 7.5$

D. $b^2 = 10.9375$

E. none of these

49. What is the sixth term of $a_n = 5a_{n-1} + 3$, $a_1 = 2$ where $n \geq 2$? [9.1]

A. 33

B. 1718

C. 3128

D. 8593

E. none of these

50. What is the sequence of steps in a math induction proof? [9.5]

A. I, II, III

B. I, III, II

C. II, I, III

D. II, III, I

E. III, II, I

I. Assume $P(k)$.

II. Verify $P(1)$.

III. Prove $P(k + 1)$.

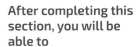

10.2 Basic Probability

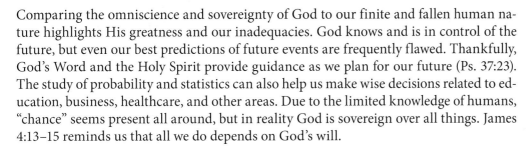

Comparing the omniscience and sovereignty of God to our finite and fallen human nature highlights His greatness and our inadequacies. God knows and is in control of the future, but even our best predictions of future events are frequently flawed. Thankfully, God's Word and the Holy Spirit provide guidance as we plan for our future (Ps. 37:23). The study of probability and statistics can also help us make wise decisions related to education, business, healthcare, and other areas. Due to the limited knowledge of humans, "chance" seems present all around, but in reality God is sovereign over all things. James 4:13–15 reminds us that all we do depends on God's will.

In the study of probability, an *experiment* consists of one or more actions whose outcome may be uncertain. An experiment can be as simple as a single trial where a coin is flipped, a die is rolled, or a name is drawn from a hat. The set S containing all the possible outcomes is the experiment's *sample space*. An *event* is any subset of a sample space and is denoted by a capital letter such as E. The outcomes are said to be *equally likely* when every outcome in the experiment has the same chance of occurring.

Sidebar: "After completing this section..."

After completing this section, you will be able to
- define terms related to basic probabilities.
- calculate basic probabilities.
- calculate probabilities of mutually exclusive and inclusive events.
- calculate probabilities of independent and conditional events.

| Example 1 | Identifying a Sample Space and an Event |

A spinner has 7 equally spaced numbers. List the sample space and the event of getting an odd number on a spin.

Answer

$S = \{1, 2, 3, 4, 5, 6, 7\}$ 1. The sample space is the set of all possible outcomes.

$E = \{1, 3, 5, 7\}$ 2. The event is the set of odd numbers.

SKILL ✔ **EXERCISE 1**

Theoretical probabilities describe long-term behaviors. If an experiment is literally conducted, the result may be quite different from the theoretical probability. These results determine the *experimental probability*. As the number of trials increases, the experimental probability approaches the theoretical probability.

▍DEFINITIONS

The **theoretical** (or **classical**) **probability** of an event, $P(E)$, is $n(E)$, the ratio of the number of favorable outcomes, to $n(S)$, the number of equally likely possible outcomes:

$$P(E) = \frac{n(E)}{n(S)}.$$

The **experimental** (or **empirical**) **probability** of an event, $P(E)$, is the ratio of the number of times the event occurs to the number of trials in an experiment:

$$P(E) = \frac{\text{number of times the event occurs}}{\text{number of trials}}.$$

Number	Freq.
1	0
2	2
3	1
4	3
5	2
6	2

Example 2 Calculating Theoretical and Experimental Probabilities

The table displays the results of Marcie's 10 rolls of a die.
State the theoretical and experimental probabilities for each event.

a. rolling a 4

b. rolling an odd number

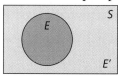

Answer

a. theoretical:

$P(4) = \frac{1}{6} = 0.1\overline{6}$ or $16.\overline{6}\%$

experimental:

$P(4) = \frac{3}{10} = 0.3$ or 30%

1. Let E = rolling a 4.

   Use $P(4) = \frac{n(4)}{n(S)}$.

2. $P(4) = \frac{\text{number of times a 4 was rolled}}{\text{number of trials}}$

b. theoretical:

$P(\text{odd}) = \frac{3}{6} = 0.5$ or 50%

experimental:

$P(\text{odd}) = \frac{3}{10} = 0.3$ or 30%

1. Let E = rolling an odd number.

   Use $P(\text{odd}) = \frac{n(\text{odd})}{n(S)}$.

2. $P(\text{odd}) = \frac{\text{number of times an odd number was rolled}}{\text{number of trials}}$

SKILL ✓ **EXERCISE 9**

Attempts to reconcile differing astronomical observations, not gaming applications, motivated much of the early research on the theory of probability. Experiments conducted with coins and dice were often studied since these were easy to perform and provided significant insight.

Since the die in Example 2 has no 7s, the probability of selecting a 7, an *impossible event*, is 0. The probability of a *certain event* (such as rolling a number less than 7) is 1. Other probabilities range from 0 to 1. If E_k is an outcome of an experiment and the sample space is $S = \{E_1, E_2, E_3, \ldots, E_n\}$, then the sum of the probabilities of all the possible events is 1.

$$P(S) = \sum_{k=1}^{n} P(E_i) = 1$$

The set of all events in the sample space that are not in E is the *complement* of E, denoted as E'. Together E and E' form the sample space.

$$P(E) + P(E') = P(S)$$
$$P(E) + P(E') = 1$$
$$P(E') = 1 - P(E)$$

Basic Probabilities

theoretical	$P(E) = \frac{n(E)}{n(S)}$
experimental	$P(E) = \frac{\text{number of times the event occurs}}{\text{number of trials}}$
event	$0 \leq P(E) \leq 1$
complement of an event	$P(E') = 1 - P(E)$
certain event	$P(C) = 1$
impossible event	$P(\varnothing) = 0$

Example 3 Calculating the Probability of the Complement

If there were 3,978,497 live births reported in the United States in 2015 and 139,862 of these were multiple births (twins, triplets, etc.), what was the probability of not having a multiple birth?

Answer

Let M = having a multiple birth.

$P(M) = \dfrac{139{,}862}{3{,}978{,}497} \approx 0.035$ or 3.5%

$P(M') \approx 1 - 0.035 = 0.965$ or 96.5%

1. Find the probability of having a multiple birth.

2. Apply $P(E') = 1 - P(E)$.

—————————— SKILL ✓ **EXERCISE 15**

An event that has a single outcome, such as rolling a die, is a *simple event*. A *compound event*, such as flipping a coin several times, is made of two or more simple events. Section 10.1 introduced independent events, where the outcome of one event has no influence on the outcomes of the other event(s).

▎ **PROBABILITY OF INDEPENDENT EVENTS**

If A and B are independent events, $P(A \text{ and } B) = P(A) \cdot P(B)$.

Pierre-Simon de Laplace was able to show mathematically that small deviations from Newton's predicted paths of celestial objects were due to effects of gravitational forces after all. This finding supported a Platonic view of the universe.

Example 4 Calculating Probabilities of Independent Events

An experiment consists of flipping a coin followed by rolling a 6-sided die. Find the probability of each event.

a. getting heads and a 5

b. getting tails and an even number

Answer

a. $P(H \text{ and } 5) = P(H) \cdot P(5) = \dfrac{1}{2} \cdot \dfrac{1}{6} = \dfrac{1}{12}$

b. $P(T \text{ and even}) = P(T) \cdot P(\text{even}) = \dfrac{1}{2} \cdot \dfrac{3}{6} = \dfrac{1}{4}$

Since the compound events consist of two independent events, apply $P(A \text{ and } B) = P(A) \cdot P(B)$.

—————————— SKILL ✓ **EXERCISE 25**

When the events are dependent, the probability of one event changes the probability of the other event(s). The Fundamental Counting Principle implies that the formula for independent events then needs to be changed to $P(A \text{ and } B) = P(A) \cdot P(B|A)$, where $P(B|A)$ is the *conditional probability* of B, given that A has happened.

▎ **PROBABILITY OF DEPENDENT EVENTS**

If A and B are dependent events, $P(A \text{ and } B) = P(A) \cdot P(B|A)$.

Example 5 Probabilities of Independent and Dependent Events

A hat contains 2 red marbles and 8 blue marbles. What is the probability of drawing 2 red marbles from the hat under the following conditions?

a. The first marble drawn is replaced before the second is drawn.

b. The first marble drawn is not replaced before the second is drawn.

Answer

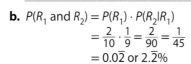

a. $P(R_1 \text{ and } R_2) = P(R_1) \cdot P(R_2)$

$\qquad = \dfrac{2}{10} \cdot \dfrac{2}{10} = \dfrac{4}{100}$

$\qquad = 0.04 \text{ or } 4\%$

The events are independent because the first marble is replaced.

b. $P(R_1 \text{ and } R_2) = P(R_1) \cdot P(R_2|R_1)$

$\qquad = \dfrac{2}{10} \cdot \dfrac{1}{9} = \dfrac{2}{90} = \dfrac{1}{45}$

$\qquad = 0.0\overline{2} \text{ or } 2.\overline{2}\%$

1. The events are dependent because the first marble is not replaced.

Check

$P(R_1 \text{ and } R_2) = \dfrac{2}{10} \cdot \dfrac{1}{9} = \dfrac{2}{90} = \dfrac{1}{45}$

2. Notice how a tree diagram can be used to verify the probability of dependent events.

SKILL ✓ **EXERCISE 21**

When events A and B are independent, the probability of B is not affected by the fact that A has happened and $P(B|A) = P(B)$.

Example 6 Applying Conditional Probabilities

In a 2014–15 school-year survey of 12–18-yr-old students, 20.8% of the students reported being bullied. The survey indicated that 53.8% of the students were from households with annual incomes of $50,000 or more. If 10.2% of the students reported being bullied and being from households with higher incomes, are the events of being bullied and being in a household with a higher income independent or dependent?

Answer

Let B = bullied student
and H = higher-income household student.

1. Define the events.

$P(B|H) = \dfrac{0.102}{0.538} \approx 0.190 \text{ or } 19.0\%$

$\neq P(B) = 20.8\%$

2. Find $P(B|H) = \dfrac{P(B \text{ and } H)}{P(H)}$ and compare it to $P(B)$.

Events B and H are dependent.

3. Since $P(B|H) \neq P(B)$, the events are not independent.

SKILL ✓ **EXERCISE 37**

To find the probability of event A or event B happening, consider whether the occurrence of one event prevents the other from occurring. The events are *mutually exclusive* or *disjoint* if both events cannot happen. If events A and B can both happen, they are *mutually inclusive* events.

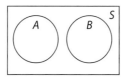

mutually exclusive

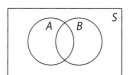

mutually inclusive

PROBABILITY OF *A* OR *B*

If *A* and *B* are mutually inclusive events, $P(A \text{ or } B) = P(A) + P(B) - P(A \text{ and } B)$.
If *A* and *B* are mutually exclusive, $P(A \text{ and } B) = 0$ and $P(A \text{ or } B) = P(A) + P(B)$.

Example 7 Calculating Combined Probabilities

A survey of 371 teens shows that 266 own a dog and 157 own a cat. If 108 own both a dog and a cat, what is the probability that a randomly selected teen owns either a dog or a cat?

Answer

Let *D* = owns a dog
and *C* = owns a cat.

$P(D \text{ or } C) = P(D) + P(C) - P(D \text{ and } C)$
$= \frac{266}{371} + \frac{157}{371} - \frac{108}{371}$
$= \frac{315}{371} \approx 0.85 \text{ or } 85\%$

The probability that a randomly selected teen owns a dog or cat is 85%.

The Venn diagram shows that the events are mutually inclusive.

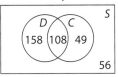

SKILL ✓ **EXERCISE 35**

Example 8 Calculating Combined Probabilities

The table summarizes the results of a survey that asked 434 students how many books they read last summer. Determine the probability that a randomly selected student read each number of books.

a. 4 or fewer books

b. 5 or more books

Answer

a. $P(\leq 4) = P(0) + P(1-2) + P(3-4)$
$= 0.039 + 0.141 + 0.198$
$= 0.378 \text{ or } 37.8\%$

Find $P(\leq 4) = P(0) + P(1-2) + P(3-4)$
since these events are mutually exclusive.

b. $P(\geq 5) = 1 - P(\leq 4) = 1 - 0.378$
$= 0.622 \text{ or } 62.2\%$

Apply the Complement Property.

Number of Books	Percent of Students
0	3.9%
1–2	14.1%
3–4	19.8%
5–6	16.1%
7–8	8.1%
9+	38.0%

SKILL ✓ **EXERCISE 39**

Compound Probabilities	
independent events	$P(A \text{ and } B) = P(A) \cdot P(B)$
dependent events	$P(A \text{ and } B) = P(A) \cdot P(B|A)$
inclusive events	$P(A \text{ or } B) = P(A) + P(B) - P(A \text{ and } B)$
mutually exclusive events	$P(A \text{ or } B) = P(A) + P(B)$

A. Exercises

List the sample space and the event for each outcome.

1. rolling a number greater than 4 on a 6-sided die

2. getting tails and an odd number when flipping a coin and rolling a 6-sided die

3. getting heads once and tails once when flipping two coins simultaneously

4. A randomly selected student chooses a chicken sandwich and lemonade from a menu offering hamburgers, chicken sandwiches, and turkey wraps to eat and lemonade and water to drink.

5. Given the options of cola, a sports drink, or tea, a randomly selected student ranks his preferred beverages as (1) sports drink, (2) tea, and (3) cola.

6. Out of the 5 starting players for the basketball team, Adam and Ben are randomly chosen to carry the equipment. The other starting players are Chris, Dave, and Ethan.

The table displays the results from 60 rolls of a die. State the theoretical and experimental probabilities of each event.

Number	Times Rolled
1	10
2	12
3	10
4	9
5	6
6	13

7. a 1

8. a prime number

9. a number greater than 4

10. an even number

11. Examine the table of results.

   a. For which outcome(s) did the experimental probability equal the theoretical probability?

   b. If the experiment was increased to 1000 rolls, would you expect to continue getting a 2 in 20% of the trials and a 5 in 10% of the trials? Explain your reasoning.

A standard deck of 108 Uno® cards has four regular "Wild" cards and four "Wild Draw 4" cards. The remaining 100 cards are evenly divided into red, blue, yellow, and green cards. Each color has one 0 and two each  **of the numbers 1 through 9, "Reverse," "Draw 2," and "Skip" cards. Determine each probability.**

12. P(red)

13. P("Skip")

14. P(purple)

15. P(not blue)

16. P("Reverse" or regular "Wild")

17. P("Wild Draw 4" or blue "Reverse")

18. P(red or blue)

19. P(4 or yellow)

20. P(odd number or green)

B. Exercises

Using the standard deck of Uno cards described above, find the probability of drawing the stated cards consecutively under the following conditions.
a. The first drawn card is replaced.
b. The first drawn card is not replaced.

21. 5, 8

22. "Reverse," regular "Wild"

23. yellow 5, yellow

24. numbered card less than 5, "Wild Draw 4"

Find each probability when a 6-sided die and an 8-sided die are rolled.

25. an odd number on the 6-sided die and a number greater than 2 on the 8-sided die

26. a number greater than 2 on the 6-sided die and a number less than 4 on the 8-sided die

Make a table listing the sums for all possible outcomes when a 6-sided die and an 8-sided die are rolled. Then find the probability for each event.

27. a sum of 11

28. a sum less than 7

29. a sum greater than 10

30. a sum that is prime

Emily and Tim each bought a bag of chocolate candies from King's Kandy Shop and recorded how many of each color of candy were in their bag. Assume candies are randomly drawn without replacement and express probabilities to the nearest tenth of a percent.

Emily	Color	Tim
6	purple	3
13	green	8
2	red	9
20	orange	14
9	yellow	14
13	blue	18
63	**Total**	66

31. What is the probability that the first candy drawn from Emily's bag is purple and the first candy drawn from Tim's bag is red?

32. What is the probability that none of the first three candies drawn from Emily's bag are orange?

33. What is the probability that Lily randomly selects Tim's bag and then draws a red candy?

34. If three identical bags are placed beside the original two, what is the probability that Lily randomly chooses an orange or a yellow candy from Emily's bag?

35. Of the church youth group's 78 teens, 48 teens went to camp last year. Of these 48, 38 teens will be going back to camp this summer, while 15 teens who did not go last year plan to join them. Draw a Venn diagram illustrating this scenario and then express the probability of each random selection as a fraction.

   a. a teen attending last summer but not this summer

   b. a teen attending just one summer

   c. a teen not attending either summer

   d. a teen attending at least one summer

36. Of Eastside Christian High School's 120 students, 72 students play fall sports, 70 students play spring sports, and 42 of these students play both. Draw a Venn diagram and label each region with its corresponding number of students. Express each probability for a randomly chosen student as a reduced fraction.

   a. The student plays in the fall but not in the spring.

   b. The student plays in either season.

   c. The student does not play in either season.

   d. Are playing fall sports and spring sports independent events or dependent events? Explain your reasoning.

37. Jim estimates that he experiences pain during 8% of his working hours. Draw a Venn diagram illustrating the time he doesn't feel well if his neck hurts 7% of the time, and his hand is sore 4% of the time.

   a. What percent of the time does he experience both neck and hand pain?

   b. Are his neck pain and hand pain independent events or dependent events? Explain your reasoning.

38. Apple's iPhone® sales accounted for 216.8 million of the 1536.5 million smartphones sold worldwide in 2017. The table records the quarterly iPhone sales (in millions) for that year. Find each probability to the nearest tenth of a percent.

2017 iPhone Sales	
Qtr	Millions
1st	78.3
2nd	50.8
3rd	41.0
4th	46.7

   a. A person who purchased a smartphone in 2017 bought an iPhone.

   b. An iPhone bought in 2017 was purchased in the last quarter.

   c. An iPhone bought in 2017 was purchased in one of the first three quarters.

39. Use the 2017 world population of 7.6 billion people and the smartphone information from excersise 38 to find each probability to the nearest tenth of a percent.

   a. A randomly chosen person did not purchase a smartphone in 2017.

   b. A randomly chosen person purchased an iPhone in the first half of 2017.

> **C. Exercises**

Exercises 40–42 refer to the table used for exercises 31–34.

40. How much more likely is Emily to first draw a purple candy than Tim?

41. Whose bag should Lily choose from if she would like to randomly draw a blue and then a green candy? How much higher (to the nearest tenth of a percent) are her chances?

42. Whose bag should Lily choose from if she would like to randomly draw one blue and one green candy simultaneously? How much higher (to the nearest tenth of a percent) are her chances?

43. Mrs. Ream randomly selects 6 essay questions from a list of 12 that she has given to her class for the final exam. If Jon knows 8 of the answers, find the probability (to the nearest percent) that he will answer each number of questions correctly.

   a. all 6 questions

   b. exactly 3

   c. at least 4

44. To demonstrate that experimental probabilities approach theoretical probabilities, write a calculator program that randomly generates n numbers from 1 to 6 and tallies the frequency of each outcome. The program's output should display the number of times each number was "rolled." Run the program for $n = 10, 20, 100,$ and 1000 and then calculate the experimental probability for each outcome.

CUMULATIVE REVIEW

Solve each system using technology. Round answers to the nearest tenth if necessary. [7.1]

45. $y = 2x^3 + 9x^2 + 7x - 6$
   $y = 3x + 4$

46. $y = |x - 3|$
   $y = x^2 + 2x + 4$

Write the standard form equation of a conic with the given characteristics.

47. hyperbola with vertices at $(\pm 6, 0)$ and perpendicular asymptotes [8.3]

48. ellipse with vertices at $(3, 5)$ and $(3, -9)$ and an eccentricity of $\dfrac{\sqrt{13}}{7}$ [8.2]

If $\displaystyle\sum_{k=1}^{200} a_k = 45$ and $\displaystyle\sum_{k=1}^{200} c_k = 505$, use properties of summations to evaluate each sum. [9.5]

49. $\displaystyle\sum_{k=1}^{200} 7a_k$

50. $\displaystyle\sum_{k=1}^{200} (5c_k - 6)$

51. What is the angle (to the nearest degree) between the vectors $\mathbf{p} = \langle 3, 4, 6 \rangle$ and $\mathbf{q} = \langle -4, 5, 3 \rangle$? [6.3]

   A. $25°$ **C.** $61°$ **E.** none of
   B. $39°$ **D.** $118°$ these

52. Which matrix is in reduced row echelon form? [7.3]

   A. $\begin{bmatrix} 3 & 5 & 2 & -7 \\ 0 & -2 & 8 & 4 \\ 0 & 0 & 0 & 6 \end{bmatrix}$ **D.** $\begin{bmatrix} 1 & 0 & 0 & 3 \\ 0 & 1 & 0 & 2 \\ 0 & 0 & 1 & 0 \end{bmatrix}$

   B. $\begin{bmatrix} 1 & 0 & 0 & -7 \\ 0 & 1 & 0 & 2 \\ 0 & 0 & 3 & 3 \end{bmatrix}$ **E.** none of these

   C. $\begin{bmatrix} 1 & 5 & 2 & 4 \\ 0 & 1 & 8 & 4 \\ 0 & 0 & 1 & 2 \end{bmatrix}$

53. What is the domain for the graph of the parametric equations $x = 2 - t$ and $y = t; t \in [-3, 2]$? [8.5]

   A. $x \in [-3, 2]$ **C.** $x \in [-5, 0]$ **E.** $x \in \mathbb{R}$
   B. $x \in [0, 5]$ **D.** $x \in [-1, 4]$

54. How many ways can the letters in the word *MISSISSIPPI* be arranged? [10.1]

   A. 24   **C.** 34,650   **E.** none of
   B. 330   **D.** 39,916,800   these

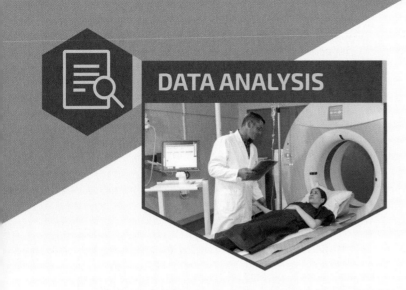

DATA ANALYSIS

Medical Screenings and Probability

Suppose that, during a routine physical examination, you test positive for a serious but rare (only 1 in every 200,000) medical condition. The test accurately identifies an individual with the condition 95% of the time and gives a false positive only 2% of the time. What is the probability that you actually have this condition? Many of us would assume it is 98%, 95%, or maybe only 93%. Doing the math provides surprisingly counterintuitive results.

Let C represent having the condition and let T represent testing positive.

1. Which conditional probability is represented by the 95% effectiveness of the test, $P(T|C)$ or $P(C|T)$?

2. Which conditional probability represents the likelihood that a person who tests positive actually has the condition?

Recall that the probability for these conditional events is found using $P(C|T) = \dfrac{P(C \text{ and } T)}{P(T)}$. Because C and T are dependent events, the probability that you have the condition and test positive is $P(C \text{ and } T) = P(C) \cdot P(T|C)$.

3. State $P(C)$ if 1 person out of 200,000 has the condition.

4. Find $P(C \text{ and } T)$ in this scenario.

To find the probability of a positive test, $P(T)$, consider the number of true positives from those who have the condition and the number of false positives from those who do not. In a sample of 200,000 people, the one person with the condition tests positive 95% of the time and the 199,999 who do not will test positive 2% of the time for a total of $0.95(1) + 0.02(199,999) = 0.95 + 3999.98 = 4000.93$ positive tests. Therefore, $P(T) = \dfrac{4000.93}{200,000} \approx 0.02$.

5. Find $P(C|T) = \dfrac{P(C \text{ and } T)}{P(T)}$.

6. What is the probability that you actually have the condition?

In this hypothetical scenario, the effective rate of the test, $P(T|C)$, was given along with the percentage of false positives. To find the likelihood of having the condition knowing that you have tested positive, $P(C|T)$ was found using

$$P(C|T) = \frac{P(C \text{ and } T)}{P(T)} = \frac{P(C) \cdot P(T|C)}{P(T)}.$$

Breast cancer is the second leading cause of cancer deaths in women in the United States. In 2017 over 40,000 women died from the disease. In 2009 the United States Preventive Services Task Force made headlines when they revised previously issued guidelines for when and how often women with no unusual risk factors should be screened for breast cancer. In particular, the task force found that the risks outweighed the benefits of mammograms for women 40–50 yr old, and changed the recommended age for women to begin routine screenings from 40 to 50. Risks noted in the task force report include overdiagnosis and overtreatment of non-life-threatening cancers, false-positive results leading to unnecessary and sometimes invasive follow-up testing, psychological harm, and false reassurance from false-negative tests.

Assume that screening mammograms are 80% effective and give false positives 10% of the time. Let C represent a woman who has breast cancer and T represent a positive result from a screening.

7. Find each probability for a woman in her 40s if on average 14 out of 1000 women will develop breast cancer in their 40s.

    a. $P(T)$ **b.** $P(C|T)$

8. Find the probability that a woman in her 30s who has tested positive actually has breast cancer if on average 4 out of 1000 women will develop breast cancer in their 30s.

In 2016, after reviewing multiple studies involving over 600,000 women, the task force issued another report supporting their 2009 conclusions. This report noted that routine screening of women 39–49 yr old would likely prevent 3 deaths per 10,000 women screened over a 10 yr period.

9. **Discuss:** While statistical analysis is obviously helpful, it cannot prescribe solutions to ethical questions. How should a biblical worldview influence the recommendations on when and how often screenings should take place?

10. **Discuss:** In lieu of more screenings, what could be done to reduce the number of deaths due to breast cancer?

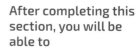

10.3 Representing Data Graphically

Our ultimate goal in the study of mathematics should be to glorify God and to help others reach their God-given potential. The study of statistics plays an important part in that goal. God created humans in His image as reasoning beings and expects us to use these abilities as we plan and make decisions for the future. While God directs our steps, He expects us to plan our ways (Prov. 16:9). Careful planning can be facilitated by information and predictions derived from statistics.

The study of statistics seeks to predict (or *infer*) outcomes based on the results of similar situations. Mathematicians have developed techniques that permit the study of a manageable number of trials to reasonably predict outcomes. For example, a statistician may predict the average weight of one-year-old boys in the United States based on a sample of 300 one-year-old boys. The larger overall set being considered is called the *population*. The *sample* is a carefully selected subset of the population. The sample is *random* if all members of the population have an equal chance of being included. If the sample is biased in any way, the inferences made will not be reliable.

▌DEFINITIONS

A **parameter** is the actual value for a characteristic of the population. A **statistic** is an estimate of the population's parameter based on a sample.

In the example above, the average weight of all one-year-old boys in the United States is a parameter of the population and the average weight of the 300 boys in the study is a statistic. In larger populations, the actual value of a parameter is difficult or even impossible to determine. The results of studying a sample are summarized with *descriptive statistics*. The use of statistics from a sample to make predictions about the population's parameters is called *inferential statistics*.

It is difficult to estimate probabilities for events that have no history. For example, how could the probability of losing a space shuttle be predicted before any shuttles had been launched? Bayesian statistics provide an alternative form of analysis for these situations.

KEYWORD SEARCH

Bayesian statistics

Example 1   Identifying Parameters and Statistics

State whether each characteristic is a parameter or a statistic. Explain your reasoning.

a. In a study of the health of cats in humane societies, the average weight of cats at the local humane society was found.

b. When reviewing the performance of students in the university's Calculus I course, Dr. Holcomb found the range of homework averages for all the students in the six sections of the class.

Answer

a. statistic; The limited number of cats represents a sample of the larger population.

b. parameter; This is the value for the entire population being studied.

──────────────────────────────── SKILL ✓ **EXERCISE 5**

Data collected for a statistical study falls into one of four levels of measurement. *Nominal* data represents unordered groups or classifications. *Ordinal* data describes ordered categories within the set without indicating the interval between values. *Interval* data measures a characteristic on a scale having a fixed width without a meaningful zero. *Ratio* data is measured on a scale with a fixed width and an absolute zero. The mathematical significance of the measurement increases at each level.

Measurement Levels	
nominal	unordered categories examples: political party, eye color, gender
ordinal	ordered categories without distances examples: customer satisfaction rating, class rank
interval	distances without an absolute zero examples: Fahrenheit temperature, time of day
ratio	distances with an absolute zero examples: test score, precipitation, income, height

Example 2 Identifying Levels of Measurement

State the level of measurement for each characteristic. Explain your reasoning.

a. grade point average   **b.** place in a race   **c.** favorite professional baseball team

Answer

a. ratio; GPA has an absolute zero and a scale with a fixed width.

b. ordinal; The data describes an ordering without a fixed scale.

c. nominal; The categories are unordered classifications.

SKILL ✓ EXERCISE 9

A statistical graph organizes the data and illustrates its distribution. Categorical data is usually illustrated with a bar graph or a pie chart. Spreadsheet programs can be used to quickly produce accurate graphs.

KEYWORD SEARCH

online statistical graph 🔍
generator

Example 3 Illustrating Categorical Data

Create a bar graph and a pie chart illustrating the grades on a Statistics test.

Grade	A	B	C	D	F
Frequency	4	7	10	3	1

Answer

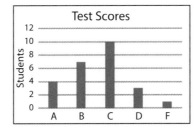

1. Create a bar graph with the vertical axis representing the frequencies and the horizontal axis representing the grades.

	A	B
1	Grade	Freq.
2	A	4
3	B	7
4	C	10
5	D	3
6	F	1

or

In a spreadsheet, enter grades in one column and the frequency of each grade in a second column. Select both columns and insert a bar graph. Then enter a title and label the axes as needed.

CONTINUED ➡

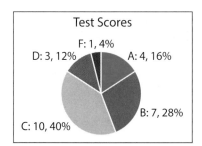
Test Scores

	A	B	C	D
1	Grade	Freq	Percent	Angle (°)
2	A	4	16%	57.6
3	B	7	28%	100.8
4	C	10	40%	144
5	D	3	12%	43.2
6	F	1	4%	14.4
7	Total	25		

2. Calculate the percentage of students who received each letter grade and multiply each percentage by 360°. Create a pie chart demonstrating the distribution of the letter grades. Label each sector appropriately.

or

In a spreadsheet, select the grade labels and frequency data and then insert a pie chart. Add a title and labels and adjust the format as needed.

Florence Nightingale made polar graphs that represented the number of Crimean War deaths due to combat, disease, and other causes. Each sector represented a different month and different colors indicated different causes of death.

SKILL ✓ **EXERCISE 25**

Dot plots and stem plots are used to organize and illustrate interval and ratio data. Relatively small sets of data, such as the following heights (in inches) of choir members, can be represented by a dot plot.

{58, 61, 65, 72, 70, 66, 62, 70, 66, 64, 71, 70, 62, 66, 60, 71, 73, 68, 66, 59, 60, 73, 71, 64}

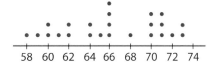

From this dot plot it is easy to see that the heights range from 58 in. to 73 in. and that the majority of heights range from 62 in. to 71 in.

This data can also be illustrated with a stem plot (or a stem-and-leaf plot). The largest digit that adequately groups the data acts as the stem and the remaining digit(s) are the leaves. The tens digit of a choir member's height is the stem and the ones digit is the leaf.

Occasionally it is helpful to split a stem plot into smaller categories. The first row with the same stem contains leaves 0–4 and the second row with that stem contains leaves 5–9.

Two similar data sets can be compared using back-to-back stem plots. The leaves of one data set are placed to the right of the shared stem and the leaves of the second data set are placed to its left.

Stem	Leaves
5	8 9
6	0 0 1 2 2 4 4 5 6 6 6 6 8
7	0 0 0 1 1 1 2 3 3

Stem	Leaves
5	
5	8 9
6	0 0 1 2 2 4 4
6	5 6 6 6 6 8
7	0 0 0 1 1 1 2 3 3
7	

Example 4   Using a Back-to-Back Stem Plot

Create a back-to-back stem plot summarizing the ages of US presidents when they took office in the 1800s and the 1900s. Then compare the two data sets.

1800s: 47, 61, 46, 64, 48, 49, 51, 55, 57, 58, 56, 57, 54, 54, 50, 49, 57, 54, 51, 52, 55

1900s: 42, 51, 56, 55, 51, 54, 51, 60, 62, 43, 55, 56, 61, 52, 69, 64, 46

Answer

1800s	Stem	1900s
9 9 8 7 6	4	2 3 6
8 7 7 7 6 5 5 4 4 4 2 1 1 0	5	1 1 1 2 4 5 5 6 6
4 1	6	0 1 2 4 9

Use the tens digit as the stem for both data sets and the ones digits as the leaves. Notice that the digits for the leaves are arranged to increase as they extend farther from the stem.

There is a wider range of ages in the 1900s and the average age when assuming office seems to be higher in the 1900s.

SKILL ✓ **EXERCISES 15, 27**

Interval and ratio data can also be illustrated by a *histogram*. Begin by organizing the data in a *frequency distribution table*. Ungrouped frequency distribution tables are made for data sets whose *range* (the difference between the maximum and minimum values) is relatively small (often ≤ 15).

Example 5   Making a Frequency Distribution Table and Histogram

Construct a frequency distribution table and histogram to illustrate the following cockatiel weights (in grams).

$$W = \begin{Bmatrix} 87, 83, 92, 86, 88, 86, 90, 85, 86, 85, \\ 88, 84, 87, 86, 89, 86, 90, 87, 86, 87 \end{Bmatrix}$$

Answer

TIP

To draw the histogram on your calculator, enter the 20 original data values in L_1. Define Plot1 and the WINDOW as illustrated with Xscl = 1.

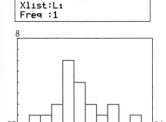

1. Since the range of the data is $92 - 83 = 9$, use an ungrouped frequency distribution table. List all the possible weights from 82 to 94 and tally their occurrences to determine the frequency for each weight.

Data x_i	Tally	Frequency f_i
83	I	1
84	I	1
85	II	2
86	IIII I	6
87	IIII	4
88	II	2
89	I	1
90	II	2
91		0
92	I	1

$$\sum f_i = 20$$

2. Construct a histogram placing the weights along the horizontal axis and frequency (or percent) along the vertical axis. Draw a bar to the frequency for each data value. Clearly label the axes and title the graph.

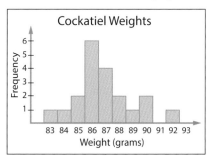

SKILL ✓ **EXERCISE 19**

A *grouped frequency distribution table* is usually used if the range of the data is greater than 15. Every data value is placed within classes that have the same width. Sturges's formula is often used to find an appropriate number of classes.

STURGES'S FORMULA

The number of classes, k, for a sample with n values is $k = 1 + 3.3(\log n)$, in which k is always rounded up to the next integer.

The width of each class, w, is then found using $w = \dfrac{\text{range}}{k}$, where w is also rounded up.

Example 6   Creating and Using a Grouped Frequency Distribution

Construct a frequency distribution table and histogram to illustrate the SAT® math scores received by students at Pinbrook Christian School.

291, 312, 321, 329, 365, 365, 382, 402, 417, 418, 421, 424, 428, 439, 443, 445, 463, 464, 465, 471, 473, 487, 492, 494, 501, 507, 510, 510, 511, 515, 518, 519, 521, 529, 538, 552, 557, 567, 572, 582, 584, 593, 607, 609, 612, 615, 641, 665, 682, 705

Answer

$1 + 3.3 \log n = 1 + 3.3 \log 50 \approx 6.6$
$\therefore k = 7$

1. Use Sturges's formula with $n = 50$ to determine the number of classes, rounding up to the next integer.

$\dfrac{\text{range}}{k} = \dfrac{705 - 291}{7} = 59.1; \therefore w = 60$

2. Find the width of each class.

	A	B	C
1	Class	Tally	Freq
2	291–350	||||	4
3	351–410	||||	4
4	411–470	卌 卌 |	11
5	471–530	卌 卌 卌	15
6	531–590	卌 ||	7
7	591–650	卌 |	6
8	651–710	|||	3
9	Total	$\Sigma f_i =$	50

3. A spreadsheet can be used to construct a frequency distribution table with 7 classes of width 60.

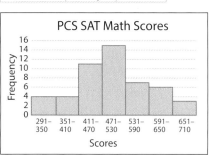

4. Draw the related histogram.

In a spreadsheet, highlight the class limits and frequency data and insert a bar graph. Add a title and label the axes.
Click on one of the bars to access the Series Options; then set the gap width to 0 and draw borders to separate the bars.

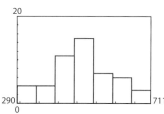

 SKILL ✓ **EXERCISE 33**

A *percentile graph* or *ogive* (pronounced ō'jíve) is a line graph that represents the cumulative frequencies of the data as percentages.

Example 7 Constructing a Percentile Graph

Construct a percentile graph for the data in Example 6.

Answer

1. Add Cumulative Frequency and Cumulative Percentage columns to the frequency distribution table and calculate the percentages.

2. Plot ordered pairs representing each class's upper limit and its cumulative percentage. Add a point at (290, 0) to show that there are no scores below 291. Connect the points to make the line graph.

	A	B	C	D
1	Class	Freq	Cumulative Frequency	Cumulative Percentage
2	291–350	4	4	8%
3	351–410	4	8	16%
4	411–470	11	19	38%
5	471–530	15	34	68%
6	531–590	7	41	82%
7	591–650	6	47	94%
8	651–710	3	50	100%

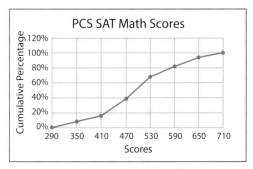

SKILL ✓ EXERCISE 37

A. Exercises

1. A _____ represents a characteristic of a population while a _____ measures a characteristic of a sample.

Identify each group as a population or a sample.

2. all the students taking the SAT in the spring of 2020

3. 100 randomly selected 16-yr-olds in Ohio

4. the students in 1 of 6 randomly selected sections of Calculus I

State whether each of the following is most likely a parameter or a statistic.

5. the favorite sport of 25 randomly selected students from Riverside High

6. the average height of a 17-yr-old boy in America

7. the median household income of residents in California

8. the range of scores on 1 of the 10 Precalculus quizzes

Identify the level of measurement.

9. the day of the week

10. the number of questions answered correctly on a math test

11. class salutatorian

12. blood type

Create a dot plot for each data set.

13. heights of students in a fifth-grade class:
51, 55, 52, 54, 55, 54, 53, 52, 55,
54, 54, 52, 56, 55, 54, 55, 56, 55

14. number of pets owned by classmates:
1, 0, 3, 2, 2, 1, 6, 2, 1, 0, 3,
2, 0, 5, 4, 2, 1, 1, 3, 0, 4

Create a stem-and-leaf plot for each data set.

15. grades from an AP History test:
85, 92, 76, 49, 84, 82, 73, 60, 84, 90

16. ages of employees:
37, 32, 49, 27, 62, 57, 46, 31, 26,
48, 51, 55, 52, 34, 61, 58, 38, 29

17. point totals in Super Bowls XXXIII through LII:
53, 39, 41, 37, 69, 61, 45, 31, 46, 31
50, 48, 56, 38, 65, 51, 52, 34, 62, 74

18. Use the survey results represented by the bar graph to find each percentage of the sample.

a. those preferring chocolate chip cookies

b. those preferring oatmeal raisin cookies

B. Exercises

Draw a histogram representing each frequency distribution table.

19.

Students in a Class	Freq.
21	4
22	0
23	3
24	6
25	5

20.

Quiz Scores	Freq.
10	3
9	5
8	4
7	2
6	1

Represent the British Literature grades of 20 students with the indicated graph.

Grades	Percent of Students
A	20%
B	35%
C	25%
D	15%
F	5%

21. pie chart

22. bar graph showing the number of students per grade

Represent the Algebra 2 grades with the indicated graph.

Grades	Number of Students
A	5
B	8
C	4
D	1
F	2

23. bar graph

24. pie chart

25. Make a bar graph and a pie chart to illustrate the 2017 iPhone sales.

Quarter	Millions
1st	78.3
2nd	50.8
3rd	41.0
4th	46.7

26. Which graph from exercise 25 better illustrates the quarterly sales? Explain your reasoning.

27. Make a back-to-back stem plot for the top two teams in the 2018 NCAA basketball tournament. Then compare the two teams's scoring.

Michigan: 61, 64, 99, 58, 69, 62
Villanova: 87, 81, 90, 71, 95, 79

28. Make a back-to-back stem plot for the point totals in Super Bowls I–XX (listed below) and the point totals in Super Bowls XXXIII–LII (listed in exercise 17). Compare the two sets of data.
45, 47, 23, 30, 29, 27, 21, 31, 22, 38,
46, 37, 66, 50, 37, 47, 44, 47, 54, 56

29. Make a split back-to-back stem plot for each player's total touchdowns scored per season played. The first stem should represent 0–4, the second should represent 5–9, and so on. Then compare their statistics. How does the fact that Brown played, on average, one fewer game per season affect your comparison?
Walter Payton: 7, 13, 16, 11, 16, 7, 8, 1, 8, 11, 11, 11, 5
Jim Brown: 10, 18, 14, 11, 10, 18, 15, 9, 21

30. Describe the error in each set of classes for a frequency distribution table.

a.

Ages
0–5
6–10
11–15
16–20
21–25
26–30
31–35

b.

Ages
20–30
30–40
40–50
50–60
60–70
70–80

31. The numbers of vehicles owned as reported in a random sampling of 40 households are listed below.

5, 1, 1, 2, 0, 1, 1, 2, 1, 1,
1, 3, 3, 0, 2, 5, 1, 2, 3, 4,
2, 1, 2, 2, 1, 2, 2, 1, 1, 1,
4, 2, 1, 1, 2, 1, 1, 4, 1, 3

  a. Make a frequency distribution table to organize the data.

  b. Draw a histogram representing the data.

  c. Draw a pie chart representing the data.

  d. Which graph better illustrates the data? Explain your reasoning.

32. Use technology to create a histogram illustrating the grouped frequency distribution table.

Ages	Freq.
20–29	5
30–39	8
40–49	9
50–59	10
60–69	6
70–79	2
Total	**40**

33. Complete the following steps to organize and illustrate the following ages of players in a recreational league soccer game.

16, 26, 26, 35, 28,
29, 22, 30, 28, 31,
33, 35, 42, 37, 27,
30, 32, 29, 26, 31,
34, 27, 31, 26, 28

  a. Use Sturges's formula to determine the appropriate number of classes for a grouped frequency distribution table and their corresponding widths.

  b. Create a frequency distribution table with the first class having a lower limit of 15.

  c. Use technology to create a histogram illustrating the frequency distribution.

34. The approximate numbers of bridges (in thousands) in 30 different states are listed below.

7, 11, 14, 18, 24, 24, 14, 14, 17, 28,
8, 7, 13, 22, 26, 13, 13, 7, 19, 17, 12,
26, 48, 16, 23, 11, 17, 9, 25, 15

  a. Use Sturges's formula to determine the appropriate number of classes for a grouped frequency distribution table and their corresponding widths.

  b. Make a frequency table from the information provided and the results from part *a*.

  c. Use technology to create a histogram illustrating the distribution.

35. Frequency polygons are line graphs that are made by connecting the midpoints of the top of each bar in a histogram. Create a frequency polygon for the data from the following.

  a. Example 6   **b.** exercise 34

C. Exercises

36. Create a double bar graph from the favorite cookie survey data. Then explain how the data from this survey might be valuable to a school.

Cookie Flavor	Males	Females
chocolate chip	35	25
peanut butter	8	10
double chocolate	10	12
sugar	18	2
oatmeal raisin	4	16

37. Create a percentile graph for the cockatiel weight distribution given in Example 5.

38. Create a percentile graph for the data from the survey of vehicles owned per household in exercise 31.

39. The numbers of NCAA Division I schools per state are listed below. Using Sturges's formula, create a frequency distribution table, histogram, and cumulative percentile graph for the data. Use Sturges's formula to find the appropriate number of groups and their corresponding widths.

9, 0, 3, 5, 24, 5, 7, 2, 13, 7,
1, 3, 13, 10, 4, 3, 7, 12, 1, 9,
6, 7, 1, 6, 5, 2, 3, 2, 2, 8, 2,
22, 18, 2, 13, 4, 4, 14, 4, 12,
2, 12, 21, 6, 1, 14, 5, 2, 4, 1

Use a half-angle identity to find the exact value of each expression. [5.5]

40. $\sin \frac{7\pi}{12}$

41. $\tan \frac{7\pi}{12}$

42. Write the recursive formula and a simplified explicit formula for the sequence 7, 10, 13, 16, 19, ... [9.2]

43. Write an explicit formula for the geometric sequence with $a_3 = 45$ and $a_6 = 1215$ and use the formula to find a_{10}. [9.3]

Marbles are drawn from a bag that contains 5 red, 7 blue, and 8 green marbles. Express each probability below to the nearest tenth of a percent. [10.2]

44. What is the probability that the first 3 marbles drawn (without replacement) are red?

45. What is the probability that the first 3 marbles drawn (with replacement) are all blue or green?

46. Which of the following is NOT true for $y = \cot x$? [4.5]

   A. period: $p = \pi$

   B. VA: $x = n\pi, n \in \mathbb{Z}$

   C. zeros: $x = (2n + 1)\frac{\pi}{2}, n \in \mathbb{Z}$

   D. It is an increasing function.

   E. all of these

47. Which describes the graph of $r = \dfrac{5}{2 + 3 \cos \theta}$? [8.6]

   A. line   **C.** ellipse   **E.** hyperbola

   B. circle   **D.** parabola

48. How many different ways can 5 of 7 pictures be arranged on a shelf? [10.1]

   A. 21   **C.** 120   **E.** 5040

   B. 25   **D.** 2520

49. Which of the following is a trigonometric identity? [5.5]

   A. $\cos (\alpha - \beta) = \sin \alpha \sin \beta + \cos \alpha \cos \beta$

   B. $\cos (\alpha + \beta) = \sin \alpha \sin \beta - \cos \alpha \cos \beta$

   C. $\sin (\alpha + \beta) = \sin \alpha \cos \beta - \cos \alpha \sin \beta$

   D. $\sin (\alpha - \beta) = \cos \alpha \sin \beta - \sin \alpha \cos \beta$

   E. all of these

Describing Data Numerically

Statistics play an ever-increasing role in sports.

After completing this section, you will be able to

- calculate measures of central tendency.
- calculate measures of variability.
- illustrate the distribution of data using a box plot.
- calculate quartiles and percentiles.
- choose appropriate descriptive statistics based on the data's distribution.

The previous section presented several ways to organize and illustrate a set of data. This section discusses several statistics that help describe the overall shape of the distribution of data by numerically describing its central tendency and variation. The mean, median, and mode are measures of central tendency that describe the typical or middle value of a set of data.

▌DEFINITIONS

The **mode** is the most frequently appearing value(s) in a data set.
The **median** is the middle value when the data is arranged in ascending or descending order (or the average of the two middle values when there is an even number of values).
The **mean** is the sum of the values divided by the number of values.

Population Mean	Sample Mean
$\mu = \dfrac{\sum\limits_{i=1}^{N} x_i}{N}$	$\bar{x} = \dfrac{\sum\limits_{i=1}^{n} x_i}{n}$

Notice that the Greek letter μ (mu) represents the population's mean (or average), while $\bar{x}$ (x bar) represents the sample's mean. The bar over the x distinguishes the sample mean from an individual value of the variable x. The total number of values is notated as N for a population and n for a sample. In general, parameters are represented by Greek letters, while statistics are represented by Latin letters.

Example 1 Finding Measures of Central Tendency

Find the sample mean, median, and mode of the following scores.
$S = \{24, 15, 20, 17, 25, 19, 20, 21, 24, 17, 24\}$

Answer

mean: $\bar{x} = \dfrac{\sum\limits_{i=1}^{11} x_i}{n} = \dfrac{226}{11} \approx 20.5$

{15, 17, 17, 19, 20, 20, 21, 24, 24, 24, 25}
The median is the 6th value, 20.

mode: 24

1. Find the mean by dividing the sum of the scores by the number of scores, $n = 11$.

2. Arrange the scores in ascending order and find the middle (the $\frac{n+1}{2}$th) value.

3. The most frequently occurring value is 24.

SKILL ✓ **EXERCISE 3**

Multiple modes can occur. If Example 1 had one less value of 24, there would be three modes: 17, 20, and 24. If no two data points are the same, then no mode exists.

While the mean and median of each data set A, B, and C are both 6, the values are spread out in different ways around the mean. The *range, variance, standard deviation*, and *interquartile range* describe how far the values are spread apart in the distribution. The simplest measure of variability, the range, was defined in Section 10.3 as the difference between the maximum and minimum values. The range for A is 4 while the range for both B and C is 8. While this shows that the data in A is less spread out, it does not reveal that the data in C is more clustered at the mean than the data in B.

The *deviation* of each data value is its difference from the mean, $x_i - \bar{x}$ or $x_i - \mu$. Since the sum of the deviations is always 0 (see exercise 35), an average of the deviations is meaningless. Instead, an average of the squares of the deviations is calculated and the square root of this average, the standard deviation, provides a measure of variableness for the data. The sum of the squares of the deviations, either $\sum_{i=1}^{n} (x_i - \bar{x})^2$ or $\sum_{i=1}^{N} (x_i - \mu)^2$, is often called the *sum of the squares* and is often abbreviated as *SS*.

$A = \{4, 5, 6, 7, 8\}$
$B = \{2, 4, 6, 8, 10\}$
$C = \{2, 6, 6, 6, 10\}$

❚ DEFINITIONS

The **variance** is an average of the squared deviations.
The **standard deviation** is the square root of the variance.

Population Variance	Sample Variance
$\sigma^2 = \dfrac{\sum_{i=1}^{N} (x_i - \mu)^2}{N}$ or $\dfrac{SS}{N}$	$s^2 = \dfrac{\sum_{i=1}^{n} (x_i - \bar{x})^2}{n-1}$ or $\dfrac{SS}{n-1}$
Population Standard Deviation	**Sample Standard Deviation**
$\sigma = \sqrt{\dfrac{\sum_{i=1}^{N} (x_i - \mu)^2}{N}}$	$s = \sqrt{\dfrac{\sum_{i=1}^{n} (x_i - \bar{x})^2}{n-1}}$

Note that the sample variance and sample standard deviation are divided by $n - 1$ instead of n. The fact that this allows the statistic to more accurately predict the actual variance and standard deviation of the population is proved in higher-level statistics classes.

Example 2 Finding the Sample Variance and Standard Deviation

Calculate the sample variance and standard deviation for data set $B = \{2, 4, 6, 8, 10\}$.

Answer
$\bar{x} = 6$

Values	Deviation^2
x_i	$(x_i - \bar{x})^2$
10	$(10 - 6)^2 = 16$
8	$(8 - 6)^2 = 4$
6	$(6 - 6)^2 = 0$
4	$(4 - 6)^2 = 4$
2	$(2 - 6)^2 = 16$

$$SS = \sum_{i=1}^{5} (x_i - \bar{x})^2 = 40$$

1. Find the mean.

2. Make a table to organize the calculation and recording of the squared deviations.

3. Find the sum of the squared deviations.

In the 1930s Walter A. Shewhart of Bell Labs developed process-control charts that are still widely used in many manufacturing processes. The relationship between the mean of a random sample and the mean of the population is used to determine whether a process is within normal variance limits or is out of control.

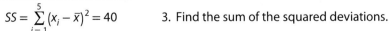

CONTINUED ➡

$$s^2 = \frac{\sum\limits_{i=1}^{n}(x_i - \bar{x})^2}{n-1} = \frac{40}{5-1} = 10$$

4. Find the sample variance by dividing the total by $(n-1)$.

$$s = \sqrt{10} \approx 3.16$$

5. The standard deviation is the square root of the variance.

_____ SKILL ✔ **EXERCISE 7**

Similar calculations for set $C = \{2, 6, 6, 6, 10\}$ produce $SS = 16 + 0 + 0 + 0 + 16 = 32$, $s^2 = \frac{32}{4} = 8$, and $s \approx 2.83$. This lower standard deviation indicates that more data values are closer to the mean in set C than in set B.

Since the calculations can become tedious, technology is often used to automate the computations.

Example 3 Using a Frequency Distribution

Use a spreadsheet to find the mean and population standard deviation of the class's test scores.

Answer

Test Scores
73, 75, 75, 78, 80, 80, 80, 83, 83, 83, 83, 83, 85, 85, 88, 88, 88, 90, 90, 93, 93, 95, 95, 95, 98

TIP

The $ symbols prevent the reference to B12 from changing when the formula is copied. Otherwise cell references are copied relative to the cell's position in the spreadsheet.

	A	B	C	D
1	Score (x_i)	Freq (f_i)	$x_i f_i$	$f_i(x_i - x_{bar})^2$
2	73	1	73	157.75
3	75	2	150	223.03
4	78	1	78	57.15
5	80	3	240	92.74
6	83	5	415	32.77
7	85	2	170	0.63
8	88	3	264	17.86
9	90	2	180	39.43
10	93	2	186	110.71
11	95	3	285	267.34
12	98	1	98	154.75
13		n	Sum	Sum
14		25	2139	1154.16
15		Mean:	85.56	
16			Variance:	46.1664
17			Standard Deviation:	6.79

1. Enter the headings in row 1, the data values in cells A2 through A12, the frequencies in cells B2 through B12, and the headings in row 13.

2. Find each product $x_i f_i$ by entering the formula =B1*A1 in cell C2 and then dragging the fill handle (small square in the lower right corner of the cell) down to fill in the formulas for C3 through C12.

3. Find the mean by entering =SUM(B2:B12) in cell B14, =SUM(C2:C12) in cell C14, and then =C14/B14 in cell C15. Enter a label for the mean in cell B15.

4. Calculate the squares of the deviations by entering =B2*(A2−C15)^2 in cell D2 and then dragging the fill handle down to fill in the formulas for D3 through D12.

5. Calculate the sum of the squares by entering =SUM(D2:D12) in cell D14.

6. Find the sample variance, s^2, by entering =D14/B14 in cell D16 and find the standard deviation, s, by entering =SQRT(D16) in cell D17; label these values appropriately.

_____ SKILL ✔ **EXERCISE 9**

The median value in Example 3, a test score of 85, divides the ordered list of data into two parts, each containing the same amount of data. _Quartiles_ divide the ordered data into four sets containing the same amount of data. After finding the median (the second quartile, Q_2), find Q_1 and Q_3 by finding the median of the lower and upper halves of the data. When finding quartiles for data sets with an odd number of values, do not include the median in either the upper or lower half of the data. For the test scores in Example 3, $Q_1 = 80$ and $Q_3 = 91.5$. A _box plot_ (often called a box-and-whisker plot) is used to illustrate the *five-number summary* of a set of data which includes the minimum, Q_1, Q_2 (the median), Q_3, and the maximum values.

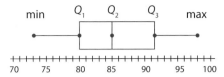

The *interquartile range* (*IQR*), the difference between Q_3 and Q_1, is another measure of variability. The *IQR* "box" contains the middle half (50%) of the data, while the "whiskers" represent the lower and upper fourths of the data.

An *outlier* is a value that is significantly higher or lower than the rest of the data. Any value more than 1.5(*IQR*) below Q_1 or above Q_3 is usually considered an outlier. It may be an extreme, nonrepresentative value or the result of an error in collecting the data. Because the value does not fit the data's overall distribution, it is sometimes excluded from the data set.

Excluding outliers is one way researchers may either intentionally or unintentionally bias their results. Stanford professor John Ioannidis cites "serendipitous inclusion or exclusion" as one factor that contributes to his claim that most published research findings are false.

Example 4   Comparing Data Sets with Box-and-Whisker Plots

Identify the outlier in the following heights. Find the population mean, median, and interquartile range, and then draw box plots when the outlier is included and when it is excluded. Then compare the resulting means, medians, and interquartile ranges.

$H = \{64, 58, 61, 68, 74, 25, 56, 62, 70, 64, 61, 59\}$

Answer

The value of 25 appears to be an outlier.	
With	Without
$\{25, 56, 58, 59, 61, 61,$ $62, 64, 64, 68, 70, 74\}$	$\{56, 58, 59, 61, 61, 62,$ $64, 64, 68, 70, 74\}$
$\mu = \dfrac{\sum x_i}{N} = \dfrac{722}{12} \approx 60.2$	$\mu = \dfrac{\sum x_i}{N} = \dfrac{697}{11} \approx 63.4$
median: $\dfrac{61 + 62}{2} = 61.5$	median: 62
$Q_1: \dfrac{58 + 59}{2} = 58.5$	Q_1: 59; Q_3: 68
$Q_3: \dfrac{64 + 68}{2} = 66$	
$IQR = 66 - 58.5 = 7.5$	$IQR = 68 - 59 = 9$

$Q_1 - 1.5(IQR) = 58.5 - 1.5(7.5) = 47.25$
$Q_3 + 1.5(IQR) = 66 + 1.5(7.5) = 77.25$
25 is an outlier.

1. Arranging the data in ascending order helps to identify potential outliers.

2. Find the mean of each data set.

3. Find the median of each data set.

4. Find Q_1 and Q_3 for each data set.

5. Use $IQR = Q_3 - Q_1$ to find each interquartile range.

6. Since 25 is the only value outside the interval [47.25, 77.25], it is the only outlier.

7. Enter the first data set as L1 and the second as L2. Then use [STAT PLOT] to graph box plots ([STAT]) of L1 with Plot1 and L2 with Plot2.

Including the outlier lowers the mean by ≈ 3.2 but lowers the median by just 0.5. While the *IQR*s with and without the outlier were about the same, the *IQR* actually decreases by 1.5 when the outlier is included.

8. Compare the means, medians, and interquartile ranges.

Your calculator can also be used to find statistics related to a univariate (one-variable) set of data. Enter the data in L1. Then select [STAT], CALC, 1:1-Var Stats, [2nd], L1, [ENTER].

```
1-Var Stats
x̄=60.16666667
Σx=722
Σx²=45084
Sx=12.22392091
σx=11.70351324
n=12
minX=25
Q₁=58.5
Med=61.5
Q₃=66
maxX=74
```

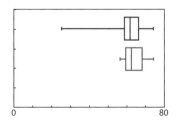

SKILL ✓ **EXERCISES 17, 27, 31**

The results of standardized tests are frequently reported in terms of *percentiles*. It is important to understand that getting a score in the 70th percentile is not the same as getting 70% of the possible points on the test. Scoring in the 70th percentile means that your score was higher than 70% of all the scores. In general $P\%$ of the data is less than the number at the Pth percentile. The first quartile Q_1 is the 25th percentile, the median is the 50th percentile, and the third quartile Q_3 is the 75th percentile.

Finding Percentiles from an Ordered List of Data

1. Find the rank, R, of the Pth percentile using $R = \dfrac{P}{100}(n+1)$ and identify the rank's integer part (IR) and its fractional part (FR). (For example, if $R = 3.25$, then $IR = 3$ and $FR = 0.25$.)

2. Let A equal the data value at the IR position and B equal the next value in the ordered list.

3. Apply the formula: Pth percentile $= A + FR(B - A)$.

Example 5 Finding the Data Value for a Given Percentile

Find the data value at the 87th percentile.
$W = \{41, 42, 46, 47, 47, 48, 48, 50, 51, 52, 53, 56, 61\}$

Answer

$R = \dfrac{87}{100}(13 + 1) = 12.18$ 1. Use $n = 13$ and $R = \dfrac{P}{100}(n+1)$ to find R;
$IR = 12$; $FR = 0.18$ then identify IR and FR.

Let $A = 56$ and $B = 61$.   2. Let $A = x_{12}$ and $B = x_{13}$ in the ordered data.

87th percentile $= 56 + 0.18(61 - 56) = 56.9$ 3. Use Pth percentile $= A + FR(B - A)$ to find the value at the 87th percentile.

SKILL ✓ **EXERCISE 19**

The shape of a distribution can often be classified as negatively skewed, normal, or positively skewed by examining the overall shape of the histogram or box plot and the relationship between the mean and median.

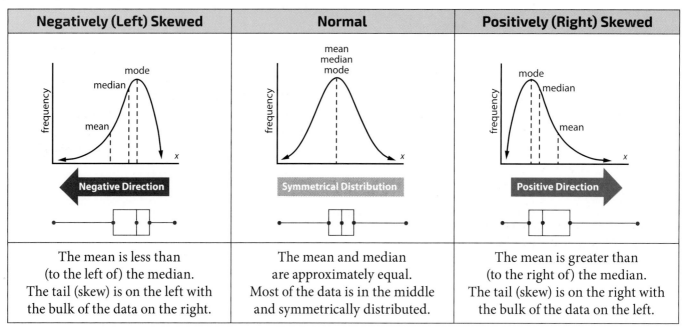

Negatively (Left) Skewed	Normal	Positively (Right) Skewed
The mean is less than (to the left of) the median. The tail (skew) is on the left with the bulk of the data on the right.	The mean and median are approximately equal. Most of the data is in the middle and symmetrically distributed.	The mean is greater than (to the right of) the median. The tail (skew) is on the right with the bulk of the data on the left.

Example 6 Analyzing a Distribution

Classify the shape of the illustrated distribution and predict the relationship between the data's mean and median.

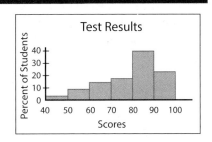

Answer

The distribution of scores is negatively (left) skewed, so the mean is less than the median.

_____ SKILL ✓ **EXERCISE 13**

Which measures of central tendency and variation should be used to describe a distribution of data? The median, interquartile range, and five-number summary are frequently used to describe skewed distributions and those with significant outliers. The median and interquartile range are said to be *resistant* since they are not as easily affected by the presence of extreme values. Note in Example 4 how the outlier had a greater effect on the mean than on the median and caused the distribution to be negatively skewed. The outlier also had a much greater effect on the sample standard deviation ($s \approx 12.2$ with the outlier and $s \approx 5.4$ without) than on the interquartile range.

The mean and standard deviation are used to describe normally distributed data. Many naturally occurring phenomena produce normal distributions, so these measures are the most commonly used statistics. They will be explored further in Sections 10.5 and 10.6.

❯ A. Exercises

1. Match each definition to the correct term.

   a. the middle value in a sorted list of data

   b. the quotient of the sum of the data values and the number of values

   c. the most frequently occurring data value

   d. the difference between a data value and the mean

   I. deviation
   II. mean
   III. median
   IV. mode
   V. standard deviation
   VI. variance

2. Match each definition to the correct term.

   a. the average of the squared deviations

   b. the square root of the variance

   c. one of the values that separate an ordered data set into four equal sets

   d. a value that is significantly higher or lower than the rest of the data

   I. deviation
   II. outlier
   III. quartile
   IV. standard deviation
   V. variance

Find the mean, median, and mode for each set of data.

3. 96, 87, 91, 90, 88, 83

4. 28, 28, 31, 35, 35, 36, 39, 40, 43, 43, 43, 43, 47

5. heights of 24 choir members

```
  .   .     .    . .
. . . . . . . . . . . . . .
58 60 62 64 66 68 70 72 74
```

6. ages of US presidents when they took office in the 1900s

Stem	Leaves
4	2 3 6
5	1 1 1 2 4 5 5 6 6
6	0 1 2 4 9

Use a table to find the mean, variance, and standard deviation (to the nearest tenth).

7. sample:
   96, 87, 91, 90, 88, 83

8. population:
   28, 31, 35, 35, 36, 39, 40, 43, 43, 47

Complete the frequency distribution table for the sample data to find the mean and the standard deviation.

9. population data

x_i	f_i	x_if_i	$f_i(x_i - \mu)^2$
55	2		
63	2		
67	2		
69	5		
70	3		
72	3		
73	2		
75	1		
Total			

10. sample data

x_i	f_i	x_if_i	$f_i(x_i - \bar{x})^2$
33	3		
35	1		
38	2		
39	2		
42	2		
46	3		
48	2		
50	1		
Total			

Determine whether each minimum or maximum value is an outlier.

11. min: 1, Q_1: 5, Q_2: 6.5, Q_3: 8, max: 14

12. 2, 4, 5, 5, 6, 6, 7, 9, 9

13. Classify the shape of the illustrated distribution as negatively skewed, normal, or positively skewed.

a.
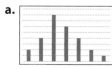

b.
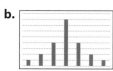

c.
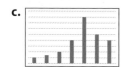

14. Classify the data represented by each box plot as left skewed, normal, or right skewed.

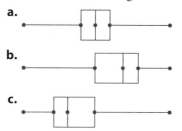

a.

b.

c.

15. Classify each described data distribution.
   a. approximately equal mean and median
   b. mean significantly to the right of the median
   c. tail of data to the left
   d. symmetric distribution

   I. negatively skewed
   II. normal
   III. positively skewed

16. Which set of statistics should be used to describe each type of data distribution?
   a. negatively skewed
   b. normally distributed
   c. data set with outliers

   I. mean and standard deviation
   II. five-number summary

> **B. Exercises**

State the five-number summary for each data set. Then sketch a box plot illustrating the data.

17. quiz scores: 10, 7, 8, 7, 9, 9, 6, 8, 9

18. sizes of women's shoes sold on Friday:
5, 6, 6, 6.5, 7, 7, 7, 7.5, 7.5, 7.5,
7.5, 8, 8, 8, 8.5, 8.5, 9, 9, 10, 11

Determine the data value at each percentile.

19. 50th and 20th percentiles for these cockatiel weights:
82, 83, 84, 85, 86, 86, 86, 86, 86, 86,
87, 87, 87, 87, 88, 88, 89, 90, 92, 94

20. 75th and the 90th percentiles for these test scores:
62, 65, 72, 75, 79, 80, 82, 85, 88,
88, 89, 90, 90, 92, 95, 95, 96, 97

21. 30th and 75th percentiles for these heights:
58, 59, 60, 60, 61, 62, 62, 64,
64, 65, 66, 66, 66, 66, 68, 70,
70, 70, 71, 71, 71, 72, 73, 73

22. 10th and 80th percentiles for these SAT scores:
312, 382, 402, 417, 418, 424,
428, 439, 463, 465, 487, 491,
492, 501, 507, 510, 510, 511,
515, 518, 538, 557, 567, 582,
607, 612, 615, 641, 665, 682

Use the sample AP History test scores to complete exercises 23–25.

$T = \{73, 42, 67, 78, 99, 84, 91, 82, 86, 94\}$

23. Use technology to find the mean and sample standard deviation.

24. Use technology to create a box plot. Then identify any outliers.

25. Use technology to find the mean and sample standard deviation without the outlier(s). Compare these statistics to those found in exercise 24.

Use the ages of presidents when they took office during the 1800s to complete exercises 26–28.

$A = \{47, 61, 46, 64, 48, 49, 51,$
$\quad 55, 57, 58, 56, 57, 54, 54,$
$\quad 50, 49, 57, 54, 51, 52, 55\}$

26. Use technology to find the mean and the population standard deviation.

27. Use technology to create a box plot. Then identify any outliers.

28. Analyze the distribution of the data.

   a. Classify the distribution as negatively skewed, normal, or postively skewed. Explain your reasoning.

   b. Which set of statistics better describes the data set—the mean and standard deviation or a five-number summary? Explain your reasoning.

29. The number of games won by each NFL team during the 2016–17 season is summarized in the frequency distribution table.

Wins	0	3	4	5	6	7	8	9
Teams	1	1	2	4	3	3	1	6
Wins	10	11	12	13	14	15	16	
Teams	2	3	2	1	1	1	1	

   a. Does the data represent a population or a sample?

   b. Find the data's mean and standard deviation.

   c. Draw a box plot illustrating the five-number summary.

   d. Draw a histogram and classify the shape of the distribution. Explain your reasoning.

30. An average of 1224 tornadoes occurred annually in the United States from 1991 to 2015. The list displays how 12 different states contributed to that number.
146.7, 49.5, 54.6, 92.4, 65.4, 54.6,
46.7, 54.0, 49.2, 41.9, 45.1, 47.1

   a. Find the data's mean and sample standard deviation.

   b. Draw a box plot illustrating the five-number summary and identify any outliers.

   c. Classify the shape of the distribution and explain your reasoning.

   d. Which set of statistics better summarizes the data?

Create box plots and write a brief statement comparing the two distributions.

31. **Super Bowl Total Points**

1–20		33–52
9 7 3 2 1	2	
8 7 7 1 0	3	1 1 4 7 8 9
7 7 7 6 5 4	4	1 5 6 8
6 4 0	5	0 1 2 3 6
6	6	1 2 5 9
	7	4

32.

2003–17 Hurricane Occurrences	
Eastern Pacific	7, 6, 7, 10, 4, 7, 7, 3, 10, 10, 9, 15, 13, 13, 9
Atlantic	7, 9, 15, 5, 6, 8, 3, 12, 7, 10, 2, 6, 4, 7, 10

33. The midrange of a data set, the average of the minimum and maximum values, is another measure of central tendency. Find the midrange for each set of data in exercise 32. Which measure is most resistant to the presence of outliers—the midrange, mean, median, or mode?

C. Exercises

34. Generalize: The ordered data set $x_1, x_2, x_3, \ldots, x_{10}$ has the five-number summary: $x_1, x_3, \dfrac{x_5 + x_6}{2}, x_8, x_{10}$. Write a generalized five-number summary for each data set with n values.

a. $n = 11$ **b.** $n = 12$ **c.** $n = 13$

35. Prove: Show that the sum of the deviations from the mean is 0: $\displaystyle\sum_{i=1}^{n}(x_i - \bar{x}) = 0$.

36. Find the indicated statistics for each player from the information provided.

	Alex Rodriguez	Hank Aaron
seasons played	22	23
total home runs	696	755
sum of the squared deviations, SS	5769.09	2751.30

a. Find the average number of home runs per season and the population standard deviation for each player.

b. Use the results of part *a* to compare the players' home run hitting careers.

37. Use a spreadsheet to create a frequency distribution and calculate the mean and the population standard deviation.

Ages of Presidents Who Took Office in the 1900s

Stem	Leaves
4	2 3 6
5	1 1 1 2 4 5 5 6 6
6	0 1 2 4 9

38. Given the ages from a random sample of employees, use Sturges's formula and a spreadsheet to create a grouped frequency distribution for the data. Using each class's median age as its value, calculate the data's mean and standard deviation.

37, 32, 49, 62, 57, 46, 31, 48, 51, 55, 52, 34, 61, 58, 38

A *weighted mean* is often used to ensure that various types of assessments within a class contribute the desired percentage (or weight) toward the final grade. After the mean is calculated for each category, the percentage is multiplied by each mean, and the final grade is the sum of those products.

39. Find the weighted average for each student.

	Exam	Tests	Projects	Quizzes	Home-work
weight	15%	50%	10%	15%	10%
student A	98	95	97	92	91
student B	78	80	90	83	85

40. The semester grade for Ralph's Precalculus class is determined by six chapter tests and one final exam, which is weighted as 20% of the final grade. His six chapter test scores were 85, 89, 90, 86, 92, and 89. Assuming that an 89.5 rounds up to an A-, what minimum grade would he need on his final exam to receive an A- for the semester?

41. Use the percentile graph to estimate each value.

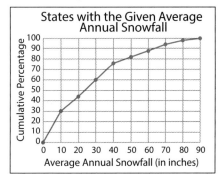

a. What is the percentile rank of a state with an annual snowfall of 10 in.?

b. What is the percentile rank of a state with an annual snowfall of 35 in.?

c. What annual snowfall is at the 80th percentile?

d. Use the Internet to find your state's average annual snowfall and then determine your state's approximate percentile rank.

Solve each system of equations using Cramer's rule. [7.4]

42. $x + y = 1$
$3x + 2y = -2$

43. $4x - 5y = 8$
$3x + 2y = 4$

44. Write a simplified explicit formula for the arithmetic sequence with $b_6 = 21$ and $b_{10} = 37$. Then use the formula to find b_{20}. [9.2]

45. Find n in the geometric sequence if $a_3 = 112$, $r = 4$, and $a_n = 7168$. [9.3]

Use the table to complete exercises 46–47. [10.3]

Goals Scored	Number of Players
0	2
1	5
2	8
3	10
4	6
5	4
6	1

46. Construct a histogram representing the data.

47. Construct a pie chart representing the data.

48. Solve $x^3 > x$. [2.7]

A. $x \in (-\infty, -1)$ **D.** $x \in (1, \infty)$

B. $x \in (-\infty, 1)$ **E.** none of these

C. $x \in (-1, \infty)$

49. Which equation represents an asymptote of $f(x) = \dfrac{8x - 5}{9x + 10}$? [2.5]

A. $y = 0$ **C.** $y = \dfrac{8}{9}$ **E.** $y = -\dfrac{10}{9}$

B. $x = -\dfrac{1}{2}$ **D.** $x = \dfrac{5}{8}$

50. Find the standard form of a parabola with a focus $F(-2, 3)$ and a directrix $x = 2$. [8.1]

A. $x = -\dfrac{1}{8}(y + 3)^2$ **D.** $y = -\dfrac{1}{8}(x - 3)^2$

B. $x = -\dfrac{1}{8}(y - 3)^2$ **E.** none of these

C. $y = \dfrac{1}{8}(x + 3)^2$

51. The administration can nominate up to 3 of the school's 6 eligible seniors for a local award. How many different sets of nominations can the school submit if at least 1 senior is nominated? [10.2]

A. 20   **C.** 120   **E.** none of these

B. 41   **D.** 156

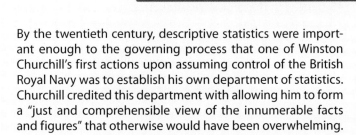

POLITICAL ARITHMETIC AND PROBABILITY

Half a league, half a league,
Half a league onward,
All in the valley of Death
Rode the six hundred.

These lines open Alfred Tennyson's "The Charge of the Light Brigade," a poem memorializing a doomed British cavalry charge during the Crimean War. The descriptive statistics recorded by Florence Nightingale reveal that the army's casualties due to preventable diseases were nearly four times greater than those due to battle in the same month of October 1854. Her polar area graphs present the data in a clear and compelling visual format. Statistics summarize data in a form that aids understanding. The derivation of the word *statistics* from the Latin word for a nation-state indicates the origin of statistics as a mathematical aid to governments in carrying out their responsibilities. In fact, the term *political arithmetic* was frequently used before the term *statistics* was adopted. Governments have kept various records from antiquity, but John Graunt, a seventeenth-century British merchant, is generally credited as the first to systematically study and interpret collected data. His 1662 publication *Natural and Political Observations . . . Made Upon the Bills of Mortality* analyzed the reported deaths published weekly by local parishes. "Men of great experience" estimated London's population to be in the millions, possibly as high as six or seven million. Graunt used the available data to more accurately estimate the population as 384,000.

By the twentieth century, descriptive statistics were important enough to the governing process that one of Winston Churchill's first actions upon assuming control of the British Royal Navy was to establish his own department of statistics. Churchill credited this department with allowing him to form a "just and comprehensible view of the innumerable facts and figures" that otherwise would have been overwhelming.

The first attempt to create a mathematical theory of probability occurred in correspondence between Blaise Pascal and Pierre de Fermat in 1654. Their discussion was prompted by a gambler's question regarding a dice game. They developed a theory of probability for games of chance but did not attempt to apply the theory to other areas or to infer properties of the games based on outcomes. Dutch mathematician Christiaan Huygens published the first book on probability in 1657. In the early 1800s Pierre-Simon de Laplace published the comprehensive treatise *The Analytical Theory of Probabilities* and a simplified version called *A Philosophical Essay on Probabilities*. The historian Carl Boyer claims that probability theory "owes more to Laplace than to any other mathematician."

Understanding probability is important since we see both regularity and chance events in our world. Physical determinism says that nothing occurs by chance; if we could at one instant know the state of every particle, then we would know both the future and the past. Others claim that chance events are beyond even the control of God. A biblical worldview recognizes the sovereignty of God as well as the uncertainty that exists from a human perspective. As American theologian Vern Poythress states, "God controls small, unpredictable events as well as big patterns and regularities in history. . . . God in his wisdom has given us the whole tapestry of regularities and unpredictabilities and their connections with one another. This tapestry . . . reflects his wisdom and his character, as Romans 1:19–20 indicates."

COMPREHENSION CHECK

1. Describe Florence Nightingale's use of descriptive statistics.

2. What is the origin of the word *statistics*?

3. Which two Frenchmen first developed a theory of probability, and what initiated their efforts?

4. According to historian Carl Boyer, which mathematician made the greatest contribution to probability theory?

5. Describe a biblical worldview of probability.

Technology such as a graphing calculator or a spread-sheet enables us to quickly explore how transformations of a data set affect its mean and standard deviation. Enter $L_1 = \{4, 6, 7, 9, 9, 10\}$ in your calculator and use the 1-Var Stats function from the $\boxed{\text{STAT}}$, CALC submenu to determine the mean $\bar{x} = 7.5$ and the sample standard deviation $s \approx 2.26$. Then enter four transformations of the data set: $L_2 = L_1 + 5$, $L_3 = L_1 - 4$, $L_4 = L_1 \times 3$, and $L_5 = L_1 \div 2$ and find the mean and sample deviation of each transformed data set.

L1	L2	L3	L4	L5
4	9	0	12	2
6	11	2	18	3
7	12	3	21	3.5
9	14	5	27	4.5
9	14	5	27	4.5
10	15	6	30	5

After completing this section, you will be able to

- describe how the mean and variance are affected when data is translated or scaled.
- calculate z-scores and other transformed scores for data.
- apply Chebyshev's Theorem and the Empirical Rule to describe variability.

L_1	$L_2 = L_1 + 5$	$L_3 = L_1 - 4$	$L_4 = L_1 \times 3$	$L_5 = L_1 \div 2$
$\bar{x} = 7.5$	$\bar{x} = 12.5$	$\bar{x} = 3.5$	$\bar{x} = 22.5$	$\bar{x} = 3.75$
$s \approx 2.26$	$s \approx 2.26$	$s \approx 2.26$	$s \approx 6.77$	$s \approx 1.13$

Can you describe how the mean and standard deviation are affected when the same number is added to (or subtracted from) each value? What if each data value is multiplied (or divided) by the same number? The following theorems summarize these results.

TRANSLATED DATA THEOREM

If $A = \{x_1, x_2, \ldots, x_n\}$ and $B = \{y_1, y_2, \ldots, y_n\}$ where $y_i = x_i + k$, then $\bar{y} = \bar{x} + k$ and $s_y = s_x$.

Apply the properties of summations to prove this theorem.

$$\bar{y} = \frac{\sum_{i=1}^{n} y_i}{n} = \frac{\sum_{i=1}^{n} (x_i + k)}{n} = \frac{\sum_{i=1}^{n} x_i + \sum_{i=1}^{n} k}{n} = \frac{\sum_{i=1}^{n} x_i + nk}{n} = \frac{\sum_{i=1}^{n} x_i}{n} + k = \bar{x} + k$$

$$\therefore \bar{y} = \bar{x} + k$$

$$s_y^2 = \frac{\sum_{i=1}^{n} (y_i - \bar{y})^2}{n-1} = \frac{\sum_{i=1}^{n} [(x_i + k) - (\bar{x} + k)]^2}{n-1} = \frac{\sum_{i=1}^{n} (x_i - \bar{x})^2}{n-1} = s_x^2$$

$$\therefore s_y = s_x$$

SCALED DATA THEOREM

If $A = \{x_1, x_2, \ldots, x_n\}$ and $B = \{y_1, y_2, \ldots, y_n\}$ where $y_i = kx_i$, then $\bar{y} = k\bar{x}$ and $s_y = ks_x$.

The proof of this theorem is left as an exercise.

Raw data values are frequently transformed into z-scores. The z-scores measure the deviation of each individual score from the mean in units of standard deviation.

DEFINITION

Given $A = \{x_1, x_2, \ldots, x_n\}$ with a mean of $\bar{x}$ and standard deviation of s, the **z-score** for each data value is $z = \frac{x - \bar{x}}{s}$.

Both theorems on page 527 are used in the definition of a z-score. It is first translated by the subtraction of x and then scaled through the division by s.

Example 1 Exploring z-scores

Find the z-score for each value in $L_1 = \{4, 6, 7, 9, 9, 10\}$ and for each transformed value in $L_4 = \{12, 18, 21, 27, 27, 30\}$. Then compare the z-scores, the mean $\bar{z}$, and the sample standard deviation s for each standardized set of data.

Answer

$L_2 = (L_1 - 7.5)/2.26$	$L_5 = (L_4 - 22.5)/6.77$
$z_1 \approx \frac{4 - 7.5}{2.26} \approx -1.55$	$z_1 \approx \frac{12 - 22.5}{6.77} \approx -1.55$
$z_2 \approx \frac{6 - 7.5}{2.26} \approx -0.66$	$z_2 \approx \frac{18 - 22.5}{6.77} \approx -0.66$
$z_3 \approx \frac{7 - 7.5}{2.26} \approx -0.22$	$z_3 \approx \frac{21 - 22.5}{6.77} \approx -0.22$
$z_4 \approx \frac{9 - 7.5}{2.26} \approx 0.66$	$z_4 \approx \frac{27 - 22.5}{6.77} \approx 0.66$
$z_5 \approx \frac{9 - 7.5}{2.26} \approx 0.66$	$z_5 \approx \frac{27 - 22.5}{6.77} \approx 0.66$
$z_6 \approx \frac{10 - 7.5}{2.26} \approx 1.11$	$z_6 \approx \frac{30 - 22.5}{6.77} \approx 1.11$

In each set of z-scores, $\bar{z} = 0$ and $s \approx 1.00$.

1. Use $z = \frac{x - \bar{x}}{s}$ and the mean and standard deviation from each set.

   This can be done quickly by redefining L_2 and L_5.

   The z-scores are the same for both sets.

2. Use 1-Var Stats on L_2 and L_5 to determine $\bar{z}$ and s.

SKILL ✔ **EXERCISE 7**

The mean of the z-score distribution is always 0 and its standard deviation is always 1. The distribution of the z-scores reflects the distribution of the raw scores.

Example 2 Finding and Interpreting a z-score

Find the z-score for a student who scored a 79 on a test having a mean of 84 and a standard deviation of 4. Then interpret the meaning of the z-score.

Answer

$$z = \frac{x - \bar{x}}{s} = \frac{79 - 84}{4} = -1.25$$

The student's score is 1.25 standard deviations below the mean.

SKILL ✔ **EXERCISE 9**

Using z-scores is the best way to compare individual scores from different normal distributions.

Example 3 Comparing z-scores

Mary earned 9 points on a quiz for which the class average was 7 and the standard deviation was 1.5. She then earned 15 points on a second quiz for which the class average was 13 and the standard deviation was 2.1. Find the *z*-score for each quiz grade and use them to decide which quiz Mary did better on compared to her classmates.

Answer

$z_1 = \frac{9 - 7}{1.5} \approx 1.3$; $z_2 = \frac{15 - 13}{2.1} \approx 0.95$

Mary's score on the first quiz is more standard deviations above the mean than her score on the second quiz.

1. Use $z = \frac{x - \bar{x}}{s}$ to find the number of standard deviations from the mean for each score.

2. Compare the *z*-scores.

SKILL ✓ **EXERCISE 19**

A known *z*-score can be transformed to a distribution with any desired mean and standard deviation while maintaining the distribution's shape and the score's relative position.

Example 4 Transforming a z-score

The 2010 ACT® English test had a mean of 20.5 and a standard deviation of 6.4. Find Brenton's ACT English score if his *z*-score was 0.43.

Answer

$sz = x - \bar{x}$
$x = sz + \bar{x}$

$x = 6.4(0.43) + 20.5 = 23.252$
His ACT English score was 23.

1. Solve $z = \frac{x - \bar{x}}{s}$ for *x*.

2. Substitute and simplify.

3. Round to find the integral raw score.

SKILL ✓ **EXERCISE 23**

Distributions of data can have many different shapes. The shape of the distribution is generally determined by looking at the data's histogram. Section 10.4 examined unimodal distributions that were skewed and normally distributed. In other cases, the distribution may be *bimodal*, having two clusters of data as illustrated below. Bimodal distributions can represent polarized opinions or sample data from overlapping distributions.

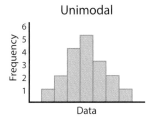

Unimodal

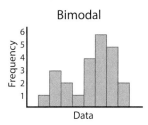

Bimodal

The Russian mathematician Pafnuty Chebyshev (1821–94) proved the following theorem describing the fraction of data values that falls within a given interval, regardless of the shape of the data distribution.

▎CHEBYSHEV'S THEOREM

When $k > 1$, at least $1 - \frac{1}{k^2}$ of the data values are within *k* standard deviations of the mean.

In 1995 the SAT recentered scaled scores for the verbal (reading and writing) and math tests so that average scores would be closer to the midpoint of the scale at 500. Average math scores had fallen to 475 and verbal scores to 425.

This implies that less than $\frac{1}{k^2}$ of the data is outside the interval $[\bar{x} - ks, \bar{x} + ks]$.

Example 5 Applying Chebyshev's Theorem

Use Chebyshev's Theorem to find the smallest percentage of data that must always lie within 2 standard deviations of the mean. Confirm the theorem using the following sample of 18 quiz scores.

$Q = \{5, 6, 7, 8, 8, 8, 9, 9, 9, 10, 10, 10, 10, 10, 10, 11, 11, 11\}$

Answer

$1 - \frac{1}{2^2} = \frac{3}{4} = 0.75$

At least 75% of the data lies within 2 standard deviations of the mean.

1. Evaluate $1 - \frac{1}{k^2}$ with $k = 2$ and interpret the results.

$\bar{x} = 9$ and $s \approx 1.71$

2. Use technology to find $\bar{x}$ and s.

$[\bar{x} - 2s, \bar{x} + 2s]$
$[9 - 2(1.71), 9 + 2(1.71)] = [5.58, 12.42]$

3. Find the interval of values within 2 standard deviations of the mean.

outside: $\frac{1}{18} \approx 5.6\%$; inside: $\frac{17}{18} \approx 94.4\%$

4. Determine the percentages of values within and outside the interval.

At least 75% of the data falls within 2 standard deviations of the mean.
(Less than 25% of the data is more than 2 standard deviations from the mean.)

5. Chebyshev's Theorem accurately describes the data.

SKILL ✓ EXERCISE 15

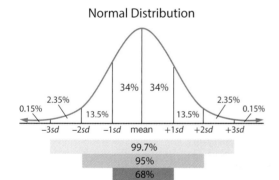

Normal Distribution

approximate percentages
of data under the curve

Since Chebyshev's Theorem applies to every set of data, it makes a very broad statement. More specific statements can be made for normally distributed data where the shape is described by the function

$$y = \frac{1}{\sqrt{2\pi}} e^{-\frac{1}{2}x^2}.$$

Recall that the mean, median, and mode are all located at the center of a normal distribution. The x-axis is the asymptote of the symmetric bell-shaped curve, and the area under the curve represents 100% of the data.

THE EMPIRICAL RULE (OR THE 68-95-99.7 RULE)

In a normal distribution, practically all the data is within four standard deviations of the mean:
(1) about 68% of the data lies within one standard deviation of the mean, $\bar{x} \pm 1s$,
(2) about 95% of the data lies within two standard deviations of the mean, $\bar{x} \pm 2s$, and
(3) about 99.7% of the data lies within three standard deviations of the mean, $\bar{x} \pm 3s$.

When data is distributed normally, the Empirical Rule can be used to estimate the amount of data within certain intervals. Remember that the z-score represents the number of standard deviations that the individual data value is above or below the mean.

Example 6 Applying the Empirical Rule

A normally distributed set of test scores has a mean of 86 and a standard deviation of 4. What percentage of the data is within each interval?

a. from 82 to 90   **b.** 94 or less   **c.** from 78 to 90

Answer

a.

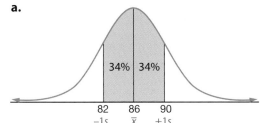

1. Sketch a normal curve centered at $\bar{x} = 86$ with the interval [82, 90]. Then shade the area under the curve within the interval.

$$z_{82} = \frac{82 - 86}{4} = -1; \; z_{90} = \frac{90 - 86}{4} = 1$$

2. Find the z-score for the lower and upper limits.

68% of the data is within [82, 90].

3. Apply the Empirical Rule.

b.

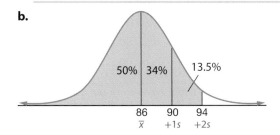

1. Sketch the normal curve with the interval $(-\infty, 94]$. Then shade the area under the curve within the interval.

$$z_{94} = \frac{94 - 86}{4} = 2$$

2. Find the z-score for the upper limit.

$50\% + 34\% + 13.5\% = 97.5\%$

3. Apply the Empirical Rule.

97.5% of the scores are 94 or less.

c.

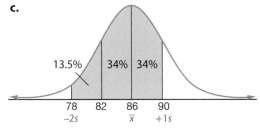

1. Sketch the normal curve with the interval [78, 90]. Then shade the area between the curve and the interval.

$$z_{78} = \frac{78 - 86}{4} = -2; \; z_{90} = \frac{90 - 86}{4} = 1$$

2. Find the z-scores for the lower and upper limits.

$13.5\% + 68\% = 81.5\%$
81.5% of the data is within [78, 90].

3. Apply the Empirical Rule.

SKILL ✔ **EXERCISE 35**

Even more specific statements regarding normal distributions will be investigated in the next section.

A. Exercises

1. The z-scores measure the _____ of each individual score from the mean in units of _____.

2. In the distribution of z-scores, the mean is _____ and the standard deviation is _____.

3. The _____, _____, and _____ are all located at the center of a normal distribution.

4. When data is distributed normally, the _____ can be used to estimate the amount of data within certain intervals.

5. What percentage of data is represented under the normal curve?

6. Explain when Chebyshev's Theorem and the Empirical Rule apply.

7. Describe the effect on each value if 5 points are added to each student's test score.
   a. mean
   b. standard deviation
   c. z-scores

8. Describe the effect on each value if each test score is doubled.
   a. mean
   b. standard deviation
   c. z-scores

If a set of test scores has a mean of 83 and standard deviation of 7, find the z-score for each test score and interpret its meaning.

9. 88   10. 96   11. 79   12. 83

13. Find the missing z-score from a set of six sample data values.
$z_1 = 0.27$, $z_2 = -0.16$, $z_3 = 0.75$, $z_4 = 1.33$, $z_5 = -1.39$, $z_6 = ?$

State the percentage of data that must lie within each stated interval.
a. when using Chebyshev's Theorem
b. when using the Empirical Rule

14. within 2 standard deviations of the mean

15. within 3 standard deviations of the mean

16. within 4 standard deviations of the mean

17. within 1 standard deviation of the mean

B. Exercises

Use z-scores to compare the students' relative performances on two different assessments.

18. Sarah's grade of 15 on Quiz 1 with a class average of 12 and standard deviation of 2.2 versus her grade of 12 on Quiz 2 with a class average of 10 and standard deviation of 1.5

19. Adam's grade of 82 on a test with a class average of 74 and standard deviation of 10 versus his grade of 162 on a project with a class average of 150 and standard deviation of 15

20. Jessi's grade of 79 on a test with a class average of 83 and standard deviation of 5 versus her grade of 120 on an essay with a class average of 127 and standard deviation of 9

21. Grace's grade of 25 on Quiz A with a class average of 22 and standard deviation of 1.8 versus her grade of 26 on Quiz B with a class average of 22 and standard deviation of 2.5

Use the data to find the integral raw score.

22. $z \approx 1.47$; $\sigma = 3.2$; $\mu = 41.3$

23. $z \approx -1.1$; $s = 2.7$; $\bar{x} = 20$

24. sample scores: 3, 4, 4, 5, 5, 6, 7, 7, 8, 9
    a. $z \approx 0.62$ b. $z \approx 1.14$ c. $z \approx -0.41$

25. sample scores: 62, 67, 68, 72, 75, 80, 86, 88, 90, 95
    a. $z \approx -1.01$ b. $z \approx 0.15$ c. $z \approx 1.50$

A fisherman recorded the following lengths (in inches) of the fish caught during his trip.
$L = \{10, 11, 11, 11, 11, 12, 15, 15, 15, 15, 15, 16, 16, 17, 20\}$

26. Find the interval $\bar{x} \pm 2s$.

27. Find the interval $\bar{x} \pm 3s$.

28. What percentage of the data actually lies within 2 standard deviations of the mean? Is this consistent with Chebyshev's Theorem?

29. What percentage of the data actually lies within 3 standard deviations of the mean? Is this consistent with Chebyshev's Theorem?

SAT scores are calculated from z-scores using the transformation SAT $= 100z + 500$.

30. State the mean score on the SAT.

31. State the standard deviation of the SAT.

32. State the SAT score that is 2.5 standard deviations above the mean.

33. Determine the number of standard deviations each score is above or below the mean.
    a. 563   b. 381

34. Use the Empirical Rule to find the percentage of data within each described interval.
   a. $\mu \pm 3\sigma$
   b. $[\mu - 2\sigma, \mu + \sigma]$
   c. $[\mu, \mu + 2\sigma]$
   d. $x_i \geq \mu + 2\sigma$

35. A set of normally distributed test scores has $\mu = 100$ and $\sigma = 15$. Find the percentage of scores within each interval.
   a. $[70, 100]$
   b. $[85, 130]$
   c. $[0, 115]$
   d. $x_i \geq 115$

A normally distributed set of test scores has a mean of 88 and a standard deviation of 3.

36. What percentage of the data is in each interval?
   a. $[88, 94]$ **b.** $[85, 94]$ **c.** $x_i \leq 85$

37. Which interval contains each described percentage of scores?
   a. the middle 68%
   b. the top 2.5%
   c. scores below the 84th percentile

C. Exercises

Prove the following relations for sets of transformed data $y_i = kx_i$.

38. $\bar{y} = k\bar{x}$

39. $s_y = ks_x$

40. The normally distributed 2016 ACT scores have a mean of 20.8 and a standard deviation of 4.7.
   a. What percentage of scores were from 16.1 to 25.5?
   b. What score represents the 84th percentile?
   c. If students whose scores are in the top 2.5% are eligible for a scholarship, what is the minimum score needed to earn the scholarship?

41. The normally distributed 2017 SAT scores have a mean of 1060 and a standard deviation of 195.
   a. What scores make up the middle 95% of the data?
   b. What is the percentile rank for a score of 865?
   c. If 1.7 million students took the test, estimate how many students scored above 1450.

42. Jeff received a 28 on the 2016 ACT and a 1355 on the 2017 SAT. Based on the means and standard deviations given in exercises 40–41, which score was better? Explain your reasoning.

CUMULATIVE REVIEW

Use technology to create a scatterplot of each set of data and determine the linear or quadratic function that best models the data. Round coefficients to the nearest thousandth. [1.9]

43.

x	−2	−1	0	2	5	6
y	10.8	4.8	1.2	−1.1	12.0	19.2

44.

x	−5	−3	−1	0	2	3	5
y	4.9	4.1	2.7	2.8	1.3	1.2	0.1

Given $A = \begin{bmatrix} 2 & 6 \\ 4 & 1 \end{bmatrix}$ **and** $B = \begin{bmatrix} 3 & -5 \\ -2 & 0 \end{bmatrix}$**, find D and E.** [7.2]

45. $D = -\frac{3}{4}B$

46. $E = A + 3B$

47. Write the standard form equation of a circle centered at $(2, -4)$ and passing through point $(5, 0)$. [8.2]

48. Classify the conic $4x^2 + 9y^2 - 16x + 54y + 61 = 0$ and then write the equation in standard form. [8.2]

49. Which strategies can be used to verify trigonometric identities? List all correct answers. [5.2]
   A. factoring
   B. combining fractions
   C. simplifying each side separately
   D. applying fundamental identities
   E. squaring both sides

50. Find the sixth term of $(2a - b)^{10}$. [9.4]
   A. $-13,440a^4b^6$
   B. $-64a^5b^5$
   C. $-8064a^5b^5$
   D. $-128a^4b^6$
   E. none of these

51. A set of 55 data values ranges from 166 to 533. What class width results from Sturges's formula for the grouped frequency distribution table or histogram representing the data? [10.3]
   A. 6.7
   B. 7
   C. 52.4
   D. 53
   E. none of these

52. Which is the formula for the sample standard deviation? [10.4]
   A. $s = \sqrt{\dfrac{SS}{n-1}}$
   B. $s^2 = \dfrac{SS}{n-1}$
   C. $\sigma = \sqrt{\dfrac{SS}{N}}$
   D. $\sigma^2 = \dfrac{SS}{N}$
   E. none of these

10.6 Normal Distributions

Some Chinook salmon have reached more than 1.5 m in length.

After completing this section, you will be able to

- use *z*-scores to find the percentage of data within a range of normally distributed values.
- find percentiles and percentile ranks for given values in a normal distribution.

z	0.00	0.01
0.0	0.0000	0.0040
0.1	0.0398	0.0438
0.2	0.0793	0.0832
0.3	0.1179	0.1217
0.4	0.1554	0.1591
0.5	0.1915	0.1950
0.6	0.2257	0.2291
0.7	0.2580	0.2611
0.8	0.2881	0.2910
0.9	0.3159	0.3186
1.0	0.3413	0.3438
1.1	0.3643	0.3665
1.2	0.3849	0.3869
1.3	0.4032	0.4049
1.4	0.4192	0.4207
1.5	0.4332	0.4345

KEYWORD SEARCH

interactive normal distribution 🔍

Remember that the area under the normal curve represents 100% of the data values. Since the normal curve is symmetric with respect to the mean, half of the data is represented by positive *z*-scores and the other half is represented by negative *z*-scores. Recall that practically all the area under the curve lies within 4 standard deviations from the mean and that the Empirical (or 68-95-99.7) Rule describes the percentages of data values within 1, 2, and 3 standard deviations from the mean. The probability that a randomly selected value in a normal distribution is within a given interval is found by determining the percentage of the area under the curve for that interval.

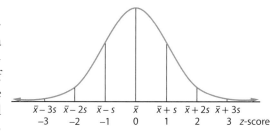

Standard normal distribution tables (available online) often list the portion of the area from the mean to a positive *z*-score. Notice that the table shows that the portion of the area from the mean to a *z*-score of 1.00 is 0.3413 or 34.13%. Other tables may list the portion of the area at or below the listed positive or negative *z*-score. Those tables indicate an area of 0.8413 or 84.13% at or below a *z*-score of 1.

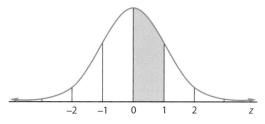

The portion of the area can also be found using your calculator.

Example 1 Finding an Area Under the Normal Curve

Find the portion of the area under the normal curve within the interval $-0.75 \leq z \leq 0$.

Answer

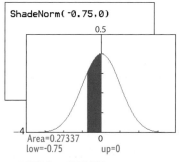

ShadeNorm(-0.75,0)

Area=0.27337
low=-0.75   up=0

≈ 0.2734 or 27.34%

Symmetry implies that ≈ 0.2734 or 27.34% of the area under the curve lies within [–0.75, 0].

Use DRAW ([2nd], [PRGM]), 1:ClrDraw to clear the graphing window. Then enter DISTR ([2nd], [VARS]), select the DRAW submenu, 1:ShadeNorm, and then enter the *lower z-score*, and the *upper z-score*.

Note that the default values of 0 and 1 for the mean and standard deviation could be added to the list of the function's parameters. A [WINDOW] of [−4, 4] × [0, 0.5] is recommended when graphing standard normal distributions.

or

Mean-centered standard normal distribution tables state that ≈ 0.2734 of the area lies between the mean and $z = 0.75$.

SKILL ✔ EXERCISE 3

Example 2   Finding an Area Under the Normal Curve

Find the area under the normal curve lying within 1.5 standard deviations of the mean.

Answer

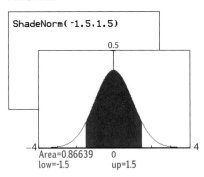

Use 1:ClrDraw from the DRAW menu to clear any previously drawn graphs.

Then select 1:ShadeNorm from the DISTR menu and enter *lower limit, upper limit.*

≈ 0.8664 or 86.64%   or

Symmetry implies that $2(0.4332) = 0.8664$ or $\approx 86.64\%$ of the data lies in the interval $-1.5 \leq z \leq 1.5$.

Mean-centered standard normal distribution tables state that ≈ 0.4332 of the area lies between the mean and $z = 1.5$.

SKILL ✓ **EXERCISE 7**

English statisticians Francis Galton and Karl Pearson made many contributions in the field of descriptive statistics. However, they also used their results to champion eugenics, an attempt to improve the gene pool by sterilizing persons of the lower class and encouraging procreation in the upper class. In 1927 the US Supreme Court ruled that involuntary sterilization of disabled persons did not violate the Constitution. The ruling was overturned in 1942.

Recall that the area under the normal curve represents the percentage of values under the normal curve in a normally distributed set of data. Therefore, the area also represents the probability of a randomly selected outcome falling within a given interval.

Example 3   Using Technology to Find a Probability

Find the probability that a data value has $z \geq 0.98$.

Answer

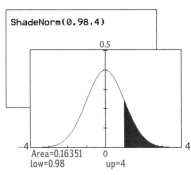

Use 1:ClrDraw to clear any previously drawn graphs.

Then use 1:ShadeNorm with 0.98 as the lower limit and 4 as the upper limit (since almost all the data is within 4 standard deviations of the mean in a standard normal distribution).

The probability that $z \geq 0.98 \approx 16.35\%$.   or

$50\% - 33.65\% = 16.35\%$
16.35% of the data has $z \geq 0.98$.

Mean-centered standard normal distribution tables state that 0.3365 of the area lies between the mean and $z = 0.98$.

SKILL ✓ **EXERCISE 15**

While the following examples are solved using technology, they could also be solved using standard normal distribution tables.

Example 4 Using Technology to Find a Probability

Find the probability that a randomly selected value in a normal distribution with a mean of 43 and standard deviation of 6.25 is within the interval [36, 51].

Answer

$z_L = \dfrac{36 - 43}{6.25} = -1.12; z_U = \dfrac{51 - 43}{6.25} = 1.28$

1. Find the z-scores for the upper and lower bounds of the interval.

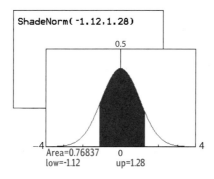

2. Clear any drawings and use 1:ShadeNorm to find the portion of the area under the standard normal distribution curve within [−1.12, 1.28].

```
normalcdf(-1.12,1.28)
              0.7683704396
```

≈ 0.768 or 76.8%

or

Using the normal cumulative density function, 2:normalcdf, from the DISTR menu and entering *lower z-score, upper z-score* returns the portion of the area under the curve within the stated z-scores.

SKILL ✓ **EXERCISE 21**

If the population's mean and standard deviation are known, the individual scores are standardized relative to the entire population by $z = \dfrac{x - \mu}{\sigma}$. The z-score formula, $z = \dfrac{x - \bar{x}}{s}$, standardizes individual scores in relation to the other scores in the sample data.

Example 5 Finding Probabilities

The Chinook salmon is the largest Pacific salmon species. If a study found that the lengths of the Chinook salmon caught were normally distributed with a mean of 78.5 cm and a standard deviation of 8.2 cm, find the probability that a randomly caught Chinook salmon has each of the following lengths.

a. 95 cm or more

b. from 70 cm to 80 cm

Answer

a. $z = \dfrac{95 - 78.5}{8.2} \approx 2.01$

1. Find the z-score for the lower limit, 95.

```
normalcdf(2.01,4)
            0.0221838387
```

$P(l \geq 95) \approx 0.022$ or 2.2%

2. Use 2:normalcdf from the [DISTR] menu to find the portion of the area under the standard normal distribution curve within [2.01, 4].

b. $z_L = \dfrac{70 - 78.5}{8.2} \approx -1.04; z_U = \dfrac{80 - 78.5}{8.2} \approx 0.18$

1. Find the z-scores for the upper and lower bounds of the interval.

```
normalcdf(-1.04,0.18)
            0.4222537389
```

$P(70 < l < 80) \approx 0.42$ or 42%

2. Use 2:normalcdf to find the portion of the area under the standard normal distribution curve within [−1.04, 0.18].

SKILL ✓ **EXERCISE 27**

Attempts to model and understand the natural world play an important role in the creation of statistical methods. British statistician R. A. Fisher developed many statistical techniques in the course of his agricultural research and was skeptical of methods proposed by pure mathematicians with no real-world scientific experience.

The *percentile rank* of a particular data value within a normally distributed set of data can be found by finding its z-score and finding the percent of data in the area to its left.

Example 6   Finding the Percentile Rank of a Data Value

Find the percentile rank of a student whose quiz score was 29 in a class whose scores were approximately normally distributed with a mean of 27 and a standard deviation of 4.

Answer

$z = \frac{x - \bar{x}}{s} = \frac{29 - 27}{4} = 0.5$

```
normalcdf(-4,0.5)
          0.6914307818
```

1. Convert to a z-score.

2. Find the portion of scores below $z = 0.5$ in the standard normal distribution.

The student scored at the 69th percentile.

——————————————————————— SKILL ✓ **EXERCISE 31**

A calculator's invNorm (inverse Normal) function or standard normal deviation tables can be used to find the z-value representing a specific percentile when data is normally distributed.

Example 7   Finding the Data Value for a Percentile Rank

Find the value at the 75th percentile in a normally distributed set of data whose mean is 19.7 and whose standard deviation is 2.8.

Answer

```
invNorm(0.75)
          0.6744897495
```

$\frac{x - 19.7}{2.8} \approx 0.674$

$x \approx 2.8(0.674) + 19.7 \approx 21.6$

∴ 21.6 is at the 75th percentile.

1. Selecting 3:invNorm from the DISTR menu and entering the percentage of data (or area) to the left of the stated percentile produces the related z-score.

2. Find the data value associated with that z-score.

——————————————————————— SKILL ✓ **EXERCISE 17**

TIP 💡

Many of your calculator's distribution functions allow you to enter the mean and standard deviation as parameters and will then return the related data value instead of the z-score.

```
invNorm(.75,19.7,2.8)
          21.5885713
```

Example 8   Finding an Interval of Scores

A normally distributed set of data has a mean of 1200 and a standard deviation of 150. Find the interval of values centered at the mean that contains 44% of the scores.

Answer

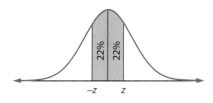

```
invNorm(.72)
          0.582841502
```

$1200 \pm (0.5828)(150) \approx 1113, 1287$

∴ [1113, 1287] contains the middle 44% of the data.

1. Sketch the desired area.

   The upper boundary of the interval is at the 72nd percentile because 50% of the data is to the left of the mean, leaving 22% between the mean and the upper boundary.

   The lower boundary is the 28th percentile.

2. Use 3:invNorm to find the z-score for the 72nd percentile.

3. Symmetry implies that the interval's bounds are ≈ 0.5828 standard deviations above and below the mean.

——————————————————————— SKILL ✓ **EXERCISE 35**

A. Exercises

Find the portion of the area of the shaded region under the normal distribution curve using the z-score tables and technology.

1.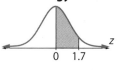
2.
3.
4.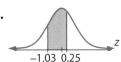

Find the percentage of data values in each interval.

5. $0 \leq z \leq 0.69$

6. $-1.21 \leq z \leq 0$

7. $-0.74 \leq z \leq 0.74$

8. $-1.85 \leq z \leq 1.85$

9. $z \geq 2.37$

10. $z \leq -1.56$

Find the probability that a randomly chosen score falls within the given interval.

11. $P(z \leq -0.92)$

12. $P(z \geq -1.4)$

13. $P(z \leq 2.0)$

14. $P(-0.3 \leq z \leq 0.3)$

15. $P(-1.4 \leq z \leq 2.3)$

16. $P(-2.83 \leq z \leq 1.11)$

B. Exercises

Find the probability that a randomly selected value in a normal distribution is within the given interval.

17. $[79, 90]$ with $\mu = 83$ and $\sigma = 5.9$

18. $[6.5, 9]$ with $\mu = 8.375$ and $\sigma = 1.04$

19. $[22, 25]$ with $\mu = 20$ and $\sigma = 7.9$

20. $[35, 40]$ with $\mu = 45$ and $\sigma = 9.26$

21. A randomly selected 16-yr-old male will have a height between 67 in. and 70 in. if the mean is 68.36 in. and the standard deviation is 2.72.

22. A randomly selected 6-mo-old baby girl will weigh between 18 lb and 20 lb if the mean is 16.44 lb and the standard deviation is 1.95.

23. A randomly selected student taking the ACT will score between 32 and 36 if the mean score is 20.9 and the standard deviation is 5.6.

24. A randomly selected student taking the SAT mathematics test in 2017 would have a score between 400 and 500 if the mean score is 527 and the standard deviation is 107.

Find the percentile rank for each student.

25. Joe's z-score of 1.07 on his college entrance exam

26. Mary's z-score of -0.26 on her economics test

27. Leesha's score of 90 on a test with a mean of 85 and a standard deviation of 3

28. Marcus's 64 in. height in an age group with a mean of 69 in. and a standard deviation of 2.94

29. Thomas's birth weight of 8.5 lb, given that the average male birth weight is 8.83 lb with a standard deviation of 1.6

Find the data value for the specified percentile in a normally distributed set of data.

30. 60th percentile if $\mu = 40$ and $\sigma = 7.2$

31. 45th percentile if $\mu = 8.2$ and $\sigma = 1.2$

32. Find the height of a 12-yr-old boy at the 5th percentile if the mean is 59 in. and the standard deviation is 3.1.

33. Find the history test score that is at the 75th percentile if the mean is 79 and the standard deviation is 6.8.

Find the z-scores for the given interval.

34. lower 20%

35. upper 10%

36. middle 34%

37. middle 97%

Find the interval of the data given the mean and the standard deviation.

38. upper 25% of data when $\mu = 7.5$ and $\sigma = 1.5$

39. lower 33% of data when $\mu = 81$ and $\sigma = 9.6$

40. middle 20% of scores with $\mu = 75$ and $\sigma = 7.8$

41. middle 50% of scores with $\mu = 50$ and $\sigma = 6.1$

C. Exercises

Use technology and the test grades below to complete exercises 42–44.

66, 70, 71, 71, 74, 75, 75, 76, 76, 77,
78, 79, 80, 80, 81, 81, 81, 82, 83, 83,
84, 84, 85, 85, 85, 86, 88, 88, 88, 88,
89, 89, 89, 89, 89, 90, 90, 90, 90, 91,
91, 92, 92, 93, 94, 95, 95, 96, 97, 98

42. Use Sturges's formula to divide the data set into intervals and create a histogram representing the data.

43. Complete a grouped frequency distribution table and use the midpoint of each class to find the estimated mean, μ, and standard deviation of the population, σ.

44. Write a normal distribution function for your data by substituting the estimated mean, μ, and variance, σ^2,

into $y = \dfrac{1}{\sqrt{2\pi\sigma^2}}e^{-\frac{(x-\mu)^2}{2\sigma^2}}$.

  a. Graph the data's normal distribution function in the window $x \in [\mu - 4\sigma, \mu + 4\sigma]$ with Xscl = σ and $y \in [0, 0.1]$.

  b. Express each interval in terms of the data values.

$[\mu - 3\sigma, \mu - 2\sigma]$	$[\mu, \mu + \sigma]$
$[\mu - 2\sigma, \mu - \sigma]$	$[\mu + \sigma, \mu + 2\sigma]$
$[\mu - \sigma, \mu]$	$[\mu + 2\sigma, \mu + 3\sigma]$

  c. Find the percentage of test scores that lie within each of the above intervals. Compare your results with the Empirical Rule to determine whether the data is normally distributed. Explain why or why not.

CUMULATIVE REVIEW

Use technology to complete a regression and write the exponential function modeling the data. Round coefficients to the nearest thousandth. [3.5]

45.

x	y
1	6
2	9
3	12
4	16
5	22
6	30

46.

x	y
0	62.2
2	57.9
4	54.8
6	49.9
8	47.5
10	44.0

Use technology to solve each system of inequalities graphically. [7.6]

47. $x + 2y > 4$
$y < 2x^2 - 1$

48. $y \geq |x + 2| - 2$
$y \leq -|x + 2| + 4$

State the five-number summary and construct a box plot for each set of data. [10.4]

49. $B = \{58, 60, 57, 73, 64, 65, 70, 71, 63, 65\}$

50. $H = \{130, 116, 133, 131, 121, 127, 123, 125, 126, 126, 127, 124, 128, 130, 112, 134, 137, 119, 129\}$

51. Use technology to estimate solutions of
$4.3x^3 - 2.45x^2 - 4.55$
$\qquad = 4.72x^4 + 5.21x^3 - 12.2x^2 - 8.22$
to the nearest hundredth. List all correct answers. [Appendix 3]

  A. -1.64 **C.** 1.46   **E.** none of
  B. -1.63 **D.** 3.71   these

52. Which of the following is true of $f(x) = g(x) + h(x)$ if $g(x) = \sin 2x$ and $h(x) = 2\cos 2x$? List all correct answers. [4.7]

  A. period: $p = \pi$ **D.** It is not a sinusoid.
  B. period: $p = 2$ **E.** none of these
  C. It is a sinusoid.

53. Find the sum $\displaystyle\sum_{n=1}^{5} 64\left(\frac{3}{4}\right)^{n-1}$. [9.3]

  A. 210.4375   **C.** 192   **E.** 101.25
  B. 195.25   **D.** 175

54. Find the z-score for a score of 33 on an exam with $\mu = 23$ and $\sigma = 6$. [10.4]

  A. 10.00   **C.** 5.50   **E.** none of
  B. 3.83   **D.** 1.67   these

Mathematical Platonism

I believe that mathematical reality lies outside us, that our function is to discover or observe it, and that the theorems which we prove, and which we describe grandiloquently as our "creations," are simply the notes of our observations.

—*G. H. Hardy (English mathematician)*

Almost everyone has heard of Plato, but not many know much about him. Plato wrote about morality, philosophy, theology, politics, aesthetics, and mathematics. While he considered mathematics his most important field of study, he is most remembered for his philosophy, which has become known as Platonism. He thought that the things we see in this world are only representations of a reality that actually exists in forms or ideas. So how did this philosophy view mathematics?

The *Stanford Encyclopedia of Philosophy* states that "*mathematical Platonism* . . . is the metaphysical view that there are abstract mathematical objects whose existence is independent of us and our language, thought, and practices. Just as electrons and planets exist independently of us, so do numbers and sets. . . . Mathematical truths are therefore discovered, not invented." The belief that mathematics is discovered dominated mathematics for nearly two millennia. Mathematical Platonism views abstract mathematical objects and truths as existing eternally, independent of God.

A biblical worldview acknowledges God as the source of all truth and humans as discoverers of mathematical truths derived from God's self-consistent character. Being created in God's image, humans are able to create a mathematical language that describes some of the underlying mathematical principles governing our universe. Many prominent mathematicians of the past gladly acknowledged the supernatural Creator God as the source of transcendent truth. For example, Johannes Kepler stated that "the chief aim of all investigations of the external world should be to discover the rational order and harmony which has been imposed on it by God and which he revealed to us in the language of mathematics."

Many modern mathematicians maintain that mathematics is simply a result of the human mind and is therefore invented or created. But this belief cannot account for math's intuitive impression of immutable truth or the striking instances of coherence between mathematics and

the physical universe. British mathematician Marcus du Sautoy wrote, "Many mathematicians fluctuate between feeling they are being creative and a sense they are discovering absolute scientific truths. Mathematical ideas can often appear very personal and dependent on the creative mind that conceived them. Yet that is balanced by the belief that its logical character means that every mathematician is living in the same mathematical world that is full of immutable truths. These truths are simply waiting to be unearthed, and no amount of creative thinking will undermine their existence."

In his 2008 essay "Mathematical Platonism and its Opposites," Harvard mathematician Barry Mazur states, "If we adopt the Platonic view that mathematics is discovered, we are suddenly in surprising territory, for this is a full-fledged theistic position." He confuses Platonism and a theistic perspective since Platonism does not necessitate theism, seeing universal mathematical truths as existing independently from God instead.

Mathematical Platonism lost some credibility when three seemingly contradictory valid geometries were developed in the nineteenth century and when paradoxes involving set theory were discovered in the early twentieth century. Several mathematicians then embarked on a quest to restore consistency to the foundations of our mathematics. Although those efforts never achieved their ultimate goal, they did produce new philosophies, including several modifications of traditional Platonism.

From a biblical point of view, the three different geometries reveal a variety of ways that mathematics can describe the physical world that God created. Understanding our finite and fallen nature allows us to accept new human insights and current inadequacies of our mathematical descriptions of our universe. Christians can have complete confidence in the infallibility of our infinite God and His system of transcendent mathematics (Ps. 147:5; Isa. 40:28).

Exercises

1. What major tenet of mathematical Platonism was the dominant view of mathematicians for the last two millennia?

2. What two mathematical objects are compared to electrons and planets in that they exist independently of humans?

3. Which famous astronomer stated that the rational order and harmony of the world was due to God?

4. What misconception of Platonism is illustrated by Barry Mazur's quote?

5. What common Platonist view is problematic for Christian mathematicians?

6. Name the key events that damaged the credibility of mathematical Platonism in the nineteenth and twentieth centuries.

7. How is God's understanding described in Psalm 147:5?

8. **Discuss:** Compare and contrast a biblical worldview of mathematics with mathematical Platonism.

9. **Discuss:** Is mathematics discovered or invented?

 # Chapter 10 Review

1. Caleb likes to wear dress pants, a dress shirt, and a tie to church on Sunday. How many different outfits can he make from his 2 pairs of dress pants, 3 dress shirts, and 2 ties? **[10.1]**

2. Determine the number of different ways 3 flavors of lollipops from a store offering 20 different flavors can be arranged in each case below. Then state whether such arrangements are independent or dependent. **[10.1]**
   a. Flavors cannot be repeated.
   b. Flavors can be repeated.

3. Eight contestants compete in the high school track meet. **[10.1]**
   a. How many ways can they line up for a group photo?
   b. Assuming there are no ties, how many possible ways could 1st, 2nd, and 3rd be secured?

4. In how many different orders can the top 4 of 15 contestants be announced as advancing to the final round of a Scripture memory competition? **[10.1]**

5. Find the number of permutations of the letters in each word. **[10.1]**
   a. *CONTEST*   b. *LOLLIPOP*

6. Evaluate each combination. **[10.1]**
   a. $_9C_4$ b. $_{10}C_4$

7. How many 4-person teams can be formed from a group of 8 boys and 4 girls if each gender will have 2 representatives? **[10.1]**

8. A regular 6-sided die is rolled. List the sample space and the event of getting a prime number. **[10.2]**

Use the results of 20 rolls of a 6-sided die listed below for exercises 9–10. [10.2]

Number	1	2	3	4	5	6
Frequency	5	3	3	2	4	3

9. State the theoretical and experimental probability for each event.
   a. $P(4)$ b. $P(\text{odd})$

10. Find the experimental probability of not getting a multiple of 3.

11. Find the probability of each event when a coin is flipped and a regular 6-sided die is rolled. **[10.2]**
   a. heads and a multiple of 2
   b. tails and a number less than 3

12. A bag contains 3 red marbles, 4 blue marbles, and 8 green marbles. Find the probability of drawing 2 blue marbles consecutively in each case. **[10.2]**
   a. The first marble is replaced.
   b. The first marble is not replaced.

In a recent survey of high school juniors, 40% played fall sports, 30% earned an A in their math class that fall, and 20% earned an A while playing fall sports.

13. Determine whether the two events are independent or dependent. **[10.2]**

14. Find the probability that a randomly selected student fits each description. **[10.2]**
   a. played fall sports or earned an A, but not both
   b. did not play fall sports and did not earn an A

15. The table summarizes the results of a survey that asked 434 students how many books they read the previous summer. Find the probability that a randomly selected student read each number of books. **[10.2]**
   a. more than 8 or fewer than 3 books
   b. between 2 and 9 books

Number of Books	Percent of Students
0	3.9%
1–2	14.1%
3–4	19.8%
5–6	16.1%
7–8	8.1%
9+	38.0%

16. Label the following as a parameter or a statistic. **[10.3]**
   a. The average speed of all vehicles traveling on Interstate 10 is 69 mi/hr.
   b. The average speed of black cars traveling on Interstate 10 between 8:05 AM and 8:10 AM is 69 mi/hr.

17. Identify the level of measurement. **[10.3]**
   a. student body president
   b. memberships in volunteer groups
   c. the number of votes received
   d. Celsius temperatures

18. Create a pie chart illustrating the Sunday school attendance data. **[10.3]**

nursery	14
preschool	23
primary	43
juniors	47
teens	97
adults	380

19. Create a back-to-back stem plot summarizing the ages of newcomers attending the local church. **[10.3]**
2017: 1, 8, 35, 12, 16, 40, 41, 14, 16, 56, 62, 66
2018: 1, 27, 28, 7, 4, 41, 41, 48, 29, 29, 50, 57, 58

20. Determine the number of classes and the class width for a grouped frequency distribution table summarizing 20 data values having a minimum value of 5 and a maximum value of 28. **[10.3]**

21. Draw a histogram representing the ages of the cousins in the Smith family. **[10.3]**

Ages	Freq.
1–3	2
4–6	2
7–9	4
10–12	3
13–15	2

22. Extend the frequency distribution table in exercise 21 by adding Cumulative Frequency and Cumulative Percentage columns and use the table to draw a percentile graph of the data. **[10.3]**

23. Find the sample mean, median, and mode of the average monthly temperatures for Charlotte, North Carolina. **[10.4]**
$T = \{51, 55, 63, 72, 79, 86, 89, 87, 81, 72, 62, 53\}$

24. Find the variance and standard deviation of sample data containing 13 values in which the sum of the squares $SS = 60$. **[10.4]**

25. Calculate the mean and sample standard deviation for the data set. **[10.4]**
$D = \{47, 61, 46, 64, 48, 49, 51, 55, 57, 58\}$

26. Use a spreadsheet to find the mean and sample standard deviation for the data in exercise 21. **[10.4]**

27. Analyze the data set $Q = \{34, 27, 28, 25, 26, 21, 24, 25, 29, 23, 28, 27\}$. **[10.4]**

   a. Find the mean, median, and interquartile range.

   b. Identify any outliers and then draw box plots that include and exclude any outliers.

28. Use technology to analyze the data set. **[10.4]**
$D = \{13, 27, 21, 18, 3, 15, 29, 21, 19, 24\}$

   a. State the five-number summary and draw the box plot.

   b. State the mean and the population standard deviation.

   c. Which provides a better summary for the data: the five-number summary or the mean and standard deviation? Explain your reasoning.

29. Find the data value at each percentile for the points scored by a sample of basketball players. **[10.4]**
$P = \{13, 15, 18, 19, 21, 21, 24, 27, 29, 31\}$

   a. 43rd percentile   **b.** 78th percentile

30. Classify a data distribution in which the bulk of the data is to the left with a tail to the right and the mean is greater than the median. **[10.4]**

   a. negatively skewed   **b.** normal distribution

   c. positively skewed

31. The data in L_1 has $\mu = 6$ and $\sigma = 2$. State the mean and standard deviation of each transformed set of data. **[10.5]**

   a. $L_2 = 5L_1$ **b.** $L_3 = L_1 + 4$

32. Find the z-score for each data value in a distribution with $\mu = 85$ and $\sigma = 5$. **[10.5]**

   a. $x_i = 100$ **b.** $x_i = 78$

33. Andrew scored a 1206 on the SAT where the mean was 1060 and the standard deviation was 195. He also received a 26 on the ACT where the mean was 21 and the standard deviation was 5.4. Find the z-score for each test and determine the test on which he received the better score. **[10.5]**

34. Find Mikayla's raw score if she had a z-score of 1.32 on an ACT test with $\mu = 20.8$ and $\sigma = 4.7$. **[10.5]**

35. Use Chebyshev's Theorem to find the smallest percentage of data that must always lie within 2 standard deviations of the mean. Confirm your results using the set of quiz scores $Q = \{1, 5, 6, 7, 7, 8, 8, 9, 9, 9\}$. **[10.5]**

36. A normally distributed set of test scores has a mean of 41 and a standard deviation of 5. What percentage of the data is in each interval? [10.5]

    a. from 36 to 46   **b.** from 26 to 51

    c. greater than 46

Find the portion of the area under the normal curve within each interval. [10.6]

37. $-1.2 \le z \le 0$

38. $-0.75 \le z \le 0.75$

39. $-0.9 \le z \le 1.85$

Find the probability that a data value chosen at random meets the following criteria. [10.6]

40. $z \le -2.1$

41. $-0.2 \le z \le 1.35$

Find the probability that a randomly selected value in a normal distribution is within the given interval. [10.6]

42. $[90, 95]$ with $\mu = 82$ and $\sigma = 7.8$

43. $[70, 89]$ with $\mu = 78$ and $\sigma = 8.6$

Use the normally distributed sample of scores that has a mean of 58 and a standard deviation of 4 to solve the following exercises. [10.6]

44. Find the probability that a randomly selected score is in the given interval.

    a. $x_i \in [53, 62]$ **b.** $x_i \ge 66$

45. Find the percentile rank for a score of 63.

46. Find the score at the 60th percentile.

47. Find the interval of values that contains the middle 50% of data.

11 Inferential Statistics

HISTORICAL CONNECTION
A theorem from the seventeenth century finds new life and expansive applications in the power of twenty-first century computing.

BIBLICAL PERSPECTIVE OF MATHEMATICS
As Platonism fell out of favor in the nineteenth century, three competing schools of thought emerged in an effort to establish a foundation and philosophical approach for mathematics.

DATA ANALYSIS
Internet search engine results owe a lot to a Russian mathematician and his probability experiments of the early twentieth century.

After completing this section, you will be able to

- classify random variables as discrete or continuous.
- construct probability distributions.
- calculate the expected value (mean) and standard deviation of a probability distribution.
- construct and apply binomial probability distributions.

The 1937 publication of Harald Cramér's *Random Variables and Probability Distributions* was the first book to use *random variable* in its title and helped standardize the term.

	1	2	3	4	5	6
1	2	3	4	5	6	7
2	3	4	5	6	7	8
3	4	5	6	7	8	9
4	5	6	7	8	9	10
5	6	7	8	9	10	11
6	7	8	9	10	11	12

Probability Distributions

Consumers rank comfortable seats and dual climate controls as key features when purchasing a car.

Frequency distributions were introduced in Chapter 10 as a way to organize data, determine measures of central tendency and variability, and visualize the overall shape of the distribution. This section relates these concepts to the outcomes for the *random variable* studied in a probability experiment.

DEFINITIONS

A **random variable** x represents all possible numerical outcomes of a probability experiment. A *discrete random variable* represents a countable number of outcomes. A *continuous random variable* represents an uncountable number of outcomes within an interval.

The number of classes that a randomly selected student attends during a school day represents a discrete outcome, while the time actually spent at school during that day represents a continuous outcome.

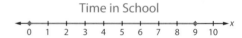

Considering whether the data is counted or measured can help distinguish discrete and continuous variables.

Example 1   Classifying a Random Variable

Classify each random variable as discrete or continuous and justify your answer.

a. Let x represent the length of newborn babies at birth.

b. Let x represent the days that it rains in a given week.

Answer

a. continuous; The value can be any reasonable real number.

b. discrete; The value is a whole number from 0 to 7.

SKILL ✓ EXERCISE 1

Different statistical techniques are used to analyze discrete and continuous random variables. This section examines the shape, center, and variability of probability distributions for discrete random variables.

DEFINITION

A **probability distribution** for the random variable, x, is a table, graph, or equation that associates each possible value of a random variable, x_i, and its probability, $P(x_i)$.

Recall that the probability of any event is $0 \leq P(x_i) \leq 1$ and that $\sum_{i=1}^{n} P(x_i) = 1$.

Consider the theoretical probability experiment examining the sum when a pair of dice is rolled. The sample space consists of the outcomes {2, 3, 4, 5, 6, 7, 8, 9, 10, 11, 12}, but each result is not equally likely. The table listing all the possible results can be used to determine the probability of each outcome. The distribution can then be represented with a table or a graph.

sum, x_i	2	3	4	5	6	7	8	9	10	11	12
probability, $P(x_i)$	$\frac{1}{36}$	$\frac{1}{18}$	$\frac{1}{12}$	$\frac{1}{9}$	$\frac{5}{36}$	$\frac{1}{6}$	$\frac{5}{36}$	$\frac{1}{9}$	$\frac{1}{12}$	$\frac{1}{18}$	$\frac{1}{36}$

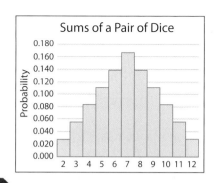

Probability distributions can also be constructed to represent experimental or observed data.

Example 2 Creating Probability Distributions

The frequency distribution table shows the results of a customer survey in which car comfort is rated from 1, very uncomfortable, to 5, very comfortable. Create numerical and graphical probability distributions for the data.

Rating	Freq.
1	2
2	3
3	12
4	20
5	13

Answer

Let x = rating.

$P(1) = \frac{2}{50} = 0.04$

$P(2) = \frac{3}{50} = 0.06$

$P(3) = \frac{12}{50} = 0.24$

$P(4) = \frac{20}{50} = 0.40$

$P(5) = \frac{13}{50} = 0.26$

x_i	$P(x_i)$
1	0.04
2	0.06
3	0.24
4	0.40
5	0.26

1. Define the random variable.

2. Determine the probability of each rating. Begin by finding the frequency total $n = 50$.

3. Verify that $0 \le P(x_i) \le 1$ for each x_i and that

$$\sum_{i=1}^{n} P(x_i) = 0.04 + 0.06 + 0.24 + 0.40 + 0.26 = 1.$$

4. Create a histogram for the probability distribution. Notice that the probability can be expressed as a percent.

SKILL ✔ **EXERCISE 27**

TIP

To graph the probability distribution on your calculator, enter each outcome x_i in L1 and their probabilities $P(x_i)$ in L2. Then use STAT PLOT to draw a histogram with List: L1 and FreqList: L2.

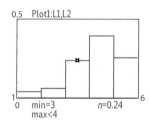

The graph of a probability distribution illustrates its overall shape. Since probability distributions include all possible outcomes, they represent the experiment's population. The mean and standard deviation are the typical measures of central tendency and variation in a discrete probability distribution. Different formulas for μ and σ must be used since the probability distribution describes what we expect to happen and N, a total number of values, is unknown.

> ## DEFINITION
>
> The **mean of a probability distribution**, μ, is the sum of the products of each outcome x_i of the random variable and its associated probability $P(x_i)$.
>
> $$\mu = \sum_{i=1}^{n} x_i P(x_i)$$

The mean of a probability distribution is also called the *expected value*, denoted as $E(x)$. The expected value is a weighted average that estimates the average result after many trials of the experiment. The expected value may not be equal to any of the outcomes for the random variable.

Is 0.5 the expected value that a newborn baby will be a boy? World Bank statistics show there are 105 male babies born in the United States for every 100 females. Your worldview will determine how you interpret this statistic.

Example 3 Finding the Expected Value of a Probability Distribution

Find the expected value of the probability distribution from Example 2.

Answer

x_i	$P(x_i)$	$x_i \cdot P(x_i)$
1	0.04	$1(0.04) = 0.04$
2	0.06	$2(0.06) = 0.12$
3	0.24	$3(0.24) = 0.72$
4	0.40	$4(0.40) = 1.60$
5	0.26	$5(0.26) = 1.30$

$$E(x) = \sum x_i P(x_i) = 3.78$$

1. Extend the table to include a column containing the products of $x_i \cdot P(x_i)$ for each possible outcome.

2. Find $\mu = E(x) = \sum_{i=1}^{n} x_i P(x_i)$.

SKILL ✓ **EXERCISE 27**

The formulas for the variance and standard deviation of a discrete probability distribution are different from the formulas for populations and samples given in Chapter 10.

DEFINITIONS

The **variance of a probability distribution**, σ^2, is the sum of the products of the squared deviation of each outcome from the mean and the outcome's probability.
The **standard deviation**, σ, is the square root of the variance.

$$\sigma^2 = \sum_{i=1}^{n} (x_i - \mu)^2 P(x_i) \text{ and } \sigma = \sqrt{\sigma^2}$$

Example 4 Finding the Standard Deviation of a Probability Distribution

Find the standard deviation of the car comfort rating data from Examples 2 and 3.

Answer

x_i	$P(x_i)$	$x_i \cdot P(x_i)$	$(x_i - \mu)^2 P(x_i)$
1	0.04	0.04	$(1 - 3.78)^2(0.04) \approx 0.309$
2	0.06	0.12	$(2 - 3.78)^2(0.06) \approx 0.190$
3	0.24	0.72	$(3 - 3.78)^2(0.24) \approx 0.146$
4	0.40	1.60	$(4 - 3.78)^2(0.40) \approx 0.019$
5	0.26	1.30	$(5 - 3.78)^2(0.26) \approx 0.387$
		$\mu = 3.78$	$\sigma^2 \approx 1.05$
			$\sigma \approx 1.03$

Check

```
      1-Var Stats
x̄=3.78
Σx=3.78
Σx²=15.34
Sx=
σx=1.025475499
n=1
minX=1
↓Q₁=3
```

1. Extend the table to include a column containing the product of $(x_i - \mu)^2 P(x_i)$ for each outcome.

2. Find $\sigma^2 = \sum_{i=1}^{n} (x_i - \mu)^2 P(x_i)$.

3. Find $\sigma = \sqrt{\sigma^2}$.

4. Enter each possible outcome x_i in L1 and their probabilities $P(x_i)$ in L2. Select 1-Var Stats from the STAT, CALC menu and enter L1 for the List: and L2 for the FreqList:. Note that μ is given as $\bar{x}$ and σ is given as σx.

SKILL ✓ **EXERCISE 27**

Section 9.4 introduced a *binomial experiment*, which consists of n identical, independent trials in which each trial results in either a success or a failure. A *binomial probability distribution* can be constructed to describe all the possible outcomes of such an experiment.

◼ CHARACTERISTICS OF A BINOMIAL PROBABILITY DISTRIBUTION

1. The experiment consists of n identical, independent trials in which each trial results in either a success (S) or a failure (F).
2. The probabilities of success and failure are $P(S) = p$ and $P(F) = q = 1 - p$.
3. The binomial random variable x is the number of successes in n trials of the experiment.

Flipping a coin three times is a simple binomial experiment. Each of the 3 trials has only two possible outcomes: heads or tails. The experiment's sample space is {*HHH, HHT, HTH, HTT, THH, THT, TTH, TTT*}. If the random variable represents the number of heads on three flips of the coin, it can have values of 0, 1, 2, or 3 and has the following binomial probability distribution.

heads, x_i	0	1	2	3
frequency, f	1	3	3	1
probability, $P(x_i)$	$\frac{1}{8} = 0.125$	$\frac{3}{8} = 0.375$	$\frac{3}{8} = 0.375$	$\frac{1}{8} = 0.125$

Recall from Section 9.4 that $_nC_x$ provides the number of ways to select x successes in n trials and that the *binomial probability distribution formula*

$$P(x) = {}_nC_x\, p^x q^{n-x}$$

gives the probability of x successes in n independent trials in which the probability of success is p and the probability of failure is $q = 1 - p$.

Example 5 Finding Binomial Probabilities

Find the probability of a randomly selected golfer getting each number of holes in one on a 9-hole miniature golf course if the probability of an average golfer getting a hole in one on each hole is 0.15.

a. 3 holes in one

b. fewer than 3 holes in one

c. 3 or more holes in one

TIP

Your calculator's binomial probability distribution function can be used to determine the probability of each outcome, $P(x_i)$. Select DISTR, A: binompdf, and enter the parameters n, p, x.

```
binompdf(9,0.15,3)
          0.1069218877
▪
```

The binomial cumulative distribution function calculates $P(\leq x_i)$.

```
binomcdf(9,0.15,2)
          0.8591465972
▪
```

Answer

x = number of holes in one
$n = 9$ holes; $p = 0.15$
$q = 1 - 0.15 = 0.85$

Define the variables for the binomial experiment.

a. $P(3) = {}_9C_3 (0.15)^3 (0.85)^{9-3}$

$\qquad = 84(0.15)^3(0.85)^6$

$\qquad \approx 0.11$ or 11%

Substitute into $P(x) = {}_nC_x\, p^x q^{n-x}$ and evaluate.

b. $P(2) = {}_9C_2 (0.15)^2 (0.85)^7 \approx 0.26$

$P(1) = {}_9C_1 (0.15)^1 (0.85)^8 \approx 0.37$

$P(0) = {}_9C_0 (0.15)^0 (0.85)^9 \approx 0.23$

$P(x_i < 3) \approx 0.26 + 0.37 + 0.23$
$\qquad\qquad \approx 0.86$ or 86%

1. Note that $P(x < 3) = P(2) + P(1) + P(0)$ and use the binomial distribution probability formula to find these 3 probabilities.

2. Calculate $P(x < 3) = P(2) + P(1) + P(0)$.

CONTINUED ➡

c. $P(x_i \geq 3) = 1 - P(x_i < 3)$
$\approx 1 - 0.86 = 0.14$ or 14%

Find $P(x \geq 3)$ using the complement rule for probabilities.

SKILL ✓ EXERCISE 21

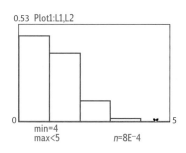

The binomial probability distribution describes the probability of each possible outcome in a binary experiment. If 4 dice are rolled with the random variable of getting a six on a die being a success, $p = \frac{1}{6}$ and $q = \frac{5}{6}$. The probabilities of the outcomes $x_i = \{0, 1, 2, 3, 4\}$ are the terms in the expansion of $(q + p)^4$, which can be found using the Binomial Theorem.

$$(q + p)^4 = \sum_{x=0}^{4} {}_nC_x\, p^x q^{n-x} = {}_4C_0 q^4 + {}_4C_1 pq^3 + {}_4C_2 p^2 q^2 + {}_4C_3 p^3 q + {}_4C_4 p^4$$

$$= 1\left(\frac{5}{6}\right)^4 + 4\left(\frac{1}{6}\right)\left(\frac{5}{6}\right)^3 + 6\left(\frac{1}{6}\right)^2\left(\frac{5}{6}\right)^2 + 4\left(\frac{1}{6}\right)^3\left(\frac{5}{6}\right) + 1\left(\frac{1}{6}\right)^4$$

$$\approx 0.4823 + 0.3858 + 0.1157 + 0.0154 + 0.0008$$

sixes, x_i	0	1	2	3	4
probability, $P(x_i)$	0.4823	0.3858	0.1157	0.0154	0.0008

The sum of these probabilities is 1 since $(q + p)^4 = \left(\frac{5}{6} + \frac{1}{6}\right)^4 = 1^4 = 1$.

While the mean and standard deviation of a binomial probability distribution can be found using the formulas given earlier in this section, simpler formulas have been derived using the properties of the binomial distribution.

Mean, Variance, and Standard Deviation of Binomial Probability Distributions		
mean: $\mu = np$	variance: $\sigma^2 = npq$	standard deviation: $\sigma = \sqrt{\sigma^2} = \sqrt{npq}$

Example 6   Analyzing a Binomial Distribution

Find the mean and standard deviation of the binomial probability distribution describing the number of sixes obtained by rolling 4 dice.

Answer

using the formulas for a binomial probability distribution:

$$\mu = np = 4\left(\frac{1}{6}\right) = \frac{2}{3} \approx 0.6667$$

$$\sigma = \sqrt{npq} = \sqrt{4\left(\frac{1}{6}\right)\left(\frac{5}{6}\right)} = \sqrt{\frac{5}{9}} \approx 0.745$$

using a spreadsheet and the general formulas for probability distributions:

	A	B	C	D
1	**Sixes**	**Probability**		
2	x_i	$P(x_i)$	$x_i \cdot P(x_i)$	$(x_i - \mu)^2 P(x_i)$
3	0	0.4823	0	0.2143
4	1	0.3858	0.3858	0.0429
5	2	0.1157	0.2315	0.2058
6	3	0.0154	0.0463	0.0840
7	4	0.0008	0.0031	0.0086
8			**Sum**	**Sum**	**Sum**
9			1	0.6667	0.5556
10				**Std Dev:**	0.7454

 TIP

The Microsoft Excel function
=BINOM.DIST(x_i,n,p,false)
returns $P(x_i)$, while
=BINOM.DIST(x_i,n,p,true)
returns $P(\leq x_i)$.
For Example 6,
=BINOM.DIST(2,4,1/6,false)
returns 0.1157, and
=BINOM.DIST(2,4,1/6,true)
returns 0.9838.

SKILL ✓ EXERCISE 23

Since the expected value (or mean) is two-thirds, we would expect a six in about 2 out of 3 rolls of the 4 dice. Any roll of the dice producing 3 sixes ($\mu + 3.13\sigma$) would be unlikely, since $P(3\text{ sixes}) \approx 1.5\%$, and 4 sixes ($\mu + 4.47\sigma$) would be extremely rare, since $P(4\text{ sixes}) \approx 0.08\%$.

A. Exercises

Classify each random variable as discrete or continuous and justify your answer.

1. Let x represent the miles per gallon your car gets on a 200 mi interstate trip.

2. Let x represent the number of questions answered correctly on a test consisting of 50 multiple-choice questions.

3. Let x represent the number of red marbles pulled on 4 successive tries (with replacement) from a bag containing 3 blue, 2 white, and 6 red marbles.

4. Let x represent the tire pressure in a car tire.

Determine whether each table could represent a probability distribution and justify your answer.

5.

x_i	3	5	7
$P(x_i)$	0.5	−0.3	0.2

6.

x_i	−2	0	2	4
$P(x_i)$	0.03	0.28	0.61	0.08

7.

x_i	4	9	15	22	30
$P(x_i)$	0.21	0.07	0.42	0.16	0.09

8.

x_i	−5	−10	−15
$P(x_i)$	0.58	0.29	0.41

Use the probability distribution to find each probability.

9.

x_i	1	2	3	4
$P(x_i)$	0.14	0.39	0.22	0.25

   a. $P(x_i > 1)$ b. P(an even number)

   c. $P(x_i \leq 2)$

10.

x_i	−100	−50	50	100
$P(x_i)$	0.75	0.10	0.10	0.05

   a. $P(x_i < 0)$ b. $P(x_i > 0)$

Use the binomial probability distribution formula to find $P(x_i)$, the probability of x successes in n independent trials where p is the probability of a success in a trial. Then find the expected value and standard deviation of the related binomial probability distribution. Round answers to the nearest hundredth if necessary.

11. $x = 8, n = 12, p = 0.75$

12. $x = 9, n = 16, p = 0.33$

13. $x = 3, n = 9, p = 0.6$

14. $x = 5, n = 22, p = 0.45$

Determine whether each of the following describes a binomial experiment. If so, state the values of p, q, and n, and if not, explain why.

15. Forty-two seniors at a high school are asked if they regularly eat breakfast before coming to school. Thirty-two of them affirm that they do. The random variable represents the number of seniors who eat breakfast.

16. A survey of 115 recent ER patients at a particular hospital asked how many minutes patients had to wait before a nurse talked with them. The random variable represents the number of minutes they waited.

17. A penny is flipped 18 times. Heads lands up 13 of those times. The random variable represents the number of times a flip resulted in heads.

18. In a group of 60 randomly selected donors, 27 have type O blood, 24 have type A, 5 have type B, and 4 have type AB. The random variable represents the number of donors having type AB blood.

B. Exercises

19. Jarnel randomly guesses on the 5 multiple-choice questions on his biology quiz. If his chance of guessing the correct answer on each question is $\frac{1}{3}$, what is the probability that he gets at least 60% correct?

20. Approximately 10% of people are left-handed. What is the probability that in a group of 12 children more than 3 are left-handed?

21. If 8% of the world's population has blue eyes, find the probability of each number of people with blue eyes in a group of 20 randomly chosen individuals.

   a. 2 blue-eyed people

   b. at most 3 blue-eyed people

   c. more than 3 blue-eyed people

22. A manufacturer claims that a regular bag of its candies has an equal distribution of its 5 colors. Use a binomial distribution in which x represents the number of red candies in a 2.17 oz bag containing 60 candies to find the following probabilities.

   a. $P(x_i = 12)$ b. $P(10 \leq x_i \leq 14)$

   c. $P(x_i = 0)$ d. $P(x_i = 60)$

   e. Give a possible explanation for a bag with either no red or all red candies.

23. A traffic light on the way to church is green 41% of the time, yellow 12% of the time, and red 47% of the time. How many times would you expect it to be green during 8 trips to church?

24. If 51% of the babies born in the United States are boys, create a probability distribution for the number of boys born into a 4-child family and determine the expected number of boys.

25. After scoring a touchdown, a football team may attempt an extra point or a 2-point conversion. The table lists the results for such plays by a high school football team over the past 6 games. Create a probability distribution for these scoring plays and use it to find the expected number of points for the team after scoring a touchdown.

Extra Points	2	1	0
Frequency	3	17	5

Create a table and a histogram representing the probability distribution for each experiment. Then use the probability distribution to find the expected value and the standard deviation.

26. A penny is flipped 3 times and the number of heads is recorded.

27. The illustrated spinners are each spun once and the resulting sum is noted.

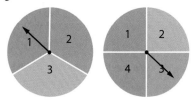

28. Two tetrahedral dice (each producing a result of 1, 2, 3, or 4) are rolled.

29. Two 6-sided dice, each having three faces with a 1, two faces with a 2, and one face with a 3, are rolled.

30. Members of the church youth group were asked the number of days per week they read their Bibles outside of church. The results are summarized in the table below.

Number of Days	0	1	2	3	4	5	6	7
Number of Members	4	2	12	9	8	7	3	5

a. Create a table and a histogram to represent the probability distribution for this data.

b. Find the mean and the standard deviation of the distribution.

c. Interpret the results.

Find the mean of a probability distribution to determine whether the warranty will likely save money for the purchaser.

31. A used car dealer offers a 1-yr extended warranty for $600 that covers 100% of all repair costs. During the next year there is a 22% chance the car will need an $800 repair, a 12% chance it will need a $1000 repair, and a 66% chance that no repairs will be needed.

32. An electronics store offers a 2-yr extended warranty covering all repairs for $10 with the purchase of a $520 camera. In the first 2 yr, 6% of these cameras require repairs costing $100 and 1.5% require repairs costing $200.

⟩ **C. Exercises**

33. Use a spreadsheet to create a probability distribution of the sums obtained by rolling a pair of dodecahedral dice. Which sum is most likely to occur? Which sum is least likely to occur? What is the expected value of the sum for this probability distribution?

34. A phone company offers two plans for a 2-yr extended warranty on broken screens. Plan A costs $130 and covers up to two screen replacements, each with a $30 copay. Plan B costs $115 and covers just one screen replacement with no copay. Screen replacement with no warranty costs $175. If 18% of screens need replacement once during the 2-yr period and 4% of screens need replacement twice during the 2-yr period, find the expected value of probability distributions for each plan (A, B, or none) to determine which would likely cost the consumer the least.

35. A CMO Impact Study completed by K. A. Whitler researched the time that chief marketing officers (CMOs) had held their current position. Let the random variable x be the number of years a CMO has held that position.

Years	$P(x_i)$
1	0.22
2	0.19
3	0.16
4	0.10
5	0.10
6	0.05
7	0.04
8	0.02
9	0.01
10+	0.11

a. Does the table satisfy the properties of a probability distribution? Explain why or why not.

b. Draw a histogram representing the data and describe the shape of the distribution.

c. Find the probability of a CMO holding that position for more than 5 yr.

d. Find the probability of a CMO holding that position less than 4 yr.

e. Use the data to determine the expected number of years a CMO has been in that position and interpret the result.

36. According to the CDC, about 1 out of 700 babies is born with Down syndrome. According to the US Census Bureau, about 10,800 babies are born each day in the United States. Let x represent the number of children born with Down syndrome each day in the United States.

a. Explain why a binomial probability distribution is an appropriate model for studying the probabilities of the number of children born with Down syndrome.

b. What is the expected number of babies born with Down syndrome on a single day in the United States?

c. Use technology to find $P(12)$.

d. Use technology to find $P(x \leq 10)$.

37. Experiment: Use an Internet coin toss simulator to flip 5 pennies and record the number of heads. Repeat this 50 times.

a. Construct an experimental probability distribution from the trials using the number of heads as the random variable and use it to find $P(3)$ and $P(\geq 2)$.

b. Construct a theoretical probability distribution for this experiment and use it to find $P(3)$ and $P(\geq 2)$.

c. Discuss the differences beteeen and the advantages or disadvantages of theoretical and experimental probabilities.

d. When would it be necessary to use an experimental probability distribution?

38. Use an Internet keyword such as *wages by education* to find approximate median salaries for US workers according to their level of education. Create a histogram representing the data. Then determine the expected median salary for a randomly selected worker.

Level of Education	Percent of Workers	Median Annual Salary
no high school diploma	8%	
high school diploma or GED	30%	
some college or associate's degree	29%	
bachelor's degree	23%	
advanced degree	10%	

Find the primary solutions of each equation. [5.3]

39. $2 \sin^2 x = 3 - 2 \sin^2 x$

40. $2 \cos^2 x + \cos x - 1 = 0$

Write and solve a matrix equation to solve each system. [7.5]

41. $2x - 5y = -16$
$3x - y = 2$

42. $4x + 7y = -1$
$6x + 2y = -10$

Find each probability for the score of a randomly selected student from a normally distributed population with a mean score of 82 and standard deviation of 6.2. [10.6]

43. $P(x_i < 85)$

44. $P(x_i > 80)$

45. What is the remainder when $p(x) = 5x^5 - 4x^4 + 3x^3 - 2x^2 + x$ is divided by $x - 2$? [2.3]

A. 114

C. 2

E. none of these

B. 57

D. -258

46. Points D and F are 19 m apart on one side of a river. If point E lies on the opposite bank with $\angle EDF = 60°$ and $\angle EFD = 50°$, which of the following represents the measure of ED? [5.6]

A. $\dfrac{(19 \text{ m}) \sin 60°}{\sin 70°}$

D. $\dfrac{(19 \text{ m}) \sin 50°}{\sin 70°}$

B. $\dfrac{(19 \text{ m}) \sin 70°}{\sin 50°}$

E. none of these

C. $\dfrac{\sin 70°}{(19 \text{ m}) \sin 60°}$

47. Which of the following represents the fifth term of $(3x - 4y)^9$? [9.4]

A. $_9C_4(3x)^4(-4y)^5$

D. $_9C_5(3x)^5(-4y)^5$

B. $_9C_5(3x)^4(-4y)^5$

E. none of these

C. $_9C_5(3x)^5(-4y)^4$

48. A sports league has an average salary of $2.1 million with a standard deviation of $1.6 million. Assuming a normal distribution, what is the probability (to the nearest percent) that a player will make between $3 million and $4 million? [10.6]

A. 63%

C. 34%

E. none of these

B. 56%

D. 17%

11.2 Central Limit Theorem

Approximately 27.5 million people watched prime time programming for the 2016 Summer Olympic Games in Rio.

The actual parameter for a population, such as the average height of 18-yr-old males in the United States, can be difficult or even impossible to determine. In these cases, statistics from a sample of the population are used to make inferences about the population's parameters. A probability distribution can be created to describe any statistic from the sample.

> ▎**DEFINITION**
>
> A **sampling distribution** is the probability distribution of a statistic from all possible samples of a given sample size from a population.

We will focus on sampling distributions for the means, $\bar{x}$, of samples with a size of n from a given population.

After completing this section, you will be able to

- create a sampling distribution and find its mean and standard deviation.
- apply the Central Limit Theorem to find probabilities.
- approximate binomial probabilities using the Central Limit Theorem.

Example 1   Analyzing a Sampling Distribution of Sample Means

Make a table listing all possible samples of size 2 (taken with replacement) from the population {7, 9, 11, 13} and their means. Use the table to create a sampling distribution for the means. Then find the mean and standard deviation of the sample means and compare them to the population's mean and standard deviation.

Answer

1. List all (4 · 4 = 16) possible samples of size $n = 2$ and their means.

Sample; $\bar{x}$	
{7, 7}; 7	{11, 7}; 9
{7, 9}; 8	{11, 9}; 10
{7, 11}; 9	{11, 11}; 11
{7, 13}; 10	{11, 13}; 12
{9, 7}; 8	{13, 7}; 10
{9, 9}; 9	{13, 9}; 11
{9, 11}; 10	{13, 11}; 12
{9, 13}; 11	{13, 13}; 13

2. Find the probability of each mean to make the sampling distribution.

Sampling Distribution	
$\bar{x}$	Probability
7	1 ÷ 16 = 0.0625
8	2 ÷ 16 = 0.1250
9	3 ÷ 16 = 0.1875
10	4 ÷ 16 = 0.2500
11	3 ÷ 16 = 0.1875
12	2 ÷ 16 = 0.1250
13	1 ÷ 16 = 0.0625

3. Enter the sampling distribution in L1 and L2 and the population in L3.

CONTINUED ➡

Compare the distribution of the population and the distribution of the sample means.

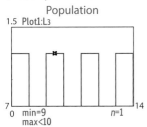

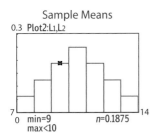

4. Use 1-Var Stats to determine the mean and standard deviation for the sampling distribution and the population.

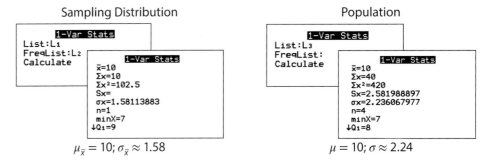

$\mu_{\bar{x}} = 10;\ \sigma_{\bar{x}} \approx 1.58$ $\mu = 10;\ \sigma \approx 2.24$

5. While the means are the same, the standard deviation of the sample means is less than the standard deviation of the population.

— SKILL ✓ **EXERCISE 21**

Properties of Sampling Distributions of Sample Means	
$\mu_{\bar{x}} = \mu$	The mean of the sample means, $\mu_{\bar{x}}$, is equal to the population's mean, μ.
$\sigma_{\bar{x}} = \dfrac{\sigma}{\sqrt{n}}$	The standard deviation of the sample means, $\sigma_{\bar{x}}$, is equal to the population standard deviation, σ, divided by the square root of the sample size, n.

Notice that the histogram illustrating the sampling distribution in Example 1 approximates a normal distribution. What effect does increasing n, the size of the sample, have on the shape of the sampling distributions from the uniform and skewed populations illustrated below?

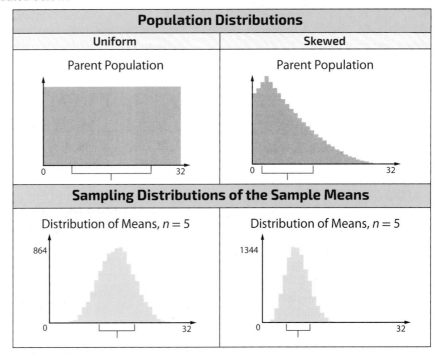

CONTINUED ➡

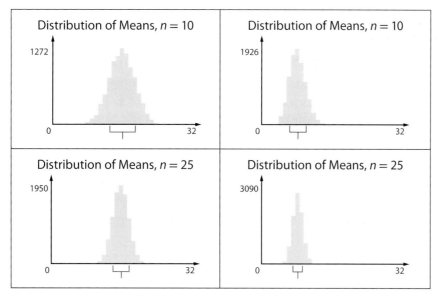

Distribution of Means, $n = 10$

Distribution of Means, $n = 10$

Distribution of Means, $n = 25$

Distribution of Means, $n = 25$

sampling distributions generated from 10,000 random samples of size n

Increasing n causes the sampling distribution of the means for both the uniform and the skewed populations to become more normally distributed with less variance. The Central Limit Theorem summarizes this idea and lays the foundation for much of the study of inferential statistics by describing the relationship between a population and its sampling distribution.

CENTRAL LIMIT THEOREM

1. In a normally distributed population, the sampling distribution of sample means is normally distributed for any sample size n.
2. Random samples of size $n \geq 30$ from other populations with a mean μ and standard deviation σ have sampling distributions of the sample means that approximate normal distributions. Better approximations result with larger sample sizes.
   In both cases $\mu_{\bar{x}} = \mu$ and $\sigma_{\bar{x}} = \frac{\sigma}{\sqrt{n}}$. The standard deviation of the sample means, $\sigma_{\bar{x}}$, is also called the *standard error of the mean*.

Pierre-Simon de Laplace developed the concepts of what would come to be called the Central Limit Theorem over the course of almost 40 yr, culminating with the publication of *Théorie Analytique des Probabilités* in 1810.

The population distribution describes the data from the entire population and is the most accurate but hardest information to gather. A sample distribution includes the data from one sample and is the least accurate but easiest information to gather. The sampling distribution does not describe individuals but a statistic from all possible samples of the same size taken from the population. Inferential statistics uses sampling distributions to predict the population distribution.

In Chapter 10, individual scores from a population were standardized within the population's distribution using $z = \frac{x - \mu}{\sigma}$, and individual scores from a single sample were standardized within the sample's distribution using $z = \frac{x - \bar{x}}{s}$. We will now use the Central Limit Theorem and $z = \frac{\bar{x} - \mu_{\bar{x}}}{\sigma_{\bar{x}}}$ to standardize the distribution of the means of all possible samples of the same size taken from the population, the sampling distribution of the means.

From Laplace's era until the twentieth century, the Central Limit Theorem was generally viewed as the expression of an underlying natural law.

Be careful to determine which distribution you are using when solving problems. Different z-score formulas are used depending on the distribution.

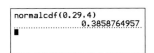 **Example 2 Analyzing Individual Values and Sample Means**

On average, 18–24-yr-olds in the United States send and receive 128 texts per day. Find each probability if the standard deviation for this normally distributed population is 41.5.

a. A randomly selected 18–24-yr-old sends and receives more than 140 texts per day.

b. The average number of texts sent and received per day for a sample of 35 randomly selected 18–24-yr-olds is more than 140.

Answer

a. $z = \frac{x - \mu}{\sigma} = \frac{140 - 128}{41.5} \approx 0.29$

1. Find the *z*-score for an individual using the population's mean and standard deviation.
2. Use technology to find the probability.

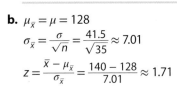

```
normalcdf(0.29,4)
             0.3858764957
■
```

$P(x > 140) = P(z > 0.29)$
$\approx 0.386 \text{ or } 38.6\%$

b. $\mu_{\bar{x}} = \mu = 128$

$\sigma_{\bar{x}} = \frac{\sigma}{\sqrt{n}} = \frac{41.5}{\sqrt{35}} \approx 7.01$

$z = \frac{\bar{x} - \mu_{\bar{x}}}{\sigma_{\bar{x}}} = \frac{140 - 128}{7.01} \approx 1.71$

1. Since $n = 35 \geq 30$, use $\mu_{\bar{x}}$ and the standard error of the mean, $\sigma_{\bar{x}}$, to find the *z*-score for the mean in a sampling distribution.

2. Use technology to find the probability.

```
normalcdf(1.71,4)
             0.0436012169
■
```

$P(x > 140) = P(z > 1.71)$
$\approx 0.044 \text{ or } 4.4\%$

SKILL ✓ **EXERCISE 23**

💡 **TIP**

The probability for the individual is found using the population's distribution: ShadeNorm (140, 1E99, 128, 41.5).

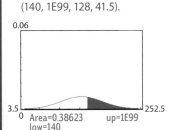

0.06

3.5   252.5
Area=0.38623
low=140   up=1E99

The probability for the sample's mean is found using the sampling distribution: ShadeNorm (140, 1E99, 128, 7.01).

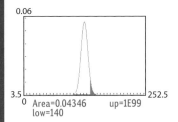

0.06

3.5   252.5
Area=0.04346
low=140   up=1E99

Example 2 demonstrates that it is not unusual for individuals to deviate from the mean. It is much more unusual for the mean of a larger sample to deviate significantly from the population's mean.

In this section we will study the means of samples from populations whose mean and standard deviation are known. In later sections we will use the Central Limit Theorem to make inferences about a population's parameters.

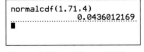 **Example 3 Applying the Central Limit Theorem**

If the average cost of a wedding in central Illinois is $19,250 with a standard deviation of $3650, find the probability that the average cost of 40 randomly selected weddings in central Illinois is less than $18,000.

Answer

$\mu_{\bar{x}} = \mu = 19,250$

$\sigma_{\bar{x}} = \frac{\sigma}{\sqrt{n}} = \frac{3650}{\sqrt{40}} \approx 577.1$

1. Since $n \geq 30$, apply the Central Limit Theorem to find the mean of the approximately normal sampling distribution, $\mu_{\bar{x}}$, and the standard error of the mean, $\sigma_{\bar{x}}$.

$z = \frac{\bar{x} - \mu_{\bar{x}}}{\sigma_{\bar{x}}} \approx \frac{18,000 - 19,250}{577.1} \approx -2.17$
$P(\bar{x} < 18,000) = P(z < -2.17)$

2. Let $\bar{x}$ = average cost of a wedding from a sample. Find the *z*-score associated with 18,000.

```
normalcdf(-4,-2.17)
             0.0149716833
```

3. Find the portion of the area under the normal curve (the probability) within the interval $-4 \leq z \leq -2.17$.

CONTINUED ➡

$P(\bar{x} < 18{,}000) = P(z < -2.17)$
≈ 0.015 or 1.5%

4. The probability that the average cost of the 40 weddings is less than \$18,000 is very unlikely.

SKILL ✓ **EXERCISE 27**

Example 4 Applying the Central Limit Theorem

Factory specifications require the weight of a candy bar coming off the production line to be 48 g with a standard deviation of 1.95 g. Weights of the candy bars are normally distributed. What is the probability that the average weight of a random sample of 10 candy bars is between 47.5 g and 48.75 g?

Answer

$\mu_{\bar{x}} = \mu = 48$

$\sigma_{\bar{x}} = \dfrac{\sigma}{\sqrt{n}} = \dfrac{1.95}{\sqrt{10}} \approx 0.617$

1. Since the population is normally distributed, all sampling distributions are normally distributed with $\mu_{\bar{x}} = \mu$ and $\sigma_{\bar{x}} = \dfrac{\sigma}{\sqrt{n}}$.

$z_{lower} = \dfrac{\bar{x} - \mu_{\bar{x}}}{\sigma_{\bar{x}}} = \dfrac{47.5 - 48}{0.617} \approx -0.81$

$z_{upper} = \dfrac{\bar{x} - \mu_{\bar{x}}}{\sigma_{\bar{x}}} = \dfrac{48.75 - 48}{0.617} \approx 1.22$

2. Find the lower and upper z-scores for the interval of sample means.

$P(47.5 < \bar{x} < 48.75) \approx P(-0.81 < z < 1.22)$
$= \text{normalcdf}(-0.81, 1.22) \approx 0.68$ or 68%

3. Use technology to find the probability.

SKILL ✓ **EXERCISE 29**

Statistical quality control, developed during World War II to improve mass production requirements for materials, is essential to success in modern manufacturing of everything from food products to computers.

The Central Limit Theorem justifies the use of the normal distribution to approximate a sampling distribution when $n \geq 30$ or when the population is normally distributed. Binomial probability distributions that represent discrete outcomes can also be approximated by a normal distribution under certain conditions. The table illustrates how binomial distributions become more normally distributed as n increases.

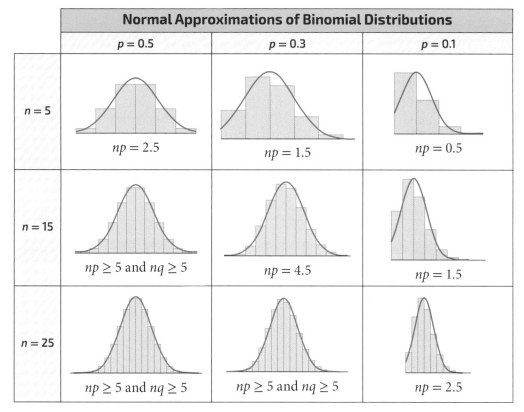

Normal Approximations of Binomial Distributions

	$p = 0.5$	$p = 0.3$	$p = 0.1$
$n = 5$	$np = 2.5$	$np = 1.5$	$np = 0.5$
$n = 15$	$np \geq 5$ and $nq \geq 5$	$np = 4.5$	$np = 1.5$
$n = 25$	$np \geq 5$ and $nq \geq 5$	$np \geq 5$ and $nq \geq 5$	$np = 2.5$

Using a normal approximation for the binomial distribution when $np \geq 5$ and $nq \geq 5$ allows binomial probabilities to be found more easily. Recall that the mean and standard deviation in a binomial distribution are given by $\mu = np$ and $\sigma = \sqrt{npq}$.

▎NORMAL APPROXIMATION OF A BINOMIAL DISTRIBUTION

A binomial distribution can be approximated by a normal distribution if $np \geq 5$ and $nq \geq 5$ where n is the number of trials, p is the probability of success, and q is the probability of failure. The distribution can be converted to standard normal distribution using
$$z = \frac{x - \mu}{\sigma} = \frac{x - np}{\sqrt{npq}}.$$

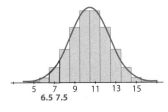

When the discrete binomial distribution is approximated by a continuous normal distribution, a *continuity correction factor* of 0.5 is subtracted from the lowest value and added to the highest value to obtain accurate results. To find $P(x = 7)$ in the discrete binomial distribution, find $P(6.5 \leq x \leq 7.5)$ in the continuous normal distribution.

	Corrections for Continuous Probability Distributions			
discrete	equal to 7	at least 11	less than 7	between 7 and 11
meaning	$x = 7$	$x \geq 11$	$x \leq 6$	$8 \leq x \leq 10$
correction for continuity	$6.5 \leq x \leq 7.5$	$x \geq 10.5$	$x \leq 6.5$	$7.5 \leq x \leq 10.5$

Example 5 Approximating a Binomial Probability

Sixty-one percent of teens volunteer to help others during the Christmas season. If 60 randomly selected teens are asked if they have volunteered to help others during the Christmas season, what is the probability that less than 35 of them answer yes?

Answer

$n = 60, p = 0.61, q = 0.39$

1. Define n, p, and q for the binomial experiment.

$np = 60(0.61) = 36.6 \geq 5$
$nq = 60(0.39) = 23.4 \geq 5$

2. Verify that the binomial distribution can be approximated with a normal distribution.

$\mu = np = 36.6$
$\sigma = \sqrt{npq} = \sqrt{60(0.61)(0.39)} \approx 3.78$

3. Find μ and σ.

$P(x < 35) \approx P(x \leq 34.5)$

4. Write the discrete probability and restate the probability with its continuity correction factor.

$z = \frac{x - \mu}{\sigma} \approx \frac{34.5 - 36.6}{3.78} \approx -0.56$
$P(z \leq -0.56) \approx 0.288$ or 28.8%

5. Convert to a z-score and use technology to find the probability.

SKILL ✔ **EXERCISE 17**

Example 6 Approximating a Binomial Probability

A survey found that 46.4% of teens like to watch the Summer Olympics. Estimate the probability that 120 out of 250 randomly selected teens like watching the Summer Olympics.

Answer

$n = 250, p = 0.464, q = 0.536$

1. Define n, p, and q for the binomial experiment.

$np = 250(0.464) = 116 \geq 5$
$nq = 250(0.536) = 134 \geq 5$

2. Verify that the binomial distribution can be approximated with a normal distribution.

CONTINUED ➡

$\mu = np = 116$

$\sigma = \sqrt{npq} = \sqrt{250(0.464)(0.536)} \approx 7.89$

$P(x = 120) \approx P(119.5 \le x \le 120.5)$

$z_{low} = \dfrac{119.5 - 116}{7.89} \approx 0.44$

$z_{high} = \dfrac{120.5 - 116}{7.89} \approx 0.57$

$P(0.44 \le z \le 0.57) \approx 0.046$ or 4.6%

3. Find μ and σ.

4. Write the discrete probability and restate the probability with its continuity correction factor.

5. Convert to a z-score and use technology to find the probability.

SKILL ✓ **EXERCISE 33**

❯ A. Exercises

For exercises 1–4, identify the described distribution as a (I) population, (II) sample, or (III) sampling distribution.

1. Which distribution represents data from each of the following?

   a. a group within the population

   b. all possible samples of the same size

   c. an entire group

2. Which distribution has values that are standardized by each z-score?

   a. $z = \dfrac{\bar{x} - \mu_{\bar{x}}}{\sigma_{\bar{x}}}$ **b.** $z = \dfrac{x - \bar{x}}{s}$ **c.** $z = \dfrac{x - \mu}{\sigma}$

3. When making predictions about a population's parameter, which distribution has each given characteristic?

   a. most accurate   **b.** least accurate

4. Which distribution describes each of the following in a study of Texas high school basketball team members?

   a. a randomly selected group of 20 basketball team members from Texas high schools

   b. all basketball team members from Texas high schools

   c. the collection of all possible groupings of 20 basketball team members from Texas high schools

Use the population {1, 3, 5, 7, 9} for exercises 5–8.

5. Find the mean and standard deviation of the population, and then draw a histogram representing the population's distribution.

6. Create a table of all possible samples of size 2 (taken with replacement) from this population and find the mean for each sample.

7. Create a table and a histogram representing the sampling distribution for the means.

8. Find the mean and standard deviation of the sampling distribution and compare them to the population's mean and standard deviation.

A population has a mean of 86 and a standard deviation of 8.2. Find the mean and the standard deviation of a sampling distribution of the means having the given sample size.

9. $n = 15$ 10. $n = 50$

11. State the two conditions for which the Central Limit Theorem implies that the sampling distribution of the means approximates a normal distribution.

Determine whether the Central Limit Theorem can be applied to each population distribution with the given mean and standard deviation using a sample size of n. If so, find $\mu_{\bar{x}}$ and $\sigma_{\bar{x}}$. If not, explain why.

12. skewed left with $\mu = 52$, $\sigma = 3.5$, and $n = 12$

13. normal with $\mu = 126$, $\sigma = 18$, and $n = 8$

14. skewed right with $\mu = 9$, $\sigma = 0.8$, and $n = 38$

15. unknown with $\mu = 37$, $\sigma = 4.9$, and $n = 19$

16. State the continuity correction factor used when using a normal approximation to find each binomial probability.

   a. $P(x = 12)$ **b.** $P(\text{at least } 9)$

   c. $P(\text{between 3 and 7})$ **d.** $P(\text{less than } 6)$

Determine whether the normal distribution can be used to approximate the binomial distribution for an experiment with n trials, each having a probability of success of p. Explain your reasoning.

17. $n = 10$, $p = 0.15$ 18. $n = 200$, $p = 0.82$

19. $n = 32$, $p = 0.78$ 20. $n = 16$, $p = 0.97$

21. Complete the following steps to create and analyze a sampling distribution of the means for the population {3, 6, 8, 10} in which $\mu = 6.75$ and $\sigma \approx 2.59$.

   a. List all possible samples of size 2 and their corresponding means, $\bar{x}$.

   b. Create a table and a histogram representing the sampling distribution for the means.

   c. Find the mean and standard deviation for the sampling distribution and compare them to the population's mean and standard deviation.

22. Find each probability if the average weight of an adult rainbow trout is normally distributed with a mean of 8 lb and a standard deviation of 2.1 lb.

   a. The adult rainbow trout you catch weighs between 9 lb and 12 lb.

   b. The average weight of 40 adult trout reported caught in a fishing magazine survey of anglers is more than 7.5 lb.

23. The average GPA of incoming freshmen at a Christian college is 3.15 with a standard deviation of 0.28. Find each probability, assuming the GPAs are normally distributed.

   a. A randomly selected freshman has a GPA less than 3.0.

   b. The average GPA of 35 randomly selected freshmen is between 3.2 and 3.8.

24. According to the Bureau of Labor Statistics, teenagers aged 15–19 get an average of 9.8 hr of sleep per night. Find each probability, assuming that the hours of sleep for teens are normally distributed and the standard deviation is 1.86 hr.

   a. A randomly chosen 17-yr-old averages less than 8 hr of sleep.

   b. Forty randomly selected 15–19-yr-olds average less than 8 hr of sleep.

25. The average annual snowfall in Bangor, Maine, is normally distributed with a mean of 66 in. Find each probability, assuming a standard deviation of 4.8 in.

   a. more than 64 in. of snow in one year

   b. an average annual snowfall of more than 64 in. over 15 yr

26. If a town has an average January high temperature of 42.2° with a standard deviation of 4.7°, what is the probability that 5 randomly chosen days in January have a high temperature greater than 45°?

27. The average smartphone in 2017 cost $363. If the standard deviation is $28.20, what is the probability that the mean cost for 36 randomly selected consumers was more than $350?

28. If a normally distributed set of test scores has a mean of 82 and standard deviation of 6.2, find the probability that a normally distributed sample of 20 scores will average greater than 85.

29. A normally distributed population of 5-yr-old girls has an average weight of 40 lb with a standard deviation of 5 lb. Find the probability that the average weight of 35 randomly selected 5-yr-old girls is between 39 lb and 41 lb.

30. If frozen chicken pot pies contain an average of 1040 mg of sodium and the sodium level is normally distributed with a standard deviation of 3.7 mg, what is the probability that 15 pot pies coming off the production line contain an average of 1038 mg to 1041 mg of sodium?

31. The time that a randomly selected student waits for a school bus is normally distributed with a mean of 5 min and a standard deviation of 2.5 min. Find the probability that the average wait time for a random sample of 10 students is less than 3 minutes.

Use a normal approximation for the binomial distribution and continuity correction factor to estimate each binomial probability.

32. Mark randomly guesses at each of the 10 true-false questions on a test. Find the probability that he gets each number of these questions correct.

   a. P(at least 7)   **b.** $P(4 \leq x \leq 6)$ **c.** P(at most 3)

33. According to AAA, 46% of teenagers admit to texting while driving. If 60 teen drivers are randomly selected, find each probability.

   a. more than 30 admit to texting while driving

   b. between 20 and 30 admit to texting while driving

34. Benson's Garage advertises a 20 min oil change. Their records indicate that this actually occurs 62% of the time. Find the probability that each number of customers from a random survey of 30 customers will have had their oil changed in less than 20 minutes.

  a. $P(x = 14)$

  b. $P(20 < x < 25)$

  c. P(at least half)

35. A score of 1200 on a recent standardized test represents the 75th percentile. Find each probability if 25 test scores are randomly selected.

  a. less than 5 have a score of 1200 or more

  b. at least 10 have a score of 1200 or more

❯ C. Exercises

36. Six sets of 5 numbers are created by randomly drawing (with replacement) from the digits 0 through 9. Use technology and these samples with $n = 5$ to complete the following.

    $A = \{8, 4, 1, 9, 3\}$; $B = \{4, 4, 6, 9, 3\}$

    $C = \{2, 0, 2, 0, 5\}$; $D = \{9, 1, 1, 8, 6\}$

    $E = \{5, 2, 5, 6, 0\}$; $F = \{8, 4, 9, 7, 5\}$

  a. Compute the population's mean and standard deviation.

  b. Find the mean of each sample and create a table representing the distribution of these means. Does the table represent a sampling distribution of the means? Explain your reasoning.

  c. Use technology to find the mean and standard deviation for the means of the samples, and then compare them to the mean and standard deviation of a sampling distribution of the means.

37. Using technology, complete the following steps to create and analyze a sampling distribution of the sample means when $n = 3$ for the population $\{3, 6, 8, 10\}$ with $\mu = 6.75$ and $\sigma \approx 2.59$.

  a. List all possible samples of size $n = 3$ and their corresponding means, $\bar{x}$.

  b. Create a table and a histogram representing the sampling distribution for the means.

  c. Find the mean and standard deviation for the sampling distribution.

38. The mean systolic blood pressure for men in a recent study was 124.71 millimeters of mercury (mm Hg). Assume the population is normally distributed with a standard deviation of 14.53 mm Hg.

  a. What is the probability that the average systolic blood pressure of a sample of 30 men selected randomly from the population is between 122.0 and 130.4?

  b. If an individual from the population is randomly selected and his blood pressure taken, what is the probability that his systolic blood pressure is between 122.0 and 130.4?

  c. Are the probabilities from parts a and b the same? Explain why or why not.

39. A telemarketer who earns $25 per sale is told that he can expect to make a sale on only 8% of his calls. During his first week, he makes 588 calls and gets 25 sales.

  a. How many sales are expected with the given number of calls?

  b. What is the probability of making 25 sales or fewer?

  c. What is the probability of making the expected number of sales or fewer?

  d. Determine his expected weekly earnings after several weeks when he can make 550 calls a week and makes a sale on 6% of his calls.

  e. What is the probability that he will make at least $900 per week?

40. A vendor selling hot dogs and hamburgers at a baseball game knows that 55% of his customers buy hot dogs. If 20 customers want to make a purchase before he restocks and he only has 12 hotdogs and 12 hamburgers in his case, what is the probability every customer gets the item he wants?

Solve each rational equation. [2.6]

41. $\dfrac{3x+1}{x^2-11x+24} + \dfrac{5}{x^2-9} = \dfrac{3x}{x^2-5x-24}$

42. $\dfrac{3x+5}{x^2-4} + \dfrac{4}{x^2+7x+10} = \dfrac{4x}{x^2+3x-10}$

Given u = $\langle 6, -12 \rangle$, v = $\langle 12, -5 \rangle$, and w = $\langle -5, 8 \rangle$, write each resultant vector in component form and as a linear combination of standard unit vectors i and j. [6.1]

43. $2\mathbf{w} + \mathbf{v}$

44. $4\mathbf{v} - \dfrac{1}{2}\mathbf{u} + 3\mathbf{w}$

Find the percentile rank for each value (to the nearest percent). [10.6]

45. an automobile weighing 4564 lb if the mean is 4021 lb and standard deviation is 421 lb

46. a student with a score of 28 on an assignment with a mean of 20.6 and standard deviation of 5.3

47. Use technology to create a scatterplot of the data. Then determine the linear, quadratic, or exponential function that best models the data. Round coefficients to the nearest thousandth. [1.9]

x	y
-4	4.4
-2	2.1
0	5.3
2	15.1
4	28.7
6	49.7
8	80.7
10	99.7

A. $f(x) = 0.749x^2 + 3.267x + 4.787$

B. $f(x) = 0.636x^2 + 3.367x + 6.527$

C. $f(x) = 7.184x + 14.161$

D. $f(x) = 7.467(1.326)^x$

E. none of these

48. Find the exact value of $\tan(\mathrm{Sin}^{-1}(-1))$ without using technology. [4.6]

A. 1   **C.** 0   **E.** none of

B. -1 **D.** ∞ these

49. Which statement is the anchor step in the inductive proof of $14 + 18 + 22 + \cdots + (4n + 10) = 2n(n + 6)$? [9.5]

A. $P(1) = 14 = 2(1)(1 + 6)$

B. $P(k) = 2k(k + 6)$

C. $P(k + 1) = 2(k + 1)((k + 1) + 6)$

D. $P(k) = P(k + 1)$

E. none of these

50. Use the binomial probability distribution formula to find the probability (to the nearest percent) of 9 successes in 15 independent trials if the probability of success in each trial is 0.73. [11.1]

A. 4%   **C.** 12%   **E.** none of

B. 11%   **D.** 27%   these

MATHEMATICAL EXPECTATION

Imagine a lottery in which the chances of winning are one in two. Winners are guaranteed a lifespan of 180 yr—and losers are immediately put to death. If the government requires participation of all citizens, then the average lifespan will be 90 yr. Would you volunteer to migrate to this country to enjoy the enviable longevity of its citizens? A similar thought experiment was used by French mathematician Jean Le Rond d'Alembert (1717–83) to argue against probability theory findings by Swiss mathematician Daniel Bernoulli (1700–82) that supported smallpox inoculations. Even if not very likely, the large immediate risk (death from purposeful exposure to smallpox) outweighed the small future benefit (living for an additional two or three years) for the majority. D'Alembert pointed out that what is optimal for the state may not be optimal for the individual.

Pierre-Simon de Laplace (1749–1827), the preeminent French mathematician and scientist of his time, laid out ten principles concerning the calculation of probabilities in the 1814 edition of his *Analytic Theory of Probability*. The first principle was the definition of probability as the ratio of favorable to possible outcomes. After nearly 200 yr, these principles have not changed. Laplace is also responsible for two major developments in probability theory that are now known as the Central Limit Theorem and Bayesian inference (known at the time as inverse probability).

English mathematician Karl Pearson (1857–1936) developed the chi-squared test to determine the reasonableness of fit between observed and expected frequencies in large data sets, while another Englishman, R. A. Fisher (1890–1962), was interested in how to make sound deductions from small data sets. Fisher was a researcher at an agricultural experimental center and published a book in 1925 entitled *Statistical Methods for Research Workers* that statistics author John Tabak claims "may well be the most successful book on statistics ever written." Fisher was particularly interested in experimental design, and one of his later books includes a discussion on how to design an experiment to test the claim that a person could tell by the taste whether milk was added to a cup before or after tea was added. Fisher's work, published initially in agricultural journals, contains a wealth of pioneering mathematics that continues to be explored and used in modern times.

In the beginning of the twentieth century, the Russian mathematician Andrey Kolmogorov (1903–87) axiomatized the theory of probability. This tremendous breakthrough brought mathematical rigor to the field and allowed mathematicians to apply the full weight of analysis to probability theory. Even so, controversy still surrounds the application of statistical findings to real-world problems. Although algorithms are written by authors who have their own worldview and prejudices, many people view algorithms as unbiased and unquestionable because the results come from a computer and are presented in terms of probabilities. Statistics-based algorithms are now common in finance (determining who gets a loan and at what rate), education, criminal justice (sentencing), and advertising. As the use of algorithms rapidly increases, an increasing number of people are warning of pitfalls and calling for experiential judgment and wisdom in interpreting and implementing algorithmic metrics.

COMPREHENSION CHECK

1. What public policy did Daniel Bernoulli's probability research support?

2. Who published ten principles of probability theory in 1814 that remain valid today?

3. What English mathematician wrote the "most successful book on statistics ever written"?

4. What was the major twentieth century contribution of Andrey Kolmogorov to probability theory?

5. **Discuss:** One problem frequently noted with applying quantitative statistics to social issues (sometimes called Campbell's law) is that inevitably the measures will succumb to corruption. Use the Internet keyword search *CompStat* to research a common modern policing tool. List some pros and cons of the system. What biblical principles can help shape our worldview concerning the use of systems like these?

There are approximately 300,000 African bush elephants in the world, some weighing over 11 tons.

After completing this section, you will be able to

- calculate point estimates for the mean of a population.
- find the critical value and margin of error for a given confidence level.
- construct and interpret confidence intervals for the mean of a population.
- calculate the minimum sample size.

What is the average weight of a male African bush elephant? You would have to find and weigh every one of them to calculate the population's mean weight, but this is not possible. How can you find a statistic to estimate the average weight, and how confident can you be of the accuracy of your estimate?

In the last section, the Central Limit Theorem was used to find the probability of a sample mean being a certain value when the mean and the standard deviation of the population were known. However, this information is rarely known since the population being studied is usually very large or inaccessible. Instead, statistics such as the mean and standard deviation of a sample are determined and used to estimate (or infer) the related parameters for the population.

There are two types of estimates: the *point estimate* and the *interval estimate*.

▌**DEFINITIONS**

A **point estimate** is a single-value estimation of a population's parameter. An **interval estimate** is a range of values used to estimate a population's parameter.

We will limit our discussion to estimates of the mean for populations in which the Central Limit Theorem applies. When the population is normally distributed or the sample size $n \geq 30$, the mean of the sampling distribution of the sample means is equal to the mean of the population ($\mu_{\bar{x}} = \mu$). In this case, a sample's mean, $\bar{x}$, is the best point estimate of the population's mean, μ.

Estimates from small samples ($n < 30$) of populations that are not normally distributed and estimates for other parameters are reserved for later courses in statistics. Any estimate needs to be *unbiased*, which means the estimate is a value that does not consistently underestimate or overestimate the parameter.

Example 1 Finding a Point Estimate

Find the best point estimate for μ using the following random sample of values from a population.

{51, 49, 56, 81, 44, 65, 69, 72, 57, 48, 55, 64, 73, 57, 63, 64, 71, 69, 73, 58, 70, 67, 74, 86, 75, 69, 83, 67, 77, 58, 74, 66, 84, 75, 71, 68, 64, 76, 81, 77}

Answer

$$\bar{x} = \frac{\sum\limits_{i=1}^{40} x_i}{40} = \frac{2701}{40} = 67.525$$

67.525 is the point estimate of μ.

Since $n = 40$, the Central Limit Theorem applies and the sample's mean is the best point estimate of μ.

SKILL ✓**EXERCISE 15a**

It is extremely unlikely that the mean μ of the population in Example 1 is exactly $\bar{x} = 67.525$, but there is a good chance it is fairly close to the sample's mean. Statisticians typically report an interval around the point estimate in which they are reasonably sure the actual parameter lies. The larger the interval, the more confident we can be that it includes the parameter. The normal distribution predicted by the Central Limit Theorem allows us to quantify the *confidence level*, c, as the probability that this interval estimate (called a *confidence interval*) contains the population parameter.

The level of confidence is the area under the standard normal distribution curve between the *critical values*, $\pm z_c$. To find the critical values for an 80% confidence level, find the z-scores, which define the interval containing the middle 80% of the area under the standard normal distribution curve. In this case, 10% of the area is in each tail, so 90% of the data lies below $z_c \approx 1.28$.

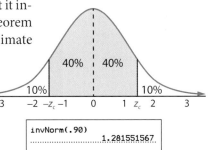

Example 2 Determining the Critical Value

Use technology to find the critical value, z_c, for a 95% confidence level.

Answer

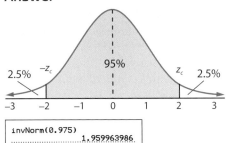

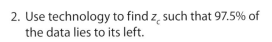

$z_c \approx 1.96$

1. Since $c = 0.95$ is the portion of the area under the curve within $\pm z_c$, each tail contains
$$\frac{1-c}{2} = 0.025 \text{ or } 2.5\% \text{ of the area.}$$

2. Use technology to find z_c such that 97.5% of the data lies to its left.

SKILL ✓ **EXERCISE 15b**

 TIP

Remembering the critical values for these frequently used confidence levels will save time and effort in the future.

Confidence Level	Critical Value
c	z_c
90%	1.645
95%	1.96
99%	2.58

To construct a confidence interval (CI) for the population mean, a *margin of error* (sometimes called the *maximum error of the estimate*) is added to and subtracted from the sample mean, $\bar{x}$. This margin of error is determined by the critical value, z_c, for the desired confidence level, the standard deviation of the population (either estimated or known), and the sample size.

▌DEFINITIONS

For a given confidence level, c, the **confidence interval for the mean** is $\bar{x} \pm E$ where E, the **margin of error for the mean**, is found using
$$E = z_c\left(\frac{s}{\sqrt{n}}\right),$$
where z_c is the critical value for the confidence level and s is the standard deviation of a randomized sample of size $n \geq 30$. If the population standard deviation is known, substitute σ for s.

In 1937 Polish mathematician Jerzy Neyman published the theory behind confidence intervals. He also developed the experimental method that the FDA uses to test medicines today.

Example 3 Finding a Margin of Error and Confidence Interval

A random sample of 35 male African bush elephants has a mean weight of 13,483 lb with a standard deviation of 1263 lb. Find the 90% margin of error and 90% confidence interval for the population mean weight and interpret the meaning of the confidence interval.

Answer

Note that $\bar{x} = 13{,}483$ and $s = 1263$.
$$E = z_c\left(\frac{s}{\sqrt{n}}\right) = 1.645\left(\frac{1263}{\sqrt{35}}\right) \approx 351$$

1. Since $n = 35$, the Central Limit Theorem applies. Use the critical value $z_c = 1.645$ for a 90% confidence level.

CONTINUED ➡

$$\bar{x} \pm E \approx 13{,}483 \pm 351$$
$$= (13{,}132, \ 13{,}834)$$

We are 90% confident that this interval contains μ.

2. The margin of error is subtracted from and added to the sample mean to construct the 90% confidence interval.

3. Interpret the confidence interval.

SKILL ✔ **EXERCISE 15c**

Confidence intervals are often misunderstood. The mean of the population, μ, is a fixed number for a given population. Different samples will produce varying confidence intervals. In Example 3, 90% of these intervals would contain μ, but 10% of them would not. We cannot be sure that μ is in our calculated confidence interval. The figure illustrates ten different 90% confidence intervals for the population mean. Notice that nine contain the population mean and one does not.

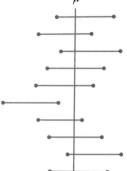

Example 4 Constructing and Interpreting a 97% Confidence Interval

Students studying earthquakes took a random sample of Richter scale values from 50 earthquakes over the past 25 yr. The mean of the values was 1.1842 with a standard deviation of 0.3449. Find the 97% confidence interval and interpret its meaning.

Answer

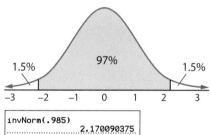

$s = 0.3449, n = 50$
$$E = z_c \left(\frac{s}{\sqrt{n}} \right) = 2.17 \left(\frac{0.3449}{\sqrt{50}} \right) \approx 0.1058$$

$$\bar{x} \pm E \approx 1.1842 \pm 0.1058 = (1.0784, 1.2900)$$

We are 97% confident that the population mean μ of the Richter scale values is in the interval (1.0784, 1.2900).

Check

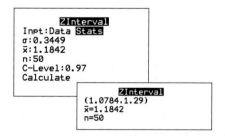

1. Since 97% of the area is within $\pm z_c$, each tail contains 1.5% of the area.

Use technology to find z_c such that 98.5% of the data lies to its left.

2. Substitute z_c, s, and n into the formula for the margin of error of the mean and evaluate.

3. Calculate the 97% CI.

4. Interpret the confidence interval.

5. The STAT, TESTS submenu contains a ZInterval function that can be used to calculate confidence intervals. Select the Stats option for Inpt: and enter the standard deviation (using the value of s for σ), the sample mean, and the confidence level.

The interval is listed in the first line.

SKILL ✔ **EXERCISE 17**

The next example examines the effect of the confidence level and sample size on the precision of the resulting confidence interval.

In the 1980s many research journals, particularly in the medical field, began to require authors to include confidence intervals in the presentation of their results.

Example 5 Analyzing Confidence Intervals

Researchers recorded the body temperatures of individuals from two samples of randomly selected adults and calculated each sample's mean and standard deviation.

a. Construct and compare the 90% CI and the 99% CI from Sample A.

b. Construct the 90% CI from Sample B and compare it to the 90% CI from Sample A.

Sample A	Sample B
$n = 40$	$n = 95$
$\bar{x} = 98.165°F$	$\bar{x} = 98.204°F$
$s = 0.687°F$	$s = 0.631°F$

Answer

a. Sample A, 90% CI

$$E = z_c\left(\frac{s}{\sqrt{n}}\right)$$
$$= 1.645\left(\frac{0.687}{\sqrt{40}}\right)$$
$$\approx 0.179$$
$$\bar{x} \pm E \approx 98.165 \pm 0.179$$
$$= (97.986°F, 98.344°F)$$

Sample A, 99% CI

$$E = z_c\left(\frac{s}{\sqrt{n}}\right)$$
$$= 2.58\left(\frac{0.687}{\sqrt{40}}\right)$$
$$\approx 0.280$$
$$\bar{x} \pm E \approx 98.165 \pm 0.280$$
$$= (97.885°F, 98.445°F)$$

1. Use $z_{90} = 1.645$ and $z_{99} = 2.58$ to determine each margin of error, the 90% CI, and the 99% CI from Sample A.

The higher (99%) level of confidence is created using a larger margin of error, which provides a less precise estimate.

2. Compare the results.

---

b. Sample A, 90% CI

$$E \approx 0.179$$
$$\bar{x} \pm E \approx (97.986°F, 98.344°F)$$

Sample B, 90% CI

$$E = z_c\left(\frac{s}{\sqrt{n}}\right)$$
$$= 1.645\left(\frac{0.631}{\sqrt{95}}\right)$$
$$\approx 0.106$$
$$\bar{x} \pm E \approx 98.204 \pm 0.106$$
$$= (98.098°F, 98.31°F)$$

1. Use $z_{90} = 1.645$ and $n = 95$ to find the 90% CI from Sample B.

The larger sample size of Sample B reduced the margin of error and the width of the confidence interval, allowing a more precise estimate. The slightly smaller value for s also made the 90% confidence interval slightly smaller.

2. Compare the results.

SKILL ✓ EXERCISES 29–31

Researchers desire the narrowest possible confidence interval while maintaining a high level of confidence. But the margin of error formula, $E = z_c\left(\frac{s}{\sqrt{n}}\right)$, implies that higher confidence levels generate larger margins of error and wider confidence intervals. The sample standard deviations, s, cannot be controlled by the researcher and will likely be close to the population standard deviation, σ. Therefore, increasing the sample size, n, is the only way to effectively lower the margin of error and obtain a more precise confidence interval with the desired level of confidence. Solving the margin of error formula for n (see exercise 27) results in a formula that can be used to find the minimum sample size required for the desired confidence level and margin of error.

$$n = \left(\frac{z_c s}{E}\right)^2$$

Example 6　Finding a Minimum Sample Size

A researcher studying body mass index (BMI) desires a 95% confidence level and the margin of error for the mean to be no more than 2. A small pilot study determined that $s = 7.4$ is a reasonable standard deviation for the population. Determine the minimum sample size for the research study.

Answer

$$n = \left(\frac{z_c s}{E}\right)^2 = \left(\frac{1.96(7.4)}{2}\right)^2 \approx 52.6$$

The minimum sample size is 53.

1. Use the sample size formula with $z_{95} = 1.96$.

2. Always round up since the formula yields the minimum number required.

_____ SKILL ✔ **EXERCISE 23**

It would be wise to include several more people in the study referenced in Example 6 since the actual sample standard deviation, s, will likely differ somewhat from 7.4 in the study.

❯ A. Exercises

Match each term with its description.
A. confidence interval
B. confidence level
C. critical value
D margin of error
E. point estimate

1. a single value that estimates a population's parameter

2. a range of values that estimates a population's parameter

3. the probability that a confidence interval contains the population's parameter

4. the maximum difference between the point estimate and the actual parameter value

5. What is the only way to effectively lower the margin of error?

6. Researchers desire the (*smallest* or *largest*) possible CI while maintaining a (*low* or *high*) level of confidence.

Use technology to find the critical value z_c (to the nearest thousandth) for each confidence level.

7. 90% confidence level

8. 99% confidence level

9. 85% confidence level

10. 78% confidence level

Find the margin of error for the mean, E, for the given confidence level, c.

11. $c = 95\%$ if $n = 42$ and $s = 2.6$

12. $c = 99\%$ if $n = 64$ and $s = 158$

13. $c = 80\%$ if $n = 120$ and $s = 5.9$

14. $c = 72\%$ if $n = 30$ and $s = 71$

Use each random sample to find
(a) the point estimate for the population's mean,
(b) the critical value for the stated confidence level,
and (c) the related confidence interval.

15. {4, 9, 1, 8, 6, 8, 5, 5, 4, 0,
6, 1, 1, 1, 1, 7, 3, 3, 5, 6,
3, 7, 7, 7, 1, 9, 2, 3, 9, 8}
$c = 95\%$

16. {42, 18, 93, 32, 92, 3, 95, 51, 48, 54,
81, 7, 62, 78, 13, 99, 49, 8, 32, 34,
34, 81, 30, 9, 22, 97, 49, 43, 6, 8}
$c = 98\%$

❯ B. Exercises

Find each confidence interval from the given sample statistics and interpret its meaning.

17. $c = 90\%$, $n = 52$, $\bar{x} = 10{,}372$, $s = 1018$

18. $c = 95\%$, $n = 115$, $\bar{x} = 38$, $s = 4.7$

19. $c = 98\%$, $n = 32$, $\bar{x} = 79$, $s = 8.2$

20. $c = 97\%$, $n = 30$, $\bar{x} = 2.81$, $s = 0.17$

Use each random sample to find the point estimate and the 90% confidence interval for the population's mean.

21. {403, 906, 387, 519, 285, 691, 592, 482, 905, 350, 987, 186, 872, 436, 362, 571, 790, 301, 815, 283, 693, 109, 363, 531, 364, 314, 780, 799, 794, 144}

22. {110, 465, 489, 284, 434, 557, 656, 694, 598, 343, 180, 346, 315, 170, 103, 477, 412, 406, 860, 632, 620, 284, 492, 391, 882, 112, 386, 328, 284, 394}

Find the minimum sample size, *n*, for the given margin of error in a normally distributed population with the given standard deviation.

23. 80% CI, $E = 1.5$, $\sigma = 7.4$

24. 90% CI, $E = 11$, $\sigma = 38.5$

25. 99% CI, $E = 0.2$, $\sigma = 0.47$

26. 95% CI, $E = 38$, $\sigma = 896$

27. Derive the formula for minimum sample size from the formula for the margin of error of the mean.

A researcher compares different-sized samples from a population. Construct the 90% confidence interval and the 99% confidence interval from each sample if $\bar{x} = 800$ and $s = 50$.

28. $n = 50$ 29. $n = 500$ 30. $n = 5000$

31. In exercises 28–30, which sample size and confidence level provide the narrowest confidence interval?

32. In 2015 a sample of 2600 teens spent an average of 81 min/day playing video games with $s = 21.4$ min/day. Find the 95% confidence interval for the population's mean. What causes the confidence interval to be so narrow?

33. The maximum drop on 55 randomly selected roller coasters in the United States was determined. If the average was 132.37 ft with a standard deviation of 64.90 ft, find a 95% confidence interval for the average maximum drop for US roller coasters.

34. The average distance of 32 randomly selected home runs hit during the 2016 MLB season was 406.81 ft with a standard deviation of 25.75 ft.
    a. Use your calculator's ZInterval function to find the 97% confidence interval for the mean distance of all the home runs hit that season.
    b. State the point estimate for the mean and the margin of error.
    c. Would a population mean distance of 400.3 ft be surprising? Why or why not?

35. An ornithologist seeks to determine the average heart rate of hummingbirds in flight. Preliminary research suggests a standard deviation of 115 bpm. What is the minimum sample size for this study if he selects a 95% confidence interval and the acceptable margin of error is 30 bpm?

36. If a study is conducted to determine the average lifespan of a certain brand of microwaves, how many microwaves should be tested if the accepted margin of error is 3 mo, the standard deviation based on past lifespans of the brand's microwaves is 0.8 yr, and a 99% confidence interval is desired?

C. Exercises

37. A random sample of 44 GPAs was selected from the seniors in a city's high schools. The 90% confidence interval for the mean was found to be (3.17, 3.43). Determine whether each statement is a correct interpretation of the result and explain your reasoning.
    a. 90% of all the students have a GPA between 3.17 and 3.43.
    b. 90% of the confidence intervals constructed from random samples of this population will contain the population's mean GPA.
    c. 90% of the sampled students have a GPA between 3.17 and 3.43.
    d. 90% of all samples of students will have average GPAs between 3.17 and 3.43.

38. A study in *Developmental Medicine & Child Neurology* reported the mean age at which 72 babies learned to roll from their back to their stomach and vice versa. Data from the study is displayed in the following table.

	Back to Stomach	Stomach to Back
mean age	4 mo	4.8 mo
95% CI	3.7 to 4.3	4.4 to 5.2

   a. State the point estimate and *E* for both rolling back to stomach and rolling stomach to back.
   b. Would you be surprised to hear that the population's mean age of rolling back to stomach was truly 4.4 mo? Why or why not?

39. A study compared the leaf widths from samples of camellia plants grown in the sun and those grown in the shade.

	Sun	Shade
n	100	30
$\bar{x}$	55.82 mm	47.67 mm
s	7.26 mm	3.96 mm

a. Construct the 90% confidence interval for the mean leaf width of each population.

b. Based on the confidence interval for the shrubs growing in the shade, do you think the mean leaf width of all camellia plants growing in the shade could be 50 mm? Why or why not?

40. A sample of the heights of 40 players in the Eastern Conference of the WNBA during the 2014 season revealed the mean to be 72.38 in. with a standard deviation of 3.76 in. Create a 98% confidence interval for the mean height of all women in the conference that year. Would it be unusual for a 5 ft 6 in. woman to be in the conference? Why or why not?

41. The number of calories per serving from 30 different brands of chocolate ice cream was determined.
{130, 260, 185, 172, 220, 214, 190, 175, 204, 218, 158, 217, 138, 159, 184, 195, 289, 174, 149, 163, 184, 173, 210, 221, 167, 180, 205, 148, 176, 221}

a. Find the point estimate for the population mean.

b. Use the sample to find 99%, 95%, and 90% confidence intervals for the population mean.

c. Describe the relationship between the level of confidence and the width of the confidence interval for a given sample.

CUMULATIVE REVIEW

Write the rule for g(x), the described transformation of f(x). [4.5]

42. The function $f(x) = \csc x$ is horizontally stretched so its period is 4π and it is shifted up 2 units.

43. The function $f(x) = \sec x$ is horizontally shrunk so its period is 2 and it is vertically shrunk by a factor of $\frac{1}{4}$.

Use identities to find each value. [5.1]

44. Find $\tan \theta$ if $\cos \theta = 0.8764$ and $\sin \theta < 0$.

45. Find $\sin \theta$ if $\sec \theta = -1.236$ and $\tan \theta < 0$.

Write the simplified explicit formula for each arithmetic sequence and then find a_{20}. [9.2]

46. 2, 9, 16, 23, . . .

47. 12, 4, −4, −12, . . .

48. Select the number of petals in the graph of the polar equation $r = 6 \cos 3\theta$ and the maximum value of $|r|$. [6.5]

A. 6; 6

B. 3; 6

C. 3; 3

D. 3; 2

E. none of these

49. Classify the graph of $4x^2 - y + 40x + 97 = 0$. [8.4]

A. circle

B. ellipse

C. hyperbola

D. parabola

E. none of these

50. Identify the value whose standardized score is $z \approx 1.47$. [10.5]
{61, 68, 69, 73, 75, 81, 85, 87, 90, 94}

A. 61

B. 68

C. 90

D. 94

E. 95

51. Which quantity is described by discrete data? List all correct answers. [11.1]

A. oranges in a box

B. orange juice in a container

C. height of a tree

D. students in a class

E. none of these

Orientation provides students with a glimpse of student life.

After completing this section, you will be able to

- write null and alternative hypotheses.
- identify type I and type II errors.
- perform hypothesis tests and interpret the results.

A university reports that the average SAT math score for incoming students is 663. A survey of 50 randomly selected freshmen found they had an average SAT math score of 672 with a standard deviation of 42.8. Do the statistics from this sample provide enough evidence to support a claim that the average SAT math score is higher than 663?

If the reported mean of $\mu = 663$ is accurate, the Central Limit Theorem implies that the sampling distribution of the sample means (with $n = 50$) is normally distributed with $\mu_{\bar{x}} = \mu = 663$ and $\sigma_{\bar{x}} = \frac{s}{\sqrt{n}} = \frac{42.8}{\sqrt{50}} \approx 6.1$. The sample mean, $\bar{x} = 672$, would have a z-score of $z = \frac{\bar{x} - \mu}{\sigma_{\bar{x}}} = \frac{672 - 663}{6.1} \approx 1.49$. Plotting this z-score on the standard normal distribution curve indicates that the amount of deviation is not that unusual, so this sample would not seem to provide enough evidence to reject the reported score of 663.

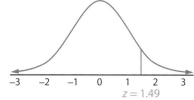

$z = 1.49$

DEFINITION

The process of using statistics from a sample to examine a *claim* about the value of a population parameter is called **hypothesis testing**.

Hypothesis testing does not determine the truth of the claim; instead, it considers whether the evidence from a sample is strong enough to reach a conclusion related to a proposed value for a population parameter. Two hypotheses are used to test the claim, which is written as a mathematical statement such as $\mu = 663$. The claim is one of the hypotheses, and its negation (or complement), $\mu \neq 663$ in this case, is the other hypothesis.

DEFINITIONS

A **null hypothesis**, H_0, is a statement about a population parameter that contains an equality such as =, ≤, or ≥.

An **alternative** (or **research**) **hypothesis**, H_a, is a statement that is the negation of the null hypothesis and contains an inequality such as ≠, <, or >.

The university's claim that $\mu = 663$ is the null hypothesis, and the alternative hypothesis is $\mu \neq 663$. Note the alternative hypothesis for each null hypothesis listed below.

If $H_0: \mu = k$, then $H_a: \mu \neq k$.　If $H_0: \mu \geq k$, then $H_a: \mu < k$.　If $H_0: \mu \leq k$, then $H_a: \mu > k$.

R. A. Fisher popularized the use of hypothesis testing with the publication of *Statistical Methods for Research Workers* in 1925, but it was Karl Pearson and Jerzy Neyman who added the concept of an alternative hypothesis.

Example 1 Stating the Null and Alternative Hypotheses

Write the null and alternative hypotheses for each statement, and identify which hypothesis represents the claim.

a. A gas station states its gasoline contains up to 10% ethanol.

b. A physical education teacher states that her students can do an average of more than 5 pull-ups.

Answer

	Null Hypotheses	Alternative Hypotheses	
a.	$H_0: \mu \leq 0.10$ (claim)	$H_a: \mu > 0.10$	Up to 10% of each gallon implies $\mu \leq 0.10$.
b.	$H_0: \mu \leq 5$	$H_a: \mu > 5$ (claim)	More than 5 implies $\mu > 5$. Since this claim does not involve an equality, it is the alternative hypothesis.

SKILL ✔ EXERCISE 15

In 2016 the US Department of Health and Human Services issued a rule requiring submission of all results from clinical trials of FDA-regulated drug, biological, and device products, regardless of whether results were statistically significant. This rule addressed the well-documented bias of underreporting negative results.

Regardless of which hypothesis represents the claim, the hypothesis test begins by assuming the null hypothesis is true. This limits the logical outcome of the test to one of two decisions:

1. Reject the null hypothesis.
2. Do not reject the null hypothesis.

Since this decision is based on a limited sample, there is always a chance that the decision is wrong. You might reject a null hypothesis that is actually true or you might fail to reject a null hypothesis that is actually false.

▌DEFINITIONS

A **type I error** occurs when the null hypothesis is rejected, but it is true.

A **type II error** occurs when the null hypothesis is not rejected, but it is false.

The table summarizes the four possible outcomes of a hypothesis test.

	True H_0	False H_0
Reject H_0.	type I error	correct decision
Do not reject H_0.	correct decision	type II error

Hypothesis testing is similar to the US legal system in that a defendant is assumed innocent (H_0) until there is enough evidence to show beyond reasonable doubt that this assumption is incorrect. Convicting the innocent is a type I error, and acquitting the guilty is a type II error. In statistics the problem being studied determines whether rejecting a true null hypothesis or accepting a false null hypothesis would be a more serious error.

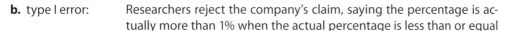

Example 2 Identifying Errors in Test Conclusions

An airbag manufacturer determines their airbags fail in at most 1% of crashes in which they are designed to deploy. Researchers examine a random sample of crashes to test whether the company's claim is accurate.

a. State the null and alternative hypotheses and identify which represents the claim.

b. State the possible type I and type II errors.

c. Which error would be more serious?

Answer

a. $H_0: \mu \leq 0.01$ (claim); $H_a: \mu > 0.01$

b. type I error: Researchers reject the company's claim, saying the percentage is actually more than 1% when the actual percentage is less than or equal to 1%.

    type II error: Researchers fail to reject the company's claim and the actual percentage of failure is greater than 1%.

c. A type I error may result in unnecessary recalls and extra expenses and may damage the company's reputation. A type II error may result in more serious injuries or fatalities during automobile crashes. A person's worldview, not mathematics, determines which set of consequences is more serious.

SKILL ✓ EXERCISE 17

In this section's introduction we saw that the mean SAT math score for the sample of freshmen was somewhat higher than the university's claimed mean of 663, but is it significantly higher? The probability of rejecting a true null hypothesis is lowered by using a lower level of significance.

DEFINITION

The **level of significance**, α, is the maximum allowable probability of making a type I error.

The level of significance is related to the desired confidence level for the test using $\alpha = 1 - c$. The level of significance is determined before data is collected and hypothesis testing is begun. Selecting $\alpha = 0.05$ implies there is a 5% chance that a true null hypothesis will be rejected (a type I error) and that there is a 95% chance that a correct decision will be made. Commonly used levels of significance are $\alpha = 0.10$, $\alpha = 0.05$, and $\alpha = 0.01$.

The *test statistic* is the statistic from a sample that is compared to a population parameter in the null hypothesis. This section focuses on using the sample mean, $\bar{x}$, to test claims about the population mean, μ. When the sample size $n \geq 30$ or the population is normally distributed, the Central Limit Theorem states that the sampling distribution of the means can be modeled by a normal distribution in which $\mu_{\bar{x}} = \mu$ and $\sigma_{\bar{x}} = \frac{\sigma}{\sqrt{n}}$.

The level of significance and the alternative hypothesis determine the *critical* (or *rejection*) *region(s)* where the differences between the test statistic and the proposed population parameter would be enough to justify rejecting the null hypothesis.

TIP

The table lists the critical values, z_c, that define the critical regions for the commonly used levels of significance.

α	Tails	z_c
0.10	left	−1.28
	two	±1.645
	right	1.28
0.05	left	−1.645
	two	±1.96
	right	1.645
0.01	left	−2.33
	two	±2.576
	right	2.33

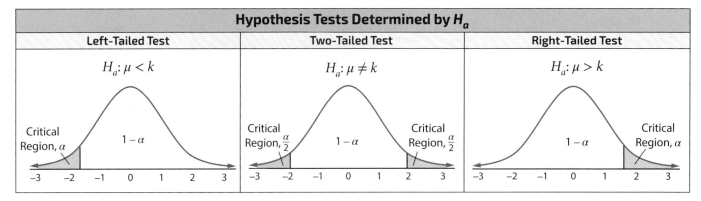

Hypothesis Tests Determined by H_a

Left-Tailed Test	Two-Tailed Test	Right-Tailed Test
$H_a: \mu < k$	$H_a: \mu \neq k$	$H_a: \mu > k$

The standardized test statistic, $z = \frac{\bar{x} - \mu}{\sigma_{\bar{x}}}$, in which $\sigma_{\bar{x}} = \frac{s}{\sqrt{n}}$, states the difference between the sample mean and the hypothesized population mean in terms of standard deviations. The null hypothesis is rejected if this z-score falls in the critical region, and the alternative hypothesis is accepted. If the z-score does not fall in the critical region, the null hypothesis is not rejected.

If the researchers studying the SAT scores of incoming freshmen discussed in this section's introduction choose a level of significance of $\alpha = 0.10$, the critical regions for $H_a: \mu \neq 663$ would be defined by $|z| \geq 1.645$. Since the standardized test statistic $z \approx 1.49$ does not fall in either critical region, they would fail to reject the null hypothesis. The sample's mean did not provide enough evidence to allow the researchers to be 90% certain that the claim made by the null hypothesis was false.

Hypothesis Testing for Means
using critical regions

1. State the null and alternative hypotheses and identify the claim.
2. Establish the level of significance.
3. Determine the critical value(s) and region(s).
4. Calculate the standardized test statistic, $z = \frac{\bar{x} - \mu}{\sigma_{\bar{x}}}$.
5. Reject or fail to reject the null hypothesis.

Example 3 Hypothesis Testing with Critical Regions

Milltown Foods manufactures granola bars with a stated net weight of 31 g, assuming the average granola bar weighs at least 31 g. A random sample of 50 bars has a mean of 30.75 g and standard deviation of 0.75 g. Complete a hypothesis test for the company's assumption about the average net weight of its granola bars at a 0.05 level of significance.

Answer

$H_0: \mu \geq 31$ (claim); $H_a: \mu < 31$

1. State the null and alternative hypotheses and identify which represents the claim.

$\alpha = 0.05$

2. Note the chosen level of significance.

$\therefore z_c = -1.645$ and a critical region $z < -1.645$

3. Determine the critical value and critical region for the left-tailed test.

CONTINUED ➡

$n = 50, \bar{x} = 30.75, s = 0.75$

$\sigma_{\bar{x}} = \dfrac{s}{\sqrt{n}} = \dfrac{0.75}{\sqrt{50}} \approx 0.106$

$z = \dfrac{\bar{x} - \mu}{\sigma_{\bar{x}}} = \dfrac{30.75 - 31}{0.106} \approx -2.357$

Reject the claim that the average weight of the granola bars is at least 31 g.

Check

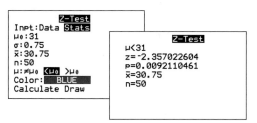

4. Since $n \geq 30$ and the Central Limit Theorem applies, calculate the standardized test statistic, $z = \dfrac{\bar{x} - \mu}{\frac{s}{\sqrt{n}}}$.

5. The standardized z-score is in the critical region.

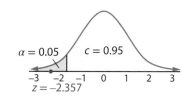

$\alpha = 0.05 \qquad c = 0.95$

$z = -2.357$

The Z-Test function from the [STAT], TESTS submenu can be used to verify the standardized z-score.

———————————— SKILL ✓ **EXERCISE 25**

Notice that the calculator also reports a *p-value* of ≈ 0.009 for the sample mean in Example 3. *P*-values provide another way to decide whether to reject the null hypothesis.

▌DEFINITION

The ***p*-value** is the probability of obtaining a test statistic as extreme as or more extreme than the one found in the sample assuming the null hypothesis is true.

The *p*-value is calculated by finding the area under the standard normal curve in the tail(s) defined by the *z*-score (left, right, or in both depending on the inequality in the alternative hypothesis). Compare the *p*-value to the level of significance to decide whether to reject the null hypothesis. If $p \leq \alpha$, then there is a statistically significant difference between the sample statistic and the population parameter at the α level of significance.

If $p \leq \alpha$, then reject the null hypothesis.
If $p > \alpha$, then fail to reject the null hypothesis.

Since the *p*-value for the sample mean in Example 3 of $p \approx 0.009$ is lower than the established level of significance $\alpha = 0.05$, the null hypothesis is rejected. In general, if $p \leq \alpha$, there is a *statistically significant difference* between the sample statistic and the population parameter at the α level of significance. The *p*-value can indicate the strength of the evidence against the null hypothesis. The smaller the *p*-value from the sample data, the more confident the researcher is in the decision to reject H_0.

TIP

The *p*-value in Example 3 can be calculated directly using the normalcdf function and the *z*-score, as shown in Section 11.2.

```
normalcdf(-4,-2.357)
          0.0091799208
```

Hypothesis Testing for Means
using *p*-values

1. State the null and alternative hypotheses and identify the claim.
2. Establish the level of significance.
3. Calculate the standardized test statistic, $z = \dfrac{\bar{x} - \mu}{\sigma_{\bar{x}}}$.
4. Calculate the *p*-value of the standardized test statistic.
5. Reject or fail to reject the null hypothesis.

Example 4   Hypothesis Testing with *p*-values

According to the National Institutes of Health (NIH), the average level of high-density lipo-protein (HDL) cholesterol, the good cholesterol, is 50 mg/dL. A sample of 88 patients has a mean HDL cholesterol level of 45.77 mg/dL with a standard deviation of 16.40 mg/dL. If the level of significance is 0.05, is the mean of this sample significantly different from the recommended cholesterol level?

Answer

$H_0: \mu = 50; H_a: \mu \neq 50$

$\alpha = 0.05$

$n = 88, \bar{x} = 45.77, s = 16.40$

$\sigma_{\bar{x}} = \dfrac{s}{\sqrt{n}} = \dfrac{16.40}{\sqrt{88}} \approx 1.748$

$z = \dfrac{\bar{x} - \mu}{\frac{s}{\sqrt{n}}} \approx \dfrac{45.77 - 50}{1.748} \approx -2.42$

```
normalcdf(-4,-2.42)
              0.0077285649
Ans*2
              0.0154571297
```

$p \approx 0.015$

$p \approx 0.015 < 0.05 = \alpha$
Reject H_0, which implies accepting H_a.

The sample mean HDL is significantly different from 50 mg/dL at the 0.05 level of significance.

1. To prove a significant difference, use equality for the null hypothesis and not equal to for the alternative hypothesis.
2. Record the stated significance level.
3. Since $n \geq 30$ and the Central Limit Theorem applies, calculate the standardized test statistic,
$$z = \dfrac{\bar{x} - \mu}{\frac{s}{\sqrt{n}}}.$$
4. Find the *p*-value in a two-tailed test. Entering normalcdf(−4, −2.42) returns the area to the left of $z \approx -2.42$, which must be doubled to account for the area to the right of $z \approx 2.42$.
5. Compare *p* with α to make and interpret the decision.

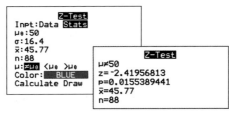

$\frac{p}{2}$ $\frac{p}{2}$

−3 −2 −1 0 1 2 3
$z = -2.42$ $z = 2.42$

Check

```
        Z-Test
Inpt:Data Stats
μ₀:50
σ:16.4
x̄:45.77
n:88
μ:≠μ₀ <μ₀ >μ₀
Color: BLUE
Calculate Draw
```

```
        Z-Test
μ≠50
z=-2.41956813
p=0.0155389441
x̄=45.77
n=88
```

6. The Z-Test function from the STAT, TESTS submenu can be used to verify the *p*-value of the test statistic.

SKILL ✓ **EXERCISE 27**

Another type of statistical test determines whether the means of two different populations are significantly different. The null hypothesis assumes the population means are the same: $H_0: \mu_1 = \mu_2, H_a: \mu_1 \neq \mu_2$. The test statistic is the difference of the sample means and the *z*-score is found using $z = \dfrac{\bar{x}_1 - \bar{x}_2}{\sqrt{\dfrac{s_1^2}{n_1} + \dfrac{s_2^2}{n_2}}}$. This formula is used in exercises 33–40.

The logic of hypothesis testing is similar to the logic used in an indirect proof. Assume the null hypothesis value for the parameter, then compare the test statistic with the proposed value. If the sample statistic is then very unlikely (its *z*-score is in a critical region, or $p \leq \alpha$), the null hypothesis is rejected and the alternative hypothesis, its negation, must be true. However, if the test statistic is not that unusual (its *z*-score is not in a critical region, or $p > \alpha$), the null hypothesis is not rejected since there is not enough evidence from the sample to show that the null hypothesis is false. This is not the same as accepting H_0; we only know that we fail to reject H_0. We need to accurately interpret and communicate the results of our statistical tests so that the results can be used to God's glory and to the benefit of others.

Bias in design, sample selection, reporting, and even in publication is a real problem in medical research. In fact, physician and Stanford professor John Ioannidis asserted, "It can be proven that most claimed research findings are false."

A. Exercises

In exercises 1–5, match each term to its definition.

A. alternative hypothesis   **D.** null hypothesis

B. confidence level   **E.** type I error

C. level of significance   **F.** type II error

1. A true null hypothesis is rejected.

2. A false null hypothesis is not rejected.

3. a statement about a population parameter that involves an equality

4. a statement about a population that involves only an inequality

5. the maximum probability of making a type I error allowed by the researcher

6. The process of using statistics from a sample to examine a claim about the value of a population parameter is called _____.

7. The statistic from a sample that is compared to the hypothetical population parameter is called a _____.

8. The probability of obtaining a statistic as extreme as or more extreme than the one found in the sample if the null hypothesis is true is the _____.

9. Order the steps (I–V) in the hypothesis testing process when using p-values.
    a. Calculate the standardized test statistic (z-score).
    b. Calculate the p-value of the standardized test statistic.
    c. Establish the level of significance.
    d. Reject or fail to reject the null hypothesis.
    e. State the hypotheses and identify the claim.

Write the null and alternative hypotheses for each statement, and identify which hypothesis represents the claim.

10. Jimmy claims that he can usually eat more than six slices of pizza.

11. A car manufacturer claims their new SUV's highway fuel economy is 35 mpg.

Determine whether the decision is a type I error, a type II error, or a correct decision.

12. A researcher fails to reject $H_0: \mu = 187.3$ when in reality the population's mean is significantly less than 187.3.

13. After testing the hypothesis, the decision is made to reject $H_0: \mu = 42$. Later it is found that μ truly is 42.

14. After choosing a 5% level of significance, a one-minute test of a company's 24-hr-a-day production line finds that approximately 42,000 candies came off the line and indicates a p-value of 0.38. The company maintains its claim that they produce 60.2 million candies each day.

State whether the hypothesis test is a left-, right-, or two-tailed test. Then calculate the z-score of the test statistic.

15. $H_0: \mu \leq 42$, $H_a: \mu > 42$, $\bar{x} = 48$, $s = 12.4$, $n = 30$

16. $H_0: \mu = 0.61$, $H_a: \mu \neq 0.61$, $\bar{x} = 0.55$, $s = 0.09$, $n = 34$

17. $H_0: \mu \geq 82$, $H_a: \mu < 82$, $\bar{x} = 78$, $s = 11.9$, $n = 45$

Use technology to calculate the p-value.

18. $H_0: \mu \leq 71$, $H_a: \mu > 71$
    $\bar{x} = 73$, $s = 5.91$, $n = 42$

19. $H_0: \mu = 1843$, $H_a: \mu \neq 1843$
    $\bar{x} = 2006$, $s = 497$, $n = 58$

State the decision that should be made for the given level of significance and p-value of the test statistic.

20. $\alpha = 0.01$, $p = 0.20$

21. $\alpha = 0.05$, $p = 0.006$

22. $\alpha = 0.001$, $p = 0.0005$

B. Exercises

In exercises 23–25, complete a five-step hypothesis test using critical regions.
    a. State the hypotheses and identify the claim.
    b. Establish the level of significance.
    c. Determine the critical value(s) and region(s).
    d. Calculate the standardized test statistic.
    e. Make a decision and interpret it relative to the problem.

23. A feed company claims their llama food keeps animals healthy and trim at an average weight of 355 lb. A sample of 58 adult llamas that eat this food have an average weight of  364 lb with a standard deviation of 38.3 lb. Can the company use these statistics to support their claim at the 95% confidence level?

24. An airline calculates that a certain flight must have at least 53 passengers to be profitable. After 60 flights, it has an average of 51 passengers with a standard deviation of 9. Is this sufficient evidence at a 95% confidence level to imply that the flight is unprofitable and should be discontinued?

25. In 2016 Experian Marketing Services reported that young adults send and receive an average of 128 text messages per day. In 2018 a random sample of 37 young adults averaged 142 texts with a standard deviation of 38.7. Can the claim be made at a 95% level of confidence that there was a significant increase in the number of text messages sent and received by young adults from 2016 to 2018?

Conduct a five-step hypothesis test using p-values.
a. State the hypotheses and identify the claim.
b. Establish the level of significance.
c. Calculate the standardized test statistic.
d. Calculate the p-value.
e. Make a decision and interpret it relative to the problem.

26. The average SAT score of the 47 seniors at Cloverdale Christian High School was 537 with a standard deviation of 100. Can they claim at the 98% confidence level that they exceed the national mean of 500?

27. The average score on a depression inventory for young adults is 90. After a sample of 52 young adults participated in an aerobic exercise routine for 20–30 min each day for 12 weeks, the average score improved to 88 with a standard deviation of 7.9. Does this research support, at the 95% level of confidence, the claim that daily aerobic exercise can improve depression?

28. According to a 2017 survey, teenagers spend about $2500 each year. A small-town survey of 41 randomly selected teens resulted in a mean of $2462 spent each year with a standard deviation of $426. Does this data support the claim that rural teens spend significantly less money per year at the 90% confidence level?

Conduct a hypothesis test to examine each claim.

29. The average duration of the common cold for a sample of 38 teenagers who took vitamin C daily after being diagnosed was 7.9 days with a standard deviation of 2.3 days. Can it be claimed that at the 95% level of confidence the sample's mean was less than the national average duration of 8.75 days?

30. Students testing a plant fertilizer find that after 5 weeks their 18 plants have a mean height of 108.5 mm with a standard deviation of 52.6 mm. Research journals report that after 5 weeks similar plants without the fertilizer have normally distributed heights with a mean of 128.1 mm. Did the fertilizer make a significant difference in the plants' growth at the 95% confidence level?

Complete exercises 31–32 using a sample with $n = 30$, $\bar{x} = 58.6$, and $s = 3.7$ to explore the relationship between confidence intervals and hypothesis testing.

31. Find the 95% confidence interval for the mean. Would a hypothesized mean of $\mu = 60$ be in the confidence interval?

32. Complete a hypothesis test with $\alpha = 0.05$ to decide if $H_0: \mu = 60$ should be rejected.

Use $z = \dfrac{\bar{x}_1 - \bar{x}_2}{\sqrt{\dfrac{s_1^2}{n_1} + \dfrac{s_2^2}{n_2}}}$ to determine the z-score used when comparing the following samples from two different populations.

33.

	Sample 1	Sample 2
$\bar{x}$	72.3	75.8
s	4.7	8.2
n	41	38

34.

	Sample 1	Sample 2
$\bar{x}$	492	483
s	17.8	9.5
n	44	52

Determine whether the means of the samples from different populations are different at the given level of significance.

35. $\alpha = 0.05$

	Sample 1	Sample 2
$\bar{x}$	16.9	18.4
s	1.69	3.18
n	30	30

36. $\alpha = 0.10$

	Sample 1	Sample 2
$\bar{x}$	56.01	55.9
s	3.6	2.1
n	100	50

〉 C. Exercises

Conduct a hypothesis test to determine whether the sample means from different populations are significantly different.

37. Mrs. D's class of 33 students had a mean score of 85 with a standard deviation of 6, while Mr. C's class of 37 students had a mean of 79 with a standard deviation of 10. Are the means statistically different at the 0.05 level?

38. Sharon and Jodi took a word processing test involving 30 samples. Sharon averaged 94 with a standard deviation of 5 and Jodi averaged 96 with a standard deviation of 6. Test for a significant difference using $\alpha = 0.025$.

39. A 30-day contest included 2 groups of 45 dieters. The first group lost an average of 10.3 lb with a standard deviation of 4.2 lb, while the second group lost an average of 8.2 lb with a standard deviation of 5.9 lb. Does the evidence suggest that the difference in effectiveness between the two diet groups is significant at the 95% level?

40. At Calvary Christian School the average SAT math score for 35 male students is 521.9 with a standard deviation of 4.597, and for 41 female students the mean is 518.7 with a standard deviation of 7.312. Is there a significant difference ($\alpha = 0.05$) in the SAT math scores of the male and female students?

CUMULATIVE REVIEW

Expand each logarithmic expression. Assume all variables are positive values. [3.3]

41. $\log_5 \dfrac{25\sqrt{y}}{x^2}$

42. $\log_3 \dfrac{\sqrt{3x}}{81y}$

Use the appropriate counting technique. [10.1]

43. How many different ways can five activities be chosen out of eight?

44. How many different ways can the letters in *MARSHMALLOW* be arranged?

Find each confidence interval from the given sample statistics. [11.3]

45. 95% CI, $n = 37$, $\bar{x} = 84$, $s = 9.7$

46. 90% CI, $n = 109$, $\bar{x} = 39$, $s = 5.3$

47. Which function represents $f(x) = x^2$ translated 3 units left and vertically shrunk by a factor of $\frac{1}{4}$? [1.5]

A. $g(x) = \frac{1}{4}(x^2 + 3)$

B. $g(x) = \frac{1}{4}(x + 3)^2$

C. $g(x) = \frac{1}{4}(x^2 - 3)$

D. $g(x) = \frac{1}{4}(x - 3)^2$

E. $g(x) = 4(x + 3)^2$

48. Identify the angle (to the nearest degree) between $\mathbf{u} = \langle 3, 4 \rangle$ and $\mathbf{v} = \langle -5, -2 \rangle$. [6.2]

A. 149°   **C.** 90°   **E.** none of

B. 119°   **D.** 31°   these

49. Write a simplified explicit formula for a_n in 5, 8, 11, 14, 17, ... and find the value of the tenth term. [9.1]

A. $a_n = 2 + 3n$; $a_{10} = 32$

B. $a_n = a_{n-1} + 3$; $a_{10} = 29$

C. $a_n = 5 + (n - 1)3$; $a_{10} = 32$

D. $a_{n+1} = a_n + 3$; $a_{10} = 29$

E. none of these

50. If 26 people are randomly selected from a normal population having a mean of 97 and a standard deviation of 7.9, compute the probability that the sample mean is between 98 and 100. [11.2]

A. 97%   **C.** 26%   **E.** 2.6%

B. 74%   **D.** 23%

Logicism, Intuitionism, and Formalism

To the biblical Christian, Gödel's results confirmed the truth that Scripture had always proclaimed. Autonomy belongs to the biblical God alone. Whenever man tries to construct any system of thought without reference to this God, it will ultimately fall short.

—James Nickel (Christian mathematician and author)

After contradictions arose in mathematics in the nineteenth century, many mathematicians viewed Platonism and its ideal realm of abstract ideas with skepticism. Scientists and some traditional mathematicians who saw mathematics as a branch of science turned to the philosophy of empiricism and its reliance on the senses and experience. In the early twentieth century, other mathematicians attempted to repair the cracks in the foundations of math as they developed three new philosophical schools: logicism, intuitionism, and formalism.

In 1910–13, British mathematicians Bertrand Russell and Alfred North Whitehead produced the three-volume work *Principia Mathematica*, which presented classical mathematics as a branch of logic. Logicism seeks to deduce all of mathematics from a few simple, undeniable axioms using valid logical steps. In an effort to reconcile such an attempt by the German philosopher Gottlob Frege, Russell discovered troubling paradoxes concerning infinite sets. Like Frege, Russell and Whitehead were also unsuccessful in developing mathematics exclusively from logic axioms. Two of their nine set theory axioms, the axiom of infinity and the axiom of choice, were not axioms of logic. Instead, they were accepted without proof based on mathematicians' daily experience with sets. Thus, modern mathematical logic is one of the branches of math, rather than math being considered a branch of logic.

Intuitionism, originated by the Dutch mathematician and philosopher L. E. J. Brouwer, views mathematics as an activity of mental construction. After observing the contradictions in classical mathematics, intuitionists attempted to rebuild mathematics from the ground up, beginning with the natural numbers. Intuitionists, like the ancient Greeks, accept that the set of natural numbers is potentially infinite since there is no largest natural number, but would reject the natural numbers as actually infinite, since the set does not exist as one finished set. Intuitionists also reject non-constructive indirect proofs as a demonstration of existence since these proofs do not

provide a means of generating an example. Math historian Howard Eves concludes, "So far, intuitionist mathematics has turned out to be considerably less powerful than classical mathematics, and in many ways it is much more complicated to develop. This is the fault found with the intuitionist approach—too much that is dear to most mathematicians is sacrificed."

The German mathematician David Hilbert was instrumental in developing formalism. Formalists say that mathematics is its own foundation rather than human intuition, nature, or logic. Math is simply a game in which one manipulates symbols according to well-defined rules. It has and needs no other basis other than itself. Hilbert's lofty goal was to produce a complete and consistent axiomatization of all of mathematics. However, mathematical logician Kurt Gödel proved in 1931 that for any robust mathematical system, deriving all true mathematics from a list of axioms is impossible. Hilbert's goal was crushed, but the formalist school of extreme axiomatization survives.

These three new schools of mathematics believe that man alone, with no need for God, can provide reliability and consistency to the foundation of an orderly mathematical system. A biblical worldview differs from all these approaches. It acknowledges that we need our created universe (empirical input), logic (axiomatic development), the human mind (intuitions), and the symbols and rules of language (formal structure). But it attributes God as the source of all these foundational elements rather than any of these being the source itself. Colossians 1:15–17 states that Jesus Christ created all things, both visible and invisible, and that by Him all things consist. Any humanistic philosophy for the foundations of mathematics is doomed to failure.

❭ Exercises

1. Match each mathematical philosophy with its view of math.

   I. empiricism   **IV.** logicism

   II. formalisim   **V.** Platonism

   III. intuitionism

   a. Math is a game of symbols played according to arbitrary rules.

   b. Math exists in an ideal realm of ideas independent of human minds.

   c. Math is part of symbolic logic rather than logic being a subset of math.

   d. Math is similar to science in its reliance on senses and experience.

   e. Math comes from and is dependent on the mind of man.

2. Name the mathematical philosophy associated with each mathematician.

   a. L. E. J. Brouwer

   b. David Hilbert

   c. Bertrand Russell

3. Name the mathematical philosophy that is challenged by each key problem.

   a. Gödel's proof that completeness with consistency is impossible

   b. much of classical mathematics sacrificed

   c. two of its necessary axioms not the type required

4. Which modern mathematical philosophy starts with the natural numbers?

5. Which modern mathematical philosophy views math as its own foundation?

6. List two key mathematical concepts rejected by logicism.

7. According to Colossians 1:15–17, who is the only sure foundation for a man's philosophy?

8. **Discuss:** Explain how a Christian philosophy of mathematics differs from the three new philosophies of the early twentieth century.

Game theory, a branch of mathematics involving the analysis of strategies in competitive decision-making, had its modern genesis in the 1944 book *Theory of Games and Economic Behavior* coauthored by mathematician John von Neumann and economist Oskar Morgenstern.

Mikayla spends a lot of time preparing for her church's Bible quiz competitions. After hearing that teens spend an average of 18.9 hr/week viewing social media, she decides to research whether this statistic is true for the teens in her national quizzing association. Considering there are approximately 2700 teenagers in this organization, how would she go about investigating this question?

Any research project begins with a compelling question or concern. A research question that clearly identifies the population and the exact characteristics (parameters) to be studied is stated. The null and alternative (research) hypotheses are then stated and the level of significance is determined.

The design of the study depends on the study's goal and the methods of data collection. The goal might be to compare parameters of two different groups, to determine whether significant relationships exist between variables, or to predict values of parameters based on other variables in the study. The sampling techniques are extremely important to the outcome of the research.

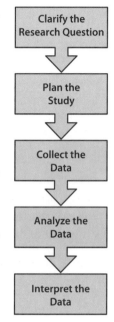

RESEARCH DESIGNS

experimental	Data is created by recording the results of treating an experimental group differently from a control group.
observational	Data is collected without the sample being treated by the researcher.
survey	Data is selected from responses given by members of the sample.

Experimental studies seek to establish a *cause and effect* relationship by comparing the effect of a specific treatment on a randomly selected experimental group to the effect of a placebo or no treatment on a similar, randomly selected control group. The cause and effect relationship can be difficult to define due to the many other factors, or *confounding variables*, that can influence the results.

Observational studies collect data without defining and applying a treatment to experimental and control groups. These studies often use preexisting data. The goal of observational studies is to determine a correlation between variables instead of a causation. A correlation between variables (one variable increases or decreases as the second variable increases) does not guarantee that a change in the first variable *causes* a change in the second variable (or vice versa). Another variable could actually cause changes in one or both variables being studied. Survey design is a form of observational design that gathers data using a survey of a sample from the population.

Example 1 **Analyzing Research Design**

Identify the population and research design for each study.

a. A study analyzed the composite ACT scores from 62 randomly selected high school seniors (31 boys and 31 girls) from schools in the Keystone Christian School Association to determine whether there was any significant difference between the girls' and boys' scores.

b. The Milwaukee Chamber of Commerce seeks to compare the commute time of workers in the Milwaukee metro area to the average commute time for US citizens of 25.5 min (as reported by the US Census Bureau). They analyzed commute-time data from questionnaires sent to 300 randomly selected workers in the metro area.

c. Before investing in a new reading curriculum, a school district randomly selects 5 first-grade classes to be taught with ABC Reading curriculum and 5 other first-grade classes to be taught with First Primer curriculum. The students' standardized test scores for reading comprehension and speed are compared at the end of the school year.

Answer

a. population: senior boys and girls in the school association

   design: observational — Scores were reported from data that had been gathered without different treatments being applied.

b. population: workers in the Milwaukee metro area

   design: survey — The questionnaire asks for information that will answer the question of concern.

c. population: first graders in the school district

   design: experimental — Different treatments were applied to similar, randomly selected groups before data was collected and compared.

SKILL ✔ **EXERCISE 7**

After the research design is selected, a detailed plan for collecting data is developed. If the inferences made are to be reliable, the sample must be large enough ($n \geq 30$ if applying the Central Limit Theorem) and *unbiased* (representing every member of the population fairly). A sample is *biased* if a factor exists that could systematically cause the sample to differ from the population being studied in a way that would cause the population's parameter to be overestimated or underestimated. Bias may be introduced into a study by the type of sample used, the conduct of the researcher, or an insufficient sample size.

Is it true that algorithms based on statistical analysis of data are free of bias? Cornell computer scientist Jon Kleinberg proved that it is mathematically impossible for a commonly used criminal justice sentencing algorithm to satisfy three reasonable criteria for fairness.

TYPES OF SAMPLES

random	Every member of the population has an equal chance of being selected.
stratified random	The population is divided into groups based on a characteristic and a random sample is taken from each group.
cluster	The population is divided into groups and then an entire group is randomly selected to be in the overall sample.
systematic	The first member is selected randomly from an ordered list of the population, and then every nth person on the list is selected.
convenience	The members are selected from the population based on accessibility.
self-selected	The members are volunteers from the population.

Random and systematic samples are usually unbiased. Convenience and self-selected samples should be avoided because of the likelihood of introducing bias. If the sample is not representative of the population, a *sampling error* has occurred. *Researcher bias* occurs when the researcher influences the respondents, either intentionally or unintentionally, by the way a question is worded or by nonverbal signals such as facial expressions during an interview. The design and execution of a research study should demonstrate precautions taken to avoid bias.

Example 2 Analyzing Sampling Techniques

Identify each type of sample and determine whether the sampling technique is likely to introduce bias.

a. The first 50 students leaving the cafeteria reported what they ate for lunch and whether they brought their lunch from home or purchased a school lunch. Researchers then calculate the calories consumed by each student and compare the mean calories consumed by those who brought lunch from home and those who ate a school lunch.

b. The 80 students taking Statistics were placed in one of two sections of the class taught by the same professor by flipping a coin. One section did not use laptops in class but the other section used them regularly. At the end of the semester, researchers compared the averages of the final grades of the students in the two sections.

c. All the third graders line up along their school gym's sidelines. A teacher randomly selects the number 3 from a stack of five index cards numbered 1–5. The third child in line and every fifth child after that is selected to be in a study.

d. The student body officers send a survey regarding food preferences for an upcoming activity to 10% of the students in each class whose names are randomly selected.

Answer

a. convenience sample; likely to be biased   **b.** random sample; not biased

c. systematic sample; not biased   **d.** stratified random sample; not biased

SKILL ✔ EXERCISE 13

The data analysis techniques found in Chapters 10 and 11 form the heart of the research study. Descriptive statistics are calculated to describe the sample's shape, center, and variability. These statistics are then used to infer estimates of the population's parameter of interest and to test hypotheses about the parameters. Proper inferential statistical techniques allow conclusions to be made about the population.

The researcher then has the responsibility to communicate these conclusions, usually in a written report and often in an oral presentation as well. A thorough knowledge of the entire research process enables the researcher to present the results effectively and credibly and allows others to carefully examine the validity of the conclusions.

Inferential statistics are invaluable tools in decision-making, but even the most carefully designed and conducted studies require moral and value judgments that are beyond the realm of mathematics.

Example 3 Evaluating a Research Project

Evaluate each step in Mikayla's research project.

Answer

Mikayla's Research Project	Analysis
Clarify the Research Question.	
Do the Bible quizzers in Mikayla's association spend an average of 18.9 hr/week on social media?	The question is clearly stated, identifying the population and parameter.
She writes the null and alternative hypotheses and determines the level of significance.	The null hypothesis states equality so the alternative hypothesis states not equal to.
$H_0: \mu = 18.9$; $H_a: \mu \neq 18.9$; $\alpha = 0.05$	A 95% level of certainty seems to be appropriate for her study.
Plan the Study.	
Mikayla creates a short, carefully worded questionnaire that has been reviewed by several students and teachers to help eliminate bias. It asks, "How many hours do you spend each week on social media?" She will ask all 5 members of each of the 10 teams competing at the regional tournament to complete the anonymous survey.	The cluster sample may not be representative of the 2700 members of the national association, since only the top teams compete at a regional tournament and her region may not be representative of quizzers from the entire nation.
Collect the Data.	
Mikayla numbers the returned surveys and then randomly selects 30 cards from a stack of similarly numbered index cards to choose the surveys to include in her research.	Her selection of 30 surveys from the 50 possible surveys allows for some surveys to not be completed while keeping a sufficient number to apply the Central Limit Theorem. The random selection of the surveys has made some provision for eliminating bias.
Analyze the Data.	
The 30 surveys indicate $\bar{x} = 16.65$ and $s = 5.68$. She calculates a standardized test statistic $z = -2.17$ with a p-value of 0.03 in a two-tailed test.	$\sigma_{\bar{x}} = \dfrac{s}{\sqrt{n}} = \dfrac{5.68}{\sqrt{30}} \approx 1.037$ $z = \dfrac{\bar{x} - \mu}{\sigma_{\bar{x}}} \approx \dfrac{16.65 - 18.9}{1.037} \approx -2.17$ $2 \times \text{normalcdf}(-4, -2.17) = 0.030$ Her calculations are correct.

CONTINUED ➡

Interpret the Data.

Since $p < \alpha$, she rejects the null hypothesis and states that the time spent on social media by quizzers in her association is significantly different from the average of 18.9 hr/week.	Mikayla correctly rejects the null hypothesis. The possible bias in the sample causes some concern about the validity of generalizing her results to all the quizzers in the national association.
Wondering if she could have shown that the quizzers spend significantly less time on social media, Mikayla does a second hypothesis test. She rewrites her hypotheses. $H_0: \mu \geq 18.9$; $H_a: \mu < 18.9$ (claim) Then she compares the p-value for the standardized test statistic in a left-tailed test to the level of significance and concludes that the quizzers spend significantly less time on social media than the average teenager at the 0.05 level of significance.	The p-value for a z-score of -2.17 in a left-tailed test, $p = 0.015$, is less than the previously established level of significance, $\alpha = 0.05$, so her conclusion is valid.

SKILL ✓ **EXERCISES 29–33**

Reading and evaluating research studies is an important skill in many careers. An *abstract* is a brief summary that precedes a formal research report. When evaluating a study, refer to the diagram at the beginning of this section and determine whether all the necessary steps are included and whether the conclusions are correct.

Example 4 Analyzing an Abstract

Use the flow chart from the beginning of this section to analyze the following abstract from "A Water Availability Intervention in New York City Public Schools: Influence on Youths' Water and Milk Behaviors," a study published in the *American Journal of Public Health*.

Objectives. We determined the influence of "water jets" [drinking water dispensers] on observed water and milk taking and self-reported fluid consumption in New York City public schools.

Methods. From 2010 to 2011, before and 3 months after water jet installation in 9 schools, we observed water and milk taking in cafeterias (mean 1000 students per school) and surveyed students in grades 5, 8, and 11 (n = 2899) in the 9 schools that received water jets and 10 schools that did not. We performed an observation 1 year after implementation (2011–2012) with a subset of schools. We also interviewed cafeteria workers regarding the intervention.

Results. Three months after implementation we observed a 3-fold increase in water taking (increase of 21.63 events per 100 students; $P < .001$) and a much smaller decline in milk taking (-6.73 events per 100 students; $P = .012$), relative to comparison schools. At 1 year, relative to baseline, there was a similar increase in water taking and no decrease in milk taking. Cafeteria workers reported that the water jets were simple to clean and operate.

Conclusions. An environmental intervention in New York City public schools increased water taking and was simple to implement.

CONTINUED ➡

Answer

Clarify the Research Question.

The research question (whether the installation of the water jets would benefit students by encouraging them to take in more fluids) and the population (students in the New York City public school system) are clearly communicated.

Plan the Study.

The study is mainly observational but also includes two surveys. Data was to be collected by observing students in schools with newly installed water jets and schools without them. The study compared milk and water intake by students prior to, 3 mo after, and 1 yr after the installation of the water jets. The null and alternative hypotheses and the level of significance are not stated.

Collect the Data.

The sample includes fifth-, eighth-, and eleventh-grade students in schools having water jets installed and students in the same grades in schools without water jets. It is difficult to determine whether a sampling error has occurred, since the methods of choosing which grades were studied or which schools without water jets were included are not discussed. The reported sample sizes appear to be more than adequate for the study.

Analyze the Data.

While the abstract states significant p-values, hypothesis testing procedures are not reported in the abstract.

Interpret the Data.

The abstract's conclusion clearly interprets the results of the study relative to New York City public schools.

SKILL ✓ **EXERCISE 35**

A. Exercises

1. List the order of the steps in a research study.

A. Analyze the data.   **D.** Plan the study.

B. Collect the data.   **E.** Clarify the research question.

C. Interpret the data.

In which stage of the research study (listed in exercise 1) should each of the following occur?

2. Perform an experiment, gather data, or conduct a survey.

3. Define the population and parameters related to a compelling concern.

4. Calculate test statistic(s).

5. Decide whether to reject the null hypothesis.

6. Determine the research design that best fits the goal of the research question.

Identify the population and research design for each study.

7. People at a local restaurant are asked which college team they support.

8. Preexisting test score data is collected from the Pickens County school district to determine the math aptitude of their high school graduates.

9. The relationship between drinking coffee and risk of death was studied by analyzing data from a NIH-AARP Diet and Health Study that included 229,119 men and 173,141 women ranging in age from 50 to 71.

10. The average yield of oyster mushrooms in the control group was compared to the average yield of groups in which a nutritional supplement of alfalfa meal, soybean meal, or vermicompost was added to the substrate.

11. The school nutritionist asks students from one class in each grade to record what they ate for breakfast each day in an attempt to determine whether the school's students are getting enough fiber in their breakfast.

12. A pharmaceutical company randomly selects half the lactose-intolerant patients who are volunteering to participate in a study to receive an experimental drug while the other half is given a placebo. They compare symptom reduction rates of the two groups during a 3 yr period.

Identify each type of sample. Then determine whether the sampling technique is likely to introduce bias.

13. Mrs. King chooses a banquet committee by randomly placing all the junior girls on a numbered list, rolling a die to choose the first girl, and then selecting every eighth girl on the list.

14. A cat food company testing its claim to prevent iron-deficiency anemia asks cat owners to volunteer their cats for participation in the study.

15. Mr. Siebert wonders if students' grades are affected by whether the students choose to sit in the front, middle, or back of the classroom. At the end of the semester, he compares the grades of students sitting in the front, middle, and back of his classroom.

16. A research company documenting the effect of a stair-climbing-machine workout on the resting heart rates of males randomly selects 45 males from major US cities to exercise 20 min on the machine 5 times a week for 6 weeks.

▶ B. Exercises

17. Explain the difference between a sampling error and researcher bias.

Describe how you might select a representative sample from the population for each described study.

18. the names on voter registration lists for a poll regarding an upcoming election

19. a study examining the time spent on community service by students attending Edwards Academy

Identify the sampling technique and discuss any potential sampling errors or researcher bias.

20. Forty teens walking in a mall, some of whom are accompanied by their mother, are selected to rate their mother's cooking on a scale of 1 to 10.

21. When studying the average tenure of teachers in Arkansas, researchers found that 15% of its teachers belong to a minority group and randomly selected 15% of their sample from minority teachers.

22. A magazine advertisement states that the first 100 hearing-impaired people who call a given number will be able to participate in a study of micro hearing aids at no cost.

23. A reading coach tests a new reading program by randomly selecting 5 of the 32 second-grade classes in the district, which include several classes for advanced students.

24. State officials conducting a yearlong study investigating the impact of weekly multiplication speed drills on fourth-grade achievement test scores select 15 fourth-grade classes, each composed of a wide range of student abilities.

25. When attempting to determine whether gas prices in their state have increased significantly in the last month, students record the current gas price at 30 gas stations within 15 mi of the school.

26. In order to study the average time Americans watch the news each day, researchers purchase data describing the viewing habits of 4300 American households that was gathered by a television ratings company by using viewing diaries. The number 7 was randomly selected and the researchers selected data from the 7th, 57th, 107th, . . . households as their sample.

27. Statistics students use a random number generator to select 40 students from a list of the 723 students in their school to determine whether the average number of pairs of shoes by students at their school differs significantly from the national average of 13.28 pairs.

28. A researcher using data from the US Census Bureau finds that housing expenses in Ohio are fairly typical of the housing expenses in the United States, so he selects the homeowners in Ohio to be the sample for his study.

Complete exercises 29–33 to plan and evaluate a research project.

29. Jack reads that 12–17-yr-olds spend an average of 18.1 hr/week watching television. He wonders if this average is accurate for 12–17-yr-olds who attend churches similar to his church. State the following.

   a. the population and parameter

   b. the null and alternative hypotheses

   c. an appropriate level of significance

30. Jack gets permission to put a question on the sign-up form for the regional church youth rally.

   a. How should he word the question?

   b. Which research design is he using?

31. Of the 1200 12–17-yr-olds signed up for the rally, 600 teens answer Jack's question. Describe a method he can use to randomly select a sample of 50 responses for his research.

32. Identify the sampling techniques used and discuss the possibilities for sample error and researcher bias.

33. If his sample has a mean of 17.2 hr with a standard deviation of 3.4 hr, find the standardized test score and determine whether he should reject the null hypothesis at a 0.05 level of significance. Explain your reasoning.

❯ C. Exercises

34. A math professor is interested in finding a method of quizzing that helps her students learn better. She institutes daily quizzes in her courses for a semester and compares the average final grade of her 105 students during this semester with the average final grade of students in her previous courses, an 81.4. The mean grade of her students during this semester is 83.5 with a standard deviation of 15.2.

   a. Clarify the objective by writing a research question.

   b. Identify the population and parameters.

   c. Write null and alternative hypotheses.

   d. Identify the research design.

   e. Identify the sampling technique and discuss possible sample errors and researcher bias.

   f. Calculate the standardized test statistic.

   g. Should null hypotheses be rejected at a level of significance of 0.10? of 0.05?

In exercises 35–36, use the flow chart at the beginning of the lesson and the given abstract to evaluate each study.

35. *The Effectiveness of Implementing the Classic Reading Program*

   Objective: to determine whether implementing the Classic Reading program as an intervention for struggling students increases their reading comprehension and speed of reading

   Methods: From 2014 to 2015 struggling readers from first and second grade took part in a 90-day trial implementing the Classic Reading program. Students were taken from 30 different classrooms in 5 different Nashville-area schools and were considered to be at least 8 mo behind in their reading level. Similar reading comprehension tests were given to these students before and after the program.

   Results: While their speed of reading showed slight improvement, significant improvement was observed in the students' reading comprehension. According to the posttest results, 80% of the students improved to no more than 4 mo behind grade level.

   Conclusions: The Classic Reading program allows struggling readers to improve their skills, quickly preventing them from falling further behind. The earlier the implementation of this reading program, the better the results.

36. *The Ability of Al's Feed to Control Weight in Alpacas*

   Objective: to test the effectiveness of the alpaca food supplied by the feed company to keep the weight of alpacas at its average of 150 lb with 97% confidence

   Methods: From a farm of 75 alpacas, 30 are provided the special feed in an area with no other significant food source. After one year the average weight for the special feed group will be compared to the average weight of the other alpacas.

   Results: One year after implementation, the average weight of the test group was 158 lb with a standard deviation of 21.2 lb ($p = 0.039$).

   Conclusion: The food produced by the feed company helps alpacas maintain their average weight.

37. Research: Use the Internet to find a research report on a topic you find interesting. Use the flow chart from the beginning of the lesson to analyze the study.

38. Research: Use the flow chart from the beginning of the lesson to design and complete a research study. Write a report summarizing your study and presenting your interpretation of the results.

Graph each function. Then state its domain, range, and whether it is continuous or discontinuous. [1.3]

39. $g(x) = \begin{cases} -x+1 & \text{if } x < 1 \\ 2x-2 & \text{if } x \geq 1 \end{cases}$

40. $f(x) = \begin{cases} 2x+3 & \text{if } x < -1 \\ 3^x & \text{if } x > 0 \end{cases}$

Solve each $\triangle ABC$. Round answers to the nearest tenth. [5.7]

41. $b = 24, c = 17, A = 57°$ **42.** $a = 42, b = 53, c = 70$

Determine whether each minimum or maximum value is an outlier. [10.4]

43. min: 2, Q_1: 4.5, Q_2: 6, Q_3: 8, max: 9

44. 1, 3, 5, 5, 6, 7, 8, 8, 10, 13

45. Simplify $\ln \sqrt[3]{e^4}$. [3.2]

A. 0.2877   **C.** $\frac{3}{4}$ **E.** none of these

B. $\sqrt[3]{4}$ **D.** $\frac{4}{3}$

46. If $\cos\theta = -\frac{9}{41}$ and $\tan\theta < 0$, what is $\cot\theta$? [4.3]

A. $-\frac{9}{40}$ **C.** $-\frac{40}{41}$ **E.** $\frac{9}{41}$

B. $\frac{9}{40}$ **D.** $-\frac{40}{9}$

47. Which polar coordinates are equivalent (to the nearest degree) to the rectangular coordinates (3, 6)? List all correct answers. [6.4]

A. $(3\sqrt{5}, -297°)$ **D.** $(3\sqrt{5}, 243°)$

B. $(3\sqrt{5}, 63°)$ **E.** $(3\sqrt{5}, 603°)$

C. $(-3\sqrt{5}, 243°)$

48. Find the minimum sample size, n, for a 95% confidence interval with a maximum margin of error of 2.1 in a population with a standard deviation of 8.4. [11.3]

A. 8   **C.** 44   **E.** 62

B. 16   **D.** 61

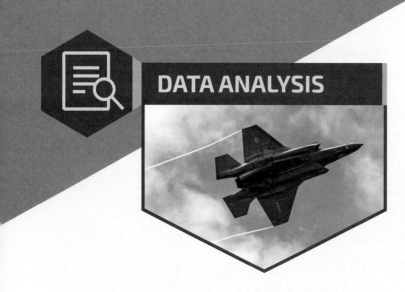

Markov Chains

In 1903 Orville Wright ushered in the aircraft era with a flight that lasted little more than 10 sec and covered only 120 ft. Just 3 yr later Andrey Markov, a student of Pafnuty Chebyshev, published the first results in his study of probabilistic processes that are now called Markov chains. In June 2017 the first operational F-35A Lightning II squadron of stealth fighter jets received its final aircraft. It's hard to say who would be more surprised to see this jet—the Wright brothers, who pioneered the aerodynamics, or Markov, whose work was crucial to the development of the voice-controlled cockpit.

Applications of Markov chains are found in biological science, business, and engineering in addition to voice recognition algorithms. Unlike traditional probability that considers independent events, Markov chains model processes in which the current state depends only on the previous state. Consider a token on an integer number line. You flip a coin and move the token one number to the right for heads and one to the left for tails. If the token starts on 5 and you flip a fair coin, the probability of the token landing on 4 is 50% and the probability of landing on 6 is 50%. It doesn't matter how the token got to 5, but the fact that it is at 5 determines the possible outcomes after the next coin flip. Since the current state depends only on the state immediately preceding it, this is an example of a Markov chain.

A transition graph is a useful tool in exploring Markov chains. The graph consists of nodes that represent the states and arrows between the nodes that represent transitions. Arrows are labeled with the appropriate probability, and the sum of probabilities from each node must equal one.

Suppose every day is either calm, breezy, or windy. The following transition graph shows that if it is calm today, there is a 40% chance it will be breezy tomorrow.

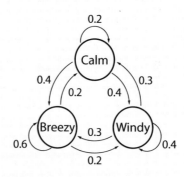

1. If it is windy today, what is the chance it will be calm tomorrow?

2. What is the probability it will be calm two days in a row?

3. In our model, does the condition yesterday affect the probability that it will be calm tomorrow? Why or why not?

Transition graphs with n states can be written as an $n \times n$ transition matrix T in which entry t_{ij} represents the probability of transitioning from state i to state j. Using the order of calm (c), breezy (b), and windy (w) for both the rows and the columns:

$$T = \begin{bmatrix} 0.2_{cc} & 0.4_{cb} & 0.4_{cw} \\ 0.2_{bc} & 0.6_{bb} & 0.2_{bw} \\ 0.3_{wc} & 0.3_{wb} & 0.4_{ww} \end{bmatrix}.$$

The product of a row matrix C representing the current condition and the transition matrix T gives the probabilities for the next day's condition. For example, using $C = [1 \quad 0 \quad 0]$ to represent a calm day, the product $CT = [0.2 \ 0.4 \ 0.4]$ represents the probabilities that tomorrow will be a calm, breezy, or windy day. Raising the transition matrix to the nth power gives the probability for transitioning to each state in n days. Therefore, the probability a certain state will exist after n iterations is the product of the initial condition matrix and the nth power of the transition matrix, CT^n.

4. If it is windy today, what is the probability it will be windy 3 days from today?

5. Using technology set to display results to the nearest thousandth, find T^4, T^5, T^6, T^7, T^8, and T^9. Describe the result as the power of T increases.

Google® search results are ranked by an algorithm based on a Markov chain. The Internet's vast size and continual growth make the important task of ranking results difficult. The page-ranking algorithm rates importance by the probability that the searcher will choose a particular page based on hyperlinks as well as the amount of time spent on each page.

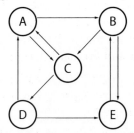

This web with 5 pages and links indicated by arrows would be represented by

$$T = \begin{bmatrix} 0 & 0.5 & 0.5 & 0 & 0 \\ 0 & 0 & 0.5 & 0 & 0.5 \\ 0.5 & 0 & 0 & 0.5 & 0 \\ 0.5 & 0 & 0 & 0 & 0.5 \\ 0 & 1 & 0 & 0 & 0 \end{bmatrix}.$$

The page-ranking algorithm also assumes that the searcher may access a page directly without linking from another site.

6. To simulate the matrix obtained by the page-ranking algorithm, replace each zero in the transition matrix with 0.05 and then reduce the other original entries by the same amount so that the sum of each row still equals one.

7. Using technology set to display results to the nearest hundredth, find the probability of each state after 100 iterations.

8. Use the results to rank the web pages.

9. Discuss: The word *google* now appears in dictionaries as a verb. The vast amount of information at our fingertips makes information and expertise easily accessible. How can understanding the process of ranking search results affect the confidence that should be placed in this information?

Chapter 11 Review

Classify each random variable as discrete or continuous and justify your answer. [11.1]

1. Let *x* represent the number of pizzas sold each day over a two-week period at Pizza Pizzaz.

2. Let *x* represent the actual number of ounces in a gallon of milk coming off a dairy's processing line.

3. The table lists results of a survey of 158 people that asked the number of days per week they use a cell phone. Create a table and a histogram representing the probability distribution. Then use the distribution to find the expected value and standard deviation. [11.1]

Days Used	Frequency
0	7
1	4
2	8
3	10
4	17
5	23
6	38
7	51

4. Use the probability distribution from exercise 3 to find the probability of a survey participant using a cell phone each number of days. [11.1]
   a. *P*(at least 6)   b. *P*(fewer than 6)

Use the binomial probability distribution formula to find the probability of *x* successes in *n* independent trials where *p* is the probability of a success in a trial. Then find the mean and standard deviation of the binomial probability distribution. Round answers to the nearest hundredth if necessary. [11.1]

5. $x = 8$, $n = 15$, $p = 0.6$ 6. $x = 4$, $n = 10$, $p = 0.25$

7. An insurance company's data shows that 33% of men in a given age group receive a traffic ticket each year. Create a table and a histogram representing the probability distribution for the number of men from a randomly selected sample of 5 men in that age group who received a traffic ticket in the past year. Then find the expected number of traffic tickets for this sample and the distribution's standard deviation. [11.1]

8. Use the probability distribution from exercise 7 to find the probability that each number of men in the sample received a ticket. [11.1]
   a. *P*(all 5)   b. *P*(at most 2)   c. *P*(at least 2)

9. A die with 3 twos, 2 threes, and 1 four is rolled and a nickel is flipped with heads recorded as 1 and tails recorded as 2. Create a table and a histogram representing the probability distribution for the sums of this two-step experiment. Then find the distribution's expected value and standard deviation. [11.1]

10. The number of months that 4 patients lived after being diagnosed with a rare disease was recorded. {18, 21, 16, 23} [11.2]
    a. Create a table containing all possible samples of size 2 (taken with replacement) from this population.
    b. Create a table and a histogram representing the sampling distribution for the means.
    c. Find and compare the means and standard deviations for the population and the sampling distribution.

11. Determine whether the Central Limit Theorem can be applied to each population distribution with the given mean and standard deviation using a sample size of *n*. If so, find $\mu_{\bar{x}}$ and $\sigma_{\bar{x}}$. If not, explain why. [11.2]
    a. normal with $\mu = 5200$, $\sigma = 1450$, $n = 12$
    b. $\mu = 16$, $\sigma = 3.92$, $n = 48$

12. State the continuity correction factor for using a normal approximation to find each binomial probability. [11.2]
    a. *P*(between 52 and 81)
    b. *P*(at most 19)

13. A survey of 15–24-yr-olds reveals their average Christmas spending is $243. Assume the standard deviation of the amount spent was $328.25. Find each probability for the average spending of 50 randomly selected people in this age bracket. [11.2]
    a. The average is less than $200.
    b. The average is between $125 and $150.

14. Find each probability if the height of mature sunflowers is normally distributed with an average height of 64 in. and a standard deviation of 3.5 in. [11.2]

   a. A randomly selected mature sunflower is between 58 in. and 62 in. tall.

   b. The average height of 150 mature sunflower plants is more than 64.5 in.

15. A manufacturer found that the lifespan of its 40-watt light bulbs is normally distributed with a mean of 10,000 hr and a standard deviation of 1150 hr. What is the probability that the average lifespan of a random sample of 15 bulbs is less than 9315 hr? [11.2]

16. A cannery packs 32 oz of tomato sauce in cans with an acceptable standard deviation of 0.77 oz. If the variation is normally distributed, what is the probability that a random sample of 16 cans has a mean weight of 32.5 oz? [11.2]

17. Pew Research Center reports that 31% of adult Internet users use Pinterest. Find each probability for a sample of 200 randomly selected adult Internet users. [11.2]

   a. at least 55 use Pinterest

   b. more than 75 use Pinterest

18. A manufacturer recalls a car part that has a 28% failure rate. In a randomly selected sample of 70 cars, what is the probability of having a faulty part in each number of cars? [11.2]

   a. P(fewer than 20 cars)   **b.** P(from 20 to 25 cars)

19. In June 2018, Scooter Gennett of the Cincinnati Reds led the National League in batting averages at 0.332, meaning that his probability of getting a hit is 33.2%. How many hits is Gennett expected to get in his next 60 at bats? Find the probability of Gennett getting at most 20 hits in the next 60 at bats. [11.2]

20. Use technology to find the critical value, z_c, for each confidence level. [11.3]

   a. 80%   **b.** 85%

21. Find the 99% confidence interval for a sample with $n = 50$, $\bar{x} = 19.6$, and $s = 3.87$ and interpret its meaning. [11.3]

Use each random sample to find the point estimate for the population's mean, the margin of error for the stated confidence level, and the related confidence interval. [11.3]

22. {46, 33, 13, 20, 45, 80, 77, 64, 71, 2, 37, 10, 40, 47, 75, 84, 39, 10, 52, 6, 55, 23, 80, 49, 63, 33, 54, 64, 0, 8}
   $c = 90\%$

23. {51, 49, 56, 81, 44, 65, 69, 72, 57, 48, 55, 64, 73, 57, 63, 64, 71, 69, 73, 58, 70, 67, 74, 86, 75, 69, 83, 67, 77, 58, 74, 66}
   $c = 95\%$

24. A test was given to predict success in a Calculus 1 course. Normally distributed results with $s = 3$ show that a mean score of 15.5 predicted an A in the course. Find the 90% and 95% confidence intervals for an A if 18 students take the test. [11.3]

25. Using the information from exercise 24, find the 90% and 95% confidence intervals if 180 students take the test. [11.3]

26. A sample of 70 students report spending an average of $267.40 per semester on books. If the standard deviation is $185.67, find the 90% confidence interval for the mean and interpret its meaning. [11.3]

27. Find the minimum sample size for an 88% confidence interval with a margin of error of 2.3 if the population standard deviation is 7.64. [11.3]

28. A researcher studying the price of comic books desires a 95% confidence level and the margin of error for the mean to be no more than $0.27. A previous study determined that $s = \$1.39$ is a reasonable standard deviation for the population. Determine the minimum sample size for the research study. [11.3]

Write the null and alternative hypotheses for each statement and identify which hypothesis represents the claim. [11.4]

29. A manufacturer tests the 250 mg dose of its pain reliever.

30. A local clothing store predicts they will have more than 2500 customers on Black Friday this year.

For exercises 31–33, classify each decision as a type I error, type II error, or correct decision given $H_0: \mu \geq 50$ and $H_a: \mu < 50$. [11.4]

31. Researchers reject H_0 and μ is found to be 70.

32. Researchers fail to reject H_0 and μ is found to be 40.

33. Using a sample of classmates in which the average height is 61.5 in., Joshua fails to reject that the average height of all high school seniors is 60.75 in. Later studies reveal that the average height of high school seniors is 66.8 in.

34. Researchers use 52 randomly selected teens to test the claim that the average weekly earnings for 16–19-yr-olds is at least $420. The mean of the sample's weekly earnings is $415/week with a standard deviation of $24.18. Perform a hypothesis test to determine whether the data supports their claim at a 0.01 level of significance. [11.4]

35. The average morning commute time for US residents is 26.1 min. Mrs. Krackenbush's statistics class wanted to know if this was true for the commuters in their city. They found the average commute time for 40 randomly selected commuters from their city to be 30.4 min with a standard deviation of 8.2 min. Perform a hypothesis test at the 95% confidence level to answer their question. [11.4]

36. State the 5 major steps involved in a research project. [11.5]

37. Explain the differences between an observational study and an experimental study. [11.5]

38. Identify each sampling technique. [11.5]

   a. The population is divided into representative groups and an entire group is randomly selected to be in the sample.

   b. The first member of the sample is randomly selected from a list and then every nth member of the list is selected.

   c. The researcher selects members of the population that are easily accessible.

Identify the population and research design for each study. [11.5]

39. A researcher randomly selects 60 eighth graders from area schools and divides them into two groups. The members of the first group continue to study using methods of their own choice. The members of the second group are coached in specific methods of studying. Average test scores from the two groups are then compared.

40. A researcher collects information about Asian US citizens from the US Census Bureau to see how their level of education relates to their rate of moving to a different state.

Identify the sampling technique and discuss potential sampling error or researcher bias. [11.5]

41. A 3-question survey is distributed to customers in a store. Participants will be added into a drawing for a gift card.

42. A researcher studying recreational spending examines median home prices in neighborhoods within the city and randomly selects participants in proportion to the number of homes in each price range.

43. Fifty dirt bike owners at a dirt bike rally are randomly selected to fill out a survey that includes the cost of their bike.

Complete exercises 44–46 to analyze a research study. [11.5]

44. A social researcher reads that the average age women in the United States get married is 27.4 yr but thinks that men are significantly older when they marry.

   a. Identify the population and parameter.

   b. State an appropriate research question for the study.

   c. State the null and alternative hypotheses.

45. The researcher decides to obtain data from the 360 weddings recorded at the county courthouse last year.

   a. Which type of research design is used?

   b. Describe a method of selecting a representative sample of size $n = 60$.

   c. Discuss any possible sampling error or research bias.

46. The researcher finds the average age of the men in the sample from exercise 45 is 29.1 yr with a standard deviation of 1.59 yr.

   a. Calculate the standardized test statistic and determine whether the null hypothesis should be rejected at a 0.05 level of significance.

   b. Interpret the results of the study.

12 Limits, Derivatives, and Integrals

BIBLICAL PERSPECTIVE OF MATHEMATICS

From simple arithmetic to the most complex mathematics, there is no avoiding the concept of infinity. How should we think biblically about this idea we cannot fully comprehend?

DATA ANALYSIS

Whenever a process can be modeled mathematically, derivatives provide insight into instantaneous rates of change. In business and economics this is known as marginal analysis.

HISTORICAL CONNECTION

When you hear the name Berkeley, you probably think of a research university in the city of Berkeley, California. Both the university and the city were named after an Irish bishop who motivated mathematicians to place calculus on a firm foundation.

12.1 Evaluating Limits

(80)

Limits govern our lives in many ways (Ps. 90:10).

The study of calculus focuses on two foundational problems related to the graph of a function: finding the equation of the line tangent to the curve and finding the area between the graph and the x-axis. The concept of a limit is essential in the solutions of both problems. Section 1.4 defined $\lim_{x \to a} f(x) = L$ if the function value $f(x)$ approaches a unique real number L as x approaches a from both sides.

Examining the function's graph over a small interval around $x = a$ will help you evaluate limits and prepare you for the more technical definition of a limit used in calculus.

After completing this section, you will be able to

- evaluate limits of functions.
- use limits to describe the end behavior of a function.
- find limits of sequences.
- solve real-world problems involving limits.

Example 1 Finding Limits Graphically

Find each limit of the greatest integer function $f(x) = [x]$.

a. $\lim_{x \to 1} f(x)$

b. $\lim_{x \to -2.5} f(x)$

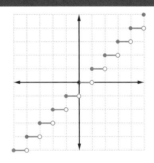

Answer

a. Consider the one-sided limits.

$\lim_{x \to 1^-} f(x) = 0$ and $\lim_{x \to 1^+} f(x) = 1$

$\therefore \lim_{x \to 1} f(x)$ does not exist.

Since the one-sided limits are not equal at $x = 1$, the function does not have a limit as $x \to 1$.

---

b. Consider the one-sided limits.

$\lim_{x \to -2.5^-} f(x) = -3$ and $\lim_{x \to -2.5^+} f(x) = -3$

$\therefore \lim_{x \to -2.5} f(x) = -3$

Since both one-sided limits are equal to -3, the two-sided limit exists.

SKILL ✓ **EXERCISE 5**

Recall from Section 1.4 that if the function is discontinuous at $x = a$, the limit exists only if both one-sided limits are equal to a unique real number L. You also learned that $\lim_{x \to a} f(x) = f(a)$ if the function is continuous over an interval of x containing a. Therefore the limits of polynomial, exponential, logarithmic, sinusoidal, or any other continuous functions can be found using direct substitution.

Example 2 Finding Limits by Substitution

Find each limit.

a. $\displaystyle\lim_{x\to-8}(x^2-6x+17)$ **b.** $\displaystyle\lim_{x\to4}5\ln(x+3)$ **c.** $\displaystyle\lim_{x\to\frac{\pi}{6}}\cos 2x$

Answer

a. $\displaystyle\lim_{x\to-8}(x^2-6x+17)=(-8)^2-6(-8)+17$
$$=64+48+17=129$$

Since quadratic functions are continuous, use direct substitution.

b. $\displaystyle\lim_{x\to4}5\ln(x+3)=5\ln(4+3)\approx9.73$

Since logarithmic functions are continuous, use direct substitution.

c. $\displaystyle\lim_{x\to\frac{\pi}{6}}\cos 2x=\cos 2\left(\frac{\pi}{6}\right)=\cos\frac{\pi}{3}=\frac{1}{2}$

Since sinusoidal functions are continuous, use direct substitution.

SKILL ✓ **EXERCISE 9**

The formula modeling continuously compounded interest, $P=e^{rt}$, is derived by evaluating the limit as $n\to\infty$ of the compound interest formula, $A=P\left(1+\frac{r}{n}\right)^{nt}$.

In Chapters 1 and 2, limit notation was used to describe the end behavior of a function and the function's behavior at vertical asymptotes and point discontinuities. Recall that the end behavior of a polynomial function can be determined by examining the leading term, since other terms become relatively insignificant as $x\to\pm\infty$.

Example 3 Describing Polynomial End Behavior with Limits

Use limits to describe the end behavior of $g(x)=x^3-8x-57$ and $h(x)=-x^4+3x^2+9x$.

Answer

a. $\displaystyle\lim_{x\to\infty}g(x)=\infty$ and $\displaystyle\lim_{x\to-\infty}g(x)=-\infty$

The end behavior of $g(x)$ matches that of $f(x)=x^3$.

b. $\displaystyle\lim_{x\to\pm\infty}h(x)=-\infty$

The end behavior of $h(x)$ matches that of a reflection of $f(x)=x^4$ across the x-axis.

SKILL ✓ **EXERCISE 15**

Note that *infinite limits* such as $\displaystyle\lim_{x\to\infty}g(x)=\infty$ describe a function's behavior, but they are not true limits since $g(x)$ does not approach a unique real number L.

Example 4 Finding Limits Involving Infinity

Evaluate each limit for $f(x)=\dfrac{2x^4}{x(x-3)(x+1)^2}$.

a. $\displaystyle\lim_{x\to\pm\infty}f(x)$ **b.** $\displaystyle\lim_{x\to-1}f(x)$ **c.** $\displaystyle\lim_{x\to3}f(x)$ **d.** $\displaystyle\lim_{x\to0}f(x)$

Answer

a. $\displaystyle\lim_{x\to\pm\infty}f(x)=2$

Since the degrees of the polynomials in the numerator and the denominator are the same, $f(x)$ has a horizontal asymptote at $y=2$.

b. $\displaystyle\lim_{x\to-1^-}f(x)=\infty$ and $\displaystyle\lim_{x\to-1^+}f(x)=\infty$
$\therefore\ \displaystyle\lim_{x\to-1}f(x)=\infty$

Since the function approaches infinity on both sides of $x=-1$, its behavior as $x\to-1$ is described with an infinite limit.

c. $\displaystyle\lim_{x\to3^-}f(x)=-\infty$ and $\displaystyle\lim_{x\to3^+}f(x)=\infty$
$\therefore\ \displaystyle\lim_{x\to3}f(x)$ does not exist.

Since the function approaches $-\infty$ on one side of $x=3$ and ∞ on the other side, its behavior as $x\to3$ cannot be described using a limit.

CONTINUED ➡

d. $\lim\limits_{x\to 0^-} f(x) = 0$ and $\lim\limits_{x\to 0^+} f(x) = 0$

$\therefore \lim\limits_{x\to 0} f(x) = 0$

Since the function approaches the same real number from both sides of $x = 0$, the limit as $x \to 0$ exists.

SKILL ✓ **EXERCISE 29**

A table can also be used to examine the values of the function near $x = 0$.

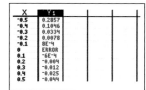

$Y_1 = 2X^4/(X(X-3)(X+1)^2)$

In Example 4*d* the fact that $f(x)$ is not defined at $x = 0$ but $\lim\limits_{x\to 0} f(x)$ is a real number indicates a point discontinuity. The fact that $\lim\limits_{x\to 0} f(x) \neq f(0)$ illustrates an important property of limits: a limit describes what occurs to the function's values as the function approaches (or is in the neighborhood of) $x = a$. If a function is discontinuous at $x = a$, then $\lim\limits_{x\to a} f(x) \neq f(a)$.

When finding the limit of a sequence as $n \to \infty$, consider the effect of substituting large numbers for the variable.

Example 5   Finding Limits of Sequences

Find the limit of each sequence.

a. $a_n = \dfrac{2n + 7}{3n - 4}$ **b.** $b_n = (-1)^n$ **c.** $c_n = \left(-\dfrac{2}{3}\right)^n$ **d.** $d_n = -\dfrac{2}{3}n$

Answer

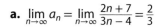

$Y_1 = (2X+7)/(3X-4)$

Define $Y_1 = a_n$, $Y_2 = b_n$, $Y_3 = c_n$, and $Y_4 = d_n$. In the TABLE SETUP menu set Indpnt: to Ask and Depend: to Auto. Then Select Table and enter increasingly larger values for X.

In a 1693 letter Leibniz wrote, "I am so much in favor of the actual infinite that instead of admitting that nature abhors it, as is commonly said, I hold that it assumes it everywhere, in order to better show the perfections of its author."

a. $\lim\limits_{n\to\infty} a_n = \lim\limits_{n\to\infty} \dfrac{2n + 7}{3n - 4} = \dfrac{2}{3}$

As n increases, a_n converges to $\dfrac{2}{3}$.

b. $\lim\limits_{n\to\infty} b_n = \lim\limits_{n\to\infty} (-1)^n$ does not exist.

As n increases, b_n alternates between 1 and -1 and the sequence is divergent.

c. $\lim\limits_{n\to\infty} c_n = \lim\limits_{n\to\infty} \left(-\dfrac{2}{3}\right)^n = 0$

As n increases, c_n converges to 0.

d. $\lim\limits_{n\to\infty} d_n = \lim\limits_{n\to\infty} -\dfrac{2}{3}n = -\infty$

As n increases, d_n continues to decrease and the sequence is divergent.

SKILL ✓ **EXERCISE 33**

You can use limits and graphing calculators to model many real-world situations.

Example 6   Applying Limits to Depreciation

Philip buys a new car for $45,000. The estimated depreciation is 20% per year.

a. Write a function $f(x)$ modeling the value of the car after x years.

b. Use technology to graph the function and find $\lim\limits_{x\to\infty} f(x)$.

c. Find the value of the car after 10 yr.

d. When will the car's estimated value drop below $1000?

Answer

a. $f(x) = 45{,}000(0.8)^x$

The modeling function will be exponential with a rate of $100\% - 20\% = 80\%$.

CONTINUED ➡

b.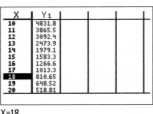

The graph of $f(x)$ has a horizontal asymptote at $y = 0$.

$$\lim_{x \to \infty} f(x) = 0$$

c. $f(10) = \$4831.84$

d. During the 18th year the estimated value will drop below $1000.

A table of values can also be helpful.

X	Y₁
10	4831.8
11	3865.5
12	3092.4
13	2473.9
14	1979.1
15	1583.3
16	1266.6
17	1013.3
18	810.65
19	648.52
20	518.81

X=18

SKILL ✓ **EXERCISE 41**

The key concepts in solving fundamental problems in calculus, the derivative and the integral, are both defined in terms of limits. Limit theorems that make the deductive development of the derivative possible are discussed in the following sections.

❯ A. Exercises

Use the graph of

$$f(x) = \frac{x(x-3)(x+1)}{x(x+2)(x-1)^2}$$

to find each limit.

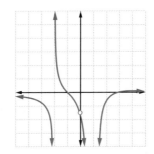

1. $\displaystyle\lim_{x \to \infty} f(x)$

2. $\displaystyle\lim_{x \to 0^-} f(x)$

3. $\displaystyle\lim_{x \to -2^+} f(x)$

4. $\displaystyle\lim_{x \to -2^-} f(x)$

5. $\displaystyle\lim_{x \to -2} f(x)$

6. $\displaystyle\lim_{x \to 1} f(x)$

7. $\displaystyle\lim_{x \to 3} f(x)$

Evaluate each limit, if it exists.

8. $\displaystyle\lim_{x \to 2} (7x - 5)$

9. $\displaystyle\lim_{x \to -1} |x - 4|$

10. $\displaystyle\lim_{x \to -2^+} (x^3 + 2x - 6)$

11. $\displaystyle\lim_{x \to -3} [x + 1]$

12. $\displaystyle\lim_{x \to \frac{7\pi}{6}} (4 \sin x)$

13. $\displaystyle\lim_{x \to 17} \sqrt{x - 8}$

Use limits to describe the end behavior of each polynomial function.

14. $g(x) = x^6 - 3x^3 + 94$

15. $f(x) = -x^3 - 7x + 5$

❯ B. Exercises

Use technology to graph each function. Then state the function's domain and evaluate the limit of the function at the given value of x.

16. $f(x) = |x|; x \to -3$

17. $g(x) = 5x^4 + 2x - 7; x \to -1$

18. $h(x) = \ln(x - 8); x \to 9$

19. $n(x) = \dfrac{3}{x^2}; x \to 0$

20. $m(x) = \sqrt{2x + 6}; x \to 5$

21. $j(x) = \tan x; x \to \dfrac{\pi}{2}$

22. $p(x) = \dfrac{x + 5}{x^2 - 49}; x \to 7$

23. $q(x) = \dfrac{4}{x^2 + 1}; x \to -1$

Write the equation of the asymptote in the graph of $f(x)$ that is implied by each limit.

24. $\displaystyle\lim_{x \to -\infty} f(x) = 7$

25. $\displaystyle\lim_{x \to -2} f(x) = -\infty$

26. $\displaystyle\lim_{x \to 5^-} f(x) = \infty$

27. $\displaystyle\lim_{x \to \infty} f(x) = -4$

Use technology to graph each function. Then state the limit, if it exists. If the limit does not exist, explain why.

28. $\displaystyle\lim_{x \to 4} \dfrac{2}{(x - 4)^2}$

29. $\displaystyle\lim_{x \to 2} \dfrac{3}{x - 2}$

30. $\displaystyle\lim_{x \to 5} \sqrt{x - 5}$

31. $\displaystyle\lim_{x \to 0} \sqrt{x + 4}$

Find the limit of the each sequence.

32. $a_n = \frac{3 - 2n}{n}$

33. $a_n = \frac{n+1}{3n}$

34. $a_n = \frac{8}{4n^3}$

35. $a_n = 3 + \frac{1}{n}$

36. $a_n = 5$

37. $a_n = 2n$

38. $a_n = 4(1.5)^n$

39. $a_n = (-2)^n$

40. A construction company buys a new piece of equipment for $359,000. The estimated depreciation is 30% per year.

  a. Write a function $f(x)$ modeling the value of the equipment after x years.

  b. Find $\lim_{x \to \infty} f(x)$.

  c. In which year will the equipment's value become less than $30,000?

41. A real estate investor buys a new property for $4.575 million. The estimated appreciation is 6% per year.

  a. Write a function $f(x)$ modeling the value of the property after x years.

  b. Find $\lim_{x \to \infty} f(x)$.

  c. In which year will the property's value become greater than $8 million?

C. Exercises

42. Graph the function $f(x) = e^x + x^e + \ln(x + e)$.

  a. State the domain. **b.** Find $f(0)$.

  c. Find $\lim_{x \to 0^+} f(x)$. **d.** Find $\lim_{x \to 0} f(x)$.

  e. Why should the graph of an unfamiliar function be considered when finding limits?

43. Find $\lim_{x \to -\infty} r(x)$ and $\lim_{x \to \infty} r(x)$ for each case of the rational function $r(x) = \frac{ax^m}{bx^n}$.

  a. $m = n$

  b. $m < n$

  c. $m - n > 0$ and even, $ab > 0$

  d. $m - n > 0$ and even, $ab < 0$

  e. $m - n > 0$ and odd, $ab < 0$

  f. $m - n > 0$ and odd, $ab > 0$

44. Find $\lim_{n \to \infty} a_n$ for each sequence.

  a. $a_n = a_0 + nd$ and $d < 0$

  b. $a_n = a_0 + nd$ and $d > 0$

  c. $a_n = a_0 r^n$ and $r < 0$

  d. $a_n = a_0 r^n$ and $0 < r < 1$

  e. $a_n = a_0 r^n$ and $r = 1$

  f. $a_n = a_0 r^n$, $a_0 > 0$, and $r > 1$

CUMULATIVE REVIEW

45. Write the slope-intercept form equation of a line passing through $(3, 7)$ and parallel to $y = \frac{4}{3}x + 2$. [1.2]

46. If $f(x) = 3x + 7$, find the simplified expression for $\frac{f(x + h) - f(x)}{h}$. [1.7]

Evaluate each infinite geometric series. [9.3]

47. $5 + 1 + \frac{1}{5} + \cdots$

48. $\sum_{n=1}^{\infty} 6\left(\frac{1}{4}\right)^n$

Determine the p-value and then use it to determine whether to reject the null hypothesis at a 0.05 level of significance. [11.4]

49. $H_0: \mu \geq 84; H_a: \mu < 84$

  $\bar{x} = 82, s = 5.92, n = 32$

50. $H_0: \mu = 850; H_a: \mu \neq 850$

  $\bar{x} = 878, s = 123, n = 55$

51. Find the length of side a (to the nearest tenth) in $\triangle ABC$ with $\angle A = 51°$, $b = 12$, and $c = 18$. [5.7]

  A. 196.1 **C.** 14.2 **E.** none of

  B. 21.6 **D.** 6 these

52. Use technology to find the probability that a randomly selected value in a normal distribution with $\mu = 83$ and $\sigma = 12.7$ is within $[69, 92]$. [10.6]

  A. 13.6% **C.** 62.6% **E.** none of

  B. 23.9% **D.** 86.4% these

53. Which sampling technique is used when the population is divided into distinguishable groups and members of each group are randomly selected for the sample? [11.5]

  A. random **D.** stratified random

  B. convenience **E.** none of these

  C. cluster

54. Evaluate $\sum_{i=1}^{n} c$. [9.5]

  A. c **C.** nc **E.** none of

  B. i **D.** n these

12.2 Properties of Limits

Investing in the lives of others produces eternal rewards.

The French mathematician Augustin-Louis Cauchy (1789–1857) proved many of these properties and established the theoretical foundation of calculus. He wrote so much that the periodical in which many of his proofs were published, *Comptes Rendus*, decided not to accept any article exceeding four pages, a rule still in use today.

The concept of limits can be used to illustrate an important truth. If you lived 80 yr and there was no life after death, your life on the earth would be $\frac{80}{80}$, or 100%, of your existence. If your life after death was 80 yr long, your earthly life would be $\frac{80}{160}$, or 50%, of your entire existence. If your life after death was 720 yr, your life here would be only $\frac{80}{80 + 720}$, or 10%, of your existence. Extending this pattern to an eternal life after death, $\lim_{x \to \infty} \frac{80}{80 + x} = 0$, demonstrates that the duration of life spent on earth is insignificant in comparison to the duration spent in eternity. In light of eternity, earthly life and its current joys and troubles are like a vapor, appearing for a little time and then vanishing away (James 4:14). Any selfish achievements are also worthless. Only what you do for the Lord becomes important to the infinite, eternal God whom you serve. With the little time we have here on earth, we should focus more on things with eternal, heavenly benefits than on those with temporary, earthly benefits (Col. 3:2).

In the previous section we intuitively evaluated limits using graphs and tables of values. Algebraic methods of evaluating limits are necessary if limits are to serve as the foundation of calculus. The following properties of limits (some of which simply state what we have already learned about continuous functions and direct substitution) are the basis of these computational techniques.

LIMIT OF A CONSTANT

If $f(x) = c$, where c is a constant, then $\lim_{x \to a} f(x) = c$ for all a.

The graph of $y = c$ is a horizontal line, which implies that the function's value remains constant for all values of x.

LIMIT OF THE IDENTITY FUNCTION

If $f(x) = x$ for all x, then $\lim_{x \to a} f(x) = a$.

Since the graph of $y = x$ is continuous, if $x = a$, then $y = a$ also.

LIMIT OF A SCALAR MULTIPLE

If f is a function such that $\lim_{x \to a} f(x) = L$, then $\lim_{x \to a} cf(x) = c \lim_{x \to a} f(x) = cL$, where $c \in \mathbb{R}$.

In other words, the limit of the product of a constant and a function is equal to the constant times the limit of the function.

LIMIT OF A SUM

If f and g are functions such that $\lim_{x \to a} f(x) = L_1$ and $\lim_{x \to a} g(x) = L_2$, then $\lim_{x \to a} [f(x) + g(x)] = \lim_{x \to a} f(x) + \lim_{x \to a} g(x) = L_1 + L_2$.

Simply put, the limit of a sum is the sum of the limits. This powerful property allows you to consider the limit of each term of a function separately. It also applies to the limit of a difference since subtraction is equivalent to adding the opposite.

▎LIMIT OF A POWER

If f is a function such that $\lim_{x \to a} f(x) = L$, then $\lim_{x \to a} [f(x)]^n = \left[\lim_{x \to a} f(x)\right]^n = L^n$.

Example 1 Finding a Limit Using Properties

Evaluate $\lim_{x \to 2} (2x^2 - 3x + 5)$.

Answer

$\lim_{x \to 2} (2x^2 - 3x + 5)$ 1. Apply the limit of a sum.

$= \lim_{x \to 2} 2x^2 - \lim_{x \to 2} 3x + \lim_{x \to 2} 5$

$= 2 \lim_{x \to 2} x^2 - 3 \lim_{x \to 2} x + \lim_{x \to 2} 5$ 2. Apply the limit of a scalar multiple.

$= 2 \left[\lim_{x \to 2} x\right]^2 - 3 \lim_{x \to 2} x + \lim_{x \to 2} 5$ 3. Apply the limit of a power.

$= 2(2)^2 - 3(2) + 5$ 4. Apply the limit of an identity and the limit of a constant
$= 7$ and simplify.

_____ SKILL ✓ **EXERCISE 7**

Example 1 validates finding the limit of the continuous quadratic function by direct substitution. Since all polynomials are continuous, direct substitution can be used to find limits of any polynomial function.

▎LIMIT OF A PRODUCT

If f and g are functions such that $\lim_{x \to a} f(x) = L_1$ and $\lim_{x \to a} g(x) = L_2$,
then $\lim_{x \to a} [f(x) \cdot g(x)] = \lim_{x \to a} f(x) \cdot \lim_{x \to a} g(x) = L_1 \cdot L_2$.

▎LIMIT OF A QUOTIENT

If f and g are functions such that $\lim_{x \to a} f(x) = L_1$ and $\lim_{x \to a} g(x) = L_2 \neq 0$,

then $\lim_{x \to a} \dfrac{f(x)}{g(x)} = \dfrac{\lim_{x \to a} f(x)}{\lim_{x \to a} g(x)} = \dfrac{L_1}{L_2}$.

The limit of a quotient allows us to find limits for rational functions.

Example 2 Finding the Limit of a Rational Function

Find $\lim_{x \to -3} \dfrac{x^3 - 8x^2 + 4}{5x - 10}$.

Answer

$\lim_{x \to -3} \dfrac{x^3 - 8x^2 + 4}{5x - 10} = \dfrac{\lim_{x \to -3} (x^3 - 8x^2 + 4)}{\lim_{x \to -3} (5x - 10)}$ 1. Apply the limit of a quotient.

$= \dfrac{\lim_{x \to -3} x^3 - \lim_{x \to -3} 8x^2 + \lim_{x \to -3} 4}{\lim_{x \to -3} 5x - \lim_{x \to -3} 10}$ 2. Apply the limit of a sum.

CONTINUED ➡

$$= \frac{\left(\lim_{x \to -3} x\right)^3 - 8\left(\lim_{x \to -3} x\right)^2 + \lim_{x \to -3} 4}{5 \lim_{x \to -3} x - \lim_{x \to -3} 10}$$

3. Apply the limit of a power and limit of a scalar multiple.

$$= \frac{(-3)^3 - 8(-3)^2 + 4}{5(-3) - 10} = \frac{-27 - 72 + 4}{-15 - 10} = \frac{-95}{-25} = \frac{19}{5}$$

4. Apply the limit of an identity and limit of a constant and simplify.

SKILL ✓ EXERCISE 9

Since the only discontinuity in the function in Example 2 occurs where $5x - 10 = 0$ (at $x = 2$), direct substitution can be used to find the limit approaching any point except $x = 2$.

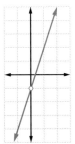

Using direct substitution to find $\lim_{x \to 0} \frac{3x^2 - x}{x}$ produces $\frac{0}{0}$, which is called an *indeterminate form* since it does not contain enough information to determine the limit. In these cases, the limit may not exist, it may diverge to ∞ or $-\infty$, or it may be a real number. Factoring and reducing $f(x) = \frac{3x^2 - x}{x} = \frac{(3x - 1)x}{x} = 3x - 1$ (where $x \neq 0$) reveals that the original expression represents a line with a point discontinuity at $x = 0$. Therefore, $\lim_{x \to 0} \frac{3x^2 - x}{x} = \lim_{x \to 0} (3x - 1) = 3(0) - 1 = -1$.

Example 3   Canceling to Find a Limit

Evaluate $\lim_{x \to 2} \frac{x - 2}{x^2 - x - 2}$.

Answer

$$\lim_{x \to 2} \frac{x - 2}{x^2 - x - 2} = \frac{(2) - 2}{(2)^2 - (2) - 2} = \frac{0}{0}$$

1. Using direct substitution produces an indeterminate form.

$$\lim_{x \to 2} \frac{x - 2}{x^2 - x - 2} = \lim_{x \to 2} \frac{x - 2}{(x - 2)(x + 1)} = \lim_{x \to 2} \frac{1}{x + 1}$$

2. Factor and cancel. The result implies the original function has a point discontinuity at $x = 2$.

$$= \frac{1}{(2) + 1} = \frac{1}{3}$$

3. Use direct substitution to find the limit.

Check

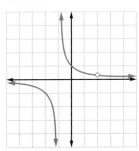

4. A graph of the function can be used to verify the limit.

SKILL ✓ EXERCISE 21

Since $\lim_{x \to 2} f(x)$ considers only values approaching $x = 2$ without reaching it, the reduced form clearly shows that both one-sided limits are equal to $\frac{1}{3}$ for $x = 2$, the location of the hole in the graph.

Some limits with indeterminate forms can be evaluated by rationalizing the numerator or the denominator.

Example 4 **Rationalizing a Numerator to Find a Limit**

Find $\lim\limits_{x \to 0} \dfrac{\sqrt{x+3} - \sqrt{3}}{x^2 - x}$.

Answer

$\lim\limits_{x \to 0} \dfrac{\sqrt{x+3} - \sqrt{3}}{x^2 - x} = \dfrac{\sqrt{0+3} - \sqrt{3}}{0^2 - 0} = \dfrac{0}{0}$

1. Using direct substitution produces an indeterminate form.

$\lim\limits_{x \to 0} \dfrac{(\sqrt{x+3} - \sqrt{3})(\sqrt{x+3} + \sqrt{3})}{(x^2 - x)(\sqrt{x+3} + \sqrt{3})}$

2. Multiply both the numerator and the denominator by the conjugate of the numerator.

$= \lim\limits_{x \to 0} \dfrac{(x+3) - 3}{x(x-1)(\sqrt{x+3} + \sqrt{3})}$

$= \lim\limits_{x \to 0} \dfrac{x}{x(x-1)(\sqrt{x+3} + \sqrt{3})}$

3. Simplify the numerator and cancel.

$= \lim\limits_{x \to 0} \dfrac{1}{(x-1)(\sqrt{x+3} + \sqrt{3})}$

$= \dfrac{1}{(0-1)(\sqrt{0+3} + \sqrt{3})} = -\dfrac{1}{2\sqrt{3}}$

4. Use direct substitution to find the limit.

Y₁=(√(X+3)–√(3))/(X²–X)

X=0   Y=

_____ SKILL ✓ **EXERCISE 25**

A graph of the function in Example 4 and the canceling of x in step 3 indicate that the limit of the function exists despite a point discontinuity at $x = 0$.

You may need to use trigonometric identities to rewrite an expression whose limit is an indeterminate form.

Example 5 **Using a Trigonometric Identity to Find a Limit**

Evaluate $\lim\limits_{x \to \pi} \dfrac{1 - \cos^2 x}{\sin x}$.

Answer

$\lim\limits_{x \to \pi} \dfrac{1 - \cos^2 x}{\sin x} = \dfrac{1 - \cos^2 \pi}{\sin \pi} = \dfrac{1 - (-1)^2}{0} = \dfrac{0}{0}$

1. Using direct substitution produces an indeterminate form.

$\lim\limits_{x \to \pi} \dfrac{1 - \cos^2 x}{\sin x} = \lim\limits_{x \to \pi} \dfrac{\sin^2 x}{\sin x}$

$= \lim\limits_{x \to \pi} \sin x$

2. Use a Pythagorean identity to rewrite the expression in the numerator and reduce. The result implies the original function has point discontinuities where $\sin x = 0$ (at $x = n\pi, n \in \mathbb{Z}$).

$= \sin \pi = 0$

3. Use direct substitution to find the limit.

Y₁=(1–cos(X)²)/sin(X)

_____ SKILL ✓ **EXERCISE 27**

A graph of the function in Example 5 and the canceling of $\sin x$ in step 2 indicate that the limit of the function exists despite a point discontinuity at $x = \pi$ (where $\sin x = 0$).

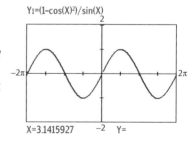

X=3.1415927   −2 Y=

A final property of limits is used to find limits of rational functions at infinity.

▌ LIMIT OF A RECIPROCAL POWER FUNCTION AT INFINITY

$\lim\limits_{x \to \pm\infty} \dfrac{1}{x^n} = 0$ when n is a natural number.

Example 6 Finding the Limit of a Rational Function at Infinity

Find $\lim\limits_{x\to\infty}\dfrac{6x^3-7x-11}{2x^3+x+3}$.

Answer

$$\lim_{x\to\infty}\frac{6x^3-7x-11}{2x^3+x+3}=\lim_{x\to\infty}\frac{\dfrac{6x^3}{x^3}-\dfrac{7x}{x^3}-\dfrac{11}{x^3}}{\dfrac{2x^3}{x^3}+\dfrac{x}{x^3}+\dfrac{3}{x^3}}$$

1. Divide each term by x^d, where d is the degree of the denominator.

$$=\lim_{x\to\infty}\frac{6-\dfrac{7}{x^2}-\dfrac{11}{x^3}}{2+\dfrac{1}{x^2}+\dfrac{3}{x^3}}$$

2. Simplify by reducing each term in the numerator and denominator.

$$=\frac{\lim\limits_{x\to\infty}6-7\lim\limits_{x\to\infty}\dfrac{1}{x^2}-11\lim\limits_{x\to\infty}\dfrac{1}{x^3}}{\lim\limits_{x\to\infty}2+\lim\limits_{x\to\infty}\dfrac{1}{x^2}+3\lim\limits_{x\to\infty}\dfrac{1}{x^3}}$$

3. Apply the limit of a sum and limit of a scalar multiple.

$$=\frac{6-7(0)-11(0)}{2+0+3(0)}=\frac{6}{2}=3$$

4. Apply the limit of a constant and limit of a reciprocal power function, and simplify.

Check

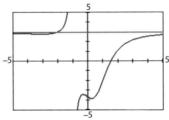

5. The horizontal asymptote of the function's graph at $y=3$ illustrates that the limit as $x\to\pm\infty$ of a rational function with a numerator and a denominator of the same degree is the ratio of leading coefficients.

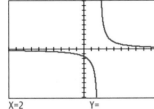

Y1=3/(X-2)

X=2   Y=

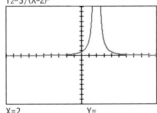

Y2=3/(X-2)²

X=2   Y=

SKILL ✓ EXERCISE 35

While algebraic methods of finding limits are preferred when applicable, graphs and tables can provide confirmation of algebraic answers or valuable insight when direct substitution produces an undefined expression $\frac{k}{0}$, where k is a constant. Notice that evaluating the limit as $x\to2$ of both $f(x)=\dfrac{3}{x-2}$ and $g(x)=\dfrac{3}{(x-2)^2}$ by direct substitution produces the result of $\frac{3}{0}$. Such a result indicates a vertical asymptote at $x=2$, and graphing the functions illustrates that $\lim\limits_{x\to2}\dfrac{3}{x-2}$ does not exist, while $\lim\limits_{x\to2}\dfrac{3}{(x-2)^2}=\infty$. Graphs should also be considered for limits such as $\lim\limits_{x\to3}[x]$ and $\lim\limits_{x\to3}\sqrt{x-3}$ in which the one-sided limits differ.

▶ A. Exercises

Name the property of limits that justifies each statement.

1. $\lim\limits_{x\to-4}(-3)=-3$

2. $\lim\limits_{x\to a}x^4=\left(\lim\limits_{x\to a}x\right)^4$

3. $\lim\limits_{x\to15}9f(x)=9\lim\limits_{x\to15}f(x)$

4. $\lim\limits_{x\to\infty}\dfrac{1}{x^5}=0$

5. $\lim\limits_{x\to7}[8x]\sqrt{2x+1}=\lim\limits_{x\to7}[8x]\cdot\lim\limits_{x\to7}\sqrt{2x+1}$

6. $\lim\limits_{x\to7}(5x^2-4x)=\lim\limits_{x\to7}5x^2-\lim\limits_{x\to7}4x$

Evaluate each limit by applying the properties of limits.

7. $\lim\limits_{x\to0}5x$

8. $\lim\limits_{x\to-1}(x^2-3x)$

9. $\lim\limits_{x\to1}\dfrac{-2x-9}{x+1}$

10. $\lim\limits_{x\to2}\dfrac{x^4-x^2+4x}{2x^2-3x-9}$

Evaluate each limit using direct substitution or explain why this method fails.

11. $\lim\limits_{x\to4}(x+3)^2$

12. $\lim\limits_{x\to2}\dfrac{3}{x^2}$

13. $\lim\limits_{x\to-1}\dfrac{x^2-1}{x+1}$

14. $\lim\limits_{x\to3}x^3$

15. $\lim\limits_{x \to -1} \dfrac{x^2 + 2x - 1}{x + 1}$

16. $\lim\limits_{x \to -1} \dfrac{2x^2 + 5x + 3}{x + 1}$

17. $\lim\limits_{x \to 0} \dfrac{1}{x - 1}$

18. $\lim\limits_{h \to 0} \dfrac{3h^2 - h + 1}{h}$

19. $\lim\limits_{\theta \to \frac{\pi}{3}} \sin \theta$

20. $\lim\limits_{\theta \to \pi} \sec \theta$

❭ B. Exercises

Evaluate each limit.

21. $\lim\limits_{x \to 1} \dfrac{x^2 - 1}{x - 1}$

22. $\lim\limits_{x \to 1} \dfrac{x^3 - 1}{x - 1}$

23. $\lim\limits_{x \to 2} \dfrac{2 - x}{x^2 - 4}$

24. $\lim\limits_{t \to 0} \dfrac{\sqrt{t + 1} - 1}{t}$

25. $\lim\limits_{x \to 0} \dfrac{\sqrt{x + 2} - \sqrt{2}}{x}$

26. $\lim\limits_{a \to 0} \dfrac{\sqrt{a + 4} - 2}{a}$

27. $\lim\limits_{\theta \to 0} \dfrac{\cos^2 \theta - 1}{\sin \theta}$

28. $\lim\limits_{\theta \to \frac{\pi}{2}} \dfrac{\tan \theta - 1}{\sec \theta}$

29. $\lim\limits_{x \to 3} \dfrac{x^2 - 2x - 3}{4x^2 - 12x}$

30. $\lim\limits_{x \to 0} \dfrac{5x^2 - 8}{4x^2 - 3x + 1}$

31. $\lim\limits_{x \to -4^-} \sqrt{x + 4}$

32. $\lim\limits_{x \to 7} [x]$

33. $\lim\limits_{h \to 0} \dfrac{(4 + h)^2 - 4^2}{h}$

34. $\lim\limits_{h \to 0} \dfrac{(x + h)^2 - x^2}{h}$

Apply the properties of limits to find the limit of each rational function at infinity.

35. $\lim\limits_{x \to \infty} \dfrac{x^2 + 4x - 7}{x^3 - 5x^2 + 8}$

36. $\lim\limits_{x \to \infty} \dfrac{-6x^4 - x + 15}{8x^4 + 11x^2 - 2}$

Apply the properties of limits to find the limits of each sequence.

37. $a_n = \dfrac{8n - 1}{2n}$

38. $a_n = \dfrac{4n - 1}{7n^2 - 2n + 3}$

❭ C. Exercises

39. When does $\lim\limits_{x \to a} \dfrac{\sec x}{\sin x} = 0$?

40. When does $\lim\limits_{x \to a} \dfrac{e^{x^2} - e^x}{e^x} = e^{20} - 1$?

Given the general rational function

$$f(x) = \dfrac{a_m x^m + a_{m-1} x^{m-1} + \cdots + a_2 x^2 + a_1 x + a_0}{b_n x^n + b_{n-1} x^{n-1} + \cdots + b_2 x^2 + b_1 x + b_0}, \text{ use the}$$

properties of limits to derive the formulas for asymptotes found on page 107.

41. $m < n$

42. $m = n$

CUMULATIVE REVIEW

43. If $f(x) = x^2 - 4x$, find the simplified expression for $\dfrac{f(x + h) - f(x)}{h}$. **[1.7]**

44. State functions $u(x)$ and $v(x)$ such that $f(x) = e^{6x} = (u \circ v)(x)$. **[1.7]**

45. Verify the identity $\dfrac{\tan x}{1 - \tan^2 x} = \dfrac{\sin x \cos x}{2 \cos^2 x - 1}$. **[5.2]**

46. Use the explicit formula for the sum of the first 50 perfect squares to evaluate $\sum\limits_{k=1}^{50} k^2$. **[9.5]**

Classify each conic. Then state its center, vertices, and focal length. **[8.2–8.3]**

47. $\dfrac{(x - 1)^2}{25} - \dfrac{y^2}{144} = 1$

48. $\dfrac{(x - 9)^2}{9} + \dfrac{(y + 2)^2}{16} = 1$

49. State the equation for the bounds of $y = 2 \sin 3x + x$. **[4.7]**

    A. $y = \pm 2$ **C.** $y = x \pm 2$ **E.** none of these

    B. $y = x$ **D.** $y = 2x \pm 2$

50. Given $P(2, 3, -1)$ and $Q(6, 5, 2)$, find the length of $\overrightarrow{PQ}$ to the nearest tenth. **[6.3]**

    A. 4.5   **C.** 9   **E.** none of these

    B. 5.4   **D.** 29

51. According to AAA, 21% of fatal accidents involving teen drivers are caused by cell phone distraction. If a random sample of 30 fatal accidents involving teens is investigated, list all the reasons that a normal approximation of a binomial distribution can be used. **[11.2]**

    A. The population size is 30.

    B. If p is the probability of success, $np = 6.3$.

    C. If q is the probability of failure, $nq = 23.7$.

    D. The continuity correction factor is 0.5.

    E. none of these

52. A food processing company buys a new piece of equipment for \$312,000. The estimated depreciation is 15% per year. In which year will the equipment's value become less than \$80,000? **[12.1]**

    A. first year   **C.** eighth year   **E.** none of these

    B. fourth year   **D.** ninth year

Mathematics and Infinity

The infinite! No other question has ever moved so profoundly the spirit of man; no other idea has so fruitfully stimulated his intellect; yet no other concept stands in greater need of clarification than that of the infinite.

—David Hilbert (German mathematician; key proponent of formalism)

In 1930 the German mathematician and philosopher Hermann Weyl opened a speech with the statement, "Mathematics is the science of the infinite." Few mathematicians would place that great of an emphasis on the term "infinite," but the concept of infinity does permeate all of mathematics.

Even the simple skill of counting leads quickly to the idea that natural numbers continue on and on without end. In college-level mathematics natural numbers are referred to as "countably infinite." Surprisingly, rational numbers are also countably infinite because they can be placed in one-to-one correspondence with natural numbers. However, the subset of real numbers in the interval between zero and one is referred to as "uncountably infinite" due to the irrational numbers involved.

In 1900 David Hilbert declared the greatest unsolved modern mathematical problem to be the continuum hypothesis, which states that there is not a level of infinity between the countably infinite natural numbers and the uncountably infinite real numbers. In the 1960s American mathematician Paul Cohen proved that the continuum hypothesis is independent of the axiomatic framework of set theory. In other words, the continuum hypothesis is impossible to either prove or disprove. Cohen's work demonstrates that as powerful as axiomatic systems are, they still have limitations.

Beginning geometry students quickly encounter infinite sets when they contemplate the basic definition of space as the set of all points and the three undefined terms *point*, *line*, and *plane*. A line contains an infinite number of points, a plane contains an infinite number of lines, and space contains an infinite number of planes. Non-Euclidean geometries consider the infinite sets of points on a sphere, on a saddle shape, and on many other unusual surfaces.

Algebra students describe infinite sets when they use set builder notation to represent a line as $\{(x, y) \mid y = mx + b\}$, any conic section as $\{(x, y) \mid Ax^2 + Bxy + Cy^2 + Dx + Ey + F = 0\}$, a basic trigonometric curve as $\{(x, y) \mid y = a \cos bx\}$, or a sphere as $\{(x, y, z) \mid (x - h)^2 + (y - k)^2 + (z - j)^2 = r^2\}$. Domains and ranges of algebraic and transcendental functions are also described with infinite set notation. For example, the domain of the logarithmic function $f(x) = \log_2 x$ is $\{x \mid x > 0\}$ and the range of the trigonometric function $f(x) = \sin x$ is $\{f(x) \mid -1 \leq f(x) \leq 1\}$.

Calculus uses the concept of infinity to define its three big ideas: limits, derivatives, and integrals. Defining the limit requires *infinitesimals*, infinitely small quantities. The derivative is defined as the limit of the slope of a segment with endpoints on the graph of a function, which makes it possible to find instantaneous velocities or to find maximums in algebraic and geometric applications. The integral is defined as the limit of the sum of rectangle areas under a function curve with the number of rectangles approaching infinity. The integral allows the calculation of the amount of work done in physics or the volume of a solid of revolution.

Although the concept of infinity is pervasive in mathematics, the mystery surrounding its use has been a source of irritation for mathematicians throughout history. Irrational numbers, which cannot be expressed as ratios of integers and whose decimal expansions are infinite, shattered the cult-like natural number philosophy of the Pythagoreans. The ancient Greek Zeno stated many paradoxes involving infinity. Contradictions involving infinity occurred early in the development of calculus before the introduction of the formal limit resolved those contradictions. The development of set theory gave rise to paradoxes such as "the set of all sets."

The concept of infinity has been a source of inspiration and amazement for Christian mathematicians, as it points to our infinite God. One reason the Renaissance mathematicians and scientists made such great advances was due to their belief in an infinite God who controls the universe in an orderly manner. They realized that God's infinite wisdom was far above their finite knowledge (Isa. 55:9; Rom. 11:33). So Kepler, Galileo, Newton, and others searched for and discovered principles of order in God's creation (Gen. 1:1; Isa. 66:1), successfully inventing mathematical descriptions for those discoveries.

Mathematical infinity is quantitative, while God's infinity is qualitative. By this we mean that God cannot be reduced to His smallest parts to be understood better. God is essentially different from us in His being, not just infinitely more intelligent or present. God is unlimited yet retains His oneness and simplicity. The famous theologian Herman Bavinck describes God's infinity as "not limited by anything finite and creaturely." God's eternality transcends time and He is not bound by it. If the concept of infinity in mathematics creates wonder and awe, how much more should we worship and praise our limitless and infinite God (Ps. 90:2; Ps. 139:1–12)!

Exercises

1. Classify each infinite set of numbers as countable or uncountable.

   a. integer
   b. irrational
   c. natural
   d. rational
   e. real

2. Match each mathematical concept with its algebraic description.

   I. $\{x \mid x \in \mathbb{R}\}$
   II. $\{f(x) \mid f(x) > 0\}$
   III. $\{(x, y) \mid y = mx + b\}$
   IV. $\{(x, y) \mid Ax^2 + Bxy + Cy^2 + Dx + Ey + F = 0\}$
   V. $\{(x, y, z) \mid (x - h)^2 + (y - k)^2 + (z - j)^2 = r^2\}$

   a. line on a plane
   b. range of the exponential function
   c. sphere
   d. domain of the sine function
   e. conic section

3. How did Herman Wyle define mathematics?

4. Which famous statement asserts there is not a level of infinity between the infinities of the natural and real numbers?

5. How do the geometric concepts of a line, a plane, and space relate to the concept of infinity?

6. Name each of the described big ideas of calculus.

   a. represents the slope of the tangent to a function's graph
   b. represents the area under a function's graph
   c. used to define the other two big ideas

7. Which big idea of calculus can be used to find maximums in algebra and geometry?

8. **Discuss:** Give several examples of how the concept of infinity has been a source of frustration to mathematicians over the history of mathematics.

9. **Discuss:** Explain how a belief in an infinite God helped make Renaissance mathematicians successful in discovering mathematical laws in the universe.

To solve the Tower of Hanoi problem, move only one disk at a time to rebuild the tower in the correct order on a different peg without placing a larger disk on top of a smaller disk.

After completing this section, you will be able to

- find the slope of the tangent to a curve at a given point.
- determine the derivative of a function.
- find average and instantaneous velocities in real-world applications.

Classic problems, such as the Tower of Hanoi, have challenged mathematicians for centuries. One such problem in calculus was finding the slope of the line tangent to a curve at a given point. The solution to the "tangent problem" involves the slopes of secants through the point. To find the slope of the tangent to $f(x) = \frac{1}{4}x^2$ at $P(2, 1)$, begin by examining the slopes of several secants that are successively better approximations for the tangent.

using secant $\overleftrightarrow{PQ}$ with $Q(6, 9)$:	using secant $\overleftrightarrow{PQ}$ with $Q(4, 4)$:	using secant $\overleftrightarrow{PQ}$ with $Q\left(3, \frac{9}{4}\right)$:
graph $f(x) = \frac{1}{4}x^2$, $Q(6, 9)$, $P(2, 1)$, 8, 4	*graph* $f(x) = \frac{1}{4}x^2$, $Q(4, 4)$, $P(2, 1)$, 3, 2	*graph* $f(x) = \frac{1}{4}x^2$, $Q\left(3, \frac{9}{4}\right)$, $P(2, 1)$, $\frac{5}{4}$, 1
$m = \dfrac{\Delta y}{\Delta x} = \dfrac{8}{4} = 2$	$m = \dfrac{\Delta y}{\Delta x} = \dfrac{3}{2} = 1.5$	$m = \dfrac{\Delta y}{\Delta x} = \dfrac{\frac{5}{4}}{1} = \dfrac{5}{4} = 1.25$

The challenge is finding the exact slope of the tangent to the curve at P. When Q reaches P, the secant becomes a tangent (intersecting the curve at just one point), but applying the formula for slope produces $\frac{0}{0}$, an indeterminate form. This difficulty is solved by finding the limit of the secant line's slope as $\Delta x \to 0$.

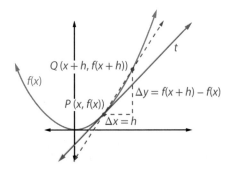

Generalizing the problem, let $P(x, f(x))$ represent the point of tangency on the graph, and let the second point be $Q(x + h, f(x + h))$ where $h = \Delta x$, the difference between the x-coordinates. The slope of secant $\overleftrightarrow{PQ}$ is $m = \dfrac{\Delta y}{\Delta x}$

$= \dfrac{f(x + h) - f(x)}{(x + h) - x} = \dfrac{f(x + h) - f(x)}{h}$, an expression called the *difference quotient*.

Finding $\displaystyle\lim_{h \to 0} \dfrac{f(x + h) - f(x)}{h}$ produces the exact slope of the tangent line t.

▌ DEFINITION

The **derivative** of the function f at the point where $x = a$, denoted by $f'(a)$ and read "f prime of a," is

$f'(a) = \displaystyle\lim_{h \to 0} \dfrac{f(a + h) - f(a)}{h}$, if the limit exists.

The slope of the line tangent to $f(x)$ at $x = a$ is $f'(a)$.

If $f'(a)$ exists, the function is said to be *differentiable* at $x = a$. All three of the following conditions must be true in order for a function to be differentiable at $x = a$.

1. The function must be continuous at $x = a$ (no asymptote, jump, or point discontinuities).

2. The function cannot have a sharp point at $x = a$.

3. The function cannot have a vertical tangent at the point. (The slope would be undefined.)

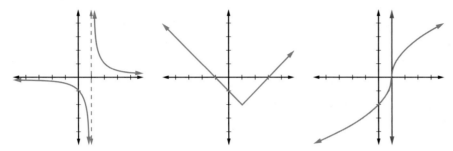

None of these graphed functions are differentiable at $x = 1$. At this value of x, the first is discontinuous, the second has a sharp point, and the third has a vertical tangent.

Example 1   Finding the Derivative at a Point

Find $f'(1)$ if $f(x) = 2x^2 - 4$.

Answer

$f'(1) = \lim_{h \to 0} \dfrac{f(1 + h) - f(1)}{h}$

1. Substitute for a in the definition of the derivative at a point: $f'(a) = \lim_{h \to 0} \dfrac{f(a + h) - f(a)}{h}$.

$= \lim_{h \to 0} \dfrac{[2(1 + h)^2 - 4] - [2(1)^2 - 4]}{h}$

2. Rewrite the difference quotient using substitutions for $f(1 + h)$ and $f(1)$.

$= \lim_{h \to 0} \dfrac{2(1 + 2h + h^2) - 4 - (2 - 4)}{h}$

3. Simplify the difference quotient.

$= \lim_{h \to 0} \dfrac{2 + 4h + 2h^2 - 4 + 2}{h}$

Note that division by h is allowed since $h \neq 0$; h is only approaching 0.

$= \lim_{h \to 0} \dfrac{4h + 2h^2}{h} = \lim_{h \to 0} (4 + 2h)$

$= 4 + 2(0) = 4$

4. Evaluate the limit of the polynomial by substituting 0 for h.

SKILL ✓ EXERCISE 13

Notice that the slope of the tangent to the parabola $f(x) = 2x^2 - 4$ at $x = 1$ is 4.

The definition of a derivative can be used to find a function for the slope of the tangent to the graph of $f(x)$ at any differentiable point.

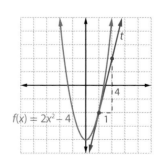

$f(x) = 2x^2 - 4$

▌DEFINITION

The **derivative function** represents the derivative for any value of x where the limit exists. It is denoted $f'(x)$ where $f'(x) = \lim_{h \to 0} \dfrac{f(x + h) - f(x)}{h}$.

Example 2 Finding and Applying a Derivative Function

Given the parabola $f(x) = \frac{1}{4}x^2$, find its derivative function $f'(x)$.

Then use $f'(x)$ to find the slope of the tangent to the parabola at $x = -2$ and $x = 1$.

Answer

$f'(x) = \lim_{h \to 0} \dfrac{f(x+h) - f(x)}{h}$

1. State the definition of the derivative function.

$= \lim_{h \to 0} \dfrac{\frac{1}{4}(x+h)^2 - \frac{1}{4}x^2}{h}$

2. Rewrite the difference quotient using substitutions for $f(x + h)$ and $f(x)$.

$= \lim_{h \to 0} \dfrac{\frac{1}{4}(x^2 + 2xh + h^2 - x^2)}{h}$

3. Simplify the difference quotient.

$= \lim_{h \to 0} \dfrac{2xh + h^2}{4h} = \lim_{h \to 0} \left(\dfrac{x}{2} + \dfrac{h}{4} \right)$

$= \dfrac{x}{2} + \dfrac{0}{4} = \dfrac{x}{2}$

4. Evaluate the limit by substituting for h.

$\therefore f'(x) = \dfrac{x}{2}$

$f'(-2) = \dfrac{(-2)}{2} = -1 \qquad f'(1) = \dfrac{(1)}{2} = \dfrac{1}{2}$

5. Substitute $x = -2$ and $x = 1$ into $f'(x)$ to find the slope of the tangent to the parabola at those points.

SKILL ✔ **EXERCISE 31**

To indicate a derivative, Leibniz used $\frac{dy}{dx}$ notation but Newton used a dot, as in $\dot{y}$. When Charles Babbage, a founding member of the Analytical Society (1812) of Cambridge, stated that one of the society's purposes was to promote "The Principles of pure D-ism in opposition to the Dot-age of the University," he was referring to a preference for Leibniz's notation.

Since the slope of any tangent to the function $f(x) = \frac{1}{4}x^2$ is given by $f'(x) = \frac{1}{2}x$, the slope varies and depends on the x-coordinate of the point. To find the exact slope of the tangent to $f(x) = \frac{1}{4}x^2$ at $x = 2$ as sought in the introduction of the lesson, evaluate $f'(2) = \frac{1}{2}(2) = 1$. The ability to find the slope of the tangent to the curve at multiple points using the single $f'(x)$ function demonstrates the power of the derivative function.

Alternative notations for the derivative function, $f'(x)$, include $\dfrac{dy}{dx}$ (read "the derivative of y with respect to x"), y' (read "y prime"), and $\dfrac{d}{dx} f(x)$ (where $\dfrac{d}{dx}$ is the *differential operator* indicating the derivative of the following function).

Example 3 Finding the Derivative Function

Find $\dfrac{dy}{dx}$ if $y = 3x + 5$.

Answer

$\dfrac{dy}{dx} = f'(x) = \lim_{h \to 0} \dfrac{f(x+h) - f(x)}{h}$

1. State the definition in function form.

$= \lim_{h \to 0} \dfrac{[3(x+h) + 5] - (3x+5)}{h}$

2. Rewrite the difference quotient using substitutions for $f(x + h)$ and $f(x)$.

$= \lim_{h \to 0} \dfrac{3x + 3h + 5 - 3x - 5}{h}$

3. Simplify the difference quotient.

$= \lim_{h \to 0} 3 = 3$

4. Find the limit, recalling that the limit of a constant is the constant.

$\therefore f'(x) = 3$

SKILL ✔ **EXERCISE 17**

Since $f(x) = 3x + 5$ is a linear function, its slope at every point is the coefficient of the first degree term, $m = 3$. For other types of functions, the derivative function will not be a constant.

Example 4 Finding the Derivative of a Radical Function

Find $\frac{d}{dx}\sqrt{x}$.

Answer

$\frac{d}{dx}f(x) = \lim_{h\to 0}\frac{f(x+h) - f(x)}{h}$

$\frac{d}{dx}\sqrt{x} = \lim_{h\to 0}\frac{\sqrt{x+h} - \sqrt{x}}{h}$

1. Using the definition of the derivative, rewrite the difference quotient using substitutions for $f(x+h)$ and $f(x)$.

$= \lim_{h\to 0}\frac{(\sqrt{x+h} - \sqrt{x})(\sqrt{x+h} + \sqrt{x})}{h(\sqrt{x+h} + \sqrt{x})}$

$= \lim_{h\to 0}\frac{x+h-x}{h(\sqrt{x+h} + \sqrt{x})}$

2. Rationalize the numerator, then simplify and cancel to eliminate the common factor h.

$= \lim_{h\to 0}\frac{h}{h(\sqrt{x+h} + \sqrt{x})} = \lim_{h\to 0}\frac{1}{\sqrt{x+h} + \sqrt{x}}$

3. Simplify.

$= \frac{1}{\sqrt{x+0} + \sqrt{x}} = \frac{1}{2\sqrt{x}}$

$\therefore \frac{d}{dx}\sqrt{x} = \frac{1}{2\sqrt{x}}$ or $\frac{1}{2}x^{-\frac{1}{2}}$

4. Evaluate the limit by substitution.

Note that the function can be expressed using rational exponents.

SKILL ✓ **EXERCISE 27**

Geometrically the derivative represents the slope of the tangent to the curve at a given point. In real-world applications the derivative is used to model rates of change. The following examples illustrate how the derivative can be used to find *instantaneous velocities*. The *average velocity* of an object is defined as $\frac{\text{change in position}}{\text{change in time}} = \frac{\Delta d}{\Delta t}$. If the object's position is given by $f(t)$, its average velocity from time a to time b can be calculated using $v_{avg} = \frac{\Delta d}{\Delta t} = \frac{f(b) - f(a)}{b - a}$.

Example 5 Finding Average Velocity

The height (in meters) of a ball t seconds after it is shot straight up at 20 m/sec can be modeled by the equation $f(t) = -10t^2 + 20t$. Find the ball's average velocity from 0.5 sec to 1.0 sec.

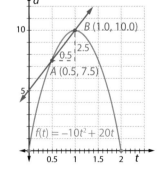

Answer

$f(0.5) = -10(0.5)^2 + 20(0.5) = 7.5$ m
$f(1.0) = -10(1.0)^2 + 20(1.0) = 10.0$ m

1. Find the ball's height at $t = 0.5$ sec and $t = 1.0$ sec.

$v_{avg} = \frac{\Delta d}{\Delta t} = \frac{f(1.0) - f(0.5)}{1.0 - 0.5}$

$= \frac{10.0 - 7.5}{0.5} = 5$ m/sec

2. Substitute into the formula for average velocity and evaluate.

SKILL ✓ **EXERCISE 21**

The average velocity of the ball in Example 5 is represented by the slope of the secant connecting the two points on the distance-time graph of $f(t)$. Its instantaneous velocity is represented by the slope of the tangent to the curve. To find the instantaneous velocity of the ball at $t = 0.5$ sec, take the limit of the average velocity as $\Delta t \to 0$. In the following definition, $h = \Delta t$.

Newton's notation is still often used in science and physics applications, particularly when the independent variable is time. When location (y) is a function of time (t), then velocity is $\dot{y}$ and acceleration, the derivative of velocity, is denoted $\ddot{y}$.

DEFINITION

If the position of an object is represented by a function of time $f(t)$, then its **instantaneous velocity** at time t is $v_{inst}(t) = f'(t) = \lim\limits_{h \to 0} \dfrac{f(t+h) - f(t)}{h}$.

Example 6 Finding Instantaneous Velocity

The height of an object dropped from a bridge 150 ft above a river is modeled by $f(t) = -16t^2 + 150$. Find the object's instantaneous velocity and height after falling for 3 sec.

Answer

$$v_{inst}(t) = f'(t) = \lim_{h \to 0} \frac{f(t+h) - f(t)}{h}$$

$$= \lim_{h \to 0} \frac{-16(t+h)^2 + 150 - (-16t^2 + 150)}{h}$$

$$= \lim_{h \to 0} \frac{-16(t^2 + 2th + h^2) + 150 + 16t^2 - 150}{h}$$

$$= \lim_{h \to 0} \frac{-32th - 16h^2}{h}$$

$$= \lim_{h \to 0} (-32t - 16h) = -32t - 16(0)$$

$$\therefore v_{inst}(t) = -32t$$

$$v_{inst}(3) = -32(3) = -96 \text{ ft/sec}$$
$$\text{or } 96 \text{ ft/sec down}$$

$$f(3) = -16(3)^2 + 150 = 6 \text{ ft above the ground}$$

1. Apply the limit definition and simplify to find the instantaneous velocity function $f'(t)$.

2. Substitute 3 into $v_{inst}(t)$.

3. Substitute 3 into $f(t)$ to find its height.

SKILL ✔ **EXERCISE 23**

The fact that the derivative represents the slope of the tangent to a curve (its rate of change at that instant) is a foundational concept in calculus.

❯ A. Exercises

Find a simplified expression for the difference quotient, $\dfrac{f(x+h) - f(x)}{h}$, of each function.

1. $f(x) = 2x + 3$

2. $f(x) = -5x - 7$

3. $f(x) = x^2 + 3x$

4. $f(x) = 3x^2 - 4x$

5. State whether each function is differentiable at the given point. If not, explain why.
  a. $f(x) = 5x^2 + 6; x = -2$
  b. $g(x) = \sqrt{x}; x = 0$
  c. $h(x) = \cos x; x = \pi$

6. State whether each function is differentiable at the given point. If not, explain why.
  a. $f(x) = |x|; x = 1$
  b. $f(x) = \dfrac{6}{x^2 - 2x - 15}; x = -3$
  c. $f(x) = \tan x; x = \dfrac{\pi}{2}$

7. State whether each function is differentiable over its entire domain. If not, explain why.
  a. $f(x) = [x]$
  b. $f(x) = \log x$
  c. $f(x) = \sin x$
  d. $f(x) = |x^2 - 2|$

Find the derivative of each function at the given point.

8. $f(x) = 6x; x = 4$

9. $f(x) = 2x - 60; x = -1$

10. $f(x) = x^2; x = 3$

11. $f(x) = 7; x = -8$

Find $f'(x)$ for each function.

12. $f(x) = x$

13. $f(x) = 3$

14. $f(x) = -2x + 5$

15. $f(x) = \dfrac{x}{5} - 3$

16. $f(x) = 3x^2$

17. $f(x) = x^3$

❯ B. Exercises

The height (in meters) of an object after t seconds is modeled by the equation $f(t)$. Find the average velocity of the object between a and b seconds.

18. $f(t) = -1.6t^2 - 5t; a = 0, b = 3$

19. $f(t) = 0.9t^2 + 1.1t; a = 1, b = 2.5$

20. $f(t) = -9.8t^2 + 7t; a = 0.4, b = 0.5$

21. $f(t) = 48t^2; a = 0.25, b = 0.75$

Find the instantaneous velocity function $v_{inst}(t)$ for each distance function $f(t)$.

22. $f(t) = 19t$

23. $f(t) = -12t + 15$

24. $f(t) = 19t^2 - 6t$

25. $f(t) = 8t^2 - 13t$

Find $f'(x)$ for each function.

26. $f(x) = 2\sqrt{x}$

27. $f(x) = \sqrt{3x}$

Find $f'(x)$ for each function and then determine the equation of the tangent at the given x-value.

28. $f(x) = x^2 - 4; x = -1$

29. $f(x) = x^2 - x; x = -4$

Find the derivative of each function.

30. the constant function: $f(x) = c$

31. the linear function: $f(x) = mx + b$

32. If the height (in meters) of an object thrown into the air from a height of 2 m with an initial vertical velocity of 20 m/sec is modeled by $d(t) = -4.9t^2 + 20t + 2$, find the average vertical velocity for the first 2 sec.

33. If the height (in feet) of an object dropped from a height of 200 ft is modeled by $d(t) = -16t^2 + 200$, find the average vertical velocity from its drop until it reaches 56 ft.

34. If the height (in meters) of an object dropped from a height of 320 m is modeled by $d(t) = -4.9t^2 + 320$, find the object's instantaneous vertical velocity at 1 sec and at 4 sec.

35. If the height (in feet) of an object shot into the air from ground level with an initial vertical velocity of 120 ft/sec is modeled by $d(t) = -16t^2 + 120t$, find the object's instantaneous vertical velocity at 3 sec and at 6 sec.

❯ C. Exercises

Find the derivative of each function.

36. the quadratic function $f(x) = ax^2 + bx + c$

37. the inverse variation $f(x) = \frac{k}{x}$

38. the absolute value function $f(x) = \begin{cases} x \text{ if } x \geq 0 \\ -x \text{ if } x < 0 \end{cases}$

39. Examine a graph of the greatest integer function and state its derivative function.

40. The derivative of $f(x) = x^2$ is $f'(x) = 2x$. The derivative of $g(x) = x^3$ is $g'(x) = 3x^2$.

   a. Make a conjecture predicting the derivative of $h(x) = x^4$.

   b. Use the definition of a derivative to confirm your conjecture.

   c. Predict the derivative of $j(x) = x^5$.

CUMULATIVE REVIEW

Given $z_1 = 2$ cis $30°$ and $z_2 = 3$ cis $60°$, express each complex number in standard form. [6.7]

41. $z_1 z_2$

42. $\dfrac{z_1}{z_2}$

Evaluate each determinant. [7.4]

43. $\begin{vmatrix} -4 & 5 \\ 6 & 1 \end{vmatrix}$

44. $\begin{vmatrix} -7 & 1 & -2 \\ 5 & -8 & 0 \\ 3 & -3 & 3 \end{vmatrix}$

Evaluate each infinite geometric series or state that the series is divergent. [9.3]

45. $\displaystyle\sum_{n=1}^{\infty} 3n$

46. $\displaystyle\sum_{n=1}^{\infty} 4\left(\frac{-1}{2}\right)^n$

47. Find the general solution of the equation $\sin 2\theta + \sin \theta = 0$ (assuming $n \in \mathbb{Z}$). [5.5]

   A. $\theta = n\pi, n2\pi \pm \frac{2\pi}{3}$

   B. $\theta = \frac{n2\pi}{3}$

   C. $\theta = n\pi$

   D. $\theta = n2\pi \pm \frac{2\pi}{3}$

   E. none of these

48. Eliminate the parameter $\theta \in [0, 2\pi]$ to find the standard form equation for the ellipse $x = 2 \cos \theta$ and $y = 4 \sin \theta$. [8.5]

   A. $\frac{x^2}{2} + \frac{y^2}{4} = 1$

   B. $\frac{x}{2} + \frac{y}{4} = 1$

   C. $\frac{x^2}{4} - \frac{y^2}{16} = 1$

   D. $\frac{x^2}{4} + \frac{y^2}{16} = 1$

   E. none of these

49. Which expression is used to evaluate $\displaystyle\sum_{k=1}^{n} k$? [9.5]

   A. $\frac{n(n+1)}{2}$

   B. $\frac{n(n-1)}{2}$

   C. $\frac{n(n+1)(2n+1)(3n^2+3n-1)}{30}$

   D. $\frac{n^2(n+1)^2}{4}$

   E. $\frac{n(n+1)(2n+1)}{6}$

50. Find the equation of the asymptote of $f(x)$ implied by $\displaystyle\lim_{x \to -\infty} f(x) = 4$. [12.1]

   A. $x = 4$

   B. $x = 2$

   C. $y = 4$

   D. $y = 0$

   E. none of these

12.4 Basic Derivative Theorems

Issac Newton's Principia *is one of the most profound achievements in the field of science.*

Isaac Newton discovered many famous scientific laws, but did not publish his findings until he was persuaded to do so by Edmond Halley, the discoverer of Halley's Comet.

Isaac Newton and Gottfried Leibniz are credited with many of the theorems related to derivatives. These theorems provide a faster and easier way of finding derivatives than repeatedly applying the definition. This section develops theorems that can be used to find the derivatives of power and polynomial functions.

▌ THE DERIVATIVE OF A CONSTANT OR LINEAR FUNCTION

The derivative of any constant function $f(x) = c$ is $f'(x) = 0$.
The derivative of any linear function $f(x) = mx + b$ is $f'(x) = m$.

The proofs of these theorems were completed in exercises 30–31 in Section 12.3. These theorems emphasize that constant and linear functions have a constant slope, either 0 or m.

The following theorem is extremely useful when finding derivatives of powers. The proof of the theorem when $n \in \mathbb{N}$ is demonstrated here, and the case of n being a negative integer is proved in exercise 43 of the next section. The theorem is also true for rational and irrational powers, but the proofs for these other cases will not be required in this text.

▌ THE POWER RULE

If $f(x) = x^n$ and $n \in \mathbb{R}$, then $f'(x) = nx^{n-1}$.

Proof: (for $n \in \mathbb{N}$)

$$f'(x) = \lim_{h \to 0} \frac{(x+h)^n - x^n}{h}$$

$$= \lim_{h \to 0} \frac{\left(x^n + nx^{n-1}h + \frac{n(n-1)}{2}x^{n-2}h^2 + \cdots + h^n\right) - x^n}{h} \quad \text{(using the Binomial Theorem)}$$

$$= \lim_{h \to 0} \frac{h\left(nx^{n-1} + \frac{n(n-1)}{2}x^{n-2}h + \cdots + h^{n-1}\right)}{h}$$

$$= \lim_{h \to 0} \left(nx^{n-1} + \frac{n(n-1)}{2}x^{n-2}h + \cdots + h^{n-1}\right)$$

$$= nx^{n-1} + 0 + \cdots + 0 = nx^{n-1}$$

Example 1　Applying the Power Rule

Find the derivative function for each function.

a. $f(x) = x^{21}$　　　　**b.** $g(x) = \dfrac{1}{x^6}$　　　　**c.** $h(x) = \sqrt[3]{x^2}$

Answer

a. $f'(x) = 21x^{21-1} = 21x^{20}$　　　　Apply the power rule for $n = 21$.

b. $g(x) = x^{-6}$　　　　1. Rewrite the function as a power.

　$g'(x) = -6x^{-6-1} = -6x^{-7}$　　　　2. Apply the power rule for $n = -6$.

CONTINUED ➡

c. $h(x) = \sqrt[3]{x^2} = x^{\frac{2}{3}}$

$h'(x) = \frac{2}{3}x^{\frac{2}{3}-1} = \frac{2}{3}x^{-\frac{1}{3}}$ or $\frac{2}{3x^{\frac{1}{3}}} = \frac{2}{3\sqrt[3]{x}}$

1. Rewrite the function as a power.
2. Apply the power rule for $n = \frac{2}{3}$.

SKILL ✓ **EXERCISE 11**

THE DERIVATIVE OF A SCALAR MULTIPLE OF A FUNCTION

If $f(x) = cg(x)$, where g is differentiable, then $f'(x) = cg'(x)$.

Proof: $f'(x) = \lim\limits_{h \to 0} \dfrac{cg(x+h) - cg(x)}{h} = \lim\limits_{h \to 0}\left(c \cdot \dfrac{g(x+h) - g(x)}{h}\right) = c \lim\limits_{h \to 0} \dfrac{g(x+h) - g(x)}{h} = cg'(x)$

Combining the results of this theorem with the power rule produces a rule for the derivative of a power function.

THE DERIVATIVE OF A POWER FUNCTION

The derivative of any power function $f(x) = cx^n$ is $f'(x) = ncx^{n-1}$.

To find the derivative of a power function $f(x) = cx^n$, simply multiply the coefficient by the exponent and then decrease the exponent by 1.

Example 2   Finding the Equation of a Tangent Line

Find $f'(x)$ if $f(x) = 3x^4$. Then find the equation of the tangent to the curve at $x = 2$.

Answer

$f'(x) = (4)3x^{4-1} = 12x^3$

1. Apply the power rule and simplify.

$m = f'(2) = 12(2)^3 = 96$

2. Evaluate $f'(2)$ to find the slope of the tangent.

$y = f(2) = 3(2)^4 = 48$
$\therefore P\,(2, 48)$

3. Evaluate $f(2)$ to find the point of tangency, P.

$y - y_1 = m(x - x_1)$
$y - 48 = 96(x - 2)$
$y - 48 = 96x - 192$
$\qquad y = 96x - 144$

4. Find the equation of the line through P with $m = 96$.

Check

5. Graph the function $f(x) = 3x^4$ and the line $y = 96x - 144$ and confirm that they intersect at $P\,(2, 48)$.

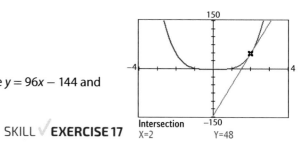

SKILL ✓ **EXERCISE 17**

Apply the following theorem describing the derivative of a sum or difference to quickly find the derivative of any polynomial function.

DERIVATIVE OF A SUM OR DIFFERENCE

If $f(x) = u(x) \pm v(x)$ when u and v are differentiable, then $f'(x) = u'(x) \pm v'(x)$.

Proof: $f'(x) = \lim\limits_{h \to 0} \dfrac{[u(x+h) + v(x+h)] - [u(x) + v(x)]}{h} = \lim\limits_{h \to 0} \dfrac{u(x+h) - u(x) + v(x+h) - v(x)}{h}$

$\qquad = \lim\limits_{h \to 0}\left[\dfrac{u(x+h) - u(x)}{h} + \dfrac{v(x+h) - v(x)}{h}\right]$

$\qquad = \lim\limits_{h \to 0} \dfrac{u(x+h) - u(x)}{h} + \lim\limits_{h \to 0} \dfrac{v(x+h) - v(x)}{h}$

$\qquad = u'(x) + v'(x)$

The proof of the derivative of a difference is left as an exercise.

Example 3 Finding the Derivative of a Polynomial Function

Find the derivative of $f(x) = 2x^3 - 6x^2 + x - 5$.

Answer

$$f'(x) = (3)2x^{3-1} - (2)6x^{2-1} + 1x^{1-1} - 0$$
$$= 6x^2 - 12x + 1$$

Apply the derivative of a power function or the derivative of a constant function to each term and simplify.

SKILL ✔ **EXERCISE 7**

TIP

The slope of the tangent to a graph can also be 0 at a point of inflection. Examine the graph of $f(x) = x^5 - x^3$.

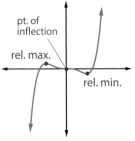

Its derivative,
$f'(x) = 5x^4 - 3x^2$
$= x^2(5x^2 - 3)$, is 0
if $x = \pm 0.77$ (the relative

maximum and minimum) or if $x = 0$, where the slope of the function is zero but doesn't have opposite signs to the left and right of the point as it does at a relative maximum or minimum.

With practice you should be able to use these theorems to differentiate polynomial functions mentally without showing any work.

Calculus is frequently used in real-world applications to find relative extrema. For example, businesses seek to maximize profit and minimize expenses. Since the tangent to a curve is horizontal at any relative minimum or maximum point, the derivative of the function at these points is zero. The x-coordinates of any relative extrema can be found by setting the derivative of the function equal to zero and solving for x. The relative extrema can often be identified by evaluating the function at these values of x and by examining the overall shape of the function.

Since the slope of the graph changes from positive to negative at a relative maximum $(a, f(a))$, $P'(x) > 0$ as $x \to a^-$ and $P'(x) < 0$ as $x \to a^+$. The slope of the graph changes from negative to positive at a relative minimum $(b, f(b))$, so $P'(x) < 0$ as $x \to b^-$ and $P'(x) > 0$ as $x \to b^+$.

Example 4 Finding the Maximum for a Function

An open container can be made from a 20 in. square piece of metal by cutting congruent squares from each corner and bending up and welding the sides. Determine what size square should be cut from each corner to maximize the volume and then calculate maximum volume.

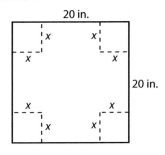

Answer

$V = lwh$ with $h = x =$ side of the square
$V(x) = (20 - 2x)(20 - 2x)x$

$V(x) = (400 - 80x + 4x^2)x$
$= 4x^3 - 80x^2 + 400x$

$V'(x) = 12x^2 - 160x + 400$

$12x^2 - 160x + 400 = 0$
$3x^2 - 40x + 100 = 0$
$(3x - 10)(x - 10) = 0$
$x = \dfrac{10}{3}, 10$

1. Write a function modeling the volume, the quantity that is to be maximized.

2. Express $V(x)$ as a polynomial function.

3. Apply the derivative theorems to find the derivative.

4. Solve $V'(x) = 0$.

CONTINUED ➡

$V(10) = [20 - 2(10)][20 - 2(10)](10) = 0$

$V\left(\frac{10}{3}\right) = \left[20 - 2\left(\frac{10}{3}\right)\right]\left[20 - 2\left(\frac{10}{3}\right)\right]\left(\frac{10}{3}\right)$

$= \left(\frac{40}{3}\right)\left(\frac{40}{3}\right)\left(\frac{10}{3}\right) \approx 592.6$

The maximum volume of ≈ 592.6 in.^{3} is obtained by cutting a $3\frac{1}{3}$ in. square from each corner.

5. Evaluate $V(x) = (20 - 2x)(20 - 2x)x$ at each resulting value to identify the relative maximum.

─────────────────── SKILL ✓ **EXERCISE 23**

In manufacturing, the instantaneous cost (the cost to produce the next item), is often modeled by an upward-opening parabola. Setting the derivative of this quadratic function equal to zero and solving yields the level of production where instantaneous cost is at a minimum, which is modeled by the vertex of the parabola.

The height of a projectile was modeled (ignoring air resistance) in Section 1.6 with the quadratic function $h(t) = -\frac{1}{2}gt^2 + v_0 t + h_0$ where h_0 is the initial height, v_0 is the initial vertical velocity, and the magnitude of g, the acceleration due to gravity, is approximately 32 ft/sec^2 or 9.8 m/sec^2. The derivative of this function can be used to find the object's instantaneous vertical velocity. At the projectile's maximum height, its vertical velocity is 0.

Example 5   Finding Instantaneous Vertical Velocity and Maximum Height

A ball is propelled from a height of 5 ft with an initial vertical velocity of 72 ft/sec.

a. Determine the ball's instantaneous vertical velocity after 2 sec.

b. Find the maximum height of the ball during its flight.

Answer

a. $h(t) = -\frac{1}{2}(32)t^2 + (72)t + (5)$

$= -16t^2 + 72t + 5$

1. Substitute $g = 32$ ft/sec^2, $v_0 = 72$ ft/sec and $h_0 = 5$ ft into $h(t) = -\frac{1}{2}gt^2 + v_0 t + h_0$.

$h'(t) = 2(-16t^{2-1}) + 72 + 0$

$\therefore v(t) = h'(t) = -32t + 72$

2. Use the derivative theorems to find the instantaneous vertical velocity function, $h'(t)$.

$v(2) = h'(2) = -32(2) + 72 = 8$ ft/sec

3. Evaluate $h'(2)$ to find the instantaneous vertical velocity after 2 sec.

---

b. $0 = -32t + 72$

$32t = 72$

$t = 2.25$ sec

1. Find the time it takes to reach the maximum height by setting $v(t) = 0$ and solving for t.

$h(2.25) = -16(2.25)^2 + 72(2.25) + 5$

$= 86$ ft

2. Evaluate $h(2.25)$ to find the maximum height.

─────────────────── SKILL ✓ **EXERCISE 29**

❯ **A. Exercises**

Find the derivative of each function by applying derivative theorems.

1. $f(x) = 10$

2. $f(x) = 2x^{12}$

3. $f(x) = 11x^4$

4. $h(x) = 6x^4 + 5x^2 + 7$

5. $g(x) = x^5 + x^4 + x^3 + x^2 + x + 1$

6. $h(x) = 7x^3 - 2x^2 + 5x - 6$

7. $p(x) = x^4 - 3x^3 + 9$

8. $n(x) = e^5$

9. $f(x) = x^{-15}$

10. $g(x) = \frac{1}{x^4}$

11. $t(x) = \sqrt[3]{x}$

12. $v(x) = \sqrt[5]{x^{17}}$

Find the slope of the tangent to the graph of the given function at each value of x.

13. $f(x) = 3x^2$ at $x = 4$ and $x = -2$

14. $m(x) = x^2 - 3x + 4$ at $x = 1$ and $x = 3$

15. $h(x) = \frac{1}{x}$ at $x = 1$ and $x = -3$

16. $g(x) = \sqrt{x}$ at $x = 4$ and $x = 9$

B. Exercises

Derive an equation of the tangent to the function at the given value of x.

17. $f(x) = 3x^2$ at $x = 1$

18. $g(x) = x^3$ at $x = -1$

19. $r(x) = \sqrt{x}$ at $x = 4$

20. $h(x) = \frac{12}{x^2}$ at $x = -2$

Use derivatives to find the relative extrema of each polynomial function.

21. $P(x) = \frac{1}{2}x^2 + 2x - 6$

22. $P(x) = x^4 + 2x^2 - 3$

23. $P(x) = 2x^3 + 3x^2 - 12x - 5$

24. $P(x) = 2x^3 + 9x^2 - 108x - 240$

Use derivatives to solve exercises 25–32.

25. If the sum of two positive integers is 120, find the maximum value of the product of one integer and the square of the other.

26. What is the largest possible area for Jill's rectangular garden if she plants the garden next to her garage and uses 40 ft of fencing for the other three sides?

27. Find the maximum area possible for a triangle if the sum of the base and the height is 30 m.

28. Jenna drops a ball off the roof of a building from a height of 40 ft.
   a. State the function modeling the ball's height and determine how long it takes to hit the ground.
   b. Derive a function for its instantaneous vertical velocity and determine its velocity after 1.5 sec.

29. John throws a ball upward with an initial vertical velocity of 63 ft/sec, releasing the ball when it is 4 ft high.
   a. State the function modeling the ball's height and determine its height after 1, 2, and 3 sec.
   b. Derive a function for its instantaneous vertical velocity and determine the vertical velocity of the ball after 1, 2, and 3 sec.
   c. Determine how long it takes for the ball to hit the ground and its vertical velocity as it hits.
   d. How long does it take for the ball to reach its maximum height and what is that maximum height (to the nearest foot)?

30. Blake shot a ball into the air from a height of 1.5 m with an initial upward velocity of 50 m/sec. Find the maximum height.

31. Frank throws a ball straight up from a height of 1.5 m. Find the upward velocity required for the ball to reach the roof of a building that is 30 m high.

32. If the vertical velocity of an object thrown upward from a height of 1.5 m is -14.7 m/sec after 4 sec, what was its initial vertical velocity?

33. Find the derivative of $h(t) = -\frac{1}{2}at^2 + v_0t + h_0$. What does this derivative function represent? Compare your result to the formula for vertical velocity of a projectile presented in Section 1.2.

34. Prove: If $f(x) = u(x) - v(x)$ when u and v are differentiable, prove $f'(x) = u'(x) - v'(x)$.

Express each product or quotient as a sum or difference, then find the derivative of the function.

35. $p(x) = (x^2 - 5)(2x^6)$

36. $h(x) = 12x(x^3 + 5x)$

37. $q(x) = \frac{2x + 5}{x}$

38. $f(x) = \frac{-11x^3 - 7x + 2}{x^5}$

C. Exercises

The *second derivative* of $f(x)$, denoted $f''(x)$, is the derivative of $f'(x)$. It can be used to classify a point where $f'(x) = 0$ as a relative minimum if $f''(x) > 0$, a relative maximum if $f''(x) < 0$, or a point of inflection if $f''(x) = 0$.

Identify any points where $f'(x) = 0$ and use $f''(x)$ to classify each point.

39. $f(x) = x^3 - 6x^2 + 9x + 1$

40. $f(x) = x^4 - 2x^3 + 1$

Instantaneous acceleration is defined as the derivative of the instantaneous velocity function (the second derivative of the displacement-time function).

41. The distance (in feet) that a ball rolls down a ramp after t seconds is modeled by $d(t) = 5t^2 + 4t$. Derive the functions that model its velocity and its acceleration down the ramp.

42. If a rocket's acceleration for several seconds after launch is modeled by $a(t) = 250t$ and its initial height and initial velocity are both zero, find the velocity function in m/sec.

43. State functions $u(x)$ and $v(x)$ such that
$f(x) = 3(x^4 + 2x^2 + 5)^{10} = (u \circ v)(x)$. **[1.7]**

44. Describe the graph of $g(x) = 3^{x+3} - 2$ as a transformation of $f(x) = 3^x$. Then sketch both $f(x)$ and $g(x)$. **[3.1]**

45. Find the angle (to the nearest degree) between $\mathbf{u} = \langle 7, 2 \rangle$ and $\mathbf{v} = \langle 1, 9 \rangle$. **[6.2]**

46. Write and solve a system of equations to find the dimensions of a rectangle with a perimeter of 58 m and an area of 154 m². **[7.1]**

Use the properties of limits to find the limit of each rational function. **[12.2]**

47. $\lim\limits_{n \to \infty} \dfrac{6n^3 - 5n^2 + 7n - 3}{2n^3 + n^2 - 4n + 3}$

48. $\lim\limits_{x \to \infty} \dfrac{-4x^4 + 2x^2 - 3x}{3x^2 + 4x - 17}$

49. Identify the function rule for $(f + g)(x)$ if $f(x) = -2x + 7$ and $g(x) = 5x^2$. **[1.7]**

A. $(f + g)(x) = -10x^2 + 35x^2$

B. $(f + g)(x) = 20x^2 - 140x + 245$

C. $(f + g)(x) = -10x^2 + 7$

D. $(f + g)(x) = 5x^2 - 2x + 7$

E. none of these

50. Find c (to the nearest tenth) in $\triangle ABC$ in which $A = 65°$, $B = 68°$, and $a = 20$. **[5.6]**

A. 47   **C.** 20.5   **E.** none of

B. 22.1   **D.** 16.1   these

51. Which point is the focus of the parabola $y = \frac{1}{8}(x - 2)^2 + 4$? **[8.1]**

A. $(2, 4)$ **C.** $(2, 6)$ **E.** none of

B. $(2, 2)$ **D.** $(4, 2)$ these

52. Which formula is used to evaluate $\sum\limits_{i=1}^{n} i^3$, the sum of the first n cubes? **[9.5]**

A. $\dfrac{n(n + 1)}{2}$ **D.** $\dfrac{n^3(n + 1)^3}{8}$

B. $\dfrac{n(n + 1)(2n + 1)}{6}$ **E.** none of these

C. $\dfrac{n^2(n + 1)^2}{4}$

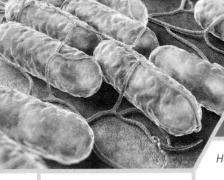

How quickly can salmonella bacteria grow?

By 1680 Leibniz had discovered and published rules for differentiating products and quotients.

The formula for the derivative of the sum (and difference) of two functions was proved in Section 12.4. This section illustrates the application of the more complicated formulas for the product, quotient, and composition of functions. The proofs of many of these theorems are studied in calculus.

PRODUCT AND QUOTIENT RULES

Given the differentiable functions $u(x)$ and $v(x)$:

if $f(x) = u(x) \cdot v(x)$, then $f'(x) = u'(x) \cdot v(x) + u(x) \cdot v'(x)$. (product rule)

if $f(x) = \dfrac{u(x)}{v(x)}$ and $v(x) \neq 0$, then $f'(x) = \dfrac{u'(x) \cdot v(x) - u(x) \cdot v'(x)}{[v(x)]^2}$. (quotient rule)

The product rule states that the derivative of a product is the derivative of the first function times the second function plus the first function times the derivative of the second function.

Example 1   Finding the Derivative of a Product

Find the derivative of $f(x) = x^5(2x^3 - 1)$.

Answer

$u(x) = x^5$ and $v(x) = 2x^3 - 1$
$u'(x) = 5x^4$ and $v'(x) = 6x^2$

1. Identify the functions forming the product and determine their derivatives.

$f'(x) = 5x^4(2x^3 - 1) + x^5(6x^2)$

2. Substitute into $f'(x) = u'(x) \cdot v(x) + u(x) \cdot v'(x)$.

$\quad = 10x^7 - 5x^4 + 6x^7$
$\quad = 16x^7 - 5x^4$

3. Simplify.

Check

$f(x) = 2x^8 - x^5$
$f'(x) = 16x^7 - 5x^4$

4. Find the derivative of the equivalent polynomial function.

SKILL ✓ **EXERCISE 7**

In Example 1, finding the derivative of the polynomial function obtained by distributing was simpler than applying the product rule, but this rule is essential when finding the derivative of functions such as $f(x) = x^3 \cos x$ or $h(x) = e^x \sqrt{x - 5}$.

The derivatives of rational functions are found using the quotient rule.

Example 2 Finding the Derivative of a Quotient

Find the derivative of $f(x) = \dfrac{5x^3 - 2x^2 - 1}{3x}$.

Answer

$u(x) = 5x^3 - 2x^2 - 1$ and $v(x) = 3x$
$u'(x) = 15x^2 - 4x$ and $v'(x) = 3$

1. Identify the functions forming the quotient and determine their derivatives.

$f'(x) = \dfrac{(15x^2 - 4x)(3x) - (5x^3 - 2x^2 - 1)(3)}{(3x)^2}$

2. Substitute into $f'(x) = \dfrac{u'(x) \cdot v(x) - u(x) \cdot v'(x)}{[v(x)]^2}$.

$= \dfrac{45x^3 - 12x^2 - (15x^3 - 6x^2 - 3)}{9x^2}$

3. Simplify.

$= \dfrac{30x^3 - 6x^2 + 3}{9x^2} = \dfrac{10x^3 - 2x^2 + 1}{3x^2}$

SKILL ✓ **EXERCISE 11**

Recall that function composition involves substituting one function into another function. For example, if $u(x) = x^{25}$ and $v(x) = x^2 - 9$, then $u \circ v = u(v(x)) = (x^2 - 9)^{25}$. In this example $u(x)$ is often called the outside function and $v(x)$ is often called the inside function. The chain rule is used to find derivatives of functions expressed as a function composition.

▌CHAIN RULE

If $f(x) = (u \circ v)(x) = u(v(x))$, where u and v are differentiable, then $f'(x) = u'(v(x)) \cdot v'(x)$.

Applying the chain rule requires finding the product of the derivative of the outside function (leaving the inside alone) and the derivative of the inside function. Therefore the derivative of
$$f(x) = u \circ v = u(v(x)) = (x^2 - 9)^{25} \text{ is}$$
$$f'(x) = 25(x^2 - 9)^{24}(2x^1 - 0) = 50x(x^2 - 9)^{24}.$$

Example 3 Applying the Chain Rule

Find $\dfrac{dy}{dx}$ for each function.

a. $y = 2(x^2 - 1)^3$ **b.** $y = \sqrt[3]{x^2 + 7x}$

Answer

a. $y = 2(x^2 - 1)^3$
$\quad = u \circ v$ where $u(x) = 2x^3$ and $v(x) = x^2 - 1$
$\quad \therefore u'(x) = 6x^2$ and $v'(x) = 2x$

1. Identify the outer cubic function and the inner polynomial function and determine their derivatives.

$y' = \dfrac{dy}{dx} = 6(x^2 - 1)^2(2x)$

2. Apply the chain rule, substituting $v(x)$ into $u'(x)$ and multiplying by $v'(x)$.

$y' = 12x(x^4 - 2x^2 + 1)$
$\quad = 12x^5 - 24x^3 + 12x$

3. Simplify.

b. $y = (x^2 + 7x)^{\frac{1}{3}}$

1. Change the radical to exponential form.

$\quad = u \circ v$ where $u(x) = x^{\frac{1}{3}}$ and $v(x) = x^2 + 7x$

2. Identify the outer cube root function and the inner polynomial function and determine their derivatives.

$\quad \therefore u'(x) = \dfrac{1}{3}(x)^{-\frac{2}{3}}$ and $v'(x) = 2x + 7$

CONTINUED ➡

$$y' = \frac{dy}{dx} = \frac{1}{3}(x^2 + 7x)^{-\frac{2}{3}}(2x + 7)$$

$$= \frac{2x + 7}{3\sqrt[3]{(x^2 + 7x)^2}}$$

3. Apply the chain rule, substituting $v(x)$ into $u'(x)$ and multiplying by $v'(x)$.

4. The result can also be written in radical form. (Rationalizing the denominator's radical is not necessary when it contains variables.)

——————— SKILL ✔ **EXERCISE 15**

The chain and quotient rules enable the derivatives of the trigonometric functions to be derived from the derivative of the sine function, whose proof is beyond the scope of this text.

▌**DERIVATIVE OF THE SINE FUNCTION**

If $f(x) = \sin x$, then $f'(x) = \cos x$.

> 💡 **TIP**
>
> To graphically verify that $\frac{d}{dx}[\sin x] = \cos x$, confirm that the graph of the numerical derivative of the original function (using MATH, 8:nDeriv) and the graph of the derivative function coincide.
>
>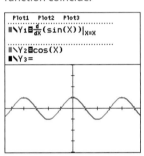

Example 4 Finding the Derivatives of Trigonometric Functions

Find the derivative of each trigonometric function.

a. $\frac{d}{dx}[\cos x]$ **b.** $\frac{d}{dx}[\cot x]$

Answer

a. $\frac{d}{dx}[\cos x] = \frac{d}{dx}\left[\sin\left(\frac{\pi}{2} - x\right)\right]$

1. Use a cofunction identity to express $\cos x$ in terms of $\sin x$.

$= \cos\left(\frac{\pi}{2} - x\right)(-1)$

2. Apply the chain rule, $f'(x) = u'(v(x)) \cdot v'(x)$, using $u(x) = \sin x$ and $v(x) = \frac{\pi}{2} - x$.

$= -\sin x$

3. Apply a cofunction identity and simplify.

---

b. $\frac{d}{dx}[\cot x] = \frac{d}{dx}\left[\frac{\cos x}{\sin x}\right]$

1. Express $\cot x$ in terms of $\cos x$ and $\sin x$.

$= \dfrac{\frac{d}{dx}[\cos x](\sin x) - (\cos x) \cdot \frac{d}{dx}[\sin x]}{(\sin x)^2}$

2. Apply the quotient rule, $\dfrac{d}{dx}\left[\frac{u(x)}{v(x)}\right] = \dfrac{u'(x) \cdot v(x) - u(x) \cdot v'(x)}{[v(x)]^2}$.

$= \dfrac{(-\sin x)(\sin x) - (\cos x)(\cos x)}{\sin^2 x}$

$= \dfrac{-(\sin^2 x + \cos^2 x)}{\sin^2 x}$

3. Simplify the expression.

$= -\dfrac{1}{\sin^2 x} = -\csc^2 x$

——————— SKILL ✔ **EXERCISE 13**

Transformations of the exponential function $f(x) = e^x$ are frequently used to model growth in real-world applications. This function is the only function whose value at a point is always equal to the value of its derivative at that point.

▌**DERIVATIVE OF THE NATURAL EXPONENTIAL FUNCTION**

If $f(x) = e^x$, then $f'(x) = e^x$.

This theorem's proof is studied in calculus.

Example 5 Applying Derivatives of Special Functions

Find the derivative function for $f(x) = 15e^x + e^4 \cos x$.

Answer

$f'(x) = \frac{d}{dx}[15e^x] + \frac{d}{dx}[e^4 \cos x]$ 1. Apply the derivative of a sum and the derivative of a scalar multiple.

$= 15\frac{d}{dx}[e^x] + e^4\frac{d}{dx}[\cos x]$

$= 15e^x + e^4(-\sin x)$ 2. Find the derivative of e^x and $\cos x$.

$= 15e^x - e^4 \sin x$ 3. Simplify.

SKILL ✓ **EXERCISE 9**

The derivative of $f(x) = e^x$ is used to find the derivative of many other exponential functions.

Example 6 Applying the Chain Rule to Exponential Growth

A biologist models the number of bacteria in a culture after t hours with $f(t) = 250e^{0.6t}$.

a. How many bacteria were initially in the culture?

b. What is the rate of growth after 10 hr?

c. When will the rate of growth reach 750,000 bacteria/hr?

Answer

a. $f(0) = 250e^{0.6(0)} = 250(1) = 250$ bacteria   Evaluate $f(x)$ when $t = 0$.

b. $f'(t) = \frac{d}{dt}[250e^{0.6t}]$ 1. The derivative function describes the rate of change at any time t.

$= 250\frac{d}{dt}[e^{0.6t}]$ 2. Apply the derivative of a scalar multiple.

Let $u(t) = e^t$ and $v(t) = 0.6t$.   3. Identify $e^{0.6t}$ as a composition of u and v and find their derivatives.
$u'(t) = e^t$ and $v'(t) = 0.6$

$f'(t) = 250[e^{(0.6t)}(0.6)]$ 4. Apply the chain rule and simplify.
$= 150e^{0.6t}$

$f'(10) = 150e^{0.6(10)}$ 5. Evaluate $f'(10)$ to find the rate of growth after 10 hr.
$= 60,514$ bacteria/hr

c. $750,000 = 150e^{0.6t}$ 1. Substitute 750,000 for $f'(t)$.

$5000 = e^{0.6t}$ 2. Solve for t.

$\ln 5000 = \ln e^{0.6t}$

$\ln 5000 = 0.6t$

$t = \frac{\ln 5000}{0.6} \approx 14.2$ hr

SKILL ✓ **EXERCISE 33**

Benjamin Gompertz published a paper in 1825 introducing a growth function that could be applied to human mortality, a rate that increases exponentially with age. Gompertz's growth curve is often used today to model cancerous tumor growth.

❯ A. Exercises

Find the derivative of each function with respect to x.

1. $y = e^\pi$

2. $f(x) = 8 \sin x$

3. $f(x) = e \cos x$

4. $k(x) = 3e^x - 7x^3 + 10^9$

5. $f(x) = 7e^x$

6. $f(x) = \frac{e^x}{5}$

Use the product rule or quotient rule to find the derivative of each function.

7. $h(x) = 2x^6(x^2 - 5)$

8. $h(x) = (x^2 - 9)(3x - 5)$

9. $f(x) = e^x \cos x$

10. $g(x) = 7x \sin x$

11. $f(x) = \frac{x^2 - 3}{x^2 + 5}$

12. $f(x) = \frac{3x}{5x - 6}$

13. $y = \tan x$

14. $y = \sec x$

Use the chain rule to find the derivative of each function.

15. $y = (2x + 1)^5$

16. $y = (3x + 5)^{100}$

17. $f(x) = \sin(x^2 - 8)$

18. $f(x) = (3 + e^x)^5$

❯ B. Exercises

Find the derivative of each function.

19. $f(x) = x^3 \cos x$

20. $y = \cos x \sin x$

21. $h(x) = (3x^2 + x)\sqrt{x}$

22. $k(x) = (x^2 + 4x + 2)(x^2 - x - 1)$

23. $y = \csc x$

24. $k(x) = \dfrac{\cos x}{x^2 + 3}$

25. $f(x) = \dfrac{x^2 - 5x + 1}{e^x}$

26. $y = \dfrac{\cos x}{3e^x}$

27. $g(x) = 5(x - 8)^{50}$

28. $h(x) = \sqrt{3x + 5}$

29. $h(x) = \sqrt[4]{(2x + 1)^7}$

30. $f(x) = (5x^7 - x^4 + 3x)^{17}$

31. $y = \sin^2 x$

32. $k(x) = e^{x^2}$

Solve each exponential growth problem using the chain rule.

33. A researcher models the number of cells in a culture after t days with $f(t) = 50e^{0.8t}$.
    a. What is the rate of growth after 5 days?
    b. When will the rate of growth reach 1,000,000 cells per day?

34. A biologist models the number of bacteria in a culture after t days with $f(t) = 100e^{0.4t}$.
    a. What is the rate of growth after 20 days?
    b. When will the rate of growth reach 500,000 bacteria per day?

35. If $20,000 is invested in an account at 4.5% APR compounded continuously, find the investment's instantaneous rate of growth (in $/yr) 7 yr later.

36. If $80,000 is invested in an account at 2.5% APR compounded continuously, find the investment's instantaneous rate of growth (in $/yr) 10 yr later.

❯ C. Exercises

Find a simplified expression for the derivative of each function.

37. $f(x) = e^{x^3 - 4}$

38. $h(x) = e^x \sqrt{x - 5}$

39. $k(x) = 5x(x - 8)^{50}$

40. $f(x) = \left(\dfrac{x}{x^2 - 1}\right)^2$

41. $f(x) = \dfrac{x}{\sqrt{x^2 - 1}}$

42. **Prove:** Use the product and chain rules to prove the quotient rule.

43. **Prove:** Show that the power rule $\dfrac{d}{dx}[x^n] = nx^{n-1}$ is true if n is a negative integer by letting k be a natural number such that $n = -k$.

CUMULATIVE REVIEW

44. Find the y-intercept and zeros of $f(x) = 6x^2 - 2x - 4$. [1.6]

45. Find the dot product of $\mathbf{u} = \langle 3, 6 \rangle$ and $\mathbf{v} = \langle 12, -6 \rangle$; then state whether the angle between the vectors is $> 90°$, $< 90°$, or $= 90°$. [6.2]

46. Use the distributive property to state a summation equivalent to $\displaystyle\sum_{i=1}^{n} cx_i$. [9.5]

47. true or false: $\displaystyle\sum_{i=1}^{n} (x_i + y_i) = \sum_{i=1}^{n} x_i + \sum_{i=1}^{n} y_i$ [9.5]

Find and interpret the meaning of the z-score for each test score if the test scores have a mean of 118 and a standard deviation of 12. [10.5]

48. 123

49. 97

50. Identify the solution to $\dfrac{x^2 + x - 6}{2x^2 + 11x + 15} \geq 0$. [2.7]
    A. $(-\infty, -3) \cup (-3, -2.5) \cup [2, \infty)$
    B. $(-\infty, -2.5] \cup [2, \infty)$
    C. $(-\infty, -3) \cup (-3, -2.5) \cup (2, \infty)$
    D. $(-\infty, -3) \cup (-2.5, 2]$
    E. none of these

51. Evaluate $\displaystyle\sum_{n=1}^{20} 7n - 4$. [9.2]
    A. 136
    B. 1390
    C. 1420
    D. 2780
    E. none of these

52. Evaluate $\displaystyle\lim_{x \to 4} 7x^2$. [12.2]
    A. 28
    B. 112
    C. 56
    D. 784
    E. none of these

53. Which equation represents the tangent to the graph of $f(x) = 2x^2$ at $x = -1$? [12.4]
    A. $y = 2x + 4$
    B. $y = -4x - 9$
    C. $y = 4x + 6$
    D. $y = -4x - 2$
    E. none of these

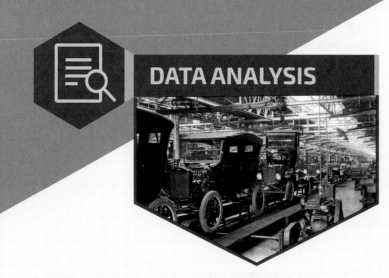

Marginal Analysis in Economics

The benefits (and liabilities) of assembly line mass production burst on the scene in the early twentieth century with Ford's Model T production line. Today it is hard to imagine a business not impacted by these developments. But how do businesses decide how many items to produce and the price at which they should be marketed? Once a process has been modeled with a mathematical equation, it can be investigated with calculus—the mathematics of change. Marginal analysis is the process of examining unit changes (instantaneous rates of change) of functions. Note these commonly used terms.

cost function—the cost of producing and marketing x units of an item; denoted $C(x)$

marginal cost—an estimate of the cost of producing one more item; denoted $C'(x)$

revenue function—the income from the sale of x units at a price of p each; denoted $R(x) = px$

marginal revenue—an estimate of the revenue obtained by selling one more item; denoted $R'(x)$

The graph illustrates a typical cost function. The total cost of manufacturing x items typically increases rapidly when only a few items are produced, increases at a lower rate as higher production rates benefit from economies of scale, and then increases rapidly again as production approaches the plant's capacity.

The marginal cost describes the rate of change in cost at a particular time, which is the slope (or derivative) of the cost function. The graph of the marginal cost is generally parabolic. The marginal cost is high when production is minimal,

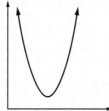

decreases as more items are produced, but then increases as production approaches plant capacity. Similarly, marginal revenue is the derivative of the revenue function.

Marginal functions allow businesses to understand the rate at which cost or revenue is changing at various production levels. Suppose a company produces an item where $C(x) = 0.04x^3 - 3x^2 + 320x + 150$. The marginal cost $C'(x)$ is a parabola whose vertex is a minimum. The minimum marginal cost is found by setting the derivative of $C'(x)$, the second derivative of $C(x)$, which is denoted $C''(x)$, equal to zero and solving for x. This provides the x-value of the point of inflection in the cost function, which represents the production level at which the cost to produce the next item is the lowest. $C'(x)$ is also used to find the cost of producing the xth item by simply substituting the desired value for x and evaluating.

1. Given $C(x) = 0.04x^3 - 3x^2 + 320x + 150$, find $C'(x)$.

2. Find the marginal cost of the twentieth and the thirtieth items.

3. At what production level is the cost to produce the next item the lowest? What is that cost?

The price at which a company can sell an item varies with the availability of the item. The price is often a decreasing function $p = f(x)$ that models the price people are willing to pay as the supply increases. Recall that the revenue function is $R(x) = px$. If the price function is linear, then the revenue function is parabolic with a maximum point that occurs where the marginal revenue, $R'(x)$, is zero.

4. Find $R(x)$ for a product whose demand equation is $p = 20 - 0.1x$.

5. Find $R'(x)$ and use it to determine the production level that produces the maximum revenue. Then state the maximum revenue.

Companies seek to find the production level that maximizes their profit, which is a function of revenue and costs: $P(x) = R(x) - C(x)$. Consider a product with $p = 200 - 0.01x$ and $C(x) = 25x + 500$.

6. Find $P(x)$ for a product if $C(x) = 25x + 500$ and $p = 200 - 0.01x$.

7. Use the derivative of $P(x)$ to find the production level that produces the maximum profit and state the maximum profit.

8. Find the price, p, that the company should charge per item to maximize profit. Then find the cost of the production level required to maximize profit.

9. Determine the average cost of producing each item and the percent markup on each item.

10. **Discuss:** Profit margins are the topic of heated debate in pharmaceuticals. Opinions range from those who maintain that companies should seek to maximize profits in order to fulfill their shareholder obligations to those who contend that life-saving drugs should be provided at manufactured cost or even at no cost to anyone who needs them.

   a. Research arguments concerning pharmaceutical company profits. Summarize convincing arguments for increasing profit margins and arguments for decreasing profit margins.

   b. Discuss how the principles found in these Scripture verses can apply to the debate.
   Leviticus 25:14; Psalm 112:1–3; Proverbs 11:1; Ecclesiastes 5:19; Isaiah 10:1–2; Matthew 25:14–23; 1 Timothy 6:10

12.6 Area Under a Curve and Integration

Archimedes was very close to discovering parts of calculus.

After completing this section, you will be able to

- approximate the area under a curve using rectangular areas or summation formulas.
- use definite integrals to determine the exact area under a curve.
- calculate the area under a velocity-time graph to find the distance traveled.

Previous sections demonstrated how limits are used to perform one of the fundamental tasks in calculus: finding the equation of a tangent to a curve. The final two sections address the second fundamental task: finding the area between a function's graph and the x-axis.

Since geometric area formulas frequently cannot be applied to find these areas, the area under the curve will be approximated using the sum of several rectangles. To estimate the area under the parabola $y = x^2$ over the interval $[0, 1]$ on the x-axis, we can divide (or *partition*) the interval into equal parts and draw several rectangles of equal width whose heights are determined by the function's value at the largest x-value (the right endpoint) in each partition. The area under the curve is then approximated by finding the sum of these rectangular areas. Partitioning $[0, 1]$ into 5 parts causes each rectangle to have a width of 0.2.

$R_1 = 0.2\, f(0.2) = 0.2(0.2)^2$
$R_2 = 0.2\, f(0.4) = 0.2(0.4)^2$
$R_3 = 0.2\, f(0.6) = 0.2(0.6)^2$
$R_4 = 0.2\, f(0.8) = 0.2(0.8)^2$
$R_5 = 0.2\, f(1.0) = 0.2(1.0)^2$
Sum $= 0.2\,(0.04 + 0.16 + 0.36 + 0.64 + 1.00) = 0.2(2.2) = 0.44\ \mathrm{u}^2$

This approximation overestimates the area. Rectangles whose height is the function value at the smallest x-value (the left endpoint) of each partition could be used, but this approximation would underestimate the area. Rectangles whose height is the function value at the midpoint of each partition frequently provide a better estimate.

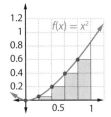

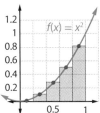

$Area \approx 0.2(0^2 + 0.2^2 + 0.4^2 + 0.6^2 + 0.8^2)$
$\quad = 0.2(0 + 0.04 + 0.16 + 0.36 + 0.64)$
$\quad = 0.2(1.2) = 0.24$

$Area \approx 0.2(0.1^2 + 0.3^2 + 0.5^2 + 0.7^2 + 0.9^2)$
$\quad = 0.2(0.01 + 0.09 + 0.25 + 0.49 + 0.81)$
$\quad = 0.2(1.65) = 0.33$

This process can be generalized to find the area beneath the function $f(x)$ over the interval $x \in [a, b]$. Each rectangle has a width of $\Delta x = \frac{b - a}{n}$, and the right endpoints of the partitions used to determine the rectangle's height can be expressed as $x_i = a + i\Delta x$ for $i = 1, 2, 3, \ldots, n$. The area of each rectangle is then found using $A = \Delta x \cdot f(x_i)$, and the sum of these rectangular areas approximates the area under the curve.

The Greek mathematician Archimedes accurately determined the area under a parabola around 200 BC with a method similar to those used today. Georg Riemann pioneered today's methods of integration in the early nineteenth century.

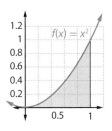

Example 1 Approximating the Area Under a Curve

Approximate the area between $f(x) = -x^2 + 6x$ and the x-axis over the interval $[0, 4]$ using four rectangles. Use the right endpoint of each partition to determine each rectangle's height.

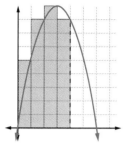

Answer

$\Delta x = \dfrac{b-a}{n} = \dfrac{4-0}{4} = 1$
$x_i = 1, 2, 3, 4$

1. Find the width of each rectangle and list the right endpoint of each partition.

$R_1 = 1 \times f(1) = 1[-(1)^2 + 6(1)] = 5 \text{ u}^2$
$R_2 = 1 \times f(2) = 1[-(2)^2 + 6(2)] = 8 \text{ u}^2$
$R_3 = 1 \times f(3) = 1[-(3)^2 + 6(3)] = 9 \text{ u}^2$
$R_4 = 1 \times f(4) = 1[-(4)^2 + 6(4)] = 8 \text{ u}^2$

2. Sketch the parabola and the rectangles used to approximate the area. Then determine the area of each rectangle using $A = \Delta x \cdot f(x_i)$.

$S = 5 + 8 + 9 + 8 = 30 \text{ u}^2$
$Area \approx 30 \text{ u}^2$

3. Find the sum of the rectangular areas to estimate the area under the curve.

SKILL ✔ **EXERCISE 13**

 TIP

The partition's right endpoints can be described recursively using $x_1 = a + \Delta x$ and $x_j = x_{j-1} + \Delta x$. The left endpoints are described recursively using $x_1 = a$ and $x_j = x_{j-1} + \Delta x$. The midpoints are described recursively using $x_1 = a + \frac{1}{2}\Delta x$ and $x_j = x_{j-1} + \Delta x$.

Using a greater number of thinner rectangles can provide a better estimate of the area under a curve. The summation properties and formulas presented in Section 9.5 are used to simplify the calculation of the sum of the rectangular areas.

$$\sum_{i=1}^{n} c = nc \qquad \sum_{i=1}^{n} cx_i = c\sum_{i=1}^{n} x_i \qquad \sum_{i=1}^{n}(a_i + b_i) = \sum_{i=1}^{n} a_i + \sum_{i=1}^{n} b_i$$

$$\sum_{i=1}^{n} i = \frac{n(n+1)}{2} \qquad \sum_{i=1}^{n} i^2 = \frac{n(n+1)(2n+1)}{6} \qquad \sum_{i=1}^{n} i^3 = \frac{n^2(n+1)^2}{4}$$

Example 2 Approximating the Area Under a Curve

Estimate the area under the polynomial curve $f(x) = x^3$ over the interval $[0, 10]$ using 1000 rectangles.

Answer

$\Delta x = \dfrac{b-a}{n} = \dfrac{10-0}{1000} = \dfrac{1}{100}$
$x_i = \dfrac{1}{100}, \dfrac{2}{100}, \dfrac{3}{100}, \ldots, \dfrac{1000}{100}$

1. Find the width of each rectangle and use $x_i = a + i\Delta x$ to find the right endpoint for each partition.

$S = \dfrac{1}{100} f\left(\dfrac{1}{100}\right) + \dfrac{1}{100} f\left(\dfrac{2}{100}\right)$
$\qquad + \dfrac{1}{100} f\left(\dfrac{3}{100}\right) + \cdots + \dfrac{1}{100} f\left(\dfrac{1000}{100}\right)$

2. Using $f(x_i)$ for the height of the rectangles, write an expression for the sum of the rectangular areas.

$S = \dfrac{1}{100}\left(\dfrac{1}{100}\right)^3 + \dfrac{1}{100}\left(\dfrac{2}{100}\right)^3$
$\qquad + \dfrac{1}{100}\left(\dfrac{3}{100}\right)^3 + \cdots + \dfrac{1}{100}\left(\dfrac{1000}{100}\right)^3$

3. Substitute for the function values.

$S = \left(\dfrac{1}{100}\right)^4(1^3 + 2^3 + 3^3 + \cdots + 1000^3)$

4. Factor out the common factor of $\left(\dfrac{1}{100}\right)^4$.

$S = \left(\dfrac{1}{100}\right)^4 \sum_{i=1}^{1000} i^3$

5. Write the sum in sigma notation.

$S = \left(\dfrac{1}{100}\right)^4\left(\dfrac{1000^2(1001)^2}{4}\right) = \dfrac{1001^2}{4(100)}$
$Area \approx 2505.0025 \text{ u}^2$

6. Substitute with the formula for the sum of the first 1000 cubes and simplify.

SKILL ✔ **EXERCISE 17**

The sum in Example 2 can be written as $S = \sum_{i=1}^{n} f(x_i) \Delta x = \sum_{i=1}^{1000} \left(i\frac{1}{100}\right)^3 \frac{1}{100}$. More accurate estimates can be found by using even more rectangles. Note that as $n \to \infty$, $\Delta x \to 0$. Finding the limit of this sum yields the exact value for the area under the curve over the stated interval.

DEFINITION

The area of a region between the graph of a function $f(x)$ and the interval $[a, b]$ on the x-axis is given by the **definite integral** $\int_a^b f(x)\, dx = \lim_{n \to \infty} \sum_{i=1}^{n} f(x_i) \Delta x$, where a and b are the *lower limit* and *upper limit* (or bounds), respectively, $\Delta x = \frac{b-a}{n}$, and $x_i = a + i\Delta x$ for $i = 1, 2, 3, \ldots, n$.

Notice how a definite integral is used to find the exact area that was approximated in Example 1.

Example 3 Evaluating a Definite Integral

Use the definition of a definite integral to evaluate $\int_0^4 (-x^2 + 6x)\, dx$.

Answer

$\int_a^b f(x)\, dx = \lim_{n \to \infty} \sum_{i=1}^{n} f(x_i) \Delta x$

1. Apply the definition of a definite integral, noting that
$\Delta x = \frac{b-a}{n} = \frac{4-0}{n} = \frac{4}{n}.$

$\int_0^4 (-x^2 + 6x)\, dx = \lim_{n \to \infty} \sum_{i=1}^{n} (-x_i^2 + 6x_i)\left(\frac{4}{n}\right)$

$= \lim_{n \to \infty} \sum_{i=1}^{n} \left(-\left(\frac{4i}{n}\right)^2 + 6\left(\frac{4i}{n}\right)\right)\left(\frac{4}{n}\right)$

2. Substitute for x_i using
$x_i = a + i\Delta x = 0 + i\left(\frac{4}{n}\right) = \frac{4i}{n}.$

$= \lim_{n \to \infty} \sum_{i=1}^{n} \left(-\frac{64 i^2}{n^3} + \frac{96 i}{n^2}\right)$

3. Distribute and simplify.

$= \lim_{n \to \infty} \left(-\frac{64}{n^3} \sum_{i=1}^{n} i^2\right) + \lim_{n \to \infty} \left(\frac{96}{n^2} \sum_{i=1}^{n} i\right)$

4. Apply the scalar and sum properties to rewrite the limit of the sum.

$= \lim_{n \to \infty} \left(-\frac{64}{n^3} \cdot \frac{n(n+1)(2n+1)}{6}\right) + \lim_{n \to \infty} \left(\frac{96}{n^2} \cdot \frac{n(n+1)}{2}\right)$

5. Substitute using summation formulas.

$= \lim_{n \to \infty} \left(-\frac{32}{n^2} \cdot \frac{2n^2 + 3n + 1}{3}\right) + \lim_{n \to \infty} \left(\frac{48(n+1)}{n}\right)$

6. Simplify, distributing the division.

$= \lim_{n \to \infty} \left(-\frac{64}{3} - \frac{32}{n} - \frac{32}{3n^2}\right) + \lim_{n \to \infty} \left(48 + \frac{48}{n}\right)$

$= \left(-\frac{64}{3} - 0 - 0\right) + (48 + 0) = \frac{80}{3}$ or $26.\overline{6}$

7. Evaluate each limit and simplify.

_____ SKILL ✔ **EXERCISE 21**

The evaluation of definite integrals in which the lower limit is not zero can be simplified by horizontally translating the function and interval to make the lower limit zero.

Example 4 **Evaluating a Definite Integral with a Nonzero Lower Limit**

Use the definition of a definite integral to evaluate $\int_{-5}^{-2}(x^2 + 8x + 17)dx$.

Answer

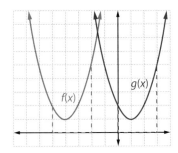

$f(x) = x^2 + 8x + 17$
$g(x) = f(x-5) = (x-5)^2 + 8(x-5) + 17$
$\quad = x^2 - 10x + 25 + 8x - 40 + 17$
$\quad = x^2 - 2x + 2$

1. Translate the interval and parabola 5 units right so the new interval is [0, 3].

$\int_0^3 (x^2 - 2x + 2)\,dx = \lim_{n\to\infty} \sum_{i=1}^{n}(x_i^2 - 2x_i + 2)\left(\frac{3}{n}\right)$

2. State the equivalent definite integral and apply the limit definition, noting that $\Delta x = \frac{b-a}{n} = \frac{3-0}{n} = \frac{3}{n}$.

$= \lim_{n\to\infty} \sum_{i=1}^{n}\left[\left(\frac{3i}{n}\right)^2 - 2\left(\frac{3i}{n}\right) + 2\right]\left(\frac{3}{n}\right)$

3. Substitute for x_i using $x_i = a + i\Delta x = 0 + i\left(\frac{3}{n}\right) = \frac{3i}{n}$.

$= \lim_{n\to\infty} \sum_{i=1}^{n}\left(\frac{27i^2}{n^3} - \frac{18i}{n^2} + \frac{6}{n}\right)$

4. Distribute and simplify.

$= \lim_{n\to\infty} \frac{27}{n^3}\sum_{i=1}^{n}i^2 - \lim_{n\to\infty}\frac{18}{n^2}\sum_{i=1}^{n}i + \lim_{n\to\infty}\frac{1}{n}\sum_{i=1}^{n}6$

5. Apply the scalar and sum properties to rewrite the limit.

$= \lim_{n\to\infty}\frac{27}{n^3}\left(\frac{n(n+1)(2n+1)}{6}\right) - \lim_{n\to\infty}\frac{18}{n^2}\left(\frac{n(n+1)}{2}\right) + \lim_{n\to\infty}\frac{6n}{n}$

6. Substitute using summation formulas.

$= \lim_{n\to\infty}\frac{9}{n^2}\left(\frac{2n^2+3n+1}{2}\right) - \lim_{n\to\infty}\left(\frac{9(n+1)}{n}\right) + 6$

7. Simplify and apply limit theorems.

$= \lim_{n\to\infty}\left(9 + \frac{27}{2n} + \frac{9}{2n^2}\right) - \lim_{n\to\infty}\left(9 + \frac{9}{n}\right) + 6$

$= (9 + 0 + 0) - (9 + 0) + 6 = 6$

8. Evaluate each limit and simplify.

SKILL ✓ **EXERCISE 25**

In Section 12.3 you learned that instantaneous velocity is represented by the slope of the tangent to the distance-time graph and is described using the derivative of the function that expresses position in terms of time. In this velocity-time graph of a car traveling 60 mi/hr for 3 hr, the area under the curve represents the distance traveled. Definite integrals allow us to determine the distance represented by similar areas when the velocity-time graph is not constant.

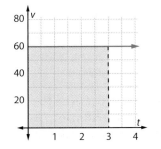

$A = bh = (3\text{ hr})(60\text{ mi/hr})$
$\quad = 180\text{ mi} = \text{distance traveled}$

Example 5 **Finding Distance Traveled by Evaluating a Definite Integral**

If the velocity of a dropped object (in m/sec) is modeled by $v(t) = 10t$, how far did the object fall from 3 sec to 5 sec?

Answer

$\int_3^5 10t\,dt$

1. State the definite integral of the velocity-time function with the desired time interval (using t instead of x).

$= \lim_{n\to\infty}\sum_{i=1}^{n}(10t_i)\left(\frac{2}{n}\right)$

2. State the equivalent definite integral and apply the limit definition, noting that $\Delta t = \frac{5-3}{n} = \frac{2}{n}$.

CONTINUED ➡

$$= \lim_{n \to \infty} \sum_{i=1}^{n} \left[10 \left(3 + \frac{2i}{n} \right) \right] \left(\frac{2}{n} \right)$$

3. Substitute for t_i using
$$t_i = a + i\Delta t = 3 + i \left(\frac{2}{n} \right) = 3 + \frac{2i}{n}.$$

$$= \lim_{n \to \infty} \sum_{i=1}^{n} \left(\frac{60}{n} + \frac{40i}{n^2} \right)$$

4. Distribute and simplify.

$$= \lim_{n \to \infty} \frac{60}{n} \sum_{i=1}^{n} 1 + \lim_{n \to \infty} \frac{40}{n^2} \sum_{i=1}^{n} i$$

5. Apply the scalar and sum properties to rewrite the limit of the sum.

$$= \lim_{n \to \infty} \frac{60}{n} (n) + \lim_{n \to \infty} \frac{40}{n^2} \left(\frac{n(n+1)}{2} \right)$$

6. Substitute using summation formulas.

$$= \lim_{n \to \infty} 60 + \lim_{n \to \infty} \frac{20n + 20}{n}$$

7. Simplify and apply limit theorems.

$$= \lim_{n \to \infty} 60 + \lim_{n \to \infty} \left(20 + \frac{20}{n} \right)$$

$$= 60 + (20 + 0) = 80 \text{ m}$$

8. Evaluate each limit and simplify.

SKILL ✔ **EXERCISE 31**

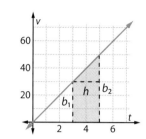

If the velocity-time function in Example 5 is graphed, it becomes apparent that the area under the curve in this case is a trapezoid and therefore could have been found using a formula from geometry.

$$A = \tfrac{1}{2}(b_1 + b_2)h = \tfrac{1}{2}\left(30\tfrac{\text{m}}{\text{sec}} + 50\tfrac{\text{m}}{\text{sec}} \right)(2 \text{ sec}) = 80 \text{ m}$$

Both of these velocity-time graphs illustrate constant accelerations (changes in velocity): 0 m/sec^2 in the first graph and 10 m/sec^2 in the second. In other cases the definite integral will likely need to be used instead of a geometric formula.

The Fundamental Theorem of Calculus, which is discussed in the next section, simplifies the solution to many integration problems just as theorems describing derivatives of basic functions simplified the differentiation of many functions.

> **A. Exercises**

State the value of Δx used to estimate the area under the graph of $f(x)$ over the interval $[a, b]$ on the x-axis with a sum of n rectangles. Then list the right endpoint of each partition, x_i.

1. $[0, 3]; n = 6$ **2.** $[-2, 3]; n = 5$

3. $[-1, 2]; n = 6$ **4.** $[2, 4]; n = 8$

Write a definite integral representing the area of each shaded region. Then evaluate the integral using a geometric formula.

5.

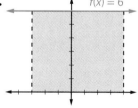

$f(x) = 6$

6.

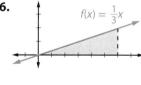

$f(x) = \frac{1}{3}x$

7.

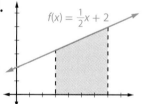

$f(x) = \frac{1}{2}x + 2$

8.

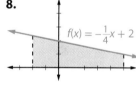

$f(x) = -\frac{1}{4}x + 2$

Estimate the area of the shaded region between $f(x)$ and the x-axis using the stated number of rectangles. Use the right endpoint of each partition to determine the height of each rectangle.

9. $f(x) = x^2$ over $[-2, 3]$ with 5 rectangles

10. $f(x) = -\frac{1}{2}x^2 + 4x$ over $[2, 6]$ with 4 rectangles

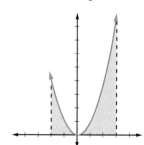

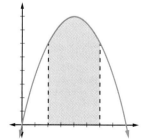

11. $f(x) = \sqrt{x}$ over $[1, 7]$
with 6 rectangles

12. $f(x) = x^2 + 2$ over $[0, 3]$
with 6 rectangles

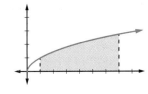
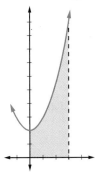

Estimate the area under *f(x)* over the given interval on the *x*-axis using the stated number of rectangles. Use the right endpoint of each partition to determine the height of each rectangle.

13. $f(x) = \frac{1}{10}x^2$ over $[0, 10]$ with 5 rectangles

14. $f(x) = \frac{1}{10}x^2$ over $[0, 10]$ with 10 rectangles

15. $f(x) = -\frac{1}{2}x^3 + 3x^2$ over $[0, 4]$ with 4 rectangles

16. $f(x) = -\frac{1}{2}x^3 + 3x^2$ over $[0, 4]$ with 8 rectangles

> **B. Exercises**

Approximate the area (to the nearest hundredth) under the curve over $[0, b]$ on the *x*-axis using 1000 rectangles.

17. $f(x) = 3x^2$; $[0, 1]$

18. $f(x) = x^3$; $[0, 2]$

19. $f(x) = 2x^3$; $[0, 4]$

20. $f(x) = 7x^2$; $[0, 5]$

Use the definition of a definite integral to evaluate each definite integral.

21. $\int_0^3 (-x + 4)\, dx$

22. $\int_0^5 4x^2\, dx$

23. $\int_0^3 (x^2 + 1)\, dx$

24. $\int_0^3 6x^3\, dx$

Evaluate each definite integral after applying a translation.

25. $\int_2^4 (x - 2)^3 dx$

26. $\int_{-3}^2 (x^2 + 6x + 4)\, dx$

27. $\int_{-3}^{-2} (-x^2 - 6x + 11)\, dx$

28. $\int_{-1}^3 (x^2 - 2x + 4)\, dx$

The function $v(t) = 10t$ models the velocity (in m/sec) of a dropped object.

29. How far did the object fall in the first 3 sec?

30. How far did the object fall from 3 to 5 sec?

The function $v(t) = 32t$ models the velocity (in ft/sec) of a dropped object.

31. How far did the object fall from 2 to 3 sec?

32. How far did the object fall in the first 6 sec?

33. Explore: Complete the following steps to compare the methods of using a geometric formula and evaluating a definite integral to find the area under $f(x) = -2x + 12$ over $[2, 5]$ on the *x*-axis.

   a. Graph the function and shade the desired region.

   b. Calculate the area using a geometric formula.

   c. State the definite integral representing this area.

   d. Use the definition of the definite integral to evaluate the integral.

   e. How do the answers for *b* and *d* compare?

> **C. Exercises**

34. Explore: Estimate the area of the shaded region under $f(x) = -(x - 1)^2 + 9$ over $[0, 4]$ on the *x*-axis using 4 rectangles by using the following points in each partition to determine the height of the rectangles.

   a. the right endpoint

   b. the left endpoint

   c. the midpoint

   d. Compare each result and the average of the right-end and left-end sums to the exact area of $26\frac{1}{3}$ u^2, found using $\int_0^4 (-(x - 1)^2 + 9)\, dx$.

35. Analyze: Use sketches of an increasing function $f(x)$ and a decreasing function $g(x)$ to explain when each sum overestimates the area under the graph and when it underestimates the area.

   a. right-end sum   **b.** left-end sum

36. Explain: Why doesn't it matter whether the left endpoint, right endpoint, or midpoint of each partition is used in the definition of the definite integral,
$$\int_a^b f(x)\, dx = \lim_{n \to \infty} \sum_{i=1}^{n} f(x_i)\, \Delta x?$$

37. Evaluate: $\int_0^b (x^2 + 3)\, dx$

38. Use the result from exercise 37 to find an expression for $\int_a^b (x^2 + 3)\, dx$.

39. Find B^{-1} if $B = \begin{bmatrix} 5 & 6 \\ -3 & 8 \end{bmatrix}$. [7.5]

40. Solve $\begin{bmatrix} 3 & 7 \\ 2 & 4 \end{bmatrix} X = \begin{bmatrix} 4 \\ -8 \end{bmatrix}$. [7.5]

41. Determine the mean, median, and mode for home runs hit in a season by Henry Aaron. [10.3–10.4]

Home Runs in a Season	
1	0 2 3
2	0 4 6 7 9
3	0 2 4 4 8 9 9
4	0 0 4 4 4 4 5 7

42. What is the range of home runs hit by Henry Aaron in a season? [10.4]

43. Given $f(x) = 2x$, evaluate $\lim\limits_{h \to 0} \dfrac{f(x+h) - f(x)}{h}$. [12.3]

44. Given $f(x) = 4x^2 + 3x - 6$, find $f'(-2)$. [12.4]

45. Find the fourth term in the expansion of $(5m + 2n)^4$. [9.4]

   A. $16n^4$ **C.** $1000mn^3$ **E.** none of

   B. $40mn^3$ **D.** $160mn^3$ these

46. Find the probability that a randomly selected value in a normally distributed population with $\mu = 87$ and $\sigma = 8.2$ falls within the interval $[76, 94]$. [10.6]

   A. 0.140   **C.** 0.051   **E.** none of

   B. 0.713   **D.** 1.000   these

47. Find $\dfrac{d}{dx} \sqrt{x}$. [12.4]

   A. $\dfrac{1}{2\sqrt{x}}$ **C.** $-\dfrac{3}{2\sqrt{x}}$ **E.** none of these

   B. $-\dfrac{1}{2\sqrt{x}}$ **D.** $\dfrac{1}{\sqrt{x}}$

48. Find the derivative of $f(x) = \dfrac{2x^2 + 7}{x^2 - 3}$. [12.5]

   A. $f'(x) = -\dfrac{26x}{(x^2 - 3)^2}$ **D.** $f'(x) = -\dfrac{2}{x^2 - 3}$

   B. $f'(x) = \dfrac{2x}{(x^2 - 3)^2}$ **E.** none of these

   C. $f'(x) = \dfrac{8x^4}{(x^2 - 3)^2}$

12.7 The Fundamental Theorem of Calculus

The distance fallen during a given time interval can be calculated with integration.

After completing this section, you will be able to

- find antiderivatives of a function using antiderivative rules.
- represent the general form of an antiderivative as an indefinite integral.
- state the Fundamental Theorem of Calculus and apply it to find areas using substitution.
- solve real-world problems involving integrals.

When the height of a thrown ball is modeled by $h(t)$, its instantaneous vertical velocity (the slope of the tangent to the height-time graph) is represented by the derivative $h'(t)$ (see Section 12.4, Example 5). In this section we seek a way to reverse the process. If the function $v(t) = -32t + 72$ represents the ball's instantaneous vertical velocity, how can a function representing the ball's height be found? In general terms, given the function $f(x)$, how can a function $F(x)$ be found such that its derivative, $F'(x)$, is $f(x)$?

> **DEFINITION**
>
> If $F'(x) = f(x)$, the function $F(x)$ is an **antiderivative** of $f(x)$.

Example 1   Finding an Antiderivative

Find an antiderivative for each function.

a. $f(x) = 5$ **b.** $g(x) = 6x^2$

Answer

a. $F(x) = mx + b = 5x + b$
Note that b can be any constant.

$F(x) = 5x$ is the simplest antiderivative.

Recall that $\frac{d}{dx}(mx + b) = m$.

Therefore, the antiderivative of a constant is a linear function with that slope.

b. $G(x) = \frac{6}{2+1}x^{2+1}$

$G(x) = 2x^3$ is the simplest antiderivative.

Recall that $\frac{d}{dx}(cx^n) = ncx^{n-1}$. To reverse the process of taking the derivative, increase the exponent by one and divide the constant by the new exponent.

SKILL ✓ **EXERCISE 3**

Another antiderivative of $g(x)$ would be $G(x) = 2x^3 - 4$ since the derivative of a constant is zero. The variable C (the *constant of integration*) is commonly used for this real number constant that can vary depending on the application. Antiderivatives that include this constant are said to be in *general form* and actually represent an entire family of functions.

Example 2   Finding a Specific Antiderivative

If $f(x) = 2x$, find the antiderivative function passing through the point $(-2, 3)$.

Answer

$F(x) = \frac{2}{1+1}x^{1+1}$

$F(x) = x^2 + C$

1. Find the general form of the antiderivative. Then check your work with differentiation.

$\frac{d}{dx}(x^2 + C) = \frac{d}{dx}x^2 + \frac{d}{dx}C = 2x + 0 = 2x$

CONTINUED ➡

$3 = (-2)^2 + C$
$3 = 4 + C$
$-1 = C$

2. Substitute $(-2, 3)$ into $F(x)$ and solve to find C.

$F(x) = x^2 - 1$

3. State the antiderivative passing through $(-2, 3)$.

SKILL ✓ **EXERCISE 17**

The family of antiderivatives for a function $f(x)$ is usually stated with integral notation.

▎DEFINITION

The **indefinite integral** of $f(x)$ is defined as $\int f(x)\,dx = F(x) + C$, where $F(x) + C$ is a family of antiderivative functions for $f(x)$ and C is the *constant of integration*.

You should know the following basic indefinite integral rules, which can be verified by differentiation.

Indefinite Integral Rules	
Constant	**Power Function**
$\int k\,dx = kx + C$	$\int kx^n\,dx = \dfrac{k}{n+1}x^{n+1} + C$
Sine Function	**Cosine Function**
$\int (\sin x)\,dx = -\cos x + C$	$\int (\cos x)\,dx = \sin x + C$
Natural Exponential Function	
$\int e^x\,dx = e^x + C$	

The scalar multiple and sum rules for integrals are also essential.

$$\int cf(x)\,dx = c\int f(x)\,dx \quad \text{and} \quad \int [f(x) \pm g(x)]\,dx = \int f(x)\,dx \pm \int g(x)\,dx$$

Example 3   Finding Indefinite Integrals

Find each indefinite integral.

a. $\int 12x^3\,dx$ **b.** $\int (2\cos x)\,dx$ **c.** $\int (3x^2 - e^x)\,dx$

Answer

a. $\int 12x^3\,dx = \dfrac{12}{3+1}x^{3+1} + C = 3x^4 + C$ Apply the power rule.

b. $\int (2\cos x)\,dx = 2\int (\cos x)\,dx$
     1. Apply the scalar multiple rule to factor out the numerical coefficient.

$= 2\sin x + C$ 2. Then use the cosine rule.

c. $\int (3x^2 - e^x)\,dx = \int 3x^2\,dx - \int e^x\,dx$
     1. Apply the sum rule.

$= (x^3 + C_1) - (e^x + C_2)$
$= x^3 - e^x + C$
     2. Apply the power and exponential rules and simplify by combining the constants.

SKILL ✓ **EXERCISE 21**

The notation indicating an indefinite integral is similar to that of the definite integral introduced in Section 12.6. This similarity reflects the fact that the antiderivative provides a shorter alternative to using the limit of a sum to evaluate definite integrals. The Fundamental Theorem of Calculus describes this shorter method.

THE FUNDAMENTAL THEOREM OF CALCULUS

If $f(x)$ is continuous over $[a, b]$ and $F(x)$ is an antiderivative of $f(x)$,

then $\int_a^b f(x)\,dx = F(b) - F(a)$.

The difference $F(b) - F(a)$ is often notated as $[F(x)]_a^b$ so that $\int_a^b f(x)\,dx = [F(x)]_a^b$. If possible, choose the simplest antiderivative function $F(x)$ by letting $C = 0$.

Example 4   Applying the Fundamental Theorem of Calculus

Evaluate $\int_2^5 (-x^2 + 6x + 1)\,dx$.

Answer

$\int_2^5 (-x^2 + 6x + 1)\,dx = \left[-\dfrac{x^3}{3} + 3x^2 + x\right]_2^5$

1. Use the sum rule to find the antiderivative.
   $\int -x^2\,dx = -\dfrac{x^3}{3}, \int 6x\,dx = 3x^2, \int 1\,dx = x$

$= \left[-\dfrac{(5)^3}{3} + 3(5)^2 + 5\right] - \left[-\dfrac{(2)^3}{3} + 3(2)^2 + 2\right]$

$= -\dfrac{125}{3} + 75 + 5 + \dfrac{8}{3} - 12 - 2 = 27$

2. Apply the Fundamental Theorem of Calculus, finding $F(b) - F(a)$ by substituting into the antiderivative and simplifying.

Check

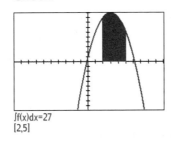

∫f(x)dx=27
[2,5]

3. Graph $f(x) = -x^2 + 6x + 1$, select 7: $\int f(x)dx$ from the [CALC] menu ([2nd], [TRACE]), and enter the lower limit of 2 and upper limit of 5 to calculate the area below the parabola over [2, 5] on the x-axis.

———— SKILL ✓ **EXERCISE 27**

It is important to note that definite integrals can be positive, negative, or equal to zero. When the function $f(x)$ is nonnegative over $[a, b]$, each nonzero term in $\sum\limits_{i=1}^{n} f(x_i)\,\Delta x$ represents the area of a rectangle above the x-axis and $\int_a^b f(x)\,dx$ represents the area under the graph of $f(x)$ and above $[a, b]$ on the x-axis. If $f(x)$ is nonpositive over $[a, b]$, the nonzero terms in $\sum\limits_{i=1}^{n} f(x_i)\,\Delta x$ are negative and $\int_a^b f(x)\,dx$ is the opposite of the area above $f(x)$ and under $[a, b]$ on the x-axis. Therefore, special care should be taken when using integrals to find areas.

DEFINITE INTEGRALS AND THE AREA BETWEEN A CURVE AND THE X-AXIS

The area, A, between the graph of a continuous function $f(x)$ and the x-axis over the interval $[a, b]$ can be found using the definite integral.

$$A = \begin{cases} \int_a^b f(x)\,dx & \text{if } f(x) \geq 0 \text{ over } [a, b] \\ -\int_a^b f(x)\,dx & \text{if } f(x) \leq 0 \text{ over } [a, b] \end{cases}$$

Example 5 Relating the Definite Integral Value to Area

Evaluate each definite integral.

a. $\int_0^\pi (\sin x)\, dx$

b. $\int_\pi^{2\pi} (\sin x)\, dx$

c. $\int_0^{2\pi} (\sin x)\, dx$

Then state the area between the graph of $y = \sin x$ and the x-axis over each interval.

d. $[0, \pi]$

e. $[\pi, 2\pi]$

f. $[0, 2\pi]$

Answer

1. Use the antiderivative to evaluate each definite interval.

a. $\int_0^\pi (\sin x)\, dx$

$= [-\cos x]_0^\pi$

$= -\cos \pi - (-\cos 0)$

$= -(-1) - (-1) = 2$

b. $\int_\pi^{2\pi} (\sin x)\, dx$

$= [-\cos x]_\pi^{2\pi}$

$= -\cos 2\pi - (-\cos \pi)$

$= -1 - 1 = -2$

c. $\int_0^{2\pi} (\sin x)\, dx$

$= [-\cos x]_0^{2\pi}$

$= -\cos 2\pi - (-\cos 0)$

$= -1 - (-1) = 0$

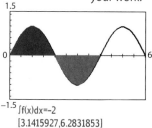

$\int f(x)dx=-2$

[3.1415927,6.2831853]

2. Use the values of the definite integrals to state each area.

d. $\sin x \geq 0$ over $[0, \pi]$

$A_{[0, \pi]} = 2\ u^2$

e. $\sin x \leq 0$ over $[\pi, 2\pi]$

$A_{[\pi, 2\pi]} = -(-2) = 2\ u^2$

f. $A_{[0, 2\pi]} = A_{[0, \pi]} + A_{[\pi, 2\pi]}$

$= 2 + 2 = 4\ u^2$

_____ SKILL ✔ **EXERCISE 25** _____

Example 5 illustrates an important property of definite integrals:

if $a < b < c$, then $\int_a^b f(x)\, dx + \int_b^c f(x)\, dx = \int_a^c f(x)\, dx.$

Example 6 examines the real-world application introduced at the beginning of this section.

Example 6 Modeling Height from a Vertical Velocity Function

The vertical velocity (in ft/sec) of a ball propelled upward with an initial vertical velocity of 72 ft/sec is modeled by $v(t) = -32t + 72$. Find a function modeling its height above the ground (in feet) if it reaches its maximum height of 86 ft in 2.25 sec.

Answer

$h(t) = \int(-32t + 72)\, dt = -16t^2 + 72t + C$

1. since $v(t) = h'(t)$, $\int v(t)\, dt = h(t)$

   Note: C represents h_0, the height at $t = 0$.

$h(2.25) = -16(2.25)^2 + 72(2.25) + C = 86$

$\qquad\qquad\qquad\qquad 81 + C = 86$

$\qquad\qquad\qquad\qquad\qquad C = 5$

2. Substitute into $h(t)$ using $h(2.25) = 86$ and solve for C.

$h(t) = -16t^2 + 72t + 5$

3. Write the function modeling the ball's height where $C = 5$ ft represents the ball's initial height.

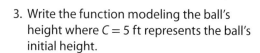

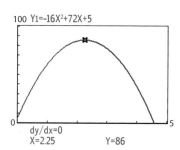

_____ SKILL ✔ **EXERCISE 31** _____

A graph of the height function $h(t)$ confirms that the height of the ball after 2.25 sec is 86 ft. At this time, the derivative of the height function $\frac{d}{dt} h(t)$ (the slope of the tangent to the curve) is 0, as predicted by $v(2.25) = -32(2.25) + 72 = 0$ ft/sec. The area below the graph of the velocity function $v(t) = -32t + 72$ and over $[0, 2.25]$ on the t-axis represents the 81 ft that the ball has risen during the first 2.25 sec of its flight.

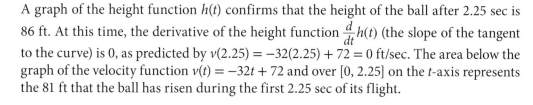

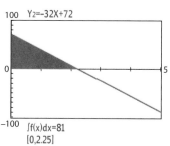

Given a function $f(x)$, the derivative function $f'(x)$ represents the slope of the tangent to $f(x)$ at any x-value. Definite integrals can be used to find the area between the graph of a function and the x-axis. These definite integrals are evaluated using indefinite integrals (or antiderivatives). Who would have thought that the area between a curve and the x-axis could be found by "undoing" the slopes of tangent lines!

A. Exercises

Find the simplest antiderivative for each function.

1. $f(x) = 10$
2. $r(x) = 8x$
3. $h(t) = t^4$
4. $g(\theta) = 6 \sin \theta$

Find each indefinite integral.

5. $\int 3 \, dx$
6. $\int x^2 \, dx$
7. $\int 7 \cos \theta \, d\theta$
8. $\int e^x \, dx$
9. $\int 2x^{19} \, dx$

Evaluate each definite integral.

10. $\int_1^{10} 2 \, dx$
11. $\int_0^3 y^2 \, dy$
12. $\int_{-2}^2 x^3 \, dx$
13. $\int_{-1}^1 e^x \, dx$
14. $\int_0^\pi 2 \sin \theta \, d\theta$

15. Classify each statement as *always*, *sometimes*, or *never* true.
    a. The constant of integration is zero.
    b. The antiderivative of a quadratic function is a linear function.
    c. The value of a definite integral is positive.
    d. An indefinite integral is a family of functions.

B. Exercises

For each function, find the specific antiderivative that contains the given point.

16. $f(x) = 8x$; $(-2, 1)$
17. $g(x) = 2x - 3$; $(-4, 5)$
18. $h(x) = -x^2 + 6x$; $(3, 0)$
19. $k(x) = -9x^2 - 4$; $(7, -2)$

Find each indefinite integral.

20. $\int \frac{1}{2} x \, dx$
21. $\int (2x^2 - x + 1) \, dx$
22. $\int (e^x + \sin x - 2) \, dx$
23. $\int 7(\cos x + e^x) \, dx$
24. $\int \frac{x^4 - 6x^3 - x^2}{x^2} \, dx$

Evaluate each definite integral.

25. $\int_{-5}^0 (3x + 4) \, dx$
26. $\int_1^3 (-3x^2 + 30) \, dx$
27. $\int_0^{10} (4x^3 + 3x^2 + 2x) \, dx$
28. $\int_1^2 (e^x - 9) \, dx$
29. $\int_4^9 \sqrt{x} \, dx$

30. If the velocity (in ft/sec) of a wrench dropped from the roof of a building is modeled with $v(t) = -32t$ and its height after 1 sec is 4 ft, write a function modeling the wrench's height.

31. If the vertical velocity (in ft/sec) of a ball thrown from the top of a building is modeled by $v(t) = -32t + 20$ and its height after 2 sec is 14 ft, write a function modeling the ball's height.

32. If the velocity (in m/sec) of ball dropped from a drone is modeled by $v(t) = -9.8t$, what was its change in height from 1 to 4 sec?

33. If the vertical velocity (in ft/sec) of a kicked football is modeled by $h(t) = -32t + 64$, use definite integrals to determine the change in height for each time interval.
    a. from 0 to 1 sec
    b. from 1 to 2 sec
    c. from 2 to 4 sec
    d. Draw a velocity time graph and find the area between the curve and the x-axis for each time interval above.
    e. Explain how the areas in step d relate to the changes in height for each time interval and the height of the ball after 4 sec.

C. Exercises

Work is defined as the product of the applied force and the distance traveled in the direction of that force. It is frequently measured in Newton meters (N·m), which are also called joules (J). The force required to lift a portion of a chain is directly proportional to the length of the chain lifted. The work required to lift the chain is represented by the area under the force-distance graph and can be calculated using a definite integral.

34. Determine the work required to raise one end of a 10 m chain weighing 400 N to a height of 5 m.

35. Determine the work required to raise one end of a 5 m chain weighing 250 N to a height of 3 m.

36. Evaluate each definite integral and find its associated area.

a. $\int_0^{\frac{\pi}{2}}(\cos x)\,dx$ **b.** $\int_{\frac{\pi}{2}}^{\pi}(\cos x)\,dx$ **c.** $\int_0^{\pi}(\cos x)\,dx$

37. Evaluate each definite integral and find its associated area.

a. $\int_{-2}^{0}x^3\,dx$ **b.** $\int_0^2 x^3\,dx$ **c.** $\int_{-2}^2 x^3\,dx$

38. Use symmetry to evaluate $\int_{-7}^7 |x|\,dx$.

39. Use two definite integrals to evaluate $\int_3^5 [x]\,dx$.

Use the Venn diagram illustrating the relationship of integrable (I), continuous (C), and differentiable (D) functions.

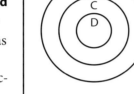

40. Classify each statement as true or false.

a. All differentiable functions are continuous.

b. All integrable functions are continuous.

c. All continuous functions are integrable.

d. All continuous functions are differentiable.

41. Name a type of function contained in each set but not its subset(s).

a. C (continuous)   **b.** I (integrable)

c. F (functions)

42. Use technology to graph $f(x) = -\frac{1}{2}x^2 - x + \frac{15}{2}$. Then use the calculator's definite integral function, found on the [CALC] ([2nd], [TRACE]) menu, to find the area between the function's graph and the x-axis over the interval $[1, 5]$.

43. Use technology to graph $f(x) = \frac{1}{2}x^2$ and $g(x) = x + 4$. Then use the calculator's definite integral function, found on the [CALC] ([2nd], [TRACE]) menu, to find the area between the graphs of the functions over the interval $[-2, 4]$.

44. Find the simplest antiderivative for each formula and identify the resulting formula.

a. circumference of a circle: $c(r) = 2\pi r$

b. surface area of a sphere: $S(r) = 4\pi r^2$

45. Use technology to graph $f(x) = x^{-2}$.

a. Find $\int x^{-2}\,dx$.

b. Use the Fundamental Theorem of Calculus to evaluate $\int_{-1}^1 x^{-2}\,dx$.

c. Explain why the definite integral found in step b does not represent the area under the curve over $[-1, 1]$ on the x-axis.

CUMULATIVE REVIEW

Write the slope-intercept form equation of each line. [1.2]

46. a line passing through $(-1, 2)$ and $(-9, -4)$

47. a line passing through $(0, 7)$ and perpendicular to the line $y = \frac{1}{3}x + 2$

Find a_0, a_1, a_2, a_3, and a_4 for each sequence. [9.1]

48. $a_n = \dfrac{4n!}{3n+1}$ **49.** $a_n = \dfrac{(-2)^n}{3(n+1)!}$

Find the slope of the tangent to the graph of the function at the given value of x. [12.4]

50. $f(x) = 5x^2$ at $x = 3$

51. $f(x) = 2x^2 + 4x + 12$ at $x = -2$

52. Identify the conic $49x^2 + 16y^2 - 294x + 128y - 87 = 0$. [8.4]

A. parabola   **C.** circle   **E.** cannot be
B. ellipse   **D.** hyperbola   determined

53. How many different committees of 7 people can be made from a group of 22 people? [10.1]

A. 170,544   **D.** 2.23×10^{17}
B. 859,541,760   **E.** none of these
C. 2,494,357,888

54. Find the derivative of $h(x) = (2x^2 - 4x + 5)(3x^2 - 2x + 11)$. [12.5]

A. $6x^4 - 16x^3 + 45x^2 - 54x + 55$
B. $24x^3 - 48x^2 + 90x - 54$
C. $24x^2 - 32x + 8$
D. $6x^4 + 8x^2 + 55$
E. none of these

55. Evaluate the definite integral $\int_2^5 2x\,dx$ using a geometric formula. [12.6]

A. 15   **C.** 25   **E.** none of these
B. 21   **D.** 42

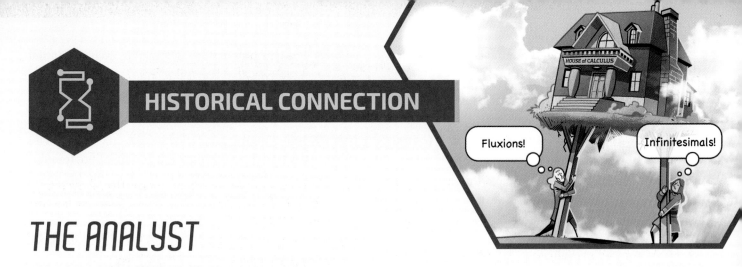

Fluxions!

Infinitesimals!

THE ANALYST

Finding the area under a curve and finding a tangent to a point on a curve are both problems that have been studied and solved in various ways even before Euclid's contributions in these areas during the fourth and third centuries BC. But precise algebraic solutions and an understanding of how the problems relate to each other (what is now called the Fundamental Theorem of Calculus) are due primarily to the efforts of Isaac Newton (1643–1727) and Gottfried Leibniz (1646–1716). Most historians agree that the development of calculus by Newton in England and Leibniz in Germany is an example of near simultaneous independent discovery. Newton is usually credited with developing his method of fluxions before Leibniz developed the same ideas with infinitesimals, but Leibniz published first and his notation using $\frac{dy}{dx}$ was more widely used than Newton's $\dot{y}$. The bitter priority dispute that raged between Newton and Leibniz became an issue of national pride and effectively isolated the mathematicians in England from advancements being made on the European continent.

Despite the obvious power of the new method of "analysis" to solve complex problems, not everyone was convinced that the methods rested on a firm foundation. One of the most ardent critics was George Berkeley, an Irish bishop in the Anglican church and a prominent philosopher.

In his work *The Analyst; Or, A Discourse Addressed to an Infidel Mathematician* (1734), Berkeley argues that men who disdain religion because it calls for faith in things not fully understood were nevertheless willing to embrace mathematical procedures on faith alone. Using diagrams and displaying in-depth understanding of mathematical methods, he points out the absurdity of both Newton's fluxions and Leibniz's infinitesimals. He takes mathematicians to task for wholeheartedly embracing concepts they cannot explain to reasonable and intelligent men.

Cambridge scientist James Jurin, who wrote under the pen name Philalethes Cantabrigiensis ("Lover of truth at Cambridge University"), responded by publishing *Geometry No Friend to Infidelity: Or, A Defence of Sir Isaac Newton and the British Mathematicians, in a Letter to the Author of the Analyst* (1734). Berkeley countered Jurin's emotional and often invective critique with *A Defence of Free-Thinking in Mathematics* (1735), wherein he maintains that Jurin answered none of his objections and that any thinking man could recognize the fallacies inherent in fluxions and infinitesimals. The tone of Berkeley's rebuttal is evident from the first sentence: "WHEN I read your Defence of the British Mathematicians, I could not, Sir, but admire your Courage in asserting with such undoubting Assurance things so easily disproved."

Another 100 yr passed before the development of the concept of limits allowed mathematicians, principally Augustin-Louis Cauchy, Karl Weierstrass, and Riemann, to place calculus on a firm foundation. Others, particularly Jean le Rond d'Alembert, had espoused limits as a better approach, but they were unable to develop a precise definition that was both rigorous and useful. A modern calculus course typically reverses the order of development by beginning with limits, using limits to define derivatives and integrals, and then using derivatives and integrals to solve problems similar to the ones that led Newton and Leibniz to develop analysis in the first place.

COMPREHENSION CHECK

1. Which two persons are generally credited with developing calculus? What two basic problems does calculus address?

2. Name the author of *The Analyst* and state in your own words his primary objection to analysis.

3. Which mathematical concept was used to finally place calculus on a firm foundation?

4. **Discuss:** The Fundamental Theorem of Calculus unites the mathematical ideas of tangents to a curve and the area under a curve in an unexpected way. How do the harmony of these inverse operations, their effectiveness in modeling real-world problems, and our ability to conceptualize them all reflect the glory of God and His attributes?

Chapter 12 Review

1. Use technology to graph $f(x) = \dfrac{1}{x+6}$ and find each limit. **[12.1]**

   a. $\lim\limits_{x \to \infty} f(x)$ **b.** $\lim\limits_{x \to -5^-} f(x)$ **c.** $\lim\limits_{x \to -6} f(x)$

2. Find each limit, if it exists. If it does not exist, explain why. **[12.1]**

   a. $\lim\limits_{x \to 1} \dfrac{2}{x^2 - 9}$ **b.** $\lim\limits_{x \to -2} |x - 2|$ **c.** $\lim\limits_{x \to 4} \sqrt{x - 5}$

3. Use limits to describe the end behavior of each polynomial function. **[12.1]**

   a. $h(x) = x^3 + 2x^2 - 8$ **b.** $g(x) = 5x^2 + 35$

State the domain of each function. Then evaluate the limit of the function at the given value of x. **[12.1]**

4. $k(x) = [x + 9]; x = -\dfrac{1}{7}$

5. $g(x) = 2x^3 + 2x^2 + 8; x = -3$

6. Evaluate $\lim\limits_{h \to 0} \dfrac{(7 + h)^2 - 7^2}{h}$. **[12.1]**

7. Find the limit of each sequence. **[12.1]**

   a. $a_n = \dfrac{4n + 3}{n - 2}$ **b.** $b_n = \dfrac{3n}{5n^2 + 1}$

8. A new diesel bus is purchased for \$495,000 with an estimated depreciation of 12.5% per year. **[12.1]**

   a. Write a function $f(x)$ modeling the value of the bus after x years.

   b. Find $\lim\limits_{x \to \infty} f(x)$.

   c. What would be the value of the bus at the end of 7 yr?

   d. If the owners want to sell the bus for at least \$100,000, what is the last year they could sell it?

Evaluate each limit. **[12.2]**

9. $\lim\limits_{x \to 4} 5x^3$

10. $\lim\limits_{x \to -2} \dfrac{x^3 - 5x}{x + 3}$

11. $\lim\limits_{\theta \to \frac{\pi}{2}} \csc \theta$

12. $\lim\limits_{x \to 3} \dfrac{x - 3}{x^2 - 2x - 3}$

13. $\lim\limits_{x \to 0} \dfrac{\sqrt{x + 3} - \sqrt{3}}{x}$

14. $\lim\limits_{x \to -\infty} \dfrac{8x^4 - 3x + 12}{2x^4 + 2x^2 + 3}$

15. $\lim\limits_{x \to \infty} \dfrac{-9x^2 + 2x + 5}{2x^4 - 5x^3 - 9x}$

16. Using $f(x) = 3x^2 + 14$, find the following. **[12.3]**

   a. $\lim\limits_{h \to 0} \dfrac{f(x + h) - f(x)}{h}$ **b.** $f'(2)$

17. Using the limit definition of a derivative, show that the derivative of the direct variation $f(x) = kx$ is k, the constant of variation. **[12.3]**

18. Use the limit of the difference quotient to find the derivative function of $f(x) = \sqrt{5x}$. **[12.3]**

19. The height of an object thrown into the air from a height of h_0 meters with an initial vertical velocity of v_0 is modeled by the function $d(t) = -4.9t^2 + v_0 t + h_0$. Find the average velocity during the first 2 sec for an object thrown from a height of 12 m with an initial vertical velocity of 30 m/sec. **[12.3]**

20. Find the instantaneous velocity (in m/sec) at 1.5 sec if the height of an object (in meters) is modeled by $d(t) = -4.9t^2 + 425$. **[12.3]**

21. Find $\dfrac{dg}{dx}$ if $g(x) = 10x^{23} - 4x^{17} - 3x^{11} + 2x^5 - x$. **[12.4]**

22. Find the derivative of $f(x) = \sqrt[3]{x}$. **[12.4]**

23. Find the equation of the tangent to the graph of $f(x) = x^2 + 3$ at $x = -3$. **[12.4]**

24. Use the derivative of $P(x) = 2x^3 - 27x^2 + 120x - 150$ to identify its relative extrema. **[12.4]**

25. An object is launched from ground level with an initial upward velocity of 176.4 m/sec. **[12.4]**

   a. State the function modeling the height of the object and determine how long it takes to hit the ground.

   b. State the function modeling the vertical velocity of the object and find its instantaneous velocity at 4 sec and at 20 sec.

   c. Give the maximum height of the object.

Use the product rule or quotient rule to find each derivative. **[12.5]**

26. $f(x) = (3x - 4)(2x + 4)$ 27. $h(x) = \dfrac{3x - 4}{2x + 4}$

28. $g(x) = \dfrac{2x^2 - 4}{3x^2 + 7}$ 29. $y = 2x \cos x$

30. $f(x) = \dfrac{\sin x}{3x^2 - 4}$

Use the chain rule to find each derivative. [12.5]

31. $f(x) = (3x - 2x^2)^3$

32. $h(x) = \sqrt{x^2 + 4}$

Find each derivative. [12.5]

33. $\dfrac{d}{dx}(10e^x + e^2x^2)$

34. $\dfrac{d}{dx}\tan x$

35. A pathologist models the number of diseased cells in a culture after t days with $f(t) = 45e^{0.62t}$. Determine the instantaneous rate of growth after 4 days. When will the instantaneous rate of growth be 50,000 cells per day? [12.5]

36. State the value of Δx used to estimate the area under the graph of $f(x)$ over the interval $[-2, 4]$ on the x-axis using 12 rectangles. Then list the right endpoint of each partition, x_i. [12.6]

37. Write a definite integral representing the area of the shaded region. Then evaluate the integral using geometric formulas. [12.6]

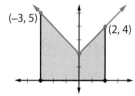

38. Approximate the area under the graph of $f(x) = 4x^2$ over $[1, 3]$ on the axis using 4 rectangles. Use the right endpoint of each partition to determine the height of each rectangle. [12.6]

39. Estimate the area (to the nearest hundredth) under $f(x) = 5x^2$ over $[0, 2]$ on the x-axis using 1000 rectangles. [12.6]

40. Use the limit definition to evaluate $\int_0^4 2x^3\, dx$. [12.6]

41. Find the simplest antiderivative for each function. [12.7]

   a. $f(x) = 8$ **b.** $h(t) = t^3$

   c. $g(x) = 3e^x$ **d.** $f(x) = 2x + 3\cos x$

42. Find the specific antiderivative through the given point. [12.7]

   a. $g(x) = 4x + 7;\ (-2, 5)$

   b. $p(x) = -6x^2 - 7;\ (3, -1)$

43. Find each indefinite integral. [12.7]

   a. $\int 3y\, dy$ **b.** $\int 6\sin\theta\, d\theta$

44. Evaluate each definite integral. [12.7]

   a. $\int_1^{12} 4\, dx$ **b.** $\int_{-3}^{3} y^2\, dy$

45. If the velocity (in ft/sec) of a wrench dropped from the roof of a building is modeled by $v(t) = -32t$ and its height after 2 sec is 18 ft, write a function modeling the wrench's height. [12.7]

46. Determine the work required to raise an end of a 10 m chain weighing 550 N to a height of 4 m. [12.7]

47. Use technology to graph $f(x) = x^3 - 4x^2 + 3x$. Then use the calculator's definite integral function, found on the [CALC] ([2nd], [TRACE]) menu, to find the area (to the nearest thousandth) between the function's graph and the x-axis over the interval $[0, 3]$. [12.7]

A.1 Sets and Real Numbers

After completing this section, you will be able to

- use set notation to describe relationships between groups of objects.
- perform unions, intersections, and complements of sets.
- use Venn diagrams to illustrate set operations and subsets.

A *set* is a collection of objects. Each object in the set is called an *element* of the set. A set with no elements is called the *empty set*, denoted ∅. Consider the following sets $A = \{1, 3, 7, 8, 10\}$ and $B = \{1, 4, 6, 10\}$. The fact that 7 is an element of set A but not of set B can be stated symbolically as $7 \in A$ and $7 \notin B$.

Union and *intersection* are the two main set operations. The union of two sets contains all elements that appear in both sets, while the intersection of the two sets contains only the elements common to both sets. Relationships between two or more sets are often represented with a *Venn diagram*.

Example 1 Finding the Union and Intersection of Sets

Given $A = \{1, 3, 7, 8, 10\}$ and $B = \{1, 4, 6, 10\}$, complete each set operation and illustrate the operation with a Venn diagram.

a. $A \cup B$

b. $A \cap B$

Answer

a. $A \cup B = \{1, 3, 4, 6, 7, 8, 10\}$

Combine all the elements into one set.

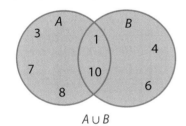

$A \cup B$

Shade all regions of both circles.

b. $A \cap B = \{1, 10\}$

List the elements in common to both sets.

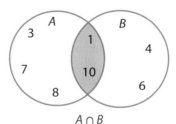

$A \cap B$

Shade the overlapping area.

─────────────────── SKILL ✔ **EXERCISES 3, 11**

TIP

Sets are named using capital letters and denoted using braces, { }, which are read "the set whose elements are."

Set C is a *subset* of set D (denoted $C \subseteq D$) if every element of C is also in D. Sets D and E are *disjoint* since they have no common elements. The *universal set* U contains all possible elements for a problem. The *complement* of D, symbolized by D', is the set that contains everything in the universal set except the elements in set D.

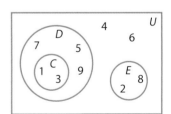

Example 2 Determining Subsets

Determine whether each statement is true or false for the illustrated sets C, D, and E. Explain your reasoning.

a. $\{5, 9\} \subseteq D$

b. $D \cup E \subseteq D$

c. $2 \subseteq E$

d. $C \cap D = C$

e. $D \cap E = \varnothing$

f. $D \cup E = U$

Answer

a. true; Both 5 and 9 are in D.

b. false; $D \cup E = \{1, 2, 3, 5, 7, 8, 9\}$ includes 2 and 8, neither of which are in D.

c. false; $2 \in E$; it is not a subset of E. Instead, $\{2\} \subseteq E$.

d. true; $C \cap D = \{1, 3\}$, and these are all the elements of C.

CONTINUED ➡

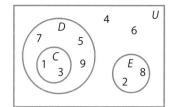

e. true; Sets D and E are disjoint.

f. false; $D \cup E = \{1, 2, 3, 5, 7, 8, 9\}$, but U also includes 4 and 6.

SKILL ✓ **EXERCISE 19**

Sets are often described using *set-builder notation*. The vertical bar, |, is read "such that" and is followed by the conditions for the variable expression that precedes the bar. For example, $A = \{n \mid n \in \mathbb{W}$ and $n > 50\}$ is read "Set A is the set of all n such that n is a whole number greater than 50." Can you list the numbers that belong in set A?

Classifying numbers with a shared characteristic enables mathematicians to make generalized statements about their relationships. Note the following subsets of the real numbers, $\mathbb{R}$, which are all the numbers found on a number line. Complex numbers were introduced in ALGEBRA 2 and will be reviewed in Appendix Lesson 5.

Number Set	Symbol	Description
natural	$\mathbb{N}$	counting numbers $\mathbb{N} = \{1, 2, 3, \ldots\}$
whole	$\mathbb{W}$	$\mathbb{W} = \{0, 1, 2, 3, \ldots\}$
integers	$\mathbb{Z}$	whole numbers and their opposites $\mathbb{Z} = \{\ldots, -3, -2, -1, 0, 1, 2, 3, \ldots\}$
rational	$\mathbb{Q}$	numbers that can be written as a ratio of integers $\mathbb{Q} = \left\{ \frac{a}{b} \mid a \in \mathbb{Z}, b \in \mathbb{Z},$ and $b \neq 0 \right\}$
irrational	$\mathbb{Q}'$	real numbers that cannot be written as a ratio of integers on a number line
real	$\mathbb{R}$	all the numbers that can be graphed on a number line

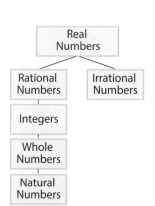

Every counting number is a whole number. The integers are composed of the natural numbers, their opposites, and 0. Therefore, $\mathbb{N} \subseteq \mathbb{W} \subseteq \mathbb{Z}$. Since any integer can be written over 1, the integers are a subset of an even larger set of numbers, the rational numbers.

Decimals that either terminate or repeat are also rational numbers because they can be written as a ratio of integers. The repeating portion is signified by a line over the sequence of repeating digits. Non-terminating, non-repeating decimals such as π, $\sqrt{2}$, and e are irrational numbers. Every real number is either a rational or an irrational number.

648   **APPENDIX LESSON 1**

Example 3 Determining Elements of Number Sets

State the most specific named subset of real numbers to which each number belongs.

a. $\sqrt{6}$ **b.** $\sqrt{9}$ **c.** 3.14159

d. $\frac{\pi}{8}$ **e.** $0.1\overline{6}$ **f.** 0.121221222...

Answer

a. irrational $\sqrt{6} \approx 2.4494...$; The decimal does not terminate and does not repeat.

b. natural $\sqrt{9} = 3$, a natural (or counting) number

c. rational   The decimal terminates.

d. irrational   This fraction cannot be expressed as a ratio of integers. The quotient of an irrational number and a rational number is irrational.

e. rational   The decimal repeats. $0.1\overline{6} = \frac{1}{6}$

f. irrational   The decimal does not terminate or repeat.

SKILL ✓ **EXERCISE 27**

❭ Exercises

Use the Venn diagram to complete exercises 1–8.

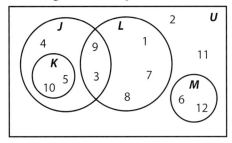

1. List the universal set.

2. Which set is a subset of set J?

3. Name two sets that are disjoint from set L.

Determine the result of the set operations.

4. $J \cap L$ **5.** $L \cap M$ **6.** $(J \cap L) \cup M$

7. J' **8.** $L' \cap M$

Use $A = \{1, 3, 5, 7, ...\}$, $B = \{2, 4, 6, 8, ...\}$, $C = \{1, 5\}$, $D = \{5, 6, 7\}$, and the named subsets of the real numbers to complete exercises 9–14.

9. $D \cap B$ **10.** $C \cup D$

11. $B \cap \mathbb{Z}$ **12.** $\mathbb{N} \cup \mathbb{W}$

13. State the smallest universal set for A, B, C, and D.

14. Given $U = \mathbb{N}$, find B'.

Use the sets given for exercises 9–14 to determine whether each of the following is true or false. If the statement is false, explain why.

15. $8 \in A$ **16.** $A \cup B = \mathbb{W}$

17. $A \cap B = \varnothing$ **18.** $A \subseteq \mathbb{Z}$

19. $D \subseteq (B \cap C)$ **20.** $\mathbb{Q}$ and $\mathbb{Q}'$ are disjoint.

Draw a Venn diagram representing the relationship between the named subsets of the real numbers. Then place each number within the smallest named subset to which it belongs.

21. $\sqrt{169}$ **22.** -17

23. $\sqrt{2\pi^2}$ **24.** $-\frac{2}{9}$

25. 0.353553555...   **26.** 0

List all the number sets, $\mathbb{N}$, $\mathbb{W}$, $\mathbb{Z}$, $\mathbb{Q}$, $\mathbb{Q}'$, and $\mathbb{R}$, to which each number belongs.

27. $\sqrt{25}$ **28.** $\frac{2}{3}$ **29.** $-\frac{\sqrt{16}}{2}$

Write each set as a list of elements.

30. $\{2n \mid n \in \mathbb{N}\}$

31. $\{2z + 1 \mid z \in \mathbb{Z}\}$

32. $\left\{ \frac{2a - 1}{3} \mid a \in \mathbb{W} \right\}$

Write each set using set builder notation.

33. all real numbers greater than or equal to -5

34. all odd natural numbers less than 100

35. all even integers between -10 and 48

36. $\{2, 5, 8, 11, ..., 44\}$

After completing this section, you will be able to

- solve linear and quadratic equations.
- solve linear inequalities and inequalities involving absolute value.

A.2 Solving Equations and Inequalities Algebraically

A challenge in every mathematics course involves remembering and applying concepts from previous courses. Every rule becomes a tool in your toolbox to be used in solving various situations. For example, the properties of equality and real numbers are used to solve first-degree equations in one variable.

Properties of Equality $(a, b, c \in \mathbb{R})$		Properties of Real Numbers $(a, b, c \in \mathbb{R})$	
Reflexive	$a = a$	Commutative	$a + b = b + a$ $a \cdot b = b \cdot a$
Symmetric	If $a = b$, then $b = a$.	Associative	$a + (b + c) = (a + b) + c$ $a \cdot (b \cdot c) = (a \cdot b) \cdot c$
Transitive	If $a = b$ and $b = c$, then $a = c$.	Identity	$a + 0 = a$ and $0 + a = a$ $a \cdot 1 = a$ and $1 \cdot a = a$
Addition	If $a = b$, then $a + c = b + c$.	Inverse	$a + (-a) = 0$ $a \cdot \frac{1}{a} = 1; a \neq 0$
Multiplication	If $a = b$, then $ac = bc$.	Distributive (of Multiplication over Addition)	$a(b + c) = ab + ac$

The first step to solve a linear equation should be to simplify by combining like terms or removing parentheses. Applying any of these properties produces an *equivalent equation*, one that has the same solution as the original equation. When an equation contains more than one operation, these operations are "undone" by doing the inverse operations in reverse order on both sides of the equation.

Example 1 Solving a Linear Equation

Solve $-3(x + 2) = 5(x + 9) - 3$.

Answer

$-3x - 6 = 5x + 42$ 1. Use the Distributive Property to simplify both sides.

$-6 = 8x + 42$
 $-48 = 8x$ 2. Add $3x$ to both sides and subtract 42 from both sides to collect the terms containing the variable on one side of the equation and constant terms on the other side.

$-6 = x$ 3. Divide both sides by 8.

$x = -6$ 4. Apply the Symmetric Property of Equality.

$-3[(-6) + 2] = 5[(-6) + 9] - 3$
 $12 = 12$ 5. Check mentally.

SKILL ✓ **EXERCISE 3**

Equations often contain fractions or decimals. Even though calculators are useful in dealing with these types of equations, it is often helpful to eliminate the fractions or decimals before solving. An equation can be cleared of fractions by multiplying both sides by a common denominator, preferably the *least common denominator* (LCD).

Example 2   Solving by Clearing Fractions

Solve $\frac{x}{4} + \frac{x-1}{3} = \frac{x+3}{6}$.

Answer

$$12\left(\frac{x}{4} + \frac{x-1}{3}\right) = 12\left(\frac{x+3}{6}\right)$$
$$3x + 4(x-1) = 2(x+3)$$

1. Multiply both sides by the LCD.

$$7x - 4 = 2x + 6$$

2. Simplify both sides.

$$5x = 10$$
$$x = 2$$

3. Solve.

$$\frac{2}{4} + \frac{2-1}{3} = \frac{2+3}{6}$$

4. Check the solution.

SKILL ✓ **EXERCISE 9**

Mathematical inequalities compare unequal quantities. The *Trichotomy Property* states that every comparison of two real numbers a and b has one of three results: $a < b$, $a = b$, or $a > b$. While there are no reflexive or symmetric properties of inequality, there is a *Transitive Property of Inequality*: if $a > b$ and $b > c$, then $a > c$. This also is true for the other inequalities $<$, $\leq$, and $\geq$.

Solving *linear inequalities* is identical to solving linear equations, with one exception. When multiplying or dividing both sides of an inequality by a negative number, the inequality sign is reversed.

Example 3   Solving a Linear Inequality

Solve $0.05n + 0.1(20 - n) \geq 1.65$ and graph the solution set.

Answer

$$100[0.05n + 0.1(20 - n)] \geq 100(1.65)$$
$$5n + 10(20 - n) \geq 165$$
$$200 - 5n \geq 165$$

1. Multiply each term on both sides by 10^2 since there are at most 2 decimal places.

$$\frac{-5n}{-5} \leq \frac{-35n}{-5}$$
$$n \leq 7$$

2. Reverse the inequality sign whenever both sides are multiplied or divided by a negative number.

$$-1 \quad 0 \quad 1 \quad 2 \quad 3 \quad 4 \quad 5 \quad 6 \quad 7 \quad 8$$

3. Use a solid dot to indicate that 7 is part of the solution.

SKILL ✓ **EXERCISE 11**

A *compound inequality* combines two inequalities into one statement that can be used to describe a range of numbers. A *conjunction* joins inequalities with the word *and* (or the symbol $\wedge$). Since the solution to a conjunction must satisfy both inequalities, it is the intersection of the inequalities' solutions. A *disjunction* joins two inequalities with the word *or* (or the symbol $\vee$). Since the solution to a disjunction can satisfy either inequality, the solution is the union of the inequalities' solutions.

Conjunction	Sketch the inequalities.	State the intersection.
$x > -2 \wedge x \le 1$ $x > -2$ and $x \le 1$	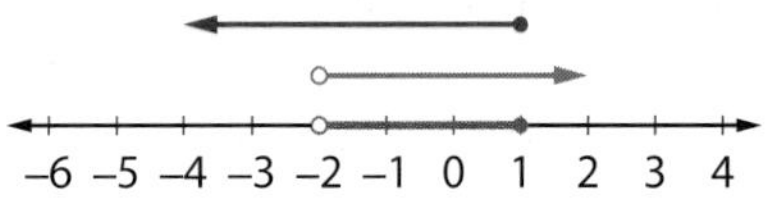 -6 -5 -4 -3 -2 -1 0 1 2 3 4	$-2 < x \le 1$
Disjunction	Sketch the inequalities.	State the union.
$x \ge 2 \vee x > 4$ $x \ge 2$ or $x > 4$	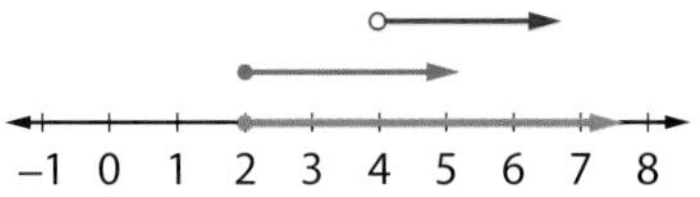 -1 0 1 2 3 4 5 6 7 8	$x \ge 2$

Example 4   Solving Compound Inequalities

Solve each inequality.

a. $5x + 9 \le 24 \wedge -3x - 7 > 14$ **b.** $2x + 3 < -7 \vee 9x - 4 > 5$

Answer

a. $5x + 9 \le 24$ and $-3x - 7 > 14$ 1. Solve each inequality separately.
       $5x \le 15$ $-3x > 21$
         $x \le 3$ $x < -7$

    -8   -6   -4   -2   0   2

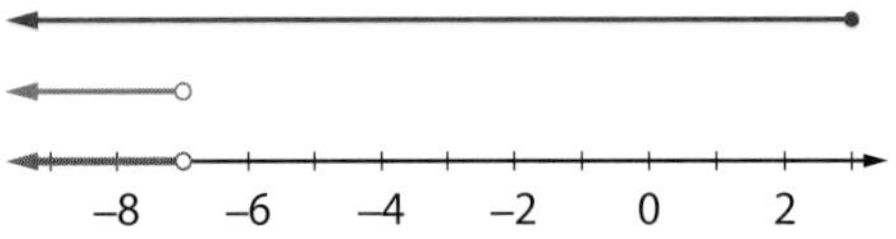

2. Find the intersection of the graphs of the two inequalities.

$x < -7$ 3. State the solution to the conjunction.

b. $2x + 3 < -7$ or $9x - 4 > 5$ 1. Solve each inequality separately.
       $2x < -10$ $9x > 9$
         $x < -5$ $x > 1$

    -6   -4   -2   0   2

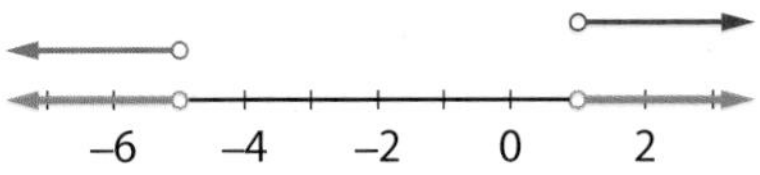

2. Find the union of the graphs of the two inequalities.

$x < -5$ or $x > 1$ 3. State the solution to the disjunction.

SKILL ✔ **EXERCISES 17, 19**

The conjunction $5x - 7 > 3$ and $5x - 7 < 23$ can be rewritten as $3 < 5x - 7 < 23$, which more clearly indicates that $5x - 7$ lies between 3 and 23. Disjunctions cannot be written this way.

When the same steps are used to solve each inequality, the properties can be used on each of the three parts of a combined conjunction as illustrated below.

TIP

If a similar compound inequality contains variables in more than one part, rewrite the compound inequality as a conjunction of two inequalities.

Example 5   Solving a Compound Inequality

Solve $3 < 5x - 7 < 23$.

Answer

$10 < 5x < 30$ 1. Add 7 to each expression.

   $2 < x < 6$ 2. Divide each expression by 5.

SKILL ✔ **EXERCISE 25**

The equation $|x| = 3$ can be interpreted as "x is 3 units from 0 on the number line," and has the solution of $x = -3$ or $x = 3$. The inequality $|x| > 3$ describes all the numbers more than 3 units from the origin, and the inequality $|x| < 3$ describes all the numbers less than 3 units from the origin. The solution to an absolute value inequality can be written as a compound inequality.

ABSOLUTE VALUE INEQUALITY THEOREM

If $c \geq 0$, then
$|x| < c$ is equivalent to the conjunction $-c < x < c$ and
$|x| > c$ is equivalent to the disjunction $x < -c$ or $x > c$.

Example 6   Solving Absolute Value Inequalities

Solve each inequality and graph its solution set.

a. $|2x - 9| < 4$ **b.** $|-4x + 9| - 11 \geq 4$

Answer

a. $-4 < 2x - 9 < 4$
1. Write a conjunction stating that $2x - 9$ is less than 4 units from the origin.

$5 < 2x < 13$
2. Solve the combined conjunction.

$\frac{5}{2} < x < \frac{13}{2}$

3. Graph the solution set.

b. $|-4x + 9| \geq 15$
1. Isolate the absolute value.

$-4x + 9 \leq -15$ or $-4x + 9 \geq 15$
2. Write a disjunction stating that $-4x + 9$ is at least 15 units from the origin.

$-4x \leq -24$ or $-4x \geq 6$
$x \geq 6$ $x \leq -\frac{3}{2}$
3. Solve. Remember to reverse the inequality signs when dividing by a negative value.

$x \leq -\frac{3}{2}$ or $x \geq 6$
4. State the solution as a disjunction.

5. Graph the solution set.

SKILL ✓ EXERCISES 27, 29

A *quadratic equation* can be written in the standard form $ax^2 + bx + c = 0$, where a, b, and $c \in \mathbb{R}$ and $a \neq 0$. The first step in solving most quadratic equations is to write the equation in standard form. If the trinomial can be factored, the equation can be solved using the *Zero Product Property*.

ZERO PRODUCT PROPERTY

If $pq = 0$, then $p = 0$ or $q = 0$.

Example 7 Solving Quadratic Equations

Solve each quadratic equation.

a. $6x^2 + 13x = -5$ **b.** $2x^2 - 7x - 15 = 0$

Answer

a. $6x^2 + 13x + 5 = 0$ 1. Write the equation in standard form.

$(3x + 5)(2x + 1) = 0$ 2. Factor the trinomial.

$3x + 5 = 0$ or $2x + 1 = 0$ 3. Apply the Zero Product Property

$\quad 3x = -5 \qquad\qquad 2x = -1$ and solve.

$\quad\quad x = -\dfrac{5}{3} \qquad\qquad x = -\dfrac{1}{2}$

$\therefore x = -\dfrac{5}{3}, -\dfrac{1}{2}$

b. $2x^2 - 7x - 15 = 0$ 1. The equation is written in standard form.

$(2x + 3)(x - 5) = 0$ 2. Factor the trinomial.

$2x + 3 = 0$ or $x - 5 = 0$ 3. Apply the Zero Product Property and solve.

$\quad 2x = -3 \qquad\qquad x = 5$

$\quad\quad x = -\dfrac{3}{2}$

$\therefore x = -\dfrac{3}{2}, 5$

SKILL ✔ **EXERCISE 35**

When a trinomial cannot be factored, use the *quadratic formula*.

▌QUADRATIC FORMULA

If $ax^2 + bx + c = 0$, where a, b, and $c \in \mathbb{R}$ and $a \neq 0$, then $x = \dfrac{-b \pm \sqrt{b^2 - 4ac}}{2a}$.

Example 8 Using the Quadratic Formula

Solve $7x^2 = 8 - 2x$.

Answer

$7x^2 + 2x - 8 = 0$ 1. Write the equation in standard form and
$a = 7, b = 2, c = -8$ identify a, b, and c.

$x = \dfrac{-b \pm \sqrt{b^2 - 4ac}}{2a} = \dfrac{-(2) \pm \sqrt{(2)^2 - 4(7)(-8)}}{2(7)}$ 2. Substitute into the quadratic formula.

$= \dfrac{-2 \pm \sqrt{4 - (-224)}}{14} = \dfrac{-2 \pm \sqrt{228}}{14}$ 3. Simplify.

$= \dfrac{-2 \pm 2\sqrt{57}}{14} = \dfrac{-1 \pm \sqrt{57}}{7}$

SKILL ✔ **EXERCISE 39**

Exercises

Solve.

1. $-2(x - 9) = 3(x - 4) - 5$

2. $2(n + 4) - 5(3n - 7) = -113$

3. $3a + 6(2a - 3) - (2a + 6) = 41$

4. $23x + 11(x - 6) = 7(3x - 5) + 8$

5. $\dfrac{b}{3} - \dfrac{8b}{7} = \dfrac{68}{21}$

6. $\dfrac{x + 2}{9} - \dfrac{x}{3} = 10$

7. $\dfrac{3x}{8} + 5 = \dfrac{x + 17}{3}$

8. $\dfrac{1}{2}(6b + 3) - 8b - (3b - 9) = \dfrac{13}{2}$

9. $0.3x + 0.89 = 5.321$

10. $0.5(4x + 12) - 0.9(x - 3) = 18.6$

11. $2x - (x + 4) \neq 7$

12. $-2x - 1 \leq 3(x + 1)$

13. $10a - 5(a + 9) \leq 4a + 12$

14. $-5x + 3(2x - 4) < 5x - 36$

15. $5(0.06y - 0.09) > 3(0.3y - 0.06) + 0.6y$

16. $5(0.04y - 0.08) > 3(0.2y - 0.05) - 0.4y$

Solve each inequality and graph its solution set.

17. $4x + 9 \leq 2 \wedge x + 8 \geq \dfrac{25}{4}$

18. $4x - 5 \leq 7 \wedge -3x + 4 \leq 19$

19. $-2x + 9 \geq 15 \vee 2x + 7 \geq 17 - 3x$

20. $8(z - 2) + 4(z + 1) \geq 4z \vee 5z - 7 < 0$

21. $\dfrac{1}{2}(d + 9) > \dfrac{1}{3}(6 - d) \wedge \dfrac{1}{3}(d - 4) > \dfrac{1}{2}(d + 5)$

22. $9(z - 2) + 3(z + 1) \leq 4z \vee 5z - 7 > 2$

Solve.

23. $6 < 7x - 8 \leq 41$

24. $7 \leq 2(x + 7) + 3x - 9 < 35$

25. $a - 6 < 5(a + 2) < 4a + 10$

26. $|8y - 8| > 12$

27. $|4x - 8| > 8 - x$

28. $|24z - 80| < 6z + 70$

29. $\left| \dfrac{x}{3} + \dfrac{5}{6} \right| + 4 \leq 9$

30. $|10 - 7x| \leq -8$

Solve by factoring.

31. $x^2 - 6x + 5 = 0$

32. $y(y + 16) = -28$

33. $x^2 - 3x - 54 = 0$

34. $8x^2 + 8x = 3 - 15x$

35. $12z^2 + z - 6 = 0$

36. $2y^2 + 9y = -10$

Use the quadratic formula to solve.

37. $6x^2 + 13x = -5$

38. $2x^2 + 2x = 2x + 4$

39. $4x^2 + 5x - 3 = 0$

40. $9x + 6x^2 = 12$

Solving Equations and Inequalities Graphically

You can use your graphing calculator to solve or check the solution(s) to an equation. If the equation is written in the form of $f(x) = 0$, the x-coordinate of any x-intercept (a point where the graph intersects the x-axis) is a solution of the equation. These values are also called the *zeros* of $f(x)$. If the graph does not intersect the x-axis, then the equation has no real solution.

Example 1   Solving a Quadratic by Graphing

Solve the equation $x^2 - 2x - 8 = 0$ by finding the zeros.

Answer

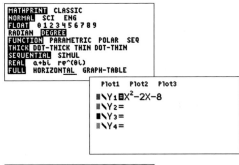

1. Press MODE and check that the calculator is in function mode. Then press Y= and enter the equation as Y_1. If Plot1, Plot2, or Plot3 is highlighted, move the cursor to that stat plot and press ENTER to turn it off.

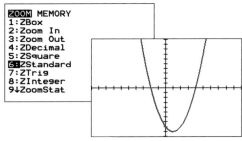

2. GRAPH the function and then select 6:ZStandard from the ZOOM menu. If necessary, adjust the WINDOW until all the x-intercepts are visible.

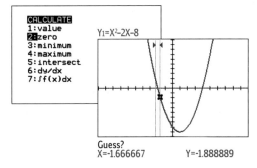

3. Press [CALC] (2nd, TRACE), 2:zero, ENTER to find the zeros. Set the left boundary by moving the cursor to the left of the zero and press ENTER. Similarly, set the right boundary and a guess. Pressing ENTER reveals the zero between the boundaries closest to the guess.

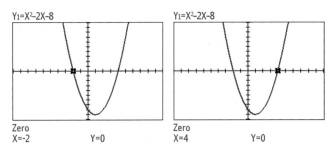

4. Repeat the process to find the second x-intercept.

   x-intercepts: (−2, 0), (4, 0)
   solutions: $x = -2, 4$

SKILL ✔ **EXERCISE 3**

Equations containing nonzero expressions on both sides of the equality can be expressed as $f(x) = g(x)$ and solved by finding the x-coordinates of any points of intersection for the graphs of $f(x)$ and $g(x)$.

Example 2 Solving a Polynomial by Finding Points of Intersection

Solve the equation $x^3 - x^2 - 21x - 24 = x^2 + 9$ by finding the points of intersection.

Answer

1. Enter $Y_1 = x^3 - x^2 - 21x - 24$ and $Y_2 = x^2 + 9$, and then [GRAPH] the functions.

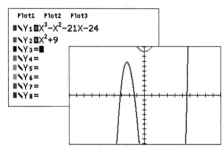

2. Adjust the [WINDOW] to view the points of intersection and press [GRAPH]. Notice that the Xscl and Yscl can be set to convenient values.

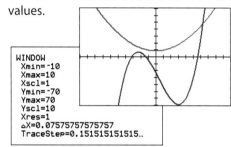

3. Select 5:intersect from the [CALC] menu ([2nd], [TRACE]). Use ▲ or ▼ and [ENTER] to select each function. Then move the cursor near the desired intersection and [ENTER] this guess. The x-value of the point of intersection is a solution to the equation.

solution: $x \approx 6.225$

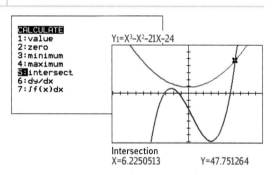

SKILL ✓ **EXERCISE 7**

It may be necessary to zoom out to verify that all points of intersection have been identified. The end behaviors of the functions in Example 2 indicate there is only one solution. An alternative method of solving Example 2 involves subtracting all the terms on one side of the equation to obtain an equivalent equation in the form of $h(x) = 0$ and finding its zeros, as illustrated in Example 1.

The method used in Example 2 can also be applied to solve equations of the form of $f(x) = k$, where k is a constant.

Example 3 Solving a Quadratic of the Form $f(x) = k$

Solve $2x^2 - x - 2 = 4$.

Answer

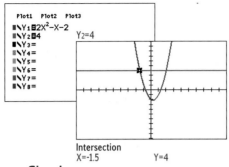

1. Define $Y_1 = 2x^2 - x - 2$ and $Y_2 = 4$ and graph the functions in the standard window as shown. Find the x-value of any intersection of the graphs using the 5:intersect function from the [CALC] menu.

   The solution includes the illustrated solution of $x = -1.5$ and the x-coordinate of the second point of intersection, $x = 2$.

Check

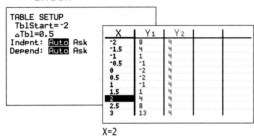

2. The TABLE SETUP menu is accessed using [TBLSET] ([2nd], [WINDOW]) and is used to define the TblStart and ΔTbl values. Select [TABLE] ([2nd], [GRAPH]) to generate a table that verifies that Y_1, the value of the left side of the equation, is 4 when $x = -1.5$ and when $x = 2$.

SKILL ✓ **EXERCISE 13**

These graphing techniques can also be used to solve inequalities. To solve inequalities of the form $f(x) > g(x)$, graph $Y_1 = f(x)$ and $Y_2 = g(x)$ and identify the interval(s) of x-values for which the graph of Y_1 is above the graph of Y_2.

Example 4 Solving an Absolute Value Inequality

Solve the inequality $|2x + 1| \geq 5$.

Answer

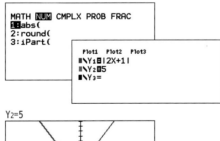

1. Use the absolute value function 1: abs on the [MATH], NUM submenu to enter $Y_1 = |2x + 1|$, and then enter $Y_2 = 5$. Then graph the functions in the standard window.

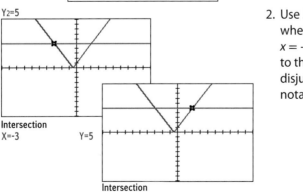

2. Use 5:intersect to identify the x-coordinates where $Y_1 = Y_2$. Since $Y_1 > Y_2$ to the left of $x = -3$ and to the right of $x = 2$, the solution to the inequality can be stated with the disjunction $x \leq -3$ or $x \geq 2$ or in interval notation as $(-\infty, -3] \cup [2, \infty)$.

SKILL ✓ **EXERCISE 19**

Inequalities of the form $f(x) < g(x)$ can also be solved by applying the same graphing steps, and then identifying the interval(s) of x-values for which the graph of Y_1 is below the graph of Y_2.

❯ Exercises

Solve each equation graphically by finding zeros. Round to the nearest hundredth if necessary.

1. $x^2 - 2x - 15 = 0$

2. $-x^2 - x + 6 = 0$

3. $10x^2 - 3x - 4 = 0$

4. $21x^2 + 2x - 3 = 0$

5. $2x^2 - 4x - 3 = 0$

Solve each equation graphically by finding points of intersection. Round to the nearest hundredth if necessary.

6. $7x^2 - 4x + 8 = 3x + 8$

7. $3x^3 + 3x + 6 = x^2 - 8$

8. $x^2 + 2x - 15 = \sqrt{5x - 9}$

9. $-4x^2 + 8 = 2x^2 - 3$

10. $0.5x^2 - 2.1x - 3.27 = -2.37x^2 + 5.8x + 10.7$

Solve each equation graphically. Then use a table to verify the solution numerically.

11. $x^2 - 2x - 6 = 2$

12. $2x^2 + 5x - 4 = 3$

13. $5x^3 - 6x^2 - 9x + 5 = 3$

14. $25x^3 + 45x^2 - 16x - 15 = -3$

15. $4x^4 + 4x^3 - 7x^2 - 4x + 8 = 5$

Use graphing technology to solve the following inequalities.

16. $|4x + 2| < 12$

17. $|-5x + 2| \geq 7$

18. $|x^2 + 4x - 12| > 17$

19. $|3x^2 + 3| \leq 5$

20. $|4x + 7| - 4x > 3$

21. $|-2x - 8| + x < 5$

22. $x^2 > |2x + 12|$

23. $x^2 \leq |4x - 8|$

24. $|3x^2 - 2| > 1$

25. $8 < |5x - 7| < 20$

A.4 Roots and Exponents

After completing this section, you will be able to
- simplify expressions with radicals.
- simplify expressions with rational exponents.
- convert between radical and exponential expressions.

The ability to simplify radicals and expressions with rational exponents is crucial to success in advanced math courses. You will also need to know how to convert between radicals and expressions with rational exponents. We will review real roots in this lesson and complex roots in Appendix Lesson 5.

DEFINITIONS

For any real numbers a and b and any positive integer n, if $a^n = b$, then a is an **nth root of b**. The *radical sign* indicates a root. The expression under a radical sign is called the *radicand*.

$index \quad \sqrt[n]{b} \quad radical\ sign$
$radicand$

Real *n*th Roots of *b*		
Radicand	*n* is even	*n* is odd
$b > 0$	one positive and one negative	one positive
$b = 0$	one (0)	one (0)
$b < 0$	none	one negative

When n is even, the radical sign indicates the nonnegative or *principal root*.

$$\sqrt{9} = 3 \text{ and } -\sqrt{9} = -3$$

Example 1 Simplifying Numerical Radicals

Find each real number root. If no real root exists, state so.

a. $\sqrt[3]{-512}$ **b.** $\sqrt[4]{-81}$ **c.** $\sqrt{0.36}$ **d.** $\sqrt{10{,}000}$ **e.** $\sqrt[3]{\frac{64}{27}}$

Answer

a. $\sqrt[3]{-512} = \sqrt[3]{(-8)^3} = -8$ **b.** no real root exists

c. $\sqrt{0.36} = \sqrt{(0.6)^2} = 0.6$ **d.** $\sqrt{10{,}000} = \sqrt{10^4} = 10^2 = 100$

e. $\sqrt[3]{\frac{64}{27}} = \sqrt[3]{\frac{4^3}{3^3}} = \frac{4}{3}$

SKILL ✔ **EXERCISES 1, 5**

Other radicals are also simplified using the Product Property of Radicals.

Product Property of Radicals
If $\sqrt[n]{x}$ and $\sqrt[n]{y}$ are real numbers, $\sqrt[n]{xy} = \sqrt[n]{x} \cdot \sqrt[n]{y}$.

Example 2 Simplifying Variable Radicals

Simplify each radical.

a. $\sqrt[3]{54x^7 y^{12}}$ **b.** $\sqrt[4]{405a^{15} b^9}$ **c.** $\sqrt{-25c^{12}}$

Answer

a. $\sqrt[3]{54x^7 y^{12}} = \sqrt[3]{(3)^3(2)(x^2)^3(x)(y^4)^3} = 3x^2 y^4 \sqrt[3]{2x}$

b. $\sqrt[4]{405a^{15} b^9} = \sqrt[4]{3^4(5)(a^3)^4 a^3(b^2)^4 b} = 3a^4 b^2 \sqrt[4]{5a^3 b}$

c. $\sqrt{-25c^{12}}$ has no real roots since the radicand is negative and the index is even.
   (The radical indicates the imaginary root $5c^6 i$.)

—————————————————————————————— SKILL ✔ **EXERCISE 9**

Be careful when finding an even root of an even power. When $x = -3$,
$\sqrt{x^2} = \sqrt{(-3)^2} = \sqrt{9} = 3$, which is $|x|$, not x.

> ### DEFINITION
> The ***n*th root of x^n** or $\sqrt[n]{x^n} = \begin{cases} |x| & \text{if } n \text{ is even.} \\ x & \text{if } n \text{ is odd.} \end{cases}$

The absolute value is used when n is even because the principal root is desired. The absolute value can be dropped when the result is an even power, which cannot be negative.

Example 3 Simplifying Variable Radicals by Using Absolute Values

Simplify each radical.

a. $\sqrt{25x^{14}}$ **b.** $-\sqrt{49y^2 z^{12}}$ **c.** $\sqrt{320x^2 yz^4}$

Answer

a. $\sqrt{5^2(x^7)^2} = 5|x|^7$ **b.** $-\sqrt{7^2 y^2(z^6)^2} = -7|y|z^6$ **c.** $\sqrt{5(8)^2 x^2 yz^4}$
$= 8|x|z^2\sqrt{5y}$

—————————————————————————————— SKILL ✔ **EXERCISE 11**

The properties of exponents apply to all integral and fractional exponents. In general, $\left(x^{\frac{1}{n}}\right)^n = x^{\frac{1}{n}(n)} = x^1 = x$; thus $x^{\frac{1}{n}} = \sqrt[n]{x}$. Note that the exponential form also indicates the principal root.

Properties of Exponents

Property or Definition		Rational Example
Product	$x^a \cdot x^b = x^{a+b}$	$x^{\frac{1}{2}} \cdot x^{\frac{1}{2}} = x^{\frac{1}{2}+\frac{1}{2}} = x^1 = x$
Quotient	$\dfrac{x^a}{x^b} = x^{a-b}; \; x \neq 0$	$x^{\frac{7}{2}} \div x^{\frac{3}{2}} = x^{\frac{7}{2}-\frac{3}{2}} = x^{\frac{4}{2}} = x^2$
Power	$(x^a)^b = x^{ab}$	$\left(x^{\frac{3}{4}}\right)^8 = x^{\frac{3}{4} \cdot \frac{8}{1}} = x^{\frac{24}{4}} = x^6$
Power of a Product	$(xy)^a = x^a y^a$	$\left(x^2 y^3\right)^{\frac{1}{6}} = x^{\frac{2}{6}} y^{\frac{3}{6}} = x^{\frac{1}{3}} y^{\frac{1}{2}}$
Power of a Quotient	$\left(\dfrac{x}{y}\right)^a = \dfrac{x^a}{y^a}; \; y \neq 0$	$\left(\dfrac{z^3}{25}\right)^{\frac{1}{2}} = \dfrac{z^{3\left(\frac{1}{2}\right)}}{5^{2\left(\frac{1}{2}\right)}} = \dfrac{z^{\frac{3}{2}}}{5^1} = \dfrac{z^{\frac{3}{2}}}{5}$
Zero Exponent	$x^0 = 1; \; x \neq 0$	$\left(\dfrac{1}{4}\right)^0 = 1$
Negative Exponent	$x^{-n} = \dfrac{1}{x^n}$ and $\dfrac{1}{x^{-n}} = x^n; \; x \neq 0$	$25^{-\frac{1}{2}} = \dfrac{1}{(5^2)^{\frac{1}{2}}} = \dfrac{1}{5^1} = \dfrac{1}{5}$ and $\left(\dfrac{1}{8}\right)^{-\frac{1}{3}} = 8^{\frac{1}{3}} = (2^3)^{\frac{1}{3}} = 2^1 = 2$

Example 4 Evaluating Exponential Expressions

Evaluate each exponential expression.

a. $16^{\frac{1}{4}}$ **b.** $-125^{\frac{1}{3}}$ **c.** $9^{-\frac{1}{2}}$

Answer

a. $\sqrt[4]{16} = \sqrt[4]{(2)^4} = 2$ **b.** $-\sqrt[3]{125} = -\sqrt[3]{(5)^3} = -5$ **c.** $\dfrac{1}{9^{\frac{1}{2}}} = \dfrac{1}{\sqrt{9}} = \dfrac{1}{3}$

SKILL ✓ EXERCISE 15

Recognizing that $x^{\frac{m}{n}} = (x^m)^{\frac{1}{n}} = \left(x^{\frac{1}{n}}\right)^m$ leads to the following definition.

RATIONAL EXPONENT

If the *n*th root of *x* is real and *m* is an integer, $x^{\frac{m}{n}} = \sqrt[n]{x^m} = (\sqrt[n]{x})^m$.

This definition indicates that you can evaluate either the power or the root first.

Example 5 Simplifying an Expression with a Rational Exponent

Evaluate $4^{\frac{3}{2}}$.

Answer

evaluating the power first: or   evaluating the root first:
$\sqrt[2]{4^3} = \sqrt[2]{64} = 8$ $\left(\sqrt[2]{4}\right)^3 = 2^3 = 8$

SKILL ✓ EXERCISE 21

Combining the properties of exponents and the definition of a rational exponent enables the conversion between radical and exponential forms of an expression.

Example 6 Converting Between Radical and Exponential Forms

Convert each expression.

a. $\sqrt[4]{75a^3b}$ to exponential form

b. $2^{\frac{3}{5}}x^{\frac{4}{5}}y^{\frac{1}{2}}$ to radical form

Answer

a. The simplest exponential form should include only prime factors.

$$75^{\frac{1}{4}}a^{\frac{3}{4}}b^{\frac{1}{4}} = \left(3 \cdot 5^2\right)^{\frac{1}{4}}a^{\frac{3}{4}}b^{\frac{1}{4}}$$
$$= 3^{\frac{1}{4}} \cdot 5^{\frac{2}{4}}a^{\frac{3}{4}}b^{\frac{1}{4}}$$
$$= 3^{\frac{1}{4}} \cdot 5^{\frac{1}{2}}a^{\frac{3}{4}}b^{\frac{1}{4}}$$

b. Rename each exponent with the lowest common denominator to rewrite the expression as a single radical.

$$2^{\frac{6}{10}}x^{\frac{8}{10}}y^{\frac{5}{10}} = \sqrt[10]{64x^8y^5}$$

SKILL ✔ EXERCISES 23, 27

The properties of exponents are used to simplify expressions with rational exponents and radical expressions.

Example 7 Simplifying Expressions with Rational Exponents

Simplify each expression, stating answers in the same form as the original expression.

a. $\left(36a^6b^{12}\right)^{1.5}$

b. $\left(\dfrac{216x^9}{125}\right)^{\frac{1}{3}}$

c. $\sqrt[4]{1024}$

d. $\dfrac{\sqrt{8}}{\sqrt[3]{4}}$

Answer

a. $\left(6^2 a^6 b^{12}\right)^{\frac{3}{2}}$
$= \left(6^2\right)^{\frac{3}{2}}\left(a^6\right)^{\frac{3}{2}}\left(b^{12}\right)^{\frac{3}{2}}$
$= 6^3 a^9 b^{18} = 216a^9b^{18}$

b. $\left(\dfrac{6^3 x^9}{5^3}\right)^{\frac{1}{3}}$
$= \dfrac{\left(6^3\right)^{\frac{1}{3}}\left(x^9\right)^{\frac{1}{3}}}{\left(5^3\right)^{\frac{1}{3}}} = \dfrac{6}{5}x^3$

c. $\sqrt[4]{2^{10}}$
$= \sqrt[4]{2^8 2^2}$
$= 2^2 \cdot \sqrt[4]{2^2}$
$= 4 \cdot 2^{\frac{1}{2}}$
$= 4\sqrt{2}$

d. $\dfrac{2^{\frac{3}{2}}}{2^{\frac{2}{3}}}$
$= 2^{\frac{3}{2}} \cdot 2^{-\frac{2}{3}}$
$= 2^{\frac{5}{6}} = \sqrt[6]{2^5} = \sqrt[6]{32}$

SKILL ✔ EXERCISE 31

❯ Exercises

Evaluate each expression without using a calculator. State "no real solution" if none exists.

1. $\sqrt{256}$

2. $\sqrt[3]{-27}$

3. $\sqrt{-324}$

4. $-\sqrt{810{,}000}$

5. $\sqrt[3]{-0.027}$

6. $\sqrt[4]{\dfrac{625}{256}}$

Simplify each radical expression. Assume variables represent positive real numbers.

7. $\sqrt{128x^8y^2z^5}$

8. $\sqrt[4]{-64\,a^{10}b^4c}$

9. $-\sqrt{192x^{10}y^{13}}$

10. $\sqrt[3]{405a^4bc^6}$

Simplify each expression, using absolute values when needed.

11. $\sqrt{4x^2}$

12. $-\sqrt{25x^8y^6}$

13. $\sqrt{(3n-4)^2}$

14. $\sqrt{81x^3y}$

Evaluate each expression.

15. $81^{\frac{1}{4}}$

16. $(-27)^{\frac{1}{3}}$

17. $125^{-\frac{1}{3}}$

18. $32^{\frac{1}{5}}$

19. $8^{\frac{2}{3}}$

20. $(-27)^{\frac{4}{3}}$

21. $81^{-\frac{3}{2}}$

22. $-256^{\frac{3}{4}}$

Convert each radical to exponential form. Assume variables represent positive real numbers.

23. $\sqrt{5xy^5}$

24. $\sqrt{25a^3b^2}$

25. $\sqrt[3]{12a^2b}$

26. $\sqrt[5]{128x^7y^3z}$

Convert each exponential expression to radical form. Assume all variables represent positive real numbers.

27. $3^{\frac{2}{3}}x^{\frac{1}{3}}$

28. $2^{\frac{3}{4}}c^{\frac{3}{2}}$

29. $7^{\frac{2}{5}}x^{\frac{3}{10}}$

30. $5^{\frac{1}{4}}x^{\frac{2}{3}}y^{\frac{5}{4}}$

Simplify each expression without using a calculator.

31. $32^{1.4}$

32. $\left(\dfrac{64x^3}{27y^6}\right)^{\frac{1}{3}}$

33. $\sqrt[4]{3^6}$

34. $\dfrac{\sqrt{27}}{\sqrt[3]{9}}$

<table>
<tr><td>

After completing this section, you will be able to

- define the imaginary unit i, imaginary numbers, and complex numbers.
- simplify powers of i.
- add, subtract, and multiply complex numbers.
- write the quotient of two complex numbers in standard form.
- find complex roots of quadratic equations.

</td></tr>
</table>

A.5 Complex Numbers

Solving $x^2 + 1 = 0$ by taking roots produces $x^2 = -1$ or $x = \pm\sqrt{-1}$. Since the result "$\sqrt{-1}$" is not a real number, it is designated as "imaginary." Leonard Euler (1707–83) first used i to represent $\sqrt{-1}$.

▎DEFINITION

The **imaginary unit**, *i*, is the square root of -1, so that $i = \sqrt{-1}$ and $i^2 = -1$.

The square roots of other negative numbers are expressed in terms of i.
$$\sqrt{-4} = \sqrt{4} \cdot \sqrt{-1} = 2i \text{ and } \sqrt{-24} = \sqrt{4} \cdot \sqrt{6} \cdot \sqrt{-1} = 2i\sqrt{6}$$

Numbers such as i, $2i$, and $2i\sqrt{6}$ are called *pure imaginary numbers*. Any *complex number*, z, can be expressed in the standard form $z = a + bi$, where $a, b \in \mathbb{R}$ and $i = \sqrt{-1}$. The set of complex numbers contains the real numbers, $a + 0i$, and the pure imaginary numbers, $0 + bi$. The set of imaginary numbers $a + bi$, $b \neq 0$ is the complement of the real numbers within the set of complex numbers. Mathematicians studied imaginary numbers for many years without any known real-life applications. Today, imaginary numbers are essential elements in electronics and engineering.

Notice the pattern in the powers of i that can be used to quickly simplify larger powers of i.

$$i = i \qquad\qquad i^5 = i^4 \cdot i = 1 \cdot i = i$$
$$i^2 = -1 \qquad\qquad i^6 = i^4 \cdot i^2 = 1 \cdot -1 = -1$$
$$i^3 = i^2 \cdot i = -1 \cdot i = -i \qquad\qquad i^7 = i^4 \cdot i^3 = 1 \cdot -i = -i$$
$$i^4 = i^2 \cdot i^2 = -1 \cdot -1 = 1 \qquad\qquad i^8 = i^4 \cdot i^4 = 1 \cdot 1 = 1$$

To simplify large powers of i, divide the exponent by 4. The remainder (which will be 3 or less) will give a power of i equivalent to the original.

Example 1   Simplifying a Power of *i*

Simplify i^{27}.

Answer

$27 \div 4 = 6 \text{ R. } 3$

1. Divide the exponent by 4 to determine the number of groupings of i^4 and the number of factors of i leftover.

$i^{27} = (i^4)^6 \cdot i^3 = 1^6 \cdot i^3$
$\quad = i^3 = -1$

2. Use the fact that each group of $i^4 = 1$ and simplify the remaining power of i.

SKILL ✓ **EXERCISE 1**

The set of complex numbers is governed by most of the properties that have been established for the set of real numbers. The Commutative, Associative and Distributive Properties hold true for the complex numbers. The Product Property of Radicals cannot be applied to negative radicands of even roots: $\sqrt{-1} \cdot \sqrt{-1} \neq \sqrt{1}$. Always write complex numbers in standard form before simplifying.
For example, $\sqrt{-4} \cdot \sqrt{-9} = 2i \cdot 3i = 6i^2 = -6$.

To add or subtract complex numbers, simply add or subtract their real and imaginary components. The same result is obtained by treating complex numbers as binomials and combining like terms. When the FOIL method is used to multiply complex numbers, the product of the last terms has a factor of i^2 that is simplified to -1 before that term is combined with the real product of the first terms. To divide complex numbers, write the division as a fraction and multiply both the numerator and the denominator $c + di$ by its conjugate, $c - di$. The product in the denominator, $(c + di)(c - di) = c^2 + d^2$, no longer contains the radical $i = \sqrt{-1}$.

Operation	Rule
addition	$(a + bi) + (c + di) = (a + c) + (b + d)i$
subtraction	$(a + bi) - (c + di) = (a - c) + (b - d)i$
multiplication	$(a + bi)(c + di) = (ac - bd) + (ad + bc)i$
division	$\dfrac{(a + bi)}{(c + di)} \cdot \dfrac{(c - di)}{(c - di)} = \dfrac{(ac + bd) + (bc - ad)i}{c^2 + d^2}$

Example 2 Performing Basic Operations with Complex Numbers

Complete each operation, given $z_1 = 3 + 4i$ and $z_2 = 5 - 6i$.

a. $z_1 + z_2$ **b.** $z_1 - z_2$ **c.** $z_1 \cdot z_2$ **d.** $z_1 \div z_2$

Answer

a. $(3 + 4i) + (5 - 6i)$
$= 8 - 2i$

Combine the real parts and imaginary parts as you would combine like terms.

b. $(3 + 4i) - (5 - 6i)$
$= -2 + 10i$

Combine the real parts and imaginary parts as you would combine like terms.

c. $(3 + 4i)(5 - 6i)$
$= 15 - 18i + 20i - 24i^2$
$= 15 + 2i + 24$
$= 39 + 2i$

Multiply using the FOIL method, substitute for i^2, and then simplify.

d. $\dfrac{3 + 4i}{5 - 6i} \cdot \dfrac{5 + 6i}{5 + 6i}$
$= \dfrac{15 + 18i + 20i + 24i^2}{25 - 36i^2} = \dfrac{-9 + 38i}{25 + 36}$
$= \dfrac{-9 + 38i}{61} = -\dfrac{9}{61} + \dfrac{38}{61}i$

Multiply the numerator and the denominator by the denominator's conjugate and simplify, expressing the result in standard form.

—— SKILL ✔ **EXERCISES 9, 13, 15**

Recall that the product of conjugates is a difference of squares: $(a + b)(a - b) = a^2 - b^2$. This pattern is used to factor the difference of squares. It is also helpful to recognize that the product of *complex conjugates* is a sum of squares: $(c + di)(c - di) = c^2 + d^2$. This pattern can be used to factor a sum of squares into the product of two complex numbers.

$9x^2 + 25 = (3x + 5i)(3x - 5i)$

An alternate method of factoring a sum of squares is to rewrite the expression as an equivalent sum using i^2 as a factor in the second term before factoring as a difference of squares.

$9x^2 + 25 = 9x^2 - 25i^2 = (3x + 5i)(3x - 5i)$

This method provides insight into factoring expressions such as $x^2 + ix + 2$.

$x^2 + ix + 2 = x^2 + ix - 2i^2 = (x + 2i)(x - i)$

Example 3 Factoring Over the Set of Complex Numbers

Factor each expression over the set of complex numbers.

a. $x^2 + 25$
b. $x^2 - 7xi - 10$

Answer

a. $x^2 + 25 = (x + 5i)(x - 5i)$ Apply the sum of squares factoring pattern.

b. $x^2 - 7xi - 10 = x^2 - 7xi + 10i^2$

1. Replace the last term with an equivalent expression containing i^2.

$\qquad = (x - 5i)(x - 2i)$

2. Factor the resulting trinomial.

SKILL ✔ **EXERCISES 17, 19**

Many quadratic equations have complex solutions. Since these equations cannot be factored over the real numbers, they are usually solved using the *quadratic formula*.

> ## QUADRATIC FORMULA
> If $ax^2 + bx + c = 0$, where $a, b, c \in \mathbb{R}$ and $a \neq 0$, then $x = \dfrac{-b \pm \sqrt{b^2 - 4ac}}{2a}$.

Example 4 Using the Quadratic Formula

Solve $2x^2 + 4x + 7 = 0$. Express the roots in standard form.

Answer

$a = 2, b = 4, c = 7$

1. Identify the values of a, b, and c.

$x = \dfrac{-4 \pm \sqrt{4^2 - 4 \cdot 2 \cdot 7}}{2 \cdot 2}$

2. Substitute into the quadratic formula.

$x = \dfrac{-4 \pm \sqrt{-40}}{4} = \dfrac{-4 \pm 2\sqrt{10}\,i}{4}$

3. Simplify.

$x = -1 \pm \dfrac{\sqrt{10}}{2}i$

4. Express the complex roots in standard form.

SKILL ✔ **EXERCISE 23**

❯ Exercises

Simplify each power.

1. i^{15} **2.** i^{46} **3.** i^{73} **4.** i^{156}

Perform each indicated operation. Express answers in standard form.

5. $(5 + 9i) + (4 - 6i)$ **6.** $(8 + i) + (3 - 7i)$

7. $(-5 + 11i) + (11 - 23i)$ **8.** $(11 + 5i) - 5i$

9. $(-7 - 5i) - (5 - 2i)$ **10.** $(8 - 15i) - (17 + 12i)$

11. $13(4 + 2i)$ **12.** $7i(5 + 3i)$

13. $(5 + 3i)(5 - 3i)$ **14.** $(-8 - 5i)(4 + 3i)$

15. $\dfrac{6 + 5i}{2 - 3i}$ **16.** $\dfrac{7 + 6i}{4 + 3i}$

Factor each expression over the set of complex numbers.

17. $x^2 + 49$ **18.** $9x^2 + 16$

19. $x^2 - 9xi - 14$ **20.** $x^2 - 3xi + 28$

Solve each equation using the quadratic formula. Express answers in standard form.

21. $x^2 - 6x + 13 = 0$ **22.** $3x^2 + 5x + 13 = 0$

23. $-x^2 + 8x - 18 = 0$ **24.** $4x^2 - 10x + 9 = 0$

Section 1.4 (continued / right column)

43. −24, 3, 0, −375
45. $x = 6$
47. $f(x) = 3x$
49. E **51.** C

39c. even; $f(-x) = (-x)^4 - 3(-x)^2 + 5$
$= x^4 - 3x^2 + 5 = f(x)$
39d. odd; $f(-x) = (-x)^3 - 4(-x)$
$= -x^3 + 4x = -(-x^3 + 4x) = -f(x)$
39e. neither; $f(-x) = (-x)^2 - 5(-x) - 2 = x^2 + 5x - 2$
$-f(x) = -(x^2 - 5x - 2) = -x^2 + 5x + 2$
$f(-x) \neq f(x)$ and $f(-x) \neq -f(x)$
41. Since $(-1)^n = -1$ when n is odd,
$f(-x) = k(-x)^n = k(-1)^n x^n = -kx^n = -f(x)$.
43a. $T^2 = kR^3$ **43b.** $k \approx 1.66 \times 10^{-19}\ \frac{\text{days}^2}{\text{miles}^3}$ **43c.** ≈ 165.2 yr
45. $(3x + 2)^2$ **47.** $f(x) = 2x + 1$ **49a.** -2 **49b.** 0
49c. does not exist **51.** B **53.** C

Section 1.5

1. $f(x)$ is translated 3 units down. **3.** $f(x)$ is reflected in the x-axis and shrunk vertically by a factor of $\frac{1}{4}$. **5a.** III **5b.** IV
5c. I **5d.** II **7.** $f(x)$ is stretched horizontally by 2 (or shrunk vertically by a factor of $\frac{1}{8}$) and is translated 5 units down.
9. $f(x)$ is stretched vertically by 2 and is translated 3 units down.

11. [graph]
13. [graph]
15. [graph]
17. [graph]

19. [graph] $D = \mathbb{R};\ R = \{2x \mid x \in \mathbb{Z}\}$
$D = \{x \mid x \neq -2\}$
$R = \{y \mid y \neq -1\}$

21. [graph] $D = \mathbb{R};\ R = (-\infty, 4]$

23. $g(x) = \sqrt{x + 4} - 3$ **25.** $r(x) = \frac{1}{2}\sqrt{x} + 3$
27. $g(x) = |x + 2| + 3$ **29.** $g(x) = \frac{1}{3}(x - 5)^2$
31. $f(x)$ is translated 7 units right and 4 units up. **35a.** $g(x) = -x^2 + 2$ **35b.** $h(x) = -x^2 - 2$
33. $f(x)$ is translated 7 units right and
37. $g(x) = f(-x)$ is the reflection in the y-axis, and
$h(x) = -g(x) = -f(-x)$ is the reflection in both axes.
$-f(-x) = -g((-x + 2)^2 + 1)$
$= -(-x - 2)^2 - 1$
$= -((-1)(x + 2))^2 - 1$
$= -(-1)^2(x + 2)^2 - 1$
$= -(x + 2)^2 - 1$

Section 1.4

41. 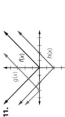 [shaded graph]

1a. 3, $-\frac{1}{4}$ **1b.** −7, $-\frac{2}{3}$ **1c.** −1, 22.4 **1d.** 2, $-\frac{\sqrt{3}}{4}$

3. [graph]
$\lim_{x\to-\infty} f(x) = -\infty$
$\lim_{x\to\infty} f(x) = \infty$

5. [graph]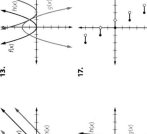

7. [graph]
$\lim_{x\to-\infty} g(x) = 0$
$\lim_{x\to\infty} g(x) = 0$

9. [graph]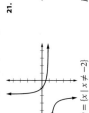

11. [graph]
incr.: $(-\infty, 0)$ and $(0, \infty)$

odd; SWRT origin

13. $m = 12n^3$ **15.** $d = 2a^{-2}$
17. $D = \mathbb{R};\ R = (-\infty, 0]$
$\lim_{x\to-\infty} f(x) = -\infty$
$\lim_{x\to\infty} f(x) = -\infty$; cont.: $\mathbb{R}$;
incr.: $(-\infty, 0]$; decr.: $[0, \infty)$;
even; SWRT y-axis
19. $D = \mathbb{R};\ R = \mathbb{R}$; $\lim_{x\to-\infty} f(x) = \infty$; $\lim_{x\to\infty} f(x) = -\infty$; cont.: $\mathbb{R}$;
decr.: $\mathbb{R}$; odd; SWRT origin
21. $D = \{x \mid x \neq 0\};\ R = \{y \mid y \neq 0\}$; $\lim_{x\to-\infty} f(x) = 0$; $\lim_{x\to\infty} f(x) = 0$; odd;
cont.: $(-\infty, 0)$ and $(0, \infty)$; decr.: $(-\infty, 0)$ and $(0, \infty)$; odd;
SWRT origin
23. C **25.** B **27.** 4.9 in. **29.** 216 ft **31.** 5×10^{-21} N **33.** 8
35. [graph]

37a. $R = \{y \mid y = 1\}$; $\lim_{x\to-\infty} f(x) = 1$; $\lim_{x\to\infty} f(x) = 1$; constant: $\mathbb{R}$
37b. $R = \{y \mid y = k\}$; $\lim_{x\to-\infty} f(x) = k$; $\lim_{x\to\infty} f(x) = k$; constant: $\mathbb{R}$
39a. odd; $f(-x) = 6(-x) = -6x = -(6x) = -f(x)$
39b. neither; $f(-x) = 3(-x) + 5 = -3x + 5$
$-f(x) = -(3x + 5) = -3x - 5$
$f(-x) \neq f(x)$ and $f(-x) \neq -f(x)$

Section 1.1

1. [graph]
3. {(0, 0), (1, −1), (1, 3), (2, −3), (4, 2)}; not a function **5.** function **7.** function
9. $(-\infty, 12)$
11. $(-4, 10]$
$D = \{x \mid x = 1, 3, 4, 6\};\ R = \{y \mid y = -1, 2, 4\}$
13. $D = [0, 3) \cup (3, 6];\ R = (2, 5]$
15. $D = (-3, 1) \cup (1, 4];\ R = [-2, 5]$
17. $D = \{x \mid x = 3\};\ R = (-\infty, \infty)$
19. $\{(-1, -7), (1, -3), (4, 3)\}$ **21.** $\{(-2, 6), (-1, 5), (0, 4), (3, 1)\}$

[Domain / Range diagrams]
Domain · Range
Range · Domain

$D = (-\infty, \infty)$
$R = \{y \mid y = -3\}$

27. [graph]
29. [graph]

$D = (-\infty, 1) \cup (1, \infty); R = (0, \infty)$
$R = (-\infty, 0) \cup (0, \infty)$
35a. function $D = [0, \infty); R = [0, \infty)$
35b. $2x + h + 2$
31. not a function **33.** function **35a.** function
35b. $s \approx 676.2$ km/hr **37a.** 1 **37b.** $2x + h + 2$
39. $D_f = \{x \mid x \neq -\frac{11}{2}\}$ or $(-\infty, -\frac{11}{2}) \cup (-\frac{11}{2}, \infty)$;
$D_g = \{x \mid x < 6\}$ or $(-\infty, 6)$ **41.** $\mathbb{Q}';\ \mathbb{R}$ **43.** $\mathbb{Z}$ **45.** $\mathbb{Q}'$
47. C **49.** D

Section 1.2

1. line **3.** $m = \frac{3}{4}$
5. [graph]
7. [graph]
9. [graph, (0, 5), (2, 0)]
11. [graph, (2, 0), $(0, -\frac{3}{2})$]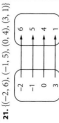
13. (2, 0); (0, 1); none; undefined
15. (−5, 0); none; undefined
17. $(\frac{3}{2}, 0)$; (0, 1); $m = -\frac{1}{2}$
19. $y = \frac{2}{3}x + 2$ **21.** $y = \frac{4}{3}x - \frac{17}{3}$
23. $y = -\frac{16}{7}x + 5$ **25.** 15; $(\frac{1}{2}, 0)$ **27.** $5\sqrt{17}$; $(-\frac{9}{2}, 11)$
29. $r = 13$ **31.** $C(-1, \frac{7}{2})$; $r = 2.5$
33. −80 ft/sec; The watermelon is traveling down.
35a. $f(x) = 3x + 2$; $17.00 **35b.** $f(x) = 3.25x + 3$; $19.25
35c. $f(x) = 3.5x + 5$; $22.50 **35d.** $f(x) = 4x + 8$; $28.00
39a. $x^2 + y^2 = 49$ **39b.** $(x - 1)^2 + (y + 4)^2 = 4$
41. Adding or subtracting a constant moves the y-intercept up or down the y-axis while maintaining the same slope.
43. $y = -\frac{3}{4}x - 2$ **45.** Plot $C(x_2, y_1)$ and draw right $\triangle ABC$.
by the Pythagorean Theorem,
$AB^2 = AC^2 + CB^2$
$d^2 = (x_2 - x_1)^2 + (y_2 - y_1)^2$
$d = \sqrt{(x_2 - x_1)^2 + (y_2 - y_1)^2}$
47. 1 **49.** 2 **51.** vertical **53.** D **55.** D

Section 1.3

1. $\{(-4, 16), (-\frac{1}{2}, 2), (0, 0), (\frac{3}{4}, 3), (2, 8)\}$
3. $\{(-4, -4), (-\frac{1}{2}, -1), (0, 0), (\frac{3}{4}, 0), (2, 2)\}$
5. $\{(-4, 24), (-\frac{1}{2}, 3), (0, 2), (\frac{3}{4}, \frac{11}{4}), (2, 4)\}$
7. [graph] $D = \mathbb{R};\ R = [0, \infty)$; cont.
9. [graph] 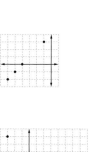 $D = \mathbb{R};\ R = [1, \infty)$; cont.
11. [graph] $D = \mathbb{R};\ R = (0, \infty)$; cont.
13. discont.; jump **15.** discont.; point **17.** discont.; infinite **19.** B
21. [graph] $D = \mathbb{R};\ R = [-1, \infty)$; cont.
23. [graph] 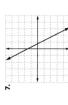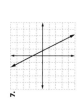 $D = \mathbb{R};\ R = \mathbb{R}$; discont.

$D = \mathbb{R};\ R = \mathbb{Z}$; discont.
25. 3, 1 **27.** −1, −1 **29.** −1 **31.** does not exist **33.** 5
35. discont.; infinite **37.** cont. **39a.** always **39b.** never
39c. sometimes

SELECTED ODD ANSWERS (668b)

21. $f(g(x)) = 3\left(\dfrac{x-9}{3}\right) + 9 = x - 9 + 9 = x$
$g(f(x)) = \dfrac{(3x+9)-9}{3} = x$

23. $f(g(x)) = \dfrac{\left(\frac{-7x-1}{x-1}\right)-1}{\left(\frac{-7x-1}{x-1}\right)+7}$

$= \dfrac{\frac{-7x-1}{x-1} - \frac{x-1}{x-1}}{\frac{-7x-1}{x-1}+\frac{7x-7}{x-1}} = \dfrac{-8x}{x-1} \cdot \dfrac{x-1}{-8} = x$

$g(f(x)) = \dfrac{-7\left(\frac{x-1}{x+7}\right)-1}{\left(\frac{x-1}{x+7}\right)-1}$

$= \dfrac{\frac{-7x+7}{x+7}-\frac{x+7}{x+7}}{\frac{x-1}{x+7}-\frac{x+7}{x+7}} = \dfrac{-8x}{x+7} \cdot \dfrac{x+7}{-8} = x$; not inverses

25. $f(g(x)) = x - 1;\ g(f(x)) = \dfrac{2x-1}{2}$; not inverses

27.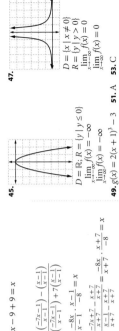

29.

31. $y = \sqrt[5]{\dfrac{x+4}{3}}$
$D = (0, \infty)$ **33.** $y = x^2 + 2;\ D = [0, \infty)$ **35.** $y = \dfrac{9}{4x^2} - 1$;

37a. $(0, 2), (3.75, 2.69), (7.5, 2.78), (11.25, 2.24)$;
≈ 2.82 m **37b.** $f(x) = -\dfrac{49}{2250}x^2 + \dfrac{49}{15}x + 2$ **37c.** ≈ 6.12 m;
$(15, 1.1)$ **37d.** ≈ 17.49 m **39.** $-\dfrac{a}{b},\ \dfrac{a}{b}$ **41.** never

45. **47.** discont. **49.** odd **51.** E **53.** B

Section 1.9
1. A **3.** C **5.** decreasing; It is negative. **7.** ≈ 0.992
9. $f(x) \approx 1.586x + 1.5$ **11.** The positive value for slope confirms a positive correlation. **13.** both; It is weak.
15. ≈ 0.937 **17.** $f(x) = 2.981x - 4.968$
19. $f(x) \approx 0.990x^2 - 2.983x + 1.057$ **21.** $l(x) = 3.312x - 18.917$;
$r^2 \approx 0.822$; yes **23a.** $\approx \$1.55$ **23b.** $\approx \$2.96$
27. $l(x) \approx 3.5x - 7;\ r^2 \approx 0.9722;\ g(x) = 0.5x^2 - 0.5x;\ r^2 \approx 1$
29. 4950 connections **31.** $f(x) = 13.315x - 157.567$;
$r^2 \approx 0.9793$; no **33.** The linear model appears to be a good fit within the data set, but extrapolated values are likely not accurate. **35a.** $\approx 1,424,000$ **35b.** $\approx 260,000$ **35c.** $\approx 260,000$
37. 1940s; 1940s **39.** Female life expectancy increased at a faster rate than male life expectancy.
41. $m(x) \approx -0.0946x^2 + 3.3982x + 49.1946;\ r^2 \approx 0.9714$
$f(x) = -0.3060x^2 + 6.5393x + 44.7274;\ r^2 \approx 0.9895$
43a. The current US life expectancies are very close to his 70–80 yr estimate.

47.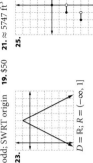
$D = \{x \mid x \neq 0\}$
$R = \{y \mid y > 0\}$
$\lim_{x \to -\infty} f(x) = 0$
$\lim_{x \to \infty} f(x) = 0$ **53.** C

45.
$D = \mathbb{R};\ R = \{y \mid y \leq 0\}$
$\lim_{x \to -\infty} f(x) = -\infty$
$\lim_{x \to \infty} f(x) = -\infty$
49. $g(x) = 2(x+1)^3 - 3$ **51.** A

Data Analysis
1. $y \approx 0.2535x + 19.2861$ **1a.** $r = 0.8764$ **1b.** $r^2 = 0.7680$;
$\approx 77\%$ of the variation in height is explained by a variation in horizontal distance. **1c.** The ball must return to the earth.
3. $y = -0.0015x^2 + 0.719x - 0.2226;\ r^2 \approx 0.9855$
3a. $\approx 99\%$ of the variation in height is explained by a variation in horizontal distance. **3b.** yes **5a.** 3.0 ft **5b.** 67 ft
5c. The effect of air resistance causes the ball's trajectory to be non-parabolic.

Review
1. $D = \{-1, 0, 1\};\ R = \{-1, 0, 1, 2, 3\}$; not a function
3. $D = (-\infty, -5) \cup (-5, \infty);\ R = (-\infty, 0) \cup (0, \infty)$; function
5. $\{(-4, 6), (-2, 4), (0, 2), (2, 0), (4, 2)\}$
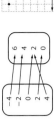 
7. $(6, 0), (0, -4);\ m = \dfrac{2}{3}$

9. $y = -\dfrac{2}{3}x + 5$
11.
13.
$D = \mathbb{R};\ R = [0, \infty)$; cont.
15a. point **15b.** jump **15c.** infinite **17.** $D = \mathbb{R};\ R = \mathbb{R}$;
$\lim_{x \to \infty} f(x) = -\infty;\ \lim_{x \to -\infty} f(x) = \infty$; cont.; $\mathbb{R}$; incr.: $(-\infty, \infty)$;
odd; SWRT origin **19.** $\$50$ **21.** ≈ 5747 ft³
23. $D = \mathbb{R};\ R = (-\infty, 4]$
discont.
$D = \mathbb{R};\ R = (-\infty, 1]$
25. $D = \mathbb{R};\ R = \{x \mid 2x \in \mathbb{Z}\}$

SELECTED ODD ANSWERS (668a)

39a. I **39b.** IV **41.** $x = -12, 2$ **43.** $a = \pm 4\sqrt{2}$ **45.** $x = -5, 9$
47. B **49.** B

Section 1.6
1. $V(0, 0)$; min; $x = 0$ **3.** $V(5, 7)$; max; $x = 5$
5. **7.**
9. $-8, \dfrac{7}{2}$ **11.** $\dfrac{-5 \pm \sqrt{33}}{2}$ **15.** $(0, 24);\ 4, 6$
13. $\dfrac{1}{2} \pm \dfrac{3}{2}i$
17. $(0, 0);\ 0, -4$
19. $f(x) = (x - 1)^2 - 1$
21. $h(x) = \left(x + \dfrac{5}{2}\right)^2 - 4$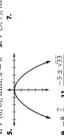

23. $g(x) = 4(x + 1)^2 - 5$
25. $V(-2, -4)$; min; y-int: $(0, 0)$; x-int: $(0, 0), (-4, 0)$
27. $V\left(1, -\dfrac{1}{2}\right)$; min; y-int: $\left(0, \dfrac{1}{2}\right)$; x-int: $\left(1 \pm \dfrac{\sqrt{2}}{2}, 0\right)$
29a. always **29b.** never **29c.** always **31.** $f(x) = \dfrac{1}{9}x^2 - \dfrac{4}{9}x - \dfrac{5}{9}$
33a. 400 ft **33b.** 1 sec **33c.** 400 ft
33d. 6 sec **35a.** $f(x) = -6000x^2 + 84{,}000x + 9{,}547{,}500$
35b. 7 price drops; $\$810$ **35c.** $\$9{,}841{,}500$
37a. $h(t) = -4.9t^2 + 4t + 2$ **37b.** ≈ 2.82 m; ≈ 0.41 sec
37c. ≈ 1.17 sec **37d.** yes; yes
39. $ax^2 + bx = -c$
$x^2 + \dfrac{b}{a}x = -\dfrac{c}{a}$
$x^2 + \dfrac{b}{a}x + \left(\dfrac{b}{2a}\right)^2 = -\dfrac{c}{a} + \dfrac{b^2}{4a^2}$
$\left(x + \dfrac{b}{2a}\right)^2 = \dfrac{b^2 - 4ac}{4a^2}$
$x + \dfrac{b}{2a} = \dfrac{\pm\sqrt{b^2 - 4ac}}{2a}$
$x = \dfrac{-b}{2a} \pm \dfrac{\sqrt{b^2 - 4ac}}{2a}$
$x = \dfrac{-b \pm \sqrt{b^2 - 4ac}}{2a}$

Section 1.7
1. $(f + g)(x) = -x - 2;\ (g - f)(x) = 3x - 16$
$(fg)(x) = -2x^2 + 25x - 63;\ D_f \cap D_g = \mathbb{R}$
3. $(f + g)(x) = 5x^2 + \dfrac{1}{x};\ (g - f)(x) = \dfrac{1}{x} - 5x^2$
$(fg)(x) = 5x;\ D_f \cap D_g = \{x \mid x \neq 0\}$
5. $\dfrac{f}{g}(x) = \dfrac{x-2}{x};\ D_{f/g} = \{x \mid x \neq 0\}$
$\dfrac{g}{f}(x) = \dfrac{x}{x-2};\ D_{g/f} = \{x \mid x \neq 2\}$
7. $\dfrac{f}{g}(x) = \dfrac{x^3 - 4x}{2};\ D_{f/g} = \{x \mid x \neq 0\}$
$\dfrac{g}{f}(x) = \dfrac{2}{x^3 - 4x};\ D_{g/f} = \{x \mid x \neq 0, \pm 2\}$
9. $-2x^2 + 7$ **11.** $45a^2 + 30ab + 5b^2$ **13.** $-2a^2 - 8a + 25$
15a.
15b. $(f + g)(x) = \mathbb{R}$
17. $f(g(x)) = x^2 + 1;\ f(g(3)) = 10$
$g(f(x)) = x^2 - 14x + 57$
$g(f(3)) = 24$
19. Commutative Property; $f \circ g \neq g \circ f$
21. $f(g(x)) = x^2 + 10x - 3;\ D_{f \circ g} = \mathbb{R}$
$g(f(x)) = x^2 - 4x - 17;\ D_{g \circ f} = \mathbb{R}$
23. $f(g(x)) = \sqrt{x^2 - 9};\ D_{f \circ g} = (-\infty, -3] \cup [3, \infty)$
$g(f(x)) = \sqrt{(x - 5)^2} - 4;\ D_{g \circ f} = [5, \infty)$
25. $f(g(x)) = -10x^2 + 40x - 39;\ D_{f \circ g} = \mathbb{R}$
$g(f(x)) = \dfrac{1}{(x-2)^2 - 12};\ D_{g \circ f} = \{x \mid x \neq \pm 2\sqrt{3}\}$
27. $f(x) = \sqrt{x},\ g(x) = x^2 - 3$ or $f(x) = \sqrt{x-3},\ g(x) = x^2$
29. $f(x) = x^2 - 7,\ g(x) = x + 2$ or $f(x) = x,\ g(x) = (x + 2)^2$
31a. $m(x) = 1000x;\ c(x) = 100x$ **31b.** $(m \circ c)(x) = 100{,}000x$
31c. 500,000 cm **33a.** $A(r) = \pi r^2;\ r(t) = 2t + 3$
33b. $A(r(t)) = 4\pi t^2 + 12\pi t + 9\pi$; the area of the circle as a function of time **33c.** 5 sec
35.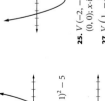

37. always **39.** sometimes **41a.** $\dfrac{f}{g}(x) = x + 6, x \neq 1$
$D = \{x \mid x \neq 1\};\ R = \{y \mid y \neq 7\}$
$\lim_{x \to \infty} f(x) = -\infty$
$\lim_{x \to \infty} f(x) = \infty$; PD at $x = 1$
41a. $\dfrac{1}{\sqrt{2x + 3}};\ D = \left(-\dfrac{3}{2}, \infty\right)$
41b. $\dfrac{1}{\sqrt{2x} + 3};\ D = \left(-\dfrac{3}{2}, \infty\right)$ **43.** $l = \dfrac{1}{2}p - w$ **45.** $y = \pm\sqrt{x + z}$
47. $f(x) = -3x + 11$ **49.** B **51.** A

Section 1.8
1. $(-9, 5)$
3. 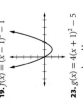 function
5. not a function
7. The relation is a function; its inverse is not.
9. The relation is a function; its inverse is not.
11. not a function **13.** function **15.** function
17. $y = \dfrac{\sqrt{x-2}}{x}$ **19a.** $y = \dfrac{x}{0.2642} \approx 3.785x$
19b. $f^{-1}(4.5) \approx 17.03$ L

Section 2.4 (continued)

35. SA: $y = x + 2$; VA: $x = 2$; PD at $x = 2$
y-int.: $(0, 0)$, $(-1, 0)$

137. SA: $y = x$; PD at $x = 2$
x-int.: $(-2, 0)$
y-int.: $(0, \frac{1}{2})$; x-int.: $(-2, 0)$

39a. linear; Factors of $x + 3$ cancel, leaving $f(x) = 2x - 5$, $x \neq -3$, a line with a point discontinuity.

39b. parabolic; Factors of $2x + 1$ cancel, leaving $f(x) = x^2 + x$, $x \neq -\frac{1}{2}$, a parabola with a point discontinuity.

41a. $D = (5, \infty)$ 41b. VA: $x = 5$ 41c. ≈ 5.13 cm

43. NLA: $y = -x^2 - 1$ 47. $\frac{2a^2 - a + 3}{a^2 - 1}$ 49. $x = 1.5, 1$
VA: $x = 1$; y-int.: $(0, 0)$
x-int.: $(0, 0)$

51. $\pm 1, \pm 2, \pm 3, \pm 4, \pm 6, \pm 12$
53. E 55. C

Section 2.6

1. $x = 8$ 3. no solution 5. $x = 0$ 7. $r = -2, -\frac{4}{3}$ 9. $n = \frac{5}{3}$
11. $x = -0.925, 0.675$ 13. $x = 2, -\frac{2}{3}$ 15. $x = -\frac{1}{3} \pm \frac{\sqrt{3}}{2}$
17. $r = -3$ 19. $x = -5$ 23. 8 25. 4 and 12, $-\frac{2}{3}$ and 1
27. 1 hr 29. 6 hr; 9 hr 31. 60 mi/hr 35a. ≈ 7.06 ohms
35b. 40 ohms 37. $p(w) = 2w + \frac{74}{w}$
37a. $(11 + 2\sqrt{21})$ ft $\times (11 - 2\sqrt{21})$ ft
39. no 41. $\lim_{x \to \infty} f(x) = \infty$; $\lim_{x \to -\infty} f(x) = -\infty$ 43. $\frac{x+4}{x^2-9}$
45. D 47. D

Section 2.7

1a. $(-\infty, -4) \cup (3, \infty)$ 1b. $(-4, 2)$ 3a. $(-3, 1) \cup (1, \infty)$
3b. $(-\infty, -3)$ 5. $\left(-\infty, -\frac{1}{2}\right] \cup [6, \infty)$ 7. $(-\infty, -1)$
9. zeros: 0; VA: $x = 2$ 9a. $(-\infty, 0) \cup (2, \infty)$
9b. $(0, 2)$ 11. PD at $x = -1$; VA: $x = 0$ 11a. $\left(\frac{4}{5}, \infty\right)$
11b. $(-\infty, -1) \cup \left(-1, \frac{4}{5}\right)$ 13. A, C 15. $\left(\infty, -\frac{3}{2}\right)$
17. $(-\infty, -7] \cup \left[\frac{1}{2}, 2\right)$ 19. $(2, \infty)$
21. $(-\infty, -5) \cup (1, 4]$ 23. $(-4, 0) \cup (2, \infty)$
25. $\left(-\infty, -2\right] \cup \left[\frac{1}{2}, 3\right]$ 27. ℝ 29. $(-\infty, -1) \cup (-1, 2]$
31. [7.21 cm, 9.50 cm] 33. [1.04 in., 2.06 in.]
35. $[-4 - \sqrt{22}, -6) \cup (0, -4 + \sqrt{22}]$ 37. $(5, \infty)$
39. $\left(-\infty, 1\right) \cup \left(1, \frac{5}{3}\right)$ 41. 1.475 ft $\times$ 1100 ft 43. $D = (-\infty, \infty)$
$R = [-2, \infty)$; discont. 45. $\frac{g}{f}(x) = x + 3$; $D = ℝ$
47. $y = 1.118x + 1.5273$ 49. D 51. C

Section 2.4

1. $\pm 1, \pm 2, \pm\frac{1}{2}$ 3. $x = \pm 2, \pm 4$ 5. $x = -3, -1, 4$ 7. $x = 4, 1$
(both multiplicity 2) 9a. 4, 2, or 0 positive zeros; 0 negative
zeros 9b. zero(s) exist in $[0, 4]$ 11. $p(x) = x^3 - 3x^2 - 2x + 6$
13. $x = -\sqrt{3}, 6$ 15. $x = 0, -1, \pm 2i$ 17. $x = -1 + 2i, 1$
19. $x = 0, \pm 2, 3$ 21. $x = -6, \frac{5}{2}, 2$ 23. $x = -5, 1 \pm 2\sqrt{2}i$
25. $x = 1$ (multiplicity 3), $-\frac{1}{4}$ 27. $x = \pm\frac{1}{2}, -\frac{3}{2}, -\frac{1}{3}$
29. $p(x) = x^3 - 4x^2 + 2x + 4$
31. $p(x) = 4x^3 - 29x^2 + 76x + 75$
33. $p(x) = x^6 - 2x^5 - 3x^4 + 34x^3 - 24x^2 - 248x - 208$
35. $(5x + 2)(x^2 - 2)$ 37. yes 39. no
41a. $p(x) = x^2 + (2 - \sqrt{3})x - 2\sqrt{3}$ 41b. $p(-\sqrt{3}) \neq 0$
43a. $x^2 - 2ax + a^2 + b^2$ 43b. $x^2 - 2ax + a^2 - bc^2$
45. $6\sqrt{2}$; $(1, 2)$ 47. $f(x)$ is translated 4 units right and
3 units up. 49. $\lim_{x \to \pm\infty} p(x) = \infty$ 51. D 53. D

Section 2.5

1. VA: $x = 0$; HA: $y = 0$; $D = \{x \mid x \neq 0\}$; $R = \{y \mid y < 0\}$
3. VA: $x = -1$; HA: $y = -2$ 5. VA: $x = 3$; HA: $y = 0$

7. VA: $x = -2$; PD at $x = 2$ 9. VA: $x = -4$; PD at $x = -2, 4$
11. B 13. C 15. A 17. C 19. proper; HA: $y = 0$; VA: $x = 4$;
PD at $x = -4$ 21. improper; HA: $y = 2$; VA: $x = \pm 2$
23. improper; SA: $y = x$; VA: $x = \pm 1$
25. improper; NLA: $y = x^2 + 3x + 4$; VA: $x = 2$
27. improper; NLA: $y = 1$; VA: $x = 1$ 29. HA: $y = 0$; VA: $x = 0, x = 4$
y-int.: $(0, -2)$; x-int.: $(-2, 0)$y-int.: none; x-int.: none

31. HA: $y = 0$; VA: $x = 0$ 33. HA: $y = -1$; VA: $x = 0$
y-int.: none; x-int.: none PD at $x = 3$; y-int.: none
x-int.: $(\pm 1, 0)$ x-int.: $(-3, 0)$

---

27. 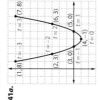 $D = ℝ$; $R = [0, \infty)$

29. $V(1, 4)$; max; y-int.: $(0, 3)$
x-int.: $(3, 0)$, $(-1, 0)$
31. $(f + g)(x) = x^2 - 3x + 2$
$(g - f)(x) = -x^2 + 5x - 6$
$(fg)(x) = x^3 - 6x^2 + 12x - 8$

33. $\frac{f}{g}(x) = x - 2$, $x \neq 2$
$D = \{x \mid x \neq 2\}$
$R = \{y \mid y \neq 0\}$
PD at $x = 2$

35. $f(x) = -2x + 5$, $g(x) = (x - 3)^2$
37. inverses
39. $f^{-1}(x) = \frac{3x + 1}{x}$ or $\frac{1}{x} + 3$

41a.
41b. $y = x^2 - 8x + 15$
43a. $V(t) = 4t$ 43b. $H = \frac{1}{100\pi}V$
43c. $H(t) = \frac{1}{25\pi}t$ 43d. ≈ 2.3 ft
43e. ≈ 314 min or 5 hr 14 min
45. ≈ 1154 ft; 8.4 sec 47. no 49. \$81,300

45. $25a^6 - 49b^2$ 47. $(x + 2)(x - 2)(x - 7)$ 49. 125,794
51. C 53. D

Section 2.2

1a. degree 5; $a_n = 7$ 1b. It is not a polynomial function since
the exponent $-1 \notin \mathbb{W}$. 1c. degree 4; $a_n = -6$ 1d. degree 0;
$a_n = 28$ 3. n is odd; $a_n < 0$ 5. n is even; $a_n > 0$
7. $\lim_{x \to \infty} p(x) = \infty$; $\lim_{x \to -\infty} p(x) = -\infty$ 9. $\lim_{x \to \infty} p(x) = \infty$,
$\lim_{x \to -\infty} p(x) = \infty$ 11. 6 (multiplicity 4) 13. 4 (multiplicity 2);
-1 (multiplicity 3) 15. $p(1) = -3$ and $p(2) = 69$; The sign
change between $x = 1$ and $x = 2$ implies there must be a zero
within $[1, 2]$. 17. 2; 1; $x = 1$ 19. 3; 2; $x = -\frac{1}{4}, 0$ 21. 5; 4;
$x = 0, \pm 1$ 23. 3; 4; $x = 0, \pm\frac{3}{2}, \pm 1$

25. zeros: $-2, \frac{1}{2}, 5$ 27. zeros: -0.5
rel. min.: $(3.21, -50.55)$ rel. min.: $(-0.5, 0)$, $(1.35, 7.46)$
rel. max.: $(-0.88, 18.18)$ rel. max.: $(0.65, 10.29)$
29. zeros: $-\frac{3}{2}, 0, 2$ 31. zeros: $\pm\sqrt{3}, \pm 2$
y-int.: $(0, 0)$ y-int.: $(0, 8)$
$\lim_{x \to \infty} p(x) = -\infty$ $\lim_{x \to \infty} p(x) = \infty$; $\lim_{x \to -\infty} p(x) = \infty$
$\lim_{x \to -\infty} p(x) = -\infty$

33. Real zeros occur between -1 and 0, 1 and 2, and 3 and 4.
35a. $V = 4x^3 - 76x^2 + 360x$ 35b. $D = (0, 9)$ 35c. 504.9 in.³;
13.7 in. $\times$ 11.7 in. $\times$ 3.2 in.
Maximum X=3.1535356 Y=504.91398
37a. neither 37b. even 37c. odd
39. 0 (multiplicity $n - 1$), 1 43. $x^3 - 27$
(multiplicity 1)
45. $(2x - 3)(x + 6)$
47. $x^2 + 3x + 11$ 49. C 51. D

Section 2.3

1. $2x - 3$ R. 13 3. $4x^2 + 22x + 121$ 5. $x^3 - 3x^2 - 2x + 1$
7. $-x^4 + x^3 - 2x^2 + 5x - 1$ R. 1 9. $3x^2 - 5x + 2$
11a. 9 11b. 0 11c. 0 13a. 8 13b. 0 13c. -30
15. 2, 12, 0 17. 2, 0, -12 19. B, D 21a. $x^2 - 4x + 16$
21b. $(x + 4)(x^2 - 4x + 16)$ 23. $p(x) = (x - 1)(x + 1)$; $x = 1$ (multiplicity 2), $\frac{3}{2}, -1$ 27. $p(x) = (3x - 7)(9x^2 + 21x + 49)$; $x = \frac{7}{3}$
29. $p(x) = x^3 - 6x^2 + 12x - 8$ 31. $p(x) = 4x^3 - 24x^2 + 21x - 5$
33. $p(x) = 9x^4 - 10x^2 + 1$ 35a. $p(x) = 0.0568x^4 - 2.0444x^3$
$+ 21.6662x^2 - 49.8841x + 105.6926$ 35b. \$136.52/ft²;
\$289.33/ft² 35c. 2005; 2011 37. $k = 9$ 39. $j = 4$; $k = 5$
41. $3x^5 - 6x^4 + x^3 + 3$ 43. $x = \pm\frac{3}{2}i$ 45. $(-\infty, -2) \cup \left[\frac{1}{4}, \infty\right)$
47. A 49. C

Section 2.1

1. $D = ℝ$; $R = ℝ$; incr.: $(-\infty, \infty)$; cont.; odd
3. $D = [0, \infty)$; $R = [0, \infty)$; incr.: $(0, \infty)$; cont.; neither
5. $D = (-\infty, 4]$; $R = [0, \infty)$; decr.: $(-\infty, 4]$; cont.; neither
9b. odd 9c. neither 9d. neither 9e. even 9a. even
11. $g(x) = x^{4/3}$; $D_g = [0, \infty)$ 13. $g(x) = \sqrt[5]{x^3}$; none
15. $x = -64$ 17. $x = 4$
19. $D = [-3, \infty)$; $R = [0, \infty)$
21.
23. $D = ℝ$; $R = ℝ$

25. $f^{-1}(x) = x^2 + 1$
$D = (-\infty, 2]$; $R = [0, \infty)$
27. $f^{-1}(x) = x^3 + 2$

29. $x = 4$ 31. $x = 19$
33. $x = \pm 8$ 35. $x = 16$
37. 500π ft³ ≈ 1570.8 ft³
39. 11 ohms 41. $x = 0, 1, -4$
43. $y = \pm\sqrt{x + 4}$; If $D_f = [0, \infty)$, then $f^{-1}(x) = \sqrt{x + 4}$.
If $D_f = (-\infty, 0]$, then $f^{-1}(x) = -\sqrt{x + 4}$.

41. Let $\log_b m = x$ and $\log_b n = y$;
$b^x = m$ (exp. form) and $b^y = n$ (exp. form)
$\dfrac{b^x}{b^y} = \dfrac{m}{n}$ (subst.)
$\dfrac{m}{n} = b^{x-y}$ (÷ Prop. of Exp.)
$\log_b \dfrac{m}{n} = x - y$ (log form)
$\log_b \dfrac{m}{n} = \log_b m - \log_b n$ (subst.)

45. inverses **47.** ±1, ±2, ±3, ±6; $f(x) = (x+1)(x+3)(x-2)$
49. $x = \dfrac{3}{2}, \dfrac{3}{4}$ **51.** B **53.** D

C3 Section 3.4

1. 6 **3.** 7 **5.** 1.303 **7.** 1.387 **9.** 0.126 **11.** 4 **13.** 3
15. $2\sqrt{2}$ **17.** $10^{6.2}$ **19.** −4 **21.** 0.463 **23.** −1.768 **25.** 5.585
27. 1.099, 3.178 **29.** no solution **31.** −1 **33.** 400 **35.** −1
37. 4 **39a.** no **39b.** yes **41.** 13 **43.** $\frac{5}{6}$ **45.** ±2
47a. ≈ 0.0236 **47b.** $T(t) = 25 - 45e^{\left(\frac{1}{5}\ln\frac{8}{9}\right)t}$ **47c.** −3.09°C
49. $x = 0, 4$ **51.** $f(x)$ is translated 3 units up.
53. $1 + \frac{2}{3}\log x + \frac{1}{3}\log y$ **55.** B **57.** C

C3 Section 3.5

1a. II **1b.** I **1c.** IV **1d.** III **3.** C **5.** A **7.** C **9.** A
11. $y \approx 76.919\,l(0.8002)^x$; $f(14) \approx 3.4$
13. $y = \dfrac{29.8494}{1 + 12.0516e^{-0.4023x}}$; $f(14) \approx 28.6$
15. $y \approx 1.9927 + 7.9839\ln x$; $f(19) \approx 25.5$
17a. ≈ 0.21%; $P(t) \approx 8.008.278(1.0021)^t$
17b. ≈ 8.3 million **17c.** 2028 **19.** $f(x) = 14.9773(0.9604)^x$
21. ≈ 39,800 ft **23.** $f(x) \approx \dfrac{17,514.32}{1 + 50.258.15e^{-0.1031x}}$ 9200; 11,000
25. $f(x) = 17.3123 \ln x - 56.3763$ **27.** ≈ 1318.5 Hz
29. exponential or power **31.** $y = 19.8050(1.3017)^x$
41. logarithmic (ln x, y); $Y = 4.0125X + 0.9686$
41. logarithmic (ln x, y); $Y = 0.4343X$; $r^2 \approx 1.0000$
43. ≈ 2; ≈ 3; ≈ 4 **45.** HA: $x = 0$; VA: $x = -5$; PD at 5
47. $\left[-4, \frac{5}{3}\right]$ **49.** \$13,938.10 **51.** B **53.** A

C3 Data Analysis

3a. ≈ 60.6 million **3b.** ≈ 7.75 billion **3c.** 2050
5. exponential $(x, \ln y)$; $Y \approx 0.0154X + 0.2450$
7. $P(x) = 1.2776(1.0155)^x$; $r^2 \approx 0.9934$; They are the same.
9a. yes **9c.** at a significantly slower rate

C3 Review

1a. exponential **1b.** exponential **1c.** power

3.
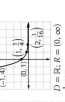
$D = \mathbb{R}$; $R = (0, \infty)$ decay

C2 Data Analysis

3a. quartic
3b. $f(x) \approx 0.113x^4 - 3.140x^3 + 23.225x^2 - 14.897x + 141.900$

C2 Review

1. A, C, D **3.** $D = (-\infty, \infty)$; $R = [2, \infty)$; decr.: $(-\infty, 0]$; incr.: $[0, \infty)$; cont.; even
5. $f^{-1}(x) = (x+1)^2$
$D = [-1, \infty)$

7. $x = \pm 27$
9. $\lim_{x\to-\infty} p(x) = \infty$, $\lim_{x\to\infty} p(x) = -\infty$
11. max: (0, 0); min: (1.66, −5.25), (−0.91, −1.05)
13. $x = \pm 2\sqrt{2}$

15. zeros: ±1, ±2
y-int.: (0, −4)
$\lim_{x\to\pm\infty} p(x) = -\infty$

17. $2x^2 + 3x + 1$ R. 1
19a. $p(2) = -10$
19b. $p(3) = 0$
19c. $p(-1) = 8$
21. $p(x) = (3x - 2)^3$
23. $p(x) = 8x^3 + 2x - 3$
25. $x = -2, 1, 3$
27. $p(x) = x^3 + x^2 - 19x + 5$

29. zeros: −2, 1, 3
y-int.: (0, 6)
$\lim_{x\to-\infty} p(x) = -\infty$
$\lim_{x\to\infty} p(x) = \infty$

31. B
33. VA: $x = 0$; HA: $y = 1$

35. proper; HA: $y = 0$
VA: $x = 6$; PD at
$x = -6$

37. HA: $y = 0$; VA: $x = -2$
PD at $x = 2$; y-int.: $\left(0, \frac{1}{2}\right)$
x-int.: none

39. SA: $y = x - 2$; VA: $x = -1$
y-int.: (0, 0)
x-int.: (0, 0), (1, 0)

41. $n = 34$ **43.** 6 and 12
45. 4.8 hr
47. ≈ 8.6 mi/hr; ≈ 6.58 min/mi
49a. $\left(-3, -\frac{3}{2}\right) \cup (1, \infty)$
49b. $(-\infty, -3) \cup \left(-\frac{1}{2}, 1\right)$
51. $\left[-4, \frac{3}{2}\right]$ **53.** $\left(-\infty, -\frac{4}{3}\right] \cup [2, 4]$

C3 Section 3.1

1a. exponential **1b.** power **1c.** exponential **1d.** power
3a. $\frac{1}{3}$ **3b.** $\frac{1}{2}$ **3c.** $\frac{25}{9}$
5. $D = \mathbb{R}$; $R = (0, \infty)$; growth **7.** $D = \mathbb{R}$; $R = (0, \infty)$; decay

9. $f(x)$ is translated 3 units left and 2 units down.

11. $f(x)$ is reflected in the x-axis and translated 3 units up.

13. $g(x) = 3^{-x} + 2$ **15.** $D = \mathbb{R}$; $R = (0, \infty)$; x-int.: none; y-int.: (0, 1); HA: $y = 0$; $\lim_{x\to-\infty} f(x) = 0$; $\lim_{x\to\infty} f(x) = \infty$
17. $f(x)$ is translated 3 units right and 4 units up; $D = \mathbb{R}$; $R = (4, \infty)$
HA: $y = 4$; x-int.: none; y-int.: (0, 4.05)
$\lim_{x\to-\infty} f(x) = 4$; $\lim_{x\to\infty} f(x) = \infty$

19. $g(x) = e^{(-x+4)}$ implies that $f(x)$ is translated 4 units left and then reflected in the y-axis, or $g(x) = e^{-(x-4)}$ implies that $f(x)$ is reflected in the y-axis and then translated 4 units right.
$D = \mathbb{R}$; $R = (-\infty, 0)$; HA: $y = 0$
x-int.: none; y-int.: (0, 54.60)
$\lim_{x\to-\infty} f(x) = \infty$; $\lim_{x\to\infty} f(x) = 0$

21. $f(x)$ is translated 3 units right, stretched vertically by a factor of 3, then translated 1 unit up.

23. The growth is faster for larger values of b.
25a. $\lim_{x\to-\infty} f(x) = k$; $\lim_{x\to\infty} f(x) = \infty$
25b. $\lim_{x\to-\infty} f(x) = \infty$;
$\lim_{x\to\infty} f(x) = k$ **27a.** ≈ \$10,644.60 **27b.** ≈ \$10,644.93 **27c.** ≈ \$10,644.94
27d. ≈ \$10,644.82 **27e.** ≈ \$10,643.91
29a. Bank A **29b.** Bank B **31.** ≈ 4.43%; ≈ 95,087 sea lions
33. 427 mg **35.** $APY = \left(1 + \frac{APR}{n}\right)^n - 1$
37. $APY_{CD} \approx 2.020\%$; $APY_{MM} \approx 2.269\%$; \$1506.87
39. $f(x) = \frac{1}{27} \cdot 9^x$; $g(x) = \left(\frac{1}{81}\right)^x$; $h(x) = \frac{1}{27} \cdot 9^x$; $f(x)$ and $h(x)$
41a. $(-\infty, 0)$ **41b.** $(0, \infty)$ **43.** Car A: ≈ 19.6%, ≈ \$5180; Car B: 20.3%, ≈ \$4467 **45.** $5x - 8y = -23$
47. When $f(x) = ax^2 + bx + c$ has $b = 0$ and $c = 0$, it is a second-degree power function. **49.** $\frac{9}{7}$ **51.** B **53.** C

C3 Section 3.2

1a. $\log_5 125 = 3$ **1b.** $\log_8 64 = 2$ **1c.** $\log_2 \frac{1}{16} = -4$
1d. $\log_{\frac{1}{3}}\left(\frac{1}{9}\right) = 2$ **3a.** $10^0 = 1$ **3b.** $10^3 = 1000$ **3c.** $10^{0.8451}$
3d. $10^{-2} = 0.01$ **5.** 8 **7.** −3 **9.** $\frac{1}{2}$ **11.** 1 **13.** $\frac{1}{4}$ **15.** 0.001
17. 1 **19.** −4 **21.** 0.4343 **23.** −7 **25.** 4.6052

27.

$y = 4^x$ $(-1, \frac{1}{4})$ $(0, 1)$ $y = \log_4 x$ $(1, 0)$ $(\frac{1}{4}, -1)$
$D = (0, \infty)$; $R = \mathbb{R}$

29.
$y = 8^x$ $(-1, \frac{1}{8})$ $(0, 1)$ $y = \log_8 x$ $(1, 0)$ $(\frac{1}{8}, -1)$
$D = (0, \infty)$; $R = \mathbb{R}$

31. $f(x)$ is translated 3 units down.

33. $f(x)$ is reflected in the x-axis and vertically shrunk by a factor of $\frac{1}{2}$.

35. $g(x) = \ln(5 - x)$

39. ≈ 3.1
41a. ≈ 78
41b. ≈ 70
41c. ≈ 64

C3 Section 3.3

1. $\log x + 3\log y$ **3.** $\ln 7 + 4\ln x$ **5.** $4\ln a - 2\ln b$
7. $\frac{3}{5}\log x - \log y$ **9.** $\log xy^2$ **11.** $\ln \frac{y^3}{9}$ **13.** $\log 10x^{\frac{2}{3}}$
15. 5.6439 **17.** 2.1935 **19.** 3.8640 **21.** −0.3562 **23.** 4.3666
25. $2 + \frac{2}{3}\log x$ **27.** $\frac{1}{2}\log_2 y - \log_2 x + 2$ **29.** $\log \frac{3^x \sqrt[3]{z}}{y^2}$
31. $\ln 16x^3$ **33.** vertical shrink of $f(x)$ by a factor of $\frac{1}{\ln 20}$
35. $R = \frac{\ln A - \ln A_0}{\ln 10}$ **37a.** 29 notes **37b.** 392 Hz
39a. $10^{-7.0}$ moles/L **39b.** ≈ 1.6×10^{-12} moles/L, less
39c. ≈ 5.01×10^{-11} moles/L **39d.** $[H_3O^+][OH^-] = 10^{-14}$

43. $g(x) = \log_4(-x+4) \Rightarrow$ translated 4 units left, then reflected in the y-axis, or $g(x) = \log_4 - (x-4) \Rightarrow$ reflected in the y-axis, then translated 4 units right.
$D = (-\infty, 4)$; $R = \mathbb{R}$
VA: $x = 4$; x-int.: (3, 0)
y-int.: $(0, \approx 0.60)$
$\lim_{x\to-\infty} g(x) = \infty$; $\lim_{x\to 4^-} g(x) = -\infty$

45a. true **45b.** false **45c.** true **47.** 82; 68; 58; 51; 45
49. 3^{x+8} **51.** 2^{7x+12} **53.** $x = 162$ **55.** D **57.** C

(page 671a — left)

5. 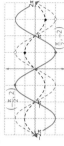 $f(x)$ is translated 3 units right, reflected in the x-axis, and vertically stretched by a factor of 4.
$D = \mathbb{R}; R = (-\infty, 0)$
x-int.: none; y-int.: $(0, -0.5)$
HA: $y = 0$; $\lim_{x\to\infty} g(x) = 0$
$\lim_{x\to-\infty} g(x) = -\infty$

7. $g(x) = -3e^{x-2} - 1$
9. $x \approx 2.81\%$; 125 panthers
11a. $\log_7 49 = 2$ 11b. $\log_{64} 64 = 3$ 11c. $\log_6 \frac{1}{36} = -2$
11d. $\log_{1/5} \frac{1}{125} = 3$ 13. 4 15. 5
17.
$(1, 6)$
$f(x) = 6^x$
$(0, 1)$
$g(x) = \log_6 x$ $(1, 0)$
$\left(\frac{1}{6}, -1\right)$
$D = (0, \infty)$
$R = \mathbb{R}$

19. $f(x)$ is reflected in the x-axis, vertically stretched by a factor of 2, and translated 2 units up.
$D = (0, \infty); R = \mathbb{R}$; VA: $x = 0$
x-int.: $(3, 0)$; y-int.: none
$\lim_{x\to 0^+} f(x) = \infty$; $\lim_{x\to\infty} f(x) = -\infty$

21. $2 \log x + \log y$ 23. $\frac{1}{3}(2 \ln a - 4 \ln b)$ 25. $\log \frac{x^2\sqrt{y}}{z^2}$
27a. ≈ 1.6332 27b. ≈ 1.5343 29a. ≈ 2.2925 29b. ≈ 2.7712
31. $x = -4$ 33. $x = 7$ 35. $x \approx 2.020$ 37. $x = \frac{1}{12}$
39a. $k = -\frac{1}{3}\ln\frac{20}{23} \approx 0.0466$; $T(t) = 71 + 115e^{\left(\frac{1}{3}\ln\frac{20}{23}\right)t}$
39b. $k \approx 143°F$ 41. $\approx 3.50\%$; $P(t) = 465{,}622(1.0350)^t$
41a. 1,100,000 41b. 2018 43. $P(t) = \frac{1706.53}{1 + 95.3535e^{-0.0403t}}$
43a. 1,707,000 43b. 884,000 43c. 2038 45a. logarithmic
45b. power 45c. exponential
47. $Y \approx 4.0223X - 2.1096$; $y \approx 0.1213x^{4.0223}$

Section 4.1
1a. 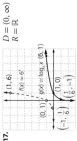 1b. 1c. 1d.
3. $-2°52'12''$ 5. $48°2'143.2''$ 7. $98.762°$ 9. $\frac{7\pi}{36} \approx 0.61$
11. $6\pi \approx 18.85$ 13. $36°$ 15. $15°$

17. A: $\frac{\pi}{4}$; C: $\frac{3\pi}{4}$; E: π; G: $240°$; I: $300°$; K: $\frac{11\pi}{6}$ 19. $148° \pm n360°$,
$508°, -212°$ 21. sample answers: $\frac{\pi}{4} + n2\pi$; $\frac{9\pi}{4}, -\frac{7\pi}{4}$
23. B, C, D 25. $\frac{3\pi}{2}$ 27. $\frac{\pi}{2}$ 29. 9.854 cm; 0.21 cm
31. 4.7 in.; 28.3 in.² 33. 157.1 radians/sec; 165.1 mi/hr
35. $\alpha = \pi + n2\pi$, $n \in \mathbb{Z}$; $\alpha = (1 + 2n)\pi$, and $2n + 1$ is odd.
37. 537 mi or 536 mi 39a. $\frac{\pi}{2} \approx 2.51$ radians/sec
39b. ≈ 41.4 mi/hr 41. 42.2 radians/sec; 42.2 radians/sec;
21.1 radians/sec 43. $D = [-7, \infty)$ 45. $\pm1, \pm2, \pm4, \pm8, \pm16$
47. $P(t) = 2000(1.08)^t$ 49. D 51. A

Section 4.2
1. $\sin A = \frac{\sqrt{21}}{5}$, $\csc A = \frac{5\sqrt{21}}{21}$, $\cos A = \frac{2}{5}$; $\sec A = \frac{5}{2}$
$\tan A = \frac{\sqrt{21}}{2}$, $\cot A = \frac{2\sqrt{21}}{21}$
3. $\sin Q = \frac{\sqrt{2}}{3}$, $\csc Q = \frac{3\sqrt{2}}{4}$, $\cos Q = \frac{1}{3}$; $\sec Q = 3$
$\tan Q = 2\sqrt{2}$; $\cot Q = \frac{\sqrt{2}}{4}$
5. $\sin L \approx 0.1667$; $\csc L = 6$; $\cos L \approx 0.9860$; $\sec L \approx 1.0142$
$\tan L \approx 0.1690$; $\cot L \approx 5.9161$
9. $x \approx 3.4$ 11. $m\angle A \approx 27°$ 13. 64.0 ft
15. $\sin\theta = \frac{24}{25}$, $\tan\theta = \frac{24}{7}$, $\csc\theta = \frac{25}{24}$
$\sec\theta = \frac{25}{7}$, $\cot\theta = \frac{7}{24}$
17. $\sin\theta = \frac{5}{13}$; $\tan\theta = \frac{5}{12}$; $\csc\theta = \frac{13}{5}$; $\cot\theta = \frac{12}{5}$; $\cos\theta = \frac{12}{13}$
19. $\cos\theta \approx 0.8660$; $\tan\theta \approx 0.5774$; $\sec\theta \approx 1.1547$
$\csc\theta = 2$; $\cot\theta \approx 1.732$
21. $\sin 60° = \frac{\sqrt{3}}{2}$; $\cos 60° = \frac{1}{2}$; $\tan 60° = \sqrt{3}$
$\sec 60° = 2$; $\csc 60° = \frac{2\sqrt{3}}{3}$; $\cot 60° = \frac{\sqrt{3}}{3}$
23. $\sin 42° \approx 0.6691$; $\csc 42° \approx 1.4945$; $\cos 42° \approx 0.7431$
$\sec 42° \approx 1.3456$; $\tan 42° \approx 0.9004$; $\cot 42° \approx 1.1106$
25. $b = 7.48$; $a = 14.41$; $b = 6.96$; $B = 25.8°$ 33. $43.0°$
$A = 77.3°$ 29. $a = 14.41$; $b = 6.96$; $B = 56.3°$ 27. $b = 4.51$; $c = 20.50$;
35. 7791 ft 37. 6445.5 ft or 1.2 mi 39. $x \approx 45$; $y \approx 69.0$;
$z \approx 27.9$ 41. ≈ 1839 ft 43a. 7.8 nm 43b. $3.1°, 2.8°$
45. y-int.: $(0, 3)$; VA: $x = -2$; $D = \{x \mid x \neq -2\}$ 47. $x = -1, -2$
49. $\frac{\pi}{5} \approx 0.63$ 51. A 53. E

Section 4.3
1. $\sin\theta = \frac{4\sqrt{17}}{17}$; $\csc\theta = \frac{\sqrt{17}}{4}$; $\cos\theta = \frac{\sqrt{17}}{17}$; $\sec\theta = \sqrt{17}$
$\tan\theta = 4$; $\cot\theta = \frac{1}{4}$
3. $\sin\theta = \frac{2\sqrt{13}}{13}$; $\csc\theta = \frac{\sqrt{13}}{2}$; $\cos\theta = -\frac{3\sqrt{13}}{13}$; $\sec\theta = -\frac{\sqrt{13}}{3}$
$\tan\theta = -\frac{2}{3}$; $\cot\theta = -\frac{3}{2}$
5. $\sin\theta = 1$; $\csc\theta = 1$; $\cos\theta = 0$; $\sec\theta$: undefined
$\tan\theta$: undefined; $\cot\theta = 0$
7. $\alpha = 20°$
9. $\alpha = \frac{\pi}{6}$
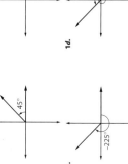

(page 671b — right)

21. $|a| = 2$; $p = 2\pi$; $h = -\pi$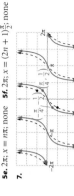
23. $|a| = 1$; $p = \frac{2\pi}{3}$; $h = \frac{\pi}{6}$; $k = 3$; The graph of $f(x)$ is horizontally shrunk by a factor of $\frac{1}{3}$ and translated $\frac{\pi}{6}$ units right and 3 units up.
25.
27.

11. $-\frac{\sqrt{3}}{2}$ 13. $-\sqrt{3}$ 15a. -0.9848 15b. -1.0819 15c. 0.4142
17. $\sin\theta = \frac{21}{29}$; $\cot\theta = -\frac{20}{21}$ 9. $\sin\theta = -\frac{2\sqrt{10}}{7}$; $\cos\theta = \frac{3}{7}$
$\tan\theta = -\frac{2\sqrt{10}}{3}$ 21. $\frac{\sqrt{3}}{2}$ 23. $-\frac{\sqrt{3}}{2}$ 25. $-\frac{2\sqrt{3}}{3}$ 27. $-\sqrt{2}$
29. undefined 31. 1 33. $-\frac{7}{8}$ 35a. at E.P.
35b. 3 in. above E.P. 35c. 0.927 in. below E.P.
35d. 3 in. below E.P. 39. $\Delta h = L(1 - \cos\theta)$
41a. $\cos\theta = a$ and $\cos(\pi - \theta) = -a = -\cos\theta$
41b. $\sin\theta = b$ and $\sin(\pi - \theta) = b = \sin\theta$ 43. $f(x)$ is reflected in the x-axis and stretched vertically by a factor of 4.
45a. II 45b. III 45c. I 47. even 49. C 51. D

Section 4.4
1. $(0, 0)$, $\left(\frac{\pi}{6}, \frac{1}{2}\right)$, $\left(\frac{\pi}{4}, \frac{\sqrt{2}}{2}\right)$, $\left(\frac{\pi}{3}, \frac{\sqrt{3}}{2}\right)$, $\left(\frac{\pi}{2}, 1\right)$, $\left(\frac{2\pi}{3}, \frac{\sqrt{3}}{2}\right)$, $\left(\frac{3\pi}{4}, \frac{\sqrt{2}}{2}\right)$, $\left(\frac{5\pi}{6}, \frac{1}{2}\right)$, $(\pi, 0)$, $\left(\frac{7\pi}{6}, -\frac{1}{2}\right)$, $\left(\frac{5\pi}{4}, -\frac{\sqrt{2}}{2}\right)$, $\left(\frac{4\pi}{3}, -\frac{\sqrt{3}}{2}\right)$, $\left(\frac{3\pi}{2}, -1\right)$, $\left(\frac{5\pi}{3}, -\frac{\sqrt{3}}{2}\right)$, $\left(\frac{7\pi}{4}, -\frac{\sqrt{2}}{2}\right)$, $\left(\frac{11\pi}{6}, -\frac{1}{2}\right)$, $(2\pi, 0)$
3. $\frac{1}{4}$; 2π 5. 2; $\frac{1}{2}$ 7a. The graph of $f(x)$ is vertically stretched by a factor of 3. 7b. The graph of $f(x)$ is reflected in the x-axis, vertically stretched by a factor of 4, and horizontally stretched by a factor of 2. 7c. Since the sine function is odd, $g(x) = -\sin 2x$. The graph of $f(x)$ is reflected in the x-axis and horizontally shrunk by a factor of $\frac{1}{2}$.
9a. $|a| = 1$; $p = \frac{2\pi}{3}$; $f = \frac{3}{2}$ 9b. $|a| = 5$; $p = \frac{1}{5}$; $f = 3$
9c. $|a| = 1$; $p = \pi$; $f = \frac{3}{4}$
11. $|a| = 1$; $p = 2\pi$
13. $|a| = 1$; $p = 2\pi$; $h = \frac{\pi}{2}$
15. $|a| = 2$; $p = \frac{2\pi}{3}$
17. $y = 105 \sin(940\pi t)$
19. $|a| = 1.5$; $p = 3\pi$

29. $f(x) = \pm\sin 4\left(x - \frac{\pi}{8}\right) + 3$ or $f(x) = \pm\sin\left(4x - \frac{\pi}{2}\right) + 3$
31. $f(x) = \pm 3\cos 2\left(x + \frac{\pi}{6}\right) + 4$ or $f(x) = \pm 3\cos\left(2x + \frac{\pi}{3}\right)$
33. $f(x) = 3\sin 2x$ 35. $y = 3\cos 2x - 2$ 37a. 160 mm Hg;
90 mm Hg 37b. $|a| = 35$; $p = \frac{2}{3}$ 37c. 1 sec; 60 times
41a. 9:48 PM; 10:12 AM 41b. $d(t) = 10.2\cos\frac{\pi}{6.2}(t - 4) + 15.67$
41c. 23.41 ft 41d. 12:54 AM, 7:06 AM, 1:18 PM, 7:30 PM
43b. $[-1.7, 1.7]$ 45. $f(x) = x^4 - 23x^2 + 24x + 144$
47. 5 49. when the leading coefficients are additive inverses
51. B 53. D

Section 4.5
1. $\left(-\frac{\pi}{3}, -\sqrt{3}\right)$, $\left(-\frac{\pi}{4}, -1\right)$, $\left(-\frac{\pi}{6}, -\frac{\sqrt{3}}{3}\right)$, $(0, 0)$, $\left(\frac{\pi}{6}, \frac{\sqrt{3}}{3}\right)$, $\left(\frac{\pi}{4}, 1\right)$, $\left(\frac{\pi}{3}, \sqrt{3}\right)$,
3. $\left(\frac{\pi}{6}, 2\right)$, $\left(\frac{\pi}{4}, \sqrt{2}\right)$, $\left(\frac{\pi}{3}, \frac{2\sqrt{3}}{3}\right)$, $\left(\frac{\pi}{2}, 1\right)$, $\left(\frac{2\pi}{3}, \frac{2\sqrt{3}}{3}\right)$, $\left(\frac{3\pi}{4}, \sqrt{2}\right)$, $\left(\frac{5\pi}{6}, 2\right)$,
$\left(\frac{3\pi}{4}, \sqrt{2}\right)$, $\left(\frac{5\pi}{6}, -\sqrt{2}\right)$, $\left(\frac{7\pi}{6}, -2\right)$, $\left(\frac{5\pi}{4}, -\sqrt{2}\right)$, $\left(\frac{4\pi}{3}, -\frac{2\sqrt{3}}{3}\right)$,
$\left(\frac{3\pi}{2}, -1\right)$, $\left(\frac{5\pi}{3}, -\frac{2\sqrt{3}}{3}\right)$, $\left(\frac{11\pi}{6}, -2\right)$
5a. 2π; none 5b. 2π; none; $(2n + 1)\frac{\pi}{2}$ 5d. π; $x = n\pi$
5c. π; $x = (2n + 1)\frac{\pi}{2}$; $n\pi$ 5f. 2π; $x = (2n + 1)\frac{\pi}{2}$; none
5e. 2π; $x = n\pi$; none
7.

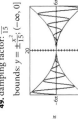

23a. $\frac{\sqrt{2}}{2}$ **23b.** $-\frac{1}{2}$

25. $|a| = \frac{1}{2}$; $p = 2\pi$; vertical shift up 2 units

27. $|a| = 1$; $p = \pi$ phase shift left $\frac{\pi}{2}$ units vertical shift down 1 unit

29. $y = -2 \cos \pi x - 4$

31. $p = 2\pi$ VA: $x = (2n+1)\frac{\pi}{2}$, $n \in \mathbb{Z}$ zeros: none

33.

35. The graph of $f(x)$ is reflected in the x-axis, stretched horizontally and vertically by a factor of 2, and translated right 2π units. **37a.** II **37b.** III **37c.** I **41b.** undefined **41c.** $\approx 0.8727 \approx 50°$

41a. $\approx 0.6405 \approx 36.7°$ **43b.** $\frac{3}{2}$ **45.** $\frac{3\pi}{2} = 135°$

43a. $-\frac{\pi}{6}$ **47.** bounds: $y = \frac{x^2}{3} \pm 2$

49. damping factor: $\frac{x^2}{15}$ bounds: $y = \pm\frac{x^2}{15}$; $(-\infty, 0]$

51. $y = e^{-0.5x} \sin (4x - \pi)$

C5 Section 5.1

1a. $\frac{1}{\cos \theta} = \frac{1}{\frac{x}{r}} = \frac{r}{x} = \sec \theta$ **1b.** $\frac{\cos \theta}{\sin \theta} = \frac{\frac{x}{r}}{\frac{y}{r}} = \frac{x}{y} = \cot \theta$

3a. $\tan \left(\frac{\pi}{2} - \theta\right) = \frac{b}{a} = \cot \theta$ **3b.** $\sec \left(\frac{\pi}{2} - \theta\right) = \frac{c}{a} = \csc \theta$

5. $\sin \theta = \frac{2\sqrt{2}}{3}$; $\tan \theta = 2\sqrt{2}$ **7.** $\sec \theta = -\frac{17}{8}$; $\cos \theta = -\frac{8}{17}$

9. B, D **11.** 0.27 **13.** 0.35 **15.** 1 **17.** -1 **19.** $-\tan x$

21. $-\tan^3 x$ **23.** B **25.** B **27.** $\sec^2 \theta$ **29.** $2 \csc x$

31. $2 \cot^2 x$ **33.** $1 + \sin x$ **35.** $\tan x + \sin x$

37. $-2 \ln |\sin x|$ **39.** $f(g(x)) = 7 |\sin \theta|$ **41.** $v_c = -V_c \cos (\omega t)$

43. $\frac{3x+1}{2x-3}$ **45.** $\frac{5x+6}{2x^2+4x}$ **47.** by raising both sides to an even power or by multiplying both sides by a variable expression **49.** A **51.** C

C5 Section 5.2

1. not an identity **3.** appears to be an identity

5. $\csc x \sin x = \frac{1}{\left(\frac{\sin x}{1}\right)}\left(\frac{\sin x}{1}\right) = 1$

7. $\sec \theta - \sin \theta \tan \theta = \frac{1}{\cos \theta} - \sin \theta \left(\frac{\sin \theta}{\cos \theta}\right)$
$= \frac{1 - \sin^2 \theta}{\cos \theta} = \frac{\cos^2 \theta}{\cos \theta} = \cos \theta$

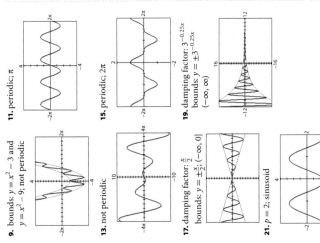

9. bounds: $y = x^2 - 3$ and $y = x^2 - 9$; not periodic

11. periodic; π

13. not periodic

15. periodic; 2π

17. damping factor: $\frac{x}{2}$ bounds: $y = \pm\frac{x}{2}$; $(-\infty, 0]$

19. damping factor: $3^{-0.25x}$ bounds: $y = \pm 3^{-0.25x}$; $(-\infty, \infty)$

21. $p = 2$; sinusoid

23. C **25.** A **27.** C **29.** A **31.** C **33.** B **35.** A

37. $y = 0.2x^2 \sin (\pi x - \pi^2)$ **39.** 0.12 cm **41.** $\sec x \cos x = 1$; Secant and cosine are reciprocal functions.

43. $f(x) \approx 1.41 \cos (x - 0.79)$ **45.** $f^{-1}(x) = \frac{3}{2}x + \frac{15}{2}$

47. $\sin x = \frac{2\sqrt{53}}{53}$ **49.** $x = n\pi$, $n \in \mathbb{Z}$ **51.** A **53.** D

C4 Data Analysis

5a. ≈ 10.22 yr **5b.** $y \approx 75.6$ **5c.** $|a| \approx 65.7$ **5d.** $\approx [9.9, 141.3]$

5e. $h \approx -2.39$

C4 Review

1a. $168°19'12''$ **1b.** $29.621°$ **3a.** $-18°$ **3b.** $-75°$ **3c.** $\approx 160.43°$

5. $\alpha = -175° \pm n360°$; $185°, -535°$ **7.** ≈ 136.1 radians/sec

9. $\sin A = \frac{2\sqrt{6}}{7}$; $\csc A = \frac{7\sqrt{6}}{12}$; $\cos A = \frac{5\sqrt{6}}{12}$; $\sec A = \frac{7}{5}$

$\tan A = \frac{2\sqrt{6}}{5}$; $\cot A = \frac{5\sqrt{6}}{12}$ **11.** $\sin \theta = 0.514$; $\csc \theta = 1.9437$

$\cos \theta = 0.8575$; $\cot \theta = 1.1662$; $\sec \theta = 1.6667$ **13.** $d = 7.1$

15. $b = \sqrt{21}$; $B = 24°37'$; $A = 65°23'$ **17.** $\sin \theta = -\frac{6\sqrt{61}}{61}$;

$\csc \theta = \frac{\sqrt{61}}{6}$; $\cos \theta = \frac{5\sqrt{61}}{61}$; $\sec \theta = \frac{\sqrt{61}}{5}$; $\tan \theta = -\frac{6}{5}$;

$\cot \theta = -\frac{5}{6}$ **19.** $\frac{\sqrt{3}}{3}$ **21.** $\sin \theta = 0$; $\csc \theta = $ undefined;

$\cos \theta = 1$; $\sec \theta = 1$; $\tan \theta = 0$; $\cot \theta = $ undefined

---

C4 Section 4.6

1.

3. 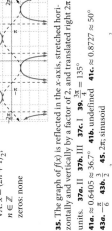 $D = \left[-\frac{\pi}{2}, \frac{\pi}{2}\right]$; $R = [-1, 1]$

5. $D = \left(-\frac{\pi}{2}, \frac{\pi}{2}\right)$; $R = (-\infty, \infty)$

7. $\frac{\pi}{3} = 60°$ **9.** $\frac{2\pi}{3} = 120°$

11. $-\frac{\pi}{4} = -45°$ **13.** $\approx 0.3490 \approx 20.0°$

15. $\approx 2.3657 \approx 135.5°$ **17.** $[-1, 1]$ **19.** $[0, \pi]$ **21.** $\frac{5\pi}{6}$

23. $\frac{\pi}{3}$ **25.** $\frac{3}{4}$ **27.** $\frac{\sqrt{2}}{2}$ **29.** $\frac{4}{5}$

31. $\frac{2}{3}$ **33.** $f(t) = \sqrt{1 - t^2}$

35. $h(t) = \frac{1}{t}$

37a. $\approx 27.4°, \approx 22.5°$ **37b.** $\theta = \tan^{-1} \frac{24}{d} - \tan^{-1} \frac{6}{d}$ **37c.** $\approx 36.9°$ at 12 ft

37d. ≈ 2.6 ft; ≈ 56.3 ft

39. [graph with $g(x) = \mathrm{Csc}\ x$, $g^{-1}(x)$]

41. $\mathrm{Csc}\ (\mathrm{Csc}^{-1}\ t) = \mathrm{Csc}\ \theta$
$t = \mathrm{Csc}\ \theta$
$t = \frac{1}{\sin \theta}$
$\sin \theta = \frac{1}{t}$
$\theta = \mathrm{Sin}^{-1} \frac{1}{t}$
$\therefore \mathrm{Csc}^{-1} x = \mathrm{Sin}^{-1} \frac{1}{x}$ **51.** D **53.** E

43a. $\tan \theta = \frac{\Delta y}{\Delta x}$ **43b.** its slope

43c. $y = 6x - 9$ **43d.** $\approx 80.5°$

45. $f(g(x)) = 4x^2 + 8x + 4$

47. [figure labeled -330]

49. $y = 3$ $D = \left[-\frac{\pi}{2}, 0\right) \cup \left(0, \frac{\pi}{2}\right]$

C4 Section 4.7

1. 2π; sinusoid **3.** 4; not a sinusoid

5. 4π; sinusoid **7.** bounds: $y = x \pm 3$ not periodic

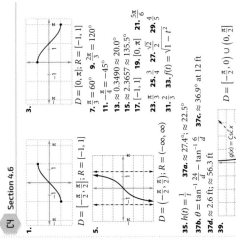

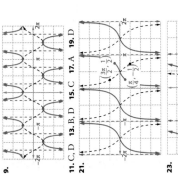

9.

11. C, D **13.** B, D **15.** C **17.** A **19.** D

21.

23.

25.

27. The graph of $f(x) = \csc x$ is shifted 2 units left (phase shift of -2). It is also vertically stretched by a factor of 4 before being shifted 8 units down. **29.** The graph of $f(x) = \cot x$ is horizontally shrunk by a factor of π ($p = 2$) before being shifted $\frac{1}{3}$ unit left $\left(h = -\frac{1}{3}\right)$. It is also vertically shrunk by a factor of $\frac{1}{3}$ and reflected across the x-axis. **35.** $y = \cos x$ or $y = \cot x$

37a. $d(t) = \frac{20}{\tan (90 - \theta)}$ **37b.** 14 ft **37c.** 58 ft; the fifth floor

39. $g(x) = \sin \left(x + \frac{\pi}{2} + n2\pi\right)$; $g(x) = -\sin \left(x - \frac{\pi}{2} + n2\pi\right)$

41. since $\triangle POQ \sim \triangle TOR$ by the AA $\sim$ Post., $\frac{TR}{PQ} = \frac{OR}{OQ}$; therefore, $\frac{TR}{\sin \theta} = \frac{1}{\cos \theta}$ and $TR = \frac{\sin \theta}{\cos \theta} = \tan \theta$

43. VA: $x = -1$; HA: $y = 0$; $D = \{x \mid x \neq -1\}$; $R = \{y \mid y \neq 0\}$ **49.** D **51.** C

45. $\frac{\pi}{5} \pm n2\pi$; $\frac{11\pi}{5}, \frac{9\pi}{5}$ **47.** 1.9

673a — Selected Odd Answers

9. $(1-\cos x)(1+\sec x)$
$= 1 + \sec x - \cos x$
$\quad -\cos x\sec x$
$= 1 + \sec x - \cos x$
$\quad -\cos x\left(\frac{1}{\cos x}\right)$
$= \sec x - \cos x$

11. $\cos\theta - \cos\theta\sin^2\theta$
$= \cos\theta(1-\sin^2\theta)$
$= \cos\theta(\cos^2\theta)$
$= \cos^3\theta$

13. working on both sides:
$\frac{\sin^2 x}{-1}$
$-\frac{\cos^2 x}{\sin^2 x} = -\left(\frac{\cos x}{\sin x}\right)\cos\theta$
$-\frac{\cos^2 x}{\sin^2 x} = -\frac{\cos^2 x}{\sin^2 x}$

15. $\cos^4 x = (\cos^2 x)^2$
$= (1-\sin^2 x)^2$
$= 1 - 2\sin^2 x + \sin^4 x$

17. $\csc\theta - \cot\theta$
$= \frac{1}{\sin\theta} - \frac{\cos\theta}{\sin\theta}$
$= \frac{1-\cos\theta}{\sin\theta}$
$= \frac{1-\cos\theta}{\sin\theta}\cdot\frac{1+\cos\theta}{1+\cos\theta}$
$= \frac{1-\cos^2\theta}{\sin\theta(1+\cos\theta)}$
$= \frac{\sin^2\theta}{\sin\theta(1+\cos\theta)}$
$= \frac{\sin\theta}{1+\cos\theta}$

19. $\frac{1+\cos\theta}{\sin\theta} + \frac{\sin\theta}{1+\cos\theta}$
$= \frac{1+\cos\theta}{\sin\theta}\left(\frac{1+\cos\theta}{1+\cos\theta}\right)$
$\quad + \frac{\sin\theta}{1+\cos\theta}\left(\frac{\sin\theta}{\sin\theta}\right)$
$= \frac{(1+\cos\theta)^2}{\sin\theta(1+\cos\theta)} + \frac{\sin^2\theta}{\sin\theta(1+\cos\theta)}$
$= \frac{1 + 2\cos\theta + \cos^2\theta + \sin^2\theta}{\sin\theta(1+\cos\theta)}$
$= \frac{2 + 2\cos\theta}{\sin\theta(1+\cos\theta)}$
$= \frac{2(1+\cos\theta)}{\sin\theta(1+\cos\theta)}$
$= \frac{2}{\sin\theta} = 2\csc\theta$

21. $\frac{\sec^2 x - 3\sec x + 2}{\sec^2 x - 1}$
$= \frac{(\sec x - 2)(\sec x - 1)}{(\sec x + 1)(\sec x - 1)}$
$= \frac{\sec x - 2}{\sec x + 1}$

23. $(\csc x - \cot x)^2$
$= \left(\frac{1}{\sin x} - \frac{\cos x}{\sin x}\right)^2$
$= \left(\frac{1-\cos x}{\sin x}\right)^2$
$= \frac{(1-\cos x)^2}{\sin^2 x}$
$= \frac{(1-\cos x)^2}{1-\cos^2 x}$
$= \frac{(1-\cos x)^2}{(1-\cos x)(1+\cos x)}$
$= \frac{1-\cos x}{1+\cos x}$

25. $\frac{\csc x}{\csc x + 1}\cdot\frac{\csc x - 1}{\csc x - 1}$
$= \frac{\csc x(\csc x - 1)}{\csc^2 x - 1}$
$= \frac{\csc x(\csc x - 1)}{\cot^2 x}$
$= \frac{\csc x - 1}{\cot^2 x}\cdot\frac{1}{\csc x}$
$= \frac{\csc x}{\cot^2 x}(\csc x - 1)$
$= \cot x\csc x(\csc x - 1)$

27. working on the left side:
$\csc^4\theta - \cot^4\theta$
$= (1 + \cot^2\theta)^2 - \cot^4\theta$
$= 1 + 2\cot^2\theta + \cot^4\theta - \cot^4\theta$
$= 2\cot^2\theta + 1$
working on the right side:
$\csc^2\theta + \cot^2\theta$
$= (1 + \cot^2\theta) + \cot^2\theta$
$= 2\cot^2\theta + 1$

29. $\csc^4 x = (\csc^2 x)(\csc^2 x)$
$= (\cot^2 x + 1)\csc^2 x$
$= \cot^2 x\csc^2 x + \csc^2 x$

31. not an identity
counterexample:
$\frac{1}{1-\sin\left(\frac{\pi}{6}\right)} + \frac{1}{1+\sin\left(\frac{\pi}{6}\right)}$
$= \frac{1}{1-\frac{1}{2}} + \frac{1}{1+\frac{1}{2}} = 2 + \frac{2}{3} = \frac{8}{3}$
$2\csc^2\left(\frac{\pi}{6}\right) = \frac{2}{\left(\frac{1}{2}\right)^2}$
$= \frac{2}{\left(\frac{1}{2}\right)^2} = 8 \neq \frac{8}{3}$

33. appears to be an identity
working on the left side: $\frac{\csc x + \cot x}{\csc x - \cot x}$
working on the right side:
$\frac{\cos^2 x + 2\cos x + 1}{\sin^2 x}$
$\frac{(\csc x + \cot x)^2}{\csc^2 x - \cot^2 x} = \csc^2 x + 2\cot x\csc x + \cot^2 x$
$= \frac{\cos^2 x + 2\cos x + 1}{\sin^2 x} = \cot^2 x + 2\cot x\csc x + \csc^2 x$

35. $\sqrt{\frac{\sec x + 1}{\sec x - 1}}$
$= \sqrt{\frac{\sec x + 1}{\sec x - 1}\cdot\frac{\sec x + 1}{\sec x + 1}}$
$= \sqrt{\frac{(\sec x + 1)^2}{\sec^2 x - 1}}$
$= \sqrt{\frac{(\sec x + 1)^2}{\tan^2 x}}$
$= \left|\frac{\sec x + 1}{\tan x}\right|$

37. $\frac{\cos\theta}{\csc\theta - 1} - \frac{\sin\theta}{\sec\theta - 1}$
$= \frac{\cos\theta}{\frac{1}{\sin\theta} - 1} - \frac{\sin\theta}{\frac{1}{\cos\theta} - 1}$
$= \frac{\cos\theta}{\frac{1-\sin\theta}{\sin\theta}} - \frac{\sin\theta}{\frac{1-\cos\theta}{\cos\theta}}$
$= \frac{\sin\theta\cos\theta}{1-\sin\theta} - \frac{\sin\theta\cos\theta}{1-\cos\theta}$
$= \sin\theta\cos\theta\left(\frac{\cos\theta}{1+\cos^2\theta} - \frac{\sin\theta}{1+\cos^2\theta}\right)$
$= \frac{\tan\theta}{1+\cos^2\theta}$

39. $\cosh^2 x - \sinh^2 x$
$= \left[\frac{1}{2}(e^x + e^{-x})\right]^2 - \left[\frac{1}{2}(e^x - e^{-x})\right]^2$
$= \frac{1}{4}[(e^x + e^{-x})^2 - (e^x - e^{-x})^2]$
$= \frac{1}{4}[(e^{2x} + 2e^0 + e^{-2x}) - (e^{2x} - 2e^0 + e^{-2x})]$
$= \frac{1}{4}[4] = 1$

41. $\text{sech}(-x) = \frac{1}{\cosh(-x)} = \frac{1}{\frac{1}{2}(e^{-x} + e^{-(-x)})} = \text{sech }x$

43. $y = -\frac{3x}{x-1}$

45a. $\frac{\sqrt3}{3}$ **45b.** $\frac{\sqrt3}{2}$ **45c.** $\frac{\sqrt2}{2}$ **47.** $\frac{\sqrt3}{2}$ **49.** C **51.** D

Section 5.3

1. $x = \frac{3\pi}{2}, \frac{3\pi}{4}, \frac{7\pi}{4}$ **3.** $x = \frac{\pi}{4}, \frac{3\pi}{4}, \frac{5\pi}{4}, \frac{7\pi}{4}$ **5.** $x = \frac{\pi}{3}, \frac{2\pi}{3}, \frac{4\pi}{3}, \frac{5\pi}{3}$
7. $x = \frac{\pi}{4}, \frac{3\pi}{4}, \frac{5\pi}{4}, \frac{7\pi}{4}$ **9.** $x = \frac{\pi}{6}, \frac{5\pi}{6}, \frac{3\pi}{2}$ **11.** $x = 0, \frac{\pi}{2}$
13. $x = \frac{\pi}{3}, \frac{5\pi}{3}$ **15.** $x \approx 0, 1.32, 3.14, 4.97$ **17.** $x = \frac{\pi}{12}, \frac{5\pi}{12}, \frac{13\pi}{12}, \frac{17\pi}{12}$
19. $x = \frac{\pi}{4} + \frac{n\pi}{2}$ **21.** $x = \frac{\pi}{6} + n2\pi, (2n+1)\pi, \frac{5\pi}{6} + n2\pi$ **25.** $x = n2\pi, \frac{4\pi}{3} + n2\pi, \frac{4\pi}{3} + n2\pi$ **31.** $\emptyset$
23. $x = \frac{\pi}{7} + n\pi, \frac{11\pi}{6} + n2\pi$ **27.** $x = \frac{\pi}{6} + n2\pi, \frac{11\pi}{6} + n2\pi$ **29.** $x = \frac{n\pi}{3}$
33. $x \approx 0.73, 2.41$ **35.** $x \approx 0, 0.59, 3.14, 3.73$ **37.** $34.2°$
39. $x \approx 0.44, 1.69, 3.58, 4.83$ **41.** $x = \frac{\pi}{3}, \frac{2\pi}{3}, \frac{3\pi}{4}, \frac{4\pi}{3}, \frac{5\pi}{3}, \frac{7\pi}{4}$
43. $x = \frac{5 + \sqrt{17}}{4}$ **45.** $x = -\frac{2}{2}$; $\ln\frac{3}{2} \approx -0.55$ **47.** $x = 21$
49. C **51.** B

Biblical Perspective of Mathematics

3a. π **3b.** e **3c.** $\frac{\pi^2}{6}$ **5.** 1.618034

Section 5.4

1. $\frac{-\sqrt6 - \sqrt2}{4}$ **3.** $-2 - \sqrt3$ **5.** $\cos\frac{11\pi}{12}$ **7.** $\frac{\sqrt2 - \sqrt6}{4}$ **9.** $\frac{\sqrt2 - \sqrt6}{4}$
11. $\frac{\sqrt6 - \sqrt2}{4}$ **13.** $-2 + \sqrt3$
15a. $\tan\left(\frac{\pi}{2} - \theta\right) = \frac{\sin\left(\frac{\pi}{2} - \theta\right)}{\cos\left(\frac{\pi}{2}-\theta\right)} = \frac{\cos\theta}{\sin\theta} = \cot\theta$
15b. $\csc\left(\frac{\pi}{2} - \theta\right) = \frac{1}{\sin\left(\frac{\pi}{2}-\theta\right)} = \frac{1}{\cos\theta} = \sec\theta$
17. $\frac{253}{325}$ **19.** $\frac{-6 - 4\sqrt5}{15}$ **21.** $\frac{x + \sqrt{3 - 3x^2}}{2}$ **23.** 1

673b — Selected Odd Answers

25. $\sin(\alpha+\beta)$
$= \sin[\alpha - (-\beta)]$
$= \sin\alpha\cos(-\beta)$
$\quad -\cos\alpha\sin(-\beta)$
$= \sin\alpha\cos\beta$
$\quad -\cos\alpha(-\sin\beta)$
$= \sin\alpha\cos\beta$
$\quad + \cos\alpha\sin\beta$

27. $\tan(\alpha - \beta)$
$= \tan(\alpha + (-\beta))$
$= \frac{\tan\alpha + \tan(-\beta)}{1 - \tan\alpha\tan(-\beta)}$
$= \frac{\tan\alpha - \tan\beta}{1 + \tan\alpha\tan\beta}$

29a. $\sin(\pi - \theta)$
$= \sin\pi\cos\theta - \cos\pi\sin\theta$
$= (0)\cos\theta - (-1)\sin\theta$
$= \sin\theta$

31. working on both sides:
$\sin\left(\frac{\pi}{2} - \theta\right) = \sin\left(\frac{\pi}{2} + \theta\right)$
$\cos\theta = (1)\cos\theta + (0)\sin\theta$
$\cos\theta = \cos\theta$
$= \sin\frac{\pi}{2}\cos\theta + \cos\frac{\pi}{2}\sin\theta$
$\cos\theta = \cos\theta$

33. $[\cos(\alpha - \beta)][\cos(\alpha + \beta)]$
$= (\cos\alpha\cos\beta + \sin\alpha\sin\beta)$
$\quad\cdot(\cos\alpha\cos\beta - \sin\alpha\sin\beta)$
$= \cos^2\alpha\cos^2\beta - \sin^2\alpha\sin^2\beta$
$= \cos^2\alpha(1 - \sin^2\beta)$
$\quad - \sin^2\alpha\sin^2\beta$
$= \cos^2\alpha - \cos^2\alpha\sin^2\beta$
$\quad - \sin^2\alpha\sin^2\beta$
$= \cos^2\alpha - \sin^2\beta\cos^2\alpha$
$\quad - \sin^2\beta\sin^2\alpha$
$= \cos^2\alpha - \sin^2\beta$

35. $\cot\alpha + \tan\beta$
$\cot\alpha - \tan\beta$
$= \frac{\cos\alpha}{\sin\alpha} + \frac{\sin\beta}{\cos\beta}$
$\quad\quad\frac{\cos\alpha}{\sin\alpha} - \frac{\sin\beta}{\cos\beta}$
$= \frac{\cos\alpha\cos\beta + \sin\alpha\sin\beta}{\cos\alpha\cos\beta - \sin\alpha\sin\beta}$
$= \frac{\cos\alpha\cos\beta + \sin\alpha\sin\beta}{\cos\alpha\cos\beta - \sin\alpha\sin\beta}$
$= \frac{\cos(\alpha - \beta)}{\cos(\alpha + \beta)}$

37. $x = 0, \pi, \frac{3\pi}{2}$ **39.** $x = 0, \pi$
41a. $\sin 2\theta = \sin(\theta + \theta)$
$= \sin\theta\cos\theta + \cos\theta\sin\theta$
$= 2\sin\theta\cos\theta$

43. $y = y_1 + y_2$
$= A_0\sin(kx - \omega t)$
$\quad + A_0\sin(kx + \omega t)$
$= A_0[\sin kx\cos\omega t$
$\quad - \sin\omega t\cos kx$
$\quad + \sin kx\cos\omega t$
$\quad + \sin\omega t\cos kx]$
$= (2A_0\sin kx)\cos\omega t$

45a. 5 **45b.** 4 **45c.** −3 **45d.** $\frac{1}{2}$
47. $(fg)(x) = 4x^3 + 8x^2 + 2x - 3$
49. $(f \circ g)(x) = 4x^2 + 2x - 3$; $(g \circ f)(x) = 8x^2 + 26x + 18$
51. C **53.** E

23. $\tan^4\theta = \frac{3 - 4\cos 2\theta + \cos 4\theta}{3 + 4\cos 2\theta + \cos 4\theta}$
25. $x = n4\pi$ or $\pi + n2\pi, n \in \mathbb{Z}$
27. $x = n2\pi, \frac{2\pi}{3} + n2\pi, \frac{4\pi}{3} + n2\pi, n \in \mathbb{Z}$
29a. $\frac{1}{2}[\sin(\alpha + \beta) + \sin(\alpha - \beta)]$
$= \frac{1}{2}(\sin\alpha\cos\beta + \sin\beta\cos\alpha + \sin\alpha\cos\beta - \sin\beta\cos\alpha)$
$= \frac{1}{2}(2\sin\alpha\cos\beta) = \sin\alpha\cos\beta$
29b. $\frac{1}{2}[\cos(\alpha - \beta) - \cos(\alpha + \beta)]$
$= \frac{1}{2}(\cos\alpha\cos\beta + \sin\alpha\sin\beta - (\cos\alpha\cos\beta - \sin\alpha\sin\beta))$
$= \frac{1}{2}(2\sin\alpha\sin\beta) = \sin\alpha\sin\beta$
31. $\frac{1}{2}\cos x + \frac{1}{2}\cos 5x$ **33.** $\frac{1}{2}(\sin 2a - \sin 2b)$
35. $2A_0\left[\cos 2\pi\left(\frac{f_1 - f_2}{2}\right)t\right]\left[\cos 2\pi\left(\frac{f_1 + f_2}{2}\right)t\right]$
37. $\frac{\pi}{4} + \frac{n\pi}{2}, 0 + n\pi$
39. $\frac{\pi}{4}, \frac{\pi}{2}$
41. $\sin^4 x - \cos^4 x$
$= (\sin^2 x - \cos^2 x)(\sin^2 x + \cos^2 x) = -(1 - 2\sin^2 x) = 2\sin^2 x - 1$
43. $\frac{\sin 3x}{\sin x} - \frac{\cos 3x}{\cos x}$
$= \frac{\sin 3x\cos x - \cos 3x\sin x}{\sin x\cos x}$
$= \frac{\sin(3x - x)}{\sin x\cos x}$
$= \frac{\sin 2x}{\sin x\cos x}$
$= \frac{2\sin x\cos x}{\sin x\cos x} = 2$
45a. $\frac{\sqrt{2 + \sqrt3}}{2}$ **45b.** $\frac{\sqrt{2 + \sqrt3}}{2}$
47a. $\tan\frac{\theta}{2} = \pm\sqrt{\frac{1-\cos\theta}{1+\cos\theta}}$
$= \pm\sqrt{\frac{1-\cos\theta}{1+\cos\theta}}\cdot\sqrt{\frac{1-\cos\theta}{1-\cos\theta}}$
$= \pm\sqrt{\frac{(1-\cos\theta)^2}{\sin^2\theta}} = \pm\left|\frac{1-\cos\theta}{\sin\theta}\right|$
47c. The signs are always the same.
49. $\frac{3}{2}; (-4, 0); (0, 6)$ **51.** 17 **53.** $p = 2; f = \frac{1}{2}$ **55.** E **57.** B

Section 5.5

1a. $\sin(\theta + \theta)$
$= \sin\theta\cos\theta + \cos\theta\sin\theta$
$= 2\sin\theta\cos\theta$
1b. $\tan(\theta + \theta) = \frac{\tan\theta + \tan\theta}{1 - \tan\theta\tan\theta}$
$= \frac{2\tan\theta}{1 - \tan^2\theta}$
3. $-\frac{7}{25}, -\frac{24}{25}, \frac{24}{7}$ **5.** $\frac{1}{2}, \frac{\sqrt3}{2}, \sqrt3$
7a. $\cos 2\theta = 2\cos^2\theta - 1$
$1 + \cos 2\theta = 2\cos^2\theta$
$\cos^2\theta = \frac{1 + \cos 2\theta}{2}$
7b. $\tan^2\theta = \frac{1 - \cos 2\theta}{1 + \cos 2\theta}$
9. $\frac{\sqrt{2 - \sqrt2}}{2}$ **11.** $-\sqrt{2 - \sqrt2}$
13. $x = 0, \frac{\pi}{3}, \pi, \frac{5\pi}{3}$
15. $x = \frac{\pi}{2}, \frac{3\pi}{2}, \frac{2\pi}{3}, \frac{4\pi}{3}$ **17.** $\cos 3\theta = 4\cos^3\theta - 3\cos\theta$
19. $\cos 4\theta = 8\cos^4\theta - 8\cos^2\theta + 1$
21. $\sin^3\theta = \frac{1}{2}(\sin\theta - \sin\theta\cos 2\theta)$

Section 5.6

1a. AAS **1b.** SSA **1c.** ASA **1d.** SSA **3.** $a = 6.1; b = 7.9$;
$B = 100°$ **5.** $R = 28°; s = 15.8; t = 16.9$ **7.** $C = 79°; a = 12.8$;
$b = 12.3$ **9.** $E = 115°; e = 16.2; f = 12.0$ **11.** $A = 51.3°$;
$B = 58.7°; a = 9.1$ **13.** $L = 68.3°; N = 29.7°; l = 16.9$ **15.** one
17. one **19.** zero **21.** $B = 35.8°; C = 127.2°; c = 8.2$ or
$B = 144.2°; C = 18.8°; c = 3.3$ **23.** $F = 74.3°; G = 59.7°; f = 6.7$
or $F = 13.7°; G = 120.3°; f = 1.6$

Section 6.3

1a. 5 **1b.** 8 **1c.** 3 **1d.** yz-plane (between 3 and 4) **1e.** 7 **1f.** 6

3.

5.

7.

9.

11. $2\sqrt{21}$; $(2, 3, -3)$ **13.** $\sqrt{(2x-2)^2 + (2y-4)^2 + (2z-6)^2}$; $(x+1, y+2, z+3)$ **15.** ≈ 1781.3 ft **17.** $a = 212$; $b = 562$; $c = 1.5$ **19.** $(12, 4, 3)$; 13; $\left\langle \frac{12}{13}, \frac{4}{13}, \frac{3}{13} \right\rangle$ **21.** $(5, -8, 9)$; ≈ 13.04; $\left\langle \frac{\sqrt{170}}{34}, -\frac{4\sqrt{170}}{85}, \frac{9\sqrt{170}}{170} \right\rangle$ **23.** $\langle -2, 1, -2 \rangle$ **25.** $\langle 16, 1, -5 \rangle$ **27.4** **29.** $63°$ **31.** $131°$ **33.** $\approx \langle -135.2, 0, 36.2 \rangle$ **35.** $\approx \langle -11.3, 133.6, 38.8 \rangle$

37. $\approx (1363.6, -1341.6, 2298.1)$ **39.** $171°$ **41a.** III **41b.** II

43. $\left(-\frac{5}{2}, \frac{5\sqrt{3}}{2} \right)$ **45.** $x^2 + y^2 = 64$ **47.** C **49.** B, C, D

Section 6.4

1., 3., 5.

7. $(2, -315°)$; $(-2, 225°)$; $(-2, -135°)$; $(2, -\pi)$; $(-2, 2\pi)$; $(2, 2\pi)$; $(2, 0)$ **9.** $(-2, -\pi)$; **11.** $(1, 0)$ **13.** $\left(\frac{5\sqrt{2}}{2}, \frac{5\sqrt{2}}{2} \right)$ **15.** $\left(-\frac{3}{2}, \frac{3\sqrt{3}}{2} \right)$ **17.** $(2\sqrt{2}, 45°)$ **19.** $(17, \approx 152°)$ **21.** 3.2 **23.** 3.9 **25.** $r = 3 \csc \theta$ **27.** $r^2 = \frac{4}{\cos^2\theta - \sin^2\theta}$ **29.** $r^2 = \frac{16}{\cos^2\theta + 4\sin^2\theta}$ **31.** $x = 5$ **33.** $x^2 + y^2 = 25$ **35.** $x^2 + (y+3)^2 = 9$ **37.** ≈ 9.5 km **39a.** $r = \frac{|k|}{2}$; $\left(\frac{k}{2}, 0 \right)$ **39b.** $r = \frac{|k|}{2}$; $\left(\frac{k}{2}, \frac{\pi}{2} \right)$ **41.** $r = \pm 2\sqrt{\sec\theta \csc\theta}$ **43.** $(x-1)^2 + (y+3)^2 = 10$

SELECTED ODD ANSWERS

5. $4\sqrt{2}$; $45°$ **7.** $\sqrt{61}$; $\approx 309.8°$

9. $\langle -1, 2 \rangle$

11. $\langle -5, 5 \rangle$

13. $\langle -3, 6.5 \rangle$; $-3i + 6.5j$ **15.** $\langle 5.5, 2 \rangle$; $5.5i + 2j$ **17.** $\left\langle \frac{4}{5}, -\frac{3}{5} \right\rangle$ **19.** $\left\langle \frac{3\sqrt{13}}{13}, \frac{2\sqrt{13}}{13} \right\rangle$ **21.** $\approx \langle 4.7, 1.7 \rangle$ **23.** $\approx \langle 1.5, -3.7 \rangle$ **25.** $\approx \langle 43.3, 25 \rangle$ **27.** $\langle -800, 0 \rangle$ **29.** $\langle 0, 500 \rangle$ **31.** 94.3 mi; $58°$ **33.** 467.0 mi; $286°$ **35.** 5.11 lb; $63°$ above horizontal **37.** ≈ 168 mi/hr at a bearing of $\approx 237°$ **39.** $\approx 301°$; ≈ 329 mi/hr **41.** $|\mathbf{F}| = 10$ lb; $|\mathbf{N}| \approx 17.3$ lb

43a. $\mathbf{r_1} = t_1 \mathbf{i}$, lb at $60°$ $\mathbf{w} = 10$ lb at $-90°$

43b. $\mathbf{r_1} = \left\langle \frac{1}{2} t_1, \frac{\sqrt{3}}{2} t_1 \right\rangle$ $\mathbf{r_2} = \left\langle -\frac{1}{2}, \frac{\sqrt{3}}{2} t_2 \right\rangle$

43c. x-components: $0 + \frac{1}{2} t_1 - \frac{1}{2} t_2 = 0$ y-components: $-10 + \frac{\sqrt{3}}{2} t_1 + \frac{\sqrt{3}}{2} t_2$

45. $\frac{2\pi}{9} \approx 0.698$ **47.** $102°$ **49.** The graph of $f(x)$ is stretched horizontally by a factor of 2, stretched vertically by a factor of 3, reflected in the x-axis, and translated 1 unit up. **51.** D **53.** C, D

Section 6.2

1. orthogonal; $90°$ **3.** $-3\sqrt{2}$ **5.** 0 **7.** 3.1; $< 90°$ **9.** 0; $= 90°$ **11.** -4; $> 90°$ **13.** $137.7°$ **15.** $64.3°$ **17.** $\frac{5}{1} k(1, 5)$ **19.** $-\frac{2}{5} k(5, -2)$ **21.** $-\frac{u_1}{u_2}$; $k(u_2, -u_1)$ or $k(-u_2, u_1)$

23. $k(\mathbf{u} \cdot \mathbf{v})$ **25.** $\mathbf{u} \cdot (\mathbf{v} + \mathbf{w})$

$= k(u_1 v_1 + u_1 v_2)$ $= (u_1, u_2) \cdot (v_1 + w_1, v_2 + w_2)$
$= (k u_1) v_1 + (k u_2) v_2$ $= u_1(v_1 + w_1) + u_2(v_2 + w_2)$
$= \langle k u_1, k u_2 \rangle \cdot \langle v_1, v_2 \rangle$ $= u_1 v_1 + u_1 w_1 + u_2 v_2 + u_2 w_2$
$= k \langle u_1, u_2 \rangle \cdot \langle v_1, v_2 \rangle$ $= (u_1, u_2) \cdot (v_1, v_2) + (u_1, u_2) \cdot (w_1, w_2)$
$= k \mathbf{u} \cdot \mathbf{v}$ $= \mathbf{u} \cdot \mathbf{v} + \mathbf{u} \cdot \mathbf{w}$

27. $\left\langle \frac{10}{17}, \frac{40}{17} \right\rangle$; $\left\langle \frac{44}{17}, -\frac{11}{17} \right\rangle$ **29.** $\left\langle \frac{34}{13}, \frac{51}{13} \right\rangle$; $\left\langle -\frac{21}{13}, -\frac{14}{13} \right\rangle$ **31a.** ≈ 32.1 lb **31b.** ≈ 32.1 lb **33a.** ≈ 59.1 lb **33b.** ≈ 46.2 lb **35.** 450 N·m **37.** 4758 ft-lb **39.** $[-xy, xy]$ **41.** 8 **43.** $A = 25.6°$; $B = 126.0°$; $C = 28.4°$ **45.** $x = 1, 38$ **47.** $\left(3, \frac{3}{2} \right)$ **49.** C $(3, 3)$; $\sqrt{34}$ **51.** C **53.** C, D

---

25. one; $B = 79°$; $b = 42.5$; $c = 43.3$ **27.** no solution **29.** one; $D = 16.0°$; $f = 4.3$ **31.** two; $P = 82.0°$; $R = 65.0°$, $r = 7.3$ or $P = 98.0°$, $R = 49.0°$; $r = 6.1$ **35.** ≈ 6.5 mi from Cape Romain ≈ 13.3 mi from Georgetown **37.** ≈ 70.0 ft **39.** ≈ 25.8 km from first tower ≈ 23.5 km from second tower **43.** $\cos\theta$

45. $\tan\theta \sin\theta + \cos\theta$
$= \left(\frac{\sin\theta}{\cos\theta} \right) \sin\theta + \cos\theta$
$= \frac{\sin^2\theta}{\cos\theta} + \frac{\cos^2\theta}{\cos\theta}$
$= \frac{\sin^2\theta + \cos^2\theta}{\cos\theta}$
$= \frac{1}{\cos\theta} = \sec\theta$

47. $x = 0, \frac{\pi}{4}, \pi$ **49.** B **51.** A

Section 5.7

1. $B = 83.5°$; $C = 41.5°$; $a = 4.9$ **3.** $W = 41.4°$; $X = 124.2°$; $Y = 14.4°$ **5.** $B = 112.1°$; $A = 39.9°$; $c = 6.6$ **7.** $A = 53.2°$; $B = 46.4°$; $C = 80.4°$ **9.** $X = 36.6°$; $Y = 83.4°$; $z = 8.7$ **11.** $X = 51.8°$; $Y = 40.0°$; $Z = 88.3°$ **13.** ≈ 56.9 cm² **15.** ≈ 96.7 ft² **17.** ≈ 2.0 mi **19.** $A = 42.8°$; $B = 60.9°$; $C = 76.2°$ **21.** $a = 4.1$; $c = 9.8$; $B = 53°$ **23.** $A = 65.4°$; $B = 71.6°$; $b = 12.5$ or $A = 114.6°$; $B = 22.4°$; $b = 5.0$ **25.** 37.0 cm² **27.** 390.7 in.² **29.** ≈ 8.4 cm and ≈ 15.2 cm **31.** ≈ 449 ft **33.** $\approx 225.2°$ and $\approx 314.8°$ **35.** $\approx 27.2°$ **39.** $\approx 44.3°$ **41.** $c \approx 13.6$ **43.** \$14,180.36 **45.** $x \approx 3.226$ **47.** $x = 3$ **49.** C **51.** C

Data Analysis

1. The light bends toward the normal. **3a.** $28.9°$ **3b.** $47.8°$

5. away from **9.** $n_1 \sin\theta_c = n_2 \sin 90°$; $\sin\theta_c = \frac{n_2}{n_1}$; $\theta_c = \sin^{-1} \frac{n_2}{n_1}$

Review

1. $\frac{\sin^2\theta}{\cos^2\theta} + \frac{\cos^2\theta}{\cos^2\theta} = \frac{1}{\cos^2\theta}$; $\tan^2\theta + 1 = \sec^2\theta$ **3a.** -0.866 **3b.** 2 **5.** $\sin^4 x$ **7.** $\sec x$

9. $\frac{\cos x}{1 + \sin x} - \frac{\cos x}{1 - \sin x} = \frac{\cos x(1 - \sin x)}{1 - \sin x} - \frac{\cos x(1 + \sin x)}{1 - \sin^2 x}$
$= \frac{\cos x - \cos x \sin x - \cos x - \cos x \sin x}{\cos^2 x}$
$= \frac{-2 \cos x \sin x}{\cos^2 x} = \frac{-2 \sin x}{\cos x} = -2 \tan x$

11. $\frac{1 + \cos\theta}{\sin\theta} \cdot \frac{1 - \cos\theta}{1 - \cos\theta} = \frac{\sin\theta(1 - \cos\theta)}{1 - \cos^2\theta}$
$= \frac{\sin\theta(1 - \cos\theta)}{\sin^2\theta} = \frac{1 - \cos\theta}{\sin\theta}$

13. $\tan^5 x = \tan x (\tan^2 x)^2$
$= \tan x (\sec^2 x - 1)^2$
$= \tan x (1 - 2\sec^2 x + \sec^4 x)$
$= \tan x - 2 \tan x \sec^2 x + \tan x \sec^4 x$

15. $\theta = \frac{\pi}{3}, \frac{2\pi}{3}, \frac{4\pi}{3}, \frac{5\pi}{3}$ **17.** $x = 1.82, 4.46$ **19.** $x = n2\pi$

21a. $\cos(x + y) = \cos(x - (-y))$
$= \cos x \cos(-y) + \sin x \sin(-y)$
$= \cos x \cos y - \sin x \sin y$

21b. $\cos\left(\frac{\pi}{2} - \theta \right)$
$= \cos\frac{\pi}{2} \cos\theta + \sin\frac{\pi}{2} \sin\theta$
$= (0)\cos\theta + (1)\sin\theta$
$= \sin\theta$

21c. $\sin(x + y)$
$= \cos\left(\frac{\pi}{2} - (x + y) \right)$
$= \cos\left(\left(\frac{\pi}{2} - x \right) - y \right)$
$= \cos\left(\frac{\pi}{2} - x \right) \cos y + \sin\left(\frac{\pi}{2} - x \right) \sin y$
$= \sin x \cos y + \cos x \sin y$

23. $\frac{-\sqrt{2} - \sqrt{6}}{4}$ **25.** $\frac{-3 - 2\sqrt{14}}{12}$

27. $\tan(\pi - \theta) = \frac{\tan\pi - \tan\theta}{1 + \tan\pi \tan\theta}$
$= \frac{0 - \tan\theta}{1 + 0 \tan\theta}$
$= -\tan x$

29a. $\cos 2x = \cos(x + x)$
$= \cos x \cos x - \sin x \sin x$
$= \cos^2 x - \sin^2 x$
$= 2 \cos^2 x - 1$

29b. $\cos 2x = 2 \cos^2 x - 1$
$2 \cos^2 x = \cos 2x + 1$
$\cos^2 x = \frac{\cos 2x + 1}{2}$

29c. $\cos^2 x = \frac{\cos 2x + 1}{2}$
$\cos^2 \frac{x}{2} = \frac{\cos 2\left(\frac{x}{2}\right) + 1}{2}$
$\cos\frac{x}{2} = \pm \sqrt{\frac{\cos x + 1}{2}}$

31. $\frac{3\sqrt{10}}{10}, \frac{\sqrt{10}}{10}, 3$ **33.** $-\frac{1}{4}$

35. $x = \frac{\pi}{3} + n4\pi, \frac{5\pi}{3} + n4\pi, \pi + n2\pi$

37. $\sin 3x + \sin x = \sin(2x + x) + \sin x$
$= \sin 2x \cos x + \cos 2x \sin x + \sin x$
$= 2 \sin x \cos x \cos x + (2 \cos^2 x - 1) \sin x + \sin x$
$= 2 \sin x \cos^2 x + (2 \cos^2 x - 1) \sin x - 1 + 1)$
$= 4 \sin x \cos^2 x$
$= 2 \sin x(2 \cos^2 x)$
$= 2 \sin x \cos 2x = 2(2 \sin x \cos x) \cos x$
$= 2 \sin 2x \cos x$

39. $A = 85.0°$; $b = 3.4$; $c = 7.5$ **41.** no solution **43.** $P = 18.2$; $Q = 33.1°$; $R = 128.7°$ **45.** $A = 145.0°$; $C = 22.0°$; $a = 15.3$ or $A = 9.0°$; $C = 158.0°$; $a = 4.2$ **47.** ≈ 19.9 in.² **49.** ≈ 29.2 ft

Section 6.1

1. $(6, 3)$

3. $(-3, 4)$

SELECTED ODD ANSWERS

Section 7.1

47. 1; cis $\frac{2\pi}{3}$, cis $\frac{4\pi}{3}$

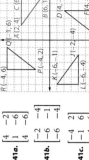

1. B 3. (4, 1) 5. (1.5, 0) 7. $\left(-\frac{1}{2}, -10\right)$, (5, 1) 9. $\left(\frac{3}{4}, -\frac{1}{8}\right)$, (-1, -1) 11. (1, 2) 13. (2, -2) 15. $\left(0, \frac{5}{2}\right)$ 17. (-1, 1), (2, 10), $\left(-\frac{1}{3}, 3\right)$ 19. (1.1, 2.7), (1.8, 2.9) 21. (2.1, 1.2); independent consistent 23. ∅; inconsistent 25. (1, -2) 27. 87.5 ft × 126 ft 29. 34,440 cars at $21.788 each 31. (-2, 3, -4) 33. (-3, 0.5, -1) 35. $\left(-\frac{8}{7}t + 3, \frac{3}{7}t + 1, t\right)$ 37. $a = 5, c = 2$ 39. $\left(\frac{\pi}{2}, 3\right)$, $\left(\frac{\pi}{2}, \frac{5\pi}{3}\right)$ 41. no solution; $\left(1 + \sqrt{7}i, \frac{3}{2} - \frac{3\sqrt{7}}{2}i\right)$, $\left(1 - \sqrt{7}i, \frac{3}{2} + \frac{3\sqrt{7}}{2}i\right)$ 43. $m = -6$ 45. $f(x) = |x|$ is reflected in the x-axis and translated 3 units right and 1 unit up. 47. $x = 7$ (multiplicity 4) 49. D 51. A, C, D

Section 7.2

1a. 4 × 3 1b. 7 1c. 4 1d. a_{32} 1e. a_{23} 3a. D 3b. E 3c. none 5. $\begin{bmatrix} -5 & -8 & 4 \\ -13 & 3 & 7 \end{bmatrix}$ 7. $\begin{bmatrix} 35 & -11 & -7 \\ -19 & 4 & 28 \end{bmatrix}$ 9. $\begin{bmatrix} 7 & -15 \\ 2 & 12 \end{bmatrix}$ 11. $\begin{bmatrix} 4 & -30 & 32 \\ -4 & 6 & -35 \end{bmatrix}$ 13. 2 × 3; $\begin{bmatrix} -5 & 20 & 30 \\ -13 & 18 & 34 \end{bmatrix}$ 15. 2 × 1; $\begin{bmatrix} 4 \\ -2 \end{bmatrix}$ 17. $\begin{bmatrix} -3 & 1 & 2 \\ -1 & 1 & -2 \\ 0 & 0 & 3 \end{bmatrix} \begin{bmatrix} x \\ y \\ z \end{bmatrix}$ 19. [50] 21. $\begin{bmatrix} 28 & 6 \\ 31 & 6 \end{bmatrix}$ 23. $\begin{bmatrix} 11 & 12 & 7 \\ -5 & -4 & 4 \\ -3 & 0 & 11 \end{bmatrix}$ 25. $\begin{bmatrix} 2 & -10 \\ 35 & -13 \end{bmatrix}$ 27. $\begin{bmatrix} 4 & -4 & 2 \\ 10 & 4 & 38 \\ 22 & 10 & 16 \end{bmatrix}$ 29. $\begin{bmatrix} 6134 & 379 \\ 2375 & 1828 \end{bmatrix}$ 31a. $\begin{bmatrix} 1 & 0 & 0 \\ 0 & 1 & 0 \\ 0 & 0 & 1 \end{bmatrix}$ 31b. $\begin{bmatrix} 1 & 0 & 0 \\ 0 & 1 & 0 \\ 0 & 0 & 1 \end{bmatrix}$ 33. $\begin{bmatrix} 0 & 0 \\ 0 & 0 \end{bmatrix}$; Zero Product Property 35. $R = [4632]$; $S = [1085]$ 39a. $A^2 - B^2 = \begin{bmatrix} 2 & 4 \\ 5 & 4 \end{bmatrix} \neq (A + B)(A - B) = \begin{bmatrix} 4 & 1 \\ 3 & 5 \end{bmatrix}$ 39b. $(A + B)(A - B) = A^2 + BA - AB - B^2$ 41a. $\begin{bmatrix} 4 & -2 \\ 1 & -6 \\ 4 & -6 \end{bmatrix}$ 41b. $\begin{bmatrix} -2 & -4 \\ -6 & -1 \\ -6 & -4 \end{bmatrix}$ 41c. $\begin{bmatrix} -4 & 1 \\ 1 & 6 \\ -4 & 6 \end{bmatrix}$

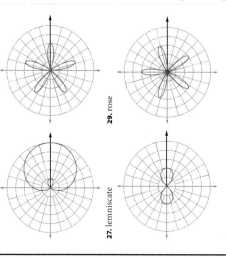

39. $\dfrac{z_1}{z_2} = \dfrac{r_1(\cos\theta_1 + i\sin\theta_1)}{r_2(\cos\theta_2 + i\sin\theta_2)} \cdot \dfrac{\cos\theta_2 - i\sin\theta_2}{\cos\theta_2 - i\sin\theta_2}$

$= \dfrac{r_1}{r_2} \cdot \dfrac{\cos\theta_1\cos\theta_2 - i\cos\theta_1\sin\theta_2 + i\sin\theta_1\cos\theta_2 - i^2\sin\theta_1\sin\theta_2}{\cos^2\theta_2 - i^2\sin^2\theta_2}$

$= \dfrac{r_1}{r_2} \cdot \dfrac{(\cos\theta_1\cos\theta_2 + \sin\theta_1\sin\theta_2) + i(\sin\theta_1\cos\theta_2 - \cos\theta_1\sin\theta_2)}{\cos^2\theta_2 + \sin^2\theta_2}$

$= \dfrac{r_1}{r_2}(\cos(\theta_1 - \theta_2) + i\sin(\theta_1 - \theta_2))$

41. 128 cis $\frac{11\pi}{6}$, $64\sqrt{3} - 64i$ 43. $\approx 29^{50}$ cis 0.35 45. $162°$ 47. $\overrightarrow{AB} = \langle 4, 5, -6 \rangle$; $|AB| = \sqrt{77}$; $u = \left\langle \frac{4\sqrt{77}}{77}, \frac{5\sqrt{77}}{77}, -\frac{6\sqrt{77}}{77} \right\rangle$ 49. 5.1 51. D 53. B

Data Analysis

1. $z_1 = i$; $z_2 = -1 + i$; $z_3 = -i$; $z_4 = -1 + i$; $z_5 = -i$; $z_6 = -1 + i$; no 3. $r(x) = \frac{6}{x}$ 3a. decrease 3b. reciprocal 5. 40,200 km; ≈ 25,000 mi

Review

1. (5, -9); $5i - 9j$ 3a. (-2, -3) 3b. (8, -2) 5. $(-3\sqrt{3}, 3)$ 7. ≈ 1042 mi; ≈ 62° 9. $20\sqrt{3}$ 11. 0; = 90° 13. $\frac{1}{3}$, $k(3, 5)$ 15a. ≈ 27.4 lb 15b. ≈ 27.4 lb

17.

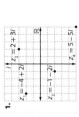

19. $\langle 2, -6, 5 \rangle$; $\sqrt{65}$; $\left\langle \frac{2\sqrt{65}}{65}, \frac{6\sqrt{65}}{65}, -8 \right\rangle$ 21. $\langle -17, 12, -8 \rangle$ 23. 90°

25.

27a. $\left(-\frac{3}{2}, \frac{3\sqrt{3}}{2}\right)$ 27b. ≈ (7.3, 105.9°) 29. $r = -3\csc\theta$ 31. $y = x$ 33a. III 33b. III 33c. I 35a. IV 35b. II 35c. I

37.

39.

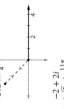

41a. ≈ 5 cis 5.64 41b. 4 cis $\frac{\pi}{4}$ 43. -12 cis $\frac{3\pi}{2}$; $12i$ 45. ≈ 625 cis 212.5°; $-527 - 336i$

675a

33. dimpled limaçon

31. rose

35. $6.25\pi \approx 19.6$ u² 39a. cardioid; $r = 12.5 + 12.5\cos\theta$ 41a. $\left(\frac{1}{2}, \frac{\pi}{6}\right)$ 41b. $\left(\frac{1}{2}, \frac{5\pi}{6}\right)$, $\left(\frac{1}{2}, \frac{5\pi}{6}\right)$ 39b. dimpled limaçon; $r = 15 + 10\cos\theta$ 41c. (0.524, 0.5), (2.618, 0.5) 43. $5 - 5i$ 45. $2 - 2i$ 47. $x = \pm 2i$ 49. B 51. C

Section 6.6

1.

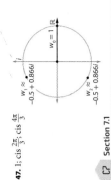

$z_1 = 2 + 3i$, $z_2 = -4 + 2i$, $z_3 = -1 - 2i$, $z_4 = 5 - 5i$

3a. $\theta = \text{Tan}^{-1}\frac{b}{a}$ 3b. $\theta = \pi + \text{Tan}^{-1}\frac{b}{a}$ 3c. $\theta = \pi + \text{Tan}^{-1}\frac{b}{a}$ 5. 7 cis π 3d. $\theta = 2\pi + \text{Tan}^{-1}\frac{b}{a}$ 7. $3\sqrt{2}$ cis $\frac{5\pi}{4}$ 9. $\frac{1}{2}$ cis $\frac{11\pi}{6}$

11.

4 cis $\frac{\pi}{6}$

13.

$2\sqrt{2}$ cis $\frac{3\pi}{4}$

15. 6 cis 0; 6 17. 6 cis 90°; $6i$ 19. $4\sqrt{2}$ cis $\frac{11\pi}{12}$ 21. ≈ 5.46 - 0.46i; ≈ 5.46 + 0.57i 23. $-8 - 8\sqrt{3}i$

$-2 + 2i$
$\frac{\sqrt{10}}{5}$ cis 1.11;
$(2 + 2\sqrt{3}) + (2 - 2\sqrt{3})i$; ≈ 0.28 + 0.57i

25. $-239 - 28{,}560i$

27. $w_0 = $ cis 0; $w_1 \approx $ cis $\frac{2\pi}{5}$; $w_2 \approx $ cis $\frac{4\pi}{5}$; $w_3 \approx $ cis $\frac{6\pi}{5}$; $w_4 \approx $ cis $\frac{8\pi}{5}$

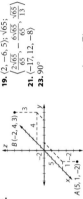

29. $w_0 \approx \sqrt[4]{3}$ cis $\frac{\pi}{5}$; $w_1 \approx \sqrt[4]{3}$ cis $\frac{3\pi}{5}$; $w_2 \approx \sqrt[4]{3}$ cis $\frac{4\pi}{5}$; $w_3 \approx \sqrt[4]{3}$ cis $\frac{7\pi}{5}$

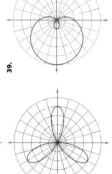

31. $w_0 = 5$ cis 0 (principal); $w_1 = 5$ cis $\frac{4\pi}{10}$; $w_2 = 5$ cis $\frac{8\pi}{10}$ 33. $w_0 = $ cis 13° (principal); $w_1 = $ cis 85°; $w_2 = $ cis 157°; $w_3 = $ cis 229°; $w_4 = $ cis 301° 35. i, $-\frac{\sqrt{3}}{2} - \frac{1}{2}i$, $\frac{\sqrt{3}}{2} - \frac{1}{2}i$ 37. ≈ -1.9 + 0.79i, ≈ 1.9 - 0.79i

45. $\mp\sin\theta$ 47. $x = 0, \pi, 2\pi$; max: $\left(\frac{\pi}{2}, 3\right)$; min: $\left(\frac{3\pi}{2}, -3\right)$ 49. $\theta = n\pi$ 51. A 53. D

Section 6.5

1a. II 1b. IV 1c. I 1d. III 3. Archimedean spiral 5. circle

7a. yes 7b. no 7c. no 7d. no 9. π; 0, 2π 11. 0, $\frac{\pi}{4}$, $\frac{3\pi}{2}$, 2π; $\frac{\pi}{4}$, $\frac{3\pi}{4}$, $\frac{5\pi}{4}$, $\frac{7\pi}{4}$

13. cardioid 15. rose

17. 12 petals; 2 19. yes; yes; no; no 21. yes; yes; yes 23. limaçon with inner loop 25. rose

27. lemniscate

29. rose

SELECTED ODD ANSWERS (676b — right page)

43. $\tan x \csc 2x$
$= \dfrac{\sin x}{\cos x} \cdot \dfrac{1}{\sin 2x}$
$= \dfrac{\sin x}{\cos x} \cdot \dfrac{1}{2\sin x \cos x}$
$= \dfrac{1}{2\cos^2 x}$
$= \dfrac{1}{2}\sec^2 x$

11. 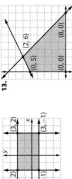 **13.** graph with (2,6), (8,0), (0,5), (0,0)

23. graph with (2,2), $\left(-\dfrac{1}{5}, \dfrac{12}{5}\right)$, (−1,0)

15. max: $f(0,6)=30$; min: $f(6,0)=-12$
17. max: $f\left(\dfrac{15}{4},0\right)=27$; min: $f(0,0)=-3$
19. no max; no min
21. graph with (0,7), (3,4), (0,2)
25. max: $f(5,0)=41$; min: $f(0,2)=2$
27. max: $f(1,6)=20$; min: 0 on segment with endpoints (1,1) and (4,4)
29. max: $f(3,2)=9$; no min
31. $R(x,y)=15x+26y$ where $x=$ number of pies and $y=$ batches of macaroons; $x\ge0$, $y\ge0$, $2x+3y\le51$, $0.5x+3.5y\le21$
33. 21 pies and 3 batches of coconut macaroons; $393
35. graph with (0,200), (75,100), (150,0), (96,72)
37. (125, $55); $937.50; $1562.50
39. by working 7 hr at the daycare and 8 hr at the gym; $190/week
41. 1.5 servings of both pancakes and protein powder
43. $-5\cos 2\theta$ **45.** 7.21 cis 4.12 **49.** D **51.** B

CP **Section 7.7**

1. $\dfrac{A}{x-2}+\dfrac{B}{x-12}$ **3.** $\dfrac{A}{x-1}+\dfrac{Bx+C}{x^2-2x-5}$ **5.** $\dfrac{A}{x-5}+\dfrac{B}{x+6}$
7. $\dfrac{5}{x-2}+\dfrac{2}{x+3}$ **9.** $\dfrac{6}{2x+1}+\dfrac{2}{x-4}$ **11.** $-\dfrac{3}{x}+\dfrac{4}{x^2}$
13. $\dfrac{5}{x-1}+\dfrac{1}{(x-1)^2}$ **15.** $\dfrac{5}{x}+\dfrac{1}{(x+1)^2}$
17. $\dfrac{3}{x-2}+\dfrac{4x-1}{x^2+2x+4}$ **19.** $\dfrac{7}{x+1}+\dfrac{4}{x^2+8x+2}$
21. $\dfrac{5x}{x^2+1}+\dfrac{x-2}{(x^2+1)^2}$ **23.** $\dfrac{3}{x}+\dfrac{2x}{x^2+3}+\dfrac{}{(x^2+3)^2}$
25. $\dfrac{3}{3x-2}-\dfrac{}{(3x-2)^2}$ **27.** $\dfrac{4x}{x^2-5x+2}-\dfrac{1}{x-1}$
29. $\dfrac{2}{2x-5}+\dfrac{5}{x-6}$ **31.** $\dfrac{2}{x}+\dfrac{1}{x-4}-\dfrac{}{(x-4)^2}$
33. $4-\dfrac{3}{x}+\dfrac{7}{x-1}$ **35.** $x-2-\dfrac{2}{x+3}+\dfrac{1}{x-1}$ **37a.** $\dfrac{1}{x}+\dfrac{3}{x+5}$
39. $162°$ **41.** $g(x)=\ln x-\ln 3$
43a. VA: $x=0$; HA: $y=0$; $D=\{x|x\ne0\}$; $R=\{y|y\ne0\}$
43b. VA: $x=0$; HA: $y=0$; $D=\{x|x\ne0\}$; $R=\{y|y>0\}$
43c. VA: $x=-3$ (hole at $x=-1$); HA: $y=0$; $D=\{x|x\ne-1$ and $x\ne-3\}$; $R=\left\{y|y\ne0 \text{ and } y\ne\tfrac{1}{2}\right\}$ **45.** C **47.** A

CP **Data Analysis**

$1.\ 5;\ 5;\ \begin{bmatrix}\frac{4}{5} & -\frac{3}{5}\\ -\frac{1}{5} & \frac{2}{5}\end{bmatrix}$ **3.** SEND FOOD **5.** SZZOQQAZD **7.** ALL IS WELL

CP **Review**

1. $(-2,-7)$; independent consistent **3.** $\left\{(x,y)\,|\,y=\tfrac{5}{3}x-\tfrac{10}{3}\right\}$; dependent consistent **5.** 24 ft × 54 ft **7.** $(2,-1,-3)$ **9a.** 3 × 4 **9b.** 3 **9c.** 14 **9d.** a_{24} **9e.** a_{31} **11a.** 3 × 3 **11b.** not defined **11c.** 4 × 2 **11d.** 2 × 5 **13.** $\begin{bmatrix}-22 & 21\\ -31 & 18\end{bmatrix}$ **15.** boys: $1483.50; girls: $1674.00 **17.** $\begin{bmatrix}1 & 0\\ 0 & 1\end{bmatrix}$ **19.** $\left(\tfrac{9-10t}{2}, 2-3t, t\right)$; dependent **21.** ∅; inconsistent **23.** 41 **25a.** −12 **25b.** −12 **27.** $(4,-5)$ **29.** 13 u² **31a.** inverses **31b.** not inverses **33.** $\begin{bmatrix}\frac{4}{5} & \frac{1}{10} & 0\\ -\frac{3}{2} & \frac{1}{2} & -\frac{1}{2}\\ -\frac{7}{10} & -\frac{1}{10} & -\frac{1}{5}\end{bmatrix}$ **35.** $\left(6, \tfrac{2}{3}, \tfrac{8}{3}\right)$
37. savings: $9500; CD: $28,000; bond: $4500
39.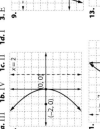
41.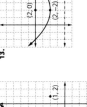
43. 20 Tropical and 40 Heartland; $220
45. $\dfrac{5}{x-6}+\dfrac{2}{x-4}$ **47.** $\dfrac{x}{x^2-3x-2}$

C8 **Section 8.1**

1a. III **1b.** IV **1c.** II **1d.** I **3.** E **5.** D
7. 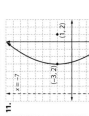 (with $x=2$, $(-2,0)$, $(0,0)$, $x=-7$)
9. graph $y=6.5$, $(1,6)$, $(1,5.5)$, $x=-4$
11. graph $(-3,2)$, $(1,2)$
13. graph $(2,0)$, $(2,-2)$, $x=-4$
15. $y=\dfrac{1}{20}(x-4)^2-6$ **17.** $x=\dfrac{1}{12}(y-3)^2+5$

SELECTED ODD ANSWERS (676a — left page)

49.

45. $(-1,4), (1,10)$ **47.** $(1,2)$ **49.** B **51.** A

43a. $2x+3y=6$
43b. $3x+2y=1$
43c. $y=k$ **45a.** 140 u³
45b. 264 u³ **47.** $x\approx-2457.38$

51. $\begin{bmatrix}2 & 3 & -1 & -6\\ 1 & 3 & -2 & -1\\ 4 & -2 & 0 & 2\end{bmatrix}$ **53.** B **55.** D

CP **Section 7.3**

1. $(-2,4)$ **3.** $\begin{bmatrix}3 & -4 & 6\\ 2 & 5 & -19\end{bmatrix}$ **5.** $\begin{bmatrix}2 & 5 & -16\\ 1 & -1 & 6\end{bmatrix}$
5a. $\begin{bmatrix}1 & -1 & 6\\ 2 & 5 & -16\end{bmatrix}$ **5b.** $\begin{bmatrix}1 & -1 & 6\\ 0 & 7 & -28\end{bmatrix}$ **5c.** $\begin{bmatrix}1 & -1 & 6\\ 0 & 1 & -4\end{bmatrix}$
7. $\begin{bmatrix}1 & 1 & 1 & 4\\ 4 & 3 & 1 & 4\\ -1 & -1 & -2 & 1\end{bmatrix}$ **7a.** $\begin{bmatrix}1 & 1 & 1 & 4\\ 0 & -1 & -3 & -12\\ 0 & -4 & -5 & -13\end{bmatrix}$ **7b.** $\begin{bmatrix}1 & 1 & 1 & 4\\ 0 & 1 & 3 & 12\\ 0 & -4 & -5 & -13\end{bmatrix}$ **7c.** $\begin{bmatrix}1 & 1 & 1 & 4\\ 0 & 1 & 3 & 12\\ 0 & 0 & 7 & 35\end{bmatrix}$
7d. $\begin{bmatrix}1 & 1 & 1 & 4\\ 0 & 1 & 3 & 12\\ 0 & 0 & 1 & 5\end{bmatrix}$ **9.** $(2,-4)$ **11.** $(2,-3,5)$
13. $(11,-9,4)$; independent consistent **15.** $\left(\tfrac{9}{2}-5t, 2-3t, t\right)$; dependent consistent
17. $\begin{bmatrix}1 & \frac{7}{2} & -2\\ 1 & -2 & -2\end{bmatrix}$ **19.** $\begin{bmatrix}1 & 0 & 2\\ 0 & 1 & -3\end{bmatrix}$ **21.** $(-2,3)$
23. $(8,1,-3)$ **25.** $\left(-\tfrac{1}{3}, -5\right)$ **27.** $\left(-\tfrac{1}{2}, 3, 2\right)$ **29.** ∅; inconsistent
31. $\left(-9t, \tfrac{2}{} +11t, t\right)$; dependent consistent **33.** (11.81, 3.14, 3.65) **35.** $\left(\tfrac{18+5t}{8}, \tfrac{10+t}{4}, t, 3\right)$
37. peanuts: $0.70; pretzels: $0.20; chocolate pieces: $2.50 **39.** 26 quarters; 16 dimes; 30 nickels **41.** ∅; inconsistent
43. $y=-2x^2-x+7$ **45.** ≈ 646 ft **47.** $f(x)=3\cos 4\left(x-\tfrac{\pi}{3}\right)$ **49.** $y=x^2$ **51.** A, D **53.** B, D

CP **Section 7.4**

1. 7 **3.** 87 **5.** −8 **7.** 15 **9.** 1 **11.** $M_{11}=-7; M_{12}=-9; M_{13}=10; C_{11}=-7; C_{12}=9; C_{13}=10$ **13.** 7 **15.** 25
17a. $|A|=98$ **17b.** $|B|=-401$ **19a.** 51 **19b.** 51 **21.** 2
23. −24 **25.** $(2,3)$ **27.** $\left(-3, \tfrac{1}{3}\right)$ **29.** $\{(x,y)\,|\,2x-3y=5\}$ **31.** $(-1,1,3)$ **33.** $(5,-2,0)$ **35.** 22.5 u² **37.** 31.5 u²
39. 31,590 ft² **41a.** using row 1:
$a(ei-hf)-b(di-gf)+c(dh-ge)$
$=aei-ahf-bdi+bgf+cdh-cge$
$=aei-bdi+cdh-gec-hfa-idb$
$=(aei+bfg+cdh)-(gec+hfa+idb)$
41b. using row 1: $a|d|-b|c|=ad-bc$

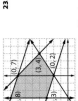

43. 2 sin 2θ **45.** graph

CP **Section 7.5**

1. singular **3.** singular **5.** inverses **7.** inverses
9. $\begin{bmatrix}\frac{1}{2} & -\frac{3}{4}\\ -1 & 2\end{bmatrix}$ **11.** $\begin{bmatrix}2 & -3\\ -3 & 6\end{bmatrix}$ **13.** $\begin{bmatrix}\frac{1}{2} & 1\\ \frac{7}{4} & -4\end{bmatrix}$
15. $\begin{bmatrix}7 & 8 & -4\\ 11 & 13 & -6\\ -12 & -14 & 7\end{bmatrix}$ **17.** $\begin{bmatrix}-9 & 7\\ 4 & -3\end{bmatrix}$ **21.** $(5,7)$ **23.** $(-2,7)$ **25.** $(9,8,-2)$
19. $\begin{bmatrix}\frac{11}{3} & -\frac{4}{3} & -2\\ -\frac{4}{3} & \frac{2}{3} & 1\\ 2 & -1 & -1\end{bmatrix}$ **27.** $\left(\tfrac{99}{10}, \tfrac{33}{2}\right)$ **29a.** dependent **29b.** inconsistent
31. 3.2 gal Mon; 2.5 gal Fri **33.** −22, 5, 52
35. $\begin{bmatrix}19 & 12 & -4\\ 4 & -32 & 18\\ 3 & 15 & -2\\ 34 & -1 & 12\end{bmatrix}$ **37.** $\begin{bmatrix}1 & 2\\ 0 & 3\end{bmatrix}$
43. 2 sin 2θ **45.** **47.** $|A|=0$ **49.** C **51.** A

CP **Section 7.6**

1.  **3.** graph
5. graph
7. $y<-\tfrac{3}{2}x-2$; $y>2x+1$
9. $y<-(x-2)^2+4$; $y\ge|x-2|$
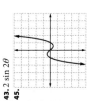

17. $3x^2 + 2xy + 3y^2 - 18 = 0$
19. $-5x^2 + 14\sqrt{3}xy + 9y^2 - 48 = 0$
21. $21x^2 - 10\sqrt{3}xy + 31y^2 - 144 = 0$

25. $\theta = \frac{\pi}{6}; v = \frac{1}{2}u^2 + 3$

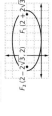

29. $12x^2 - 26xy + 12y^2 + 25 = 0$

33a. $u = \frac{v^2}{10}$ **33b.** 2.5 ft

31. parabola; $y = \frac{2}{3}x$; a line
35. $x = u\cos\theta - v\sin\theta; y = u\sin\theta + v\cos\theta$

$A(u\cos\theta - v\sin\theta)^2$
$+ B(u\cos\theta - v\sin\theta)(u\sin\theta + v\cos\theta)$
$+ C(u\sin\theta + v\cos\theta)^2 + D(u\cos\theta - v\sin\theta)$
$+ E(u\sin\theta + v\cos\theta) + F = 0$

Only the first three terms generate terms containing uv.
$A(u^2\cos^2\theta - 2uv\cos\theta\sin\theta + v^2\sin^2\theta)$
$+ B(u^2\sin\theta\cos\theta - uv\cos^2\theta - uv\sin^2\theta + v^2\sin\theta\cos\theta)$
$+ C(u^2\sin^2\theta + 2uv\sin\theta\cos\theta + v^2\cos^2\theta) + \cdots = 0$
collecting terms containing uv:
$(-2A\cos\theta\sin\theta + B(\cos^2\theta - \sin^2\theta) + 2C\sin\theta\cos\theta)uv$
and rearranging the coefficient:
$2(C - A)\sin\theta\cos\theta + B(\cos^2\theta - \sin^2\theta)$

39. $6x^2 + 4\sqrt{3}xy + 2y^2$
$+ (2\sqrt{3} + 1)x + (2 - \sqrt{3})y = 0$

47a. $y = (x - h)^2 + k$ **47c.** $\frac{(x-h)^2}{a^2} - \frac{(y-k)^2}{b^2} = 1$

37. $\theta \approx 26.6°$
$u = -(v + 1)^2 + 1$

43. $(3, -2)$ **45.** 2 **47b.** $\frac{(x-h)^2}{a^2} + \frac{(y-k)^2}{b^2} = 1$
49. C **51.** C

15. $\theta \approx 33.7°; u = \frac{1}{3}v^2$

23. $\theta \approx 18.4°; \frac{u^2}{18} + \frac{v^2}{6} = 1$

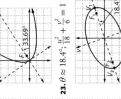

27. $x^2 + xy + y^2 - 2 = 0$

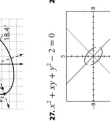

---

27. $\frac{x^2}{9} - \frac{y^2}{16} = 1$ **29.** $\frac{(x-2)^2}{16} - \frac{(y-4)^2}{16} = 1$
31. $25x^2 - 4y^2 - 100 = 0$
33. $16x^2 - 49y^2 - 224x + 490y + 343 = 0$
35. $\frac{y^2}{260,100} - \frac{x^2}{739,900} = 1$

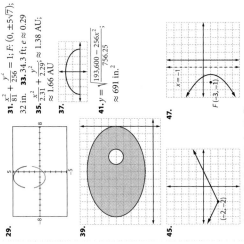

37. $C(4, -1); V: (4, -1 \pm \sqrt{5})$
$y = \frac{\sqrt{10}}{4}x - (\sqrt{10} + 1),$
$y = -\frac{\sqrt{10}}{4}x + (\sqrt{10} - 1)$

41a. $\frac{(x-100)^2}{3600} - \frac{y^2}{6400} = 1$
41b. $\frac{(y-180)^2}{5625} - \frac{x^2}{26,775} = 1$
41c. $(385, 372)$

45.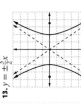
49. $\frac{4}{5}$ **51.** C **53.** D

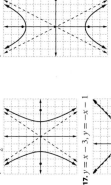

47. $\frac{\pi}{4}$

Section 8.4

1. no; hyperbola **3.** no; circle **5.** yes; parabola
7. $x = \frac{\sqrt{2}}{2}u - \frac{\sqrt{2}}{2}v, y = \frac{\sqrt{2}}{2}u + \frac{\sqrt{2}}{2}v$
9. $x = \frac{\sqrt{3}}{2}u - \frac{1}{2}v, y = \frac{1}{2}u + \frac{\sqrt{3}}{2}v$
11. $\theta = \frac{\pi}{4}; \frac{u^2}{16} - \frac{v^2}{16} = 1$
13. $\theta = \frac{\pi}{6}; \frac{u^2}{48} + \frac{v^2}{16} = 1$

---

19. $x = (y + 3)^2 - 1$
23. $y = \frac{1}{4}(x + 4)^2 + 1$

25. $y = -4x + 8$
27. $y = \frac{1}{3}x - \frac{11}{3}$

29. $y = 3(x - 4)^2 + 1$
31. $x = \frac{3}{16}x^2$, 16 in. in front of the center **35.** B, E
33. $y = \frac{3}{16}x^2$

41. $y = \frac{1}{3}x + \frac{19}{3}$ **45.** $(x + 1)^2 + (y + 3)^2 = 25$
47. **49.** $g(x) = 6(x + 4)^2 - 6$ **51.** A **53.** C

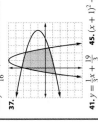

---

31. $\frac{x^2}{81} + \frac{y^2}{256} = 1; F: (0, \pm 5\sqrt{7});$
$e \approx 0.29$
33. 34.3 ft **35.** $\frac{x^2}{2.31} + \frac{y^2}{2.29} \approx 1.38$ AU;
≈ 1.66 AU

37. $y = \sqrt{\frac{193,600 - 256x^2}{756.25}};$
≈ 691 in.^{2}

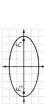

41. $y = \sqrt{\frac{193,600 - 256x^2}{756.25}};$

47.

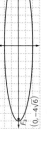

$F(-3, -1)$
$x = -1$

49. 6; 5; $x = 0, -2, 7$ **51.** A **53.** B

Section 8.3

1. difference; constant **3a.** V **3b.** IV **3c.** III **3d.** I **3e.** II
5. $C(0, 0)$; 24; 10 **7.** $C(0, 0); V: (0, \pm 8); e = \frac{5}{3}$
9. $C(0, 0); V: (0, \pm 9); F: (0, \pm 15); e = \frac{5}{3}$
11. $C(0, 0); V: (\pm 3, 0); y = \pm \frac{4}{3}x$
13. $y = \pm \frac{3}{2}x$ **15.** $y = \pm 2x$

17. $y = x - 3, y = -x - 1$
19. $C(3, -2); V: (0, -2), (6, -2)$
$y = \frac{5}{3}x - 7, y = -\frac{5}{3}x + 3$

21. $C(6, 0); V: (3, 0), (9, 0)$
$F \approx (11.8, 0), (0.2, 0)$
$e \approx 1.94; y = \frac{5}{3}x - 10,$
$y = -\frac{5}{3}x + 10$
23. $C(0, -3); V: (\pm 5, -3)$
$F: (\pm\sqrt{41}, -3)$
$e \approx 1.28; y = \pm\frac{4}{5}x - 3$

25. $C(5, 2); V: (4, 2), (6, 2)$
$F \approx (7.2, 2), (2.8, 2)$
$e \approx 2.24; y = 2x - 8,$
$y = -2x + 12$

---

19. $x = (y + 3)^3 - 1$
21. $y = -\frac{1}{8}(x - 5)^2 + 2$

25. $y = -4x + 8$
27. $y = \frac{1}{3}x - 3$

29.

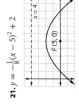

39.

45.

$(-2, -2)$

Section 8.2

1. $C(0, 0); 10; 6$ **3.** $C(0, 0); V: (0, \pm 7); cV: (\pm 5, 0)$
5. $V: (-1, -2), (-1, 7); F: (-1, -1), (-1, 7); e = 0.8$
7. $C(0, 0); V: (\pm 3, 0); e = 0.8$

9.

11. $\frac{x^2}{4} + \frac{y^2}{16} = 1$; ellipse **13.** $\frac{x^2}{9} + \frac{(y-3)^2}{25} = 1$; ellipse
15. $\frac{(x+3)^2}{25} + \frac{(y-5)^2}{16} = 1$ **17.** $\frac{(x-4)^2}{49} + \frac{(y-2)^2}{4} = 1$
19. $\frac{(x+2)^2}{9} + \frac{(y-1)^2}{25} = 1$ **21.** $\frac{x^2}{25} + \frac{y^2}{16} = 1$
23. $e \approx 0.98$

25. $e = 0$

27. $e \approx 0.87$

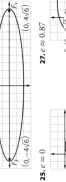

$(0, 4\sqrt{6})$

$F_1(2 + 2\sqrt{3}, 2)$ $F_1(2 + 2\sqrt{3}, 2)$

$F_1(2 - 2\sqrt{3}, 2)$

$(0, -4\sqrt{6})$

$C = F$
$(1, -2)$

23a. 144; 2584 23b. $a_1 = 1, a_2 = 1, a_n = a_{n-1} + a_{n-1}$ 33. $2.\overline{7083}$;
25. converges; 0 27. diverges 29. 190 31. $\frac{137}{15}$
$2.7\overline{16}; 2.71805$ 35. $-0.36805; -0.36786; -0.36788$
37. $0.\overline{2}$ or $\frac{2}{9}$; convergent 39. $-\infty$; divergent 41. 10!
43. $[-\pi, \pi]$ 45. $y = 3x + 8$
47.

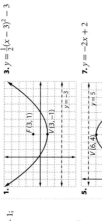

$D = \mathbb{R}; R = (0, \infty)$; decay
49. $\sin A = \frac{3\sqrt{34}}{34}$
$\cos A = \frac{5\sqrt{34}}{34}$
$\tan A = \frac{3}{5}$ 51. A 53. D

Section 9.2

1a. VI 1c. I 1e. II 3. $d = 11; 121, 132, 143$ 7. $d = 6; a_5 = 22$
9. $a_1 = 7, a_n = a_{n-1} + 12; a_n = 12n - 5; a_{20} = 235$
11. $a_1 = 1, a_n = a_{n-1} + 2; a_n = 2n - 1; a_{20} = 39$
13. $a_1 = \log 10, a_n = a_{n-1} + 2; a_n = 2n - 1; a_{20} = 39$
15. $a_n = -6n + 89; a_{20} = -31$ 17. $a_n = \frac{1}{7n-2}; a_{20} = \frac{1}{138}$
19. 41.75, 51.5, 61.25
21. $a + d = x$ and $x + d = b$ 23. $-2, 1, 4, 7, 10$; arithmetic; diverges 25. $\frac{1}{2}, \frac{1}{4}, \frac{1}{6}, \frac{1}{8}, \frac{1}{10}$; harmonic; converges 27. 1050 29. 252,000

$a = x - d$
$b = x + d$
———————
$a + b = 2x$
$x = \frac{a+b}{2}$

31. $\sum_{n=1}^{29}(4n + 1)$ 33. -10 35. 1
37. $51,500, 53,000, 54,500, 56,000$ 39. 504
41. The reciprocal of $\frac{b}{dn+c}$ is $\frac{dn+c}{b} = \frac{d}{b}n + \frac{c}{b}$, which is linear and therefore arithmetic.
45. $\frac{1}{16}$ 47. 194 mi/hr; 83.6° 49. 5, 12, 19, 26; $a_{10} = 68$
51. B 53. C

Section 9.3

1a. VI 1c. I 1e. II 3. $r = 10; 530, 5300, 53,000$
5. $r = -\frac{3}{2}; \frac{3}{2}, \frac{9}{4}, \frac{27}{8}$ 7. $a_1 = -7, a_n = -2a_{n-1}$;
$a_n = -7(-2)^{n-1}; a_{10} = 3584$ 9. $a_1 = 4, a_n = 2.5a_{n-1}$;
$a_n = 4(2.5)^{n-1}; a_{10} \approx 15,259$ 11. $a_n = -16\left(-\frac{1}{2}\right)^n; a_5 = 75$
13. $a_n = 16\left(\frac{1}{2}\right)^n$ or $a_n = -16\left(-\frac{1}{2}\right)^n; a_{12} = \frac{1}{256}$
15. $-10, -50$ 17. ± 28 19. 131,070 21. $\frac{e^{1001}}{e-1}$ 23. $\frac{16}{3}$
25. divergent 27. 1 29. 4 31. 3
33. $51,500,000, 53,045,000, 54,636.35, 56,275.44$
35. $a_6 \approx \$53,906, S_6 \approx \$300,781; b_6 \approx \$54,880, S_6 \approx \$292,482$
37. $\$525.63$ 39a. 2.5 ft 39b. 315 ft 39c. 320 ft
41. $\frac{a_n}{a_k} = \frac{a_1 r^{n-1}}{a_1 r^{k-1}} = r^{(n-1)-(k-1)} = r^{n-k}, a_n = a_k \cdot r^{n-k}$
45. ≈ 63.6 yr 47. $\frac{1}{9}, \frac{1}{3}, 3, 81, 6561, 1,594,323$ 49. yes; $d = 9$;
46, 55, 64 51. $r = \frac{7.5}{1 + 2.5\sin\theta}$; hyperbola 53. B 55. C

9. $V: (0, \pm 4); F: (0, \pm\sqrt{7})$; $e \approx 0.661$

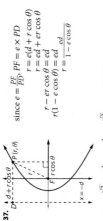

11. $F: \approx (-4.73, 1), (-1.27, 1)$, $e \approx 0.866$
13. $\frac{(x-2)^2}{25} + \frac{(y+3)^2}{169} = 1$ 15. $\frac{(x-3)^2}{9} + \frac{(y+1)^2}{25} = 1$
17. $y = \pm\frac{2}{3}x$
19. C $(15, -9)$ $V: (15, -6), (15, -12)$ $cV: (19, -9), (11, -9)$ $F: (15, -14), (15, -4)$ $e \approx 1.67$
21. $\frac{x^2}{25} - \frac{y^2}{72} = 1$ 23. $9x^2 - 25y^2 - 18x + 50y - 241 = 0$
25. $\frac{x^2}{316,969} - \frac{y^2}{1,933,031} = 1$
27. $x = \frac{\sqrt{2}}{2}u - \frac{\sqrt{2}}{2}v$, $y = \frac{\sqrt{2}}{2}u + \frac{\sqrt{2}}{2}v$
29. $\theta = \frac{\pi}{4}; \frac{u^2}{4} - \frac{v^2}{9} = 1$
31. $\theta \approx 33.7°; v = (u+1)^2$
33. $7x^2 - 6\sqrt{3}xy + 13y^2 - 100 = 0$
35. $x = (y-2)^2 + 1$ $D = [1, 5]$
37. $\frac{(x-5)^2}{64} + \frac{(y+2)^2}{9} = 1$
39. $x = 6\cos\theta + 3$, $y = 2\sin\theta + 1$
41a. $x = (60\cos 20°)t$, $y = -16t^2 + (60\sin 20°)t + 6.3$
41b. ≈ 7.9 ft 41c. ≈ 78.9 ft or 26.3 yd
43. $e = 0.2$; ellipse; directrix: $y = -25$ 45. $r = \frac{2}{1 - \frac{2}{3}\sin\theta}$ 47. $y = \frac{2}{1 + \sin\theta}$
49. $\frac{(x-2)^2}{1} - \frac{y^2}{9} = 1$

Section 9.1

1a. IV 1c. III 1e. II 3. $\frac{3}{2}, \frac{3}{5}, \frac{3}{10}, \frac{3}{17}; a_{10} = \frac{3}{101}$ 5. $\frac{1}{2}, \frac{2}{3}, \frac{3}{4}, \frac{4}{5}$,
$a_{10} = \frac{11}{10}$ 7. 3, 6, 24, 192, 3072, 98, 304 9. 2, 10, 34, 122, 434, 1546
11. 3, 1, $\frac{6}{5}, \frac{18}{7}; \frac{8}{?}$ 13. $\frac{1}{2}, -\frac{1}{2}, \frac{1}{4}, -\frac{1}{12}, \frac{1}{48}$
15. $a_n = 1 + 2n; a_{10} = 21$ 17. $a_n = \frac{n}{n+1}; a_{10} = \frac{9}{10}$
19. $a_1 = 3, a_2 = 6$, 21. $a_1 = 8, a_n = 0.1a_{n-1} + 1$ where $n \geq 2$: 1.1118, 1.11118,
$a_n = a_{n-1} + a_{n-2}$ where $n \geq 3$; 24, 39, 63   1.111118

Section 8.5

1.
t	0	1	2	3	4
x	-1	0	1	2	3
y	-2	-1	0	1	2

3.
t	-2	-1	0	1	2
x	-1	0	1	2	3
y	4	1	0	1	4

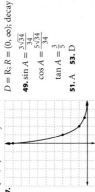

5. clockwise; lower right to upper left
7.
9. $y = -x + 1; D = [-1, 3]$ 11. $y = -(x+1)^2 + 4; D = [-3, 1]$
13. $x = (y+1)^2 - 1; D = [-3, 1]$
15. $\frac{x^2}{9} + \frac{y^2}{16} = 1$
17. $x^2 + y^2 = 9$
19. $y^2 - \frac{x^2}{9} = 1$
21. $\frac{(x-1)^2}{4} + \frac{(y-3)^2}{16} = 1$
23. $\frac{(x+4)^2}{36} + \frac{(y+8)^2}{25} = 1$
25. $x = t - 1, y = (t-1)^2 - 1, t \in [-1, 3]$ 27. $x = t - 4, y = 2(t-4) - 3; t \in [2, 5]$
29. $x = -2 + 4\tan\theta, y = 1 + 3\sec\theta$
31. $x = 1 + 8\cos\theta, y = -2 + 10\sin\theta$
33a. $x = (70\cos 15°)t, y = -16t^2 + (70\sin 15°)t + 6.5$
33b. ≈ 8.6 ft 33c. ≈ 81.1 ft 35a. ≈ 1.94 sec; 75 yd
35b. ≈ 3 ft 37a. $x^2 + y^2 = r^2$ 37b. $(x-h)^2 + (y-k)^2 = r^2$
39. (a) If $a = b$, it's a circle. (b) If $a > b$, then the cos term (x-component) is greater. ∴ an ellipse with its major axis on the x-axis
41. $x = h + a\sec\theta, y = k + b\tan\theta$ 43. $x^2 + y^2 = 64$; circle
45. $y = x^2$; parabola
47. hyperbola; $V: (\pm 2, 0); F: (\pm\sqrt{13}, 0); e \approx 1.80$
49. C, D 51. E

Section 8.6

1. $e = 1$; parabola; $y = 4$ 3. $e = 6$; hyperbola; $x = -1.5$
5. $e = \frac{4}{3}$; hyperbola; $x = -6$ 7. $e = 0.6$; ellipse; $x = -\frac{7}{3}$
9. E 11. F 13. D 15. $r = \frac{5}{1 - 2\sin\theta}$; parabola
17. $r = \frac{2}{1 - 2\sin\theta}$; hyperbola 19. $r = \frac{1.5}{1 + 0.5\cos\theta}$
21. $r = \frac{6}{1 + 2\sin\theta}$ 23. $\frac{x^2}{60} + \frac{(y+2)^2}{64} = 1$ 25. $x = \frac{1.5}{1 + 0.5\cos\theta}$
27. $\frac{(y+9)^2}{9} - \frac{x^2}{72} = 1$ 29. $a(1 - e); a(1 + e)$
31. $r = \frac{1.524(1 - 0.093^2)}{1 + 0.093\cos\theta} \approx 1.38$ AU; ≈ 1.67 AU
33. $r = \frac{4}{1 - \cos\theta}$ 35. $r = \frac{9}{4 + 5\sin\theta}$
37.

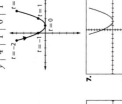

since $e = \frac{PF}{PD}, PF = e \times PD$
$r = e(d + r\cos\theta)$
$r = ed + er\cos\theta$
$r - er\cos\theta = ed$
$r(1 - e\cos\theta) = ed$
$r = \frac{ed}{1 - e\cos\theta}$

41. $x = \frac{\sqrt{3}}{2}u - \frac{1}{2}v, y = \frac{1}{2}u + \frac{\sqrt{3}}{2}v$ 43. 25, 30, 35
45. $a_1 = 4; a_2 = 8; a_{10} = 40$ 47. D 49. E

Data Analysis

1. (80, 0) 3. $\frac{x^2}{16,974,400} + \frac{y^2}{16,968,000} = 1$ 7. $r \approx \frac{109,100}{1 + 0.5376\cos\theta}$
5. 67,000 mi 7. $e \approx 0.019$

Review

3. $y = \frac{1}{2}(x-3)^2 - 3$

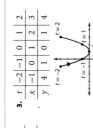

5.

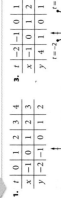

7. $y = -2x + 2$

C9 Section 9.4

1. $x^4 + 4x^3y + 6x^2y^2 + 4xy^3 + y^4$ 3. $w^8 + 8w^7v + 28w^6v^2$
$+ 56w^5v^3 + 70w^4v^4 + 56w^3v^5 + 28w^2v^6 + 8wv^7 + v^8$
5. $243a^5 - 405a^4 + 270a^3 - 90a^2 + 15a - 1$ 7. $16a^4 - 96a^3b$
$+ 216a^2b^2 - 216ab^3 + 81b^4$ 9. 15, 15 13. 1; 1
15. $a^3 + 3a^2b + 3ab^2 + b^3$ 17. $8c^3 - 12c^2 + 6c - 1$
19. $1024 + 1280z + 640z^2 + 160z^3 + 20z^4 + z^5$
21. $16a^4 - 96a^3b + 216a^2b^2 - 216ab^3 + 81b^4$
23. $3125a^5 + 12,500a^4z + 20,000a^3z^2 + 16,000a^2z^3 + 6400az^4$
$+ 1024z^5$ 25. $28x^2y^6$ 27. $-70,000m^4n^3$ 29. $-6435c^8d^7$
31. $3234w^{10}$ 33. $\approx 5.4\%$ 35. $\approx 27.3\%$ 37. $\approx 1.3\%$
39. ${}_nC_2 + {}_nC_1 = \frac{n!}{2(n-2)!} + \frac{n!}{(n-1)!} = \frac{2(n-1)!}{n(n-2)!} + \frac{(n+1)n\sqrt{n}}{2(n-1)!} \cdot \frac{(n+1)n\sqrt{n}}{2}$
$= \frac{n^2 - n}{2} + n = \frac{2n^2}{2} = n^2$
41. $x^2\sqrt{x} - 10x^2 + 40x\sqrt{x} - 80x + 80\sqrt{x} - 32$
43. $-367 + 144\sqrt{7}i$ 45a. $\approx 0.1\%$ 45b. $\approx 38.6\%$, $\approx 11.6\%$ 45c. $\approx 11.6\%$ 45d. $\approx 100\%$
47. $v = (2, -11, -3)$; $|v| = \sqrt{134} \approx 11.58$
$\frac{v}{|v|} = \langle \frac{2}{\sqrt{134}}, -\frac{11}{\sqrt{134}}, -\frac{3}{\sqrt{134}} \rangle$
49. It is not geometric since $\frac{a_n}{a_{n-1}}$ is not constant: $4, \frac{9}{4}, \frac{16}{9}, \frac{25}{16}$
51. $a_1 = 4$, $a_n = \frac{3}{2}a_{n-1}$; $a_n = 4\left(\frac{3}{2}\right)^{n-1}$; $a_{10} = \frac{19,683}{128}$
53. C 55. A

C9 Section 9.5

1a. I 1b. III 1c. V 1d. IV 1e. II 3. 4
5. $P(1): 8 = 1(1+7)$ is true.
$P(k): 8 + 10 + 12 + \cdots + 2(k+3) = k(k+7)$
$P(k+1): 8 + 10 + 12 + \cdots + 2(k+3) + 2((k+1)+3)$
$= (k+1)((k+1)+7)$
7. $P(1): 3$ is a factor of $7^1 - 4^1 = 3$.
$P(k): 3$ is a factor of $7^k - 4^k$
$P(k+1): 3$ is a factor of $7^{k+1} - 4^{k+1}$
9. If $1 + 5 + 9 + \cdots + (4k-3) = 2k^2 - k$,
then $1 + 5 + 9 + \cdots + [4(k+1) - 3] = 2(k+1)^2 - (k+1)$.
11. If $3k < 2^k + 3$, then $3(k+1) < 2^{k+1} + 3$.
13. 2216 15. 722,666 17. 31,009,903
19. $S_1 = \frac{a_1(1-r^1)}{1-r} = a_1$
Assume $P(k): S_k = \frac{a_1(1-r^k)}{1-r}$
$a_1 + a_2 + \cdots + a_1r^{k-1} = \frac{a_1(1-r^k)}{1-r}$
Add $a_{k+1} = a_1r^{(k+1)-1} = a_1r^k$ to both sides.
$a_1 + a_2 + \cdots + a_1r^{k-1} + a_1r^k = \frac{a_1(1-r^k)}{1-r} + a_1r^k$
$S_{k+1} = \frac{a_1 - a_1r^k}{1-r} + \frac{a_1r^k - a_1r^{k+1}}{1-r} = \frac{a_1 - a_1r^{k+1}}{1-r}$
$= \frac{a_1(1-r^{k+1})}{1-r}$
$P(k+1): S_{k+1} = \frac{a_1(1-r^{k+1})}{1-r}$
$\therefore P(n)$ is true for all $n \in \mathbb{N}$.

21. $P(1): \sum_{k=1}^1 k^3 = 1^3 = 1 = \frac{1^2(1+1)^2}{4} = \frac{2^2}{4} = 1$
Assume $P(k): 1^3 + 2^3 + \cdots + k^3 = \frac{k^2(k+1)^2}{4}$.
Add $(k+1)^3$ to both sides.
$1^3 + 2^3 + \cdots + k^3 + (k+1)^3 = \frac{k^2(k+1)^2}{4} + (k+1)^3$
$= \frac{k^2(k+1)^2 + 4(k+1)^3}{4}$
$= \frac{(k+1)^2[k^2 + 4(k+1)]}{4}$
$= \frac{(k+1)^2(k^2+4k+4)}{4}$
$= \frac{(k+1)^2(k+2)^2}{4}$
$= \frac{(k+1)^2[(k+1)+1]^2}{4}$
$= P(k+1)$
$\therefore P(n)$ is true for all $n \in \mathbb{N}$.
23. $P(1): 1^3 - 1 + 12 = 12 = 6(2)$; 6 is a factor.
Assume $P(k): k^3 - k + 12 = 6c$, $c \in \mathbb{Z}$.
$P(k+1): (k+1)^3 - (k+1) + 12$
$= (k^3 + 3k^2 + 3k + 1) - k - 1 + 12$
$= (k^3 - k + 12) + 3k^2 + 3k$
$= 6c + 3k(k+1)$
$= 6c + 3(2d) = 6(c + d)$
$= 6e$, $e \in \mathbb{Z}$
$\therefore P(n)$ is true for all $n \in \mathbb{N}$.
25. $P(1): 8^1 - 3^1 = 5 = 5(1)$; 5 is a factor.
Assume $P(k): 8^k - 3^k = 5c$, $c \in \mathbb{Z}$.
$P(k+1): 8^{k+1} - 3^{k+1} = 8(8^k) - (3)3^k$
$= 8(8^k) - 8(3^k) + 5(3^k)$
$= 8(8^k - 3^k) + 5(3^k)$
$= 8(5c) + 5(3^k)$
$= 5(8c + 3^k) = 5d$, $d \in \mathbb{Z}$
$\therefore P(n)$ is true for all $n \in \mathbb{N}$.
27. $P(1)$ is true; $2^1 > 1$
Assume $P(k): 2^k > k$.
since $2^k > 1$ for $k > 0$,
$2^k + 2^k > k + 1$
$2(2^k) > k + 1$
$\therefore P(k+1): 2^{k+1} > k + 1$ and $P(n)$ is true for all $n \in \mathbb{N}$.
29. $P(4): 4! (= 24) > 2^4 (= 16)$
Assume $P(k): k! > 2^k$ when $k \geq 4$.
since $k + 1 > 2$ when $k \geq 4$, $(k+1)k! > (2)2^k$
$\therefore P(k+1): (k+1)! > 2^{k+1}$
and $P(n)$ is true for all $n \geq 4$, $n \in \mathbb{N}$.
31. $S_1 = 1, S_2 = 3, S_3 = 7, S_4 = 15, S_5 = 31; S_n = 2^n - 1$
$P(n): 1 + 2 + 4 + 8 + \cdots + 2^{n-1} = 2^n - 1$
$P(1): 1 = 2^1 - 1 = 1$
Assume $P(k): 1 + 2 + \cdots + 2^{k-1} = 2^k - 1$.
$1 + 2 + \cdots + 2^{k-1} + 2^k = 2^k - 1 + 2^k$
$= 2(2^k) - 1 = 2^{k+1} - 1$
$P(k+1): 1 + 2 + \cdots + 2^k = 2^{k+1} - 1$
$\therefore P(n)$ is true for all $n \in \mathbb{N}$.
33. $\sum_{k=1}^n k^3 = \frac{n^2(n+1)^2}{4} = \left(\frac{n(n+1)}{2}\right)^2 = \left(\sum_{k=1}^n k\right)^2$
35a. 180, 360, 540, 720,... 35b. $a_n = 180(n-2)$; $n \geq 3$

35c. $P(n)$: For n vertices, the number of degrees for all interior angles is $180(n-2)$.
35d. $P(3): a_3 = 180(3-2) = 180$, and the sum of the degree measures in any triangle is $180°$.
Assume $P(k): a_k = 180(k-2)$.
An additional vertex adds another triangle and another $180°$.
$P(k+1): a_{k+1} = 180(k-2) + 180 = 180(k-2+1)$
$= 180((k+1) - 2)$
$\therefore P(n)$ is true for $n \geq 3$, $n \in \mathbb{N}$.
35e. $1440°$
37. $P(1): \sum_{k=1}^1 k^4 = 1^4 = \frac{1(1+1)(2(1)+1)[3(1)^2 + 3(1) - 1]}{30}$
$= \frac{1(2)(3)(5)}{30} = 1$
Assume $P(k):$
$1^4 + 2^4 + \cdots + k^4 = \frac{k(k+1)(2k+1)(3k^2+3k-1)}{30}$
Add $(k+1)^4$ to both sides.
$1^4 + 2^4 + \cdots + k^4 + (k+1)^4$
$= \frac{k(k+1)(2k+1)(3k^2+3k-1)}{30} + (k+1)^4$
$= \frac{k(k+1)(2k+1)(3k^2+3k-1) + 30(k+1)^4}{30}$
$= \frac{(k+1)[k(2k+1)(3k^2+3k-1) + 30(k+1)^3]}{30}$
$= \frac{(k+1)(6k^4 + 9k^3 + k^2 - k + 30k^3 + 90k^2 + 90k + 30)}{30}$
$= \frac{(k+1)(6k^4 + 39k^3 + 91k^2 + 89k + 30)}{30}$
$= \frac{(k+1)(k+2)(2k+3)[3(k^2 + 2k + 1) + 3k + 3 - 1]}{30}$
having worked backwards from the right side of $P(k+1)$:
$= \frac{(k+1)(k+2)(2k+3)[3(k^2 + 2k + 1) + 3k + 3 - 1]}{30}$
$= \frac{(k+1)((k+1)+1)[2(k+1)+1][3(k+1)^2 + 3(k+1) - 1]}{30}$
$= P(k+1)$
$\therefore P(n)$ is true for all $n \in \mathbb{N}$.
39. $P(1): \cos 1\pi = -1 = (-1)^1$ is true for all $n \in \mathbb{N}$.
Assume $P(k): \cos k\pi = (-1)^k$.
$\cos k\pi (\cos \pi) = (-1)^k (\cos \pi)$
$\cos k\pi \cos \pi - \sin k\pi \sin \pi$
$= (-1)^k \cos \pi - \sin k\pi \sin \pi$
Apply the cosine of a sum identity on the left and simplify the right.
$\cos(k\pi + \pi) = (-1)^k(-1) - (\sin k\pi)(0)$.
$\cos(k+1)\pi = (-1)^{k+1} - 0$
$P(k+1): \cos(k+1)\pi = (-1)^{k+1}$
$\therefore P(n)$ is true for all $n \in \mathbb{N}$.

C9 Data Analysis
3. 70 5a. $A - w - x - B$; 9 5b. $A - y - z$; 11

C9 Review

1a. finite sequence 1b. infinite series 3. $a_n = n^2$; $a_{10} = 100$
5. $a_1 = 1$; $a_n = \frac{1}{2}a_{n-1}$ where $n \geq 2$; $\frac{1}{16}, \frac{1}{32}, \frac{1}{64}$
7. converges; 2 9. 70, 112, 168 11. yes; $d = -15$; $-34, -49,$
-64 13. $a_1 = 0$, $a_n = a_{n-1} + 1$; $a_n = n - 1$; $a_{20} = 19$
15. 45, 36, 27 17. 5100 19. $a_n = 2n - 1$ 21. not geometric
23. $a_1 = 216$, $a_n = \frac{1}{3}a_{n-1}$; $a_n = 216\left(\frac{1}{3}\right)^{n-1}$; $a_{10} = \frac{8}{729}$
25. $a_n = \frac{5}{8}(2)^n$; $a_{10} = 640$ 27. ≈ -226.66 29. $846,272.41$
31. $a^5 - 15a^4 + 90a^3 - 270a^2 + 405a - 243$
31. $64 - 384z + 960z^2 - 1280z^3 + 960z^4 - 384z^5 + 64z^6$
35. 6; 1 37. $4 - 24\sqrt{2}i + 108z^2 - 108\sqrt{2}i + 81i^4$ 39. 25,781,
$250w^4$ 41a. $P(1): 4$ is a factor of $9^1 - 5^1 = 4$. 41b. $P(k): 4$ is a factor of $9^k - 5^k$. 41c. $P(k+1): 4$ is a factor of $9^{k+1} - 5^{k+1}$.
43a. 90 43b. 837
45. $P(1): 1^2 + 1 + 4 = 6 = 2(3)$, so 2 is a factor.
Assume $P(k): k^2 + k + 4 = 2c$, $c \in \mathbb{Z}$.
$P(k+1): (k+1)^2 + (k+1) + 4$
$= (k^2 + 2k + 1 + k + 1 + 4$
$= (k^2 + k + 4) + 2k + 2$
$= 2c + 2(k+1) = 2c + 2d = 2e$, $e \in \mathbb{Z}$
$\therefore P(n)$ is true for all $n \in \mathbb{N}$.
47. $P(2)$ is true; $3^2 > 3(2)$
Assume $P(k): 3^k > 3k$ for $k > 1$,
and therefore $3(3^k) > 3(3k)$ (Mult. Prop of Ineq.).
For any $c > 1$, $3c > c + 3$.
Substituting $3k$ for c, $3(3k) > 3k + 3$
and $3(3^k) > 3k + 3$ (Transitive Prop.).
$P(k+1): 3^{k+1} > 3(k+1)$ for $k > 1$
$\therefore P(n)$ is true for all $n > 1$, $n \in \mathbb{N}$.
49. $P(4)$ is true: $\frac{(4)(4-3)}{2} = 2$
Assume $P(k)$: A k-gon has $\frac{k(k-3)}{2}$ diagonals.
For every additional vertex, the polygon has an additional $(k+1) - 2$ or $k - 1$ diagonals.
$P(k+1): \frac{k(k-3)}{2} + (k-1) = \frac{k(k-3) + 2(k-1)}{2}$
$= \frac{k^2 - k - 2}{2} = \frac{(k+1)(k-2)}{2} = \frac{(k+1)((k+1)-3)}{2}$
$\therefore P(n)$ is true for all $n \geq 4$, $n \in \mathbb{N}$.

C10 Section 10.1

1. dependent; independent 3. 12; dependent 5. 360
7. 181,440 9. 504 11. 2184 13. 21 15. 720 17. 60,480
19. 42,504 21. 5040 23. 1260 25a. 720 25b. 48
27a. 235,620 27b. 35,343 27c. 270,963 29a. 2,049,694,920
29b. 3,092,256,688 31a. $n!$ 31b. $\frac{n!}{r!}$ 31c. $n!$ 31d. 1
33. 12,600 35a. 712,882,560 35b. 3,564,412,800
35c. 5,483,712,000

41a. $a_n = 0.005625n^3 - 0.005625n^2 + 0.07125n + 0.085$
41b. $a_n = 0n^3 + 0.125n^2 + 0.5n - 0.25$
41c. $a_n = 0n^3 + 0n^2 + 0.125n + 0.125$
41d. $a_n = 0.375n^3 - 0.875n^2 + 1.4375n - 0.78125$
43a. even 43b. neither 43c. odd 43d. even
45. inverses 47. ±39 49. D 51. A

Section 10.4

1a. III **1b.** II **1c.** IV **1d.** I **3.** 89.2; 89; none
5. 66.2; 66; 66 **7.** $\bar{x} = 89.2$; $s^2 = 19.0$; $s = 4.4$
9.

$x_i f_i$	$f_i(x_i - \mu)^2$
110	343.22
126	52.02
134	2.42
345	4.05
210	10.83
216	45.63
146	48.02
75	47.61
1362	553.80

$\mu = 68.1$; $\sigma \approx 5.3$

11. 14 is the only outlier.
13a. positively skewed **13b.** normal **13c.** negatively skewed **15a.** II **15b.** III
15c. I **15d.** II **17.** min: 6; Q_1: 7; median: 8; Q_3: 9; max: 10
19. 86.5; 85.2 **21.** 63; 70.75
23. $\bar{x} \approx 79.6$; $s \approx 16.3$
25. $\bar{x} = 83.7$; $s \approx 10.2$
27. none
29a. population **29b.** $\mu \approx 8.3$; $\sigma \approx 3.6$
29c.
29d.

31.

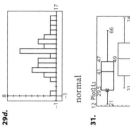

normal

---

41. $-2 - \sqrt{3}$ **43.** $a_n = \frac{5}{3}(3)^n$; 98,415 **45.** 42.2% **47.** E **49.** A

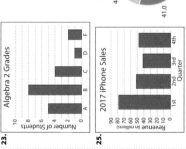

33a. $k = 6$; $w = 5$ **33b.**

Class	Frequency
15–19	1
20–24	1
25–29	11
30–34	8
35–39	3
40–44	1
Total	25

33c.

Players' Ages

35a.

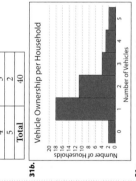

PCS SAT Math Scores

35b. Bridges per State

37.

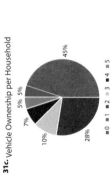

Cockatiel Weights

39.

Class	f	Σf	%	Σ%
0–3	18	18	36	36
4–7	16	34	32	68
8–11	4	38	8	76
12–15	8	46	16	92
16–19	1	47	2	94
20–23	2	49	4	98
24–27	1	50	2	100
Total	50		100	

---

37. working on both sides:

$$n\left[\frac{(n-1)!}{(r-1)![n-1-(r-1)]!}\right] \overset{?}{=} (n-r+1)\left[\frac{n!}{(r-1)![n-(r-1)]!}\right]$$

$$\frac{n(n-1)!}{(r-1)![n-r]!} \overset{?}{=} (n-r+1)\left[\frac{n!}{(r-1)![n-r+1]!}\right]$$

$$\frac{n!}{(r-1)!(n-r)!} = \left(\frac{n-r+1}{n-r+1}\right)\left[\frac{n!}{(r-1)!(n-r)!}\right]$$

39a. 35 **39b.** 6 **39c.** 2; 1 **39d.** 420 **41.** proper; HA: $y = 0$;
43. $\frac{A}{x} + \frac{B}{x^2} + \frac{C}{x+1}$ **45.** $c^3 + 3c^2d + 3cd^2 + d^3$
47. C **49.** D

Section 10.2

1. $S = \{1, 2, 3, 4, 5, 6\}$; $E = \{5, 6\}$ **3.** $S = \{HH, HT, TH, TT\}$;
$E = \{HT \text{ and } TH\}$ **5.** $S = \{CST, CTS, SCT, STC, TCS, TSC\}$;
$E = \{STC\}$ **7.** $\frac{1}{6}, \frac{1}{6}$ **9.** $\frac{1}{3}, \frac{19}{60}$ **11a.** rolling a 1 and rolling a 3
11b. no **13.** $\frac{2}{7}$ **15.** $\frac{83}{108}$ **17.** $\frac{31}{18}$ **19.** $\frac{31}{108}$ **21.** $\frac{4}{729}, \frac{16}{2889}$
23. $\frac{25}{5832}, \frac{4}{963}$ **25.** $\frac{3}{4}$ **27.** $\frac{5}{12}$ **29.** $\frac{5}{24}$ **31.** 1.3% **33.** 6.8%
35a. $\frac{5}{39}$ **35b.** $\frac{25}{78}$ **35c.** $\frac{5}{26}$ **35d.** $\frac{21}{26}$ **37a.** 3%
37b. dependent **39a.** 79.8% **39b.** 1.7%
41. Emily's bag: 1.0% **43a.** 3% **43b.** 24% **43c.** 73%
45. (−3.5, −6.6), (−1.8, −1.3), (0.8, 6.4) **47.** $\frac{x^2}{36} - \frac{y^2}{36} = 1$
49. 315 **51.** E **53.** B

C10 Data Analysis

1. $P(T|C)$ **3.** 3.5×10^{-6} or 0.0005% **5.** 2.375×10^{-4} or
0.023750% **7a.** $\approx 10.98\%$ **7b.** $\approx 10.20\%$

Section 10.3

1. parameter; statistic **3.** sample **5.** statistic **7.** parameter
9. interval **11.** ordinal
13.

```
  • •
• • •
• • • •
• • • •
• • •  •
51 52 53 54 55 56
```

15.

```
4 | 9
5 |
6 | 0
7 | 3 6
8 | 2 4 4 5
9 | 0 2
```

17.

```
3 | 1 1 4 7 8 9
4 | 1 5 6 8
5 | 0 1 2 3 6
6 | 1 2 5 9
7 | 4
```

19.

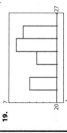

21. British Literature Grades
A, 20%; B, 35%; C, 25%; D, 15%; F, 5%

23. Algebra 2 Grades

25. 2017 iPhone Sales

27.

Michigan		Villanova
1 2 4 9	7	1 9
8 5	8	1 7
8 1	9	0 5

29.

Payton		Brown
1 0	0	9
5 7 7 8 8	1	0 0 1 4
1 1 1 1 3		5 8 8
6 6	2	1

31a.

Number of Vehicles	Frequency
0	2
1	18
2	11
3	4
4	3
5	2
Total	40

31b. Vehicle Ownership per Household

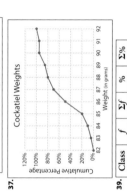

2017 iPhone Sales

31c. Vehicle Ownership per Household
0, 5%; 1, 45%; 2, 28%; 3, 10%; 4, 7%; 5, 5%

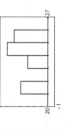

33. Eastern Pacific = 9; Atlantic = 8.5; median

35. $\sum_{i=1}^{n}(x_i - \bar{x}) = \sum_{i=1}^{n} x_i - \sum_{i=1}^{n} \bar{x}$ (3rd property)

$= \sum_{i=1}^{n} x_i - n\bar{x}$ (1st property)

$= \sum_{i=1}^{n} x_i - n\left(\dfrac{\sum_{i=1}^{n} x_i}{n}\right)$ (def. of mean)

$= \sum_{i=1}^{n} x_i - \sum_{i=1}^{n} x_i = 0$

37. $\mu \approx 54.6$; $\sigma \approx 7.02$ **39.** A: 94.8%; B: 81.65% **41a.** ≈ 30th **41b.** ≈ 68th **41c.** ≈ 47 in. **43.** $\left(\frac{36}{23}, -\frac{8}{23}\right)$ **45.** n = 6

47. Goals Scored

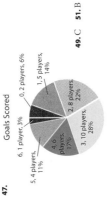

6, 1 player, 3%
0, 2 players, 6%
1, 5 players, 14%
2, 8 players, 22%
3, 10 players, 28%
4, 6 players, 17%
5, 4 players, 11%

C10 Section 10.5

1. deviation; standard deviation **3.** mean; median; mode
5. 100% **7a.** increases by 5 **7b.** remains the same
7c. remain the same **9.** z ≈ 0.71 **11.** z ≈ -0.57 **13.** -0.80
15a. ≈ 88.9% **15b.** ≈ 99.7% **17a.** does not apply
17b. ≈ 68% **19.** Since $z_1 = z_2 = 0.8$, his scores are the same number of standard deviations above the mean.
21. $z_A = 1.67$ is more standard deviations above the mean than $z_B = 1.60$. **23.** [5.45, 22.55] **25a.** 67 **25b.** 80 **25c.** 95
27. [5.45, 22.55] **29.** 100%; yes **31.** 100 **33a.** 0.63 standard deviations above the mean **33b.** 1.19 standard deviations below the mean **35a.** 47.5% **35b.** 81.5% **35c.** 84%
35d. 16% **37a.** [85, 91] **37b.** $x_i \geq 94$ **37c.** $x_i \leq 91$

39. $s_y = \sqrt{\dfrac{\sum_{i=1}^{n}(y_i - \bar{y})^2}{n-1}} = \sqrt{\dfrac{\sum_{i=1}^{n}(kx_i - k\bar{x})^2}{n-1}} = \sqrt{\dfrac{\sum_{i=1}^{n}[k(x_i - \bar{x})]^2}{n-1}} = \sqrt{\dfrac{\sum_{i=1}^{n}k^2(x_i - \bar{x})^2}{n-1}} = k\sqrt{\dfrac{\sum_{i=1}^{n}(x_i - \bar{x})^2}{n-1}} = ks_x$

41a. [670, 1450] **41b.** 16th **41c.** 42,500

C10 Section 10.6

1. 0.455 **3.** 0.145 **5.** 25.5% **7.** 54.1% **9.** 0.9% **11.** 17.9%
13. 97.7% **15.** 90.9% **17.** 63.3% **19.** 13.7% **21.** 41.8%
23. 2.0% **25.** 86th percentile **27.** 95th percentile
29. 42nd percentile **31.** ≈ 8.0 **33.** ≈ 83.6 **35.** z ≥ 1.28
37. -2.17 ≤ z ≤ 2.17 **39.** $x_i \leq 76.8$ **41.** [45.9, 54.1]
43. μ = 84.6; σ ≈ 7.5 **45.** $y \approx 4.579(1.370)^x$

47.

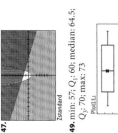

Zstandard
Standard

49. min: 57; Q_1: 60; median: 64.5; Q_3: 70; max: 73

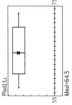

Plot1:L1
Med=64.5

51. B, C **53.** B

C10 Review

1. 1.12 **3a.** 40,320 **3b.** 336 **5a.** 2520 **5b.** 1680 **7.** 168
9a. $\frac{1}{6}$; $\frac{1}{10}$ **9b.** $\frac{1}{2}$; $\frac{1}{5}$ **11a.** $\frac{1}{4}$ **11b.** $\frac{1}{6}$ **13.** dependent
15a. 56% **15b.** 44% **17a.** ordinal **17b.** categorical
17c. ratio **17d.** interval

19.

2017		2018
8 1	0	1 4 7
6 6 4 2	1	2 7 8 9 9
5	2	3
10 4		1 1 8
6 5		0 7 8
6 2	6	6

21.

Smith Family Cousins
Frequency: 0-3, 4-7, 8-11, 12-15, 16-19
Ages

23. mean = 70.83; median = 72; mode = 72 **25.** $\bar{x} \approx 53.6$; $s \approx 6.3$ **27a.** μ = 26.64; median = 26.5; IQR = 3.5
27b. 34 is the only outlier.

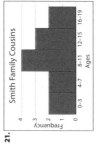

29a. 20.46 **29b.** 28.16 **31a.** μ = 30; σ = 10 **31b.** μ = 10; σ = 2 **33.** $z_{SAT} \approx 0.75$; $z_{ACT} \approx 0.93$; His ACT score was better.
35. 75% **37.** 0.385 **39.** 0.784 **41.** 49.1% **43.** 72.3%
45. 89th percentile **47.** [55.3, 60.7]

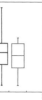

C11 Section 11.1

1. continuous **3.** discrete **5.** no **7.** no **9a.** 0.86 **9b.** 0.64
9c. 0.53 **11.** P(8) = 0.19; μ = 9; σ = 1.5 **13.** P(3) = 0.07;
μ = 5.4; σ = 1.47 **15.** yes; p ≈ 0.76; q ≈ 0.24; n = 42 **17.** yes;
p ≈ 0.72; q ≈ 0.28; n = 18 **19.** ≈ 21.0% **21a.** ≈ 27.1%
21b. ≈ 92.9% **21c.** ≈ 7.1% **23.** E(x) = μ = 3.28
25. E(x) = μ = 0.92

27. 0.3 Plot1:L1:L2 — n=0.25

29. 0.4 Plot2:L5:L6 — n=0.3333333

31. E(x) = -304: On average, the purchaser loses $304.
33. most likely: 13; least likely: 2 and 24; E(x) = 13 **35a.** yes
35b. skewed right **35c.** 0.23 **35d.** 0.57 **35e.** 3.91 yr
37a. $P_T(3) = 0.313$; $P_T(x \geq 2) = 0.813$ **39.** $\frac{\pi}{3}, \frac{2\pi}{3}, \frac{4\pi}{3}, \frac{5\pi}{3}$
41. (2, 4) **43.** ≈ 68% **45.** A **47.** C

C11 Section 11.2

1a. II **1b.** III **1c.** I **3a.** I **3b.** II **5.** μ = 5; σ = 2.83
7. 0.3 Plot2:L1:L2 — n=0.2 — min=5 max<6

9. $\mu_{\bar{x}} = 86$; $\sigma_{\bar{x}} \approx 2.1$
13. yes; $\mu_{\bar{x}} = 126$; $\sigma_{\bar{x}} \approx 6.36$
15. no **17.** no **19.** yes

21a.

Sample; $\bar{x}$	Sample; $\bar{x}$
{3, 3}; 3	{8, 3}; 5.5
{3, 6}; 4.5	{8, 6}; 7
{3, 8}; 5.5	{8, 8}; 8
{3, 10}; 6.5	{8, 10}; 9
{6, 3}; 4.5	{10, 3}; 6.5
{6, 6}; 6	{10, 6}; 8
{6, 8}; 7	{10, 8}; 9
{6, 10}; 8	{10, 10}; 10

21b. 0.25 Plot1:L1:L2 — n=0.1875 — min=8 max<8.5

21c. $\mu_{\bar{x}} = 6.75$; $\sigma_{\bar{x}} \approx 1.83$; μ = $\mu_{\bar{x}}$; but σ > $\sigma_{\bar{x}}$
23a. ≈ 29% **23b.** ≈ 15% **25a.** ≈ 66% **25b.** ≈ 95%
27. ≈ 99.7% **29.** ≈ 76% **31.** ≈ 0.6% **33a.** ≈ 31%
33b. ≈ 66% **35a.** ≈ 21% **35b.** ≈ 7%
37c. $\mu_{\bar{x}} = 6.75$; $\sigma_{\bar{x}} \approx 1.49$; μ = $\mu_{\bar{x}}$; but σ > $\sigma_{\bar{x}}$
37b. 3 Plot1:L1:L2 — n=0.40625

39a. ≈ 47 **39b.** ≈ 0.05% **39c.** 50% **39d.** $825 **39e.** ≈ 33%
41. $\frac{37}{24}$ **43.** ⟨2, 11⟩; 2i + 11j **45.** 90th **47.** B **49.** A

C11 Section 11.3

1. E **3.** B **5.** Increase the sample size. **7.** 1.645 **9.** 1.440
11. ≈ 0.79 **13.** ≈ 0.69 **15.** $\bar{x} \approx 4.67$; $z_c \approx 1.96$;
17. ≈ (10,140, 10,604); We are 90% confident that μ is within the interval (10,140, 10,604).
19. ≈ (75.6, 82.4); We are 98% confident that μ is within the interval (75.6, 82.4). **21.** $\bar{x}$ = 533.8; CI: ≈ (458.0, 609.6)
23. 40 **25.** 37

27. $E = z_c\left(\dfrac{s}{\sqrt{n}}\right)$; $E\sqrt{n} = z_c s$; $\sqrt{n} = \dfrac{z_c s}{E}$; $n = \left(\dfrac{z_c s}{E}\right)^2$

29. (796.3, 803.7); (794.2, 805.8)
31. the lower confidence level (90%) and the largest sample size (n = 5000)
33. ≈ (115.22, 149.52) **35.** n ≥ 57
37a. no **37b.** yes **37c.** no **37d.** no
39a. sum: ≈ (54.63, 57.01); shade: ≈ (46.48, 48.86)
41a. 189.3 cal/serving **41b.** 99% CI: ≈ (173.0, 205.6); 95% CI: ≈ (176.9, 201.7); 90% CI: ≈ (178.9, 199.7)
43. $g(x) = \frac{1}{4}\sec \pi x$ **45.** 0.5877 **47.** $a_n = -8n + 20$; $a_{20} = -140$
49. D **51.** A, D

C11 Section 11.4

1. E **3.** D **5.** C **7.** test statistic **9a.** III **9b.** II **9c.** II
9d. V **9e.** I **11.** H_0; μ = 35 (claim); H_a; μ ≠ 35 **13.** type I error **15.** right-tailed; z ≈ 2.65 **17.** left-tailed; z ≈ -2.25
19. p ≈ 0.012 **21.** p < α; Reject H_0. **23a.** H_0; μ = 355 (claim); H_a; μ ≠ 355 **23b.** α = 0.05 **23c.** two-tailed test with $z_c \approx \pm 1.96$; critical regions: z < -1.96 and z > 1.96
23d. z ≈ ±1.790 **23e.** Fail to reject H_0. **25a.** H_0; μ ≤ 128; **25b.** α = 0.05 **25c.** right-tailed test with $z_c \approx 1.645$; critical region: z > 1.645 **25d.** z ≈ 2.20
25e. Reject H_0 and accept H_a. **27a.** H_0; μ ≥ 90; H_a; μ < 90 (claim) **27b.** α = 0.05 **27c.** z ≈ -1.826 **27d.** p ≈ 0.03
27e. Reject H_0 and accept H_a. **29.** yes **31.** ≈ (57.3, 59.9); no
33. z = -2.30 **35.** yes **37.** Since p ≈ 0.002 < α, reject H_0. The means of the two classes are statistically different at the 0.05 level. **39.** Since p = 0.051 > α, fail to reject H_0. There is no significant difference in the weight lost between the two groups at the 95% confidence level. **41.** $\frac{1}{2}\log_3 y - 2\log_3 x + 2$
43. 56 **45.** ≈ (80.9, 87.1) **47.** B **49.** A

C11 Section 11.5

1. E, D, B, A, C **3.** E **5.** C **7.** the local community; survey
9. 50–71-yr-old men and women; observational **11.** the students in the school; survey **13.** systematic; Bias is likely. **15.** convenience; Bias is likely. **21.** stratified random **23.** random **25.** convenience; **27.** random
29a. 12–17-yr-olds from similar churches; the time spent watching TV each week **29b.** H_0; μ = 18.1; H_a; μ ≠ 18.1
29c. α = 0.10 or 0.05 are reasonable **33.** z = -1.87
39.

41. a = 20.5
B = 79.0°
C = 44.0°
43. neither **45.** D **47.** A, B, C

D = ℝ; R = [0, ∞); continuous

SELECTED ODD ANSWERS

682a — SELECTED ODD ANSWERS (left)

C11 Data Analysis
1. 30%   3. no   5. The entries in each row converge to probabilities of 0.231 (c), 0.462 (b), and 0.308 (w).   7. 0.18, 0.27, 0.22, 0.13, 0.20

C11 Review
1. discrete; The value can only be a whole number.
3. 0.35Plot1:L1L2
5. $P(8) \approx 0.18$; $\mu = 9$; $\sigma \approx 1.90$
7. 0.45Plot1:L1L2
$\mu \approx 5.18$; $\sigma \approx 1.96$

9. 0.45Plot1:L1L2

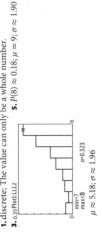

$\mu = 1.65$; $\sigma \approx 1.05$

$r = 0.417$
min=4 max=5

$E(x) = 4.17$; $\sigma^2 \approx 0.81$
$\sigma \approx 0.90$

11a. yes   11b. yes   13a. ≈ 18%   13b. ≈ 1.7%   15. ≈ 1.0%
17a. 87%   17b. 1.9%   19. 20 hits; ≈ 56%   21. ≈ (18.19, 21.01)
23. $\bar{x} \approx 65.78$; $E \approx 3.57$; CI: ≈ (62.21, 69.35)   25. 90% CI:
≈ (15.13, 15.87); 95% CI: ≈ (15.06, 15.94)
29. $H_0: \mu = 250$ (claim); $H_a: \mu \neq 250$ 31. type I error
33. type II error   35. Based on this sample, commute times in their city are significantly different from the national average at a 95% confidence level.   39. eighth grade students from area schools; experimental   41. self-selected
43. random   45a. observational

C12 Section 12.1
1. 0   3. ∞   5. does not exist   7. 0   9. 5   11. does not exist
13. 3   15. $\lim_{x\to\infty} f(x) = \infty$; $\lim_{x\to-\infty} f(x) = -\infty$ 17. $D = \mathbb{R}$; -4
19. $D = \{x \mid x \neq 0\}$; ∞   21. $D = \{x \mid x \neq (2n+1)\frac{\pi}{2}, n \in \mathbb{Z}\}$; does not exist   23. $D = \mathbb{R}$; 2   25. $x = -2$ 27. $x = -4$
29. does not exist   31. 2   33. $\frac{1}{3}$ 35. 3   37. ∞ (divergent)
39. does not exist   41a. $f(x) = 4{,}575{,}000(1.06)^x$ 41b. ∞
41c. tenth year   43a. $\frac{a}{b}, \frac{a}{b}$ 43b. 0, 0   43c. ∞, ∞
43d. -∞, -∞   43e. ∞, ∞   43f. -∞, ∞   45. $y = \frac{4}{3}x + 3$
47. $\frac{25}{4}$ 49. $p \approx 0.028$; Reject H_0 51. E   53. D

C12 Section 12.2
1. limit of a constant   3. limit of a scalar multiple   5. limit of a product   7. 0   9. $-\frac{11}{2}$ 11. 49   13. indeterminate form
15. undefined expression   17. -1   19. $\frac{\sqrt{3}}{2}$ 21. 2   23. $-\frac{1}{4}$

25. $\frac{\sqrt{2}}{4}$ 27. 0   29. $\frac{1}{3}$ 31. does not exist   33. 8   35. 0   37. 4
39. never   41. HA: $y = 0$ 43. $h + 2x - 4$
45. $\dfrac{\tan x}{1 - \tan^2 x} = \dfrac{\frac{\sin x}{\cos x}}{1 - \frac{\sin^2 x}{\cos^2 x}} = \dfrac{\sin x \cos x}{\cos^2 x - \sin^2 x}$
$= \dfrac{\sin x \cos x}{\cos^2 x - (1 - \cos^2 x)} = \dfrac{\sin x \cos x}{2\cos^2 x - 1}$
47. hyperbola; $C(1, 0)$; $V: (-4, 0), (6, 0)$; $c = 13$
49. C   51. B, C

C12 Section 12.3
1. 2   3. $2x + 3 + h$ 5a. yes   5b. no   5c. yes   7a. no
7b. yes   7c. yes   9. $f'(-1) = 2$ 11. $f'(-8) = 0$ 13. $f'(x) = 0$
15. $f'(x) = \frac{1}{5}$ 17. $f'(x) = 3x^2$ 19. 4.25 m/sec   21. 48 m/sec
25. $v_{ins}(t) = 16t - 13$ 27. $f'(x) = \frac{2\sqrt{3x}}{3}$
29. $f'(x) = 2x - 1$; $y = -9x - 16$ 31. $f'(x) = m$ 33. -48 ft/sec
35. 24 ft/sec; -72 ft/sec   37. $f'(x) = -\frac{k}{x^2}$ 39. $f'(x) = 0$ for all $x \notin \mathbb{Z}$ 41. $6i$ 43. -34   45. divergent   47. A   49. A

C12 Section 12.4
1. $f'(x) = 0$ 3. $f'(x) = 44x^3$ 5. $g'(x) = 5x^4 + 4x^3 + 3x^2 + 2x + 1$
7. $p'(x) = 4x^3 - 9x^2$ 9. $f'(x) = -15x^{-16}$ 11. $t'(x) = \frac{1}{3}x^{-3}$ or $-\frac{1}{9}$
13. $f'(4) = 24$; $f'(-2) = -12$ 15. $h'(1) = -1$; $h'(-3) = -\frac{1}{9}$
17. $y = 6x - 3$ 19. $y = \frac{1}{4}x + 1$ 21. min: $(-2, -8)$
23. max: $(-2, 15)$; min: $(1, -12)$ 25. 256,000   27. 112.5 m²
29a. $h(t) = -16t^2 + 63t + 63$; 31 ft/sec; -33 ft/sec
29b. $f(t) = v(t) = -32t + 63$; 31 ft/sec   29c. 4 sec; -65 ft/sec   29d. ≈ 1.97 sec; 66 ft
33. at least 23.6 m/sec   33. $h'(t) = -gt + v_0$; instantaneous velocity   35. $f(x) = 16x^7 - 60x^5$ 37. $q'(x) = -5x^2$
39. rel. max.: (1, 5); rel. min.: (3, 1); point of inflection: (2, 3)
41. $v(t) = (10t + 4)$ ft/sec; $a(t) = 10$ ft/sec²   43. $u(x) = 3x^{10}$; $v(x) = x^4 + 2x^2 + 5$ 45. $\theta = 68°$ 47. 3   49. C   51. C

C12 Section 12.5
1. $y' = 0$ 3. $f'(x) = 7e^x$ 5. $f'(x) = 7e^x$
7. $h'(x) = 16x^7 - 60x^5$ 9. $f'(x) = e^x(\cos x - \sin x)$
11. $f'(x) = \frac{16x}{(x^2 + 5)^2}$ 13. $y' = \sec^2 x$ 15. $y' = 10(2x + 1)^4$
17. $f'(x) = 2x \cos (x^2 - 8)$ 19. $f'(x) = 3x^2 \cos x - x^3 \sin x$
21. $h'(x) = \frac{15}{2}x^{\frac{3}{2}} + \frac{3}{2}\sqrt{x}$ or $\left(\frac{15}{2}x + \frac{3}{2}\right)\sqrt{x}$
23. $y' = -\csc x \cot x$ 25. $f'(x) = \frac{-x^2 + 7x - 6}{e^x}$
27. $g'(x) = 250(x - 8)^{49}$ 29. $h'(x) = \frac{7}{2}\sqrt[4]{(2x+1)^3}$ 33b. ≈ 12.66 days
31. $y' = \sin 2x$ 33a. ≈ 2184 cells/day   39. $k'(x) = 5(x - 8)^{49}(51x - 8)$
35. $1233.23/yr   37. $3x^2 e^{x^3 - 4}$
41. $f'(x) = -(x^2 - 1)^{\frac{3}{2}}$
43. Let k be a natural number such that $n = -k$. $f(x) = x^n = x^{-k} = \frac{1}{x^k}$

682b — SELECTED ODD ANSWERS (right)

A1
1. $U = \{1, 2, 3, \ldots, 12\}$ 3. M and K   5. ∅
7. $\{1, 2, 6, 7, 8, 11, 12\}$ 9. $\{6\}$ 11. B   13. ℕ   15. false
17. true   19. false
21, 23, 25.

ℝ Q' $\sqrt{2\pi^2}$ 0.353553555...
ℚ $\sqrt{169}$
ℤ, W, ℕ

27. ℕ, W, ℤ, ℚ, ℝ   29. ℤ, ℚ, ℝ
31. $\{\ldots, -5, -3, -1, 1, 3, 5, \ldots\}$ 33. $\{n \mid n \geq -5\}$
35. $\{z \mid z \in \mathbb{Z} \text{ and } -5 < z < 24\}$

A2
1. $x = 7$ 3. $a = 5$ 5. $b = -4$ 7. $x = 16$ 9. $x = 14.77$
11. $x \neq 11$ 13. $a \leq 57$ 15. $y < -\frac{40}{9}$ 17. $x = -\frac{7}{4}$
19. $x \leq -3$ or $x > 2$ 21. ∅   23. $3.2 < x \leq 7$ 25. $-4 < a < 0$
27. $x < 0$ or $x > \frac{16}{5}$ 29. $-\frac{35}{2} \leq x \leq \frac{25}{2}$ 31. $x = 1, 5$
33. $x = -6, 9$ 35. $x = -\frac{5}{2}, 3$ 37. $x = -\frac{1}{2}, 5$
39. $x = \frac{-5 \pm \sqrt{73}}{8}$

A3
1. $x = -3, 5$ 3. $x = -0.5, 0.8$ 5. $x = -0.58, 2.58$
7. $x = -1.38$ 9. $x = \pm 1.35$ 11. $x = -2, 4$ 13. $x = -1, 0.2, 2$
15. $x = -1.5, -1, 0.5, 1$ 17. $(-\infty, -1] \cup [1.8, \infty)$
19. $[-0.81, 0.81]$ 21. $(-13, -1)$ 23. $[-5.46, 1.46]$
25. $(-2.6, -0.2) \cup (3, 5.4)$

A4
1. 16   3. no real solution   5. -0.3   7. $8x^4 y^2 z^2 \sqrt{2z}$
9. $-8x^5 y^6 \sqrt[3]{3y}$ 11. $2|x|$ 13. $|3n - 4|$ 15. 3   17. $\frac{1}{\sqrt[5]{2}}$ 19. 4
21. $\frac{1}{729}$ 23. $5^{\frac{2}{3}}x^{\frac{1}{3}}y^2$ 25. $2^{\frac{1}{5}}3^{\frac{1}{3}}a^{\frac{1}{5}}b^{\frac{3}{5}}$ 27. $\sqrt[3]{9x}$ 29. $\sqrt[10]{240x^3}$
31. 128   33. $3\sqrt{3}$

A5
1. $-i$ 3. $3i$ 5. $9 + 3i$ 7. $6 - 12i$ 9. $-12 - 3i$ 11. $52 + 26i$
13. 34   15. $-\frac{3}{13} + \frac{28}{13}i$ 17. $(x + 7)(x - 7)$ 19. $(x - 7)(x - 2)$
21. $x = 3 \pm 2i$ 23. $x = 4 \pm \sqrt{2}i$

C12 Data Analysis
$f(x) = \dfrac{0(x^k) - 1(kx^{k-1})}{(x^k)^2} = \dfrac{-kx^{k-1}}{x^{2k}}$
$= -kx^{k-1-2k} = -kx^{-k-1} = nx^{n-1}$
45. 0; = 90°   47. true   49. $z = -1.75$ 51. B   53. D

C12 Data Analysis
1. $C'(x) = 0.12x^2 - 6x + 320$ 3. 25 items; $245
5. $R'(x) = -0.2x + 20$; $R(100) = \$1000$
7. 8750 items; $765,125   9. ≈ $25.06; ≈ 349%

C12 Section 12.6
1. $\Delta x = 0.5$; $x_i = 0.5, 1, 1.5, 2, 2.5, 3$ 3. $\Delta x = 0.5$; $x_i = -0.5, 0, 0.5, 1, 1.5, 2$ 5. $\int_0^4 6\,dx$; 42   7. $\int_1^7 \left(\frac{1}{2}x + 2\right)dx$; 18   9. 15 u²
11. 12.48 u²   13. 13.44 u²   15. 40 u²   17. 1.00 u²   19. 128.26 u²
21. $7\frac{1}{3}$ 23. 12   25. 4   27. $19\frac{2}{3}$ 29. 45 m   31. 80 ft   33b. 15 u²
33c. $\int_2^5 (-2x + 12)\,dx$ 33d. 15 u²   37. $\frac{1}{3}b^3 + 3b$

39.

$\frac{4}{29}$	$-\frac{3}{29}$
$\frac{3}{58}$	$\frac{5}{58}$

41. mean: ≈ 32.8; median: 34; mode: 44
43. 2   45. D   47. A

C12 Section 12.7
1. $F(x) = 10x$ 3. $H(t) = \frac{1}{5}t^5$ 5. $F(x) = 3x + C$
7. $F(\theta) = 7\sin\theta + C$ 9. $F(x) = \frac{1}{10}x^{20} + C$ 11. 9   13. ≈ 2.350
15a. sometimes   15b. never   15c. sometimes   15d. always
17. $G(x) = x^2 - 3x - 23$ 19. $K(x) = -3x^3 - 4x + 1055$
21. $\frac{2}{3}x^3 - \frac{3}{2}x^2 + x$ 23. $7(\sin x + e^x) + C$ 25. 17.5
27. 11,100   29. $\frac{38}{3}$ 31. $h(t) = -16t^2 + 20t + 38$ 33a. 48 ft
33b. 16 ft   33c. -64 ft   33d. $A_{[0,1]} = 48$ ft; $A_{[1,2]} = 16$ ft;
$A_{[2,4]} = 64$ ft   35. 225 J   37a. -4, 4 u²   37b. 4, 4 u²
37c. 0, 8 u²   39. 7   41. 18 u²   45a. $\frac{1}{x} + C$ 45b. -2
47. $y = -3x + 7$ 49. $\frac{1}{3}, \frac{1}{9}, \frac{2}{9}, \frac{2}{45}$ 51. $f'(-2) = -4$
53. A   55. B

C12 Review
1a. 0   1b. 1   1c. does not exist   3a. $\lim_{x\to\infty} h(x) = \infty$; $\lim_{x\to-\infty} h(x) = -\infty$ 3b. $\lim_{x\to\infty} g(x) = \infty$; $\lim_{x\to-\infty} g(x) = \infty$
5. $D = \mathbb{R}$; -28   7b. 0   9. 320   11. 1   13. $-\frac{\sqrt{3}}{6}$ 15. 0
17. $f'(x) = \lim_{h\to 0} \frac{k(x+h) - kx}{h} = \lim_{h\to 0} \frac{kx + kh - kx}{h}$
$= \lim_{h\to 0} \frac{kh}{h} = \lim_{h\to 0} k = k$
19. 20.2 m/sec   21. $g(x) = 230x^{22} - 68x^{16} - 33x^{10} + 10x^4 - 1$
23. $y = -6x - 6$ 25a. $h(t) = -4.9t^2 + 176.4t$; 36 sec
25b. $v(t) = h'(t) = -9.8t + 176.4$; 137.2 m/sec; -19.6 m/sec
25c. 1587.6 m   27. $h'(x) = \frac{(2x+4)^3}{3}$ 29. $y' = 2\cos x - 2x\sin x$
31. $f'(x) = (9 - 12x)(3x - 2x^2)^3$ 33. $10e^x + 2e^x$
35. ≈ 333.2 cells/day; ≈ 12.08 days   37. $\int_{-3}^{1} |x| + 2\,dx$; 16.5 u²
39. 13.35 u²   41a. $F(x) = 8x$ 41b. $H(t) = \frac{t^4}{4}$ 41c. $G(x) = 3e^x$
41d. $F(x) = x^2 + 2e^x$ 43a. $\frac{3}{2}y^2 + C$ 43b. $-6\cos\theta + C$
45. $h(t) = -16t^2 + 82$ 47. 3.083 u²

Glossary

absolute value function (p. 18) A function of the form $f(x) = |x|$ where $f(x) = x$ if $x \geq 0$ and $f(x) = -x$ if $x < 0$.

acceleration due to gravity (p. 14) The constant g, where g is approximately 32 ft/sec^2 or 9.8 m/sec^2.

algebraic function (p. 128) A function that involves only the algebraic operations of addition, subtraction, multiplication, division of constants and an independent variable, and raising an independent variable to a rational power.

alternative (research) hypothesis (p. 573) A statement that is the negation of the null hypothesis and contains an inequality such as $>$, $<$, or $\neq$. Denoted H_a.

ambiguous case (p. 270) The SSA case, which does not always uniquely determine a triangle.

amplitude (p. 198) Half the difference of the maximum and minimum values of a periodic function.

anchor step (p. 477) The initial step in mathematical induction that shows $P(n)$ is true for $P(1)$.

angle of depression (p. 183) The angle formed by a horizontal line and the line of sight toward an object that is below the horizontal.

angle of elevation (p. 183) The angle formed by a horizontal line and the line of sight toward an object that is above the horizontal.

angular speed (p. 175) The ratio of the angle of rotation (in radians) per unit of time: $\omega = \frac{\theta}{t}$.

annual percentage rate (APR) (p. 130) The yearly interest rate expressed as a percentage.

annual percentage yield (APY) (p. 134) The equivalent annual rate for an investment at a given annual percentage rate (APR) compounded n times after 1 yr: $P(1 + APY) = P\left(1 + \frac{APR}{n}\right)^n$.

antiderivative (p. 638) If $F'(x) = f(x)$, the function $F(x)$ is an antiderivative of $f(x)$.

aphelion (pp. 407, 438) The point at which an orbiting object is at its farthest distance from the sun.

Arccosine (p. 217) The inverse function of cosine: $y = \text{Cos}^{-1} x$.

arc length formula (p. 174) A central angle of radian measure θ in a circle with radius r intercepts an arc with length $s = r\theta$.

Arcsine (p. 216) The inverse function of sine: $y = \text{Sin}^{-1} x$.

Arctangent (p. 218) The inverse function of tangent: $y = \text{Tan}^{-1} x$.

argument (p. 324) The angle θ of a complex number in polar form $z = r(\cos \theta + i \sin \theta)$.

arithmetic means (p. 458) The terms between any two given terms of an arithmetic sequence.

arithmetic sequence (p. 456) A sequence in which the difference of any two consecutive terms is a constant.

arithmetic series (p. 459) The sum of the terms of an arithmetic sequence.

asymptote (p. 104) A line that a graph continually approaches.

augmented matrix (p. 353) A combination of the coefficient and constant matrices of a linear system.

average velocity (p. 615) $\frac{\text{change in position}}{\text{change in time}} = \frac{\Delta d}{\Delta t}$.

axis of symmetry (pp. 39, 396) The line that divides a parabola into mirror-image halves.

bias (p. 585) A factor that systematically causes a sample to differ from the population.

binomial (p. 472) The sum of two unlike terms.

binomial coefficients (p. 472) The coefficients of the terms generated by expanding $(a + b)^n$.

binomial experiment (p. 474) A statistical experiment of n identical independent trials where each trial results in either a success or a failure.

binomial probability (p. 474) The probability of x successes in n trials of a binomial experiment is $P(x) = {}_nC_x p^x q^{n-x}$, where p is the probability of success and q, the probability of failure, is $1 - p$.

binomial probability distribution (p. 549) A table describing all the possible outcomes of a binomial experiment: $P(x) = {}_nC_x p^x q^{n-x}$.

bivariate data (p. 59) Data containing two related variables.

carrying capacity (p. 158) The limit of growth supported by the environment.

center (of a hyperbola) (p. 412) The midpoint of the transverse axis of a hyperbola.

center (of an ellipse) (p. 403) The midpoint of the major axis of an ellipse.

change of base formula (p. 145) $\log_b x = \frac{\log_a x}{\log_a b}$ for $a, b \in \mathbb{N}$ when $a \neq 1$ and $b \neq 1$.

circular function (pp. 191–92) A trigonometric function, such as $\tan \theta = \frac{y}{x}$, defined in terms of a point $P(x, y)$ on the unit circle where x, y, and θ are real numbers.

closed interval (p. 4) An interval that includes both endpoints. The interval $\{x \mid a \leq x \leq b\}$ is denoted $[a, b]$.

coefficient of determination (p. 60) (r^2 value) Describes the extent to which the variation in the dependent variable can be explained by variation in the independent variable.

cofactor (p. 362) The cofactor C_{ij} of entry a_{ij} in a square matrix with minor M_{ij} is $C_{ij} = (-1)^{i+j} M_{ij}$.

cofunction (pp. 180, 234) A trigonometric function of an angle's complement.

combination (pp. 473, 492) The number of different ways to choose r out of n items where order is not important, denoted ${}_nC_r$, $C(n, r)$, or $\binom{n}{r}$.

common difference (p. 456) The difference, d, between any two consecutive terms in an arithmetic sequence.

common logarithmic function (p. 137) The function $y = \log x$ where $10^y = x$.

common ratio (p. 463) The quotient, r, between any two consecutive terms in a geometric sequence.

completing the square (p. 40) Adding the constant $\left(\frac{b}{2}\right)^2$ to an expression in the form $x^2 + bx$ to obtain a perfect square trinomial.

complex number (p. 644) Any complex number, z, can be expressed in the standard form $z = a + bi$, where $a, b \in \mathbb{R}$ and $i = \sqrt{-1}$.

complex plane (p. 324) A coordinate plane with real and imaginary axes.

components (p. 287) The horizontal and vertical parts of a vector. Denoted $\mathbf{v} = \langle a, b \rangle$, where a represents the horizontal change $(x_2 - x_1)$ and b represents the vertical change $(y_2 - y_1)$ from the tail to the head of the vector.

component vectors (p. 296) The result of decomposing a vector into two orthogonal vectors, one of which is parallel to another given vector.

composition (p. 47) The composition of two functions f and g, denoted $f \circ g$, is defined as $(f \circ g)(x) = f(g(x))$.

compound inequality (p. 651) The combination of two inequalities into one statement using *and* or *or*.

compound interest (p. 130) The interest on both the principal and any interest accumulated.

conditional equation (pp. 233, 246) An equation that is true only for certain value(s) of the variable.

conditional probability (p. 499) The probability of an event, given the occurrence of a previous event.

confidence interval (p. 567) An interval around the point estimate in which it is reasonably certain that the actual parameter lies.

confidence level (p. 567) The probability that the confidence interval actually contains the population parameter.

conic section (conic) (p. 395) The intersection of a plane with a right circular conical surface.

conjugate axis (p. 412) The segment that passes through a hyperbola's center and is perpendicular to the hyperbola's transverse axis.

conjunction (p. 651) A compound mathematical sentence of the form $a \wedge b$ (or "a and b") that is true when both statements are true (the intersection of their solutions).

constant function (pp. 12, 25–26) A function of the form $f(x) = k$ whose value does not vary.

constant of variation (proportion) (p. 27) The nonzero constant relating the variables in a variation. In the functions $y = kx$ and $y = \frac{k}{x}$, k is the constant of variation.

continuity correction factor (p. 560) A correction applied when a continuous distribution is used to approximate a discrete distribution.

continuous function (pp. 19, 21) A function with no gaps or holes.

continuous on an interval (p. 21) A function is continuous on an interval (a, b) iff it is continuous at every point in (a, b).

continuous random variable (p. 546) A variable representing an uncountable number of outcomes within an interval in a probability experiment.

convergent sequence (p. 449) A sequence whose values approach a finite real number as the position number approaches infinity.

correlation coefficient (p. 60) Denoted r, where $-1 \leq r \leq 1$. Describes the degree to which two variables are related.

cosecant (pp. 179, 188) The trigonometric ratio that is the reciprocal of sine.

cosine (pp. 179, 188) The ratio of the leg adjacent to an acute angle and the hypotenuse of a right triangle. The ratio $\frac{x}{r}$, where $P(x, y)$ is a point on the terminal side of an angle in standard position and $r = \sqrt{x^2 + y^2}$.

cotangent (pp. 179, 188) The trigonometric ratio that is the reciprocal of tangent.

coterminal angles (p. 174) Two angles in standard position with the same terminal side.

co-vertices (pp. 403, 412) The endpoints of an ellipse's minor axis or of a hyperbola's conjugate axis.

critical (rejection) region (p. 575) The area where the difference between the test statistic and the proposed population parameter is enough to reject the null hypothesis.

critical value (p. 567) The z-value that corresponds to a certain confidence level.

damped harmonic motion (p. 225) Motion that occurs when friction reduces the displacement of an oscillating object. Modeled by $f(x) = ae^{-ct} \cos bt$ or $f(x) = ae^{-ct} \sin bt$ ($c > 0$), where a is the maximum displacement.

damped sinusoid (p. 225) A function of the form $f(x) = g(x) \sin bx$ or $f(x) = g(x) \cos bx$.

damping constant (p. 225) The value of $c > 0$ in the equation $f(x) = ae^{-ct} \cos bt$ or $f(x) = ae^{-ct} \sin bt$ that affects the rate of decrease in the amplitude of oscillations.

damping factor (p. 225) A factor $g(x)$ that reduces the amplitude of a sinusoid model $f(x) = g(x) \sin bx$ or $f(x) = g(x) \cos bx$.

decay factor (p. 129) The base, b, in the exponential function $y = ab^x$, given $0 < b < 1$.

decomposition (p. 48) The process of finding simpler functions $g(x)$ and $f(x)$ such that the given function $h(x) = f(g(x))$.

decreasing function (pp. 25–26) A function in which the value of y decreases as x increases.

definite integral (p. 633) The area of a region between the graph of a function $f(x)$ and the interval $[a, b]$ on the x-axis is given by the definite integral $\int_a^b f(x)\, dx = \lim_{n \to \infty} \sum_{i=1}^{n} f(x_i)\, \Delta x$, provided the limit exists.

degenerate conic (p. 395) A point, a line, or two intersecting lines that result when a plane intersecting a conical surface contains the vertex.

dependent events (p. 490) Events in which the probability of one event changes because another event has occurred.

dependent variable (p. 3) The variable representing the values of the range in a relation.

depressed polynomial (p. 88) The quotient of a polynomial divided by one of its binomial factors.

derivative function (p. 613) The derivative of $f(x)$, denoted $f'(x)$, where $f'(x) = \lim_{h \to 0} \frac{f(x+h) - f(x)}{h}$.

descriptive statistics (p. 507) The organization of data and the determination and reporting of its numerical characteristics.

determinant (pp. 361, 363) A characteristic value associated with a square matrix that indicates whether the inverse of the matrix exists.

difference quotient (p. 612) The slope of a secant line through the given points $(x, f(x))$ and $(x + h, f(x + h))$ is $\frac{f(x+h) - f(x)}{h}$.

differentiable function (p. 613) A function that has a derivative at every point of its domain.

differential operator (p. 614) The notation $\frac{d}{dx}$ that indicates to find the derivative of a function.

directrix (p. 435) A fixed line such that all points on a conic are equidistant to a conic's focus and the line.

direct variation (proportion) (p. 27) A function of the form $y = kx$ or $k = \frac{y}{x}$, where k is a nonzero constant of variation.

discontinuity (p. 21) A gap or hole in a relation caused by excluded values.

discrete random variable (p. 546) A variable representing a countable number of outcomes of a probability experiment.

disjunction (p. 651) A compound mathematical sentence of the form $a \vee b$ (or "a or b") that is true when either statement is true (the union of their solutions).

divergent sequence (p. 449) A sequence whose values do not approach a finite real number as the position number approaches infinity.

domain (p. 2) The set of first elements of the ordered pairs in a relation.

dot product (pp. 294–95, 305) For $\mathbf{u}$ and $\mathbf{v}$, $\mathbf{u} \cdot \mathbf{v} = |\mathbf{u}|\,|\mathbf{v}| \cos \theta$, where θ is the angle between $\mathbf{u}$ and $\mathbf{v}$ when the vectors are placed in standard position ($0 \leq \theta \leq 180$). Using vector components: if $\mathbf{u} = \langle u_1, u_2 \rangle$ and $\mathbf{v} = \langle v_1, v_2 \rangle$, then $\mathbf{u} \cdot \mathbf{v} = u_1 v_1 + u_2 v_2$.

eccentricity (pp. 407, 414, 435) The measure of a conic's deviation from a circle.

elementary row operation (p. 354) An operation that transforms an augmented matrix into an equivalent system by interchanging any two rows, multiplying or dividing each entry in a row by a nonzero number, or adding a multiple of one row to another.

eliminating the parameter (p. 52) The process of expressing y in terms of x when given a set of parametric equations.

ellipse (p. 403) The set of points in a plane such that the sum of the distances from two fixed points (the foci) is constant.

empty set (p. 647) A set containing no elements. Denoted $\varnothing$. Also called a *null set*.

end behavior (p. 25) A description of the values of a function as x approaches positive or negative infinity.

equivalent equations (p. 650) Equations that have the same solution set.

even function (p. 26) A function where $f(-x) = f(x)$ for all $x \in D$.

existence theorems (p. 94) Theorems that guarantee the existence of a quantity, but do not provide a means of finding it.

expected value (p. 547) The mean of a probability distribution. Denoted $E(x)$.

experiment (p. 497) A repeatable activity resulting in exactly one of a finite set of outcomes.

experimental (empirical) probability (p. 497) The ratio of the number of times an event occurs to the number of trials in an experiment.

explicit formula (pp. 447, 456) A formula in terms of a_n that allows direct computation of any term in the sequence.

exponential decay (p. 129) The decrease of a quantity by the same percentage per unit of time.

exponential equation (p. 149) An equation in which the variable occurs in the exponent.

exponential function (p. 128) A function of the form $f(x) = ab^x$ where $a \neq 0$, $b > 0$, and $b \neq 1$.

exponential growth (p. 129) The increase of a quantity by the same percentage per unit of time.

extraneous root (p. 74) A derived solution that is invalid because it does not make the original equation true.

extrapolation (p. 60) The process of making predictions outside the range of a data set.

factorial (p. 448) The product of a number, n, and every natural number less than that number. Denoted $n!$.

family of functions (p. 32) A group of functions whose graphs share similar characteristics.

five-number summary (p. 519) The minimum, lower quartile, median, upper quartile, and maximum values of a data set.

focal axis (p. 435) The line that passes through a conic's focus and is perpendicular to the conic's directrix.

focal distance (pp. 403, 412) The distance from the center of an ellipse or a hyperbola to each focus.

focal length (p. 396) The distance from the vertex of a parabola to its focus.

focus (p. 435) A fixed point such that the distances to that point from any point on the conic and from the conic's directrix are in a constant ratio, which is the conic's eccentricity, e.

frequency (p. 199) The reciprocal of the period of a function:
$$f = \frac{1}{p} = \frac{|b|}{2\pi}.$$

function (p. 2) A relation in which every element of the domain is paired with one and only one element of the range.

future value of an annuity (p. 467) The future value, FV, of an annuity consisting of n periodic payments of P with a periodic interest rate i is given by $FV = P\left[\dfrac{1 - (1+i)^n}{1 - (1+i)}\right]$ or $FV = P\left[\dfrac{(1+i)^n - 1}{i}\right]$.

Gaussian elimination (p. 353) The process of eliminating variables from a system to find an equivalent system in row echelon form.

Gauss-Jordan elimination (p. 355) The process of applying elementary row operations to an augmented matrix until the unique reduced row echelon form is found.

geometric means (p. 465) The terms between any two given terms of a geometric sequence.

geometric sequence (p. 463) A sequence in which the ratio of any two consecutive terms is a constant.

geometric series (p. 465) The sum of the terms of a geometric sequence.

greatest integer function (p. 18) A function that returns the greatest integer less than or equal to x.

growth factor (p. 129) The base, b, in the exponential function $y = ab^x$, given $b > 1$.

growth rate (p. 131) The term r in the exponential growth function, $P(t) = P_0(1 + r)^t$, where t = time.

half-life (p. 132) The time it takes for half a radioactive isotope to decay into a stable isotope of another element.

harmonic sequence (p. 458) The reciprocals of an arithmetic sequence.

histogram (p. 510) A graphic representation of a frequency distribution.

horizontal asymptote (p. 104) The line $y = c$ is a horizontal asymptote of $f(x)$ if $\lim\limits_{x \to -\infty} f(x) = c$ or $\lim\limits_{x \to \infty} f(x) = c$.

hyperbola (p. 412) The set of points in a plane such that the difference of the distances from two fixed points (its foci) is constant.

hypothesis testing (p. 573) The process of using statistics from a sample to examine a claim about the value of a population parameter.

identity (p. 233) An equation that is true for all values in the domain of the variable.

imaginary axis (p. 324) The vertical axis in the complex plane.

imaginary unit (p. 664) The imaginary unit, i, is the square root of -1, so that $i = \sqrt{-1}$ and $i^2 = -1$.

increasing function (pp. 25–26) A function in which the value of y increases as x increases.

indefinite integral (p. 639) The indefinite integral of $f(x)$ is $\int f(x)\, dx = F(x) + C$, where $F(x)$ is the antiderivative of $f(x)$ and C is a constant.

independent events (p. 490) Events in which the occurrence of one has no influence on the probability of the other events occurring.

independent variable (p. 3) The variable representing the values of the domain in a relation.

indeterminate form (p. 606) An expression obtained, such as $\frac{0}{0}$, that implies the function does not contain enough information to determine the limit at that point.

inferential statistics (p. 507) The process of interpreting the statistics of a sample to make predictions about a population's parameters.

infinite discontinuity (pp. 21, 105) An infinite discontinuity exists for $f(x)$ at $x = a$ if a one-sided $\lim\limits_{x \to a^{\pm}} f(x) = \pm\infty$.

infinite limit (p. 600) Describes a function's behavior, but the true limit does not exist.

instantaneous velocity (pp. 615–16) If the position of an object is represented by a function of time $f(t)$, then its instantaneous velocity at time t is $v_{inst}(t) = f'(t) = \lim\limits_{h \to 0} \dfrac{f(t+h) - f(t)}{h}$.

interpolation (p. 60) The process of making predictions within the range of a data set.

interquartile range (IQR) (p. 519) The difference between the third quartile and the first quartile of a data set.

intersection of sets (p. 647) The set of elements common to the given sets.

interval (p. 4) A continuous set of real numbers.

interval estimate (p. 566) A range of values used to estimate a population's parameter.

inverse functions (p. 56) A relation and its inverse that are both functions: $(f^{-1} \circ f)(x) = (f \circ f^{-1})(x) = x$.

inverse matrix (p. 370) The multiplicative inverse of square matrix A, denoted A^{-1}, is the matrix such that $AA^{-1} = A^{-1}A = I$, the identity matrix.

inverse relation (p. 53) If a relation R contains the ordered pair (a, b), its inverse relation, R^{-1}, contains the ordered pair (b, a).

inverse variation (proportion) (p. 28) A relation in which the product of the two variables is a nonzero constant, k. That is, $xy = k$, where $k \neq 0$.

invertible (nonsingular) matrix (p. 370) A matrix for which an inverse exists.

irrational number (p. 648) A real number that cannot be expressed as a ratio of two integers.

irreducible quadratic factor (p. 99) A second-degree polynomial that cannot be factored over the integers.

leading coefficient (p. 78) The constant factor of the term with the highest degree in a polynomial expression.

least common denominator (LCD) (p. 651) The smallest positive integer that is a multiple of two or more given denominators.

left-hand limit (p. 21) The left-hand limit of $f(x)$ as x approaches a, denoted $\lim\limits_{x \to a^-} f(x)$, is the number to which $f(x)$ gets closer and closer as x approaches a from the left.

level of significance (p. 575) The maximum allowable probability of making a type I error.

limit (pp. 21, 599) The limit of $f(x)$ as x approaches a, denoted $\lim\limits_{x \to a} f(x)$, is L iff $\lim\limits_{x \to a^-} f(x) = \lim\limits_{x \to a^+} f(x) = L$.

linear combination (p. 289) A sum of vectors in the form $a\mathbf{v} + b\mathbf{w}$, where a and b are scalars.

linear correlation (p. 60) Describes how closely data points are clustered along a trend line.

linear programming (p. 377) A technique used to maximize or minimize a particular quantity under a given set of constraints.

linear regression (p. 59) A statistical method of determining the line of best fit (trend line).

linear speed (p. 175) The ratio of arc length, or distance traveled, per unit of time: $v = \dfrac{s}{t}$.

line of best fit (p. 59) See **trend line**.

logarithmic equation (p. 149) An equation of the form $\log_b x = k$ in which the variable occurs in the argument (input) of a logarithmic expression.

logarithmic function (p. 136) The inverse of the exponential function $b^y = x$, denoted $y = \log_b x$, where x and b are positive and $b \neq 1$: $y = \log_b x$ iff $b^y = x$.

logistic growth function (p. 158) A function that can be written in the form $f(x) = \dfrac{c}{1 + ae^{-bx}}$ where a, b, and c are positive constants.

magnitude (pp. 287–88) The length of vector $\mathbf{v} = \langle a, b \rangle$ is $|\mathbf{v}| = \sqrt{a^2 + b^2}$.

major axis (p. 403) The chord containing the foci of an ellipse whose endpoints are the vertices of the ellipse.

margin of error (maximum error of the estimate) (p. 567) The greatest acceptable difference between the point estimate and the actual value of the parameter for a given confidence level, c.

mathematical induction (p. 477) A method of proving a proposition $P(n)$ is true for all natural numbers by showing that $P(1)$ is true and that $P(k + 1)$ is true when $P(k)$ is true.

matrix (p. 343) A rectangular array of numbers.

mean (p. 516) The arithmetic average obtained by dividing the sum of the values by the number of values.

median (p. 516) The middle value or the mean of the two middle values in a set of data arranged in numerical order.

midline (p. 201) The horizontal line halfway between the maximum and minimum values of a function: $y = \dfrac{max - min}{2}$.

minor (p. 362) The minor of entry a_{ij} in square matrix A, notated M_{ij}, is the determinant of the matrix formed by removing the ith row and jth column of A.

minor axis (p. 403) The chord perpendicular to the major axis that passes through the center of an ellipse and whose endpoints are the co-vertices of the ellipse.

mode (p. 516) The most frequently appearing value(s) in a data set.

modulus (p. 324) The absolute value of a complex number (the distance from the complex origin). If $z = a + bi$, then the modulus of $z = \sqrt{a^2 + b^2}$.

monomial functions (p. 78) Power functions of the form $f(x) = kx^n$, where n is a natural number, and constant functions of the form $f(x) = c$, where c is a real number.

multiplicative identity matrix (p. 346) A square matrix in which entries on the main diagonal are 1 and all other entries are 0.

multiplicity (p. 81) A root of a polynomial has a multiplicity of n if the polynomial contains n identical binomial factors.

natural base (p. 130) The number $e = \lim\limits_{x \to \infty} \left(1 + \dfrac{1}{x}\right)^x \approx 2.71828$.

natural exponential function (p. 130) The function $f(x) = e^x$ where $e \approx 2.71828$.

natural logarithmic function (p. 138) The inverse of the exponential function $e^y = x$, denoted $y = \ln x$, where x is positive: $y = \ln x$ iff $e^y = x$.

nonlinear asymptote (p. 107) Given a rational function $f(x) = \dfrac{a(x)}{b(x)}$ where degree of $a(x)$ is at least 2 greater than the degree of $b(x)$, the nonlinear asymptote is the quotient (without the remainder) when $a(x)$ is divided by $b(x)$.

nonrigid transformation (p. 33) A transformation that distorts the shape of the graph.

nth partial sum (p. 450) The sum of a sequence's first n terms, denoted S_n.

nth root of a complex number (p. 327) If $w = a + bi$ and z is a complex number such that $w^n = z$, then w is an nth root of z.

nth root of unity (p. 327) If $w = a + bi$ and $w^n = 1$, then w is the nth root of unity.

null hypothesis (p. 573) A statement about a population parameter that contains an equality such as $\geq$, $\leq$, or $=$. Denoted H_0.

objective function (p. 377) A linear function representing the quantity to be optimized in a linear programming problem.

octant (p. 303) One of eight regions created in space by a three-dimensional coordinate system.

odd function (p. 26) $f(-x) = -f(x)$ for all $x \in D$.

one-sided limit (p. 21) See **right-hand limit** or **left-hand limit**.

one-to-one function (p. 55) A function in which each element of the domain corresponds to exactly one element of the range.

open interval (p. 4) An interval that includes all the points between two endpoints but does not include the endpoints. The interval $\{x \mid a < x < b\}$ is denoted (a, b).

orthogonal vectors (p. 296) Two vectors **u** and **v** are orthogonal iff $\mathbf{u} \cdot \mathbf{v} = 0$. Nonzero orthogonal vectors are also perpendicular.

outlier (pp. 60, 519) A value in a data set that is significantly higher or lower than the other values in the set.

parabola (pp. 39, 396) The set of points in a plane that are equidistant from a fixed line (the directrix) and a fixed point (the focus) not on that line.

parameter (statistical) (p. 507) The numerical value for a characteristic of a population.

parametric curve (p. 429) A set of ordered pairs (x, y) defined by the parametric equations $x = f(t)$ and $y = g(t)$, where $f(t)$ and $g(t)$ are continuous functions of t on the parameter interval, I.

parametric equations (p. 52) A set of functions representing each coordinate in terms of one or more other independent variables (the parameters).

parent function (p. 32) The basic function used as a reference for transformed functions within a family of functions.

partial fraction decomposition (p. 383) The process of expressing a proper rational expression as a sum of simpler rational functions.

percentile (p. 520) When a distribution is divided into 100 equal parts, each percentile represents the amount of the distribution that lies below that percentile's value.

perihelion (pp. 407, 438) The point at which an orbiting object is at its closest distance to the sun.

period (pp. 193, 198) The horizontal length of one cycle in a periodic function.

periodic function (p. 193) A function f with a repeating pattern of y-values so that there exists a constant c such that $f(x + c) = f(x)$ for all x in the domain.

permutation (p. 491) The number of different ways to arrange (or order) r out of n items. Denoted $_nP_r$ or $P(n, r)$.

phase shift (p. 200) A horizontal translation in the graph of a trigonometric function.

piecewise function (p. 18) A function whose value is defined by multiple function rules for various intervals of its domain.

point estimate (p. 566) A single-value estimation of a population's parameter.

point (removable) discontinuity (pp. 21, 106) A single point on the graph of $f(x)$ that is not defined.

point-slope form (p. 12) A linear equation of the form $y - y_1 = m(x - x_1)$, where m is the slope of the line and (x_1, y_1) is a point on the line.

polar axis (p. 309) An initial ray drawn from the pole in the direction of the positive x-axis.

polar coordinates (p. 309) Coordinates of the form $P(r, \theta)$, where r is a directed distance from the pole to the point P and θ is a directed angle from the polar axis.

polar (trigonometric) form (p. 324) If $z = a + bi$, then $z = r(\cos \theta + i \sin \theta)$ or $z = r \operatorname{cis} \theta$ where r is the modulus and θ is the argument of z.

pole (p. 309) A fixed point, O, that serves as the origin for the polar coordinate system.

polynomial function (p. 78) A function of the form $p(x) = a_n x^n + a_{n-1} x^{n-1} + a_{n-2} x^{n-2} + \cdots + a_1 x + a_0$, where n is a nonnegative integer and the coefficients are real numbers.

population (p. 507) The larger overall set being considered in a statistical study.

power function (p. 25) A function of the form $f(x) = kx^n$ where k and the power n are nonzero constants.

primary solution (p. 246) A solution to a trigonometric equation that falls within the interval $[0, 2\pi)$.

principal root (p. 328) When $k = 0$ in the complex root of $\sqrt[n]{r} \operatorname{cis} \frac{\theta + k2\pi}{n}$.

principal value (p. 216) A value within a restricted domain of a trigonometric function.

probability distribution (p. 546) A table, graph, or equation that associates each possible value of a random variable, x, with its probability, $P(x)$.

projection (p. 296) If $\mathbf{w}_1$ and $\mathbf{w}_2$ are orthogonal component vectors of **u** and $\mathbf{w}_1$ is parallel to vector **v**, then $\mathbf{w}_1$ is the projection of **u** onto **v**, $\operatorname{proj}_\mathbf{v} \mathbf{u}$.

p-value (p. 577) The probability of obtaining a test statistic as extreme as or more extreme than the one found in the sample, assuming the null hypothesis is true.

quadrantal angle (p. 174) An angle in standard position whose terminal side lies along either the x- or y-axis.

quadratic function (p. 40) A function that can be written in the standard form $f(x) = ax^2 + bx + c$, where a, b, and $c \in \mathbb{R}$ and $a \neq 0$.

quartiles (p. 518) Values that divide ordered data into four equal sets.

radian (p. 173) The measure of a central angle that intercepts an arc whose length is the same as the circle's radius: 1 radian $= \frac{180°}{\pi} \approx 57.3°$.

radian measure (p. 173) The ratio of a central angle's intercepted arc's length, s, to the circle's radius, r: $\theta = \frac{s}{r}$.

radical equation (p. 74) An equation of the form $\sqrt[n]{x} = k$ that contains a radical expression with a variable in the radicand, or an equation of the form $x^{\frac{p}{r}} = k$ that contains a variable with a rational exponent.

radical function (p. 72) A function that contains a radical expression with the independent variable in the radicand.

random sample (pp. 507, 586) A sample for which every member of the population has an equal chance of being selected.

random variable (p. 546) A variable representing all possible numerical outcomes in a probability experiment.

range (of a data set) (pp. 510, 517) The difference between the maximum and minimum values.

range (of a function) (p. 2) The set of second elements of the ordered pairs in a relation.

rational equation (p. 112) An equation containing at least one ratio of polynomials, $\frac{a(x)}{b(x)}$, where $b(x) \neq 0$.

rational function (p. 104) A function that can be expressed as $f(x) = \frac{a(x)}{b(x)}$, where $a(x)$ and $b(x)$ are polynomials and $b(x) \neq 0$.

rational number (p. 648) A number that can be expressed as a ratio of two integers $\frac{a}{b}$, where $b \neq 0$.

real numbers (p. 648) All the numbers that can be graphed on a number line.

recursive formula (pp. 447, 456) A formula that states the first term(s) of a sequence and defines the remaining terms using the previous term(s).

reduced row echelon form (RREF) (p. 355) The form of a coefficient matrix when the first nonzero element in each row is 1 and any other elements in that column are 0.

reference angle (p. 189) The acute angle formed by the x-axis and the terminal side of an angle in standard position.

reference triangle (p. 189) The triangle formed by a perpendicular drawn to the x-axis from the terminal side of an angle in standard position.

reflection (p. 33) A transformation across a reference line that creates a mirror image.

relation (p. 2) Any set of ordered pairs.

relative extrema (p. 80) The maximum or minimum values relative to a local region of points.

residual (p. 60) The difference between the actual y-value of a data point and the value predicted by the modeling function.

resultant vector (vector sum) (p. 288) The vector that represents the sum of two vectors. If $\mathbf{u} = \langle u_1, u_2 \rangle$ and $\mathbf{v} = \langle v_1, v_2 \rangle$, $\mathbf{r} = \mathbf{u} + \mathbf{v} = \langle u_1 + v_1, u_2 + v_2 \rangle$.

right-hand limit (p. 21) The right-hand limit of $f(x)$ as x approaches a, denoted $\lim\limits_{x \to a^+} f(x)$, is the number to which $f(x)$ gets closer and closer as x approaches a from the right.

rigid transformation (p. 33) A transformation that maintains the shape of the graph, such as a translation or reflection.

row echelon form (REF) (p. 353) A system of linear equations written in inverted triangular form in which all leading coefficients are 1.

sample (p. 507) A group selected from a population.

sample space (p. 497) All possible outcomes in an experiment.

sampling error (p. 586) An error that occurs when the sample is not representative of the population.

scalar (pp. 287–88) A real number.

scatterplot (p. 59) A graph of ordered pairs that illustrates the relationship between two sets of data.

secant (pp. 179, 188) The trigonometric ratio that is the reciprocal of cosine.

sector (p. 175) The region of a circle bound by two radii and the intercepted arc.

semi-perimeter (p. 278) One half the sum of a triangle's side lengths.

sequence (p. 446) A function whose domain is the set of natural numbers (infinite sequence) or the first n natural numbers (finite sequence) that is usually written as an ordered list of numbers.

series (p. 449) The sum of the terms in a sequence.

set (p. 647) A group or collection of numbers or objects.

sigma notation (p. 449) See **summation notation**.

simple harmonic motion (p. 225) Oscillations that continue with the same amplitude and period.

sine (pp. 179, 188) The ratio of the leg opposite an acute angle and the hypotenuse of a right triangle. The ratio $\frac{y}{r}$, where $P(x, y)$ is a point on the terminal side of an angle in standard position and $r = \sqrt{x^2 + y^2}$.

singular matrix (p. 370) A matrix for which no inverse exists.

sinusoidal function (p. 198) A function that can be written as $y = a \sin b(x - h) + k$ or $y = a \cos b(x - h) + k$.

slant asymptote (p. 107) Given a rational function $f(x) = \frac{a(x)}{b(x)}$ where degree of $a(x)$ is one more than the degree of $b(x)$, the slant asymptote is the quotient (without the remainder) when $a(x)$ is divided by $b(x)$.

slope (pp. 10, 14) The ratio of a line's rise (vertical change) to its run (horizontal change). Denoted m.

slope-intercept form (p. 11) A linear equation in the form $y = mx + b$, where m is the slope of a line and $(0, b)$ is the y-intercept.

solution (p. 233) Any value of the variable for which a conditional equation or inequality is true.

square matrix (p. 343) A matrix that has an equal number of rows and columns.

standard deviation (pp. 517, 548) A measure of variance from the mean found by finding the square root of the variance.

standard position (of an angle) (p. 172) An angle with its vertex at the origin of a coordinate plane and its initial side coinciding with the positive x-axis.

standard position (of a vector) (p. 287) A vector with its initial point at the origin.

standard unit vectors (p. 289) $\mathbf{i} = \langle 1, 0 \rangle$ and $\mathbf{j} = \langle 0, 1 \rangle$.

statistic (p. 507) An estimate of a population's parameter based on a sample.

subset (p. 647) A set whose elements are all contained in another set.

summation notation (p. 449) A series represented as $\sum\limits_{i=b}^{c} a_i = a_b + a_{b+1} + a_{b+2} + \cdots + a_c$ where the index (or counter) i has a lower bound of b and an upper bound of c.

sum of the squares (p. 517) The sum of the squares of the difference of each value from the mean.

synthetic division (p. 86) A shortened version of the long-division algorithm used when dividing a polynomial by a linear polynomial of the form $x - c$.

synthetic substitution (p. 89) Using synthetic division to evaluate a function.

tangent (pp. 179, 188) The ratio of the leg opposite an acute angle and the leg adjacent to that angle in a right triangle. The ratio $\frac{y}{x}$, where $P(x, y)$ is a point on the terminal side of an angle in standard position.

terminal side (p. 172) The side of an angle in standard position that rotates around the origin.

theoretical (classical) probability (p. 497) The ratio of the number of favorable outcomes, $n(E)$, to the number of possible outcomes, $n(S)$, where every outcome is equally likely.

transcendental function (p. 128) A function, such as an exponential, logarithmic, or trigonometric function, that goes beyond, or transcends, the basic algebraic operations.

translation (p. 32) A change in the position of a figure without rotation or resizing.

transverse axis (p. 412) The segment containing a hyperbola's vertices whose endpoints are the hyperbola's foci.

trend line (p. 59) A line drawn to model the relationship between two related variables and to make predictions related to other values of either variable.

type I error (p. 574) An error that occurs when the null hypothesis is rejected, but it is true.

type II error (p. 574) An error that occurs when the null hypothesis is not rejected, but it is false.

union of sets (p. 647) The set of all elements that appear in the given sets.

unit circle (p. 191) The circle centered at the origin with a radius of 1 unit: $x^2 + y^2 = 1$.

unit vector (p. 289) A vector with a magnitude of 1.

variance (pp. 517, 548, 550) The average of the sum of the squared deviations from the mean.

vector (p. 287) A quantity $\langle a, b \rangle$ modeled with a directed line segment having both magnitude and direction.

verifying identities (p. 240) Showing that both sides of an equation are equal for all values of the variable for which the expressions are defined.

vertex (of a conic section) (p. 435) Any intersection of a conic and its focal axis.

vertex (of a parabola) (pp. 39, 396) The minimum or maximum point (h, k) of the quadratic function $f(x) = a(x - h)^2 + k$ at the intersection of the parabola and its axis of symmetry.

vertical asymptote (p. 104) The line $x = c$ is a vertical asymptote of $f(x)$ if $\lim\limits_{x \to c^-} f(x) = \pm\infty$ or $\lim\limits_{x \to c^+} f(x) = \pm\infty$.

zero of a function (pp. 41, 656) A value of x such that $f(x) = 0$.

zero vector (pp. 288, 305) A vector having a length of 0 and no direction.

z-score (pp. 527–28) The number of standard deviations a value is from the mean.

Index

Photo Credits

Key: (**t**) top; (**c**) center; (**b**) bottom; (**l**) left; (**r**) right

Chapter 11

545 Sergieiev/Shutterstock.com; **546** Nestor Rizhniak/Shutterstock.com; **549** kali9/E+/Getty Images; **551** rvlsoft/Shutterstock.com; **552l** timquo/Shutterstock.com; **552r** ethylalkohol/Shutterstock.com; **555** msgrafixx/Shutterstock.com; **559** Photology1971/Shutterstock.com; **562** Tim Fitzharris/Minden Pictures/Getty Images; **563** Brian Doben/Photolibrary/Getty Images; **566** guenterguni/Getty Images; **569** bane.m/Shutterstock.com; **570** monkeybusinessimages/iStock/Getty Images Plus/Getty Images; **572** shihina/Shutterstock.com; **573** BJU Photo Services; **575** Benoist/Shutterstock.com; **579** jensenwy/iStock/Getty Images Plus/Getty Images; **580** PASIEKA/Science Photo Library/Getty Images; **582** Marek CECH/Shutterstock.com; **584** ibreakstock/Shutterstock.com; **585** Digital Vision./Photodisc/Getty Images; **586** Tetra Images - Jamie Grill/Brand X Pictures/Getty Images; **588** ldutko/Shutterstock.com; **590l** Dora Zett/Shutterstock.com; **590r** cate_89/Shutterstock.com; **593** the_guitar_mann/iStock Editorial/Getty Images; **596** ljubaphoto/iStock/Getty Images Plus/Getty Images; **597** grahamheywood/iStock/Getty Images Plus/Getty Images

Chapter 12

598 BRUCE BECK/Alamy Stock Photo; **599** Marko Rupena/Shutterstock.com; **604** FatCamera/E+/Getty Images; **610** sakkmesterke/Shutterstock.com; **612** Dmitry Elagin/Shutterstock.com; **618** catwalker/Shutterstock.com; **624** Tatiana Shepeleva/Shutterstock.com; **629** Science History Images/Alamy Stock Photo; **631** neftali/Shutterstock.com; **638** Sky Antonio/Shutterstock.com

Screenshots from TI-84 Plus CE Calculator courtesy of Texas Instruments

Text Acknowledgements

Chapter 1
9 Eves, Howard. *An Introduction to the History of Mathematics*, 6th ed. (Pacific Grove: Brooks/Cole, 1990), 264; **17** Wigner, Eugene. *Symmetries and Reflections: Scientific Essays* (Cambridge, MA: The MIT Press, 1970), 237; **17** Calvin, John. *Institutes on the Christian Religion*, vol. 1, trans. Henry Beveridge (Edinburgh: Calvin Translation Society, 1845), 318–19; **17** Hertz, Heinrich, quoted in E. T. Bell. *Men of Mathematics* (New York: Touchstone Books, 1986), 16; **17** Nickel, James. Mathematics: *Is God Silent?* (Vallecito, CA: Ross House Books, 2001), 223; **49** Fourier, Joseph. *The Analytical Theory of Heat*, trans. Alexander Freeman (Cambridge: The University Press, 1878), 1; **59** Alligator data from Example 2.20, Scheaffer, Richard L. *Probability and Statistics for Engineers*, 5th Edition (Boston: Brooks/Cole, 2011), 97; **64** Average US gas prices data from US Department of Energy; **65** Life expectancy data from the CDC/National Center for Health Statistics; **70** US Census Bureau.

Chapter 2
122 Formula from "International America's Cup Class," Wikipedia.

Chapter 3
134 National Marine Fisheries Service. 2013. Status Review of The Eastern Distinct Population Segment of Steller Sea Lion (Eumetopias jubatus). 144pp + Appendices. Protected Resources Division, Alaska Region, National Marine Fisheries Service, 709 West 9th St, Juneau, Alaska 99802; **134** "Fukushima Radiation: 800 Tera Becquerel of Cesium-137 to Reach West Coast of North America by 2016," Centre for Research on Globalization; **142** Cajori, Florian. *A History of Mathematics*, 2nd ed., rev. (New York: Macmillan, 1919), 149; **155** Kline, Morris. *Mathematics for the Nonmathematician* (New York: Dover Publications, 1967), 206–207; **155** Kepler, Johannes, quoted in James Nickel. *Mathematics: Is God Silent?* (Vallecito, CA: Ross House Books, 2001), 145; **155** Zimmerman, Larry L. "Mathematics: Is God Silent?," Part III, *The Biblical Educator*, 2:3, 2 (1980), n.p.; **155** Leibniz, Gottfried, quoted in Kline, Morris. *Mathematics: The Loss of Certainty* (New York: Oxford University Press, 1980), 60; **155** Fehr, Howard F. "Reorientation in Mathematics Education," *Teachers College Record*, May 1953, vol. 54, no. 8, p. 435; **163** Nesting pairs data from "Chart and Table

of Bald Eagle Breeding Pairs in Lower 48 States," US Fish and Wildlife Service.

Chapter 4
214 Einstein, Albert, quoted in Morris Kline. *Mathematics and the Physical World* (New York: Dover, 1981), 464; **214** Einstein, Albert. "Physics and Reality," *Out of My Later Years* (New York: Citadel Press, 1950), 61; **214** Nickel, James. *Mathematics: Is God Silent?* (Vallecito, CA: Ross House Books, 2001), 225; **214** Lobachevsky, Nikolai, quoted in George E. Martin. *The Foundations of Geometry and the Non-Euclidean Plane* (New York: Springer, 1998), 225; **215** Gardner, Martin, quoted in Donald J. Albers and Gerald L. Alexanderson, eds. *Fascinating Mathematical People: Interviews and Memoirs* (Princeton: Princeton University Press, 2011), ix.

Chapter 5
235 Feynman, Richard. *The Character of Physical Law* (Cambridge, MA: The MIT Press, 1985), 34; **252** Fourier, Joseph. *The Analytical Theory of Heat*, trans. Alexander Freeman (Cambridge: The University Press, 1878), 8; **252** Russell, Bertrand. *Mysticism and Logic and Other Essays* (London: George Allen & Unwin Ltd, 1959), 61; **252** Gioia, Dana. "Beauty's Place in the Christian Vision" (chapel sermon), Biola University, February 8, 2012; **252** Nickel, James. *Mathematics: Is God Silent?* (Vallecito, CA: Ross House Books, 2001), 94; **252–53** Kline, Morris. *Mathematics in Western Culture* (New York: Oxford University Press, 1953), 512; **268** Bhatia, Rajendra. *Fourier Series* (Providence, RI: American Mathematical Society, 2004), 116; **268** Bracewell, Ronald, quoted in Prestini, Elena. *The Evolution of Applied Harmonic Analysis: Models of the Real World* (Boston: Birkhäuser, 2004), xii; **282** Data table from Smith, A. Mark. *Ptolemy's Theory of Visual Perception: An English Translation of the "Optics" with Introduction and Commentary* (Philadelphia: American Philosophical Society, 1996), 233.

Chapter 6
301 Hermite, Charles, quoted in Morris Kline. *Mathematics: The Loss of Certainty* (New York: Oxford Univ. Press, 1980), 345; **301** Galilei, Galileo, quoted in Morris Kline. *Mathematics and the Physical World* (New York: Dover, 1981), 206; **301** Kasner, Edward and James Newman. *Mathematics and the Imagination* (London: G. Bell and Sons, 1949), 359; **301** Jourdain, Philip E.

B. *The Nature of Mathematics* (London: Jack and Nelson, 1919), 46; **301** Gauss, Carl, quoted in Ioan James. *Remarkable Mathematicians* (New York: Cambridge University Press, 2002), 67; **302** Zimmerman, Larry L. *Truth & the Transcendent* (Florence, KY: Answers in Genesis, 2000), n.p.

Chapter 7
351 Hardy, G. H. *A Mathematician's Apology* (Cambridge: Cambridge University Press, 2004), 94; **352** Bahnsen, Greg L. "The Great Debate: Does God Exist?," University of California, Irvine, CA 1985; **369** Huxley, Thomas, quoted in Cajori, Florian. "A Review of Three Famous Attacks upon the Study of Mathematics as a Training of the Mind," *Popular Science Monthly*, vol. 80, April 1912; **369** Sylvester, James Joseph, Ibid.

Chapter 8
427 Wiles, Andrew. "Andrew Wiles on Solving Fermat," NOVA, 1 November 2007, PBS online; **442** Hawking, Stephen. Interview by Kenneth Campbell, *Reality on the Rocks*, 1995.

Chapter 9
454 Hales, Thomas, quoted in George Szpiro. *Kepler's Conjecture* (Hoboken, NJ: Wiley, 2003), 201; **454** Hawking, Stephen, quoted in Rory Cellan-Jones. "Stephen Hawking Warns Artificial Intelligence Could End Mankind.", 2 December 2014, *BBC News* online; **454** Volkers, Cody. "A Christian View of Artificial Intelligence," 1 March 2017, *Ecclesiam Journal* online; **455** Ibid; **471** Pascal, Blaise. "Prayer to Ask of God the Proper Use of Sickness," *Minor Works*, trans. O. W. Wight (New York: P. F. Collier & Son, 1910), 371; **481** Van Til, Cornelius. A *Survey of Christian Epistemology* (Phillipsburg, NJ: P&R Publishing, 1969), 19.

Chapter 10
497 First paragraph ideas based on Tagliapietra, Ron. *Math for God's Glory* (Bloomington, IN: Xlibris, 2004); **526** Boyer, Carl B. *A History of Mathematics*, 2nd ed. (New York: John Wiley & Sons, 1992), 492; **526** Poythress, Vern S. *Chance and the Sovereignty of God: A God-Centered Approach to Probability and Random Events* (Wheaton, IL: Crossway, 2014), 101; **540** Hardy, G. H. *A Mathematician's Apology* (Cambridge: Cambridge University Press, 1969), 123–24; **540** Linnebo,

Øystein, "Platonism in the Philosophy of Mathematics," *The Stanford Encyclopedia of Philosophy* (Spring 2018 Edition), Edward N. Zalta (ed.), https://plato.stanford.edu/archives/spr2018/entries/platonism-mathematics/; **540** Kepler, Johannes, quoted in Morris Kline. *Mathematics: The Loss of Certainty* (New York: Oxford University Press), 31; **540** Du Sautoy, Marcus. *The Music of the Primes: Searching to Solve the Greatest Mystery in Mathematics* (New York: HarperCollins, 2003), 33–34.

Chapter 11

559 Graphs generated from the Controlling for Variables tool by SticiGui©. Philip B. Stark, University of California, Berkeley; **560** Teen data from Stage of Life LLC, 24 South Franklin Street, Dallastown, PA 17313. Copyright © 2011 All rights reserved; **562** Bureau of Labor Statistics, American Time Use Study; **562** Molla, Rani. "Why People Are Buying More Expensive Smartphones Than They Have in Years," January 23, 2018, *Recode* online. Vox Media, Inc.; **578** Ioannidis, John P. A. "Why Most Published Research Findings Are False," August 30, 2005, *PLOS Medicine* online; **582** Nickel, James. *Mathematics: Is God Silent?* (Vallecito, CA: Ross House Books, 1990), 59; **582** Eves, Howard. *An Introduction to the History of Mathematics*, 4th ed. (New York: Holt, Rinehart and Winston, 1976), 481; **588** Elbel, Brian, et al. "A Water Availability Intervention in New York City Public Schools: Influence on Youths' Water and Milk Behaviors," *American Journal of Public Health*, vol. 105, no. 2. Washington, DC: American Public Health Association, Feb. 2015; **597** Morning commute data from the US Census Bureau.

Chapter 12

601 Leibniz, Gottfried. *The Philosophical Works of Leibniz*, trans. George Martin Duncan (New Haven, CT: The Tuttle, Morehouse & Taylor Co., 1908), 71; **610** Hilbert, David, quoted in Eli Maor. *To Infinity and Beyond: A Cultural History of the Infinite* (Boston: Birkhäuser Boston, 1987), vii; **610** Weyl, Hermann, quoted in Peter Pesic. *Levels of Infinity* (Mineola, NY: Dover, 2012), 17; **644** Fraser, Alexander Campbell, ed. *The Works of George Berkeley, D.D.*, vol. 3 (Oxford: Clarendon Press, 1871), 301.

Quick Reference

Functions

even	$f(-x) = f(x)$ for all $x \in D$	symmetrical with y-axis
odd	$f(-x) = -f(x)$ for all $x \in D$	symmetrical with origin

Transformations of Functions

	Translation	**Stretch or Shrink**	**Reflection**
vertical	$g(x) = f(x) + k$ up if $k > 0$ down if $k < 0$	$g(x) = af(x)$ stretch by a if $\|a\| > 1$ shrink by a if $0 \le \|a\| < 1$	$g(x) = -f(x)$ reflection across x-axis
horizontal	$g(x) = f(x - h)$ right if $h > 0$ left if $h < 0$	$g(x) = f(bx)$ shrink by a factor of $\frac{1}{\|b\|}$ if $\|b\| > 1$ stretch by a factor of $\frac{1}{\|b\|}$ if $0 \le \|b\| < 1$	$g(x) = f(-x)$ reflection across y-axis

Exponents and Logarithms

	of Exponents	**of Logarithms**	
Equality Property	$b^m = b^n$ iff $m = n$	$\log_b m = \log_b n$ iff $m = n$	**change of base**
Product Property	$b^m \cdot b^n = b^{m+n}$	$\log_b mn = \log_b m + \log_b n$	$\log_b x = \dfrac{\log_a x}{\log_a b}$
Quotient Property	$\dfrac{b^m}{b^n} = b^{m-n}$	$\log_b \frac{m}{n} = \log_b m - \log_b n$	
Power Property	$(b^m)^p = b^{mp}$	$\log_b m^p = p \log_b m$	

Vectors

magnitude	**reference angle**	**Direction (θ degrees from the positive x-axis)**	
$\|\mathbf{v}\| = \sqrt{a^2 + b^2}$	$\alpha = \text{Tan}^{-1} \left\| \frac{b}{a} \right\|$	Q I: $\theta = \alpha$ Q III: $\theta = 180° + \alpha$	Q II: $\theta = 180° - \alpha$ Q IV: $\theta = 360° - \alpha$

dot product	$\mathbf{u} \cdot \mathbf{v} = \|\mathbf{u}\|\,\|\mathbf{v}\| \cos \theta$ If $\mathbf{u} = \langle u_1, u_2 \rangle$ and $\mathbf{v} = \langle v_1, v_2 \rangle$, then $\mathbf{u} \cdot \mathbf{v} = u_1 v_1 + u_2 v_2$.	**unit vector**	$\mathbf{u} = \dfrac{\mathbf{v}}{\|\mathbf{v}\|}$
		projection of u onto v	$\text{proj}_{\mathbf{v}}\,\mathbf{u} = \left(\dfrac{\mathbf{u} \cdot \mathbf{v}}{\|\mathbf{v}\|^2} \right) \mathbf{v} = \mathbf{w}_1; \ \mathbf{w}_2 = \mathbf{u} - \text{proj}_{\mathbf{v}}\,\mathbf{u}$

Complex Numbers

standard form	$z = a + bi$	**De Moivre's Theorem**
polar (trig) form	$z = r(\cos \theta + i \sin \theta)$ or $z = r \operatorname{cis} \theta$	$z^n = r^n \operatorname{cis} n\theta$
product	$z_1 z_2 = r_1 r_2 \operatorname{cis}(\theta_1 + \theta_2)$	**Corollary to De Moivre's Theorem**
quotient	$\dfrac{z_1}{z_2} = \dfrac{r_1 \operatorname{cis} \theta_1}{r_2 \operatorname{cis} \theta_2} = \dfrac{r_1}{r_2} \operatorname{cis}(\theta_1 - \theta_2)$	The n complex roots of z are $\sqrt[n]{r} \ \operatorname{cis} \dfrac{\theta + k2\pi}{n}$ where $k = 0, 1, 2, \ldots, n - 1$.

Sequences and Series

	Arithmetic	**Geometric**
recursive formula	$a_n = a_{n-1} + d$	$a_n = a_{n-1} \cdot r$
explicit formula	$a_n = a_1 + (n - 1)d$	$a_n = a_1 r^{n-1}$
finite series	$S_n = \frac{n}{2}(a_1 + a_n)$ or $S_n = \frac{n}{2}[2a_1 + (n-1)d]$	$S_n = \dfrac{a_1 - a_n r}{1 - r}$ or $S_n = \dfrac{a_1(1 - r^n)}{1 - r}$
infinite series	The series diverges.	If $\|r\| < 1$, then $S = \dfrac{a_1}{1 - r}$. If $\|r\| \ge 1$, the series diverges.

Analytic Geometry

Standard Form Equations of a Parabola

with vertex $V(h, k)$ and focal length $|p|$ where $a = \frac{1}{4p}$

$$y = \frac{1}{4p}(x - h)^2 + k \qquad\qquad\qquad\qquad x = \frac{1}{4p}(y - k)^2 + h$$

focus: $F(h, k + p)$; axis: $x = h$; directrix: $y = k - p$ $\qquad$ focus: $F(h + p, k)$; axis: $y = k$; directrix: $x = h - p$

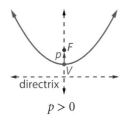
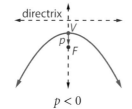
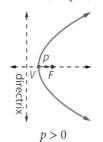
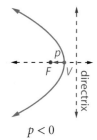

$\qquad p > 0 \qquad\qquad\qquad p < 0 \qquad\qquad\qquad\qquad\qquad p > 0 \qquad\qquad\qquad p < 0$

Standard Form Equations of an Ellipse

centered at $C(h, k)$ with $a > b$ and $c^2 = a^2 - b^2$

$$\frac{(x - h)^2}{a^2} + \frac{(y - k)^2}{b^2} = 1 \qquad\qquad\qquad \frac{(x - h)^2}{b^2} + \frac{(y - k)^2}{a^2} = 1$$

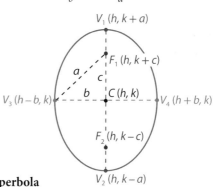

Standard Form Equations of a Hyperbola

centered at $C(h, k)$ with $c^2 = a^2 + b^2$

$$\frac{(x - h)^2}{a^2} - \frac{(y - k)^2}{b^2} = 1 \qquad\qquad\qquad \frac{(y - k)^2}{a^2} - \frac{(x - h)^2}{b^2} = 1$$

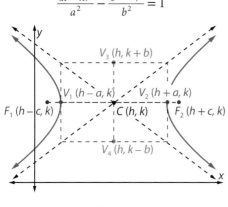
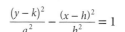
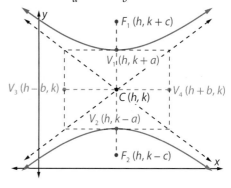

$$y = \pm\frac{b}{a}(x - h) + k \qquad\qquad \textbf{asymptotes} \qquad\qquad y = \pm\frac{a}{b}(x - h) + k$$

General Form Equation of Conics

$$Ax^2 + Bxy + Cy^2 + Dx + Ey + F = 0 \text{ with discriminant } B^2 - 4AC \text{ and eccentricity } e = \frac{c}{a}$$

Circle	Ellipse	Parabola	Hyperbola
$B^2 - 4AC < 0$;	$B^2 - 4AC < 0$;	$B^2 - 4AC = 0$	$B^2 - 4AC > 0$
$B = 0$ and $A = C$	$B \neq 0$ or $A \neq C$	$e = 1$	$e > 1$
$e = 0$	$e < 1$		

Summations

Properties

$$\sum_{i=1}^{n} c = nc \qquad \sum_{i=1}^{n} ca_i = c \sum_{i=1}^{n} a_i \qquad \sum_{i=1}^{n} (a_i + b_i) = \sum_{i=1}^{n} a_i + \sum_{i=1}^{n} b_i \qquad \sum_{i=1}^{n} a_i = \sum_{i=1}^{p} a_i + \sum_{i=p+1}^{n} a_i \text{ where } 1 < p < n$$

Partial Sums of Powers of Integers

$$\sum_{k=1}^{n} k = \frac{n^2 + n}{2} = \frac{n(n+1)}{2} \qquad \sum_{k=1}^{n} k^2 = \frac{n(n+1)(2n+1)}{6} \qquad \sum_{k=1}^{n} k^3 = \frac{n^2(n+1)^2}{4} \qquad \sum_{k=1}^{n} k^4 = \frac{n(n+1)(2n+1)(3n^2 + 3n - 1)}{30}$$

Probability

$$\text{permutation} \quad {}_nP_r = \frac{n!}{(n-r)!} \qquad\qquad \text{combination} \quad {}_nC_r = \frac{n!}{r!(n-r)!}$$

Binomial Theorem

$$(x + y)^n = {}_nC_0\, x^n + {}_nC_1\, x^{n-1}y + {}_nC_2\, x^{n-2}y^2 + {}_nC_3\, x^{n-3}y^3 + \cdots + {}_nC_n\, y^n = \sum_{r=0}^{n} {}_nC_r\, x^{n-r}y^r$$

theoretical $\quad P(E) = \frac{n(E)}{n(S)} \qquad$ **experimental** $\quad P(E) = \frac{\text{number of times the event occurs}}{\text{number of trials}} \qquad$ **complement of an event** $\quad P(E') = 1 - P(E)$

independent events $\quad P(A \text{ and } B) = P(A) \cdot P(B)$

dependent events $\quad P(A \text{ and } B) = P(A) \cdot P(B|A)$

mutually exclusive events $\quad P(A \text{ or } B) = P(A) + P(B)$

inclusive events $\quad P(A \text{ or } B) = P(A) + P(B) - P(A \text{ and } B)$

Statistics

	Population	Sample	Binomial Probability Distribution	
mean	$\mu = \dfrac{\sum_{i=1}^{N} x_i}{N}$	$\bar{x} = \dfrac{\sum_{i=1}^{n} x_i}{n}$	**formula**	$P(x) = {}_nC_x\, p^x q^{n-x}$
			mean	$\mu = np$
			variance	$\sigma^2 = npq$
variance	$\sigma^2 = \dfrac{\sum_{i=1}^{N}(x_i - \mu)^2}{N}$ or $\dfrac{SS}{N}$	$s^2 = \dfrac{\sum_{i=1}^{n}(x_i - \bar{x})^2}{n-1}$ or $\dfrac{SS}{n-1}$	**standard deviation**	$\sigma = \sqrt{\sigma^2} = \sqrt{npq}$
standard deviation	$\sigma = \sqrt{\dfrac{\sum_{i=1}^{N}(x_i - \mu)^2}{N}}$	$s = \sqrt{\dfrac{\sum_{i=1}^{n}(x_i - \bar{x})^2}{n-1}}$		
z-score	$z = \dfrac{x - \mu}{\sigma}$	$z = \dfrac{x - \bar{x}}{s}$		

Limits

sum $\quad \lim\limits_{x \to a}[f(x) + g(x)] = \lim\limits_{x \to a} f(x) + \lim\limits_{x \to a} g(x)$

product $\quad \lim\limits_{x \to a}[f(x) \cdot g(x)] = \lim\limits_{x \to a} f(x) \cdot \lim\limits_{x \to a} g(x)$

scalar multiple $\quad \lim\limits_{x \to a} cf(x) = c \lim\limits_{x \to a} f(x) \text{ where } c \in \mathbb{R}$

quotient $\quad \lim\limits_{x \to a} \dfrac{f(x)}{g(x)} = \dfrac{\lim\limits_{x \to a} f(x)}{\lim\limits_{x \to a} g(x)}$

power $\quad \lim\limits_{x \to a}[f(x)]^n = \left[\lim\limits_{x \to a} f(x)\right]^n$

reciprocal power function at infinity $\quad \lim\limits_{x \to \pm\infty} \dfrac{1}{x^n} = 0 \text{ where } n \in \mathbb{N}$

Derivatives

constant	$\frac{d}{dx}[c] = 0$	product	$\frac{d}{dx}[u(x) \cdot v(x)] = u'(x) \cdot v(x) + u(x) \cdot v'(x)$
linear	$\frac{d}{dx}[mx + b] = m$	quotient	$\frac{d}{dx}\left[\frac{u(x)}{v(x)}\right] = \frac{u'(x) \cdot v(x) - u(x) \cdot v'(x)}{[v(x)]^2}$
power	$\frac{d}{dx}[cx^n] = ncx^{n-1}$	chain rule	$\frac{d}{dx}[(u \circ v)(x)] = u'(v(x)) \cdot v'(x)$
sum or difference	$\frac{d}{dx}[u(x) \pm v(x)] = u'(x) \pm v'(x)$	basic trigonometric	$\frac{d}{dx}[\sin x] = \cos x$
natural exponential	$\frac{d}{dx}[e^x] = e^x$		$\frac{d}{dx}[\cos x] = -\sin x$

Integrals

constant	$\int k \, dx = kx + C$	scalar	$\int cf(x) \, dx = c \int f(x) \, dx$
power	$\int kx^n \, dx = \frac{k}{n+1}x^{n+1} + C$	sum	$\int [f(x) \pm g(x)] \, dx = \int f(x) \, dx \pm \int g(x) \, dx$
sine	$\int (\sin x) \, dx = -\cos x + C$	cosine	$\int (\cos x) \, dx = \sin x + C$
natural exponential	$\int e^x \, dx = e^x + C$	Fundamental Theorem of Calculus	$\int_a^b f(x) \, dx = F(b) - F(a)$
definite integral	$\int_a^b (x) \, dx = \lim\limits_{n \to \infty} \sum\limits_{i=1}^{n} f(x_i) \Delta x$		

Other Formulas

distance formula	$d = \sqrt{(x_2 - x_1)^2 + (y_2 - y_1)^2 + (z_2 - z_1)^2}$
midpoint formula	$M = \left(\frac{x_1 + x_2}{2}, \frac{y_1 + y_2}{2}, \frac{z_1 + z_2}{2}\right)$
absolute value of a complex number	If $z = a + bi$, then $|z| = |a + bi| = \sqrt{a^2 + b^2}$.
Heron's formula	$Area = \sqrt{s(s-a)(s-b)(s-c)}$, where $s = \frac{a+b+c}{2}$
compound interest	$A(t) = P\left(1 + \frac{r}{n}\right)^{nt}$
continuously compounded interest	$A(t) = Pe^{rt}$
height of a projectile	$h(t) = -\frac{1}{2}gt^2 + v_0 t + h_0$, where $g = 32$ ft/sec^2 or 9.8 m/sec^2

Trigonometry

Basic Ratios

$$\sin A = \frac{opp.}{hyp.}$$

$$\cos A = \frac{adj.}{hyp.}$$

$$\tan A = \frac{opp.}{adj.}$$

Reciprocal Ratios

$$\csc A = \frac{1}{\sin A} = \frac{hyp.}{opp.}$$

$$\sec A = \frac{1}{\cos A} = \frac{hyp.}{adj.}$$

$$\cot A = \frac{1}{\tan A} = \frac{adj.}{opp.}$$

Reciprocal Identities

$$\csc \theta = \frac{1}{\sin \theta} \qquad \sec \theta = \frac{1}{\cos \theta} \qquad \cot \theta = \frac{1}{\tan \theta}$$

Quotient Identities

$$\tan \theta = \frac{\sin \theta}{\cos \theta} \qquad \cot \theta = \frac{\cos \theta}{\sin \theta}$$

Pythagorean Identities

$$\sin^2 \theta + \cos^2 \theta = 1 \qquad \cot^2 \theta + 1 = \csc^2 \theta \qquad \tan^2 \theta + 1 = \sec^2 \theta$$

Even/Odd Identities

$$\sin(-\theta) = -\sin \theta \qquad \cos(-\theta) = \cos \theta \qquad \tan(-\theta) = -\tan \theta$$
$$\csc(-\theta) = -\csc \theta \qquad \sec(-\theta) = \sec \theta \qquad \cot(-\theta) = -\cot \theta$$

Cofunction Identities

$$\sin \theta = \cos\left(\frac{\pi}{2} - \theta\right) \qquad \tan \theta = \cot\left(\frac{\pi}{2} - \theta\right) \qquad \sec \theta = \csc\left(\frac{\pi}{2} - \theta\right)$$
$$\cos \theta = \sin\left(\frac{\pi}{2} - \theta\right) \qquad \cot \theta = \tan\left(\frac{\pi}{2} - \theta\right) \qquad \csc \theta = \sec\left(\frac{\pi}{2} - \theta\right)$$

Sum/Difference Identities

$$\cos(\alpha \pm \beta) = \cos \alpha \cos \beta \mp \sin \alpha \sin \beta$$
$$\sin(\alpha \pm \beta) = \sin \alpha \cos \beta \pm \cos \alpha \sin \beta$$
$$\tan(\alpha \pm \beta) = \frac{\tan \alpha \pm \tan \beta}{1 \mp \tan \alpha \tan \beta}$$

Double-Angle Identities

$$\cos 2\theta = \cos^2 \theta - \sin^2 \theta$$
$$\sin 2\theta = 2 \sin \theta \cos \theta$$
$$\tan 2\theta = \frac{2 \tan \theta}{1 - \tan^2 \theta}$$

Half-Angle Identities

$$\sin \frac{\theta}{2} = \pm\sqrt{\frac{1 - \cos \theta}{2}}$$
$$\cos \frac{\theta}{2} = \pm\sqrt{\frac{1 + \cos \theta}{2}}$$
$$\tan \frac{\theta}{2} = \pm\sqrt{\frac{1 - \cos \theta}{1 + \cos \theta}} = \frac{1 - \cos \theta}{\sin \theta} = \frac{\sin \theta}{1 + \cos \theta}$$

Power-Reducing Identities

$$\sin^2 \theta = \frac{1 - \cos 2\theta}{2}$$
$$\cos^2 \theta = \frac{1 + \cos 2\theta}{2}$$
$$\tan^2 \theta = \frac{1 - \cos 2\theta}{1 + \cos 2\theta}$$

Product-to-Sum Identities

$$\sin \alpha \sin \beta = \frac{1}{2}[\cos(\alpha - \beta) - \cos(\alpha + \beta)]$$
$$\cos \alpha \cos \beta = \frac{1}{2}[\cos(\alpha - \beta) + \cos(\alpha + \beta)]$$
$$\sin \alpha \cos \beta = \frac{1}{2}[\sin(\alpha + \beta) + \sin(\alpha - \beta)]$$
$$\cos \alpha \sin \beta = \frac{1}{2}[\sin(\alpha + \beta) - \sin(\alpha - \beta)]$$

Sum-to-Product Identities

$$\sin \alpha + \sin \beta = 2 \sin \frac{\alpha + \beta}{2} \cos \frac{\alpha - \beta}{2}$$
$$\sin \alpha - \sin \beta = 2 \cos \frac{\alpha + \beta}{2} \sin \frac{\alpha - \beta}{2}$$
$$\cos \alpha + \cos \beta = 2 \cos \frac{\alpha + \beta}{2} \cos \frac{\alpha - \beta}{2}$$
$$\cos \alpha - \cos \beta = -2 \sin \frac{\alpha + \beta}{2} \sin \frac{\alpha - \beta}{2}$$

angle measure

$$\pi \text{ radians} = 180°$$

arc length

$$s = r\theta \text{ (in radians)}$$

angular speed

$$\omega = \frac{\theta}{t}$$

linear speed

$$v = \frac{s}{t} = r\omega$$

area of a sector
(θ in radians)

$$A_{sector} = \frac{1}{2}r^2\theta$$

Polar-to-Rectangular Equations

$$r^2 = x^2 + y^2 \qquad x = r \cos \theta \qquad y = r \sin \theta$$

Law of Sines

$$\frac{\sin A}{a} = \frac{\sin B}{b} = \frac{\sin C}{c} \quad \text{or} \quad \frac{a}{\sin A} = \frac{b}{\sin B} = \frac{c}{\sin C}$$

Law of Cosines

$$a^2 = b^2 + c^2 - 2bc \cos A, \; b^2 = a^2 + c^2 - 2ac \cos B,$$
$$\text{and } c^2 = a^2 + b^2 - 2ab \cos C$$